ITALIAN PHYSICAL SOCIETY

PROCEEDINGS

OF THE

INTERNATIONAL SCHOOL OF PHYSICS « ENRICO FERMI »

XVIII COURSE

edited by D. S. BILLINGTON
Director of the Course

CENTRO DI STUDI NUCLEARI DI ISPRA
DEL COMITATO NAZIONALE PER L'ENERGIA NUCLEARE
ISPRA (VARESE)

SEPTEMBER 5 - SEPTEMBER 24 1960

Radiation damage in solids

1962

ACADEMIC PRESS • NEW YORK AND LONDON

SOCIETÀ ITALIANA DI FISICA

RENDICONTI

DELLA

SCUOLA INTERNAZIONALE DI FISICA «ENRICO FERMI»

XVIII Corso

a cura di D. S. Billington
Direttore del Corso

CENTRO DI STUDI NUCLEARI DI ISPRA
DEL COMITATO NAZIONALE PER L'ENERGIA NUCLEARE
ISPRA (Varese)

5-24 SETTEMBRE 1960

Radiation damage nei solidi

1962

ACADEMIC PRESS • NEW YORK AND LONDON

ACADEMIC PRESS INC.
111 Fifth Avenue
New York 3, N. Y.

United Kingdom Edition
Published by
ACADEMIC PRESS INC. (London) Ltd.
Berkeley Square House, London W. 1

Library of Congress Catalog Card Number: 62-13644

PRINTED IN ITALY

INDICE

Radiation Damage in Semiconductors.

Radiation Damage in Ionic and Covalent Crystals.

Radiation Damage in Metals.

Radiation Damage in Uranium.

Special Seminars.

1. G. Leibfried
2. J. Mahanty
3. A. Wronski
4. R. M. Walker
5. G. Hadamard
6. A. Guinier
7. J. E. Bailey
8. M. Ossona de Mendez
9. R. Fieschi
10. J. C. Pfister
11. P. R. Rudman
12. M. Giudici
13. U. Bergenlid
14. R. Bäuerlein
15. B. Knook
16. P. Gosar
17. A. Seeger
18. P. Manca
19. M. Kleman
20. A. T. Ivanov
21. G. Diehl
22. N. Van Dong
23. M. Herrschap
24. R. S. Barnes
25. G. Chiarotti
26. J. A. Brinkman
27. F. Levi
28. B. Germagnoli
29. D. K. Holmes
30. L. Van Almkerk
31. R. M. Stern
32. J. A. Grimshaw
33. C. Lehmann
34. K. Thommen
35. G. H. Vineyard
36. W. Rauch
37. J. M. Worlock
38. B. B. Goodman
39. J. Herak
40. F. Niedercorn
41. P. D. Townsend
42. E. M. Gunnersen
43. H. C. Van Elst
44. A. Al
45. E. Harnik
46. R. O. Simmons
47. K. Fischer
48. R. Gillot
49. S. Gillot
50. D. Dautreppe
51. D. S. Billington
52. M. W. Thompson
53. G. Spinolo
54. F. Pietragostini
55. C. Reale
56. G. Fabbri
57. A. De Salvo
58. G. Poletti
59. L. Passai
60. F. Perillo
61. M. Bertolotti
62. E. E. Conrad
63. D. Gelli
64. L. Verdini
65. T. Papa
66. A. Merlini

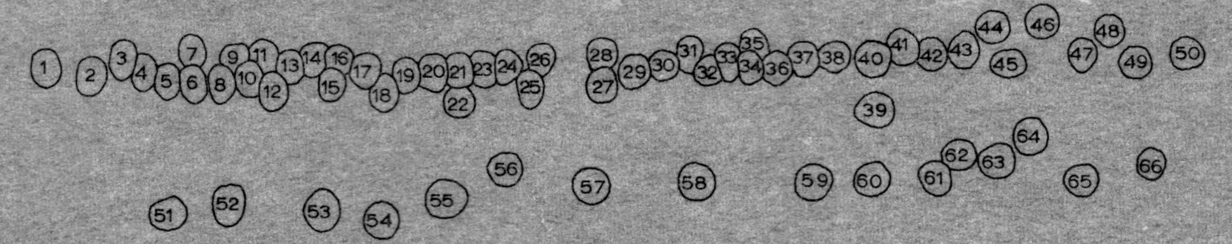

1. G. Leibfried
2. J. Mahanty
3. A. Wronski
4. R. M. Walker
5. G. Hadamard
6. A. Guinier
7. J. E. Bailey
8. M. Ossona de Mendez
9. R. Fieschi
10. J. C. Pfister
11. P. R. Rudman
12. M. Giudici
13. U. Bergenlid
14. R. Bäuerlein
15. B. Knook
16. P. Gosar
17. A. Seeger
18. P. Manca
19. M. Kleman
20. A. T. Ivanov
21. G. Diehl
22. N. Van Dong
23. M. Herrschap
24. R. S. Barnes
25. G. Chiarotti
26. J. A. Brinkman
27. F. Levi
28. E. Germagnoli
29. D. K. Holmes
30. L. Van Almkerk
31. R. M. Stern
32. J. A. Grimshaw
33. C. Lehmann
34. K. Thommen
35. G. H. Vineyard
36. W. Rauch
37. J. M. Worlock
38. B. B. Goodman
39. J. Herak
40. F. Niedercon
41. P. D. Townsend
42. E. M. Gunnersen
43. H. C. Van Elst
44. A. Al
45. E. Harnik
46. R. O. Simmons
47. K. Fischer
48. R. Gillot
49. S. Gillot
50. D. Dautreppe
51. D. S. Billington
52. M. W. Thompson
53. G. Spinolo
54. F. Pieragostini
55. C. Reale
56. G. Fabbri
57. A. De Salvo
58. G. Poletti
59. L. Passai
60. P. Perillo
61. M. Bertolotti
62. E. E. Courad
63. D. Gelli
64. L. Verdini
65. T. Papa
66. A. Merlini

SOCIETÀ ITALIANA DI FISICA

SCUOLA INTERNAZIONALE DI FISICA « E. FERMI »

XVIII CORSO - CENTRO DI STUDI NUCLEARI DI ISPRA (VARESE) - 5-24 Settembre 1960

Introduction.

D. S. BILLINGTON

Director, Solid State Division, Oak Ridge National Laboratory (*)
Oak Ridge, Tenn.

Nature has, through the agency of radioactive impurities in crystalline solids, presented us with evidence, the metamict minerals, that radiation damage is indeed an old subject. However, for man, the subject has received its principal impetus from technological requirements generated by the nuclear reactor developmental programs; and as such radiation damage is definitely established as a major area of concern in the reactor field. This aspect of radiation damage is important, challenging, and of utmost concern to ourselves and future generations in our quest for the cheap and plentiful power that all nations require for a modern technology.

On the other hand, that which begins as a problem of engineering concern is rapidly becoming a most important tool for the study of the behavior of solids. Almost coincidental with the beginnings of nuclear reactor studies has been the realization by solid state physicists of the crucial role that lattice defects play in determining so many important properties of a solid. For example, the concept of dislocations and the subsequent experimental verification of the role of dislocations in explaining the plastic properties of solids is a major example of the role of lattice defects in determining solid state behavior. The role of Schottky defects in explaining diffusion and related reactions in solids is of equal importance.

Radiation damage studies assume the aspect of a tool for solid state investigation because the interaction of energetic radiation with solids leads to the introduction of lattice defects into the solid. Thus, energetic radiation becomes a tool for manipulating a solid, in ways that are both unconventional and unique. For example, many solid state reactions will take place at lower temperatures, after or during irradiation, than in the absence of radiation.

(*) Oak Ridge National Laboratory is operated by the Union Carbide Corporation for the U.S. Atomic Energy Commission.

Crystals can be hardened by irradiation, but in a manner that is unlike either cold-working or alloying. They can be heat treated without resorting to heat. Under special conditions, transient defects can be introduced, such as the thermal spike. Phase changes can be made to take place under abnormal conditions. High-temperature phases can be made stable at room temperature by irradiation alone.

Thus, irradiation of solids by energetic radiation can lead to changes in the solid that are often similar to effects generated by other defects, but in the last analysis there remain many unique aspects.

However, we do not understand in detail the mechanism of the interaction of energetic radiation with the crystalline structure. This is partly caused by the fact that we do not have a detailed understanding of lattice defects in the absence of radiation. On the other hand, it is safe to say that we probably won't understand defects in the absence of radiation until we understand in detail the radiation damage process. This is to say that radiation damage is integrally bound up as an inseparable part of the whole field of solid state physics, and to understand the part we must understand the whole. It is my belief that the increased interaction or cross-fertilization that is taking place between the two fields of endeavor is desirable and necessary to gain ultimate understanding of solid state behavior.

In arranging the present series of lectures and seminars, it was considered important that several series of lectures should be presented: First, a series of lectures on defect solid state in the absence of radiation. Second, a thorough discussion of radiation damage theory with emphasis on the basic mechanism of interaction of radiation with matter. Third, an authoritative discussion of recent advances in the experimental observation of lattice defects. Fourth, detailed discussions of recent advances in radiation damage studies on all types of solids—metals and alloys, semiconductors, ionic and covalent crystals. Fifth, seminars on recent advances in all the above four categories.

It is my belief that the lectures and seminars that were given presented an excellent cross-section of the entire field of radiation damage in solids and should lead to an informed viewpoint of the many problems in the field that remain.

It is known that the many speakers who graciously consented to give these lectures and seminars represent an appreciable fraction of the outstanding workers in the field in the world today. Participation in the School has provided a unique opportunity, not only to the « students » but to the faculty as well, and has proven, I'm certain, to be of inestimable value to each and every one of us.

The devoted attention and skill applied to the problems of managing the School by Dr. A. Merlini, the Scientific Secretary, and his staff, are deeply appreciated. The gratitude of all is expressed for the hospitality and co-operation of CNEN and EURATOM. The assistance of Mrs. A. MERLINI, given under trying circumstances, is most appreciated. Professor POLVANI and Professor GERMANÀ, with their usual foresight and thoughtfulness, provided the congenial and challenging environment that enabled this School to meet the high traditions set by the past Summer Schools sponsored by the Italian Physical Society.

Crystalline Defects and Their Detection.

Introductory Lectures on Crystalline Defects.

J. FRIEDEL

Physique des Solides, Faculté des Sciences de Paris, Orsay

Introduction.

The purpose of these introductory lectures is to remind you of the main technical terms about defects in crystals which will be used in the study of radiation damage. Defects in crystals arise, of course, either from deviations of the nuclei from their periodic arrangement, or from excitation of electrons from their most stable state around the nuclei. There are many types of such defects, most of them of importance in radiation damage. But, very roughly speaking, one can distinguish the dynamic ones, which only last as long as some external excitation or little time afterwards; and the static ones, which remain, in a metastable state, long after the external excitation has ceased. Because time is short, I want to concentrate on the static defects. But to be complete, I shall first summarily list the dynamic ones of importance in radiation damage.

I. – Dynamic Defects.

1. – Electronic excitations.

These are of fundamental importance in the slowing-down of charged particles.

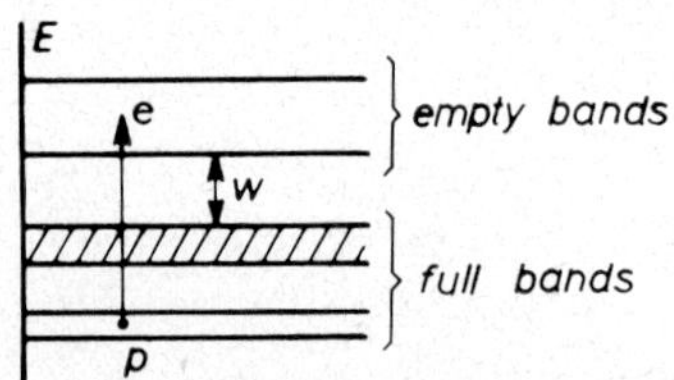

Fig. 1. – Individual electronic excitation.

Those of major importance can be thought of as excitations of *individual electrons*: in the band approximation, one electron e from a full band is excited into an empty band of higher energy E, leaving a positive hole p behind [1] (Fig. 1).

The recent studies of electronic correlations [2] have essentially confirmed this simple picture. The Coulomb interactions between the electrons e and the incoming charge Ze are merely screened off [3], so that their potential energy of interaction V is cut off in a roughly exponential way with distance r:

$$V \simeq -\frac{Ze^2}{r} \exp\left(-\frac{r}{r_0}\right). \tag{1.1}$$

For incoming charges moving slowly with respect to the electrons of the material, the screening radius r_0 is given approximately by a Debye formula,

$$r_0 \simeq \frac{v_M}{\omega}, \tag{1.2}$$

where v_M and ω are a characteristic velocity and a characteristic frequency associated with the electron gas. More precisely, ω is the « plasma » frequency:

$$\omega \simeq \left(\frac{4\pi N e^2}{m}\right)^{\frac{1}{2}}, \tag{1.3}$$

where e and m are the charge and mass of an electron, and N their density in the material. v_M is a characteristic velocity, which, for a metal, would be the Fermi velocity. For particles with higher velocities, the screening radius increases [4]. Roughly speaking, the effective ionization of the particle increases, in a way which justifies Bohr's approximate condition [5] about the particle velocity compared with the electronic velocity.

Electronic correlations now replace the long range Coulomb interactions by the « *plasma* » *waves* [8], that is longitudinal collective excitations corresponding to successive excess and lack of electronic density, as pictured in Fig. 2. Experiments on many materials have shown that such waves exist [7], with frequencies approximately given by eq. (1.3): one shoots fast electrons through thin foils and measures their energy losses, which are multiples of the plasma energy $\hbar\omega$. In formula (1.3), one must count only the easily polarizable electrons, thus those with an excitation energy w, Fig. 1, not too large compared with the plasma energy. In most materials, all the valence electrons fulfil this condition [8]. It seems, however, that the excitation of plasma waves is not very important compared with individual excitations, except in the slowing-down of fairly slow charges [3].

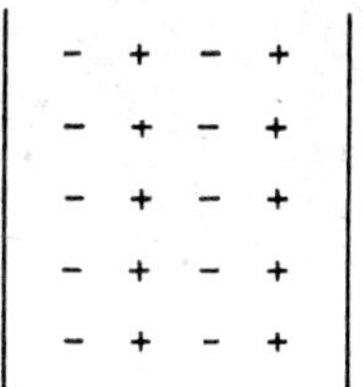

Fig. 2. – Plasma wave.

The *excitons* are another type of excitation made possible, in insulators, by electronic correlations: they occur when the excitation energy ΔE given to the electron is too small ($\Delta E < w$, Fig. 1) so that the electron is kept bound to the positive hole and forms a neutral defect [9]. This type of defect has also been very much studied in recent times [10], but is probably often of not much importance in the slowing-down processes.

2. – Photons.

These are, of course, significant both as producing radiation damage (γ-rays) and as light or X-rays emitted as result of radiation.

3. – Displacement of nuclei.

These can sometimes be analysed in terms of *phonons*, that is plane waves of atomic displacements small enough to be treated within linear elasticity. This is especially true for the general displacements produced some way from the initial displacement hits. The movements of the atoms might even be disordered enough for the concept of temperature to be used, *i.e.*, the equipartition of energy between the various phonon modes [1]. The dispersion curves of the phonons, *i.e.*, the variation of their frequency with wavelength, are also important in telling us something about the interatomic forces in the crystals. This is why these curves are so much studied nowadays by X-rays or neutron scattering [12]. It is however clear that a knowledge of phonons alone is quite insufficient to discover the nature and the value of the interatomic forces involved in the very large displacements occurring during radiation damage. The higher-order terms in elasticity (anharmonic terms) are of little use, if not pushed to very high orders indeed. One has had, therefore, to rely, in this field, up till now, on very rough theoretical estimates or on indirect evidence about surfaces, grain-boundaries and liquids.

Fig. 3. – Crowdion along a row *A B*.

We can finally list two other dynamic defects, which will be discussed at length later on at this meeting. The *focussons* [13] correspond to the possibility for kinetic energy to be transmitted not through a volume, as in a phonon, but along a close-packed row in the crystal. It would indeed be difficult to describe such a progression in terms of phonons. The *dynamic crowdions* [14] correspond to a possible transport of matter along some rows in some crystalline structures; the atoms along row *AB*, Fig. 3, push themselves in such a way that an excess atom progresses along the row.

II. – Static Defects.

These can be classified as follows, from a geometrical point of view:

1) *Point defects*: impurity atoms, either inserted into interstitial positions in the crystal, or substituted to atoms of the pure crystal. Vacancies are a particular case of the latter, where atoms are merely removed from lattice sites.

2) *Linear defects*: dislocation lines.

3) *Surface defects*: the outer surface of a crystalline sample is, of course, a break in the periodicity of the lattice; grain boundaries, between crystals of different orientation or chemical structures, are another example.

4) *Volume defects*: aggregates of various kinds, such as displacement spikes in radiation damage, Guinier-Preston zones in solid solutions.

Surface defects will be treated first, then dislocations and finally point defects.

1. – Surface defects.

1'1. Outer surfaces. – Thys type of defect, which separates the crystal from vacuum or from an atmosphere, is characterized by its surface tension.

a) The *surface tension* γ_s can be taken as the excess free energy per unit area of the surface. It has been measured for instance by heating wires of various lengths, suspended by their ends, at a temperature high enough for creep to occur [15]. One then observes the larger wires to lengthen under their own weight; the shorter ones contract, under their surface tension (Fig. 4). The measurement of the intermediary length where the weight equilibrates the surface tension gives the latter quantity. One finds values of the order of

$$\gamma_s \simeq \mu b/10 \,, \tag{1.1}$$

where μ is the elastic shear modulus and b the interatomic distance.

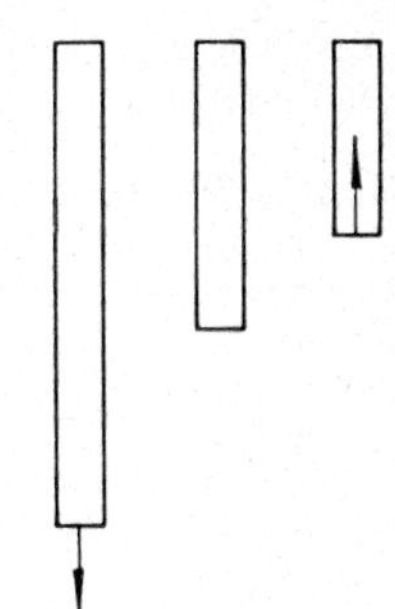

Fig. 4. – Measurement of surface tension.

Such a value can be understood from the fact

that γ_s is the work done to break in two a crystal over a unit area. Let $\sigma(x)$ be the tension exerted to displace by x the two halves of the crystal with respect to each other (Fig. 5). For very small x, *i.e.* in the elastic range, σ must be of the order of Ex/b, where E is Young's elastic modulus. One also expects σ to vanish when x is large enough, because interatomic forces are only fairly close range. $\sigma(x)$ must therefore have a form such as that pictured in Fig. 6; and

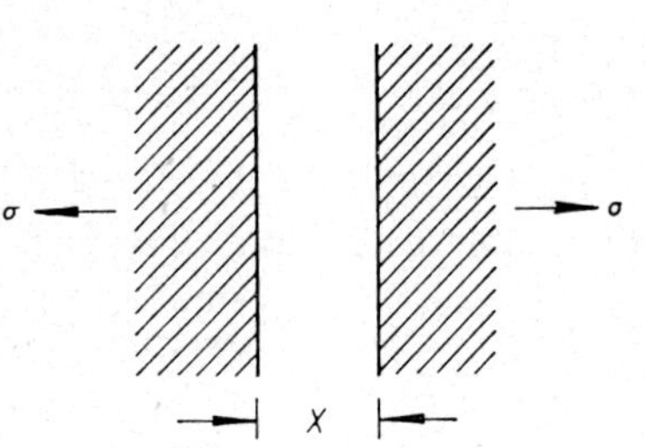

Fig. 5. – Tension to separate by x the two halves of a crystal.

$$2\gamma_s = \int_{\mathscr{A}} \sigma \, \mathrm{d}x \, .$$

A value near to (1.1) is obtained if $\sigma(x)$ is taken as a sinusoidal curve and vanishes for $x \simeq b/2$. Values of the order of (1.1) have also been obtained in a few cases where more detailed computations have been made. These involve a knowledge of the electronic structure of the surface.

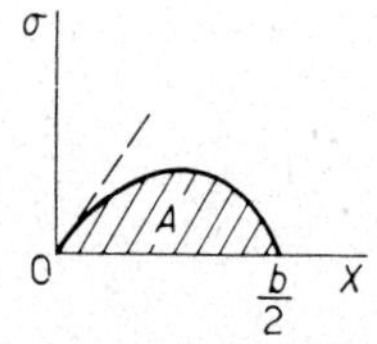

Fig. 6. – Variation of σ with x.

b) The *electronic structure* of the surface differs, of course, depending on the nature of the material considered.

In *metals*, the surface tension is due to the valence electrons and arises from two quantum mechanical effects. If the potential V in the vacuum were infinite, so that the electrons were kept completely in the metal, their wave function ψ should vanish at the surface S (Fig. 7). This effect reduces their density near to the surface, thus increases their Fermi energy [16]. In actual fact, the increase of potential towards vacuum is more progressive and finite, as pictured in Fig. 7 *b*). As a result, the electron wave functions are able to penetrate a little into the vacuum, by a kind of tunnel effet, in such a way that the electronic charge in the vacuum compensates the lack of charge, near the surface, inside the metal [17]. But the electronic charge in the vacuum is submitted to a potential higher than in the metal; this effect also produces an increase in energy [18].

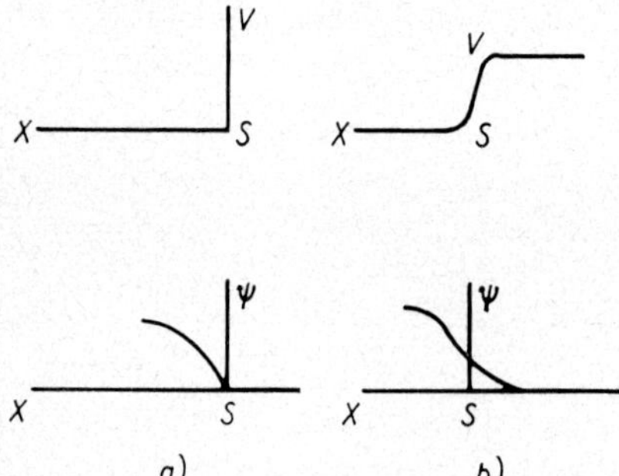

Fig. 7. – Behaviour of the electronic wave functions at the surface of a metal *a*) Impenetrable vacuum; *b*) real case.

In *covalent* structures, the surface tension is best computed by counting simply the number of bonds broken by the surface [19] (Fig. 8). Excess electrons can actually be captured on the surface to saturate these broken bonds. In other words, the surface gives rise to acceptor levels in the forbidden energy gap, which are usually fairly stable below the conduction band (Fig. 9). In an n-type semiconductor, these surface levels are thus filled at the expense of the shallow impurity levels, turning the surface layer into p character (Figs. 8 and 9). Such a layer is well established in materials such as germanium [20].

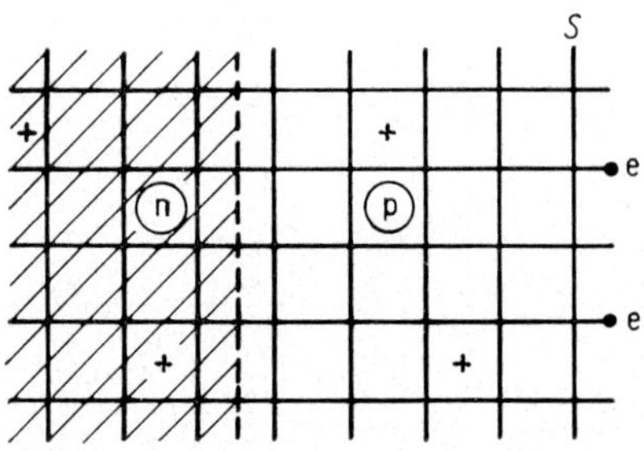

Fig. 8. – Broken bonds on the surface S of a covalent structure; p character due to captured electrons saturating some bonds.

Finally, in *ionic solids* [21], the surface tension arises from the work done against the electrostatic forces to remove one half of the crystal (Fig. 10). The removal of the dashed half of the crystal, Fig. 10, disturbs the electrostatic balance; thus part of the positive charge of ion A is no longer compensated by the negative ion B. One can think that there are now uncompensated charges of alternate signs on the surface ions, and that the surface energy arises from their Coulomb interactions. A simple reasoning shows that, for structures with equal numbers of positive and negative ions of charges $\pm Ze$ the uncompensated charges are equal (*) to $\frac{1}{2}Ze$.

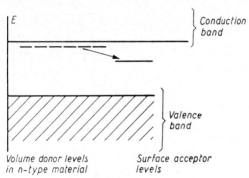

Fig. 9. – Saturation of surface acceptor levels by volume donor levels, giving rise to a p surface layer in an n-type semiconductor.

c) The surface tension is obviously *anisotropic*. In metallic or covalent structures, it is smallest for close packed planes; for covalent structures, more bonds are broken, obviously, for the atomically rough surface of Fig. 11 *b*) than for the smooth one, Fig. 11 *a*); in metals, electrons are more simply reflected by the latter than by the former, and this should correspond to a

(*) This is easily seen by thinking that the addition of the dashed plane of ions, Fig. 10, changes the signs of the uncompensated charges without altering their absolute magnitude.

more stable state. In ionic solids the uncompensated surface charges should cancel each other at close range: in Fig. 12, *a* is more stable than *b*.

Perhaps a physically more important problem is whether, for a given orientation, a roughness on an atomic scale is more or less stable than on a larger one (Fig. 11 *b* or Fig. 13). In most cases this problem is not clearly settled either theoretically or experimentally. My personal feeling is that atomic roughness should be somewhat more stable in metals and covalent structures. This is because the electrons should be able to rearrange themselves more easily on isolated atomic steps than on larger ones, so that an atomic step should be more stable when isolated than when included in a larger one: covalent bonds such as *b*, *b'*, Fig. 11, could stabilize each other; larger tunnel effects could occur on such steps in metals. Thus big steps should occur only in special cases: as configurations out of equilibrium, due to the kinetics of crystal growth or etching; or when there is an adsorbed layer of large atoms or molecules: these will obviously fit more easily to the big steps of Fig. 13. One expects the contrary to be generally true in ionic solids: each atomic step is obviously the site of an excess charge which is not necessarily compensated at very close range; in big steps between stable surfaces, of the type of Fig. 12*a*, only the corners such as *C*, Fig. 13, carry excess charges which are not compensated at close range. Observations on surfaces obtained by cleavage [22] or heated in various conditions [23] are, on the whole, in fair agreement with these conclusions.

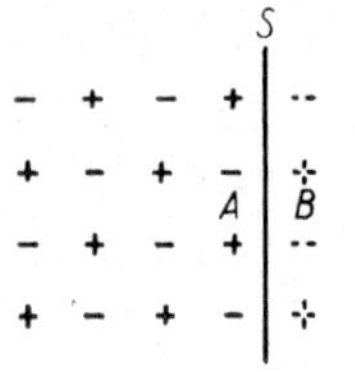

Fig. 10. – Surface tension in ionic solids.

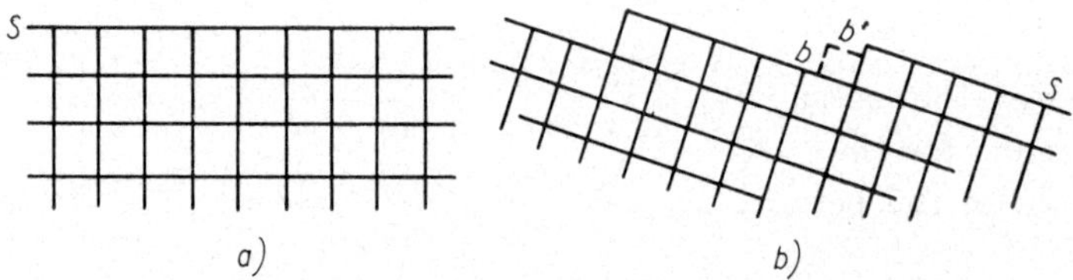

Fig. 11. – Atomically smooth and rough surfaces.

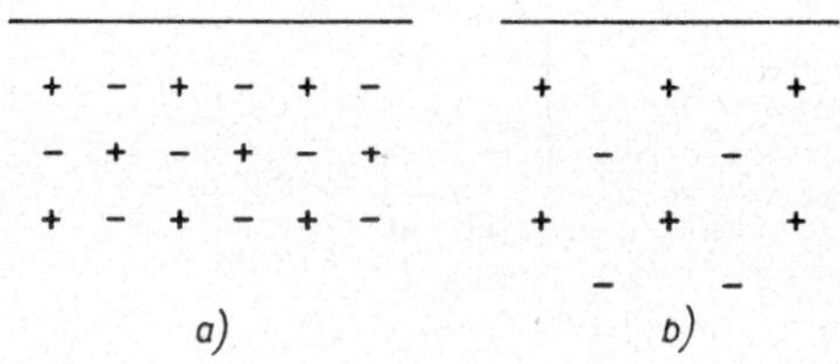

Fig. 12. – Two orientations of the surface in ionic solids.

d) As far as one can tell from the high-temperature measurements made so far, the surface tension seems to decrease somewhat with increasing temperature [15]. There is, therefore, a *positive surface entropy*.

The main part of it has probably a vibrational origin: the atoms on the surface can vibrate, normally to the surface, more easily than parallel to it or than atoms inside the crystal can do [24]. At temperatures definitely higher than the Debye temperature, the atoms can be assumed to vibrate independently from each other. The surface atoms have then one degree of freedom with a free energy:

$$F_s = kT \ln \frac{\theta_s}{T},$$

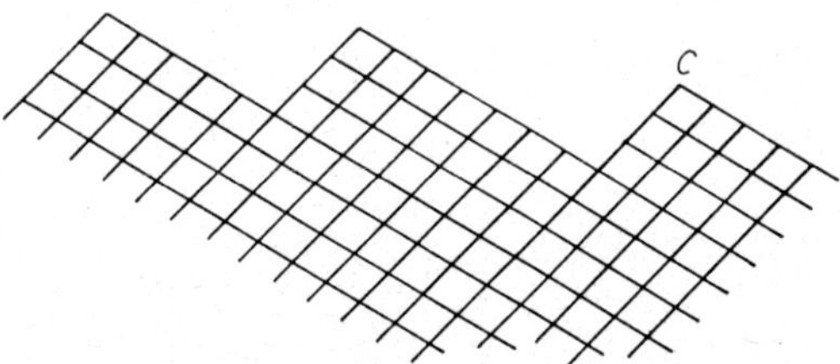

Fig. 13. – Microscopically rough surface.

which involves a Debye temperature θ_s somewhat smaller than the volume value θ_v. The corresponding excess entropy per unit area is

$$\Delta S_s \simeq \frac{1}{b^2}\left(\frac{\partial F_v}{\partial T} - \frac{\partial F_s}{\partial T}\right) = \frac{k}{b^2} \ln \frac{\theta_v}{\theta_s} > 0 \,.$$

Assuming that the elastic constant involved in θ_s is something like half that in θ_v, one finds for the entropy a reasonable order of magnitude.

There is also the possibility of a positional entropy: at finite temperature, one expects the steps on the surface to become covered with « kinks » (k, **Fig. 14**), and also adsorbed atoms and adsorbed vacancies to appear, if the crystal is in equilibrium with its vapour. All these defects are of course produced because of their entropy. However, as far as fairly rough theoretical studies indicate [25], this contribution should usually be negligible, except if surface melting occurs: above a critical temperature and by a co-operative process, the surface might become covered with kinked steps and adsorbed point defects. However, this critical temperature cannot be much lower than the (volume) melting point; and there is indeed no break in the decrease of γ_s with increasing temperature which might indicate that the process occurs when the crystal is in contact with its vapour. Indeed, surface melting seems to have been observed only for crystals in contact with their melt [26].

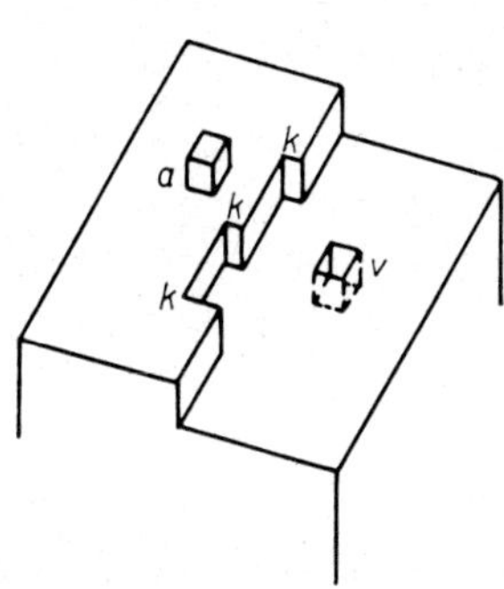

Fig. 14. – Surface at $T \neq 0^{0k}$, with kinks k, adsorbed atoms a and adsorbed vacancies v.

e) Finally, two points must be stressed in connection with *point defects.*

Surface diffusion is much more rapid than volume diffusion [27]. This is because volume diffusion occurs usually by vacancy migration. But vacancies adsorbed on the surface should be both more stable and perhaps more mobile; and there is the further possibility of diffusion by adsorbed atoms.

Atomically rough surfaces are easy sources and sinks for point defects, especially at their kinks [28]. This is because point defects created at kinks merely shift the kink along the step, without altering the total surface area. Point defects should be more difficult to create on atomically smooth surfaces, with big steps, because their formation then necessarily increases the surface area. Big steps should, however, be easy sinks for point defects, which should reduce their energy by going to any surface, except if repelled by an adsorbed layer.

1·2. Grain boundaries.

a) Ordinary *incoherent grain boundaries* must be thought of as mere surfaces along which two crystals of differents orientations stick together without being very much perturbed (Fig. 15). This is in agreement with the type of boundary observed with Bragg's bubble model [29], and is to be expected with short range interatomic forces. In such a model, the disorder along the boundary depends little on the misorientation θ between the grains. This is born out by measurements of the grain boundary tension γ_g. This varies little with θ, except for small angles θ (sub-boundaries) or for special orientations (coherent twins), where γ_g is definitely smaller [30] (Fig. 16).

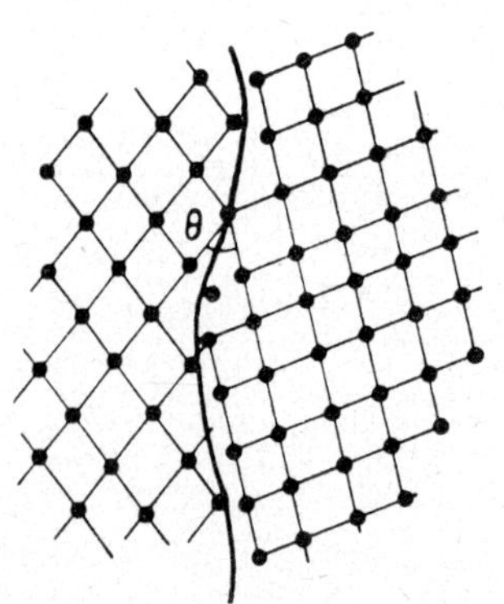

Fig. 15. – Atomic structure of a large angle grain boundary.

b) The stable state of a *sub-boundary* is for the two grains to be coherent except along some more or less equidistant lines of defect [31]. A simple case is pictured in Fig. 17. These lines are the dislocations discussed in the next section. This fact has been well established by observing the dislocation lines either as they emerge on the outer surface [32], or, in some cases, within the crystal [33]. The theory of dislocations discussed in the next section explains the variation of γ_g with small θ; starting from zero with a vertical tangent, it saturates at an angle $\theta_M \simeq 20°$, at a value which both the dislocation theory and experiment give as

$$\gamma_M \simeq \frac{\mu b}{20}.$$

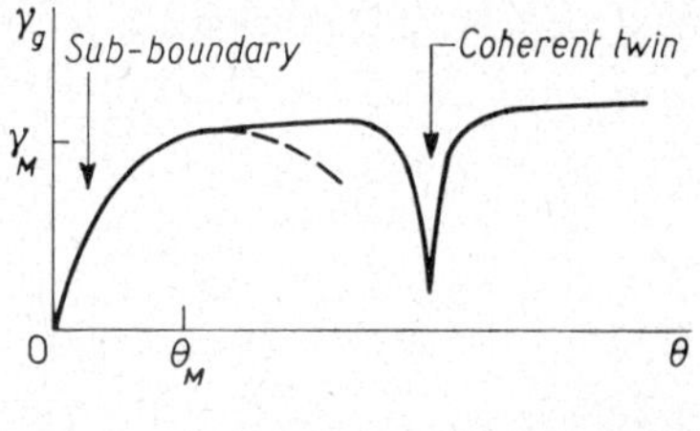

Fig. 16. – Variation of the grain boundary tension γ_g with the misorientation θ between the grains.

For larger angles θ, the dislocations are so close that they lose their identity and this theory, which predicts a decrease of γ_g along the broken curve, Fig. 17, no longer applies.

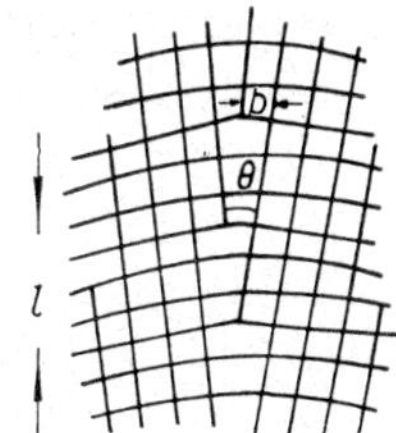

Fig. 17. – Sub-boundary as a dislocation wall.

c) *Coherent twin boundaries* join two crystal symmetrical with respect to the boundary. They can have a low energy if they do not perturb the atomic bonds too much. Fig. 18 gives a schematical example where the atomic planes are not at right angles, so that the atoms on the twin plane have the right length but not the right angles. The spinel twin boundaries of FCC metals, with a very similar structure, have indeed especially low tensions γ_t, the ratio γ_t/γ_M being of the order of 1/30 for copper and 1/5 for aluminium [34, 35].

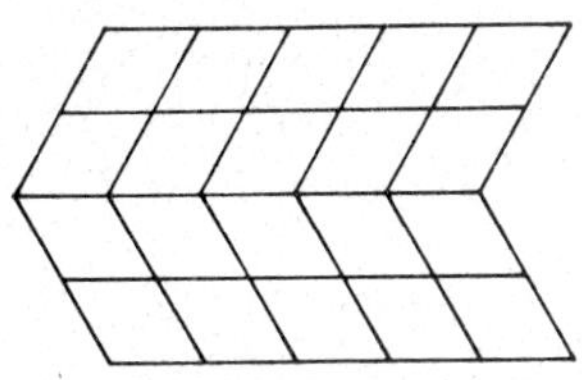

Fig. 18. – Coherent twin boundary.

Both γ_t and γ_M are measured by studying the equilibrium of the tensions at triple points between either the surface and a grain boundary or three grain boundaries. The anisotropy of these tensions makes the study somewhat difficult, so that these values are not known accurately [36]. It must also be stressed that no satisfactory computation of these tensions exists so far [37].

d) There are other possible types of coherent boundaries. An *epitaxial boundary* joins two different structures with a common lattice plane (Fig. 19*a*). A *stacking fault* is a fault, usually by twinning, in the stacking of close packed planes (Fig. 19*b*). It can indeed be considered as a winned lamella of atomic thickness, so that its surface tension γ_f should be near to twice the twin tension. It can also be considered as a layer L with a different crystalline structure than the rest of the crystal, so that its tension is the difference in free energy of the two structures. In the FCC structure, the stacking fault can be considered as a layer of HCP. Both methods seem useful to estimate γ_f in metals and alloys [38].

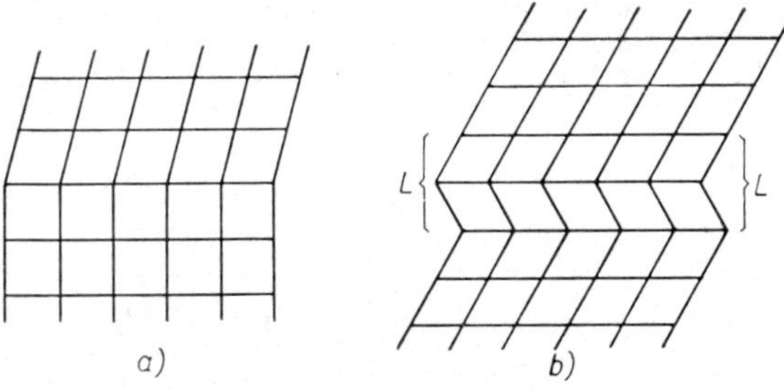

Fig. 19. – Two types of coherent boundaries: *a*) epitaxial; *b*) stacking fault.

e) As far as *point defects* are concerned, one observes, as expected, a vacancy diffusion somewhat intermediary between the surface and volume diffusions [39]: vacancies should be more stable and perhaps more mobile along the broken structure of the boundary than in the perfect crystal, but there is no equivalent to the surface adsorbed atoms. The few measurements made indicate that the selfdiffusion coefficient D_g increases linearly with the misorientation θ up to θ_M, then saturates to a fairly constant value [40] except near coherent twin positions [41] (Fig. 20). If one remembers that the regions of bad crystal at the center of dislocations coalesce for $\theta > \theta_M$, this seems to indicate that diffusion is rapid only along the regions of bad crystal, both in isolated dislocations and in grain boundaries. This conclusion is strengthened by the fact that, for sub-boundaries with only one family of parallel dislocations, as in Fig. 17, diffusion normal to the dislocation lines seems negligible up to $\theta = \theta_M$ [42].

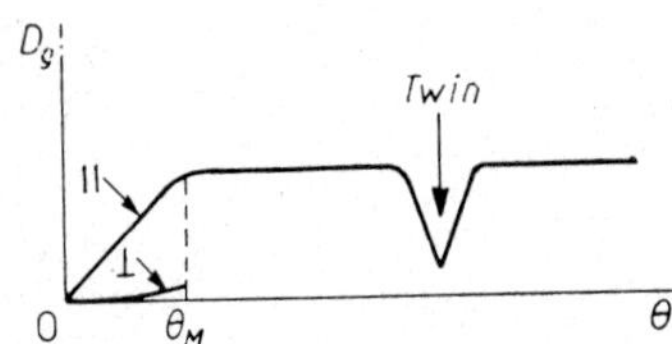

Fig. 20. – Variation with the misorientation θ of the grain boundary diffusion coefficient D_g.

One expects interstitials to move more slowly along incoherent grain boundaries or dislocations than in the perfect crystal: in such irregular structures, the interstitials will certainly be more stable in some positions than others, and will tend to stick there; in the perfect crystal, on the contrary, being nowhere very stable, they can jump more easily. This point is fairly well established for interstitial impurities such as carbon in iron [43]. It is also expected to be true, along dislocations, for interstitials with the same nature as the crystal. In large angle boundaries, they are probably rapidly absorbed by one of the grains so as to lose their identity.

Indeed incoherent boundaries are obviously easy sources and sinks for point defects [44], contrary to coherent boundaries [45].

2. – Dislocations.

2·1. Definition. – The dislocation lines used in the study of crystals can always be generated in the following way [38]:

1) Cut a volume V of matter along a surface S bounded by the line L (Fig. 21).

2) Translate the two lips of the cut by a vector $\boldsymbol{b}$ relative to each other, without deforming them.

3) Fill in the empty spaces eventually created, or remove the matter in excess.

4) Stick together the lips of the cut and remove the applied stresses.

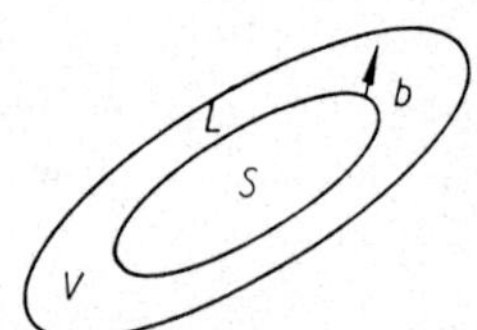

Fig. 21. – General definition of a dislocation line.

This succession of operations has obviously produced internal stresses in the material. These can be shown [46] to be continuous over the whole volume, except along the line L. Such a dislocation line is uniquely defined by its geometrical form L and its strength $\boldsymbol{b}$, or Burgers vector. The exact position of the surface S of the cut has no importance.

Take, for instance, a cylinder of isotropic matter; cut it along a half-plane S limited by the axis L; shear the lips of the cut by a vector $\boldsymbol{b}$ parallel to L. In the « screw » dislocation thus formed (Fig. 22), the planes normal to the axis have been replaced by helical surfaces. The same state of stress would obviously have been produced, starting with another surface S'. One finds that these are pure shear stresses, inversely proportional to the distance r to the line:

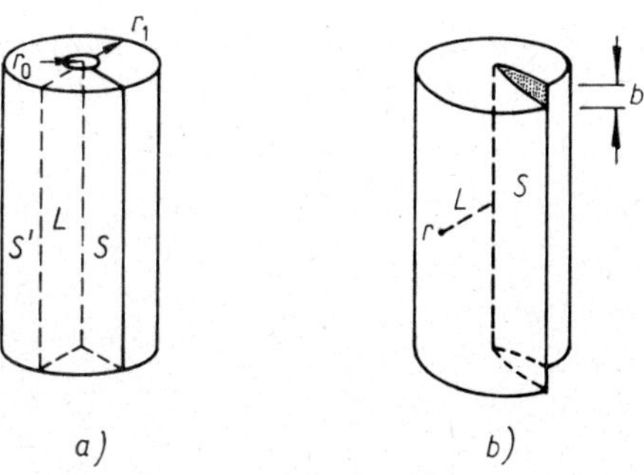

Fig. 22. – Formation of a screw dislocation.

$$\sigma = \frac{\mu b}{2\pi r}\,. \tag{2.1}$$

The energy stored per unit length of line is obtained by integrating $\sigma^2/2\mu$ over the volume of the cylinder. It acts as a line tension and is obviously given by a logarithmic expression:

$$\tau = \frac{\mu b^2}{4\pi}\ln\frac{r_1}{r_0}\,, \tag{2.2}$$

where r_1 is the outer radius of the cylinder anr r_0 a cut-off radius such that for $r < r_0$ the strains are so large that the elastic approximation used breaks down. For reasonable interactomic forces, the energy stored within the inner cylinder of radius r_0 is usually negligible.

In more complicated cases (non-screw orientation, anisotropic materials...), similar results obtain. Expression (2.2) is still approximately valid, where r_1 is the distance to another defect such as the outer surface or another dislocation. r_0 is of the order of an interatomic distance. With likely values of r_1, between a few hundred ångström and a few hundred μm, the line tension is

$$\tau \simeq \mu b^2\,. \tag{2.3}$$

2'2. Full and partial dislocations. – In crystalline structures, the Burger vector $\boldsymbol{b}$ is restricted to a few possible values.

a) The most obvious possibility is for the lips of the cut S to stick perfectly after the translation $\boldsymbol{b}$. This requires $\boldsymbol{b}$ to be a period of the Bravais lattice. The corresponding dislocations are sometimes called *full* or *perfect*. As the line tension is proportional to b^2, dislocations with a large multiple period b are not stable: they split into smaller periods b', b'', b''', ..., thus lowering the total energy (Fig. 23). Thus the only possible Burgers vectors of full dislocations are a few elementary periods of the Bravais lattice, which can be predicted for each structure.

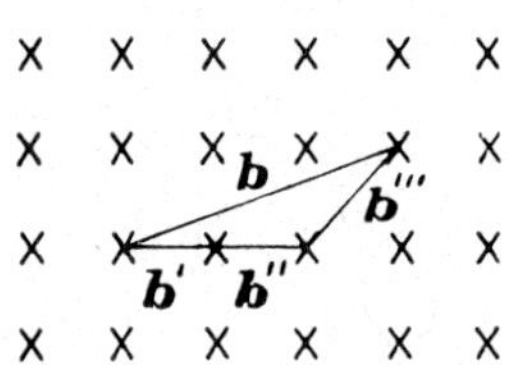

Fig. 23. – Splitting of a dislocation with a large Burgers vector $\boldsymbol{b}$ into dislocations with smaller periods $\boldsymbol{b}', \boldsymbol{b}'', \boldsymbol{b}'''$.

One of the first direct evidence of this fact comes from the study of the subgrain boundaries mentioned in the first lecture. The figure given then shows that the Burgers vector $\boldsymbol{b}$ of the dislocation lines can be deduced from a measurement of their distance l (from etch pits...) and of the misorientation θ of the grain (by X-rays):

$$b \simeq \theta l \, . \tag{2.4}$$

This leads indeed, in many substances, to a value of b equal to an elementary period of the lattice [32].

b) If $\boldsymbol{b}$ is not a period of the lattice, the atoms on the two lips of the cut will be out of step with each other, and the sticking operation will usually require a very large energy indeed. There are a few important exceptions; in some lattice structures and if the cut S is along some close-packed planes, some values of $\boldsymbol{b}$ can produce on S a stacking fault with low energy, of the kind discussed in the first lecture. The *partial* or *imperfect* dislocations thus formed are therefore always the boundary of a stacking fault, and their Burgers vector is not a period of the lattice.

Two examples will be given: the loops formed from a supersaturation of vacancies in HCP metals; the dissociated dislocations of FCC crystals.

The HCP structure can be thought of as a stacking of close packed planes with bonds between atoms of successive planes alternately inclined one way and the other (Fig. 24*a*). Vacancies can, in some cases, condense into a circular aggregate along a close-packed plane [47]. Once this plane has been removed over some area, the two neighbouring planes PP' will gain energy by moving toward each other, so as to close the gap and stick together. The possible interatomic bonds are, however, oriented in such a way that a stacking fault necessarily arises along P or P' (Fig. 24*b*). Its corresponding Burgers vector $\boldsymbol{b}$ has both a vertical and a horizontal component, because the planes PP' have moved somewaht in both directions to stick together.

It can be shown similarly that full dislocations in the FCC structure (Fig. 25*a*) become more stable by splitting into two parallel partials $\boldsymbol{b}'$, $\boldsymbol{b}''$

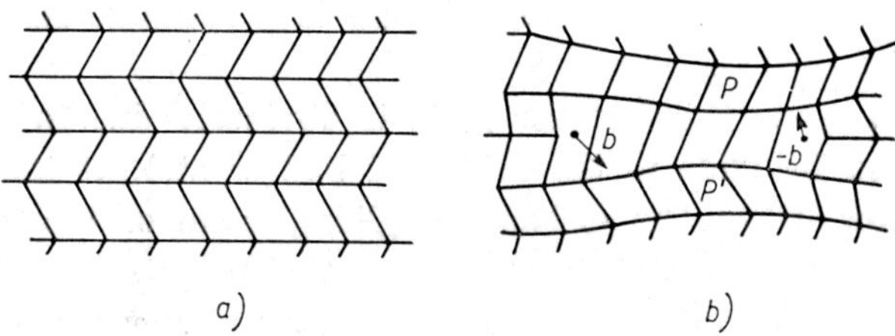

Fig. 24. – HCP structure: *a*) perfect crystal; *b*) with a Frank loop due to condensed vacancies.

bordering a narrow ribbon of stacking fault $\boldsymbol{b}'$, $\boldsymbol{b}''$ and the stacking faults are in the same close packed plane (Fig. 25*b*).

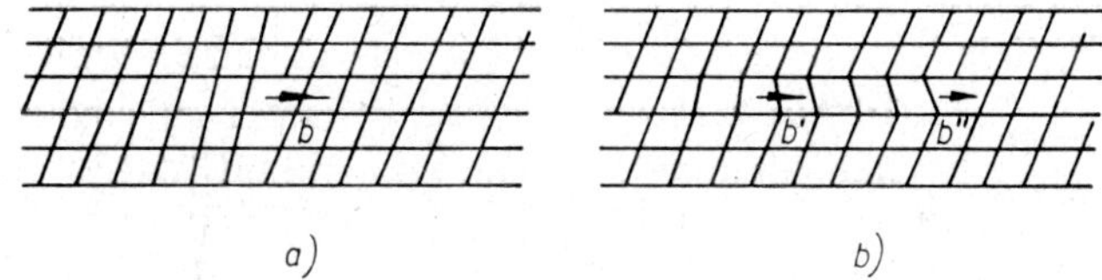

Fig. 25. – FCC structure with: *a*) a full dislocation $\boldsymbol{b}$; *b*) a dislocation split into two Shockley partials $\boldsymbol{b}', \boldsymbol{b}''$ with a stacking fault.

The partial dislocations with a Burgers vector parallel to the stacking fault, as in Fig. 25*b*, are called « glissile » or Shockley partials [48]. Those with a Burgers vector not in the plane of the stacking fault, as in Fig. 24*b*, are called « sessile » or Frank partials [49]. This distinction now will be explained.

2'3. Glide. – It is usually much easier for a dislocation to move parallel to its Burgers vector than in any other direction. Such a motion is called glide.

This is fairly clear on the simple example of Fig. 26*a*, where the dislocation has been produced by shear along the surface S: to move the dislocation horizontally, one needs only to extend or decrease the area of S by simple shear, without opening empty spaces or creating excess matter. Glide parallel to $\boldsymbol{b}$ is always the only way to move a dislocation

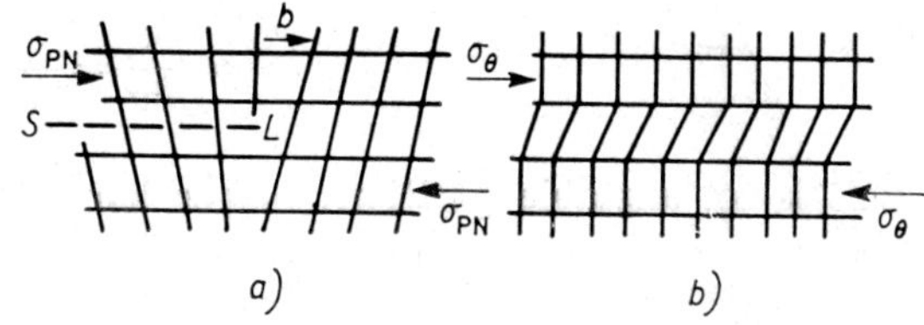

Fig. 26. – Two types of glide: *a*) by propagating a dislocation; *b*) simultaneous.

easily. One sees then for instance, that the glissile dislocation S of Fig. 25*b* can glide in the close-packed plane; the ribbon of stacking fault is merely shifted in this process. The sessile dislocation of Fig. 24*b* can glide only by creating a new stacking fault of high energy in a plane at an angle with the horizontal one.

The applied stress required for glide is obviously due to the changes of energy produced by glide in the region of bad crystal, at the center of the dislocation. Now, when the dislocation glides, some of the bonds lengthen while others shorten; they thus compensate their effects somewhat, in a way which would not be possible if glide occured simultaneously over the plane, as in Fig. 26*b*: the so-called « Peierls-Nabarro » stress σ_{PN} for dislocation glide [50] is certainly smaller than the « theoretical » elastic limit σ_θ for simultaneous glide [51], which is estimated to be of the order of $\mu/20$, or about 1 ton per square millimeter. This is indeed what led to the idea that plastic deformation occurs by dislocation glide. The exact value of σ_{PN}, and its dependence on temperature, are still poorly known, because they depend so much on the behavior of the inner core of bad crystal. All that can be said is that, in close-packed metals, it is low enough to explain observed elastic limits smaller than $10^{-4}\mu$; it seems definitely larger in covalent structures like diamond, silicon, germanium [52].

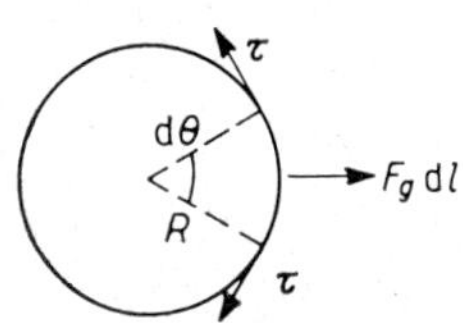

Fig. 27. – Radius of curvature R under an applied stress σ.

There is a last difficulty about plastic deformation: if dislocations glide easily, they are very hard to form in a perfect crystal. The applied stresses required are again of the order of the theoretical elastic limit. This is easily seen by computing the radius of a loop in equilibrium with an applied stress σ. If the Peierls-Nabarro stress is neglected, the curvature $1/R$ of the loop must be such that on an element dl, the action of the line tension τ equilibrates the force $F_g\,\mathrm{d}l$ due to the applied stress (Fig. 27). Now a *shear* stress $\boldsymbol{\sigma}$ acting on the glide plane of the loop produces a gliding force F_g on the loop which is obviously normal everywhere to the loop and equal to (*)

$$F_g = \boldsymbol{\sigma b}\,. \tag{2.5}$$

Thus

$$R = \frac{\mathrm{d}l}{\mathrm{d}\theta} = \frac{\tau}{\boldsymbol{\sigma b}}\,. \tag{2.6}$$

This is an unstable position: bigger loops tend to expand, but smaller ones tend to contract. Loops can therefore be created by thermal activation only

(*) This is seen [53] by computing the work $F_g S = (\boldsymbol{\sigma} S)\boldsymbol{b}$ produced by $\boldsymbol{\sigma}$ when a dislocation such as that of Fig. 26*a* sweeps over an area S.

if R is of atomic dimensions. Even with a fairly small line tension τ, the stress σ required is at least of the order of $\mu/10$.

This leads to the idea that fairly plastic crystals, especially metals, must have a pre-existing network of dislocations before any plastic deformation has occured [54]. It is indeed observed that many well-formed crystals have such a network, with an average mesh of 10 to 100 μm [38]. Often such crystals become brittle only when the dislocations of this « Frank » network are pinned down in some way (impurity atoms [55], radiation damage [56],...).

Finally, once a crystal starts deforming, its dislocation density ϱ increases in various ways. They multiply, get entangled into each other, pile up in front of grain boundaries, etc.. ϱ can reach 10^{10} to 10^{11} cm^{-2}. Such a high density corresponds to a measurable stored energy

$$W \simeq \varrho\tau \tag{2.7}$$

which can reach 10^6 erg/cm. This energy is mainly due to the long range elastic stresses σ_i set up around the dislocations, which can be measured by X-ray line broadening. The following relation applies as an order of magnitude [57]:

$$W \simeq \frac{\sigma_i^2}{\mu}\,. \tag{2.8}$$

The increase in dislocation density by work hardening makes the glide of dislocations more and more difficult in the increasingly less perfect crystal. Experiment [58] shows that the yield stress σ_c (or hardness) increases with σ_i:

$$\sigma_c = A\sigma_i\,, \tag{2.9}$$

with A very roughly of the order of unity. As a result, the yield stress σ_c should increase with the dislocation density ϱ:

$$\sigma_c = B\mu b\varrho^{\frac{1}{2}}\,.$$

Theory [59] and measurements [60] show that B is somewhat smaller than unity.

2'4. Climb. – For the dislocation line of Fig. 26*a* to move up or down, atoms must obviously be subtracted or added to the extra half plane. For a climb upwards, interstitials must be emitted or vacancies absorbed; the contrary applies to a downward climb. Such a movement is called climb and needs either large stresses or high temperatures.

a) *Instantaneous climb*: An applied *tension* σ, if large enough, can induce the dislocation to climb: the work done by the corresponding climbing force $\boldsymbol{F}_c$ on the dislocation must be larger than the energy spent in creating point defects. If U_f is the formation energy of such defects, and using a relation similar to (2.5), the condition is

$$\sigma b^3 > U_f \,. \tag{2.10}$$

This leads to enormous stresses, met only in very special cases.

Consider, for instance, two dislocations of opposite signs, gliding in parallel and neighbouring planes PP', and meeting each other. The row of vacancies created in the case of Fig. 28 can be considered as due to the mutual annihilation by climb of the two dislocations. Such a process is only possible if P and P' are not distant by more than a few interatomic distances. A similar process can in principle occur for interstitials, but P and P' must be even closer together, because the energy U_f is larger in that case. This and other analogous processes [61] probably explain why point defects, and especially vacancies, are usually formed during work hardening.

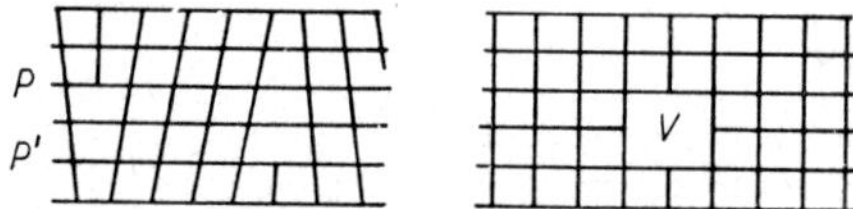

Fig. 28. – Creation of vacancies by mutual annihilation of dislocations with opposite signs.

b) *Slow climb*: When the applied stresses are too small for instantaneous climb to occur, a slow climb is still possible at high temperatures, with the use of thermal agitation. Point defects are then emitted or absorbed one by one by the dislocation line. In most cases, they will be emitted by the « jogs », where the line goes from one atomic plane to the next one (Fig. 29). The work done by the applied stresses, σb^3, is to be added to the energy U_f spent to form the point defect. The equilibrium concentration of point defects near to such a line is thus

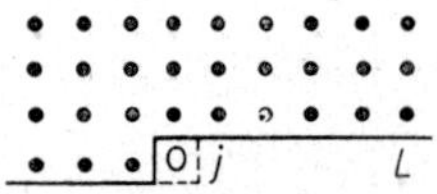

Fig. 29. – Emission of a vacancy from a dislocation line by shifting a jog j. (Picture in the half-plane, normal to $\boldsymbol{b}$).

$$c = c_0 \exp\left[-\frac{\sigma b^3}{kT}\right], \tag{2.11}$$

where $c_0 \simeq \exp[-U_f/kT]$ would be the equilibrium concentration near to a flat surface or grain boundary. The local super- or under-saturation due to the stress sets up a concentration gradient of point defects between this dislocation line and the surface (or other lines under different stresses). The climb rate is then usually controlled by the diffusion rate of the point defects between their sources and sinks, and is proportional to the applied stress, if not too large.

There are some cases, however, where the kinetics of climb are slowed down appreciably, because point defects are not so easily emitted by the dislocations. Thus, for *widely dissociated dislocations*, jogs are difficult to form [62], because one has either to pinch the two partials together against their mutual repulsion (Fig. 30*a*) or form split jogs, where usually some dislocation lines must necessarily lie on the edges *ee'* of the steps (Fig. 30*b*). In either case, the jog energy may be so high that their thermodynamic concentration becomes small, and emission from them a rare event. Point defects could also be directly emitted from the edge of a dislocation. This would, however, leave on the dislocation line a compensating adsorbed defect: adsorbed interstitial if a vacancy is emitted, and vice versa. Such a defect, pictured in Fig. 31, has an appreciable energy $U_{f'}$, which must be added to the usual energy U_f of the emitted defect.

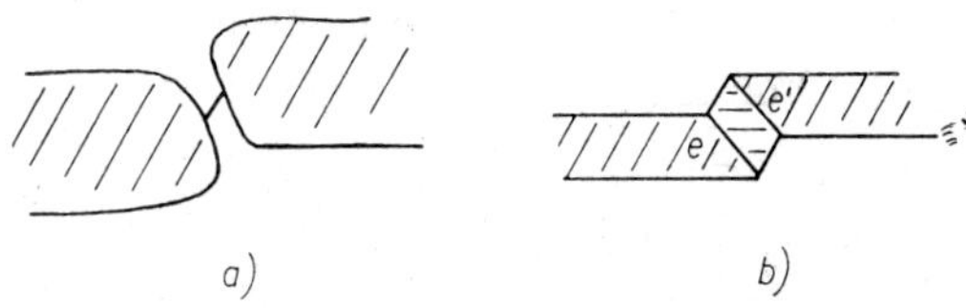

Fig. 30. – Two types of jogs on dissociated dislocations.

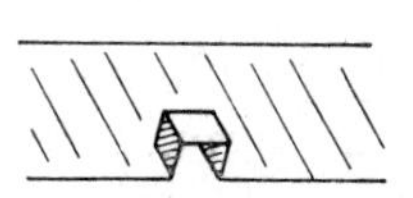
Fig. 31. – Defect produced, on a dissociated dislocation by the emission or absorption of a point defect (schematic perspective).

In conclusion, the *emission* of point defects may be the slower rate-determining process in the climb of dissociated dislocation. No such difficulty arises for their *absorption*: in that case, the energy change $U_{f'} - U_f$ of the atomic jump is usually negative: the point defect is more stable when adsorbed on the line [63].

The stress σ inducing climb can have various origins:

1) an external stress (*creep*);

2) an internal elastic stress, due to interactions between dislocation lines (*recovery, polygonization*);

3) an internal thermodynamical stress, due to *super-* or *undersaturation of point defects*.

In the last case, the climbing force F_c on the dislocation tends to move it in such a way as to remove the excess or lack of point *defects*. This force is again normal to both $\boldsymbol{b}$ and L; eq. (2.11) shows that it is constant and equal to

$$|F_c| = |\sigma b| = \frac{kT}{b^2}\left|\ln\frac{c}{c_0}\right|. \tag{2.12}$$

The equilibrium form of a dislocation line under such a force is easily seen to be a helix wound on a circular cylinder of axis parallel to $\boldsymbol{b}$ and radius

$$R \simeq \frac{\tau}{F_c}\,. \tag{2.13}$$

A particular case would be a circle [65], of radius R, normal to $\boldsymbol{b}$ (Figs. 32*a* and *b*). For the circular loop, this is again an unstable equilibrium. By the same reasoning as above, loops have no chance of nucleating if the critical radius R is not of atomic dimensions: these loops can nucleate only for fairly high super- (or under-) saturations (*) [66], given by $R \leqslant a$ few b's. For helices, it can be seen that no such stringent nucleation condition obtains: pre-existing dislocations should start climbing into helices under supersaturations for which loops cannot yet form.

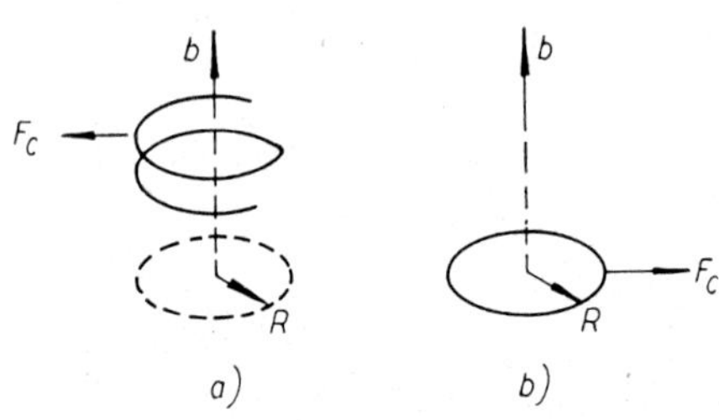

Fig. 32. – *a*) Helix; *b*) circle in equilibrium under a given supersaturation of point defects.

3. – Point defects.

3·1. Impurity atoms in general. – One of the most important properties of impurity atoms is probably that they should preserve the total electrical neutrality of the crystal.

a) *Condition of electrical neutrality*: This point has already been stressed about ionic solids: in NaCl the extra positive charge of the substitutional Ca^{++} ions must be compensated by an equal number of positive Na^+ ion vacancies (Fig. 33). These are responsible for low temperature ionic conductivity [67], when thermal agitation is still large enough to keep the vacancies mobile and free from the impurity ions [68].

$Na^+Cl^-\ Na^+$
$Cl^-\ Ca^{++}Cl^-$
Na^+Cl^- [Na^+]

Fig. 33. – Positive ion vacancy associated with Ca^{++} ion substituted in NaCl.

In a covalent crystal like tetravalent Ge, a substituted pentavalent As atom will have four of its valence electrons bound to the neighbouring germanium atoms. Thus an As^+ ion is easily substituted for a Ge atom (Fig. 34). The fifth valence electron, which should compensate the positive charge of the As^+ ion, cannot be so tightly bound. In

(*) Values of U_{f_v} discussed in the last section show that the supersaturation of vacancies formed by quenching is sufficient to nucleate dislocation loops only if the recovery remperature at which loops are formed is less than something like half or two thirds of the temperature from which one quenches.

its most stable state, it is only loosely bound by the weak Coulomb potential $-e/Kr$. If the crystal has a high dielectric constant K, this electron is easily excited thermally into the conduction band from this shallow impurity bound-state, giving rise to the characteristic semiconducting properties of n-type germanium [69].

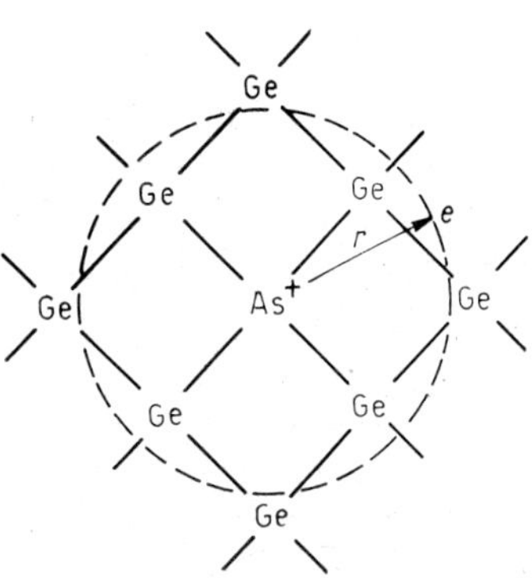

Fig. 34. – Shallow impurity states in semiconductors.

In metals, the extra nuclear charge introduced by an impurity, whether substitutional or interstitial, is screened out at very close range indeed [70]: the mobile valence electrons pile up locally so that most of the screening occurs within the impurity atom itself (Fig. 35). This is to be expected from the fact that no electrostatic field should occur, in a conductor, within the limits of classical physics—thus outside interactomic distances; it also comes from the Debye formula given in the first section, with the values of the screening radius r_0 for usual metals.

Besides this concentrated screening, each impurity atoms sets in a metal long range oscillating changes in electronic density [71], as pictured in Fig. 35. These diffraction patterns are, however, so weak that they can be safely neglected for all but a few properties, such as the long range magnetic coupling, between impurities [72] or the changes by alloying in the nuclear magnetic resonance of a metal [73].

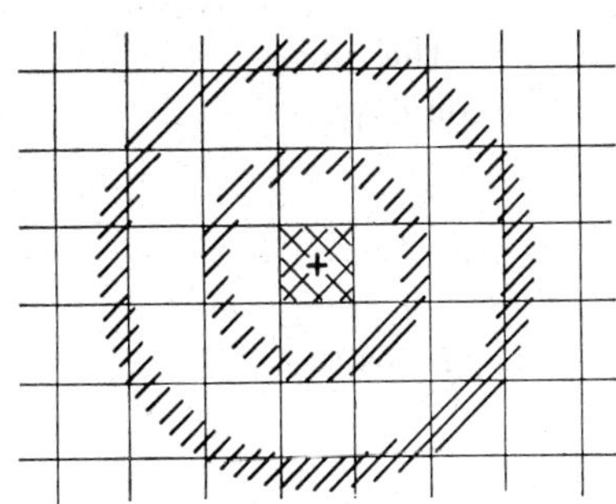

Fig. 35. – Local screening and long range changes in electronic density produced by an impurity in a metal. The squares represent schematically the atomic cells.

Ionic and covalent solids are dealt with at length in this course. The end of this section will therefore be restricted to stressing a few consequences of short range screening of impurities in *metals*. One can distinguish the « chemical » properties directly related to the detailed electronic structure, and the « elastic » ones, where a cruder model applies.

b) « Chemical » properties of metallic impurities. – Because the perturbation introduced by an impurity is localized on itself, one expects its contribution to the electric resistivity $\Delta\varrho$ to be fairly small: the effective cross-section A used to compute $\Delta\varrho$ must have atomic dimensions at most [70]

$$A \leqslant \pi r_s^2 , \tag{3.1}$$

where the radius of the atomic sphere r_s is related to the atomic volume v by

$$v = \frac{4}{3}\pi r_s^3 . \tag{3.2}$$

More precisely, cross-sections of the order of πr_s^2 are expected, and indeed measured, for impurities in transitional matrices, where the mobile conduction electrons are easily scattered into empty states of the d-band by any appreciable perturbation.

In ordinary, nontransitional matrices, cross-sections definitely smaller than πr_s^2 are observed when the impurity introduces only small changes in valence (interstitial impurity with small valency or substitutional impurity with a valence near to that of the matrix). The explanation is twofold:

1) Light interstitials (*e.g.* H) or substitutional impurities in the same period as the matrix and a neighbouring valency (*e.g.* Zn in Cu) produce only a small perturbation, which scatters the conduction electrons only slightly. This is fully born out by quantitative estimates [74] for, say, Zn, Ga ... in Cu.

2) Impurities with the same valency but in different periods scatter in much the same way as the conduction electrons of a given matrix. When one impurity atom is replaced by another in a different period, the large change in perturbing potential is more or less compensated by a large change in kinetic energy: the change in the number of inner shells leads to a change in the number of nodes around the nucleus in the wavefunctions; the corresponding change in the curvature of the wavefunctions leads, by Schrödinger's equation, to the change in kinetic energy. When, for instance, a gold atom is substituted into silver, the conduction electrons are not much scattered, because the wavefunctions just take one more node around the gold atom, without changing much their energy or their behavior at large distances from the nuclei [75]. This is shown schematically in Fig. 36 for the wavefunction at the botton of the Ag conduction band.

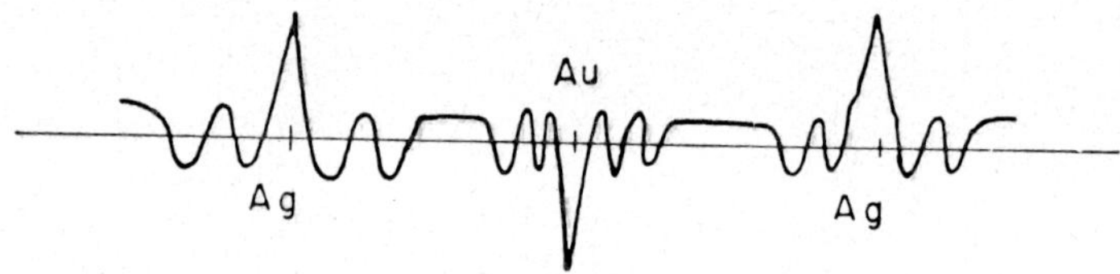

Fig. 36. – Wavefunction at the bottom of the conduction band of silver with a substituted gold atom.

Finally, when the valence effects are small, one has to take into account the size effects discussed below. The electrical resistivity is not very sensitive to the long range elastic distortions produced by an interstitial [76], or by a substitutional atom with the wrong size. But a size effect changes the screening condition: thus, for instance, too big a substitutional atom, which repels the neighbouring nuclear charges, requires locally fewer electrons for its screening than if it had the right size. In fact, if Ze is the change in valency produced by the impurity, the charge to be screened is [77]

$$Z_{\text{eff}}\,e = Ze - N\,\Delta v\,, \tag{3.3}$$

if Δv is the local expansion of the lattice produced by the impurity, and N the density of valence electrons. This screening rule explains, for instance, the fairly small resistivities observed when alkali metals are dissolved in liquid sodium ($Z=0$, cf. [78]).

As far as chemical contributions to the energies are concerned, only qualitative points can be made so far:

1) *The chemical energy of interaction* between two impurity atoms should be very short range, and then fairly small, because each impurity does not perturb very appreciably the metal outside its own atomic cell. The sign and value of this chemical interaction should be related to the long range oscillations pictured in Fig. 35, and have not been estimated correctly so far.

2) *The chemical energy of solution* of an impurity atom should be fairly small, because an impurity atom keeps most of its electronic charge as in the pure solute element, and with much the same structure if valence differences are not too large.

It is indeed well known that metallic solid solutions are often nearly « ideal », when the size effects discussed below are not too large: *i.e.*, both their energy of solution and interactions are fairly small, compared for instance with alloys with ionic or covalent characters.

c) « Elastic » properties of metallic impurities. Since impurity atoms behave in much the same way as if they were in the pure solute element, one is somewhat justified in using a rough elastic model to describe the distortions due to size effects and the change in elastic properties due to impurities [79]. This model is widely used for metallic alloys [74], but was first developed for ionic solid solutions [80]; it might also be of some use for covalent alloys. It will be therefore described in some detail, at least for metallic alloys.

In this model, the matrix and the impurity atom are both treated as classical elastic media, with compressibility and Poisson's ratio respectively χ and ν for the matrix, χ' and ν' for the impurity. The impurity atom is taken as a sphere of initial radius r'_s introduced into a spherical cavity of initial radius r_s in the matrix. The sphere and the cavity are then stuck together so as to take an intermediate radius b (Fig. 37). χ, ν, χ', ν' are taken equal to the elastic constant of the pure solvent and solute elements; r_s' is the radius of the atomic sphere for the pure solute; r_s is the same for the pure solvent, for substitutional impurities; it is taken to be very small for interstitial ones.

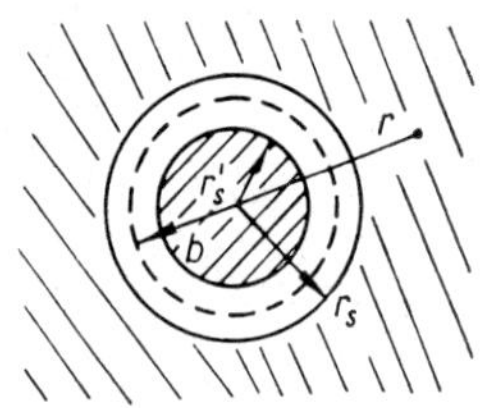

Fig. 37. – Elastic model for an impurity atom.

By sticking together, the two media are distorted: the impurity atom is under a uniform dilatation; in the matrix, there is a shear proportional to r^{-3}, and a small dilatation proportional to the concentration of impurities. The effect on various physical properties will be recalled.

A small atomic concentration c of impurities has similar effects on the *total volume* (as measured by density), the average *lattice parameter* (as measured by X-rays), and the *elastic constants* (shear modulus μ, compressibility χ):

$$\frac{\mathrm{d}V}{3V\,\mathrm{d}c} = \frac{\mathrm{d}a}{a\,\mathrm{d}c} = \alpha\,\frac{a'-a}{\bar{a}}\,, \tag{3.4}$$

$$\frac{\mathrm{d}\mu}{\mu\,\mathrm{d}c} = \alpha\,\frac{\mu'-\mu}{\bar{\mu}}\,, \tag{3.5}$$

$$\frac{\mathrm{d}\chi}{\chi\,\mathrm{d}c} = \alpha\,\frac{\chi'-\chi}{\bar{\chi}}\,, \tag{3.6}$$

with

$$\alpha = (1+x)\Big/\left(\frac{\chi'}{\chi}+x\right); \qquad x = (1+\nu)/2(1-2\nu) \simeq 2\,.$$

According to these equations, the lattice parameter should vary linearly with concentration if $\chi'=\chi$ (Vegard's law). A variation less rapid than Vegard's law is expected if the impurity is softer, more rapid if it is harder (Fig. 38). Eq. (3.4) actually predicts that the deviations from Vegard's law should keep within fairly narrow limits; it gives the correct sign and order of magnitude for these deviations in the Cu, Ag and Au base alloys [81]. Similarly, eq. (3.5) and (3.6) predict that the elastic constants should vary nearly linearly with concentration; there should, however, be a definite curvature downwards, if the elastic constants of the pure constituents are very different. The elastic constants of copper base alloys are also well explained in this way [82].

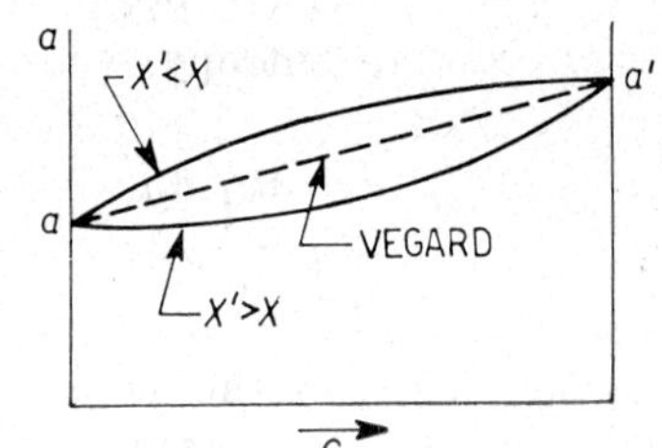

Fig. 38. – Variation of lattice parameter with concentration.

The same model gives for the elastic energy stored:

$$\varepsilon = 8\pi \frac{x}{(\chi'/\chi) + x} \mu b^3 \left(\frac{r'_s - r_s}{b}\right)^2 . \tag{3.7}$$

This elastic energy increases rapidly with the size factor, and becomes large compared with kT and with possible values of the chemical term if

$$\left|\frac{r'_s - r_s}{b}\right| \gg 10 \text{ to } 20\% . \tag{3.8}$$

This justifies Hume-Rothery's rule that only impurities with a size factor smaller than 15% have extensive solubilities [85]. For those impurities, however, the chemical term is usually preponderant in the energy of solution. The elastic term is then important only to compare the influence of a given impurity on the stability of various phases with similar electronic structures (*liquidus and solidus...* [84]).

The *entropy of solution* is of purely elastic origin: the chemical term does not lead to any appreciable contribution, except at low temperatures. There are two contributions:

1) The energy ε due to a *size factor* is really a work done, thus a free energy term. It decreases with increasing temperatures, because of the fairly strong decrease of the elastic constant μ. This gives an entropy term [74]

$$S_1 = -\frac{\partial \varepsilon}{\partial T} \simeq -\varepsilon \frac{\mathrm{d}\mu}{\mu\,\mathrm{d}T} > 0 . \tag{3.9}$$

2) If the elastic constants are different ($\mu' \neq \mu$), the variation of μ with c, Fig. 39, is such that a solid solution has a shear constant smaller than the linear average between the constituents. This gives an entropy term

$$S_2 = -\frac{3k}{2}\left(\frac{\mathrm{d}\mu}{\mu\,\mathrm{d}c} - \frac{\mu' - \mu}{\mu}\right) > 0 . \tag{3.10}$$

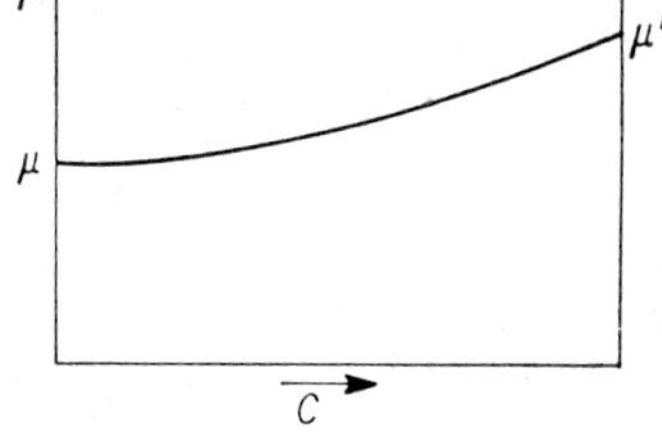

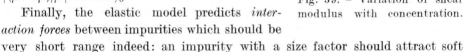

Fig. 39. – Variation of shear modulus with concentration.

S_1 and S_2 are of the same order of magnitude for a size factor of 15% and an « elastic » factor $|(\mu' - \mu)/\mu|$ of 100%.

Finally, the elastic model predicts *interaction forces* between impurities which should be very short range indeed: an impurity with a size factor should attract soft impurities and repel hard ones [79].

3'2. Vacancies, interstitials.

a) *Ionic solids.* Electrostatic neutrality also leads point defects to appear in pairs: two vacancies of opposite signs (Schottky defect [85]); or an interstitial positive ion with a positive ion vacancy (Frenkel defect [86]). The pair of interstitial negative ion plus negative ion vacancy cannot be produced thermally, because negative ion interstitials are so large that their elastic energy (eq. (7)) is prohibitive. Even positive interstitials only occur for small or polarizable ions. Thus Frenkel defects are formed thermally in silver halides, but only Schottky ones in alkali halides. Finally, after heating in some atmospheres, or after various excitations, the changes in ionic charge due to the vacancies can be screened out by bound electrons (for negative ion vacancies) or positive holes (for positive ion vacancies). These are, respectively, the *F* and *V* color centers, which absorb light by exciting their bound electrons or positive holes [67]. Fig. 40 summarizes these four types of defects.

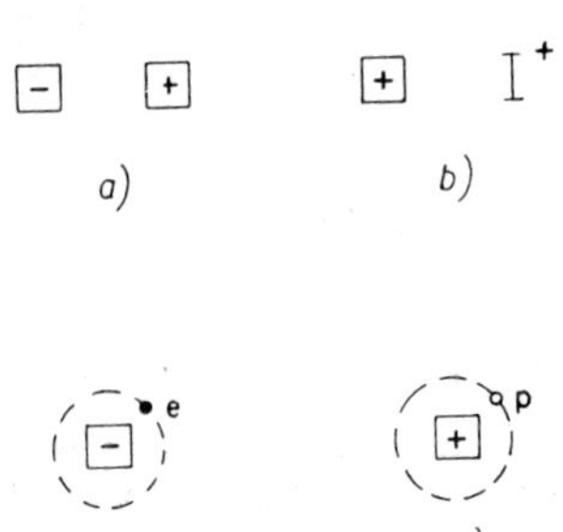

Fig. 40. – Four types of point defects in ionic solids: *a*) Schottky defect; *b*) Frenkel defect; *c*) *F* center; *d*) *V* center.

The energies of formation, displacement and association of these defects have been extensively studied, both theoretically and experimentally, as is explained in other lectures.

b) *Covalent solids.* A vacancy in germanium gives rise to four broken bonds (Fig. 41*a*). Because they are so near to each other, they will accept extra electrons even more easily than the broken bonds on the outer surface or on

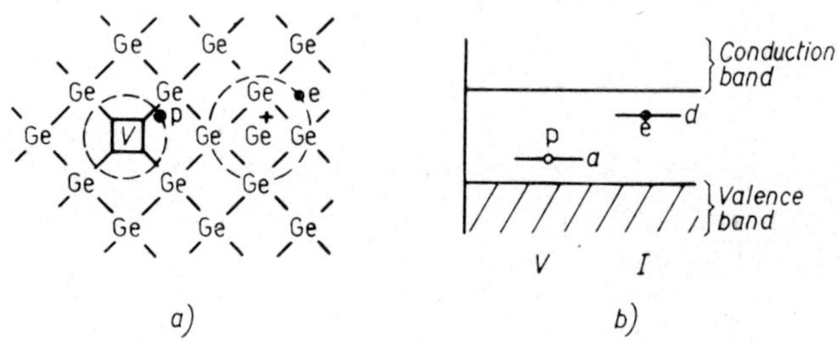

Fig. 41. – Acceptor levels on vacancies and donor levels on interstitials, in germanium: *a*) in space; *b*) in energy (schematic).

grain boundaries (cf. Sec. 1'2). The corresponding acceptor level (or levels) should be even more stable in energy than the surface levels (Fig. 41*b*).

An interstitial germanium atom will, on the other hand, be rather strongly squeezed in the narrow empty spaces of the germanium lattice. This should induce it to go into the lattice as a smaller positive ion, keeping one (or several) valence electrons in impurity states of large orbits. Interstitials should thus give rise to one or more not very stable donor levels.

Such a description of point defects is probably qualitatively correct [87], but quantitative data about the number and energy of the levels involved is lacking or confused in most substances.

In a covalent structure, the formation energy U_{fv} of a vacancy should be of the order of the cohesive energy E_c per atom. In the diamond structure, for instance, four bonds are broken to take away one atom so as to form one vacancy and one vapour atom; breaking the crystal into vapour atoms requires on the average two broken bonds per atom. Thus $U_{fv}+E_c \simeq 2E_c$ and

$$U_{fv} \simeq E_c\,.$$

The few energies U_{fv} measured seem to be somewhat smaller, no doubt because the broken bonds have interacted so as to reduce the energy.

c) *Metals.* According to the rules set up above, the cross-section for the electrical resistivity of point defects should be of the order of πr_s^2 in transitional metals, and somewhat smaller in ordinary metals of low valencies. Thus a vacancy in copper, with no valence electron, should be treated as a substitutional impurity reducing the valence by $Z=-1$, as for Ni in Cu; and an interstitial should be considered as introducing a valence $Z=1$, as H in Cu [88]. This treatment can only be approximate, because it neglects the changes in period produced by suppressing or creating all the inner shells of a copper atom. One should also take some account of the size effects, especially for the interstitials. It is therefore not surprising that the electrical resistivity of both vacancies and interstitials in copper, as deduced from various experiments, seems somewhat larger than that for Ni or H impurities, but still smaller than the maximum limit for $A=\pi r_s^2$ (1.5 to 3 $\mu\Omega$ cm/% experimentally [89], as compared with 3.5 $\mu\Omega$ cm/% if $A=\pi r_s^2$).

From eq. (4) of the elastic model, one deduces the changes in total volume V and lattice parameter a due to atomic concentrations c_i and c_v of interstitials and vacancies:

$$\left(\frac{\Delta V}{V}\right)_i = 3\left(\frac{\Delta a}{a}\right)_i - c_i\,, \tag{3.11}$$

$$\left(\frac{\Delta V}{V}\right)_v = 3\left(\frac{\Delta a}{a}\right)_v + c_v\,. \tag{3.12}$$

The corrective terms c_i and c_v take into account the fact that the interstitial atom was removed from the surface; and the atom removed from the vacancy was put on the surface. An atomic volume is therefore subtracted or added for each point defect created.

These equations show that, when point defects are created, the expression $(\Delta V/V) - 3(\Delta a/a)$ should be positive for vacancies, negative for interstitials. The point defects created by thermal agitation in aluminium and silver have been proved in this way to be vacancies [90]. Similarly, from the fact that the changes in volume and lattice parameter recover in the same way after irradiation of copper, *i.e.* $(\Delta V/V)_{i+v} - 3(\Delta a/a)_{i+v} = c_v - c_i =$ const, one has deduced that interstitials and vacancies were annihilating mutually, so as to keep $c_i - c_v$ a constant [91].

As far as actual values of $\Delta V/V$ and $\Delta a/a$ are concerned, only rough guesses are possible. Because interstitials should push away the surrounding atoms, one expects $\Delta a/a$ to be positive. If the distortions around the interstitial were small enough for linear elasticity to apply, it can be shown that one would expect $3(\mathrm{d}a/a\,\mathrm{d}c)_i = 1$. It is probable that the anharmonic terms involved in the large distortions actually occurring increase this value somewhat [92]:

$$3\left(\frac{\mathrm{d}a}{a\,\mathrm{d}c}\right)_i > 1\,, \qquad \text{thus} \qquad \left(\frac{\mathrm{d}V}{V\,\mathrm{d}c}\right)_i > 0\,.$$

Vacancies, if considered as cavities of atomic size, should tend to shrink under the action of their surface tension [93]. The effect should not be very large, because the effective surface tension involved is certainly reduced by tunnel effect from the normal value. Variation with pressure of diffusion by vacancies [94] and other more indirect evidence (interaction with dislocations...) concur to predict

$$0 < 3\left(\frac{\mathrm{d}a}{a\,\mathrm{d}c}\right)_v < \frac{1}{2}\,, \qquad \text{thus} \qquad \left(\frac{\mathrm{d}V}{V\,\mathrm{d}c}\right)_v > 0\,.$$

Treating a vacancy as a small cavity gives for its *energy of formation*:

$$U_{fv} \simeq 4\pi r s^2 \gamma_s\,. \tag{3.13}$$

By taking for the surface tension γ_s the value for flat surfaces, one finds an energy U_{fv} too large by a factor of about two. This gives the order of magnitude to be used for γ_s when computing the « shrinkage » of vacancies: one then finds a small shrinkage, $3(\mathrm{d}a/a\,\mathrm{d}c)_v \simeq 1/6$, which hardly affects the energy U_{fv}.

For interstitials, the size factor is probably preponderant and should give energies definitely larger than those observed for vacancies:

$$U_{fi} > \mu b^3 > U_{fv}\,. \tag{3.14}$$

More elaborate theoretical estimates have been made for a few metals, copper in particular. They agree with these conclusions, as the following table shows [95].

TABLE I. – *Computed energies of point defects in copper (in* eV).

U_{fv}	U_{fi}	U_{dv}	U_{di}
1 to 1.5	4 to 5	0.8 to 1.2	0.05 to 0.25

These computations predict that the interstitials should be more mobile than the vacancies ($U_{di} < U_{dv}$). This can be understood qualitatively from the fact that, in a close-packed metal, interstitials are nowhere very stable, thus need less energy to break through to a neighbouring equilibrium site. As explained below, the quantities U_{fv}, U_{dv}, U_{di} have been measured for a number of metals. U_{fi} has also been measured approximately for copper. The values found in all close-packed metals seem to agree in order of magnitude with the theoretical extimates in copper of Table I.

The entropy of formation can be estimated for vacancies, from eq. (3.10). Neglecting the small shrinkage and considering the vacancy as a completely soft material gives

$$S_{fv} \simeq (9/4)k \quad \text{per atom}.$$

The entropy for interstitials is probably mainly due to the size effect. Eq. (3.9) gives

$$S_{fi} \geqslant 30\,k \quad \text{per atom}.$$

Finally, the *interactions* of point defects with other impurities are not very well known. From the discussion above, one expects interstitials to attract soft impurities, especially vacancies, and repel hard ones, but only at very close range. Similarly, vacancies should attract impurities with a size factor; divacancies should also be stable, because of the reduction in surface tension, and mobile, because the neighboring atoms are more free to jump into a vacant site [96]. It is probable that, in FCC metals, trivacancies should be even more stable, but much harder to move: the three vacancies should empty a tetrahedron of neighbouring atoms, keeping one atom at the center of the empty tetrahedron [97].

d) Methods of production.

Work hardening has been seen to produce vacancies, and perhaps interstitials. When a material strained at low temperature is heated, these point defects disappear. This can be followed by studying a property sensitive to point defects, such as electrical resistivity [98], stored energy [99], or density [100], which was initially altered by work hardening. Comparison with a property like hardness which is more sensitive to dislocations shows that these point defects disappear more easily, *i.e.* at lower temperatures, than dislocations (Fig. 42). Changes in the temperature or in the rate of heating during recovery give a measurement of the energy of displacement U of the defect. Comparison with the quenching experiments described below shows that stage II is probably due to the disappearance of vacancies. The order of magnitude for U_{dv} is that given in Table I above. Stage I has a smaller activation energy and has been ascribed to interstitials or, less likely, to divacancies. From the amplitude of the second step, one deduces that in various polycrystals the concentration of vacancies increases with the strain ε. As an order of magnitude,

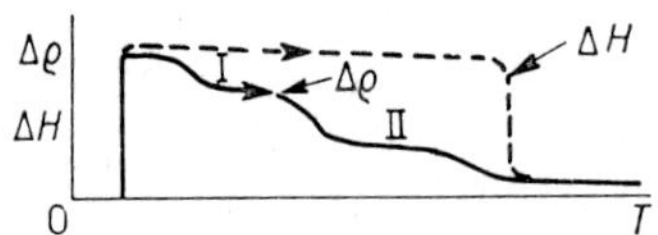

Fig. 42. – Recovery, by heating, of the increases in electrical resistivity and hardness, $\Delta\varrho$ and ΔH, produced by work hardening.

$$c_v \simeq (10^4 \text{ to } 10^{-5})\varepsilon \,. \tag{3.15}$$

The initial increase of c_v is more nearly parabolic in monocrystals ($c_v \propto \varepsilon^2$).

Irradiation produces, by Wigner effect, Frenkel pairs of point defects. A study of the fairly complicated recovery behavior of various properties after low-temperature irradiation, indicates one or several steps at low temperature, most likely due to interstitials jumping into vacancies, with an energy $U_{di} \simeq 0.1$ eV in copper [101]. These steps are pushed towards higher temperatures and higher energies U_{di} when the metal contains soft impurities [102] or dislocations [103]. This indicates probably, that the interstitials have been captured by these defects at lower temperatures, and need higher activation energies to escape from the impurities or move along the dislocations (cf. Section **2**). The step in $\Delta\varrho$ observed in the latter case is indeed somewhat similar to stage I, Fig. 10, after work hardening. There is also usually a small step, at still higher temperatures, with an energy U_{dv} which is reasonable for vacancies. This would correspond to the vacancies that have escaped interstitials. That some interstitials and vacancies disappear otherwise than by mutual annihilation is proved by the pinning down of pre-existing dislocations during irradiation (as measured by internal friction [104]), and by the formation of small loops of new dislocations, observed in the electron microscope [105]. Finally, a measurement of the stored energy released in the low temperature recovery step [106] gives in copper an energy of formation of a Frenkel pair, *i.e.* $U_{fv} + U_{fi} \simeq 5.5$ eV, which is of the order of magnitude predicted by Table I above.

The preceding types of experiments are somewhat complicated, because they involve several types of point defects. It is therefore very useful to have another group of methods, which involves only one type of defect, probably vacancies in most materials. These methods just use the fact that, in thermal equilibrium at a given temperature T, the atomic concentration of point defects is given by

$$c = \exp[S_f/k]\exp[-U_f/kT]\,. \tag{3.16}$$

From the preceding discussion, interstitials have such a large energy U_{fi} that, despite their large entropy, S_{fi}, their concentration is negligible. Even vacancies are not very numerous. With the estimate of S_{fv} given by eq. (16), the maximum concentration, at the melting point, is always well below one percent. Properties sensitive to vacancies, such as electrical resistivity [107] (in metals), lattice parameter, atomic volume [90], and specific heat [108], show exponential anomalies with *increasing temperature*, which have been attributed to these defects.

A more reliable procedure is to *quench* the solid [109]:

1) Quenches from various temperatures, give the energy of formation, U_{fv}, at least if the quench has been fast enough to retain most of the vacancies.

2) Recovery at various temperatures after a quench from a given temperature gives the energy of displacement U_{dv}. Careful measurements can even give the full diffusion coefficient for the vacancies:

$$D(\text{vac}) = D_0(\text{vac})\exp\left[-\frac{U\,dv}{kT}\right]. \tag{3.17}$$

This requires a good control of the geometry of recovery and small supersaturations of vacancies [110]. One uses, for instance, thin wires, so as to have sinks mostly on the outer surface, and few on dislocations. One quenches from fairly low temperatures, so as to have small supersaturations, and also, according to the results of the second section, no formation of dislocation loops.

These measurements can be checked by comparing the (average) volume *diffusion* coefficient, D, thus deduced with that measured directly. One should have

$$D = D(\text{vac})\,c_v\alpha\exp\left[-\frac{U_{fv}+U_{dv}}{kT}\right].$$

That the diffusion energy is equal to $U_{fv}+U_{dv}$ as measured by quenches has been checked for a number of materials [110]. Also, the measured values of U_{fv} and U_{dv} are of the order of magnitude predicted by Table I. This can be taken as a confirmation that the defects are indeed vacancies in most cases.

In conclusion, these lectures must be taken as a mere introduction to a complicated and somewhat controversial field. They are far from covering the initial program proposed. Nothing has been said, for instance, of problems of order and aggregates, or of long range interaction of dislocations with point defects, or again of the contribution of dislocations to the elastic constants and internal friction. No doubt some of these points will be covered at length by other speakers.

REFERENCES

[1] F. Seitz and J. S. Koehler: *Solid State Physics*, Vol. **2**, (New York 1956) p. **307**; G. J. Dienes and G. H. Vineyard: *Radiation Effects in Solids* (New York, 1957).

[2] D. Bohm and D. Pines: *Phys. Rev.*, **82**, 625 (1951), cf. [6].

[3] D. Pines: *Phys. Rev.*, **85**, 931 (1952).

[4] H. A. Kramers: *Physica*, **13**, 401 (1947); G. Lee Whiting: *Proc. Roy. Soc.* A **212**. 362 (1952).

[5] N. Bohr: *Kgl. Danske Videnskab. Selskab. Mat.-fys. Medd.*, **18**, 8 (1948).

[6] D. Pines: *Solid State Physics*, **1**, 369 (1955).

[7] L. Marton, L. B. Leder and H. Mendlowitz: *Adv. in Electronics*, **7**, 183 (1955); D. Pines: *Rev. Mod. Phys.*, **28**, 184 (1956).

[8] N. F. Mott: *Conférence Solvay* (Bruxelles, 1954); P. Nozières and D. Pines: *Phys. Rev.*, **109**, 1009; **111**, 442 (1958).

[9] J. Frenkel: *Phys. Z. Sowjetunion*, **9**, 158 (1936); G. H. Wannier: *Phys. Rev.*, **92**, 18 (1936).

[10] J. Elliott: *Phys. Rev.*, **108**, 1384 (1957); G. Dresselhaus: *Phys. Rev.*, **106**, 71 (1957); H. Haken: *Forts. d. Phys.*, **6**, 271 (1958); G. G. Macfarlane T. P. McLean, J. E. Quarrington and V. Roberts: *Journ. Phys. Chem. Sol.*, **8**, 388 (1959); J. J. Hopfield and D. G. Thomas: *Journ. Phys. Chem. Sol.*, **12**, 276 (1960).

[11] F. Seitz and J. S. Koehler, cf. [1].

[12] E. H. Jacobsen, *Phys. Rev.*, **97**, 654 (1955).

[13] R. H. Silsbee: *Journ. Appl. Phys.*, **28**, 1246 (1957).

[14] G. Leibfried: *Journ. Appl. Phys.*, **30**, 1388 (1959); **31**, 117 (1960).

[15] H. Udin, A. J. Shaler and J. Wulff: *Journ. Met.*, **1**, 186 (1949).

[16] A. Brager and A. Schuchowitsky: *Acta Physicochim.*, **21**, 13 (1946); M. von Laue: *Ann. d. Phys.*, **44**, 1197 (1914).

[17] J. Bardeen: *Phys. Rev.*, **49**, 653 (1935).

[18] K. Huang and G. Wyllie: *Proc. Phys. Soc.*, A **351**, 180 (1959).

[19] W. D. Harkins: *Journ. Chem. Phys.*, **10**, 268 (1942).

[20] P. Handler and W. M. Portnoy: *Phys. Rev.*, **116**, 516 (1959).

[21] M. Born and M. Göppert-Mayer: *Handb. d. Phys.*, **24/2**, 762 (1933).

[22] J. FRIEDEL: *Fracture* (New York, 1959), p. 498.
[23] R. SHUTTLEWORTH, R. KING and B. CHALMERS: *Nature*, **178**, 482 (1946); A. J. W. MOORE: *Acta Met.*, **6**, 293 (1958); J. BÉNARD, J. MOREAU and F. GRONLUND: *Compt. Rend.*, **246**, 756 (1958); C. G. DUNN and J. L. WALTER: *Acta Met.*, **7**, 649 (1959).
[24] A. BRAGER and A. SCHUCHOWITSKY: *Acta Physicoch.*, **21**, 1001 (1946).
[25] W. K. BURTON and N. CABRERA: *Disc. Farad. Soc.*, **5**, 33, 40 (1949); W. K. BURTON, N. CABRERA and F. C. FRANCK: *Phil. Trans. Roy. Soc.*, A **243**, 299 (1950-1951); W. W. MULLINS: *Acta Met.*, **7**, 746 (1959).
[26] K. A. JAKSON: *Liquid Metals and Solidification* (Cleveland, 1958); *Acta Met.*, **7**, 747 (1959).
[27] I. LANGMUIR: *Zeits. Angew. Chem.*, **46**, 719 (1933).
[28] F. R. N. NABARRO: *Bristol Conference, Physical Society* (London, 1948), cf. [15]; J. SILCOX and M. J. WHELAN: *Phil. Mag.*, **5**, 1 (1960).
[29] W. L. BRAGG and J. F. NYE: *Proc. Roy. Soc.*, A **190**, 474 (1947); W. L. BRAGG and W. M. LOMER: *Proc. Roy. Soc.*, A **196**, 171 (1949).
[30] Cf. J. C. FISHER and C. G. DUNN: *Imperfections in Nearly Perfect Crystals* (New York, 1952), p. 371; S. AMELINCKX and W. DEKEYSER: *Solid State Phys.*, **8**, 327 (1959); R. S. WAGNER and B. CHALMERS: *Journ. Appl. Phys.*, **31**, 581 (1960).
[31] J. M. BURGERS: *Proc. Kon. Ned. Akad. Wet.*, **42**, 293, 378 (1959); W. T. READ and W. SHOCKLEY: *Phys. Rev.*, **78**, 275 (1950).
[32] P. LACOMBE and L. BEAUJARD: *Bristol Conference* (London, 1948); R. CASTAING and A. GUINIER: *Compt. Rend. Acad. Sci.*, **228**, 2033 (1949); F. L. VOGEL, W. G. PFANN, H. E. COREY and E. E. THOMAS: *Phys. Rev.*, **90**, 489 (1953), etc.
[33] J. M. HEDGES and J. W. MITCHELL: *Phil. Mag.*, **44**, 223 (1949); W. DEKEYSER and S. AMELINCKX: *Les Dislocations et la Croissance des Métaux* (Paris, 1955), etc.
[34] R. FULLMAN: *Journ. Appl. Phys.*, **22**, 448 (1951).
[35] A. SEEGER: *Bristol Conference* (*Institute of Metals*) (London, 1954).
[36] C. HERRING: *Powder Metallurgy* (New York, 1951).
[37] J. FRIEDEL, B. D. CULLITY and C. CRUSSARD: *Acta Met.*, **1**, 79 (1953).
[38] Cf. W. T. READ: *Dislocations in Crystals* (New York, 1953); A. H. COTTRELL: *Dislocations and Plastic Flow* (Oxford, 1953); J. FRIEDEL: *Les Dislocations* (Paris, 1956).
[39] A. HOFFMAN and D. TURNBULL: *Journ. Appl. Phys.*, **22**, 634, 984 (1951), etc.; cf. S. AMELINCKX and W. DEKEYSER [30].
[40] D. TURNBULL and A. HOFFMAN: *Acta Met.*, **2**, 419 (1954).
[41] C. W. HAYNES and R. SMOLUCHOWSKI: *Acta Met.*, **3**, 130 (1955); P. COULOMB, C. LEYMONIE and P. LACOMBE: *Compt. Rend. Acad. Sci.*, **246**, 1209 (1958).
[42] B. OKKERSE, T. J. TIEDEMA and W. G. BURGERS: *Acta Met.*, **3**, 300 (1955); A. HOFFMAN: *Acta Met.*, **4**, 98 (1956).
[43] R. C. FRANK: *Journ. Appl. Phys.*, **29**, 1262 (1958); W. KÖSTER, L. BANGERT and R. HAHN: *Arch. Eisenhüttenw.*, **25**, **569** (1954); G. BIORCI, A. FERRO and G. MONTALENTI: *Journ. Appl. Phys.*, **30**, 1732 (1959).
[44] F. C. FRANK and D. TURNBULL: *Phys. Rev.*, **104**, 617 (1956); A. G. TWEET: *Phys. Rev.*, **106**, 221 (1957); cf. [45].
[45] R. S. BARNES G. B. REDDING and A. H. COTTRELL: *Phil. Mag.*, **3**, 97 (1958)
[46] G. WEINGARTEN: *Rendiconti Accad. Lincei* [5], **10**, 57 (1901).
[47] A. FOURDEUX, A. BERGHEZAN and W. W. WEBB: *Journ. Appl. Phys.*, **31**, 918 (1960); N. BROWN: private communication.

[48] R. D. HEIDENREICH and W. SHOCKLEY: *Bristol Conference* (*Physical Society*) (London, 1948).

[49] F. C. FRANK and J. F. NICHOLAS: *Phil. Mag.*, **44**, 1213 (1953).

[50] R. PEIERLS: *Proc. Phys. Soc.*, **52**, 34 (1940); F. R. N. NABARRO: *Proc. Phys. Soc.*, **59**, 256 (1947).

[51] J. FRENKEL: *Zeits. Phys.*, **37**, 572 (1926).

[52] Cf. A. CRACKNELL and N. J. PETCH: *Acta Met.*, **3**, 186 (1955); *Phil. Mag.*, **2**, 649 (1957) for αFe; P. HAASEN: *Acta Met.*, **5**, 598 (1957) for Ge; M. L. KRONBERG: *Acta Met.*, **5**, 507 (1957); R. CHANG: *Journ. Appl. Phys.*, **31**, 484 (1960) for sapphire.

[53] N. F. MOTT and F. R. N. NABARRO: *Bristol Conference* (*Physical Society*) (London, 1948); M. PEACH and J. S. KOEHLER: *Phys. Rev.*, **80**, 436 (1950).

[54] F. C. FRANK: *Pittsburg Conference* (ONR, 1949).

[55] A. H. COTTRELL and B. A. BILBY: *Proc. Phys. Soc.*, A **62**, 49 (1949); F. C. FISHER: *Trans. Am. Soc. Mod.*, **47**, 451 (1955); R. J. STOKES, T. L. JOHNSTON and C. H. LI: *Phil. Mag.*, **4**, 920 (1959); *Trans. AIME*, **215**, 437 (1959); A. S. KEH: *Journ. Appl. Phys.*, **31**, 1538 (1960).

[56] R. A. MEYER: *Journ. Appl. Phys.*, **25**, 1369 (1954); D. HULL and I. L. MOGFORD: *Phil. Mag.*, **3**, 1213 (1958); A. A. JOHNSON: *Phil. Mag.*, **5**, 413 (1960).

[57] J. S. L. LEACH, E. G. LOEWEN and M. B. BEVER: *Journ. Appl. Phys.*, **26**, 728, (1955).

[58] M. S. PATERSON: *Acta Met.*, **2**, 823 (1954).

[59] P. B. HIRSCH: *Internal Stresses and Fatigue in Metals* (New York, 1959); G. SAADA: *Métaux et Corrosion*, in press.

[60] M. J. WHELAN, P. B. HIRSCH and R. W. HORNE: *Proc. Roy. Soc.*, A **240**, 524 (1957); J. E. BAILEY and P. B. HIRSCH: *Phil. Mag.*, **5**, 485 (1960).

[61] F. SEITZ: *Adv. Phys.*, **1**, 43 (1952); cf. [59].

[62] A. SEEGER and G. SCHOEK: *Bristol Conference* (*Phisical Society*) (London, 1954); cf. [38].

[63] Cf. A. SEEGER and H. TRÄUBLE: *Zeits. f. Metallkunde*, **51**, 435 (1960) for unidirectional climb in zinc.

[64] J. WEERTMAN: *Phys. Rev.*, **107**, 1259 (1957); R. DE WIT: *Phys. Rev.*, **116** 592 (1959).

[65] J. BARDEEN and C. HERRING: *Imperfections in Nearly Perfect Crystals* (New York, 1952).

[66] G. SCHOECK and W. A. TILLER: *Phil. Mag.*, **5**, 43 (1960).

[67] N. F. MOTT and R. W. GURNEY: *Electronic Processes in Ionic Crystals* (Oxford, 1948).

[68] A. B. LIDIARD: *Handb. d. Phys.*, **20**, 256 (1956).

[69] Cf. W. SHOCKLEY: *Electrons and Holes in Semiconductors* (New York, 1950).

[70] N. F. MOTT and H. JONES: *Metals and Alloys* (Oxford, 1936).

[71] J. FRIEDEL: *Phil. Mag.*, **43**, 153 (1952).

[72] K. YOSHIDA: *Phys. Rev.*, **106**, 893 (1957); A. BLANDIN and J. FRIEDEL: *Journ. Phys. Rad.*, **20**, 160 (1959).

[73] A. BLANDIN, E. DANIEL and J. FRIEDEL: *Phil. Mag.*, **4**, 180 (1959); *Journ. Phys. Rad.*, **21**, 769, 849 (1959); W. KOHN and S. H. VOSCO: *Phys. Rev.*, **119**, 912 (1960); A. BLANDIN and J. FRIEDEL: *Journ. Phys. Rad.*, in press.

[74] J. FRIEDEL: *Adv. Phys.*, **3**, 446 (1954).

[75] Cf. [70]; also K. HUANG: *Proc. Phys. Soc.*, **60**, 161 (1948); J. FRIEDEL: *Can. Journ. Phys.*, **34**, 1190 (1956).
[76] A. W. OVERHAUSER and R. L. GORMAN: *Phys. Rev.*, **102**, 676 (1956); cf. [88].
[77] W. H. HARRISON: cf. F. J. BLATT: *Phys. Rev.*, **108**, 285 (1957).
[78] E. DANIEL: *Journ. Phys. Chem. Sol.*, **13**, 353 (1960).
[79] J. D. ESHELBY: *Sol. State Phys.*, **3**, 79 (1956).
[80] J. A. WASASTJERNA: cf. V. HOVI: *Acta Met.*, **2**, 335 (1954).
[81] J. FRIEDEL: *Phil. Mag.*, **46**, 514 (1955).
[82] G. BRADFIELD and H. PURSEY: *Phil. Mag.*, **44**, 437 (1953).
[83] W. HUME-ROTHERY: *Structure of Metals and Alloys* (New York, 1945).
[84] C. WAGNER: *Acta Met.*, **2**, 242 (1954); J. FRIEDEL: *Symposium on Rare Metals* (Bombay, 1957).
[85] W. SCHOTTKY and C. WAGNER: *Zeits. Phys. Chem.*, **2**, 163 (1930).
[86] J. FRENKEL: *Zeits. Phys.*, **35**, 35 (1926).
[87] K. LARK HOROWITZ: *Zeits. Phys. Chem.*, **198**, 107 (1951).
[88] P. JONGENBURGER: *Appl. Sci. Research*, B **3**, 237 (1953); *Nature*, **175**, 545 (1955); F. J. BLATT: *Phys. Rev.*, **99**, 1708 (1955); A. SEEGER and H. BROSS: *Zeits. Phys.*, **145**, 161 (1956); F. ABÉLÈS: *Compt. Rend. Acad. Sci.*, **237**, 796 (1953).
[89] M. DOYAMA and J. S. KOEHLER: *Phys. Rev.*, **119**, 939 (1960); cf. [94].
[90] R. O. SIMMONS and R. W. BALLUFFI: *Phys. Rev.*, **119**, 600 (1960).
[91] A. SEEGER: *Proceedings of the Second United Nations International Conference on Paceful Uses of Atomic Energy* (Geneva, 1958), paper n. 998 (Geneva, 1959).
[92] H. B. HUNTINGTON: *Acta Met.*, **2**, 554 (1954); G. J. DIENES: *Phys. Rev.*, **86**, 228 (1952); G. H. VINEYARD, J. B. GIBSON, A. N. GOLAND and M. MILGRAM: *Bull. Am. Phys. Soc.*, **5**, 26 (1960).
[93] H. BROOKS: *Impurities and Imperfections* (A.S.M., 1955).
[94] W. DE SORBO: *Bull. Am. Phys. Soc.*, **4**, 284 (1959); N. H. NACHTRIEB, J. A. WEIL, E. CATALANO and A. W. LAWSON: *Journ. Chem. Phys.*, **20**, 1182 (1952); R. G. BARNES, N. P. ENGARDT and R. A. HULTSCH: *Phys. Rev. Lett.*, **3**, 202 (1959).
[95] H. B. HUNTINGTON and F. SEITZ: *Phys. Rev.*, **61**, 315 (1942); **76**, 1728 (1949); H. B. HUNTINGTON: *Phys. Rev.*, **61**, 325 (1942); **91**, 1092 (1953).
[96] J. H. BARTLETT and G. J. DIENES: *Phys. Rev.*, **89**, 848 (1953).
[97] A. C. DAMASK, G. J. DIENES and V. G. WEIZER: *Phys. Rev.*, **113**, 781 (1959).
[98] J. A. MANINTVELD: *Nature*, **169**, 623 (1952); cf. T. BLEWITT: *Bristol Conference (Physical Society)* (London, 1954); M. WINTENBERGER: *Acta Met.*, **7**, 549 (1959).
[99] L. M. CLAREBROUGH, M. E. HARGREAVES, D. MICHEL and G. W. WEST: *Proc. Roy. Soc.*, A **215**, 507 (1952); A **232**, 252 (1959); D. MITCHELL and E. LOVEGROVE: *Phil. Mag*, **5**, 499 (1960).
[100] A. SEEGER: *Zeits. Phys.*, **146**, 217 (1955); L. M. CLAREBROUGH, M. E. HARGREAVES and G. W. WEST: *Phil. Mag.*, **1**, 528 (1956).
[101] J. W. CORBETT and R. M. WALKER: *Phys. Rev.*, **110**, 767 (1958); J. W. CORBETT, R. R. SMITH and R. M. WALKER: *Phys. Rev.*, **114**, 1452, 1460 (1959); H. G. COOPER, J. S. KOEHLER and J. W. MARX: *Phys. Rev.*, **97**, 599 (1955); D. THOMPSON, T. BLEWITT and D. HOLMES: *Journ. Appl. Phys.*, **28**, 742 (1957).
[102] T. H. BLEWITT, R. R. COLTMAN, C. E. KLABUNDE and T. S. NOGGLE: *Journ. Appl. Phys.*, **28**, 639 (1957).

[103] C. J. Meechan and A. Sosin: *Journ. Appl. Phys.*, **29**, 783 (1958); R. M. Walker and J. W. Corbett: *Bull. Am. Phys. Soc.*, **5**, 25 (1960); C. J. Meechan, A. Sosin and J. A. Brinkman: *Phys. Rev.*, **120**, 411 (1960).
[104] D. O. Thompson and D. K. Holmes: *Journ. Appl. Phys.*, **27**, 713 (1956); D. O. Thompson, T. Blewitt and D. K. Holmes: *Journ. Appl. Phys.*, **28**, 742 (1957); R. S. Barnes and P. M. Hancock: *Phil. Mag.*, **29**, 527 (1959); D. O. Thompson and V. K. Paré: *Journ. Appl. Phys.*, **31**, 528 (1960).
[105] Cf. M. W. Thomson: this volume p. 169.
[106] T. H. Blewitt, R. R. Coltman and C. E. Klabunde: *Phys. Rev. Lett.*, **3**, 132 (1959).
[107] D. K. C. Mac Donald: *Journ. Chem. Phys.*, **21**, 177 (1953).
[108] T. E. Pochapsky: *Acta Met.*, **1**, 747 (1953).
[109] G. Airoldi, G. L. Bacchella and E. Germagnoli: *Phys. Rev. Lett.*, **2**, 145 (1959).
[110] A. Blandin and J. Friedel: *Acta Met.*, **8**, 384 (1960).

Technique and Application of Trasmission Electron Microscopy.

P. B. HIRSCH

Cavendish Laboratory, University of Cambridge - Cambridge

I. – Technique.

1. – Introduction.

Crystals whose thickness does not exceed a few 1000 Å, are transparent to electrons in an electron microscope. The interior of such crystals can be observed directly, and lattice defects are revealed at very high magnification. Thus, by the transmission technique the distribution, nature and size of defects and inhomogeneities such as dislocations, dislocation loops, stacking faults, cavities, centres of strain, precipitates, Guinier-Preston zones, can be studied directly, and the motion of dislocations and diffusion controlled processes such as climb and precipitation can be followed in dynamic experiments in the microscope. Such observations not only give qualitative and quantitative information about the nature and distribution of defects, but can also be used to estimate values of quantities such as stacking fault energies and activation energies for climb.

Since the resolution of modern microscopes is ~ 10 Å, inhomogeneities on this scale are observable, provided they give rise to sufficient contrast.

The successful application of the transmission technique depends on two factors:

1) the ability to prepare thin specimens from bulk material;

2) the ability to interpret correctly the contrast effects observed.

In the following sections these two problems will be discussed in some detail.

2. – Thinning techniques.

In the case of metals thinning is usually accomplished by electro-polishing, a technique first applied by BOLLMANN [1] for this purpose. Essentially in this technique the specimen to be thinned acts as anode and the cathode consists of another suitable metal. Typically the anode specimen may be in the form of a strip 1-2 cm wide, a few cm long, and $\frac{1}{5}$ mm thick. The anode is coated with a varnish resistant to attack by the particular electrolyte used, except for a « window » about $(1 \div 2)$ cm in diameter (Fig. 1*a*).

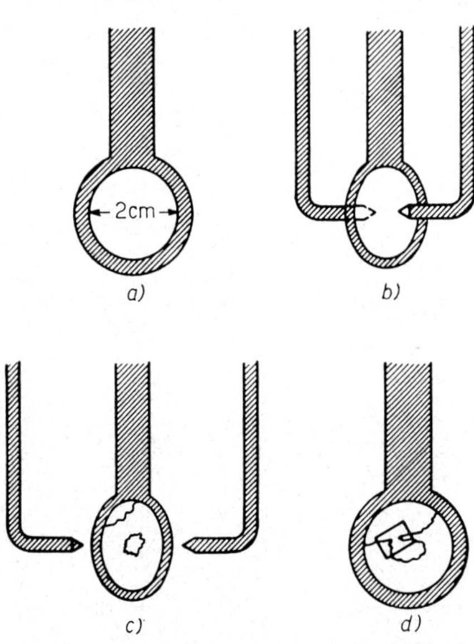

Fig. 1. – Diagram illustrating Bollmann electropolishing technique. (KELLY and NUTTING [2]; courtesy Institute of Metals).

The voltage across the cell is varied until optimum polishing conditions are obtained, by trial and error. The stainless steel points are placed close to the specimen and the current is switched on until a hole is made in the anode (Fig. 1*c*). The distance between the specimen and the cathode points is then increased and polishing continued. Perforation then spreads from the edge of the window and polishing is continued until the bridge between the two holes just disappears (Fig. 1*d*). The specimen is washed and small pieces can then be cut with a razor blade from the region near the junction of the holes and these should be transparent over areas $\sim \frac{1}{10}$ mm wide around the edges.

There are many variants of this technique. For example often it is only necessary to make a single hole and the edges are then found to be transparent (TOMLINSON [3]). In other cases a guard ring surrounding the edge of the specimen is found to be effective in giving a uniform polish (FISHER, quoted by KELLY and NUTTING [2]). This ring essentially acts to make the field uniform over much of the specimen. For particularly thick specimens, say 1 mm or so, a polishing machine is useful in which the specimen is continuously moved between the electrodes (KELLY and NUTTING [2]).

By polishing only from one side, one of the original surfaces can be preserved and in this way it is possible to study directly the topography of the surface (for example slip lines) and, its relation to the distribution of the defects inside (HIRSCH, PARTRIDGE and SEGALL [4]; THOMAS and HALE [5]).

Etching methods have also been used for thinning metal specimens, but this technique seems to have limited application (WHELAN [6]).

In the case of nonmetallic crystals, thinning has been carried out by chemical polish of cleavage slices (for example MgO; WASHBURN, GROVES, KELLY and WILLIAMSON [7]), by grinding and etching (for example Ge; PHILLIPS and HARTREE [8]), or by simple cleaving (for layer structures such as mica, graphite, etc.; *e.g.* DELAVIGNETTE and AMELINCKX [9]; WILLMIASON [10]).

Generally it appears that suitable thinning techniques can be found for most materials with relatively little effort, and the technique has therefore very wide application. Examples of the application of the various techniques used are given in the list of references, in particular in Table I of KELLY and NUTTING [2].

It should be noted also that the transmission technique is of course directly applicable to thin crystals grown by deposition from the vapour or from solution, or to very thin whiskers (*e.g.* MENTER [11]; BASSETT and PASHLEY [12]; PRICE [13]).

3. – Observational techniques.

The technique of observation of the specimen in the electron microscope is simple. Usually the specimen is first viewed at low magnification, say a few 1000 times, to find the transparent areas. The transparent areas are then examined at instrumental magnifications from ~20000 times to perhaps 100000 times depending on the nature of the defects to be observed. Since the contrast is very sensitive to orientation it is essential to tilt the specimen in the stereoholder usually provided. It is also very important to take microdiffraction patterns from the local areas examined; from these the orientation of these areas can be determined, and in this way much more complete information can be obtained about the nature of the microstructure than is possible from micrographs alone.

In order to reduce the heating of the specimen due to the electron beam it is necessary to make use of a double condenser lens in the electron gun; in modern instruments such a double condenser is usually available, and it allows the illuminating spot on the specimen to be reduced to only a few microns in diameter, so that the heating effect can be made very small. Experiments on precipitation and climb of loops have shown that under suitable conditions the temperature rise due to the electron beam can be limited to $(10 \div 20)$ °C (SILCOX and WHELAN [14]; SILCOX [15]; THOMAS and WHELAN [16]; PRICE [13]). On the other hand with other illuminating conditions it is also possible to melt the specimen. Hence care must be taken to ensure that the illuminating conditions for small temperature rises are used. A theoretical discussion of the temperature rise under different conditions has been given by GALE and HALE [17].

For some purposes heating and cooling object stages are useful, and these are now available for some microscopes, and in any case can be built fairly easily. Thus, a simple form of heating stage for the Siemens Elmiskop consists simply of a small grid, usually of platinum, heated electrically, on which the specimen is placed (WHELAN [18]). Cooling is usually carried out by contact with a cooling rod which is immersed in liquid air outside the microscope. For optimum ease of operation these object stages should also be equipped with a tilting mechanism.

In the course of observation of the object in the microscope stresses are induced in the specimen due to temperature gradients and also as a result of deposition of carbon from oil vapour in the microscope column. These stresses are often sufficient to cause movement of dislocations. Special straining devices have also been constructed for the same purpose, and with these the movement of the dislocations can be studied in a controlled manner (WILSDORF [19]; FISHER [20]).

Cine-films of the movement of dislocations, of climb, precipitation effects and of any other observable changes in the specimen can be made by photographing the image on the screen of the electron microscope from outside (HIRSCH, HORNE and WHELAN [21]).

II. – Contrast.

1. – Introduction.

Essentially three methods have been employed for revealing lattice defects. In the first of these, due to MENTER [22], the lattice planes are resolved directly by ensuring that direct and diffracted waves enter the aperture of the objective lens of the imaging system. When the spacing of the lattice planes is too small to be resolved in present-day electron microscopes, moiré patterns due to overlapping crystals can be used to give images of the crystal lattice (HASHIMOTO and UYEDA [23]; BASSETT, MENTER and PASHLEY [24]). Both these methods reveal the nature of the distortion of the lattice planes near a defect and depend for their success on good resolution and rather stringent specimen requirements. For example, the specimens must be relatively thin to avoid excessive chromatic aberration due to energy losses.

In the third method, first investigated independently by BOLLMANN [1] and by HIRSCH, HORNE and WHELAN [21], image contrast is produced by local differences in the intensities of the Bragg diffracted beams. It is generally arranged that only the direct beam (bright field image) or one diffracted beam (dark field image) enters the aperture of the objective lens (see Fig. 2). In the bright field image, dark contrast results wherever local conditions in the crystal lead to strong diffraction. This « diffraction contrast » is sensitive to changes in orientation or thickness, and to displacements of the atoms from their normal positions due to lattice strains. In the perfect crystal this type of contrast is responsible for « extinction contours », which are bands of constant orientation or of thickness corresponding to conditions of particularly strong diffraction. In the imperfect crystal, dislocations appear as lines because of the atomic displacements near them, and stacking faults give rise to a characteristic fringe pattern. This method of contrast formation has the advantage that the atomic array is not resolved, that resolution is therefore not a limiting factor, and that specimen requirements are less stringent. For example, a projection of the three-dimensional arrangement of dislocations can be obtained for crystals whose thickness would be too great for resolution of lattices or of moiré patterns of small spacings. The main application of this method is in the study of the distribution of defects and also of their behaviour, for example, on heating or straining the specimen while the first two methods are particularly suitable for the study of the nature of the atomic displacements near the defect.

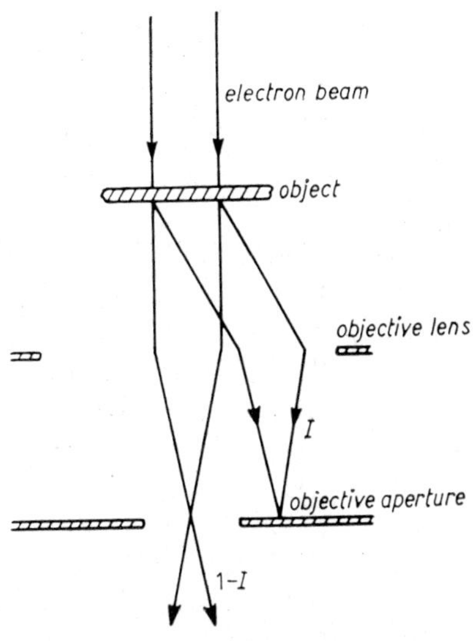

Fig. 2. – Diagram illustrating diffraction contrast. The incident electron beam is diffracted by the specimen and the diffracted beam is removed by the aperture of the objective lens. The intensity of the incident beam is unity, that of the diffracted beam I and that of the transmitted beam $1-I$. Contrast arises through local variations of the intensities of the diffracted beams (HIRSCH, HOWIE and WHELAN [25]; courtesy Royal Society).

In the following sections the theory of the « diffraction contrast » will be outlined.

2. – Basic diffraction theory.

2·1. *Electron wavelength.* – The electron wavelength in free space is given by

$$\lambda = \frac{h}{[2meE(1 + e/2mc^2)]^{\frac{1}{2}}},$$

where h = Planck's constant, m = electron mass, e = electron charge, c = velocity of light, E = accelerating voltage of electrons. Thus for 100 kV electrons λ is found to be 0.037 Å.

2·2. *Atomic scattering factor.* – When a plane wave is scattered by an atom the diverging wavelet can be represented at a distance r from the atom by

$$u(r) = \exp[2\pi ikr]\frac{f(\theta)}{r},$$

where $k = 1/\lambda$, and 2θ is the scattering angle. The function $f(\theta)$ is called the scattering amplitude, which is a function of $(\sin\theta)/\lambda$ and varies with atomic number.

For electrons, in the Born approximation, the scattering amplitude is given by the Fourier transform of the potential distribution of an atom, *i.e.*

$$f(\theta) = \frac{2\pi me}{h^2}\int V(\boldsymbol{r})\exp[2\pi i\boldsymbol{k}\cdot\boldsymbol{r}]\,\mathrm{d}\tau_r\,,$$

where $V(\boldsymbol{r})$ is the potential at any point in the atom, $\boldsymbol{K} = \boldsymbol{k} - \boldsymbol{k}_0$, where $\boldsymbol{k}_0$ and $\boldsymbol{k}$ are the wave vectors corresponding to the incident and scattered waves, and $\mathrm{d}\tau_r$ is a volume element in the atom. Since there is a connection between charge density and potential the above integral is related to the Fourier transform of the charge distribution, *i.e.* to the scattering factor for X-rays, $F_{\mathrm{X}}(\theta)$. Hence we find

$$f(\theta) = \frac{me^2\lambda}{2h^2}\left(\frac{Z - F_{\mathrm{X}}(\theta)}{\sin^2\theta}\right),$$

where Z is the atomic number. The first term in the bracket is due to the scattering from the positive nucleus, the second term to the scattering from the electron cloud. The scattering amplitude for electrons is found to be about 10^4 times as great as that for X-rays. Hence electrons can be scattered strongly by much smaller volumes of scattering material than in the case of X-rays.

Further details are given in PINSKER [26].

2·3. *Laue conditions.* – The amplitude scattered by an assembly of atoms is

$$A = \sum_n f_n \exp[2\pi i(\boldsymbol{k} - \boldsymbol{k}_0)\cdot\boldsymbol{r}_n] = \sum_n f_n \exp[2\pi i\,\boldsymbol{K}\cdot\boldsymbol{r}_n]\,,$$

where f_n is the scattering factor of the atom at $\boldsymbol{r}_n$, and $\boldsymbol{r}_n = n_1\boldsymbol{a} + n_2\boldsymbol{b} + n_3\boldsymbol{c}$, for a perfect crystal. The bracket in the exponential is the phase difference of the wave scattered by the atom at $\boldsymbol{r}_n$ relative to that scattered by an atom situated at the origin O (Fig. 3*a*), $\boldsymbol{K}$ is a vector normal to the reflecting planes, of length $(2 \sin\theta)/\lambda$ (Fig. 3*b*).

Fig. 3. – Diagrams illustrating vectors $\boldsymbol{k}_0$, $\boldsymbol{k}$, $\boldsymbol{K}$.

Now $\boldsymbol{K}$ can be expressed as a vector in reciprocal space. The reciprocal lattice unit cell is defined by the vectors $\boldsymbol{a}^x$, $\boldsymbol{b}^x$, $\boldsymbol{c}^x$, as follows:

$$\boldsymbol{a}^x = \frac{\boldsymbol{b}\times\boldsymbol{c}}{(\boldsymbol{a}\cdot\boldsymbol{b}\times\boldsymbol{c})}; \qquad \boldsymbol{b}^x = \frac{\boldsymbol{c}\times\boldsymbol{a}}{(\boldsymbol{a}\cdot\boldsymbol{b}\times\boldsymbol{c})}; \qquad \boldsymbol{c}^x = \frac{\boldsymbol{a}\times\boldsymbol{b}}{(\boldsymbol{a}\cdot\boldsymbol{b}\times\boldsymbol{c})}.$$

Then

$$\boldsymbol{a}\cdot\boldsymbol{a}^x = \boldsymbol{b}\cdot\boldsymbol{b}^x = \boldsymbol{c}\cdot\boldsymbol{c}^x = 1\,, \qquad \boldsymbol{a}\cdot\boldsymbol{b} = \boldsymbol{b}\cdot\boldsymbol{c} = \boldsymbol{c}\cdot\boldsymbol{a} = 0\,.$$

$\boldsymbol{K}$ can be written

$$\boldsymbol{K} = \xi\boldsymbol{a}^x + \eta\boldsymbol{b}^x + \zeta\boldsymbol{c}^x$$

and hence

$$A = \sum_n f_n \exp\left[2\pi i(n_1\xi + n_2\eta + n_3\zeta)\right].$$

Strong diffraction occurs if $(n_1\xi + n_2\eta + n_3\zeta)$ is an integer for all $n_1\, n_2\, n_3$, *i.e.*

$$\xi = h\,; \qquad \eta = k\,; \qquad \zeta = l\,,$$

where h, k, l are integers.

These are the usual Laue conditions, corresponding to Bragg reflexion from *hkl* planes, *i.e.* strong reflexion occurs if $\boldsymbol{K}$ coincides with a reciprocal lattice vector, say $\boldsymbol{g}$. Since $|\boldsymbol{g}| = 1/d$, where d is the spacing of a set of crystal planes, and since $|\boldsymbol{K}| = (2 \sin\theta)/\lambda$ for a strong reflexion $\lambda = 2d \sin\theta$, which is the Bragg law.

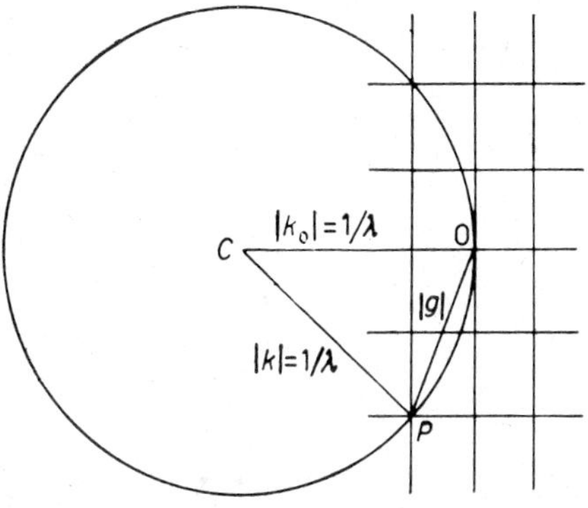

Fig. 4. – Reflecting sphere construction.

This leads to the reflecting sphere construction (Fig. 4). The vector $-\boldsymbol{k}_0$ is drawn from the origin O of the reciprocal lattice to the point C. A sphere of radius $1/\lambda$ is drawn around C; if this sphere passes through a reciprocal lattice point P, a strong Bragg reflexion occurs, the wave vector of the reflected beam, $\boldsymbol{k}$, being along CP. The radius of the reflecting sphere, $1/\lambda$, is large compared to the spacing of the reciprocal lattice ($\sim 1\,\text{Å}^{-1}$), since λ is very small ($\ll 1\,\text{Å}$) for electrons. Hence the reflecting sphere for electrons is nearly planar for the region of importance. This point is important in orientation determinations from electron diffraction patterns.

2·4. *Intensity distribution.* – The electrons are of course reflected over a range of angles, and this can be discussed in terms of a distribution of intensity in reciprocal space. Suppose we consider the diffracted intensity in a direction $\boldsymbol{k}$ corresponding to P' at a distance $\boldsymbol{s}$ from the reciprocal lattice point P (Fig. 5). Then $\boldsymbol{K}=\boldsymbol{g}+\boldsymbol{s}$. Hence

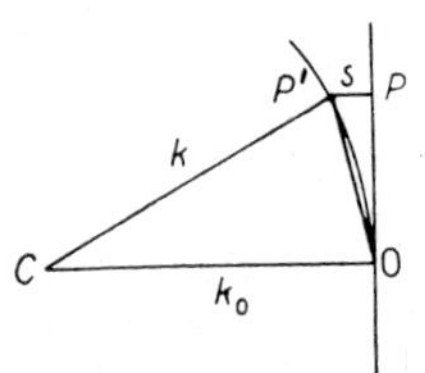

Fig. 5. – Reflecting sphere passing through P' at a distance s from P.

$$A = \sum f_n \exp[2\pi i(\boldsymbol{g}+\boldsymbol{s})\cdot\boldsymbol{r}_n]\,.$$

For a perfect crystal this simply gives

$$A(\boldsymbol{s}) = \sum f_n \exp[2\pi i\,\boldsymbol{s}\cdot\boldsymbol{r}_n]\,,$$

i.e. there is a distribution of intensity around a reciprocal lattice point. Usually we can sum over one unit cell and then over all cells and write this

$$A(\boldsymbol{s}) = F\sum_j \exp[2\pi i\,\boldsymbol{s}\cdot\boldsymbol{r}_j]\,,$$

where r_j now denotes the j-th unit cell position, and F is the scattering amplitude from one unit cell.

Usually this can be written as an integral

$$A(\boldsymbol{s}) = (F/V)\int\exp[2\pi i\boldsymbol{s}\cdot\boldsymbol{r}]\,\mathrm{d}\tau\,,$$

where V is the volume of the unit cell. This expression is the Fourier transform of the crystal.

For a rectangular parallelepiped whose edges are of lengths A, B, C, this integral is

$$A \propto \frac{\sin\pi Au}{\pi u}\cdot\frac{\sin\pi Bv}{\pi v}\cdot\frac{\sin\pi Cw}{\pi w}\,,$$

where $\boldsymbol{u}$, $\boldsymbol{v}$, $\boldsymbol{w}$ are reciprocal lattice vectors along directions parallel to A, B, C. The intensity $I \propto A^2$ is sketched in Fig. 6 along the direction u, for $v, w = 0$. The central maximum has a width of reflexion $\Delta u = 1/A$.

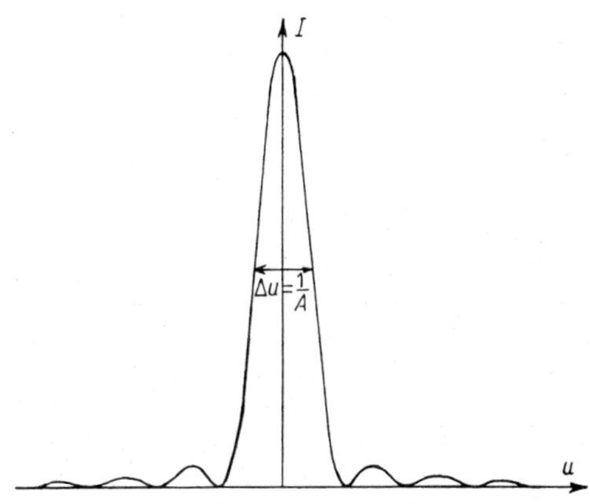

Fig. 6. – Curve of $\sin^2(\pi A u)/(\pi u)^2$ *vs.* u.

Thus for a spherical crystal the distribution in reciprocal space around a reciprocal lattice point is spherically symmetrical and has a width $\sim$ (diameter of crystal)$^{-1}$.

But in the electron case the crystal is usually in the form of a plate normal to the electron beam, and the intensity distribution is thus spread out in a spike normal to the crystal plate (Fig. 7), the central width of the spike being $\sim 1/t$, where t is the crystal thickness. Thus, if $t = 200$ Å, $d = 2$ Å, the range of reflexion $\mathrm{d}\theta \sim d/t = 10^{-2}$ rad, *i.e.* $\frac{1}{2}°$ (see Fig. 7). This may be compared with the Bragg angles $\theta = \lambda/2d = 10^{-2}$ rad; *i.e.* the width of the reflection is of the same order as the Bragg angle. The divergence of the electron beam in the microscope is $\sim 10^{-3}$ rad under usual operating conditions.

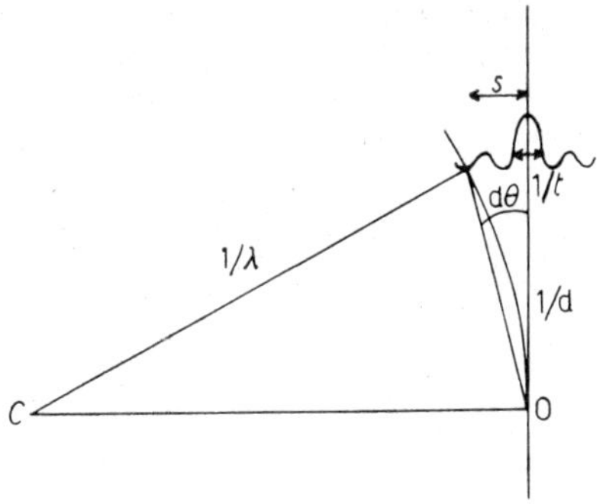

Fig. 7. – Distribution of intensity along spike through reciprocal lattice point.

As the crystal becomes thicker, t increases, $\mathrm{d}\theta$ decreases, but there is a limit because the beam is completely diffracted away by a thickness of only a few 100 Å so that the number of elements in the grating is always limited to this. Thus even if the crystal is thicker reflexion takes place over $\mathrm{d}\theta \sim d/t_0$, where t_0 = extinction distance, which may be 200 Å or so.

Further details are given in PINSKER [26] and JAMES [27].

3. – Dynamical and kinematical theory.

We are now in a position to consider the contrast.

We want to know the distribution of intensity at the lower surface of crystal (Fig. 8).

Diffraction occurs and the diffracted beam is diffracted back again into the incident beam direction so that here is an interchange of energy between the incident and diffracted waves. This is the basis of the dynamical theory. But if the orientation is far away from the reflecting position, the intensity of the diffracted beam is small and one can use the kinematical theory as a first approximation. In the kinematical theory one neglects depletion of energy of the incident beam due to diffraction. This theory gives the most important contrast effects but breaks down when the crystal orientation is near a reflecting position. In the following sections the kinematical theory will be outlined (HIRSCH, HOWIE and WHELAN [25]).

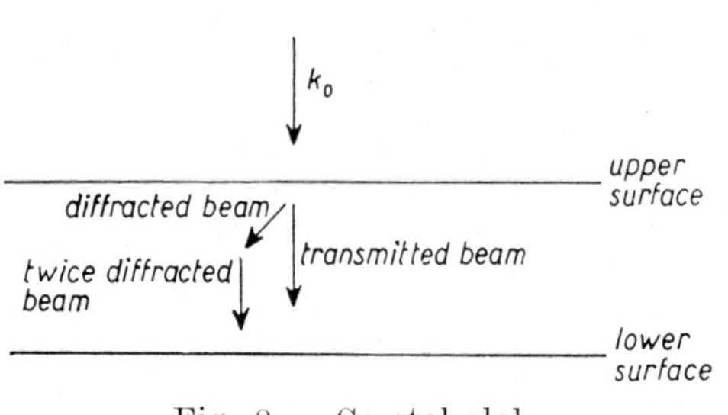

Fig. 8. – Crystal slab.

4. – Column approximation (kinematical theory).

4·1. *Perfect crystal.* – Calculations of diffraction patterns from perfect and dislocated crystals show that most of the intensity is still concentrated near reciprocal lattice points. Since most of the interference takes place inside the crystal, we may assume that at the lower surface the diffracted and incident waves are essentially plane. Then for a dark field picture at any point on the lower surface, the diffracted intensity L_{diff} comes from a column in the direction of the diffracted beam (Fig. 9). Thus for a dark field picture we calculate I_{diff} from this column and for a bright field picture the contrast is given by $1-I_{\text{diff}}$.

Then

$$A = \sum_j F_j \exp\left[2\pi i(\boldsymbol{g}+\boldsymbol{s})\cdot\boldsymbol{r}_j\right]$$

and

$$I_{\text{diff}} = \left(\frac{F^2\lambda^2}{V^2\cos^2\theta}\right)\frac{\sin^2\pi ts}{(\pi s)^2}\,,$$

the factor in brackets being appropriate

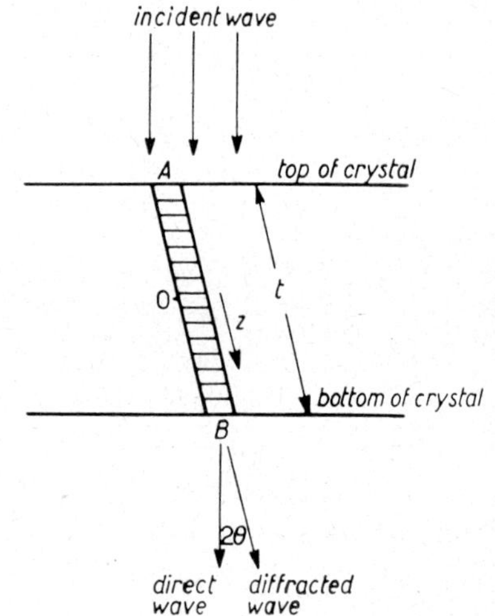

Fig. 9. – Column along diffracted beam in dark field case (HIRSCH, HOWIE and WHELAN [25]; courtesy Royal Society).

for a column of finite lateral dimensions (for discussion of this point see HIRSCH, HOWIE and WHELAN [25]). Clearly I_{diff} varies sinusoidally with t for a given s; the depth periodicity is $t'_0 = 1/s$. We can also illustrate this oscillation by

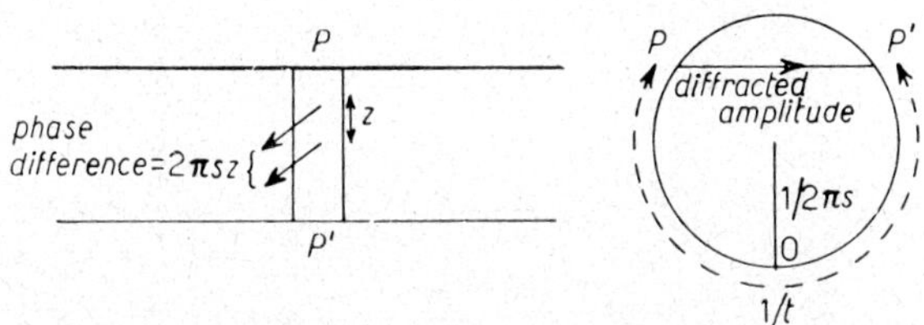

Fig. 10. – Phase difference between waves scattered from different points along column and amplitude-phase diagram for perfect crystal.

means of the amplitude-phase diagram. The amplitude scattered by an element of column lying between z and $z+dz$ (measured along the column) is proportional to dz and has a phase angle $2\pi sz$. The amplitude-phase diagram for the column is a circle with radius $1/2\pi s$, analogous to diffraction by a slit in physical optics (Fig. 10).

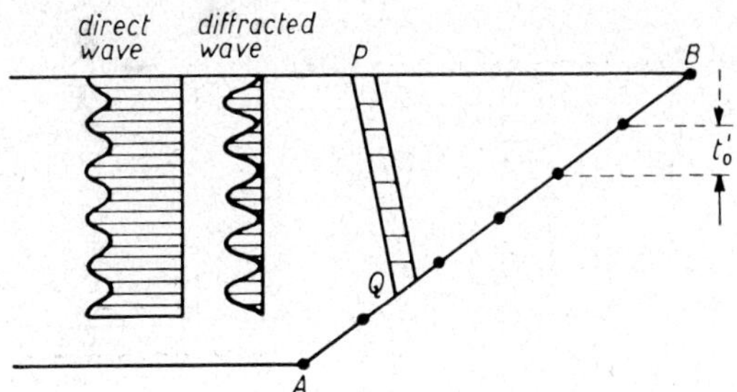

Fig. 11a. – Oscillation of waves in wedge crystal.

As t varies, A varies between 0 and $1/\pi s$, as is evident from the above equation. Thus the waves in the crystal oscillate with depth as shown in Fig. 11a. If the crystal is wedge-shaped the image will consist of a set of fringes called thickness contours, as is evident from the schematic diagram of Fig. 11a. An example of thickness contours around a hole is shown in Fig. 11b.

Again, if s varies, *i.e.* if the orientation varies, the diffracted intensity changes, producing the so-called bend extinction contours. An example is shown in Fig. 11c. It should also be noted that the intensity varies as $1/s^2$, *i.e.* it decreases quite rapidly with increasing deviation from the Bragg angle.

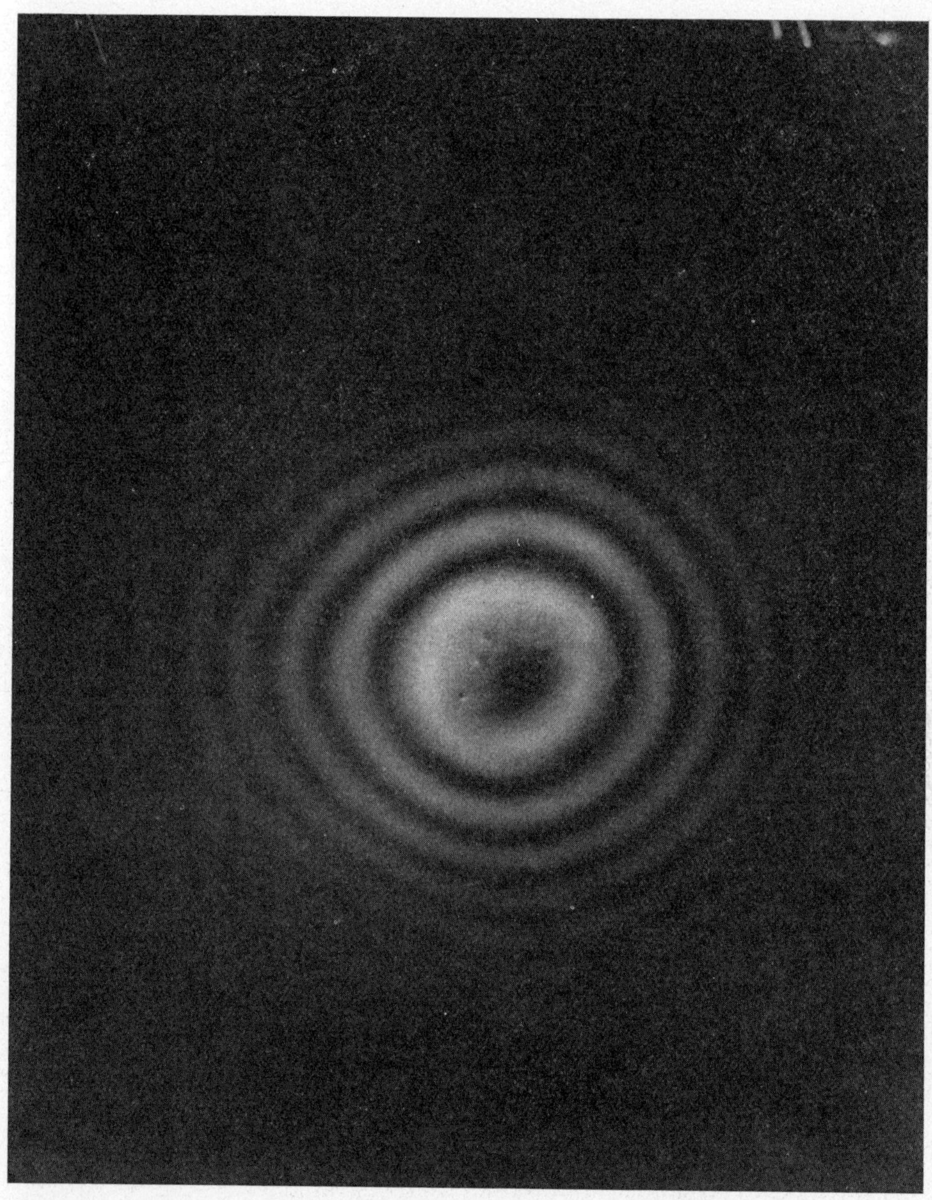

Fig. 11*b*. – Thickness extinction contours in aluminium around a hole (Mag. ×60 000) (HIRSCH, HOWIE and WHELAN [25]; courtesy Royal Society).

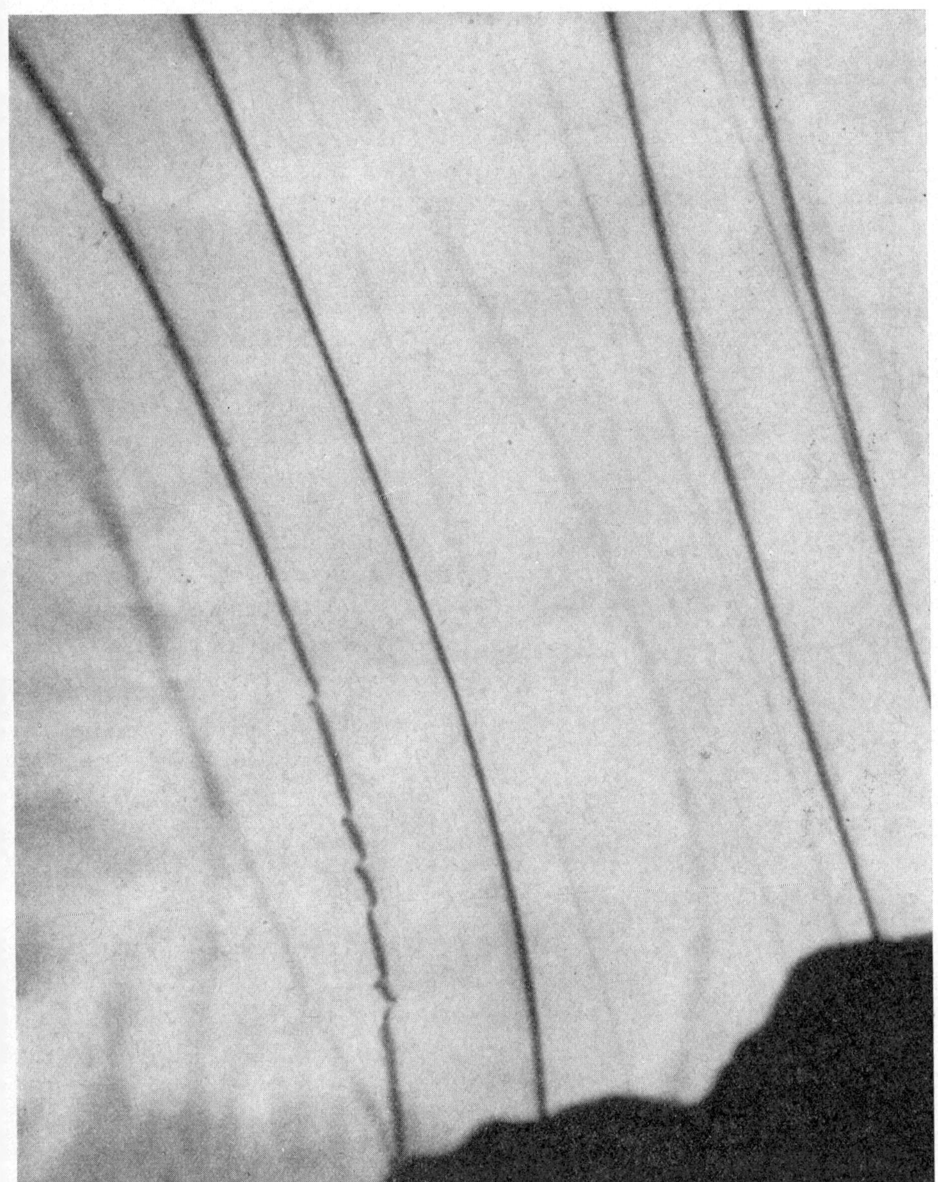

Fig. 11c. – Bend extinction countours in aluminium (SILCOX [15]) (Mag. × 66000).

4·2. *Imperfect crystal.* – If the atoms are displaced from their ideal positions

$$A = F_j \sum_j \exp[2\pi i(\boldsymbol{g} + \boldsymbol{s})\cdot(\boldsymbol{r}_j + \boldsymbol{R})]\,,$$

where $\boldsymbol{R}$ = displacement vector. We are assuming here that the scattering factors are not changed, *i.e.* that these are equal to F_j for all unit cells. Of course such changes can be taken into account, for example for precipitation or segregation effects, but generally the displacements give more important contrast effects.

The above equation reduces to

$$A = F_j \sum_j \exp[2\pi i\,\boldsymbol{g}\cdot\boldsymbol{R}]\exp[2\pi i\,\boldsymbol{s}\cdot\boldsymbol{r}_j]\,,$$

where we have neglected $\boldsymbol{s}\cdot\boldsymbol{R}$ in the exponent because $|\boldsymbol{R}|$ is usually of atomic dimensions, and $|\boldsymbol{s}|$ is the reciprocal of a macroscopic dimension. Thus the displacement of the cell produces a phase angle $\alpha = 2\pi\boldsymbol{g}\cdot\boldsymbol{R}$ in the scattered wave, and the resultant amplitude will differ from that from a perfect crystal. The contrast therefore arises through a phase contrast mechanism in the Bragg reflexions, the phase contrast being produced by atomic displacement. The above equation can be approximated by an integral; leaving out the factor F/V we obtain

$$A = \int \exp[i\alpha]\exp[2\pi isz]\,\mathrm{d}z\,,$$

where α is a function of the position in the column z, and depends on $\boldsymbol{g}$ and $\boldsymbol{R}$. The amplitude is essentially the Fourier transform of the phase factor $\exp[i\alpha]$ over the whole column.

4·3. *Stacking fault in face centred cubic crystal.* – Suppose the fault runs obliquely across the foil as shown in Fig. 12*a*.

The two parts of the crystal are displaced relative to each other parallel to the fault plane by the vector $\boldsymbol{R} = (a/6)\,[112]$. This produces a phase difference α in waves diffracted from opposite sides of the

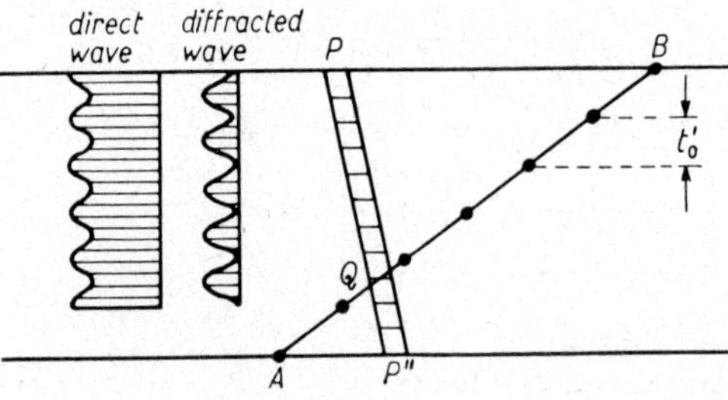

Fig. 12*a*. – Oscillation of waves in faulted crystal (HIRSCH, HOWIE and WHELAN [25]; courtesy Royal Society).

fault equal to $\alpha = \frac{1}{3}\pi \cdot (h+k+2l)$, for a reflexion h, k, l. The possible values of α are multiples of $2\pi/3$ or 2π, depending on the indices h, k, l. The amplitude-phase diagram for $\alpha = -120°$ is shown in Fig. 13.

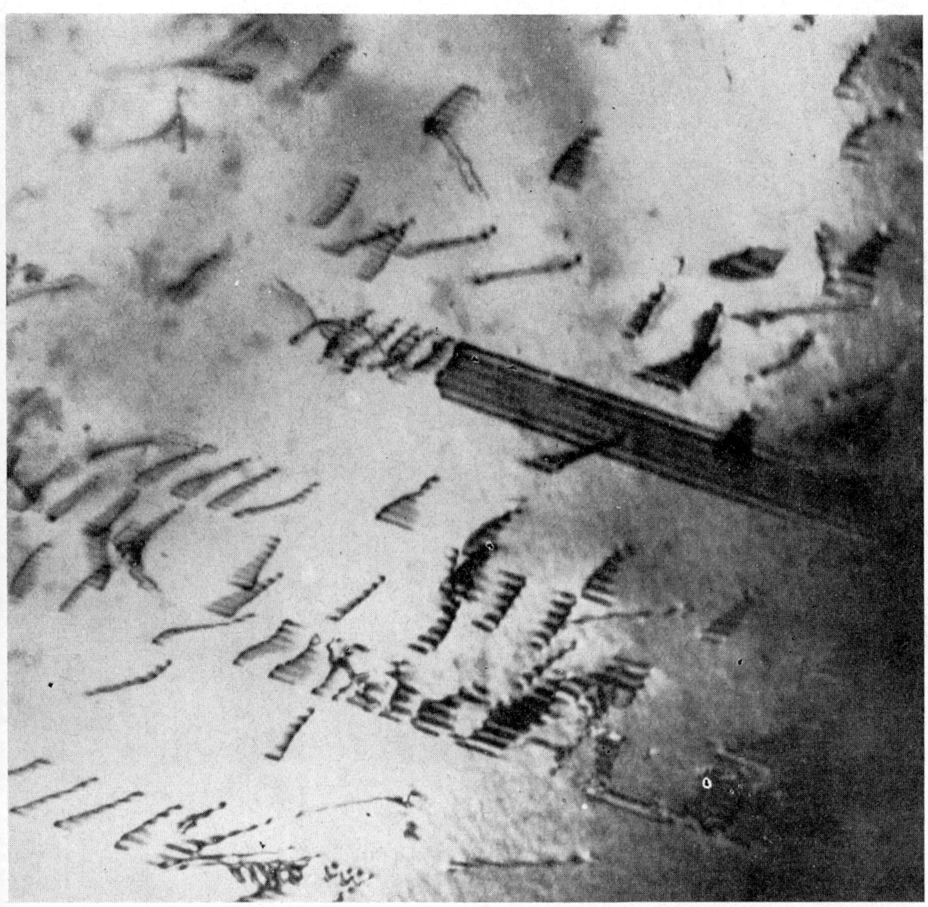

Fig. 12*b*. – Stacking fault fringes in single crystal of Cu 7 % Al alloy (Howie [28]) (Mag. × 60 000).

An abrupt change of phase of $-120°$ occurs at the point, Q, where the column meets the fault. As the position of the column is changed P is fixed but Q and P'' vary, and hence I varies. But for a change in depth of Q by t'_0, it occupies identical positions on the circle, and so does P''. Hence the intensity is periodic in t'_0. Thus fringes are produced parallel to the intersection of the fault plane with the surface, the periodicity being determined by $t'_0 = 1/s$, shown schematically in Fig. 12*a*. The intensity distribution can, of course, be calculated easily from the above equations. An example of stacking fault fringes in a single crystal of Cu 7 % Al alloy is shown in Fig. 12*b* (HOWIE [28]).

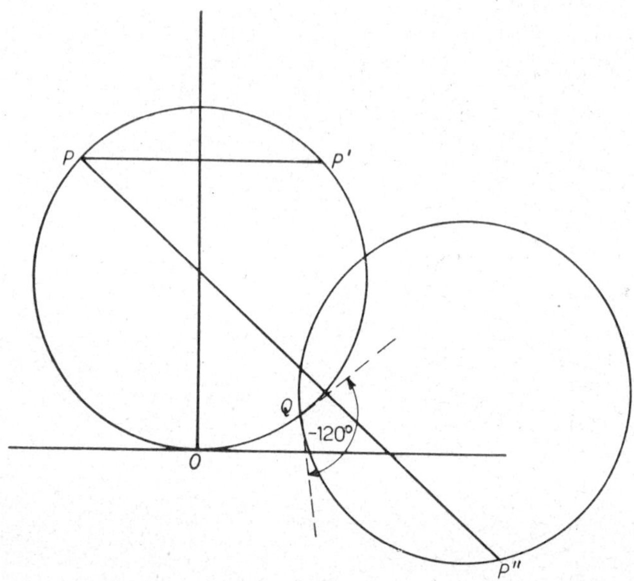

Fig. 13. – Amplitude-phase diagram for crystal with stacking fault (HIRSCH, HOWIE and WHELAN [25]; courtesy Royal Society).

4·4. *Dislocations.* – In this case there is a continuous variation of α with z. Consider for example an edge dislocation parallel to the foil plane as shown in Fig. 14.

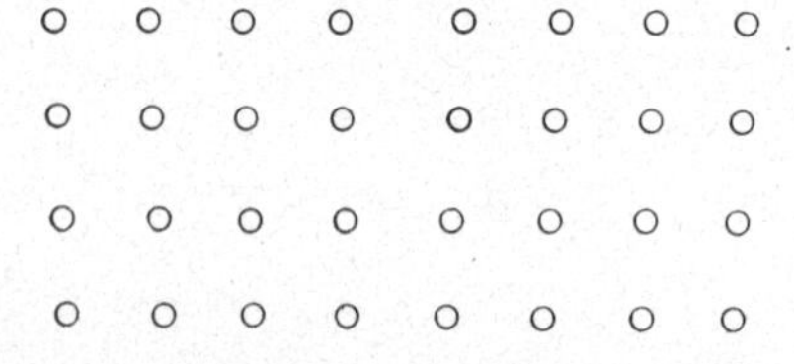

Fig. 14. – Strain field associated with edge dislocation in simple cubic lattice (COTTRELL [29]; courtesy Clarendon Press).

The displacements on opposite sides of the dislocation are in opposite senses. Hence on one side of the dislocation the phase factor α adds to $2\pi sz$ due to the change in depth of the point in the column; on the other side the two phase angles subtract. Hence on one side of the dislocation the crystal is brought nearer a reflecting position, on the other side away from it. The diffracted intensity is again proportional to $1/s^2$ and this means that contrast is only obtained on one side of the dislocation.

This can also be interpreted in terms of local rotation of lattice planes as is clear from Fig. 14; on one side the atomic planes are rotated into the reflecting position, on the other side away from it.

For the construction of amplitude-phase diagrams and associated calculations, the simplest case to consider is that of a screw dislocation parallel to the plane of the foil. The column is now distorted as shown in Fig. 15.

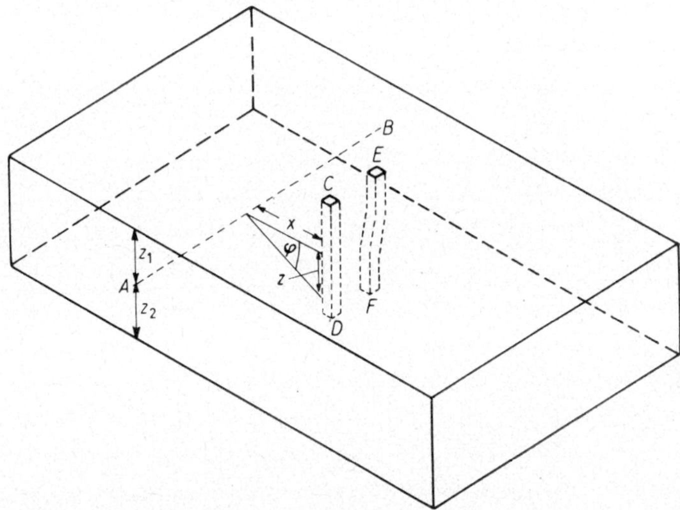

Fig. 15. – Crystal containing screw dislocation AB parallel to the plane of the foil. A column of crystal CD in the perfect crystal is deformed to shape EF after introduction of the screw dislocation. The diagram illustrates the choice of parameters x, z and φ (HIRSCH, HOWIE and WHELAN [25]; courtesy Royal Society).

The displacement vector $\boldsymbol{R} = \boldsymbol{b}\,\varphi/2\pi = \boldsymbol{b}/2\pi\,\mathrm{tg}^{-1}\,(z/x)$, where x is the closest distance of the column from the dislocation.

Hence

$$\alpha = 2\pi \boldsymbol{g}\cdot\boldsymbol{R} = \boldsymbol{g}\cdot\boldsymbol{b}\,\mathrm{tg}^{-1}\frac{z}{x} = n\,\mathrm{tg}^{-1}\frac{z}{x},$$

n is an integer which may have positive or negative values or zero; $n\pi$ is the phase difference between the waves scattered immediately above and below the dislocation. Usually the important values of n are $n = 0, 1, 2, 3, 4$. For $n = 0$, *i.e.* $\alpha = 0$, $\boldsymbol{g}\cdot\boldsymbol{b} = 0$, the screw dislocations are invisible, a case of considerable importance for the determination of Burgers vectors. This condition implies that the displacements are parallel to the reflecting planes.

We obtain for the diffracted amplitude

$$A = \int_{-z_1}^{z_2} \exp\left[in\,\mathrm{tg}^{-1}\frac{z}{x} + 2\pi i s z\right]\mathrm{d}z\,.$$

This expression can be put in a form from which it is clear that the shape of the amplitude-phase diagram only depends on n and a parameter $\beta = 2\pi s x$. The size of the diagram and therefore the amplitude, are proportional to s^{-1}, as for the perfect crystal. Fig. 16 shows an example for $n=2$ and $\beta = \pm 1$. As expected the intensity is large only on one side of the dislocation.

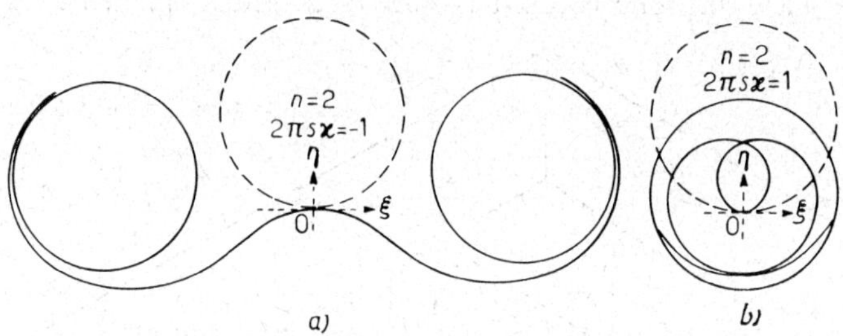

Fig. 16. – Amplitude-phase diagram for a screw dislocation for $n=2$, $2\pi s x = \pm 1$ (HIRSCH, HOWIE and WHELAN [25]; courtesy Royal Socyety).

The intensity of diffraction will depend on the distance between the centres of the circles and also on the position of the initial and final points on these circles. As the depth of the dislocation is changed, so the points on the circles will move and the intensity will vary. The average intensity is given by the vector joining the centres of the circles and dislocation profiles can be calculated for different values of β, *i.e.* x for a given s. Such profiles are shown in Fig. 17*a* for various values of n.

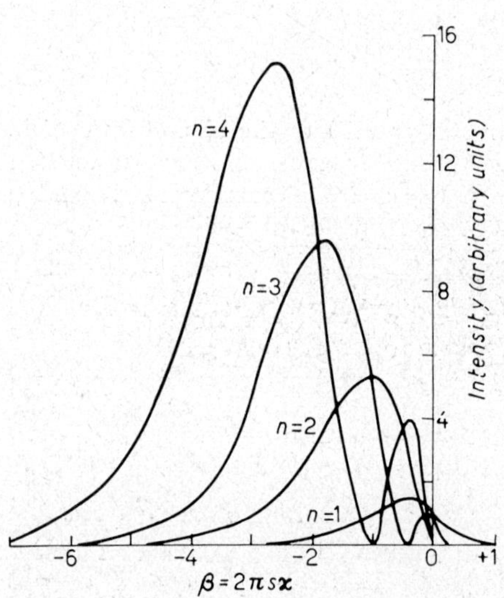

Fig. 17*a*. – Intensity profiles of a screw dislocation for various values of n, plotted as a function of $\beta = 2\pi s x$. The centre of the dislocation is at $\beta = 0$. Note that the contrast lies to one side of the centre of the dislocation (HIRSCH, HOWIE and WHELAN [25]; courtesy Royal Society).

The one-sided nature of the contrast, and the long tails on the side away from the dislocation should be noted. It is also clear that the displacement of the image from the dislocation is of the same order as the width of the dislocation. These intensity curves can be considered as profiles for a given value of s. But as s is decreased the intensity increases, the smallest value of s possible, corresponding to maximum contrast, is of the order of t_0^{-1}, where t_0 is the extinction distance. Now t_0 increases with increasing n and hence the peak heights of all these profiles are likely to be of the same order for optimum contrast conditions. But for larger n, the optimum values of s are smaller

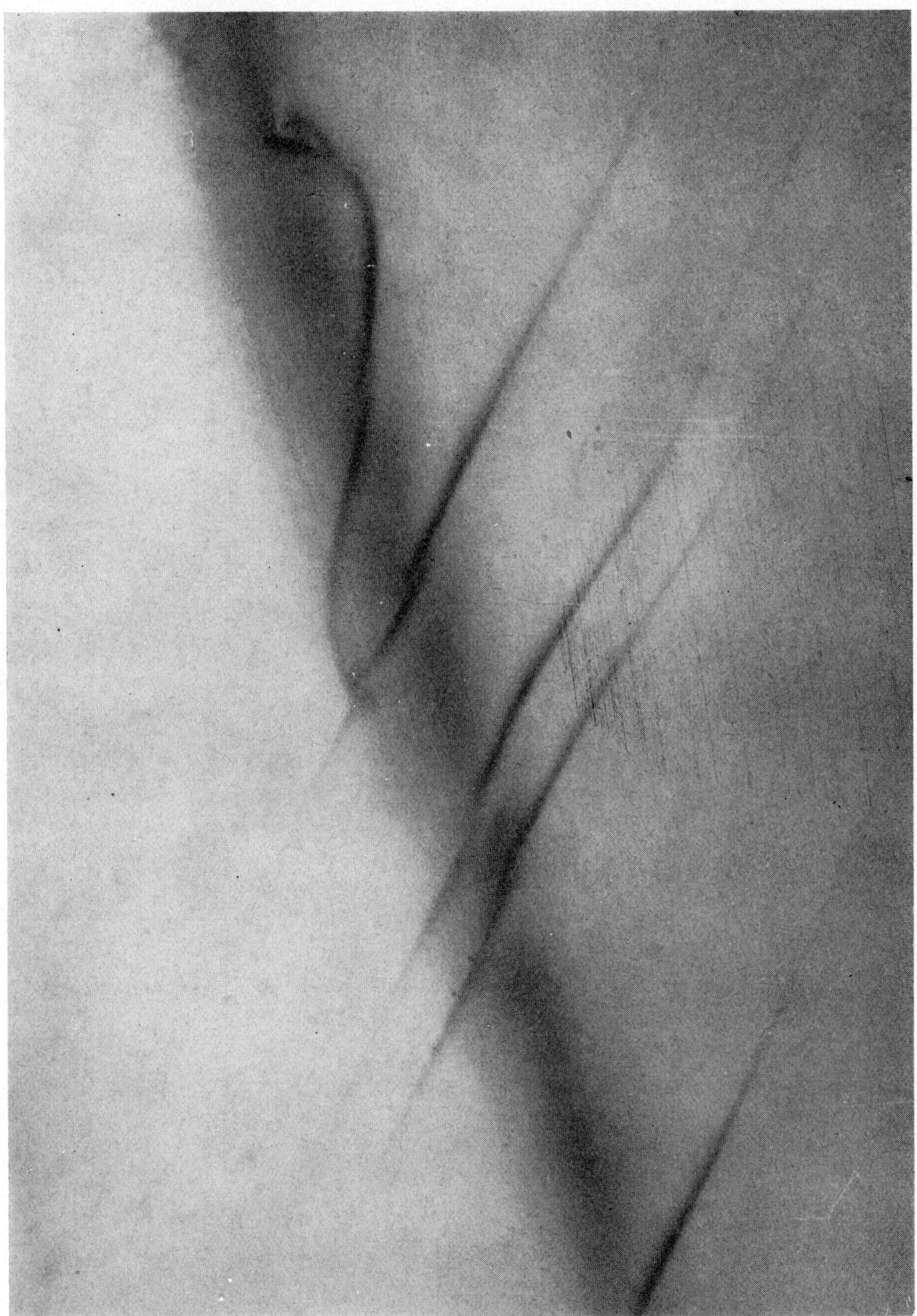

Fig. 17b. – Micrograph illustrating dislocation contrast in aluminium. Note that the contrast lies on one side of the dislocation, and changes from one side to the other where the dislocation crosses the bend extinction contour. Note also the rapid decrease in contrast on the side facing the dislocation and the slower decrease on the other side. The width and total intensity of the image are a maximum on the edge of the extinction contour. The width of the dislocation image is of the order of the displacement of the peak of the image from the centre of the dislocation (Mag. × 100 000) (Hirsch, Howie and Whelan [25]; courtesy Royal Society).

and hence the width of the image will be larger. Thus, at optimum contrast, the profile for $n=4$ is about 5 times as wide and as far away from the dislocation as that for $n=1$.

4·5. *Summary of screw dislocation image contrast effects deduced from this theory.*

1) Dislocations scatter more electrons; dark field and bright field images should be reversed; this is confirmed experimentally for thin crystals.

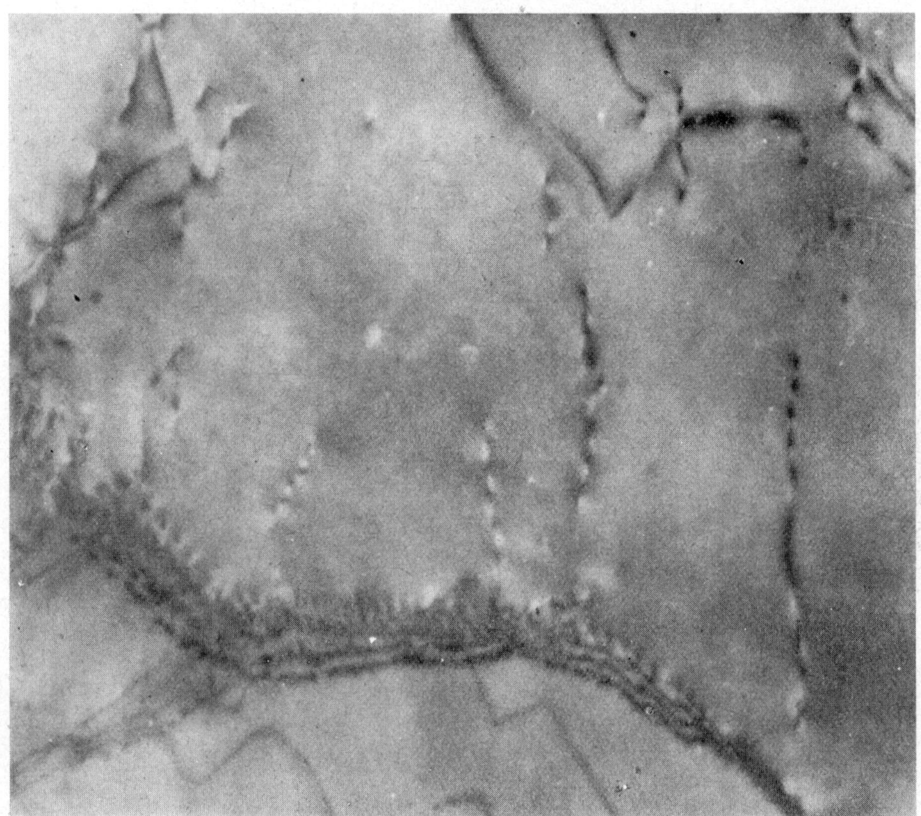

Fig. 17*c*. – Black and white contrast at dislocations in aluminium (Mag. $\times$ 150 000) (HIRSCH, HOWIE and WHELAN [25]; courtesy Royal Society).

2) The contrast is one-sided; thus, when the dislocation runs across an extinction bend contour the sign of s changes and hence the contrast should transfer from one side to the other of the dislocation. This is confirmed experimentally. An example is shown in Fig. 17*c*.

3) The width of the dislocation image is about the same as its displacement from the centre of the dislocation (see Fig. 17*b*).

4) The image has tails away from dislocation. Confirmed experimentally (see Fig. 17*b*).

5) Contrast decreases with increasing distance from a strong extinction contour; confirmed experimentally (see Fig. 17*b*).

6) Dislocations oblique to the plane of the foil will have oscillatory contrast; confirmed experimentally.

7) When $\boldsymbol{g}\cdot\boldsymbol{b}=0$ the dislocation image vanishes; confirmed experimentally.

8) If two reflexions are operating simultaneously images may be formed on both sides of the dislocation; confirmed experimentally.

9) When a screw dislocation is inclined to the plane of the foil, the calculation is similar except that x is replaced by $x/\cos\psi$, where ψ is the angle of inclination of the dislocation. The dislocation image becomes narrower by a factor $\cos\psi$ and disappears when the dislocation is normal to the plane of the foil, as observed experimentally for loops. The effect is illustrated schematically in Fig. 18*a*, and an example is shown in Fig. 18*b*.

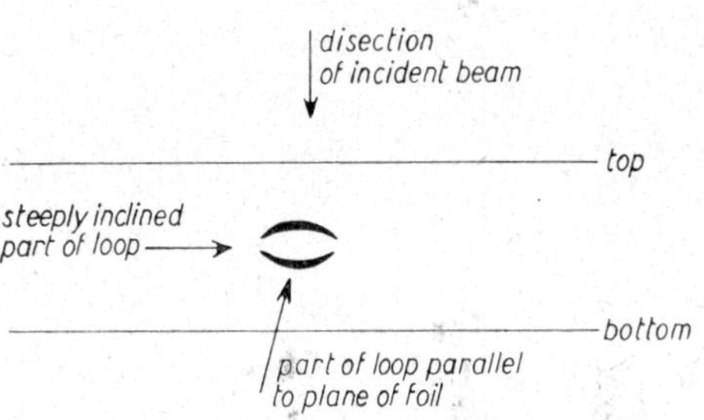

Fig. 18*a*. – Diagram illustrating nature of image of a dislocation loop inclined to the plane of the foil.

10) Since the image of the dislocation is on one side, the image will lie either completely inside or completely outside the dislocation loop. If two reflexions are operating both images can occur simultaneously; this has been confirmed experimentally.

4·6. *Edge dislocation.* – For an edge dislocation the displacements are

$$R_1=\frac{b}{2\pi}\left[\varphi+\frac{\sin 2\varphi}{4(1-\nu)}\right],$$

parallel to the Burgers vector, and

$$R_2=-\frac{b}{2\pi}\left[\frac{(1-2\nu)}{2(1-\nu)}\log|r|+\frac{\cos 2\varphi}{4(1-\nu)}\right],$$

normal to the slip plane.

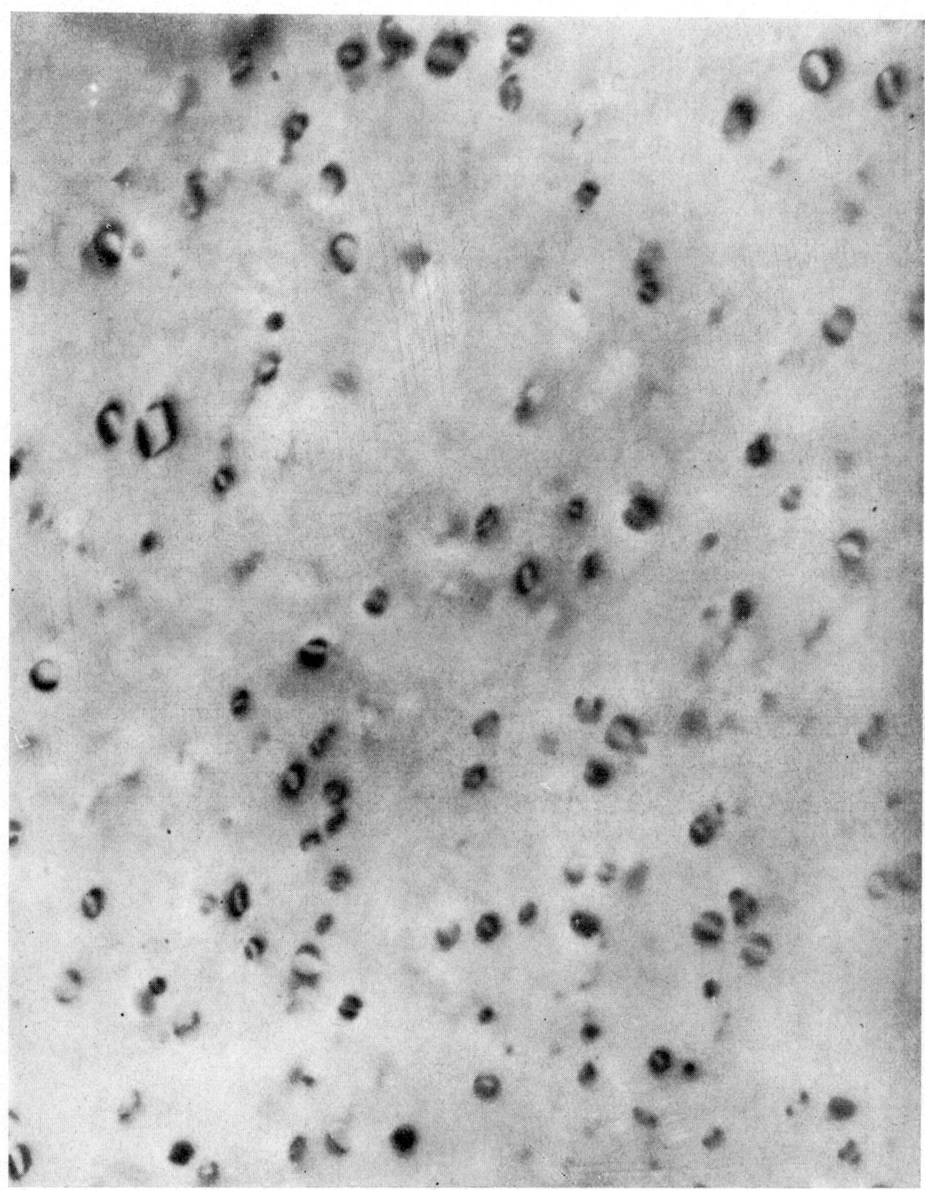

Fig. 18*b*. – Dislocation loops in quenched aluminium (Mag. × 166000) (HIRSCH, SILCOX, SMALLMAN and WESTMACOTT [30]; courtesy Philosophical Magazine).

When the slip plane is parallel to the plane of the foil only R_1 is effective since R_2 is parallel to the reflecting plane. In this case the edge dislocation image is rather similar to that of a screw dislocation, but will be rather wider than that of a screw. The condition for invisibility, *i.e.* $\boldsymbol{g}\cdot\boldsymbol{b}=0$ will still hold.

But for any other orientation of the dislocation this is not the case and the edge dislocation should be visible although $\boldsymbol{g}\cdot\boldsymbol{b}=0$. There are no detailed calculations available for dislocations of arbitrary Burgers vector and orientation, but in general contrast from the screw component is more important and the effect of R_2 is relatively small.

However for an edge dislocation with its slip plane normal to the plane of the foil only R_2 is important. An example is a prismatic dislocation loop parallel to the foil plane. We note that the contrast is now symmetrical about the dislocation, since R_2 will not change sign with φ. Loops may therefore appear double.

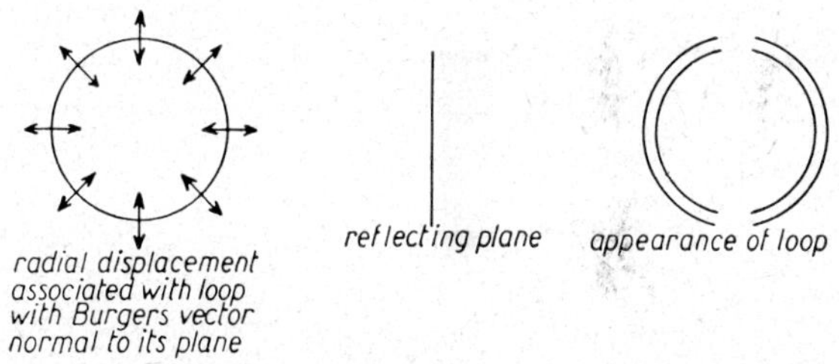

For a loop, however, part of its length will be invisible where the displacement is parallel to the reflecting planes. The appearance of the loops is therefore as sketched schematically in Fig. 19*a*.

Fig. 19*a*. – Appearance of dislocation loop parallel to plane of foil, with Burgers vector normal to this plane.

Such loops have been found in Zn (PRICE [13]; BROWN, unpublished), and an example is shown in Fig. 19*b*.

However, to explain these contrast effects in detail the dynamical theory is required since the displacements are small and the contrast effects are important only when $s\to 0$.

It should be emphasized that the contrast effects must be studied carefully before the nature of the dislocation loop can be deduced, *i.e.* whether the Burgers vector is normal to the plane of the loop, or whether there is a component parallel to the plane of the loop. It is also possible to decide in favourable cases whether the prismatic loops are produced from the collapse of discs of vacancies or from plates of interstitials. An example has been described by WILLIAMSON and BAKER [31].

4·7. *Effects not explained.*

1) Dislocation images have an oscillatory white-dark contrast and sometimes a zig-zag contrast when $s\to 0$. An example is shown in Fig. 17*c*.

2) Oscillations of the image are mainly confined to the parts of the dislocations or faults near the surface.

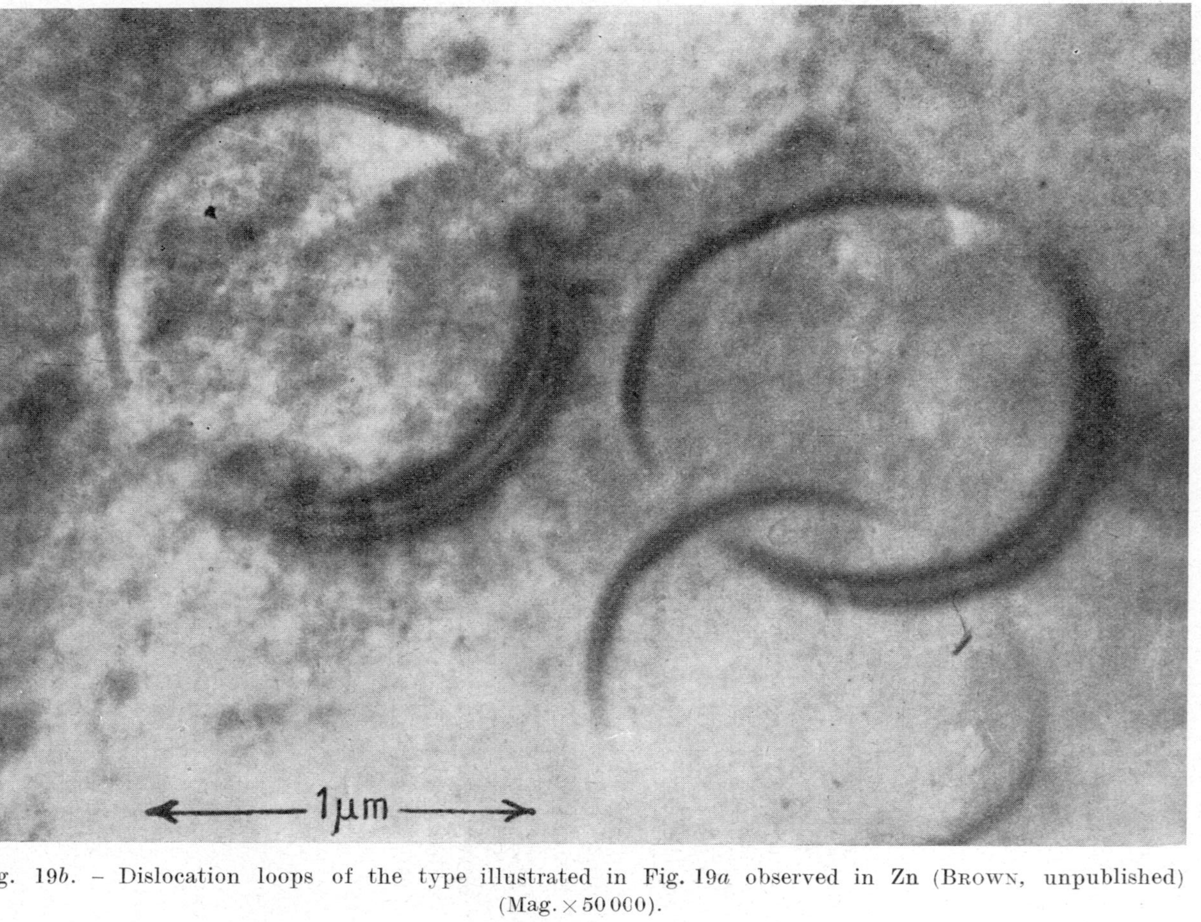

Fig. 19*b*. – Dislocation loops of the type illustrated in Fig. 19*a* observed in Zn (BROWN, unpublished) (Mag. ×50 000).

3) Dislocations sometimes appear to scatter less than the surrounding regions.

For these effects the dynamical theory must be used. The physical principles of this theory will be outlined below, without going into the mathematical details.

5. – Dynamical theory.

There is a coupling between the direct and diffracted beams in the crystal, and the situation is similar to the case of a coupled pendulum. Consequently just as in the case of the coupled pendulum, two modes of oscillation occur with slightly different wave vectors (Fig. 20), $\boldsymbol{k}_0$, $\boldsymbol{k}_0'$ for the incident waves, and $\boldsymbol{k}_g$, $\boldsymbol{k}_g'$ for the diffracted waves.

Beats are set up between the waves with $\boldsymbol{k}_0$ and $\boldsymbol{k}_0'$, and similarly for the diffracted waves, and these beats give rise to oscillations in the resultant amplitude of the incident and diffracted waves in the crystal, producing the fringes observed.

For the perfect crystal the amplitude of the resultant diffracted waves is given by

$$A = \frac{\sin \pi t\bar{s}}{\pi\bar{s}},$$

where

$$\bar{s} = \sqrt{t_0^{-2} + s^2},$$

t_0 being the extinction distance $=\pi V \cdot \cos\theta/\lambda F$. Thus the form of the oscillations in the dynamical region is similar to that in the kinematical region, except that at $s = 0$ a maximum amplitude

$$A_{\max} = t_0 \frac{\sin(\pi(t/t_0))}{\pi},$$

is obtained. As the scattering factor decreases rapidly with increasing scattering angle, F decreases and therefore t_0 increases with increasing h, k, l. Typical values of extinction distances are given in Table I.

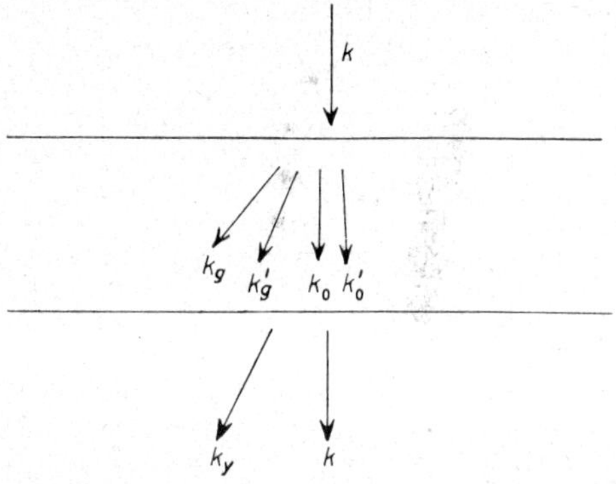

Fig. 20. – Wave vectors in dynamical treatment.

TABLE I. – *Extinction distances* (Å) *of typical metals for* 100 kV *electrons* (λ=0.037 Å).

Reflexion	111	200	220
Al	646	774	1 240
Ni	258	302	468
Cu	268	308	472
Ag	250	285	403
Pt	165	188	262
Au	181	204	281

Suppose now that there is a fault in the foil. Then the two halves of the crystal are treated as perfect crystals and the wavefunctions matched at the fault interface, taking into account the phase differences. This calculation has been carried out for stacking faults (WHELAN and HIRSCH [32]). Again contrast in the form of fringes is obtained.

This problem can be considered in another way. In general we are interested in the intensity distribution in vacuo on the lower surface of the crystal. The waves inside the crystal must be matched with the waves outside the crystal at the lower surface; *i.e.* certain boundary conditions must be satisfied. Now it turns out that if the two foil surfaces are parallel to each other there are only one incident and one diffracted wave outside the crystal below the lower surface (Fig. 20) and uniform contrast is obtained. If the lower surface is not parallel to the upper surface (*i.e.* the crystal is wedge-shaped) then two waves with slightly different wave vector, k, emerge in vacuo and we get Young type or « $\cos^2\theta$ » interference fringes (Fig. 21).

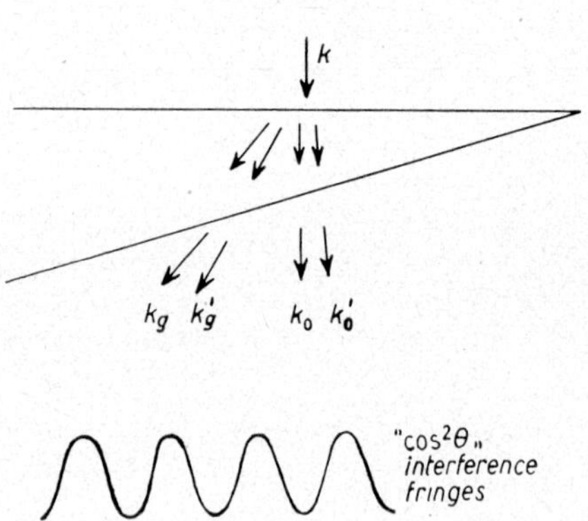

Fig. 21. – Wave vectors and nature of fringes at lower surface of wedge crystal.

If there is a fault across the crystal, each of the two waves in the top crystal excites two waves in the bottom crystal; thus there are four incident waves and four diffracted waves in the bottom crystal, and these give rise to three waves in vacuo below the bottom surface of the crystal. The fringes therefore arise from 3-beam interference (shown schematically in Fig. 22) and are more complicated than for wedge crystals.

For dislocations, one essentially takes a column and divides the crystal into narrow slabs, perfect within each slab, but with phase differences between adjacent slabs. This gives rise to a differential formulation of the dynamical equations in the distorted crystal and for a given dislocation the image can be computed on a machine. The results obtained by HOWIE and WHELAN [33, 34] so far, using this procedure (and introducing absorption (see below)), give

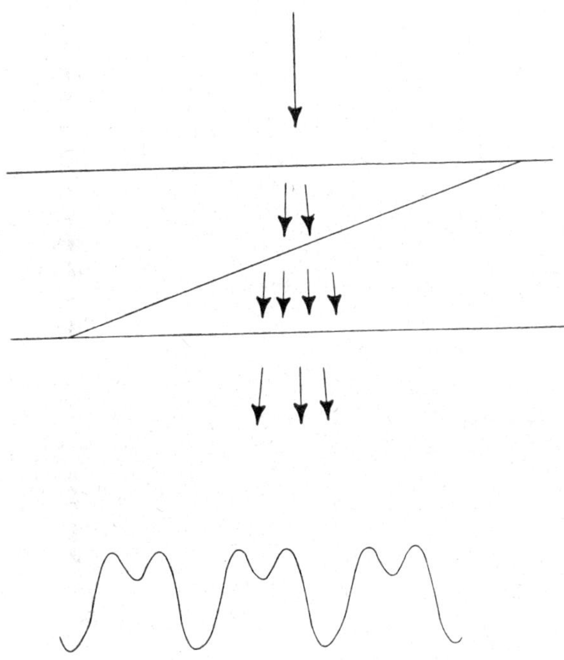

Fig. 22. – Wave vectors and nature of fringes at lower surface of faulted crystal.

dislocation profiles near extinction contours in good agreement with experiment. Thus zig-zag appearance and the black and white contrast can be explained.

However some of the effects can only be explained if absorption is taken into account. This can be done formally by assuming a complex scattering potential. The effect of absorption is rather striking and has important practical consequences (HASHIMOTO, HOWIE and WHELAN [33]).

If one considers the nature of the wavefunctions for the waves with wave vectors k_0, k_0' for example, it turns out that one of these has nodes at the atoms and for a low order reflexion antinodes between them; and the reverse is true for the other wave. If now there is some incoherent process whereby the wave suffers an energy loss at the atom, it may not reach the image because of a change in direction in its path and because of the effect of chromatic aberration. In that case one of the waves will be absorbed preferentially. This has interesting consequences:

1) Consider a (111) reflexion. On one side of the reflecting position the preferentially absorbed wave is mainly excited; hence the absorption is large. On the other side of the reflecting position the nonabsorbed wave is mainly excited, and hence there is a preferential transmission. Experimentally in thick regions dark (absorbing) bands are observed, at the edge of which there is enhanced transmission and good contrast. Thus, for example, in these regions Al foils $\sim$7 500 Å thick have been found to be transparent (THOMAS and WHELAN [16]).

2) The nature of the fringes, for example, at stacking faults, will be modified because some of the waves are preferentially absorbed. This is shown schematically in Fig. 23. The preferentially absorbed waves are dotted. The diagram shows that in region A and C, « $\cos^2 \theta$ » type fringes are produced, the two interfering waves being of comparable intensity, while in the middle of the fault, B, weak 3-beam interference fringes are produced on a uniform background, one of the transmitted waves being strong and the others weak (HASHIMOTO, HOWIE and WHELAN [35]). Thus the fringe pattern is no longer uniform, as in the case of nonabsorbing crystals. It also turns out that the fringe pattern is not identical at the top and bottom parts of the fault, A, C, when viewed in dark field. Hence the top and bottom surfaces can be distinguished from such images, and similar ones from dislocations.

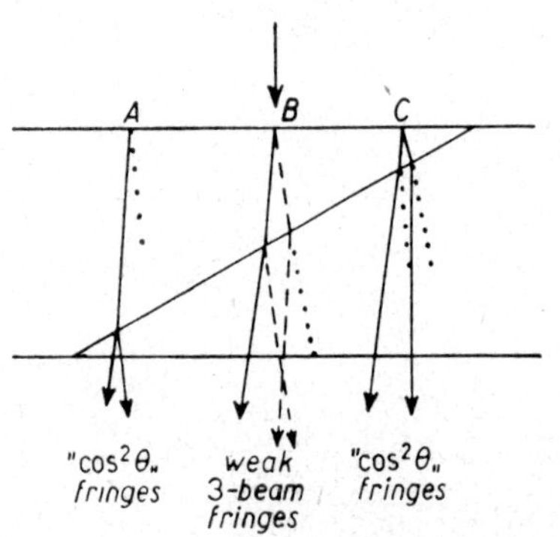

Fig. 23. – Effect of absorption on nature of fringes from faulted crystals.

6. – Other contrast effects.

There are many other contrast effects, *e.g.* due to precipitates, slip traces, cavities etc., which have not yet been studied in detail. However it may just be noted here that slip traces (example shown in Fig. 24) which are left behind when the dislocations have moved, and which are considered to arise from strains set up as the result of dislocation motion at the top and bottom metal-oxide or metal-carbon film interfaces, are very useful for determining the thickness of the foil. Such measurements are essential in studies of concentrations of loops, of dislocations, or of other defects (*e.g.* BAILEY and HIRSCH [36]).

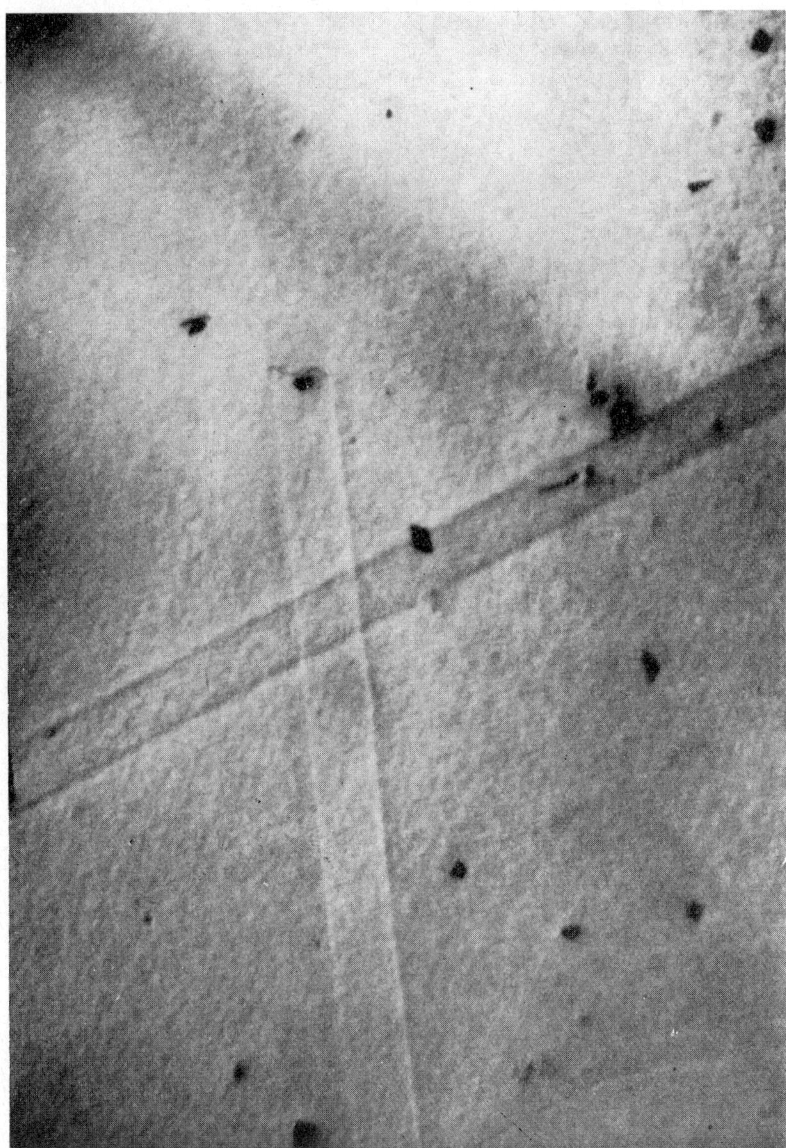

Fig. 24. – Slip traces due to movement of dislocations in gold (Mag. $\times 60\,000$) (COTTERILL, unpublished).

7. – Conclusions about contrast effects.

1) By studying the nature of contrast in different orientations one can deduce Burgers vectors of dislocations or shears at faults; the condition of invisibility of the dislocation image is particularly useful.

2) From the nature of the change-over of the image of a dislocation across extinction contours the value of $n = \boldsymbol{g}\cdot\boldsymbol{b}$, and hence the Burgers vector, can be determined. With experience one may be able to deduce the Burgers vector simply from the width of image.

3) It is possible to deduce the sign of the Burgers vector, knowing the side on which the dislocation image appears, and knowing the sign of $\boldsymbol{s}$. Thus it should be possible to distinguish between interstitial and vacancy loops, provided the plane on which the loop lies is known.

4) It is possible to distinguish between the top and bottom of the foil from dark field pictures of faults and dislocations.

5) It is possible to distinguish between prismatic loops with screw components and loops with Burgers vectors normal to the plane of the loop.

III. – Application of Transmission Electron Microscopy to the Study of Defects in Quenched and Neutron-Irradiated Crystals.

1. – Quenching.

Extensive observations have been carried out on quenched Al (Hirsch Silcox, Smallman and Westmacott [30]; Wilsdorf and Wilsdorf [37]), Al alloys (Thomas and Whelan [16]; Smallman, Westmacott and Coiley [38]; Nicholson and Nutting [39]) and Au (Silcox and Hirsch [40]) and some observations have also been made on quenched Cu, Ag, and Ni (Hirsch and Silcox [41]; Smallman, Westmacott and Coiley [38]). The results of these experiments will be summarized in the following sections.

1'1. *Quenched aluminium.* – Specimens of Al have been examined after quenching from 600 °C into iced brine, followed by thinning for electron microscope observations (Hirsch, Silcox, Smallman and Westmacott [30]). The specimens are found to contain a high density of prismatic dislocation loops ($\sim 10^{15}$ cm^{-3}), with Burgers vector $\frac{1}{2}[110]$ inclined to the plane of the loops An example is shown in Fig. 18*b*. These loops are presumably formed by the collapse of discs of vacancies on (111) planes, as predicted by Kuhlmann-Wilsdorf [42]. The average diameter of the loops is ~ 200 Å and the total vacancy concentration $\sim 10^{-4}$. The density of dislocations in the form of loops is $\sim 10^{10}$ cm^{-2}. The loops tend to be hexagonal with their sides parallel to close packed directions. Along these directions the prismatic dislocations can dissociate along intersecting (111) planes, thereby lowering the energy.

Other observations include the existence of a denuded zone near grain boundaries (Fig. 25), and the presence of very joggy dislocations. The prismatic glide of loops has also been observed directly.

SILCOX and WHELAN [14] and VANDERVOORT and WASHBURN [43] have studied the annealing of the dislocation loops in Al, the former using a

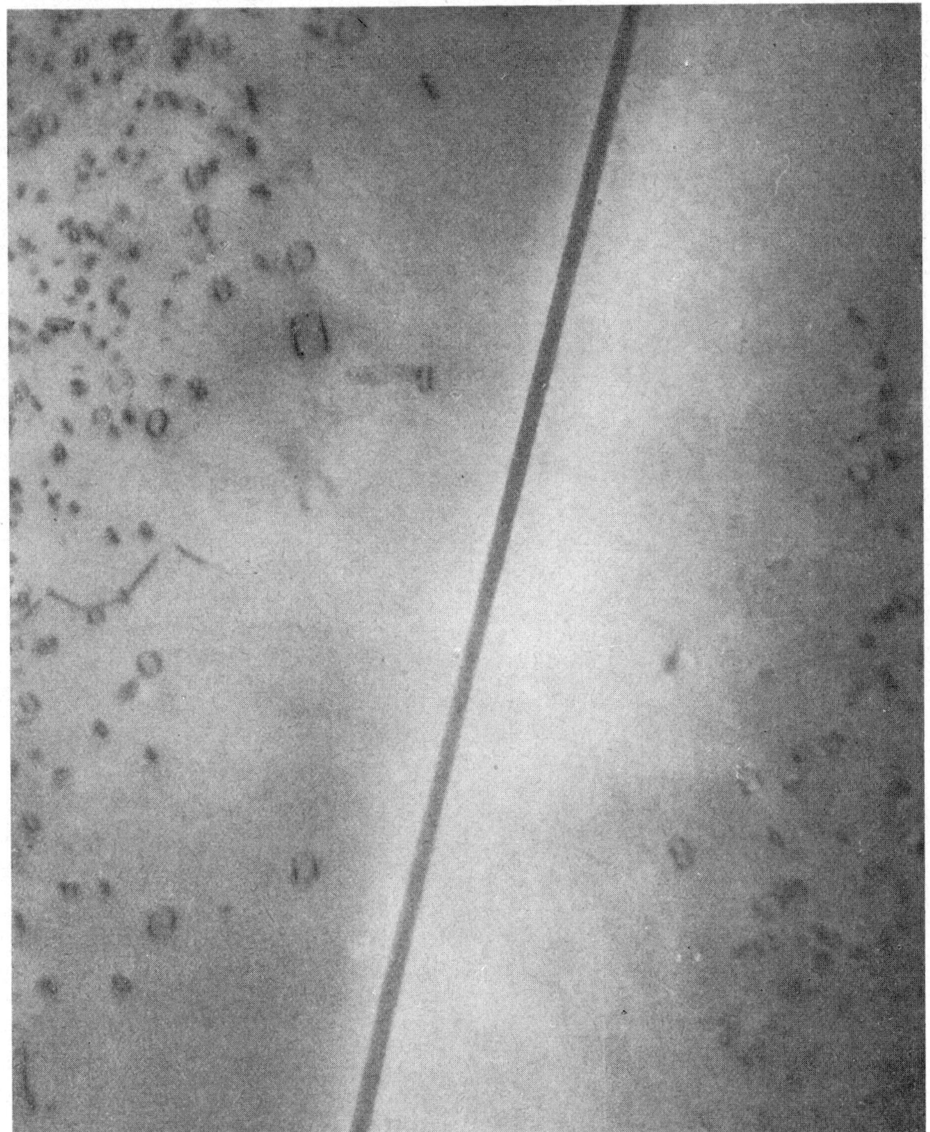

Fig. 25. – Dislocation loops in Al quenched from 600 °C into iced brine, showing a denuded zone near a grain boundary (HIRSCH, SILCOX, SMALLMAN and WESTMACOTT [30]) (Mag. × 60 000) (Courtesy *Phil. Mag.*).

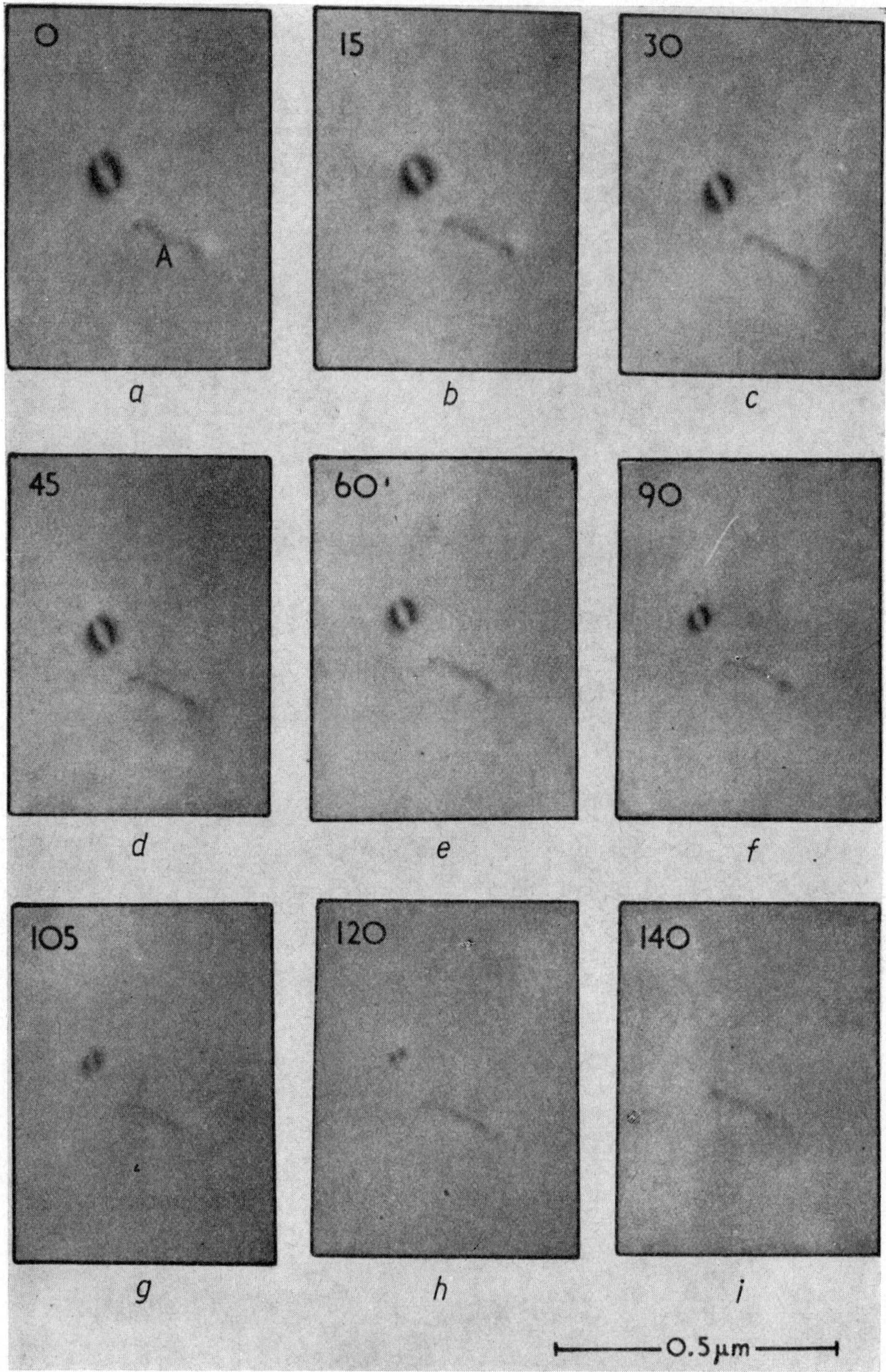

Fig. 26. – Sequence showing annealing of dislocation loop by climb in thin foil on heating stage in the electron microscope; stage temperature 197 °C. The numbers refer to the time in seconds at which exposures were made (Silcox and Whelan [14]) (Mag. × 96000) (Courtesy *Phil. Mag.*).

heating stage in the electron microscope. At about 190 °C the loops are observed to shrink and disappear in a few minutes. The process of shrinking is climb by the emission of vacancies which disappear at the surface. A sequence of micrographs illustrating this process is shown in Fig. 26. Applying Friedel's theory of climb [44] to this case it is found that the loops (of radius r_0) anneal out in a time

$$t_0 = \frac{r_0^2}{z\nu b^2 \alpha} \exp\left[U_{SD}/kT\right],$$

where z is the co-ordination number, ν an atomic frequency, b the Burgers vector, α a constant depending on the line tension of a dislocation, U_{SD} is the activation energy for self diffusion, k the Boltzmann factor and T the temperature. Values of t_0 can be measured experimentally, and U_{SD} found after substituting reasonable values for the other constants. For Al (SILCOX and WHELAN [14]), Zn (PRICE [13]) and Cu (SEGALL, PATRIDGE and HIRSCH [45]) values of U_{SD} found in this way agree to within 10% with the accepted values (1.3 eV, 0.9 eV, 2.05 eV respectively). This analysis is extremely useful; it is possible to predict with precision the temperature range in which such loops would disappear in a given time, and in this way one can test whether loops are prismatic or not.

The observations on Al are directly comparable with resistivity measurements on bulk specimens, made by FEDERIGHI [46], who finds that the resistivity anneals out in the same temperature range, also with an activation energy U_{SD}. However, the annealing of bulk specimens is more complicated because the vacancies emitted by the smaller loops disappear at the large ones, thus changing the distribution of loops to larger and larger loops.

With regard to the mechanical properties, there is some evidence which shows that at least part of the quench-hardening anneals out in the same temperature range (KINO [47]).

There is thus a good correlation between the microstructural observations and bulk properties.

1·2. *Quenched* Au. – Specimens of Au quenched from 900 °C into iced brine and subsequently aged at 100°, followed by thinning, contain a high density ($\sim 10^{15}$ cm^{-3}) of defects which have been shown, by contrast experiments, to be tetrahedra of stacking faults (usually ~ 300 Å in diameter) on (111) planes (SILCOX and HIRSCH [40]). An example is shown in Fig. 27. The difference in the nature of the defects in Al and Au after quenching is due to the difference in stacking fault energy, γ, of the two metals. In the case of Al, γ is large and the discs of vacancies collapse to form a ring of dislocation with Burgers vector $\frac{1}{2}[110]$ without a stacking fault (KUHLMANN-WILSDORF [42]). In the case of Au, γ is low, and the disc collapses forming

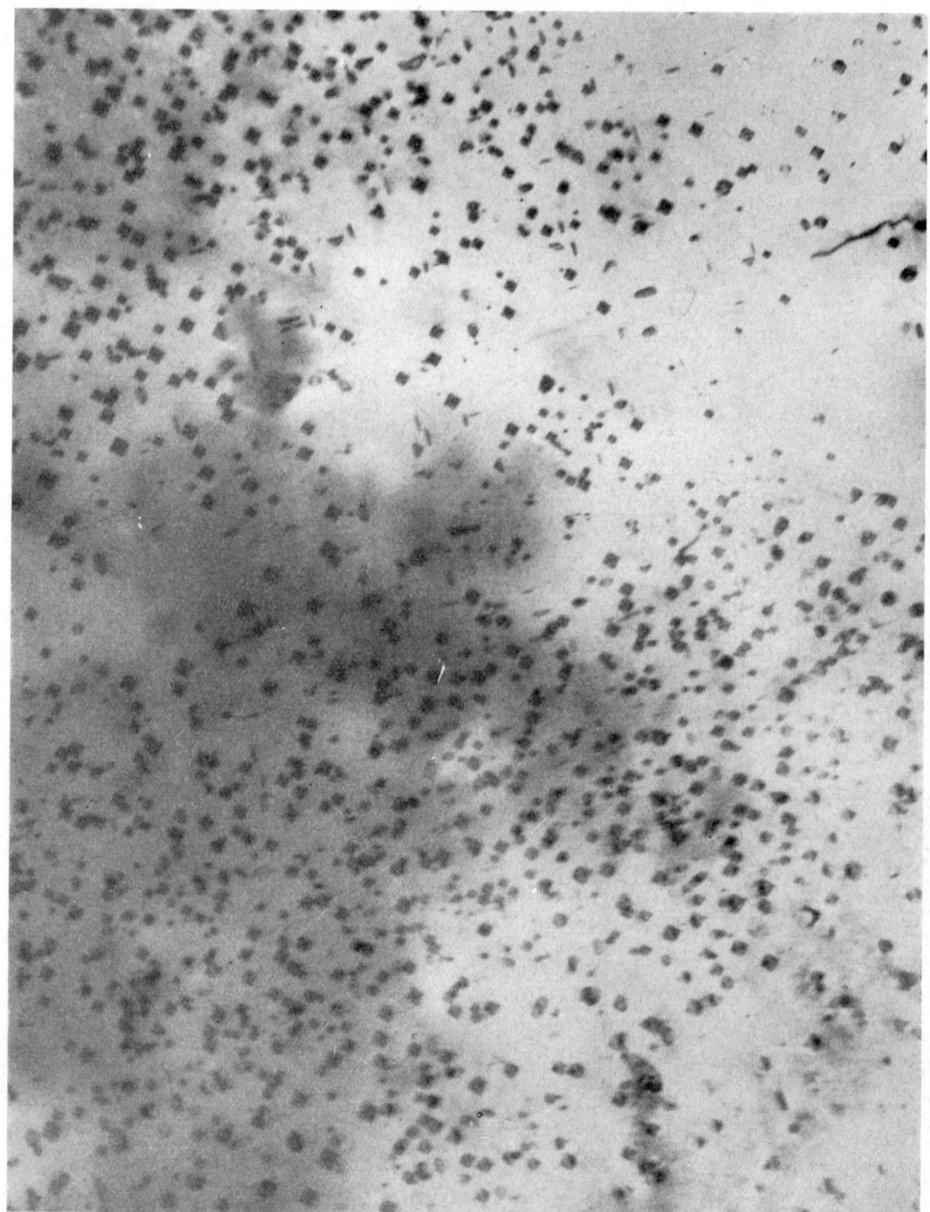

Fig. 27. – Tetrahedra of stacking faults in quenched gold (SILCOX [15]) (Mag. × 60000).

a Frank sessile dislocation $\frac{1}{3}[111]$, which has a lower energy, and a stacking fault. If the loop is in the form of a triangle the edges of which are along close packed directions, dissociation takes place and eventually a tetrahedron of stacking faults is formed the edges of which are low energy stair-rod dislocations with Burgers vector $\frac{1}{6}[110]$. The energy of this defect is about $\frac{1}{3}$ of that of the original Frank sessile loop (SILCOX and HIRSCH [40]; YOFFE [48])

These tetrahedra are extremely stable and do not anneal out till about 650 °C, when they have been observed to disappear extremely quickly in a narrow temperature range (SILCOX [15]). The quench hardening anneals out in the same temperature range, with an activation energy ~ 4.7 eV (KAUFFMANN and MESHII [49]). The mechanism of annealing is not clear; the tetrahedron is extremely stable since all other configurations to be derived from it

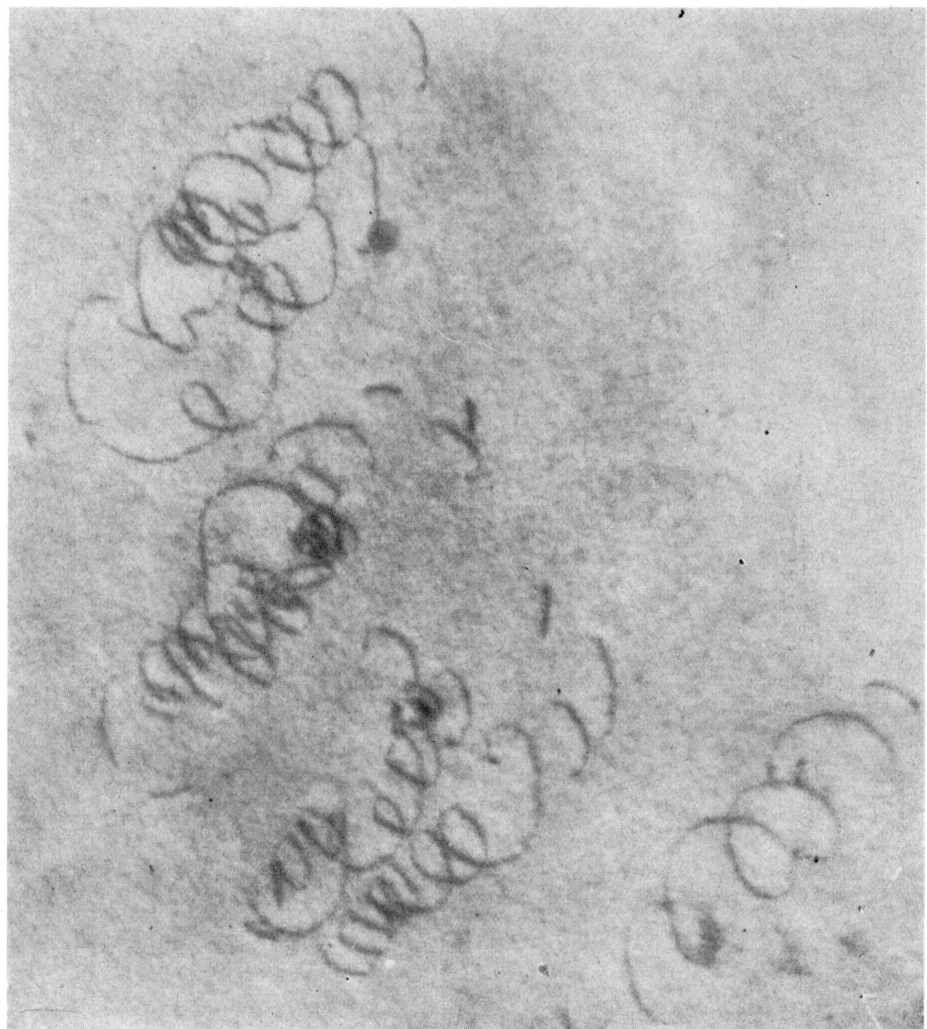

Fig. 28. – Helices in Al 4% Cu alloy quenched from 540 °C into iced brine; the helices are formed by condensation of vacancies on screw dislocations (THOMAS and WHELAN [16]) (Mag. × 66 000) (Courtesy *Phil. Mag.*).

have a higher energy. However, in the temperature range $(600 \div 700)$ °C it becomes unstable relative to the aggregate of vacancies which it represents because the free energy of the latter becomes smaller than that of the tetrahedron. This is because the entropy factor of an aggregate of vacancies is large. SILCOX has suggested that the tetrahedra might anneal out by a process in which interstitials nucleate a loop of critical size on a face; the measured activation energy would then correspond to that of interstitial diffusion.

Although there is some difficulty of interpretation, there is again good correlation between microstructure and bulk properties in this case.

It might be noted here that quenched specimens have a fairly uniform distribution of defects and can be used for making measurements of resistivity due to stacking faults or dislocation loops. In this way the resistivity of stacking faults in Au has been determined to be $2.2 \cdot 10^{-13}\,\Omega\,\text{cm}^{-1}$ per unit area of fault cm^{-3} (COTTERILL [50]).

Observations on quenched Cu, Ni and Ag are described by HIRSCH and SILCOX [41], and more extensively by SMALLMAN, WESTMACOTT and COILEY [38].

1·3. *Alloys.* – Quenched Al-Cu alloys are found to contain a high density of helical dislocations formed by precipitation of vacancies on screw dislocations. An example in Al 4% Cu alloy is shown in Fig. 28 (THOMAS and WHELAN [16]). Loop formation appears to be suppressed because nucleation is difficult as a result of vacancy-solute association. The vacancies can however still disappear at sinks, *i.e.* existing dislocations (THOMAS and WHELAN [16]; SMALLMAN, WESTMACOTT and COILEY [38]; NICHOLSON and NUTTING [39]).

2. – Irradiation with neutrons.

2·1. *Electron microscope observations.* – Specimens of Cu irradiated with neutrons in a pile, and subsequently thinned for electron microscope observations, are found to contain a high density of small regions of strain, some of which can be resolved as small dislocation loops (SILCOX and HIRSCH [51]; MAKIN, WHAPHAM and MINTER [52]). Examples are shown in Fig. 29. Table II gives the data on the specimens which have been examined. Comparing the results obtained from irradiation in BEPO, it appears that growth of loops occurs during irradiation. This suggests mobility of some defects during irradiation and this is confirmed by the existence of a small but definite denuded region near grain boundaries. It is also clear that the number of defects observed is not proportional to the number of neutron collisions. Thus both the number and size of loops increase with dose but not in simple proportion with it.

There is no doubt that these loops will give rise to some dispersion hardening although it is likely that this is not the most important hardening mechanism at low temperature (see below). The loops anneal out in a few minutes in the range (350÷370) °C, with an activation energy ~2 eV; the hard-

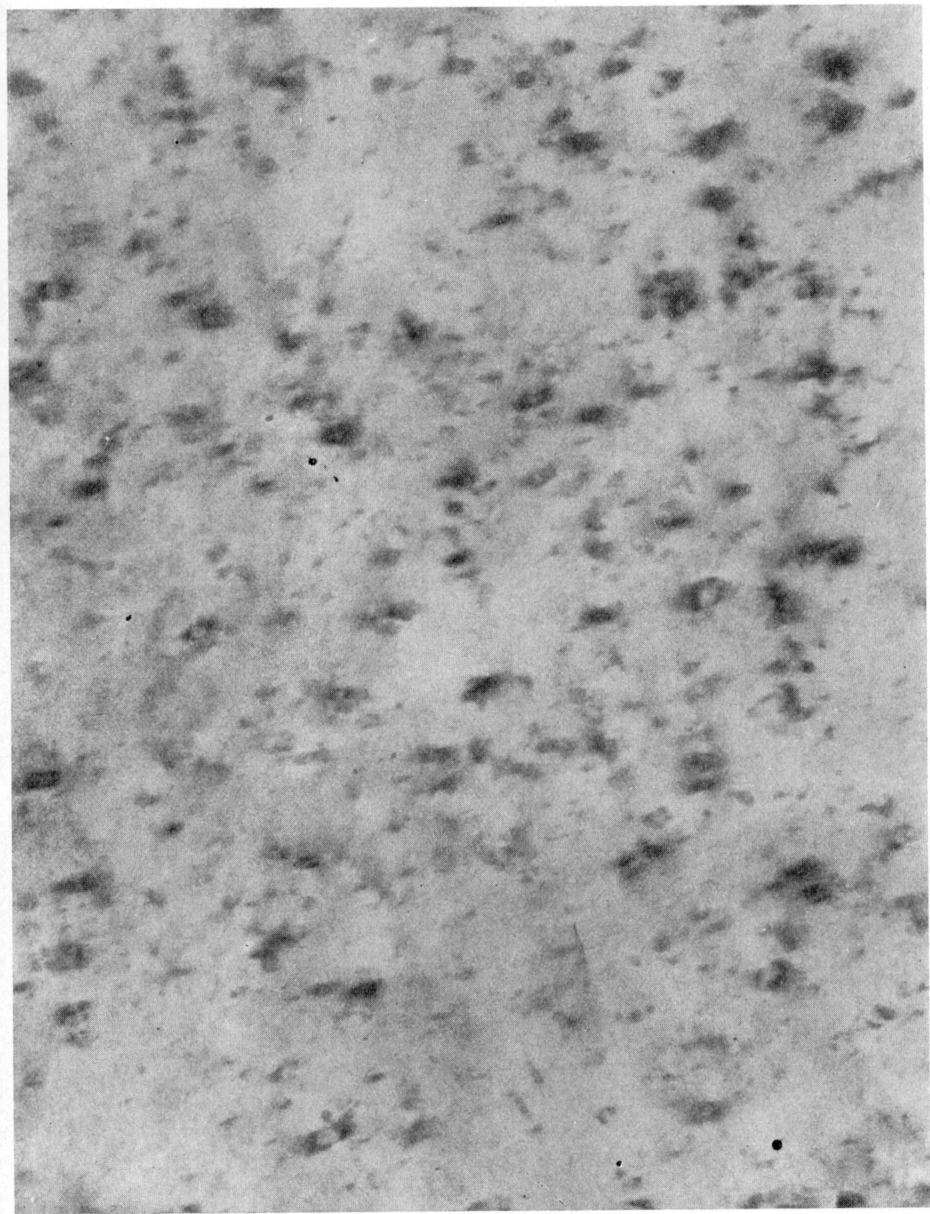

Fig. 29. – Dislocation loops in neutron irradiated Cu; dose $5.6 \cdot 10^{18}$ n cm^{-2} (SILCOX and HIRSCH [51]) (Mag. ×210 000) (Courtesy *Phil. Mag.*).

TABLE II (SILCOX-HIRSCH [51]).

Pile	BEPO	BEPO	DIDO
Total neutron flux	$6.7\cdot10^{17}$ cm^{-2}	$5.6\cdot10^{18}$ cm^{-2}	$1.4\cdot10^{20}$ cm^{-2}
Density of defects	$3\ \cdot10^{15}$ cm^{-3}	$6.5\cdot10^{15}$ cm^{-3}	$1.4\cdot10^{15}$ cm^{-3}
Density of neutron collisions	10^{17} cm^{-3}	10^{18} cm^{-3}	$2.5\cdot10^{19}$ cm^{-3}
Loop size (diameter)	75 Å	150 Å	300 Å
Number of vacancies per loop	800	3100	12400
Total number of vacancies	$2.4\cdot10^{18}$ cm^{-3}	$2\ \cdot10^{19}$ cm^{-3}	$1.7\cdot10^{19}$ cm^{-3}
Vacancies per neutron collision	24	20	0.6
Distance between collisions	215 Å	100 Å	35 Å
Distance between loops	700 Å	535 Å	900 Å
Dislocation densities (in loops)	10^{10} cm^{-2}	$4\ \cdot10^{10}$ cm^{-2}	$1.7\cdot10^{10}$ cm^{-2}

ening also disappears in this temperature range, with a similar activation energy. MAKIN, WAPHAM and MINTER [52] have suggested recently that these loops anneal out before the hardening, and that the latter is mainly due to other smaller defects which can be observed only after annealing.

Observations on Au show the existence of similar defects after irradiation (SILCOX [15]), but no extensive studies have been made. In irradiated Ni nothing has been observed which could be attributed to the result of irradiation (SILCOX [15]; WILSDORF [53]). However, after annealing at 250 °C SILCOX has observed small regions of strain on dark field photographs; this observation still requires confirmation. No defects have been observed in irradiated Al.

Thus the only extensive observations have been made on Cu, and in this metal the formation of dislocation loops as a result of irradiation has been established. In the following sections the formation of loops and the effect of loops on hardening will be discussed mainly with reference to Cu.

2·2. *Nature and formation of loops.* – BLEWITT, COLTMAN, JAMISON and REDMAN [54] have shown that irradiation hardening in Cu occurs on irradiating at 20 °K, and that it varies only little on annealing, till about (300÷400) °C, when it anneals out. Since it is likely that hardening is due to loops (SILCOX and HIRSCH [51]) or small clusters (SEEGER [55]; MAKIN, WHAPMAN and MINTER [52]) these must be produced in the spikes. SILCOX and HIRSCH [51] have suggested a model in which a neutron collision results in a region of a high concentration of vacancies (say $10^{-4}\div10^{-3}$) surrounded by a shell of vacancies and interstitials, and further out, by a shell of interstitials shot out as crowdions. The central vacancy-rich region then collapses forming a loop. The loops observed on micrographs of neutron irradiated Cu were thought by the authors to be formed in this way. MAKIN,

WHAPMAN and MINTER [52] however, have shown that observable dislocation loops occur already after irradiation and examination at temperatures below — 50 °C. Since vacancies should not be mobile at these temperatures, and since these loops are known to grow during irradiation, those authors conclude that these are of the interstitial type. Their conclusion derives support from the work of BARNES and MAZEY [56], who observed the growth of loops in the helium band of α-particle-irradiated Cu on annealing. In this case the loops grow by emitting vacancies which are absorbed by the helium bubbles; the loops must therefore be of interstitial character. On the present evidence this latter interpretation seems more probable, but further observations on the growth of loops during irradiation and on the width of the denuded zone as a function of dose and temperature of irradiation are needed to test the model in more detail. The role of impurity atoms in the nucleation and growth of the loops and clusters is also not well understood.

2·3. *Hardening.* – The flow stress of neutron-irradiated Cu and Ni is known to have a large temperature-dependence at low temperatures (BLEWITT, COLTMAN, JAMISON and REDMAN [54]; MAKIN and MINTER [57]). ADAMS and HIGGINS [58] and MAKIN and MINTER [57] have shown by experiments on the grain size-dependence of the flow stress of neutron-irradiated polycrystals of Cu and Ni, that this large temperature-dependence is associated with a frictional stress. The authors also demonstrated the presence of source hardening which was found to be relatively temperature-independent.

SEEGER [55] has interpreted the large temperature-dependence of the frictional stress in terms of dispersion hardening from small obstacles, a few atoms in diameter. The obstacle was thought to be in the form of an ill-defined vacancy cluster. MAKIN and MINTER [57] have interpreted their results in terms of a modification of this theory. The experiments of MAKIN, WHAPMAN and MINTER [52] are consistent with such a model. The latter authors also point out that although the hardening in Ni is similar to that in Cu, no loops are observed in irradiated Ni (SILCOX [15]; WILSDORF [53]). The available evidence is therefore consistent with a model in which the dispersion hardening at low temperatures is mainly due to nonobservable clusters of defects. In the case of Ni of course these defects might be both vacancy and interstitial clusters.

The larger observable loops may however make an appreciable contribution to the hardening (SILCOX and HIRSCH [51]). The hardening due to loops with diameter 100 Å or greater should however be relatively insensitive to temperature. This is confirmed by experiments on quenched Al (TANNER [59]), which show that the flow stress of quenched Al, presumably containing large loops, varies little with temperature. It is clear therefore that the large observable loops are not responsible for the large temperature-dependence of the flow stress at low temperatures. Nevertheless the large loops may effectively control an increasingly large fraction of the flow stress the higher the temperature of the test, since the smaller obstacles became increasingly transparent. MAKIN and MINTER [57] have proposed this type of model, and these authors also show that prior mild annealing has the effect of reducing considerably the temperature-dependence of the flow stress at low temperature, while the flow stress at the higher temperature is less affected. We believe, therefore, with MAKIN and MINTER [57], that the flow stress is controlled by obstacles of various sizes, that the effective obstacle size increases with test temperature, and we suggest that the observable dislocation loops make an important contribution at the highest temperatures.

The relatively temperature-independent source hardening detected by ADAMS and HIGGINS [58] and MAKIN and MINTER [57] is likely to be due to resistance from sessile jogs, which would give rise to hardening of this type at low temperatures (HIRSCH and WARRINGTON [60)].

The models discussed so far assume that the loops or clusters causing the hardening are left intact as the dislocations move through the crystal. It is likely however that the defects combine with the dislocations sweeping through the crystal forming jogs or dispersing along the dislocation in which case the dispersion hardening may be determined by the mobility of these jogs or of point defects along the dislocation line. Models of this type have been discussed by WILSDORF and WILSDORF [61], FOURIE and WILSDORF [62] and HIRSCH [63]; FOURIE and WILSDORF [62] have stressed the importance of pipe diffusion in this connection. The temperature-dependence and magnitude of this hardening mechanism are not understood at present, but electron microscope observations of deformed quenched Al (VANDERVOORT and WASHBURN [43]) and of fatigued Cu (SEGALL, PORTRDIGE and HIRSCH [45]) show that the loops disappear after a few % deformation, presumably by a mechanism in which they combine with and are swept up by the moving dislocations. The temperature-dependence of the flow stress of quenched Au (MESHII and KAUFFMAN [64]) suggests that a similar process occurs in this case (HIRSCH [63]). Although no detailed calculations are available, there is little doubt, however, that the large temperature-dependence of the flow stress of neutron irradiated metals could only be explained if the clusters are extremely small, a few atoms in diameter. Although no electron microscope observations are available on this point for irradiated metals, the strain-rate dependence of irradiated Cu decreases rapidly on deformation (THORNTON, unpublished) showing that the small defects are being swept up.

It is clear that the details of the hardening mechanism require further clarification. Electron microscope observation of the defects in a Lüders band might be useful in this connection. It may also be possible to obtain some independent information on the size of the sub-electron microscopic defect clusters from low angle scattering experiments using could neutrons (*e.g.* ATKINSON [65]).

2·4. *Conclusions.* – It seems clear that comprehensive studies including electrons microscope observations, and measurements of mechanical properties and electrical resistivity, are going to be most fruitful in the elucidation of the phenomena resulting from quenching and irradiation.

SOURCES OF FIGURES

Fig. 1. is Fig. 1. of KELLY and NUTTING, *Journ. Inst. Metals*, **87**, 385 (1959).
Fig. 2. is Fig. 1. of HIRSCH, HOWIE and WHELAN, *Phil. Trans. Roy. Soc.*, A **252**, 499 (1960). (This paper is referred to as H.H.W. below).
Fig. 9. is Fig. 2. of H.H.W.
Fig. 11*b*. is Fig. 5*a*. of H.H.W.
Fig. 12*a*. is Fig. 4. of H.H.W.
Fig. 13. is Fig. 6. of H.H.W.
Fig. 14. is Fig. 20. of COTTRELL, *Dislocations and Plastic Flow in Crystals* (Oxford, 1953).
Fig. 15. is Fig. 8. of H.H.W.
Fig. 16. is Fig. 10. of H.H.W.
Fig. 17*a*. is Fig. 15. H.H.W.
Fig. 17*b* is Fig. 20. of H.H.W.
Fig. 17*c*. is Fig. 21*e*. of H.H.W.
Fig. 18*b*. is Fig. 2. of HIRSCH, SILCOX, SMALLMAN and WESTMACOTT, *Phil. Mag.*, **3**, 897 (1958).
Fig. 25 is Fig. 7. of HIRSCH, SILCOX, SMALLMAN and WESTMACOTT, *Phil. Mag.*, **3**, 897 (1958).
Fig. 26 is Fig. 3. of SILCOX and WHELAN, *Phil. Mag.*, **5**, 1 (1960).
Fig. 28. is Fig. 6. of THOMAS and WHELAN, *Phil. Mag.*, **4**, 511 (1959).
Fig. 29. is Fig. 5. of SILCOX and HIRSCH, *Phil. Mag.*, **4**, 1356 (1959).

REFERENCES

[1] W. BOLLMANN: *Phys. Rev.*, **103**, 1588 (1956).
[2] P. M. KELLY and J. NUTTING: *Journ. Inst. Metals*, **87**, 385 (1959).
[3] H. TOMLINSON: *Phil. Mag.*, **3**, 867 (1958).
[4] P. B. HIRSCH, P. G. PARTRIDGE and R. L. SEGALI: *Phil. Mag.*, **4**, 721 (1959).
[5] K. THOMAS and K. F. HALE: *Phil. Mag.*, **4**, 531 (1959).
[6] M. J. WHELAN: *Proc. IVth International Conference on Electron Microscopy* (Berlin, 1958).
[7] J. WASHBURN, G. W. GROVES, A. KELLY and G. K. WILLIAMSON: *Phil. Mag.*, **5**, 991 (1960).

[8] R. Phillips and O. P. Hartree: *Brit. Journ. Appl. Phys.*, **11**, 22 (1960).
[9] P. Delavignette and S. Amelinckx: *Journ. Appl. Phys.*, **31**, 1691 (1960).
[10] G. K. Williamson: *Proc. Roy. Soc.*, A **257**, 457 (1960).
[11] J. W. Menter: *Advan. Phys.*, **7**, 180 (1958).
[12] G. A. Bassett and D. W. Pashley: *Journ. Inst. Metals*, **87**, 449 (1959).
[13] P. B. Price: *Phil. Mag.*, **5**, 873 (1960).
[14] J. Silcox and M. J. Whelan: *Phil. Mag.*, **5**, 1 (1960).
[15] J. Silcox: *Ph. D. Thesis*, (Cambridge, 1961).
[16] G. Thomas and M. J. Whelan: *Phil. Mag.*, **4**, 511 (1959).
[17] B. Gale and K. F. Hale: *Brit. Journ. Appl. Phys.*, **12**, 115 (1961).
[18] M. J. Whelan: *Ph. D. Thesis* (Cambridge, 1958).
[19] H. G. F. Wilsdorf: *Rev. Sci. Instr.*, **30**, 925 (1958).
[20] R. M. Fisher: *Rev. Sci. Instr.*, **30**, 925 (1959).
[21] P. B. Hirsch, R. W. Horne and M. J. Whelan: *Phil. Mag.*, **1**, 677 (1956).
[22] J. W. Menter: *Proc. Roy. Soc.*, A **236**, 119 (1956).
[23] H. Hashimoto and R. Uyeda: *Acta. Cryst.*, **10**, 143 (1957).
[24] G. A. Bassett, J. W. Menter and D. W. Pashley: *Proc. Roy. Soc.*, A **246**, 345 (1958).
[25] P. B. Hirsch, A. Howie and M. J. Whelan: *Phil. Trans. Roy. Soc.*, A **252**, 499 (1960).
[26] Z. G. Pinsker: *Electron Diffraction* (London, 1953).
[27] R. W. James: *The optical principles of the diffraction of X-rays* (London, 1948).
[28] A. Howie: *Ph. D. Thesis* (Cambridge, 1961).
[29] A. H. Cottrell: *Dislocations and plastic flow in crystals* (Oxford, 1953).
[30] P. B. Hirsch, J. Silcox, R. E. Smallman and K. H. Westmacott: *Phil. Mag.*, **3**, 897 (1958).
[31] G. K. Williamson and C. Baker: *Phil. Mag.*, **6**, 313 (1961).
[32] M. J. Whelan and P. B. Hirsch: *Phil. Mag.*, **2**, 1121, 1303 (1957).
[33] A. Howie and M. J. Whelan: *Proc. of European (Delft) Regional Conference on Electron Microscopy* (1960) (in press).
[34] A. Howie and M. J. Whelan: *Proc. Roy. Soc.* A **263**, 217 (1961).
[35] H. Hashimoto, A. Howie and M. J. Whelan: *Phil. Mag.*, **5**, 967 (1960).
[36] J. E. Bailey and P. B. Hirsch: *Phil. Mag.*, **5**, 485 (1960).
[37] D. K. Wilsdorf and H. G. F. Wilsdorf: *Journ. Appl. Phys.*, **31**, 516 (1960).
[38] R. E. Smallman, K. H. Westmacott and J. H. Coiley: *Journ. Inst. Metals*, **88**, 127 (1959).
[39] R. B. Nicholson and J. Nutting: *Acta. Met.*, **9**, 332 (1961).
[40] J. Silcox and P. B. Hirsch: *Phil. Mag.*, **4**, 22 (1959).
[41] P. B. Hirsch and J. Silcox: *Report on Conference on Growth and Perfection of Crystals* (New York, 1958).
[42] D. Kuhlmann-Wilsdorf: *Phil. Mag.*, **3**, 125 (1958).
[43] R. Vandervoort and J. Washburn: *Phil. Mag.*, **5**, 24 (1960).
[44] J. Friedel: *Les Dislocations* (Paris, 1956).
[45] R. L. Segall, P. G. Partridge and P. B. Hirsch: *Phil. Mag.*, **6**, 1493 (1961).
[46] T. Federighi: *Phil. Mag.*, **4**, 502 (1959).
[47] T. Kino: *Journ. Sci. Hiroschima Univ.*, **22**, 259 (1958).
[48] E. H. Yoffe: *Phil. Mag.*, **5**, 161 (1960).
[49] M. Meshii and J. W. Kauffman: *Phil. Mag.*, **5**, 939 (1960).
[50] R. M. J. Cotterill: *Phil. Mag.*, **6**, 1351 (1961).
[51] J. Silcox and P. B. Hirsch: *Phil. Mag.*, **4**, 1356 (1959).

[52] M. J. Makin, A. D. Whapham and F. J. Minter: *Phil. Mag.*, **6**, 465 (1961).
[53] H. G. F. Wilsdorf: *Phys. Rev. Lett.*, **3**, 173 (1959).
[54] T. H. Blewitt, R. R. Coltman, R. E. Jamison and J. K. Redman: *Journ. Nucl. Mater.* **2**, 277 (1960).
[55] A. Seeger: *Second Geneva Conf. on Paceful Uses of Atomic Energy*, **6**, 250 (1958)
[56] R. S. Barnes and D. J. Mazey: *Phil. Mag.*, **5**, 1247 (1960).
[57] M. J. Makin and F. J. Minter: *Acta. Met.*, **8**, 691 (1960).
[58] M. A. Adams and P. R. B. Higgins: *Phil. Mag.*, **4**, 777 (1959).
[59] L. E. Tanner: *Acta. Met.*, **8**, 730 (1960).
[60] P. B. Hirsch and H. D. Warrington: *Phil. Mag.*, **6**, 735 (1961).
[61] H. G. F. Wilsdorf and D. K. Wilsdorf: *Phys. Rev. Lett.*, **3**, 170 (1959).
[62] J. T. Fourie and H. G. F. Wilsdorf: *Journ. Appl. Phys.*, **31**, 2219 (1960).
[63] P. B. Hirsch: *Journ. Inst. Metals*, **89**, 303 (1961).
[64] M. Meshii and J. W. Kauffman: *Acta. Met.*, **7**, 180 (1959).
[65] H. A. Atkinson: *Phil. Mag.*, **3**, 476 (1958).

The Experimental Observation of Dislocations and Radiation Damage in Crystals by Surface Methods and Decoration Techniques.

S. AMELINCKX

Centre d'Etudes de l'Energie Nucléaire - Mol

Introduction.

These two lectures will be complementary to those given by Prof. HIRSCH since we will be concerned with methods for revealing dislocations other than by the electron microscope. In a sense they will, however, also be a complement to those of Prof. FRIEDEL, since we will have occasion to illustrate a number of geometrical features of dislocation theory which were treated in his lectures. The X-ray methods for revealing dislocations will not be considered since Prof. GUINIER will give lectures on this subject. In our discussions we will follow more or less the historical order since this turns out to have been also a logical one.

1. – Crystal growth.

The first phenomenon which was proved to be unambiguously related to the presence of dislocations was crystal growth on close-packed faces and at low supersaturations [1-3].

A growing crystal is soon bounded by its slowest growing faces, since the others eliminate themselves in the process. The slowest growing faces are in general the close-packed ones. The nucleation of a new close-packed layer on a perfect crystal face requires the formation of a two-dimensional nucleus, which is a difficult process. A large supersaturation is required (50%) in order to obtain an observable growth rate, on the assumption that two-dimensional nucleation is the rate-determining step.

In practice growth is observed at supersaturations of 1% and less. The process of two-dimensional nucleation would not be necessary if the surface were rough, *i.e.* if it contained kinked steps. BURTON and CABRERA [4] have however shown, using a Kossel crystal model, that the roughness defined as $s = (n_s - n_0)/n_0$ is *not* large enough to ensure growth at temperatures below a critical temperature, T_c, which may, moreover, be above the melting point (n_s = number of bonds protruding from the rough surface, n_0 = number of bonds protruding from a perfectly flat surface.)

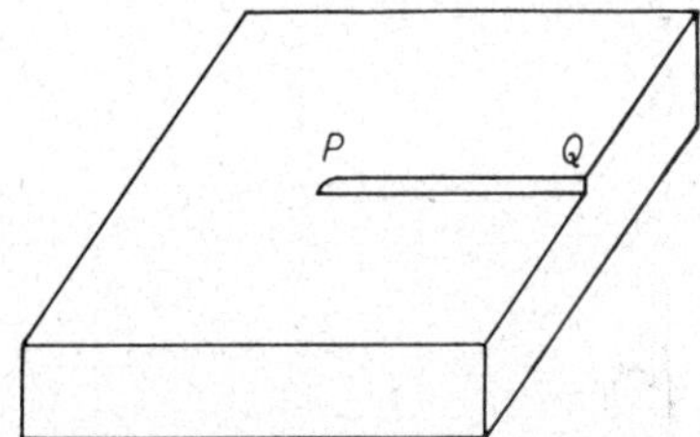

Fig. 1. – A step is attached to the emergence point P of a screw dislocation.

FRANK [1] therefore suggested that growth might be catalyzed by the presence of dislocations having a Burgers vector which has a component perpendicular to the crystal face. For geometrical reasons a step is attached to the emergence point of such a dislocation (Fig. 1). During growth, building units are attached to this step which tends, as a consequence, to be displaced parallel to itself. Since it is however anchored at the emergence point, P, it will wind up into a spiral (Fig. 2). Direct evidence for the occurrence of this process has been obtained

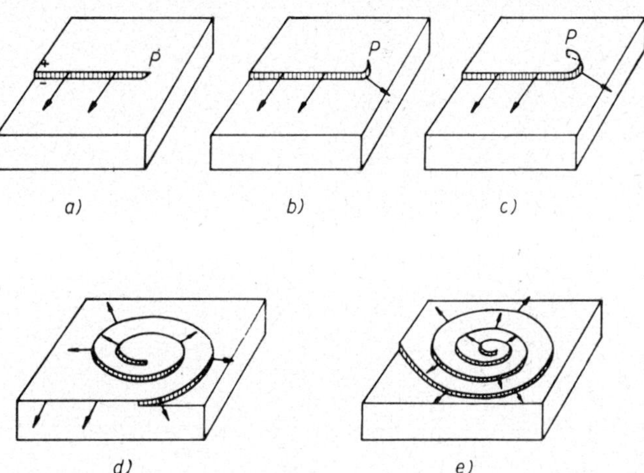

Fig. 2. – Under conditions of supersaturation the step attached to a screw winds up into a spiral. The diagram shows different phases of the process.

in a large number of cases. Fig. 3 shows examples, as observed on basal planes of silicon carbide crystals. It is clear that we now have a means of locating the emergence points of those dislocations having a Burgers vector which has a component perpendicular to the crystal face. We can, moreover,

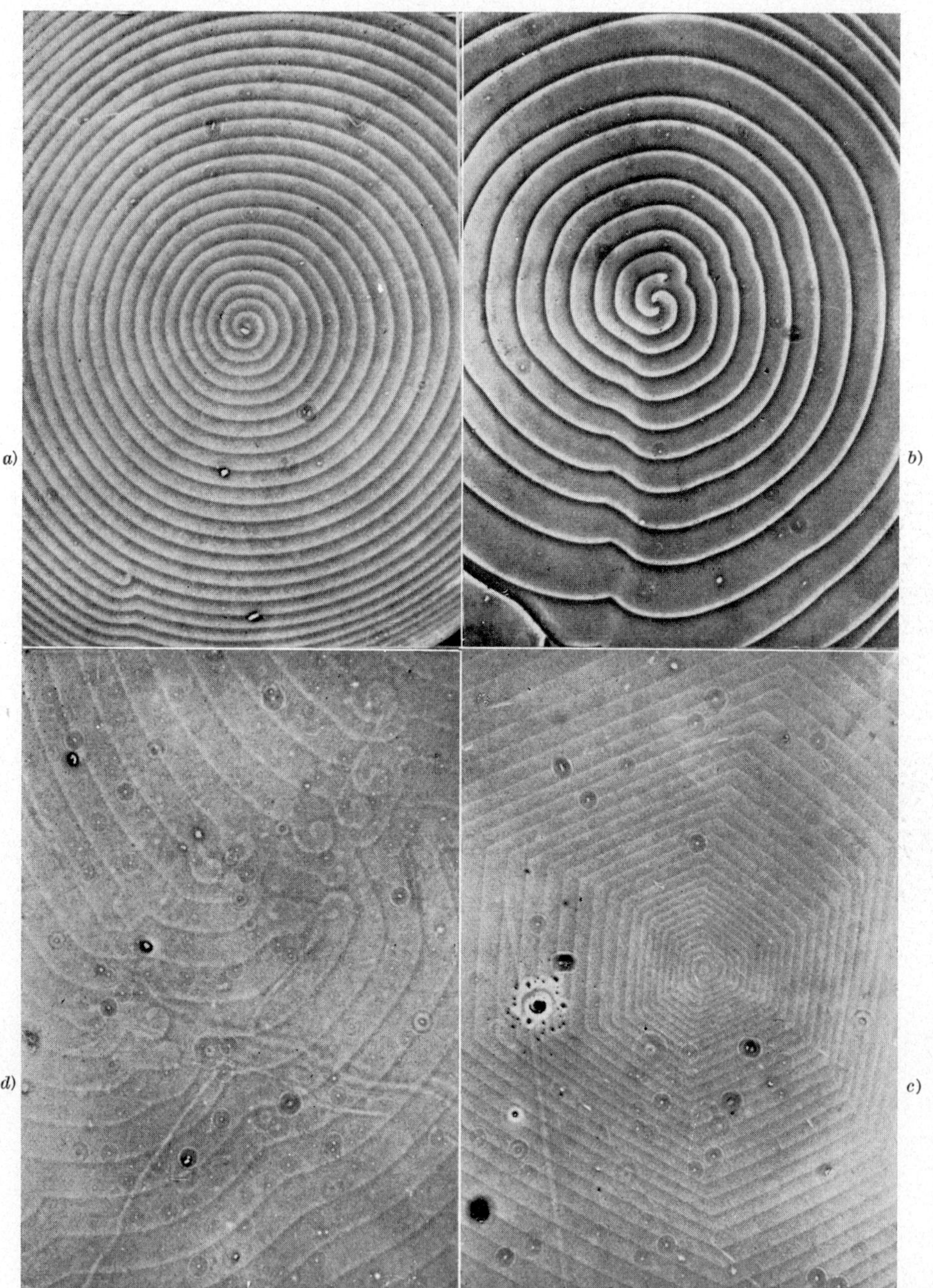

Fig. 3. – Examples of growth spirals observed on the c-face of silicon carbide. *a*) Rounded spiral. *b*) Interaction between three spirals: two of one sign and one of the opposite sign. *c*) Hexagonal spiral. *d*) Complicated group of spirals revealing the presence of an equal number of screw dislocations.

determine this perpendicular component since it is equal to the step height of the spiral.

If the emergence point of such a dislocation moves, it leaves a step in its wake, and we therefore have a means of studying its motions (see Fig. 4).

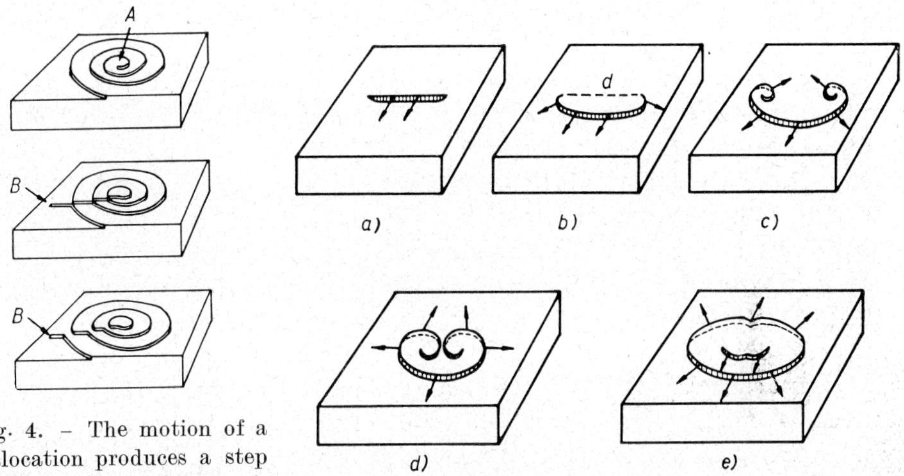

Fig. 4. – The motion of a dislocation produces a step connecting the initial position A and the final position B of the emergence point.

Fig. 5. – Growth initiated by two dislocations of opposite sign produces closed platforms.

The first evidence for the movement of dislocations was obtained in this way. The mutual annihilation of dislocations of opposite sign was also demonstrated first by the use of growth features. Two dislocations of opposite sign give rise to closed growth fronts as shown in Fig. 5. Mutual annihilation of the two dislocations just before cessation of growth leads to the features of Fig. 6; *i.e.*, to a sequence of closed growth fronts without a visible center.

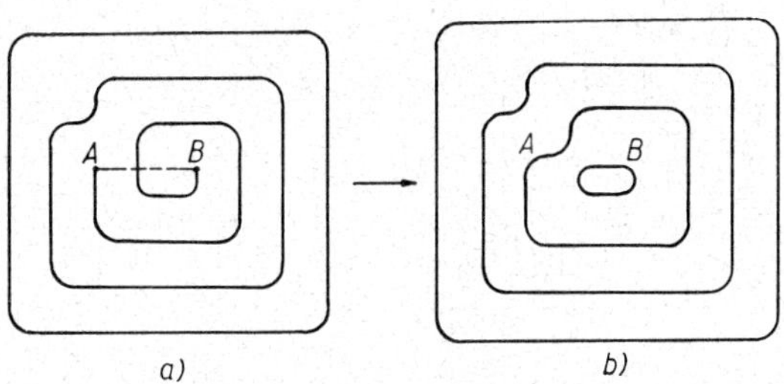

Fig. 6. – The mutual annihilation of two dislocations of opposite sign, as reflected in the growth pattern. *a*) Growth pattern due to the dislocations of opposite sign A and B. The dotted line represents the slip step that results when A and B annihilate. *b*) Pattern that results after a small amount of growth.

2. – Evaporation.

The reverse phenomenon, *i.e.* evaporation under conditions of low undersaturation, also produces spiral steps. These are now depressions instead of hills, *i.e.* their center is the lowest point instead of the highest. It is clear that this phenomenon can equally well be used to locate intersection points of dislocations with the surface and to measure the component of the Burgers vector perpendicular to that surface.

The method works beautifully on alkali halides [6], using optical microscopy. Recently TRILLAT [6] and BASSETT [7] have developed a method for making visible monatomic steps on alkali halides, such as those formed on evaporation or growth. The procedure consists of evaporating in vacuum a very thin layer of gold onto the alkali halide crystal which is heated at some $(150 \div 200)$ °C. In these circumstances the gold does not form a continuous layer, but instead small isolated gold particles nucleate epitaxially, preferentially along surface steps. A layer of carbon is deposited on top of the gold layer. The carbon replica is then taken off by dissolving the alkali halide crystal in water. The gold particles remain imbedded in the carbon film which is now examined in the electron microscope. BETGHE and co-workers [8, 9] have shown how detailed information can be obtained from surface studies by the use of this technique.

3. – Etching.

3·1. *Introduction.* – The first direct proof that dislocations can be revealed by means of etching was given independently by GEVERS *et al.* [10], GEVERS [11] and HORN [12]. These authors showed that etch pits are developed at the centers of growth spirals. The experiments were performed on silicon carbide crystals which were etched in fused borax at 900 °C for 1 hour. In these experiments etch pits were also found which were not located at the centers of spirals, and it was concluded that these correspond to edge dislocations.

3·2. *Principle of the method.* – The method simply consists of immersing the crystal in a suitably chosen medium, *e.g.* a liquid, a solution, or a chemical reagent. It is found that small pits are developed at the emergence points of dislocations.

Different methods of etching have been successful:

a) Thermal etching: Heating of silver in an atmosphere containing some oxygen produced small pits at the dislocations [13]. Heating NaCl to near the melting point for some time produces evaporation spirals [5].

TABLE I. – *Etchants for revealing dislocations.*

Crystal	Etchant	Remarks	Ref.
NaCl	*a*) anhydrous methyl alcohol *b*) acetic acid $+2\%$ $FeCl_3$ *c*) absolute ethyl alcohol with 3 g $HgCl_2$ per liter		[19] [20]
KCl	25% saturated solution $BaBr_2$ in ethyl alcohol	followed by an ether rinse	[21]
KBr	Glacial acetic acid	Etchant for KCl works for KBr as well	[20]
MgO	5 part saturated NH_4Cl 1 part H_2SO_4 1 part distilled water	Different shapes of etch pits for fresh and grown-in dislocations	[22]
CaF_2	Concentrated H_2SO_4		[14]
Ge	*a*) 50 ml HNO_3; 30 ml CH_3COOH 30 ml HF; 0.6 ml Br_2 *b*) 10 ml HF; 10 ml H_2O_2; 40 ml H_2O		[23] [24]
LiF	*a*) 1 part glacial acetic acid 1 part conc. HF saturated with FeF_3 *b*) dilute aqueous solution of FeF_3 or $FeCl_3$ ($\simeq 1.5 \cdot 10^{-4}$ molar)	Attacks all dislocations Attacks more intensely freshly formed dislocations	[25] [16]
Silicon Iron	Electrolytic polishing and etching in a chromeacetic acid bath	With C impurity	[26]
Al	47% HNO_3; 50% HCl; 3% HF	With Fe impurity	[27]
Zn	160 g chromic acid; 50 g hydrated sodium sulphate; 500 ml H_2O	With Cd impurity	[28]
Si	1 part HF; 3 parts HNO_3; 10 parts glacial acetic acid		[29]

b) Chemical etching: The reaction between molten borax and silicon carbide is of this type [10]. The etching of calcium fluoride with concentrated sulfuric acid is also a chemical attack [14].

c) Solution etching: Sodium chloride can be etched by dipping it for 1 s in anhydrous methylalcohol [15]. Lithium fluoride is etched by means of an aqueous solution of ferric fluoride [16].

d) Preferential oxydation: This can in a sense be considered as a way of etching. YOUNG [17] has shown that copper, *e.g.*, oxidizes preferentially at dislocation sites.

e) Electrolytic etching: This has been used by JACQUET [18] on specimens of α-brass.

The reasons why the emergence points of dislocations are attacked preferentially are probably complex and are not well understood at present. It seems established, however, that in metals some impurity segregation or Cottrell atmosphere formation is necessary before dislocations can be reliably etched. This is probably due to the inevitable presence of a surface film on metal specimens; one attacks in fact this film. Dislocation sites in this film are probably differentiated as a consequence of the impurities.

In ionic crystals the presence of impurities does not seem to play an important role. On clean cleavage faces of such crystals fresh dislocations (*i.e.*, newly introduced), as well as old ones (*i.e.*, grown in), can be revealed. In some cases the aspects of the pits may differ for fresh and for grown-in dislocations [16]. This is particularly useful if one wishes to study the movement of dislocations.

From the fact that fresh dislocations are better attacked one may conclude that the strain around the dislocations is responsible for the increased reactivity. When an atmosphere of impurities forms, the strain is relieved, and hence the reactivity decreases. On the other hand, an atmosphere may locally increase the solubility and hence increase the etching rate. The two cases actually occur depending on the particular etchant used (see Table I).

3·3. *Reliability of an etching method.* – When cleaved specimens are used, as *e.g.* in the ionic solids, the easiest check on reproducibility and reliability consists in comparing the two halves. The etch patterns should be mirror images, apart from small deviations, *e.g.* due to branching of the dislocations in the cleavage plane. In the latter case one pit on one face corresponds to two close pits on the second face. When metal specimens are used, successive attacks, alternated with electropolishing, should reveal consistently the same pattern.

A comparison with an independent method, *e.g.* decoration can also be used. This has been done by DASH [29] for silicon. He has shown that a deccorated dislocation line corresponds to every etch pit. The same kind of evidence was obtained for NaCl [30] and for silver bromide [31]. A direct check has also been obtained for germanium. VOGEL *et al.* [23] demonstrated that the distance between etch pits in a tilt boundary corresponds, within the experimental error, to the distance between dislocations as given by the Burgers model. The misorientation angle was determined with a refined X-ray method. In this way they proved both the correctness of the Burgers model and the reliability of the etchant.

It is possible to make use of similar evidence without the necessity for the measurement of the small angle, θ, which is difficult. It is clear that a relation exists between the dislocation densities in three meeting tilt boundaries; one simply has

$$\sum_i \varrho_i/(\cos\theta_i + \sin\theta_i) = 0\,,$$

where the ϱ_i are the densities of dislocations as measured from the etch patterns, and θ_i are the angles between the directions of the boundaries and the directions of the symmetrical tilt boundaries. This relation was verified for sodium chloride [15], germanium [32], and silicon iron [33], demonstrating the validity of the dislocation model in asymmetrical tilt boundaries and giving confidence in the etching method.

3·4. *Information obtainable from etch pits.* – Etch pits essentially reveal emergence points at the surface and they therefore give a direct measure of dislocation densities. Since the etch pits have a certain depth, they may also give some indication concerning the general direction of the dislocation lines.

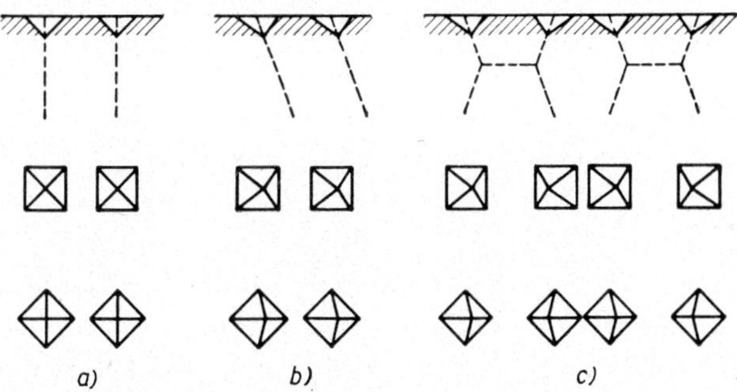

Fig. 7. – Relation between etch pit shape and the direction of the dislocations with respect to the surface. *a*) Dislocations perpendicular to the surface. *b*) Parallel dislocations inclined with respect to the surface. *c*) Crossed grid intersecting the surface.

If the line intersects the surface perpendicularly, a symmetrical pit results; if the line is oblique, the pits become slightly asymmetrical and from this asymmetry the inclination of the line can be deduced, as shown in Fig. 7.

If the dislocation line is perpendicular to the surface, and has a helical shape, the etch pit acquires the form of a conical spiral [34]. Direct evidence for this was obtained by DASH [29] in silicon, by the use of the decoration technique. Spiral etch pits were shown to be located on helical dislocations.

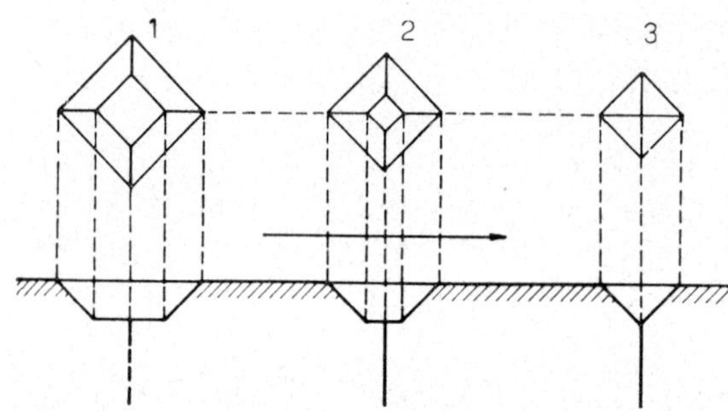

Fig. 8. – The motion of a dislocation as reflected in the etch pattern. The flat bottomed pits mark intermediate positions of the dislocations, while the centered pit marks the final position.

A flat bottomed pit results if a dislocation moves out of a pit produced by a first etching; further etching then only develops the pits laterally, but no longer in depth. Jerky motion of a dislocation during etching would result in a configuration as shown in Fig. 8. The flat bottomed pits represent intermediate positions of the dislocations; the centered pit represents the final position. Since etch pits do not pin the dislocation very much, movement can be studied [16].

A dislocation half-loop is represented as two coupled pits, which on continued etching approach one another and finally coalesce. A helix intersected along the axis is in fact equivalent to a sequence of such half-loops; helices can therefore easily be recognized in an etch pattern.

It has been shown that not only dislocations can be etched but also tracks due to fission fragments. Also « debris » left by moving dislocations etches, but discontinuously. The « debris » may consist either of agglomerates of point defects or of dislocation « dipoles » broken up in small elongated loops (X-irradiated NaCl [35] and neutron irradiated LiF [36] exhibit such a background etching of diffuse pits).

3·5. *Specimen preparation.* – In order to obtain reliable etch patterns, surface preparation is of primary importance. Whenever possible, cleavage is to be preferred if this produces a nondeformed specimen. In this case « clean » as well as aged dislocations can be etched. In metal specimens electrolytic polishing is the usual procedure; this, however, produces in general a surface covered by some oxide films. It is thus often necessary to age the specimen in order to collect impurities along the dislocations and produce « sensitive » emergence points in this surface film. In many cases intentional impurity addition may be required, *e.g.* cadmium to zinc [28], iron to aluminium [27], and tellurium to copper [17].

4. – Applications of etching.

We now review a few typical examples of application of etching techniques to dislocation problems and to radiation damage.

4·1. *Dislocation problems.* – We have already mentioned a few applications in the course of our previous discussions.

a)

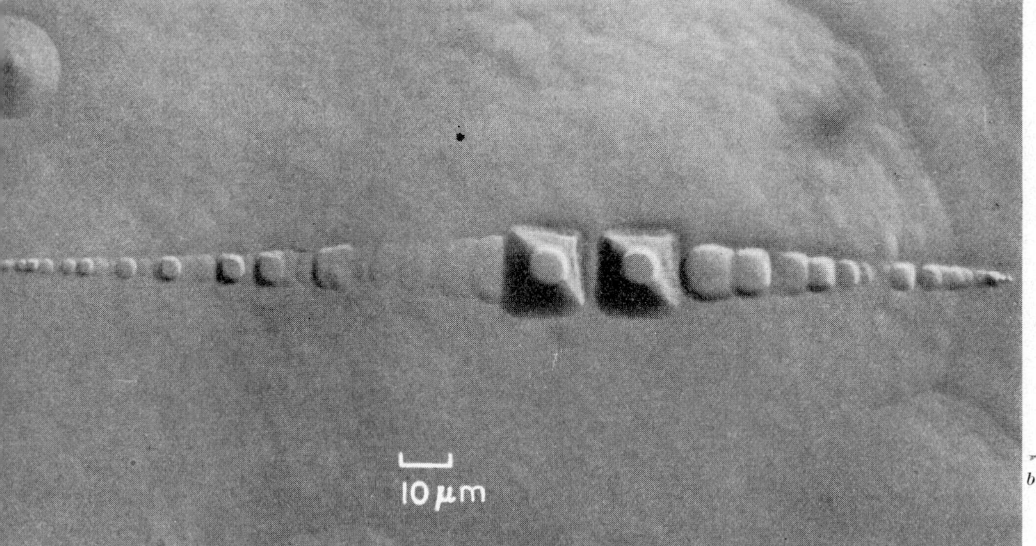

b)

. – *a*) Observed pattern in LiF, corresponding to Fig. 8 (After GILMAN and JOHNSTON). *b*) Pattern due to the extension of a half-loop (After GILMAN and JOHNSTON).

4.1.1. Stress-velocity relation. – One of the most elaborate problems that has been successfully solved using an etching procedure is probably the experimental determination of the stress-velocity relationship for an individual dislocation by GILMAN and JOHNSTON [37]. The authors first intro-

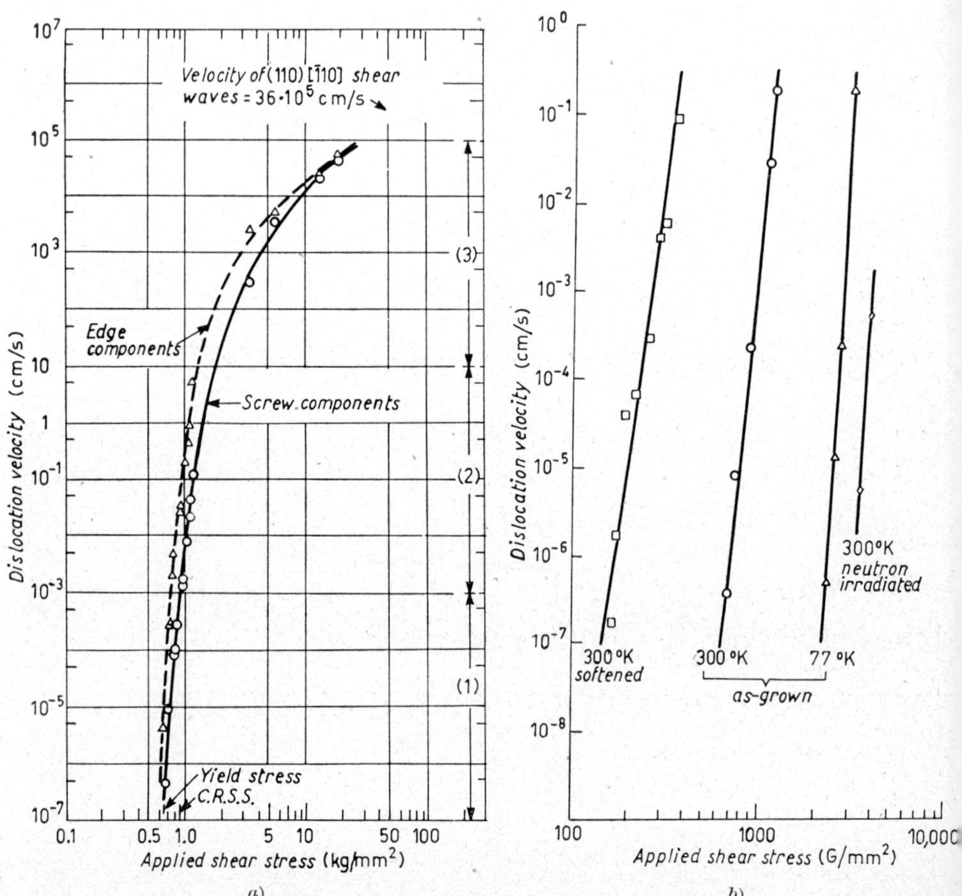

Fig. 10. – Relation between applied stress and resulting dislocation velocity, as determined by means of etch pits (After J. GILMAN and W. JOHNSTON). *a*) In an as-grown crystal. *b*) In differently treated crystals.

duced a fresh dislocation halfloop in a lithium fluoride cleavage prism. This is done by producing a small indentation rosette and then polishing away all but one of the so formed half-loops. A given stress is now applied during a known period of time and the distance travelled by the dislocations of the loop is deduced from the difference in the etch patterns before and after application of the stress. An example of the patterns obtained is shown in Fig. 9.

Several orders of magnitude of velocities can be covered by a suitable choice of the stressing device. The resulting curve is shown in Fig. 10; it appears that the following empirical relation describes the curve rather well:

$$v = \mathscr{V}_0 \exp[-A/\sigma]\,,$$

$\mathscr{V}_0$ is some limiting velocity, σ is the applied stress.

After neutron irradiation the curve undergoes a parallel displacement toward higher stresses, suggesting that friction hardening is operating.

4'1.2. Deformation patterns. – The distribution of dislocations in slip traces can be revealed by etching. In this way piling up and the formation of Lomer-Cottrell barriers have been studied [18]. Fig. 11 shows an example

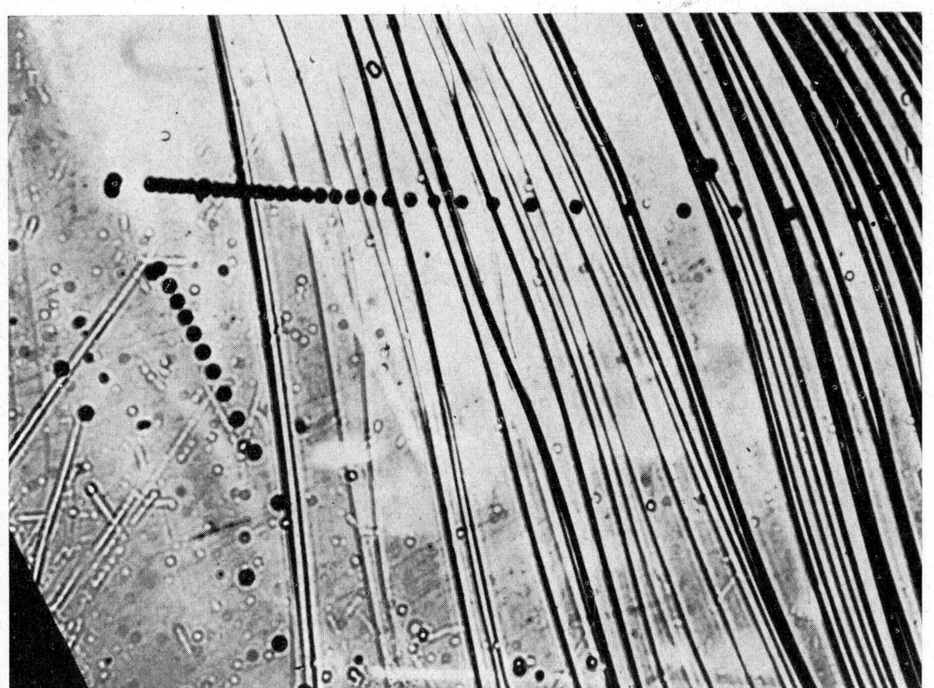

Fig. 11. – Pile-up of dislocations in SiC. The obstacle is a grown-in dislocation giving rise to a growth spiral (after ref. [40]).

of a pile-up of dislocations in silicon carbide. The obstacle is a grown-in screw dislocation which produced a growth spiral. Glide on the first system was probably relieved by glide on a second system, resulting in the observed configuration. The distribution of dislocations in a pile-up should be such that a linear relationship exists between the index of the dislocation and the square root of its distance to the leading dislocation in the pile-up [38, 39]. It is easy to verify that this is indeed very approximately the case for the sequence shown [40].

4·1.3. Polygonization. – If a crystal is bent about an axis normal to a Burgers vector and subsequently annealed, pure symmetrical tilt boundaries form. The plane of the boundaries is perpendicular to the glide planes. The formation of these boundaries is known as polygonization since curved lattice planes become polygonal during this process, as shown schematically in Fig. 12. The phenomenon essentially consists in a rearrangement of dislocations into an equilibrium configuration, which is such that the edge dislocations arrange themselves « one on top of the other ». This implies the occurrence of climb.

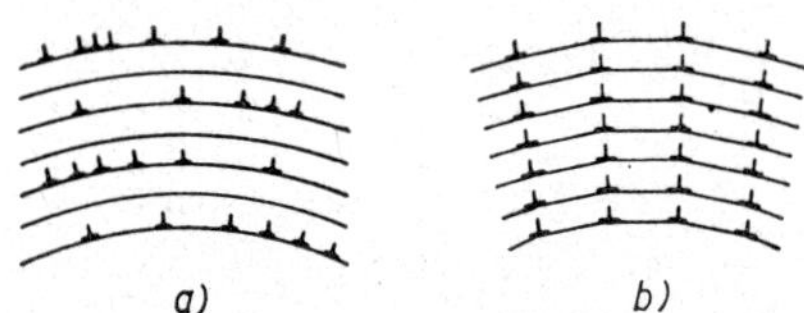

Fig. 12. – Illustrating the process of polygonization. *a*) Immediately after deformation. *b*) After anneal.

Etching and decoration [41] have convincingly illustrated the correctness of this picture which is due to Cottrell [42]. Fig. 14 shows, *e.g.*, a polygonized area of an etched silicon carbide crystal. In a few places, indicated by straight lines, characteristic configurations called « doublets » are observed; they are stable with respect to glide, but not with respect to climb.

4·2. *Radiation damage problems.* – Radiation apparently introduces defects which can be detected by etching. We will discuss some of the results for the different kinds of radiation.

4·2.1. X-rays. – If crystals of NaCl, which have been irradiated in only half their volume with X-rays, are etched in anhydrous methyl alcohol, it is found that the irradiated part dissolves faster than the other one. The cross-section becomes somewhat as shown in Fig. 13. The dislocation etch pits become smaller as a consequence. The phenomenon may be due to dissolution initiated at defect clusters.

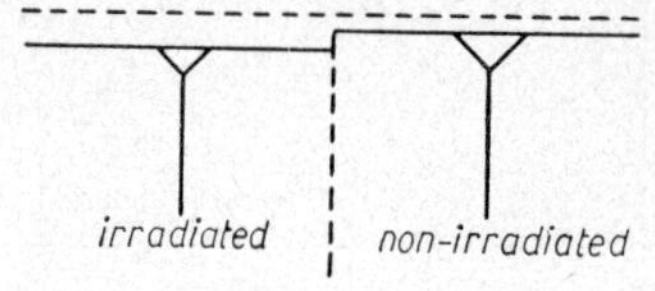

Fig. 13. – Cross-section through a crystal of NaCl of which only one half was irradiated. In the irradiated half there is overall etching; the size of the dislocation etch pits is consequently reduced.

It is further found that slip traces, originating in the unirradiated part, stop abruptly at the limit between the irradiated and the unirradiated regions showing that the X-irra-

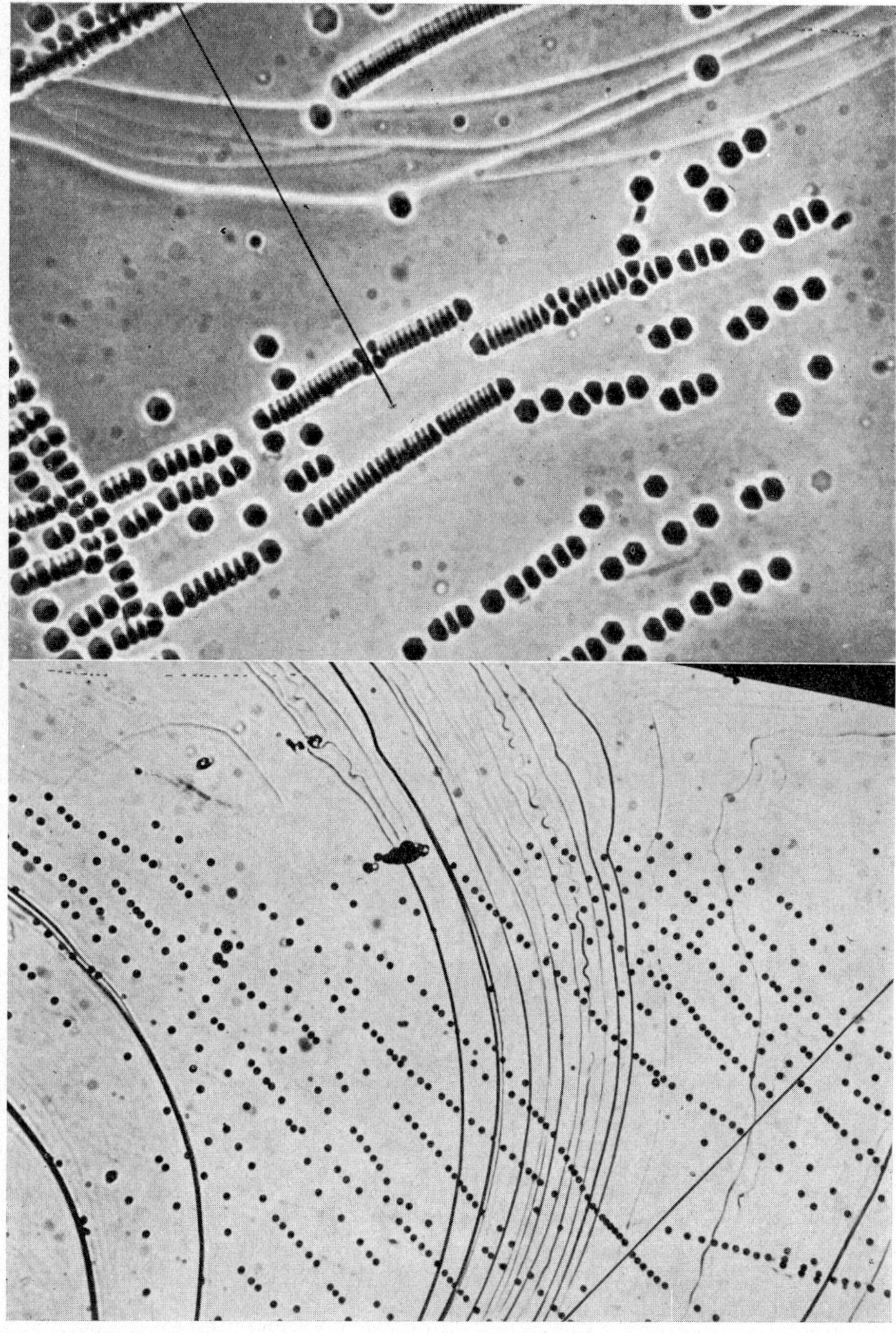

Fig. 14. – Polygonized regions in deformed SiC crystals. The dislocations form walls perpendicular to the slip plane, which is indicated on the photograph (after ref. [40]).

diation causes hardening. A simple means of studying radiation hardening consists in measuring the distance travelled by dislocations in an indentation rosette. As the dose increases, this distance, as revealed by etch pits, diminishes very rapidly. This method has been used to study radiation hardening in NaCl [43] and LiF [44].

4.2.2. Neutron irradiation.

Germanium: In an attempt to find evidence for small localized disordered regions in neutron-irradiated germanium and silicon, etching with CP 4 was used by Chang [46] and by Noggle and Stiegler [47]. An overall change in etching characteristics was found, but no evidence was discovered for the existence of p-zones in n-type material, for instance. It is not impossible that the neutron dose used was in fact too high.

Graphite: Hennig [48] has presented evidence that the controlled low-temperature burning of neutron-irradiated or quenched graphite produces etch patterns on the c-plane, observed with the electron microscope and using a replica technique. It is shown that the number of pits corresponds roughly to the number of point defects introduced.

Lithium fluoride: Lithium fluoride has been studied in greatest detail especially by Johnston and Gilman [37]. The results can be summarized as follows:

There is no evidence for movement of grown-in dislocations, and no regions which could be attributed to thermal spikes were observed. Instead there is a rather uniform roughening of the etched surface for exposures greater than 10^{15} nvt. The roughening seems to be correlated with the appearance of the 4500 Å absorption band which is due to aggregates of point defects rather than single point defects. In the range of exposures considered here, no lattice expansion is observed [49].

After annealing, the etch structure becomes much coarser. The pits become, however, flat-bottomed after having progressed a small distance into the crystal, which means that the damage is localized. A tendency to form paired pits, as would be the case for loops, is noted. After longer anneals, the number of such loops becomes smaller but their size increases (see Fig. 15). The loops are presumably prismatic with an $(a/2)[110]$ Burgers vector; they probably result from the agglomeration of vacancies in a cube plane. This disc of vacancies collapses into an $(a/2)[100]$ dislocation ring which would, however, contain a severe electrostatic fault. The latter will be eliminated by an $(a/2)[010]$ shear, transforming the loop into a perfect prismatic dislocation. After annealing at about 600 °C the etch structure disappears almost completely and instead small cavities are now found in the bulk of the crystals. The cavities, which are bound by cube planes, become quite visible after annealing at 700 °C. They are located along sub-boundaries and they are often very flat, so as to exhibit interference colors.

Fig. 15. – Etch patterns of neutron irradiated LiF. On annealing the pattern becomes coarser. The pits become paired, showing that small dislocation loops are present (After J. GILMAN and W. JOHNSTON). *a*) As irradiated, $5.4\cdot10^{17}$ nvt; $p \geqslant 10^{17}/\text{cm}^3$, $\bar{d}\simeq 50$ Å. *b*) 1 hour at 400 °C, $5.4\cdot10^{17}$ nvt; $p\simeq 2\cdot10^{14}/\text{cm}^3$, $\bar{d}\simeq 500$ Å. *c*) 1 hour at 500 °C, $5.4\cdot10^{17}$ nvt; $p\simeq 5\cdot10^{12}/\text{cm}^3$, $\bar{d}\simeq 10000$ Å. *d*) 1 hour at 500 °C, $5.7\cdot10^{16}$ nvt; $p\simeq 1.2\cdot10^{11}/\text{cm}^3$, $\bar{d}\simeq(2\div5000)$ Å.

With increased annealing temperature, large cavities grow at the expense of smaller ones. JOHNSTON and GILMAN [37] suggest that the cavities result from vacancy agglomeration. The vacancies result partly from the irradiation and partly as a consequence of the loss of material; lithium undergoes a nuclear reaction with a thermal neutron:

$$^6\text{Li}_3 + \text{n}_0^1 \rightarrow {}^4\text{He}_2 + {}^3\text{H}_1 + 4.8\ \text{MeV}\,.$$

Fluorine is also liberated under irradiation, as noted previously by SENIO and TUCKER [50], and by LAMBERT and co-workers [51]. The cavities themselves apparently do not contain gases when investigated at the end of the experiment. Presumably the cavities nucleate as a consequence of the presence of the gases, but the latter diffuse out during the anneal.

4.2.3. Fission fragments. – Tracks produced by fission fragments can be revealed in LiF by the use of the dislocation etchant. The pits are centered on the track and they become flat-bottomed at the end of the track.

5. – Decoration techniques.

5.1. *General discussion of the method.* – The methods discussed so far only reveal emergence points of dislocations and they were therefore restricted in their application. We will now discuss methods which reveal the dislocations along their whole length, and which are therefore suitable for studying the complete geometry.

The technique consists in heat-treating a crystal in such a way that small but visible particles are formed along the dislocation lines. The particles should be small enough to make the resolving power sufficiently high. On the other hand, they should be large enough to scatter sufficient light to become visible in the optical microscope. The particles can be observed either in transmitted light, if they are large enough, or in scattered light (ultramicroscopic obser-

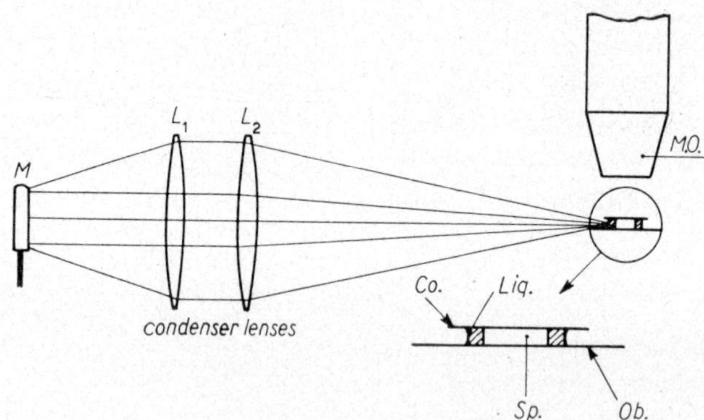

Fig. 16. – Experimental set-up for the observation of decoration patterns in transparent crystals by means of ultra microscopy: *M*: high pressure small size mercury arc; L_1 and L_2 condenser lenses; *MO*: microscope objective; *Co*: cover slide; *Sp*: specimen (thickness $\simeq \frac{1}{4}$ mm); *Liq.*: liquid of the same index of refraction as the specimen.

vation). The latter method is more sensitive, but requires longer exposure times when taking photographs. A typical set-up is shown schematically in Fig. 16. Light from a high pressure mercury arc is focussed in the specimen which is mounted between an object glass and a cover glass, and imbedded in a liquid of the same index of refraction as the crystal. The latter precaution is necessary to avoid scattering by the surface of the cleaved specimens. The use of thin slices ($\pm$ 0.5 mm) is advisable in order to obtain good contrast. In specimens which are too thick, the background scattering, from particles which are not in focus blurs the image considerably.

The possibility of producing decoration by the use of a suitable heat treatment is due to the following factors:

a) Cottrell interaction, which causes an elastic attraction of impurities to dislocations.

b) Enhanced diffusion along dislocations.

c) Preferential nucleation of particles along the dislocations.

d) The ability of a dislocation to act as a source of vacancies and to make room for the growing precipitate particles.

From this it will be clear that heat treatment is generally unavoidable in order to allow migration of the decorating agent towards the dislocations. The more easily the impurity diffuses the lower will be the temperature of the heat treatment. It is therefore convenient to use impurities which migrate along interstitial sites, *e.g.* Cu in Si, Li in Ge, etc.... In such cases impurity diffusion may be appreciable at temperatures where self-diffusion is still small. It is also required that the solubility of the decorating agent be small at room temperature and increases with temperature.

It is also possible to treat the crystal in such a way that a chemical transformation takes place, the reaction product being insoluble and therefore precipitating, *e.g.*, formation of CaO in CaF_2 [52]. The « impurity » may be a stoichiometric excess of one of the constituents, *e.g.* Na in NaCl.

The inherent limitations of the method are obviously the following:

a) The heat treatment may disturb the dislocation pattern so that only annealing structures can be observed.

b) The dislocations are pinned by the precipitates; the study of motion is therefore difficult. Whereas dislocations are observed « in vivo » in the electron microscope, they are observed « in vitro » by decoration techniques.

5·2. *Decoration methods for specific crystals.* – We will now discuss different methods that have been used for specific crystals. We will only give the practical prescription, without going into the details of the decoration mechanisms.

5·2.1. Silver halides [53]. – Exposure at room temperature to light absorbed in the tail of the fundamental absorption band is all that is needed to cause the formation of photolytic silver particles along dislocations in silver bromide and silver chloride. The pattern can be observed in transmission using inactive light.

5·2.2. Alkali halides.

a) *Sodium chloride* [54]: Heavy additive coloration of NaCl results in the precipitation of colloidal sodium along dislocations. The procedure consists of making a cavity in a cleavage block, filling this with sodium metal, and closing it, like a box, with another cleavage fragment. The whole assembly is kept together in a steel frame and heated to a temperature not far below the melting point of the alkali halide, for one or two hours and finally fairly rapidly cooled.

b) *Sodium chloride, potassium chloride and potassium bromide* [54-56]: The dislocations in these alkali halides can be decorated by doping the crystals with a small amount of the corresponding silver halide and annealing them in hydrogen at a temperature not too far below the melting point for one or two hours. After this treatment the crystals have to be cooled slowly. The silver halide is added to the melt when growing the crystal (0.5% to the melt by weight addition). The decorating particles are silver, produced by reduction in the hydrogen.

c) *Potassium chloride* [57, 58]: In crystals doped with 0.1% of silver nitrate, the decoration procedure is as follows. The crystal is first irradiated with 50 kV X-rays for 2-3 hours and then annealed at some (500÷600) °C for one hour. Small cavities, filled with the decomposition gases of the NO_3-group are then found along the dislocations. Large cavities result on annealing of the same crystals, in hydrogen. After the irradiation alone the crystal is not visibly changed apart from coloration; the only effect is the decomposition of the nitrate group. The annealing agglomerates the decomposition products.

An interesting feature in this method is that dislocations present before the irradiated are decorated much better than those introduced after the irradiation, but before the anneal. This applies as well to grown-in, as to freshly introduced dislocations.

Apparently the decomposition of the nitrate group takes place preferentially along dislocations, possibly because excitons dissipate their energy there [58].

The latter method allows one to make visible deformation structures since only a heat treatment at a moderate temperature is necessary.

d) *Undoped alkali halides* [58 *bis*]: In undoped alkali halide crystals the decoration can be achieved by diffusing in some impurities from outside. The following method is convenient for KBr and NaCl. The alkali halide crystals, together with a small quantity of the corresponding gold halide, *i.e.* $HAuCl_4$ or $HAuBr_4$, are sealed in an evacuated quartz capsule, and heated at a temperature about 100 °C below the melting point, for two or three hours, and subsequently cooled at a moderate rate. The cooling rate is rather critical, especially in small crystals. The decorating particles are gold, resulting from the thermal decomposition of the gold halide. The same method can also be applied to cesium bromide [59].

5·2.3. Calcium fluoride. – It is sufficient to heat calcium fluoride [52] in moist air for a short time, *e.g.* 30 min at 800 °C, in order to obtain a precipitation of CaO along the dislocations. The phenomenon consists in fact in a partial hydrolysis of calcium fluoride. The temperature is not critical; at lower temperatures the annealing time has to be correspondingly longer.

5·2.4. Silicon and Germanium. – Decoration in silicon [29] is achieved by diffusing copper into the crystal at about 900 °C. This is done by putting a few drops of a copper nitrate solution on the crystal slab and heating it subsequently in hydrogen. Copper then diffuses through interstitial sites and precipitates in substitutional positions along dislocations, which climb somewhat in order to produce the vacancies required [60]. Since silicon is not transparent to visible light, except in very thin samples, infrared radiation is used to view the crystal slab in transmission. An image converter, suitable for the near infrared, is used to focus the image, but photographs are made directly on infrared-sensitive emulsion. The heat treatment does not seem to disturb very much the dislocation pattern.

In germanium, lithium can be used as a decorating agent [61]. Observations, however, require the use of more elaborate infrared-sensitive detection than for silicon.

6. – Applications of the decoration techniques.

We will now discuss a few typical examples of applications where decoration techniques have been particularly successful. At the same time the theory required for a proper understanding of the features will be discussed briefly.

6·1. *Geometry of sub-boundaries.* – Since the decoration techniques involve a certain amount of annealing anyway, they are ideally suited to study, *e.g.*, sub-boundaries in an annealed crystal. The geometrical features of sub-boundaries in alkali halides were studied in detail [62, 63], and a direct verification of the models predicted by theory has been possible in this way.

The Burgers vectors of dislocations in crystals of the sodium chloride structure are of the type $(a/2)[110]$. With this type of dislocation a variety of subboundaries can be formed. They fall into three classes.

6·1.1. Boundaries consisting of parallel lines. – These are tilt boundaries, *i.e.*, the rotation axis is in the plane of the boundary and all lines are edge dislocations parallel to the rotation axis. In the simplest case all

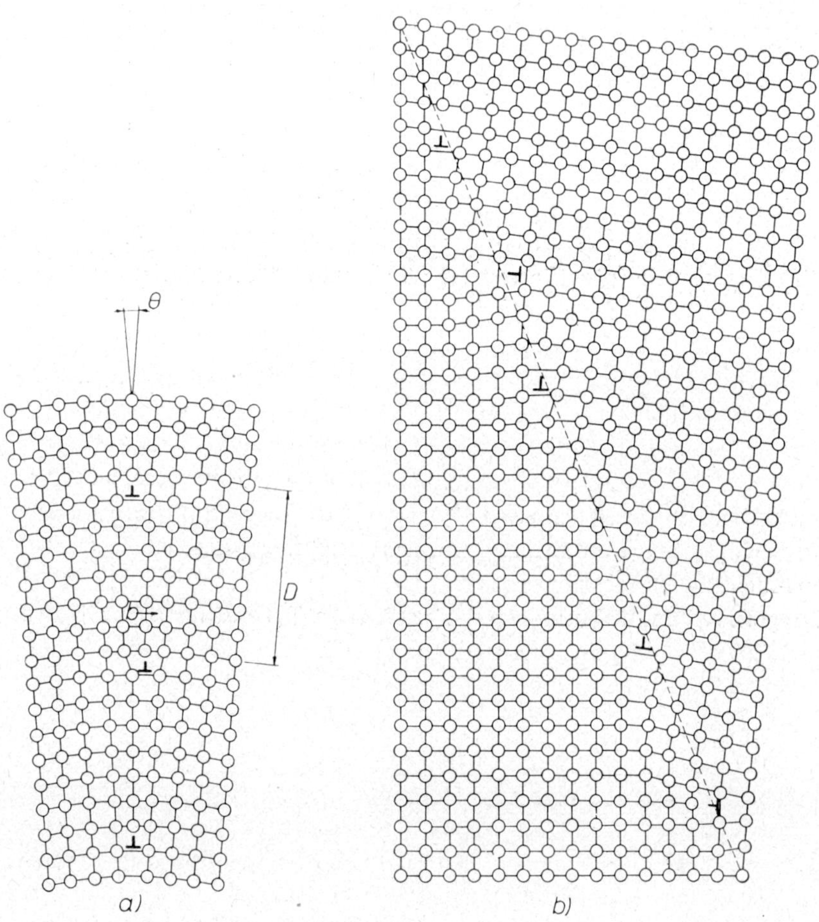

Fig. 17. – Tilt boundaries. *a*) Burgers' model of the symmetrical pure tilt boundary. *b*) Asymmetrical pure tilt boundary.

dislocations have the same Burgers vectors. The boundary plane is then a symmetry plane for the bicrystal and it is perpendicular to the Burgers vector (Fig. 17*a*). If the boundary plane has a more general orientation, more than one kind of dislocations is required (Fig. 17*b*). On a decoration pattern no difference is of course visible. An example of tilt boundaries is presented in Fig. 18*a* and Fig. 18*b*. The first refers to potassium chloride and the decorating

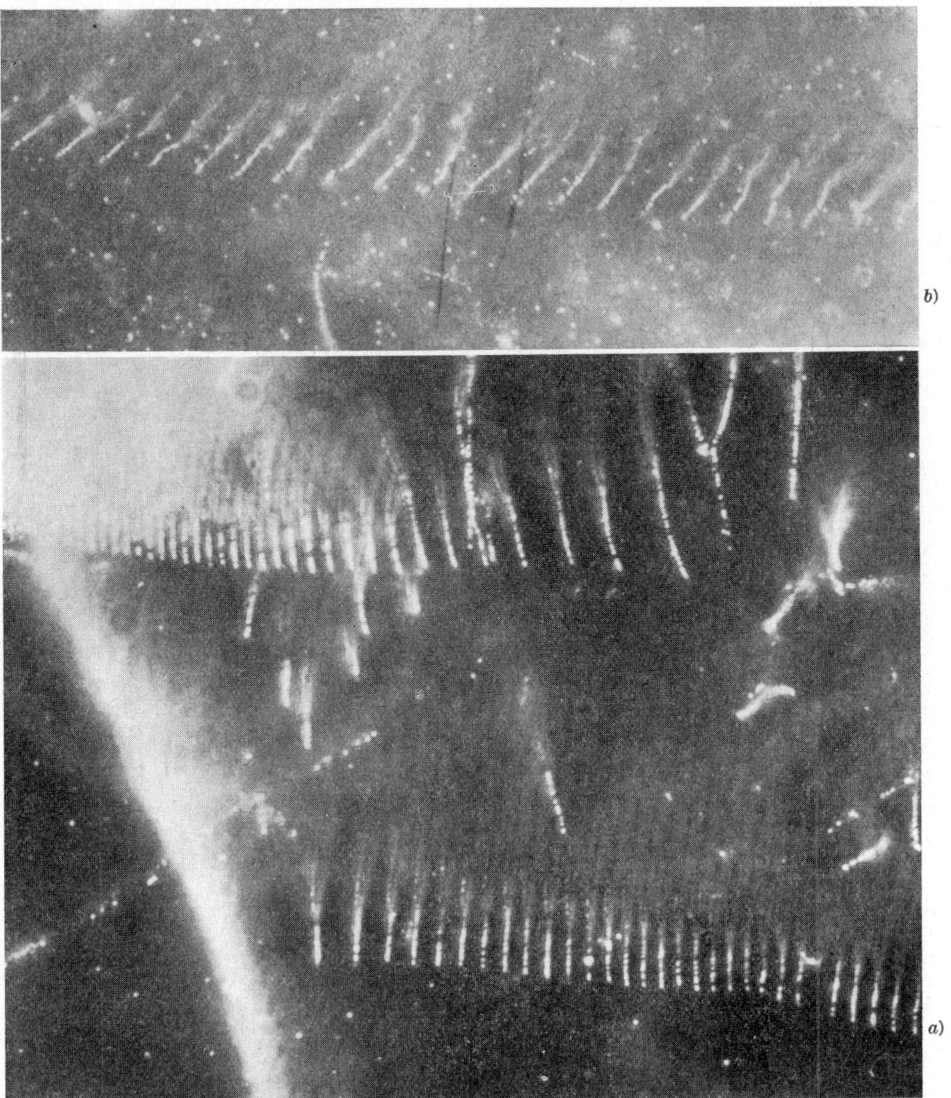

Fig. 18. – Tilt boundaries observed by decoration methods. *a*) Tilt boundary decorated by means of silver particles in potassium chloride (after ref. [56]). *b*) Tilt boundary revealed by gold particles in cesium bromide (after ref. [59]).

particles are silver. The second example is a ceasium bromide crystal, the decorating particles being gold. In the latter case the Burgers vectors are of the type $a[100]$ and the symmetrical tilt boundaries are in the cube plane.

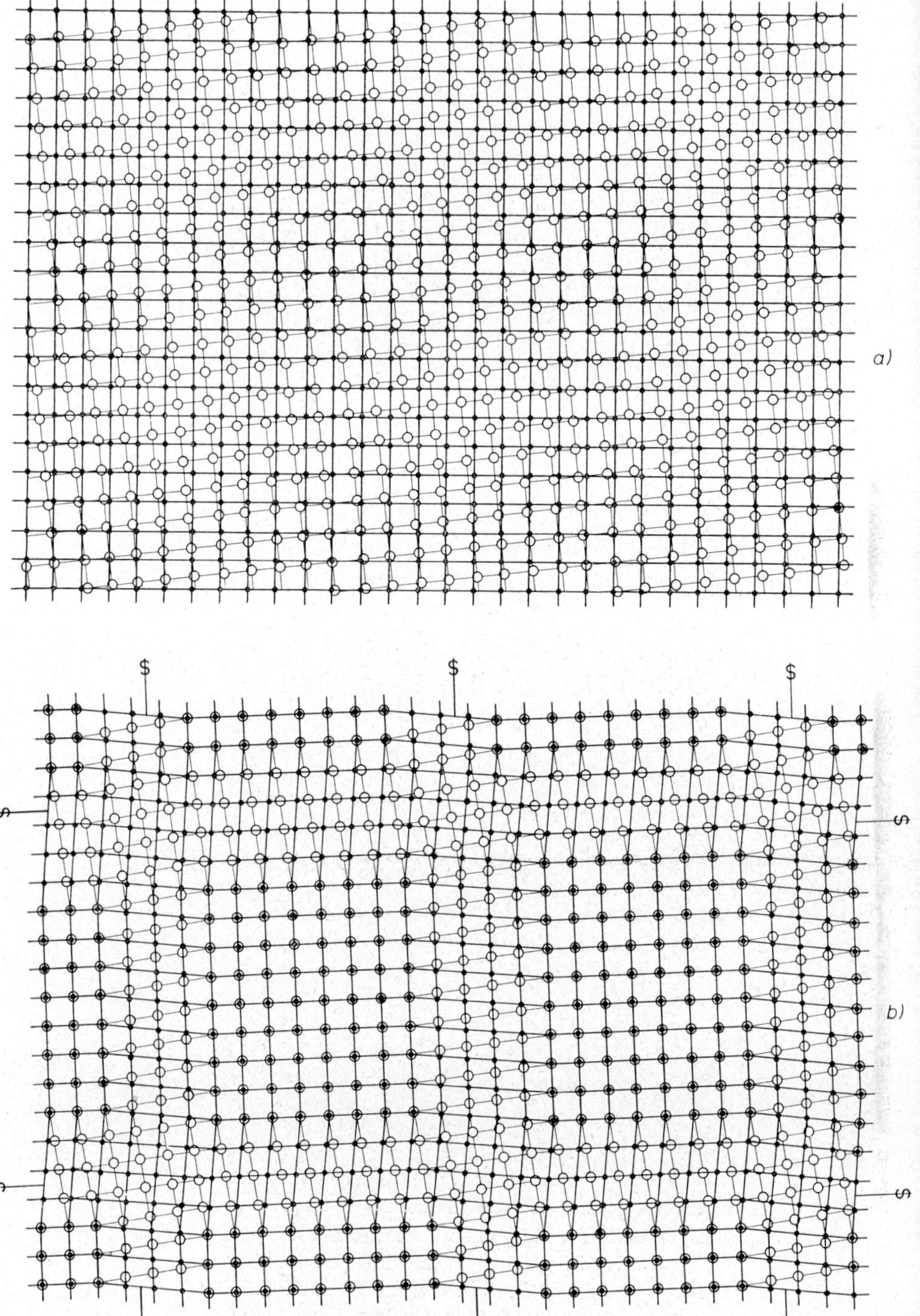

Fig. 19. – Model of twist boundary with [001] rotation axis and (001) contact plane. The model consists of a square grid of screw dislocations. *a*) One lattice plane each side of the contact plane is twisted. *b*) The atoms have relaxed and taken up equilibrium positions.

6·1.2. Square networks. – The model for a twist boundary having an

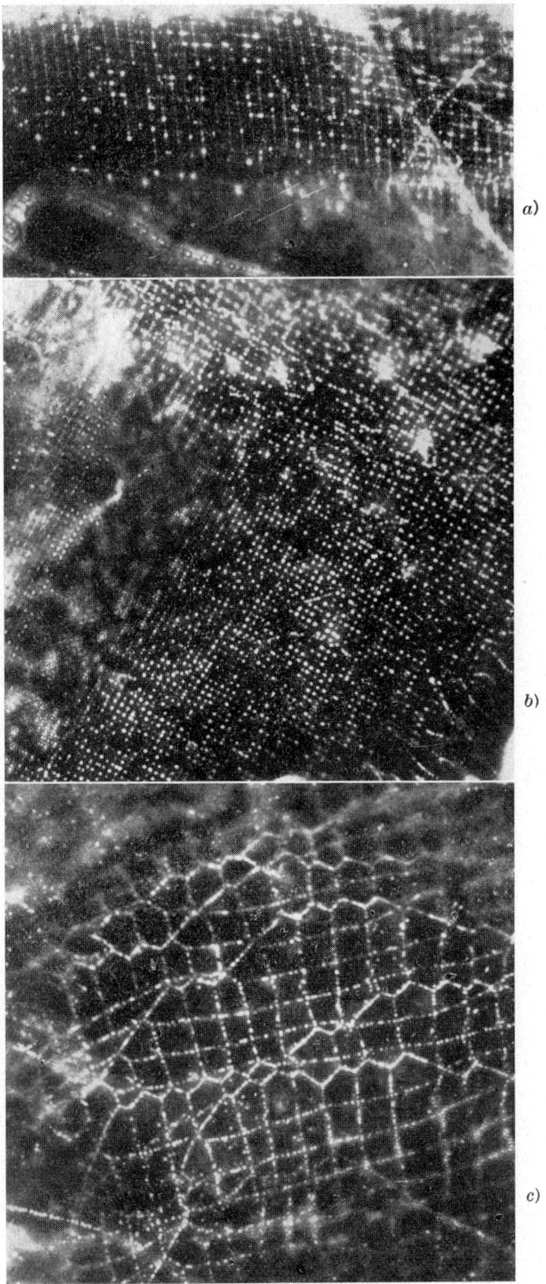

Fig. 20. – Square grids of dislocations in potassium chloride. *a*) The lines are slightly decorated. Notice the preferential decoration at node points. *b*) Only decoration at node points of the net. *c*) Singular lines in a square network.

$a[100]$ rotation axis and a (100) contact plane consists of a square grid of pure screw dislocations having directions [011] and $[01\bar{1}]$ and Burgers vectors $(a/2)[011]$ and $(a/2)[01\bar{1}]$ respectively. This is shown intuitively in Fig. 19 for a primitive lattice. If the contact plane deviates from the cube plane, the network acquires lozenge-shaped meshes; its projection along [100] on the (100) plane is however still the same square grid.

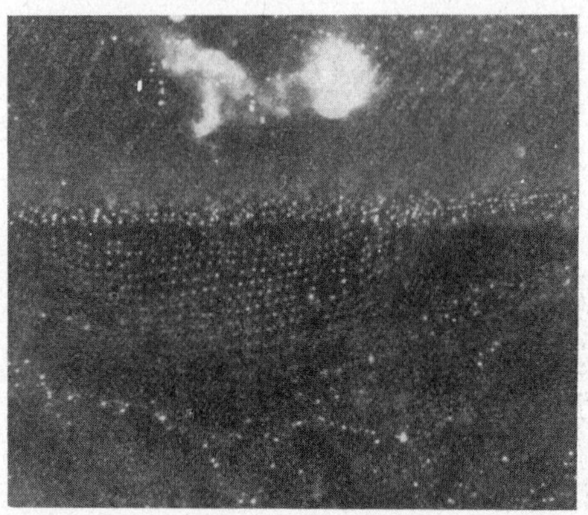

Fig. 21. – Square array of dots in CrBr, corresponding to the node points of a square grid (after ref. [59]).

Examples of square grids are shown in Fig. 20. The directions of the lines are in agreement with the theoretical predictions. It is obvious that the node points are decorated preferentially. In some cases, where the resolution of the method becomes insufficient, only the node points are decorated. Fig. 21 is an array of dots corresponding to a square network in the cube plane of CsBr.

6·1.3. Hexagonal networks. – If the contact plane of a boundary is the (111) plane, and if the rotation axis is parallel to [111], the model for the boundary consists of a hexagonal grid of screw dislocations having Burgers vectors $(a/2)[1\bar{1}0]$, $(a/2)[\bar{1}01]$ and $(a/2)[01\bar{1}]$. This is shown in Fig. 22 in an intuitive way. Provided the rotation axis remains the same, a change in boundary plane only causes a change in the mesh shape, the pattern becoming such that its projection along [111] on the (111) plane produces the same hexagonal net.

Examples of hexagonal grids are reproduced in Fig. 23. The plane of the net was near to the cube plane; the meshes are therefore elongated hexagons.

In many cases decoration is less, or even lacking completely, along one family of lines. It is found that the segments then have a [110] direction, *i.e.*, the direction of a possible Burgers vector. They are, therefore, very pre-

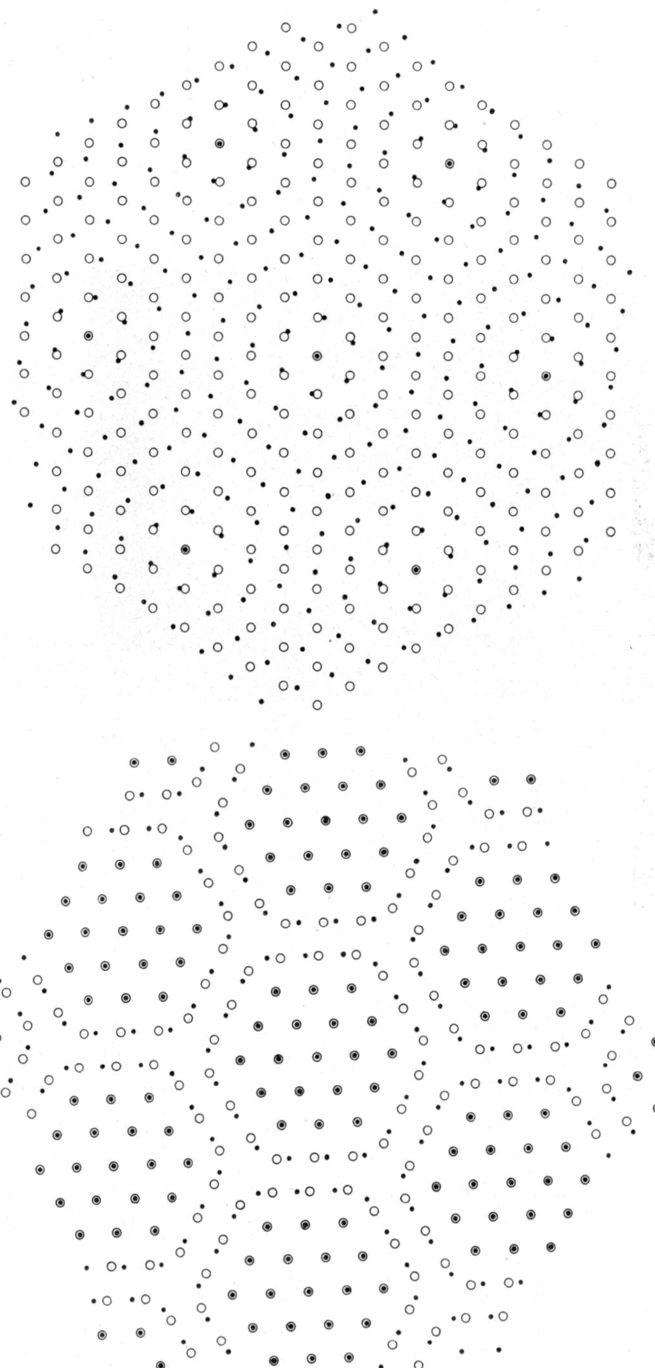

Fig. 22. – Model of a twist boundary having a [111] rotation axis and a (111) contact plane.

sumably screw segments. One can, therefore, conclude that the interaction of impurities is presumably weaker with screws.

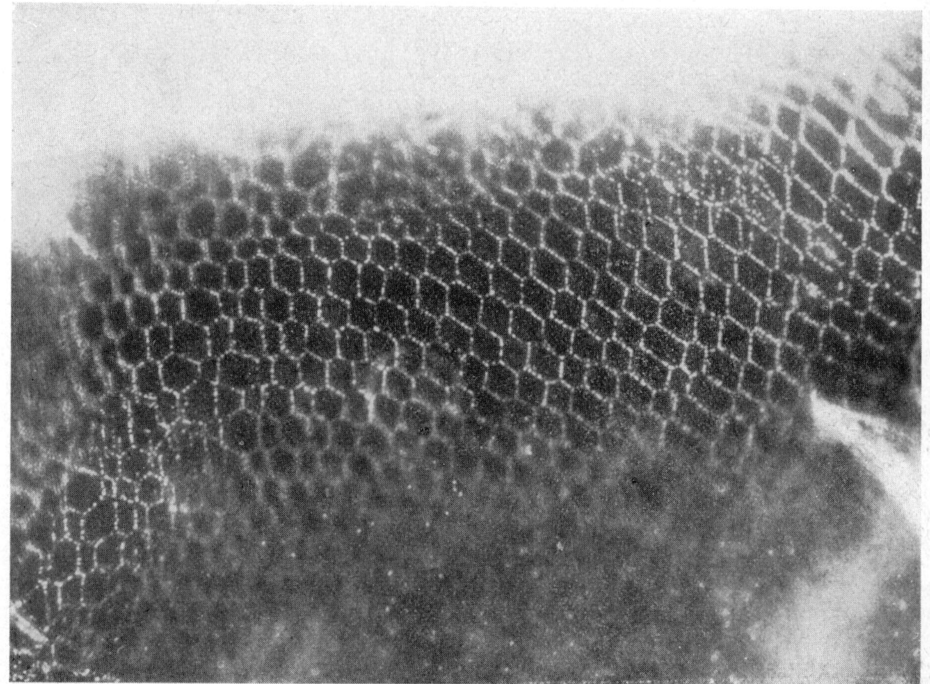

Fig. 23. – Observed hexagonal grid in potassium chloride. The boundary plane is near to the cube plane; hence the meshes have elongated shape.

6·1.4. More general patterns. – The three main types of patterns described above can be generated by the intersection of two families of dislocations at the most. In the case of the hexagonal grid the third family of dislocations is formed at the intersection points of the first two families, since this reduces the total energy. It is clear that the orientation of the rotation axis is subject to certain restrictions. This is no longer true if three families of dislocations having noncoplanar Burgers vectors are allowed.

An arbitrary boundary, *i.e.* one having an arbitrary rotation axis and an arbitrary contact plane, can now be constructed. Two dislocation boundaries, for which the rotation axis is not along a simple direction, will contain foreign dislocations of a third kind; these can often be recognized as, *e.g.*, in Fig. 20.

6·2. *Dislocation climb.* – As shown by Prof. FRIEDEL in his lectures, a screw dislocation which is subject to an over- or undersaturation of vacancies will adopt the shape of a helix. This phenomenon was first discovered in calcium fluoride [64, 14, 65] by the use of decoration techniques, in the way described in Section **5**·2.3. An example of the observed helical dislocations is shown in Fig. 24. The axis of the helix is along [110] in accordance with the assumption that the original dislocation was a screw. In some cases a sequence of loops is observed in the prolongation of the helix. These probably result from the intersection of the helix with itself. Since successive turns of the helix repel each other, and if prismatic glide in the direction of the Burgers vector is possible, loops can be blown off in this direction.

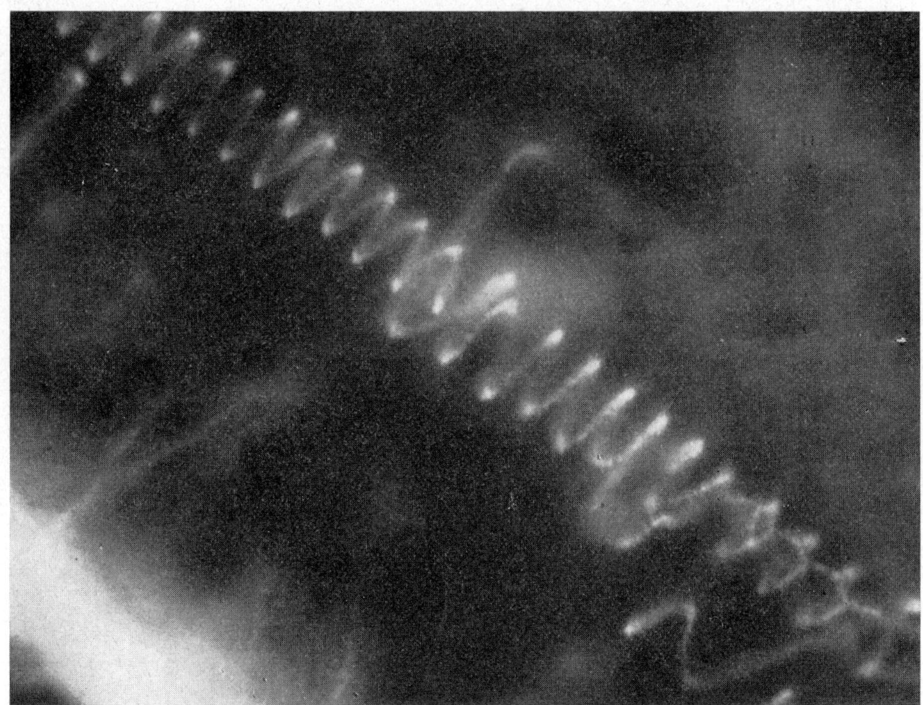

Fig. 24. – Helical dislocations in calcium fluoride. The dislocations are decorated by means of calcium oxide particles (after ref. [14]).

In NaCl, polygonized helices were found [65] by means of silver decoration. The presence of the helices could be demonstrated using an independent method, namely etching. Calcium fluoride cleaves along (111) planes; a cleavage plane may therefore intersect a helix and produce a sequence of half-loops. On etching, one observes a sequence of paired pits, which on continued etching coalesce and finally become flat-bottomed. This is shown in Fig. 25. In such a way it was demonstrated that the helices are not a consequence of the decoration procedure but are only revealed by it.

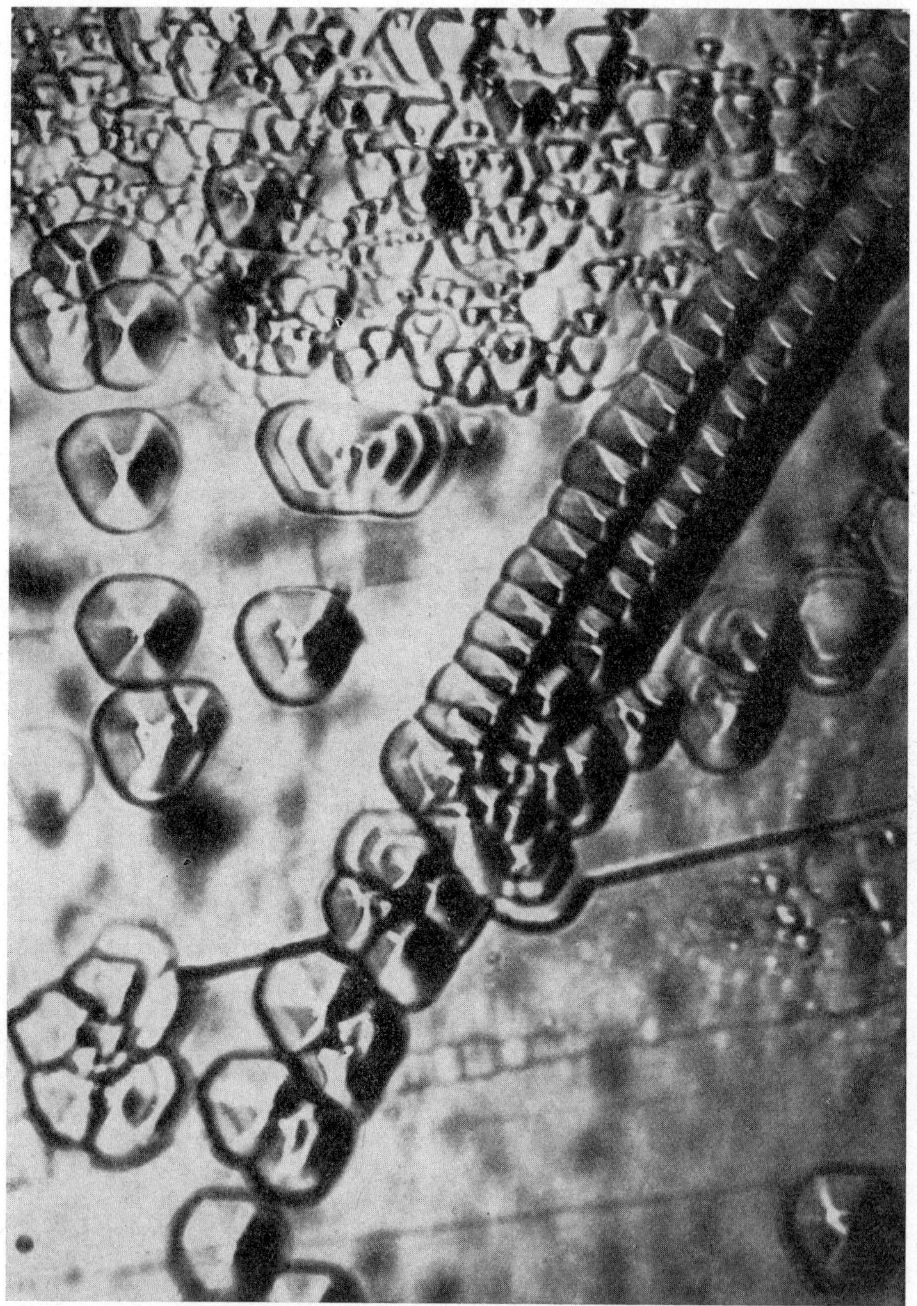

Fig. 25. – Etch patterns of a helix in CaF_2. On continued etching pairs of etch pits coalesce and finally become flat bottomed (after ref. [14]).

Electron microscopic observations in quenched metals have confirmed that helices can be generated by a supersaturation of vacancies. More recently, DASH [66] has demonstrated that an undersaturation of vacancies may cause

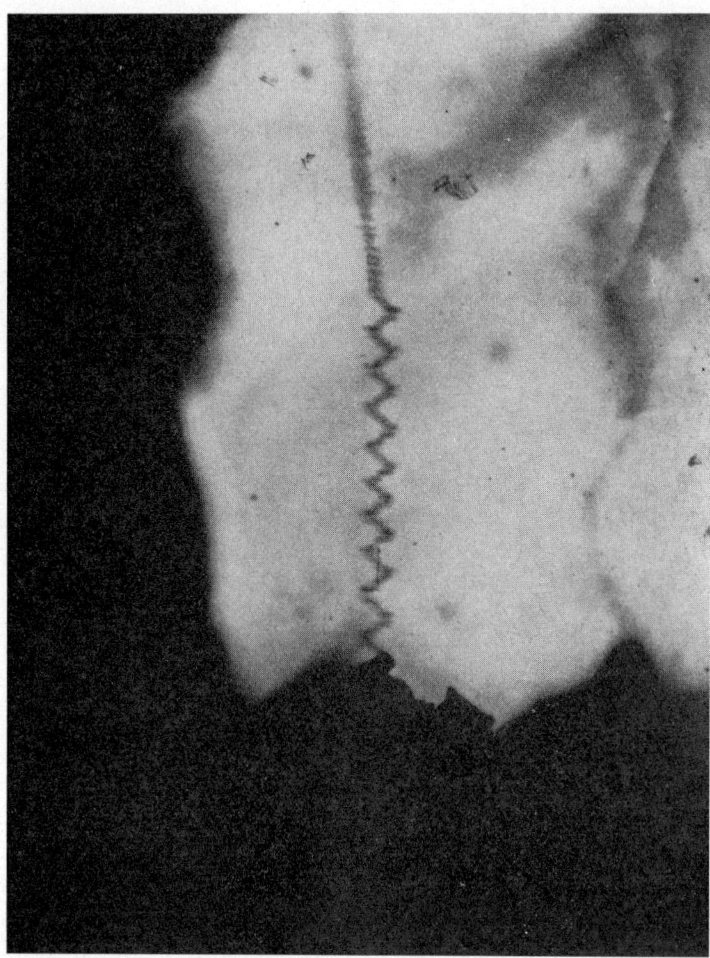

Fig. 26 *a*). – Helical dislocations revealed by copper decoration in silicon (after DASH). Helical dislocation and the etch pit centered on it.

climb as well. The experiment was performed as follows. First screw dislocations of a known sign were introduced by twisting a silicon rod about a [111] axis. Then gold was allowed to diffuse into the crystal. Gold is known to diffuse interstitially in silicon but, if captured by a vacancy, it becomes substitutional and immobilizes the vacancy. The dislocations are consequently induced to climb in order to maintain the equilibrium concentration of vacancies, and the screws are as a consequence driven into helices. The dislocations are subsequently or simultaneously decorated, using copper precipi-

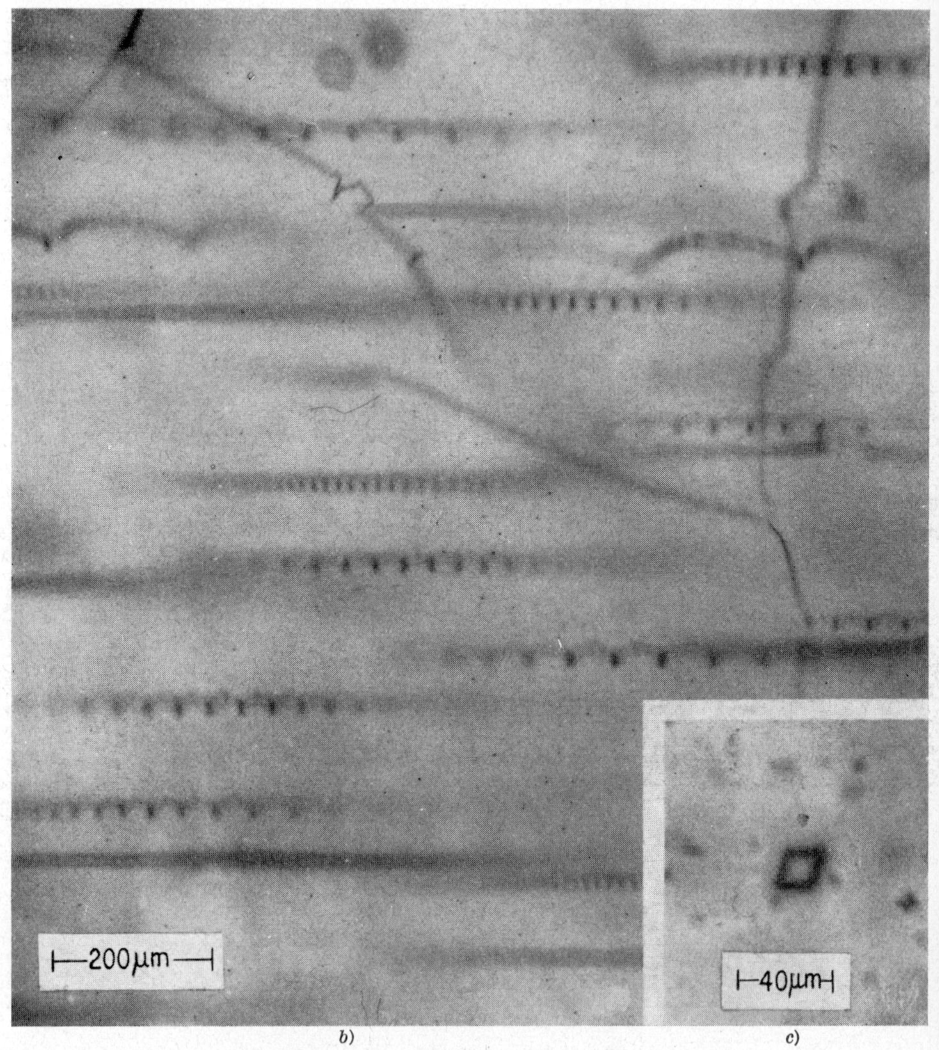

Fig. 26 *b*), *c*). – Helical dislocations revealed by copper decoration in silicon (after DASH). *b*) Sets of parallel screws driven into helices by the deficiency of vacancies resulting from diffusion of gold into silicon. *c*) Helix seen end-on, showing its polygonal shape. This observation also allows to determine the sense of winding of the helix.

tation. The sign of the helices was deduced by observing them along their axis, moving the focus of the microscope up and down. From the sense of movement of the in-focus part of the helix, the sense of winding can be deduced. It was found that left-handed screws were transformed into right-handed helices (Fig. 26). Fig. 27 demonstrates that this can only be caused by an undersaturation of vacancies.

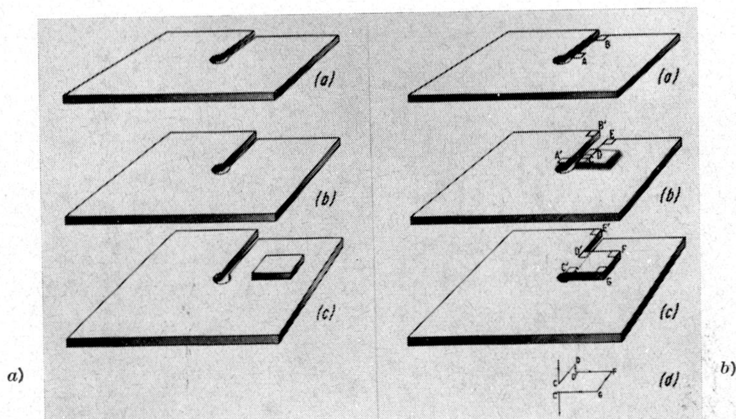

Fig. 27. – The formation at the dislocations of the vacancies required to compensate the deficiency, is geometrically equivalent to the deposition of interstitials at the dislocation. *a*) Expanded model of three adjacent planes of a crystal threaded by a left-handed screw dislocation. A prismatic dislocation loop formed by the aggregation of interstitial atoms between planes (*b*) and (*c*) is shown on top of plane (*c*). *b*) Element of a helical dislocation formed by moving the prismatic dislocation loop to the core of the screw dislocation. A and A', B and B', etc. represent adjacent atoms in the crystal when the planes (*a*), (*b*) and (*c*) are brought together. The result of this construction is the formation of one turn of a right-handed helix shown in (*d*) (After DASH).

6'3. *Dislocations in whiskers.* – Because of their unusual mechanical properties, there has been much speculation as to the dislocation content and configuration in whiskers. Their large strength has been attributed either to the absence of dislocations or to their inability to multiply. On the other hand, the particular habit of these crystals has been explained by assuming that they grow around a single axial screw dislocation.

Decoration methods have shown that (at least) the particular alkali halide whiskers studied often contain a large number of dislocations. Only in a few exceptional cases one finds that the theoretical picture of a single axial dislocation is confirmed.

Fig. 28, *e.g.*, shows a whisker containing a single axial screw dislocation. The wiskers were obtained by growth from a solution containing a small amount (2 mg per liter) of polyvinyl alcohol. This impurity acts as a « poison » which induces the crystals to grow as thin fibres rather than as isometric crystals. In fact we have to do with a form of dendrite growth; the fibres often branch. Fig. 29 shows the dislocation configuration observed in such a branching point.

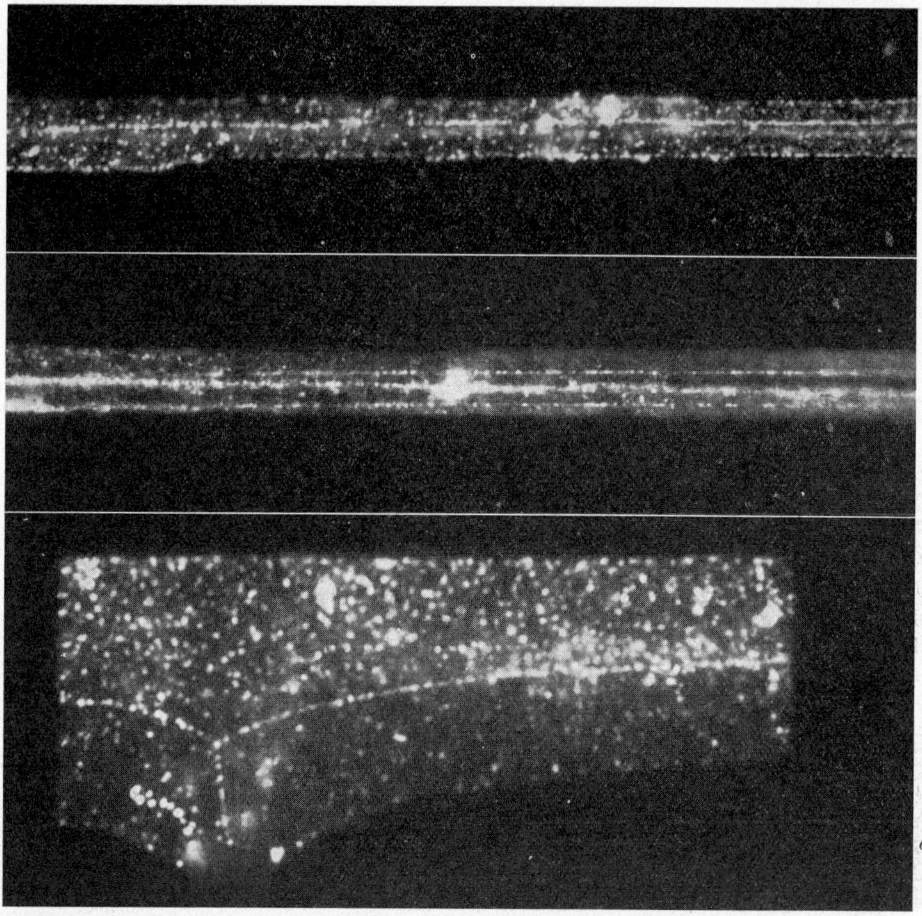

a)

b)

c)

Fig. 28. – Decorated dislocations in sodium chloride whiskers (after ref. [67]). *a*) Two dislocations parallel to the axis. *b*) Several dislocations parallel to the axis. *c*) Branching point of the whiskers and the dislocations in the three branches.

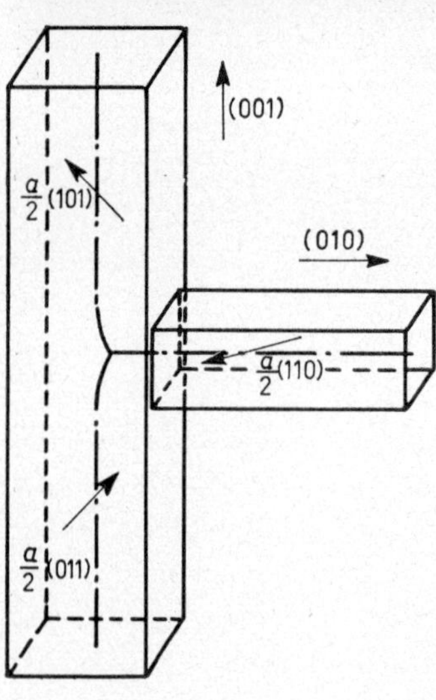

Fig. 29. – Configuration of Burgers vectors in a branching point.

From this observation the Burgers vector of the axial dislocation can be deduced in the following way. The angles at the node being approximately equal, the Burgers vectors must be equal in magnitude, and hence of the form $(a/2)[110]$. If the dislocations in the three branches are further required to emerge with a screw component in the top face, the only possible configuration is such that the axial dislocation is a 45° dislocation.

Decoration in the whiskers was achieved by diffusing in gold from outside. A large number of whiskers was enclosed in an evacuated quartz tube together with a small amount of gold chloride. After heating at 700 °C for about 1 hour the crystals were cooled fairly rapidly. For further details of the experimental procedure we refer to references [67].

6·4. *Deformation patterns.* – It is now generally accepted that dislocation multiplication is the process responsible for plastic flow. One of the possible mechanisms for dislocation multiplication is the so-called Frank-Read source [68]. In view of its importance and in order to appreciate fully the detailed confirmation by DASH [29], it is considered worth-while to describe briefly the geometry of the process, since this has not been done as yet in the course of these lectures.

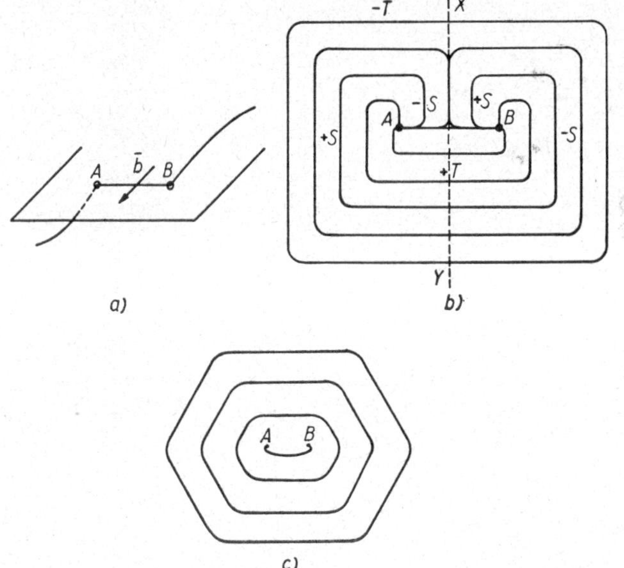

Fig. 30. – Schematic view of Frank-Read source. *a*) Initial configuration of dislocations. *b*) Successive stages in the formation of a loop. *c*) Final configuration after a number of loops has been emitted by the source.

Consider the configuration of dislocations shown in Fig. 30. The segment AB is pure edge and it is lying in the glide plane. It is therefore mobile. The other segments CD and AD are immobile since they are out of the glide plane. Under the influence of a shear stress the dislocation AB will successively adopt the shapes 1, 2, 3, ...; the sign and character of each dislocation segment is marked. Finally, in situation 4 two screws of opposite sign meet, and annihilate. One is now left with a closed dislocation loop, which will further expand, and the original segment AB is restored and can generate a new closed loop.

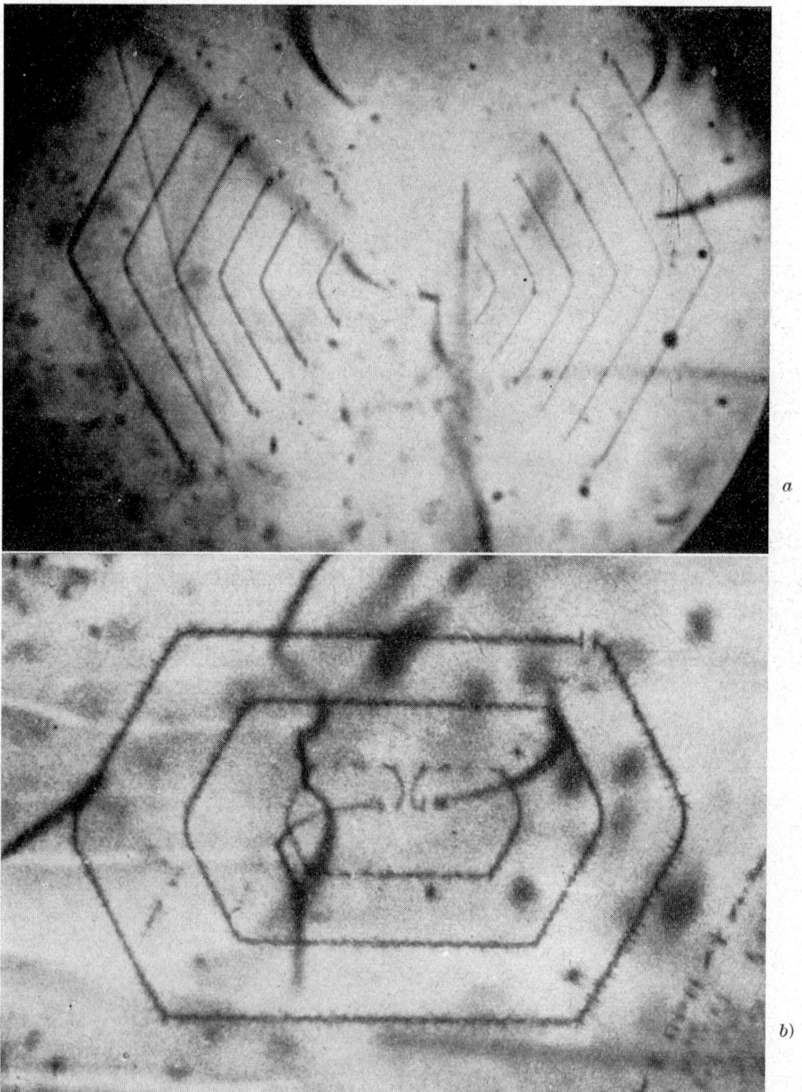

Fig. 31. – Frank-Read sources in silicon as observed by means of copper decoration (after DASH). *a*) Double ended Frank-Read source. *b*) Single ended Frank-Read source; screw segments are not decorated.

The area within the loop is hereby displaced, in the direction and sense indicated by the Burgers vector, with respect to the region outside. If, at a point, n loops have passed, the displacement in that point is nb. It is geometrically possible to obtain an unlimited amount of glide from a single source AB; in practice, however, the source will stop operating, because of the elastic back-stress caused by a number of produced loops piling up against one or another

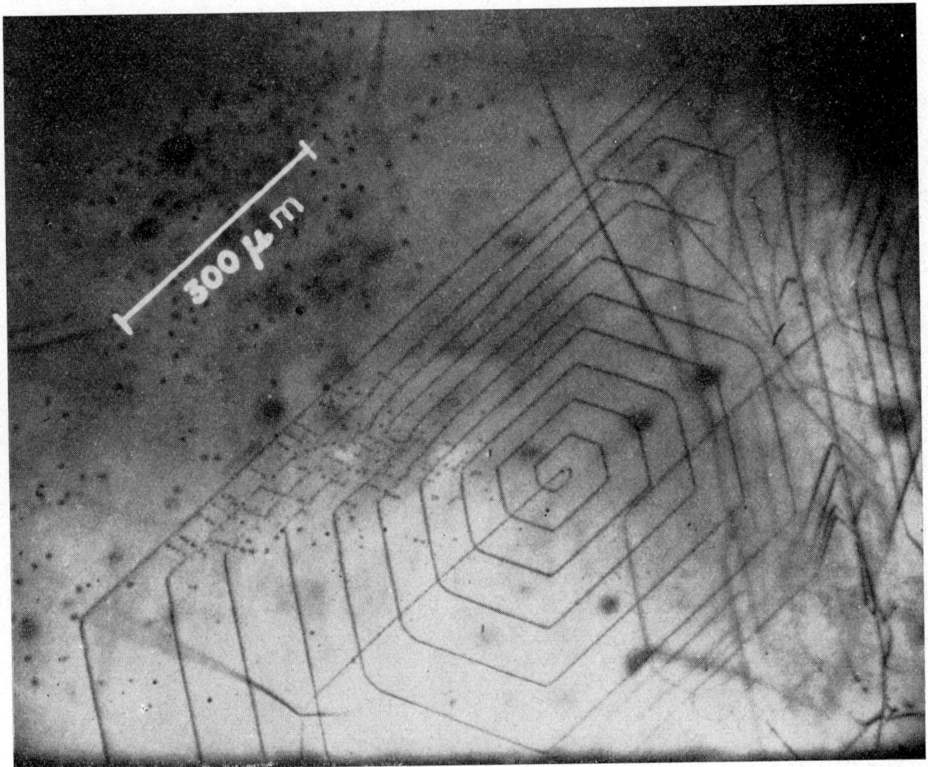

Fig. 32. – Single ended source. Notice the trails left by moving jogs (after Dash).

barrier. The configuration of dislocations resulting from the operation of a Frank-Read source is therefore as shown in Fig. 30 for the case of a glide plane with square symmetry. Dash has twisted silicon crystals at high temperature, around a [111] axis, causing glide in the (111) plane. The dislocations were then decorated using copper in the way described in Section **5**.2.4. The result is shown in Fig. 31. It is clear that the observed configuration is of exactly the kind predicted by theory. Since we have to do with a face of three-fold symmetry the loops are, of course, more like hexagons. The nondecorated segments in Fig. 31 are the screw segments. In accordance with the observation of nets in alkali halides, the interaction with impurities seems to be less with screws. An alternative reason for the lack of decoration may be that screws do not provide space for the precipitates.

Dislocation sources may also be single-ended. The source segments, instead of connecting two pinning points, may connect one node point to the surface. Such a source is equivalent, with respect to the shear stress required to operate it, to a double-ended source of double the length, *i.e.*, having its second pinning point at the mirror image of the first one with respect to the surface. The geometrical configuration resulting from the operation of a single-ended source can be deduced by cutting Fig. 30 along the line XY. An observed single-ended source is shown in Fig. 32.

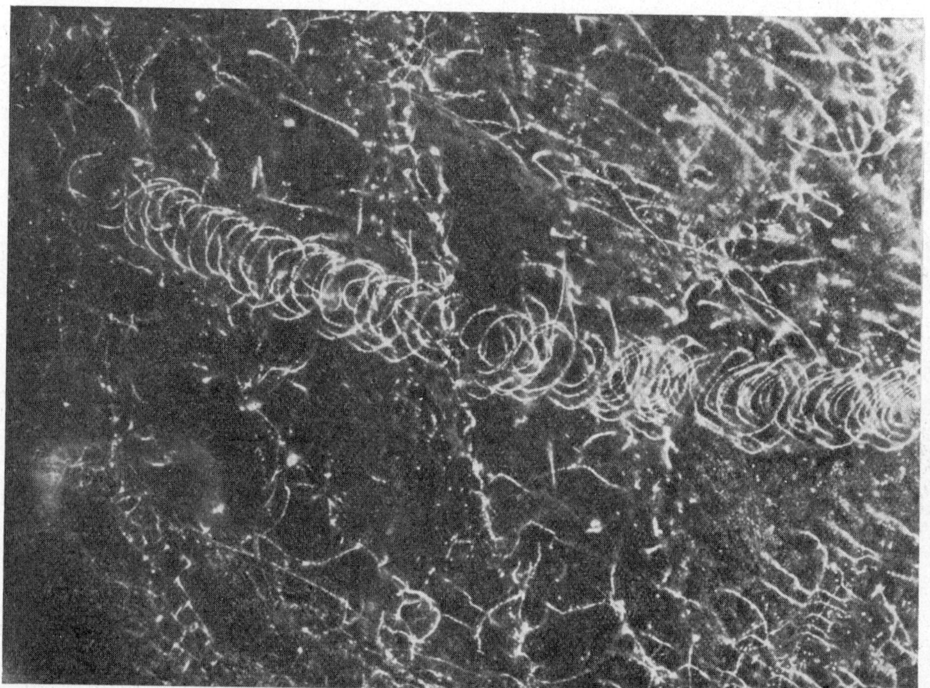

Fig. 33. – Surface sources in silver nitrate-doped KCl, as revelad by the X-irradiation-anneal method (after ref. [37]).

The same pattern exhibits a number of other remarkable features. In a number of planes the dislocations present cusps, and behind the cusps linear arrays of precipitates are visible. Similar trails have been observed in potassium chloride decorated with silver [56]. It is believed that these are due to point defects left by the movement of a jogged dislocation. In view of more recent evidence obtained with the electron microscope on other substances [69], it now seems, more plausible that they represent dislocation « dipoles » caused by large jogs. These dipoles may break up in a sequence of loops as shown by PRICE [70] in the case of zinc. In fact such linear sequences of loops in the (111) plane were found earlier by DASH, using his copper decoration technique, but he had not given any explanation. It now appears that they are related to the trails. Such small loops left in the wake of a moved dislocation have been held responsible for dislocation multiplication in LiF [71, 72].

Surface sources of a somewhat different kind are visible in Fig. 33, which represents dislocation patterns in a crystal of KCl doped with silver nitrate and decorated by X-irradiation followed by annealing. The surface loops are formed as a consequence of plastic deformation, at the tip of a moving crack. Such sequences of half-loops are very unstable and would move out of the crystal on a high temperature anneal. The picture therefore proves that the decoration technique allows one to reveal deformation patterns, *i.e.*, freshly introduced dislocations.

* * *

I would like to thank Dr. GILMAN, Dr. JOHNSTON, Dr. BONTINCK and Dr. DASH for their permission to reproduce photographs and Mr. STRUMANE who took notes which formed the basis for this written version.

REFERENCES

[1] F. C. FRANK: *Disc. Faraday Soc.*, **5**, 48 (1949).
[2] W. DEKEYSER and S. AMELINCKX: *Les dislocations et la croissance des cristaux* (Paris, 1955).
[3] A. R. VERMA: *Crystal Growth and Dislocations* (London, 1953).
[4] W. K. BURTON and N. CABRERA: *Disc. Faraday Soc.*, **5**, 53 (1949).
[5] S. AMELINCKX and E. VOTAVA: *Naturwiss.*, **44**, 422 (1954).
[6] C. SELLA, P. CONJEAUD and J. J. TRILLANT: *Compt. Rend.*, **249**, 1978 (1959).
[7] G. A. BASSETT: *Phil. Mag.*, **3**, 1042 (1958).
[8] H. BETGHE and W. Z. KELLER: *Naturforsch.*, **15**a, 271 (1960).
[9] H. BETGHE and V. SCHMIDT: *Naturforsch.*, **14**a, 307 (1959).
[10] R. GEVERS, S. AMELINCKX and W. DEKEYSER: *Naturwiss.*, **39**, 448 (1952).
[11] R. GEVERS: *Journ. Chim. Phys.*, **50**, 321 (1953).
[12] F. H. HORN: *Phil. Mag.*, **43**, 1210 (1952).
[13] E. S. MACHLIN: *Dislocations and Mechanical Properties of Crystals*, Ed. J. C. FISHER *et al.* (New York, 1957), p. 165.
[14] W. BONTINCK: *Phil. Mag.*, **2**, 516 (1957).
[15] S. AMELINCKX: *Acta Met.*, **2**, 848 (1954).
[16] J. J. GILMAN and W. G. JOHNSTON: *Dislocations and Mechanical Properties of Crystals*, Ed. J. C. FISHER *et al.* (New York, 1957), p. 116.
[17] F. W. YOUNG and A. T. GWATHMEY: *Journ. Appl. Phys.*, **31**, 225 (1960).

[18] P. A. JACQUET: *Acta Met.*, **2**, 752, 770 (1954).
[19] S. AMELINCKX: *Acta Met.*, **2**, 850 (1954).
[20] P. R. MORAN: *Journ. Appl. Phys.*, **29**, 1768 (1958).
[21] G. A. SLACK: *Phys. Rev.*, **105**, 834 (1957).
[22] A. S. KEH: *Journ. Appl. Phys.*, **31**, 1538 (1960).
[23] F. L. VOGEL, W. G. PFANN, H. E. COREY and E. E. THOMAS: *Phys. Rev.*, **90**, 489 (1953).
[24] S. G. ELLIS: *Journ. Appl. Phys.*, **26**, 1140 (1955).
[25] J. J. GILMAN and W. G. JOHNSTON: *Journ. Appl. Phys.*, **27**, 1018 (1956).
[26] J. C. SUITS and J. R. LOW: G.E. Report No. 56-RL-1575 (1956).
[27] G. WYON and P. LACOMBE: *Rept. Conf. on Defects in Crystalline Solids* (London, 1955), p. 187.
[28] J. J. GILMAN: G.E. Rept. No. 55-RL-1434 (1955).
[29] W. C. DASH: *Journ. Appl. Phys.*, **27**, 1193 (1956).
[30] S. AMELINCKX: *Phil. Mag.*, **1**, 269 (1956).
[31] J. T. BARTLETT and J. W. MITCHELL: *Phil. Mag.*, **3**, 334 (1958).
[32] W. G. PFANN and L. C. LOVELL: *Acta Met.*, **3**, 512 (1955).
[33] C. G. DUNN and W. R. HIBBARD: *Acta Met.*, **3**, 409 (1955).
[34] S. AMELINCKX, W. BONTINCK and W. DEKEYSER: *Phil. Mag.*, **2**, 355 (1957).
[35] E. AERTS, S. AMELINCKX and W. DEKEYSER: *Acta Met.*, **7**, 29 (1959).
[36] J. J. GILMAN: *Journ. Appl. Phys.*, **29**, 877 (1958).
[37] W. G. JOHNSTON and J. J. GILMAN: *Journ. Appl. Phys.*, **30**, 129 (1959).
[38] J. D. ESHELBY, F. C. FRANK and F. R. N. NABARRO: *Phil. Mag.*, **42**, 351 (1951).
[39] G. LEIBFRIED: *Zeits. f. Phys.*, **130**, 214 (1951).
[40] S. AMELINCKX, G. STRUMANE and W. W. WEBB: *Journ. Appl. Phys.*, **31**, 1359 (1960).
[41] S. AMELINCKX and R. STRUMANE: *Acta Met.*, **8**, 312 (1960).
[42] A. H. COTTRELL: *Dislocations and Plastic Flow in Crystals* (London, 1953).
[43] Y. LI: *Acta Met.*, **1**, 155 (1953).
[44] A. D. WHAPAM: *Phil. Mag.*, **3**, 103 (1958).
[45] W. H. VAUGHAN and J. W. DAVISSON: *Acta Met.*, **6**, 554 (1958).
[46] R. CHANG: *Journ. Appl. Phys.*, **28**, 385 (1957).
[47] T. S. NOGGLE and J. O. STIEGLER: *Journ. Appl. Phys.*, **30**, 1279 (1960).
[48] G. R. HENNIG and J. E. HOVE: *Proc. Conf. on the Peaceful Use of Atomic Energy*, **7**, 666 (Paper nr. 751) (1956).
[49] D. BINDER and W. J. STURM: *Phys. Rev.*, **107**, 106 (1957).
[50] P. SENIO and C. W. TUCKER: KAPL-1727 (1957).
[51] M. LAMBERT, P. BERGÉ, C. MAZIÈRES and A. GUINIER: *Compt. Rend.*, **249**, 2054 (1959).
[52] W. BONTINCK: *Physica*, **22**, 595 (1956).
[53] J. W. MITCHELL: *Dislocations and Mechanical Properties of Crystals*, Ed. J. C. FISHER *et al.* (New York, 1957), p. 69.
[54] S. AMELINCKX: *Dislocations and Mechanical Properties of Crystals*, Ed. J. C. FISHER *et al.* (New York, 1957), p. 3.
[55] W. VAN DER VORST and W. DEKEYSER: *Phil. Mag.*, **1**, 882 (1956).
[56] S. AMELINCKX: *Acta Met.*, **6**, 34 (1958).
[57] S. AMELINCKX: *Phil. Mag.*, **3**, 653 (1958).
[58] S. AMELINCKX, W. MAENHOUT-VAN DER VORST and W. DEKEYSER: *Acta Met.*, **7**, 8 (1959).
[58 *bis*] J. D. BARBER, K. B. HARVEY and J. W. MITCHELL: *Phil. Mag.*, **2**, 704 (1957).

[59] S. AMELINCKX: *Phil. Mag.*, **3**, 307 (1958).
[60] F. C. FRANK and D. TURNBULL: G.E. Rept., No. 56-RL-1607 (1956).
[61] W. W. TYLER and W. C. DASH: *Journ. Appl. Phys.*, **28**, 1221 (1957).
[62] S. AMELINCKX and W. DEKEYSER: *Solid State Physics*, Ed. F. SEITZ and D. TURNBULL, **8**, 325 (1959).
[63] F. C. FRANK: *Rep. Conf. on Strength of Solids* (London, 1955), p. 159.
[64] S. AMELINCKX, W. BONTINCK, W. DEKEYSER and F. SEITZ: *Phil. Mag.*, **2**, 355 (1957).
[65] S. AMELINCKX, W. BONTINCK and W. MAENHOUT-VAN DER VORST: *Physica*, **23**, 270 (1957).
[66] W. C. DASH: G.E. Rept. No. 60-RL-2503 G (1960) (to be published in *Journ. Appl. Phys.*).
[67] S. AMELINCKX: *Growth and perfection of crystals* (Proc. Conf. on Crystal growth, Ed. R. H. DOREMUS *et al.*) (New York, 1958), p. 139.
[68] F. C. FRANK and W. T. READ: *Phys. Rev.*, **75**, 722 (1950).
[69] J. WASHBURN, A. KELLY and G. K. WILLIAMSON: *Phil. Mag.*, **5**, 192 (1960)
[70] P. B. PRICE: *Phil. Mag.*, **5**, 873 (1960).
[71] S. AMELINCKX and W. DEKEYSER: *Journ. Appl. Phys.*, **29**, 1000 (1958).
[72] W. G. JOHNSTON and J. J. GILMAN: *Journ. Appl. Phys.*, **31**, 632 (1960).

Mise en évidence des défauts cristallins par les rayons X.

A. Guinier

Faculté des Sciences de Paris - Orsay (S.-et-O.)

I. – Effet des imperfections cristallines sur la diffraction des rayons X.

L'étude expérimentale des défauts cristallins, qui est une des bases des théories de l'état solide, a une importance particulière pour l'étude des structures des solides résultant de l'action des rayonnements assez énergiques pour perturber l'édifice cristallin. Les méthodes que l'on a utilisées peuvent se classer en deux groupes: les méthodes directes et indirectes. Les premières visent à donner des renseignements sur la structure atomique des défauts. Aux secondes, on demande de détecter ces défauts et de permettre une comparaison de deux solides de structures analogues. Par exemple, la mesure de la résistivité électrique permet de décider si tel échantillon métallique contient plus de défauts que le métal parfaitement recuit. Mais on ne peut déduire de l'augmentation de résistivité seulement la nature des défauts qui la provoque. Ces méthodes indirectes ont l'avantage d'être souvent très simples et quelquefois extrèmement sensibles. Mais il est évident que les méthodes les plus avantageuses sont celles qui nous donnent des renseignements sur la structure atomique.

Parmi celles-ci, les rayons X jouent un rôle important. Nous voudrions dans cette conférence montrer le rôle particulier des techniques de rayons X, en nous attachant à préciser quelles sont les possibilités et aussi les limites de cette méthode. Il sera important ensuite de faire la comparaison avec une technique en plein développement, le microscope électronique, dont une conférence antérieure a montré les récents succès dans l'étude des défauts cristallins [1]. Etant donné que nous avons besoin de tous les renseignements utilisables et que nos moyens expérimentaux sont, en somme, assez limités, il n'y a pas concurrence entre ces méthodes mais il faut savoir utiliser chacune d'elles dans les meilleures conditions et coordonner leurs résultats.

1. – Principes des méthodes de rayons X.

Les principes généraux qui déterminent l'action des imperfections cristallines sur les diagrammes de diffraction de rayons X ont fait l'objet d'une série de conférences à la Summer School de Varenna en 1957 qui ont été publiées dans *Il Nuovo Cimento* [2]. Nous ne reviendrons donc pas dans cet article sur les détails de cette question; nous ne ferons que rappeler les résultats en renvoyant le lecteur à l'article de *Il Nuovo Cimento* ou bien encore à un traité spécialisé [3].

On sait que les rayons X, à cause de leur courte longueur d'onde, sont susceptibles de donner les détails d'une structure avec un pouvoir séparateur suffisant pour déterminer la position des atomes individuels. Mais on sait d'autre part qu'il n'est pas possible avec la diffraction des rayons X d'obtenir une « photographie » de la structure réelle du solide. Cela provient de ce que l'expérience permet d'enregistrer seulement les intensités de faisceaux diffractés mais non leur phase relative. Certes, dans certains cas, la précision que l'on obtient dans la détermination des structures est surprenante; ainsi, avec les méthodes modernes de la cristallographie, on réussit à déterminer la position dans une maille cristalline de quelques dizaines d'atomes à quelques centièmes d'ångström près. Mais ce succès est dû à la structure régulière du cristal étudié et à ce que l'on connaît les atomes qui en constituent la maille. Dans d'autres cas au contraire, les rayons X ne peuvent donner que des renseignements assez vagues. C'est, par exemple, le cas de la structure des liquides. Ainsi, quand il s'agit de mélanges liquides d'atomes de dimensions différentes, les données des rayons X sont extrèmement pauvres.

Nous devons d'abord définir ce que nous pouvons attendre de l'étude par les rayons X d'un cristal imparfait. Nous nous limitons à un modèle défini de la façon suivante: Nous partons d'un cristal parfait, où les atomes sont rangés de façon rigoureusement périodique dans les trois dimensions, et nous faisons subir à ce cristal de *petites* altérations. Cela signifie que chaque atome est déplacé d'une quantité inférieure aux dimensions de la maille du réseau régulier moyen. En d'autres terms, on peut en général sans ambiguité rattacher chaque atome du cristal imparfait à un atome du cristal non perturbé. Toutefois, nous traiterons aussi le cas du cristal qui contient des cavités d'un volume bien supérieure à la maille ou des groupes d'atomes étrangers en insertion. Le problème est de trouver ce que ces altérations modifient dans les diagrammes de diffraction du cristal parfait et, inversement ce que, des modifications observées, on peut déduire sur la nature des altérations du réseau. Ces effets étant de différents types, nous allons commencer par étudier le cas assez simple des cristaux « presque parfaits ». Nous traiterons le problème assez rapidement parce qu'il intervient peu dans le cas particulier des cristaux irradiés.

2. – Phénomènes d'extinction dans les cristaux.

La théorie simple de la diffraction des rayons X, ou *théorie cinématique*, consiste à calculer les interférences entre les ondes diffusées par les différents atomes de la matière touchée par le faisceau de rayons X primaires. L'hypothèse implicite à la base de cette théorie cinématique, c'est que les faisceaux diffractés sont d'intensité si faible par rapport aux faisceaux primaires qu'il n'y a pas d'interactions entre ces deux faisceaux. C'est ce qui a permis à LAUE et à BRAGG de prévoir l'existence des réflexions sélectives sur les différents plans cristallins et d'en calculer les intensités et c'est la théorie qui est utilisée par tous les cristallographes pour la détermination des structures cristallines.

Cependant, assez paradoxalement, cette théorie ne s'applique pas aux cristaux parfaits à moins qu'ils ne soient de dimensions très faibles (de l'ordre du micron). En effet, si l'on considère un grand domaine où les atomes sont rangés aux nœuds du réseau cristallin de façon rigoureuse, la théorie cinémamatique tombe en défaut parce qu'il n'est plus possible de négliger les interactions entre faisceaux diffractés et incidents.

La théorie qui est alors valable, bien plus complexe, s'appelle la *théorie dynamique* [4] dont le résultat capital est le suivant: les directions dans l'espace des faisceaux diffractés sont les mêmes que celles qui avaient été prévues par la théorie cinématique, mais *les intensités diffractées sont notablement inférieures*. Il y a ce qu'on appelle « *extinction* » dans le cristal parfait étendu. La divergence entre les résultats des deux théories est notable quand la dimension du domaine qui diffracte d'une façon cohérente est grande par rapport à une longueur, dite d'extinction, qui dépend du facteur de diffusion du plan réticulaire considéré et qui, dans le cas des rayons X, est de l'ordre du μm.

Un cristal qui est composé de domaines de cet ordre de grandeur, les domaines étant parfaits à leur intérieur mais étant un peu décalés et désorientés les uns par rapport aux autres, s'appelle « *cristal mosaïque* » ou « idéalement imparfait ». L'usage du mot imparfait ne doit pas induire en erreur. En fait, dans le cristal mosaïque, l'immense majorité d'atomes est entourée de voisins dans les positions rigoureures du cristal parfait. Il n'y a que de très rares et très légères failles dans l'édifice si bien que, en un point éloigné de quelques milliers de distances atomiques de l'origine, les atomes ne sont plus sur le réseau défini au voisinage de cet atome origine. Beaucoup de cristaux naturels et la généralité des métaux s'approchent de ce modèle avec une bonne approximation. Par contre, on connaît certains cristaux exceptionnels, naturels ou artificiels (calcite, fluorure de lithium, silicium, germanium), dans lesquels les domaines cohérents sont notablement plus grands et qui vérifient plus ou moins bien les conclusions de la théorie dynamique.

Pour représenter un cristal réel, nous partons donc d'un cristal indéfini à réseau parfait et nous y introduisons des « failles » qui le morcellent en domaines incohérents plus ou moins étendus. Dans ces conditions, la figure de diffraction de l'ensemble reste très semblable à celle du cristal parfait. La seule différence c'est que l'intensité des faisceaux diffractés augmente quand la dimension moyenne des domaines croît: elle tend vers celle donnée par la théorie cinématique quand cette dimension tombe au-dessous, disons du μm. Cette image est d'ailleurs trop restrictive. Certaines déformations élastiques très faibles variant de façon continue, comme celles provoquées par suite de tensions hétérogènes, peuvent aussi diminuer l'extinction et augmenter l'intensité réfléchie. Enfin un cristal donné peut contenir des régions où ce genre d'imperfection atteint des degrés différents.

Or, il existe actuellement des méthodes qui permettent d'obtenir ce qu'on appelle maintenant l'image par diffraction d'un cristal (méthodes dérivées de celle de Berg-Barrett) [5]. Dans ces méthodes, en un point du film sur lequel on enregistre la diffraction, ne parviennent que les rayons diffractés issus d'un point donné du cristal, la correspondance se faisant avec un pouvoir séparateur de l'ordre du μm ou de quelques μm. Dans ces conditions, les régions imparfaites donneront sur les photographies des taches noires puisqu'elles correspondetn à une plus grande intensité diffractée.

Ainsi on peut faire la carte de la répartition des régions imparfaites, à condition que celles-ci soient entourées de régions assez parfaites pour que les phénomènes d'extinction y soient considérables. De nombreuses applications de cette technique [6] ont été faites au cours de ces dernières années. C'est ainsi que Lang [7] a pu déceler dans un cristal de silicium les lignes de dislocation, à condition qu'elles soient assez distantes pour pouvoir être séparées par ces méthodes qui, comme nous l'avons dit, ont un pouvoir séparateur assez faible. C'est de façon analogue que dans le cas du microscope électronique les dislocations [8] ont été mises en évidence, mais cette fois-ci avec un pouvoir séparateur bien plus considérable. Pour le moment, on en est encore à des expériences qualitatives mais on peut espérer que l'on arrivera bientôt à une évaluation d'un « degré de perfection » basé sur la comparaison des intensités diffractées.

C'est surtout dans le cas des dislocations ou bien des groupements de dislocations (sous-joints, réseau de Frank très serré) que cet effet de diminution de l'extinction est considérable. Dans le cas qui nous intéresse spécialement des cristaux irradiés, certaines expériences préliminaires ont montré que l'irradiation diminuait l'extinction d'un cristal parfait. M. Lambert [9] a étudié les lamelles de fluorure de lithium clivées d'une épaisseur de l'ordre de $\frac{1}{2}$ mm. Elle a mesuré le pouvoir réflecteur sur des plans (200) perpendiculaires aux faces de clivage et comparé des cristaux vierges et après irradiation; elle a constaté que tous les nombres mesurés se trouvaient entre les limites des deux valeurs calculées d'après la théorie dynamique et d'après la théorie cinématique. D'autre part, tous les cristaux irradiés ont des pouvoirs réflecteurs supérieurs à ceux des cristaux avant irradiation. Le fait d'utiliser des plans réflecteurs intérieurs et non les seuls plans superficiels, comme quand on opère par réflexion sur la surface libre du cristal, évite les irrégularités dues aux déformations superficielles qui rendent les résultats des mesures par réflexion extrèmement dispersés. M. Lambert a constaté que les radiations aux rayons γ ne produisaient aucun effet, seule l'irradiation aux neutrons est effective. Avant irradiation, le pouvoir réflecteur pour un cristal d'épaisseur 0.4 mm varie d'un échantillon à l'autre autour de $1\cdot10^{-4}$: le pouvoir réflecteur est multiplié par 2 environ pour une dose de l'ordre de 10^{17} neutrons/cm^2, et par 5 pour une dose de $5\cdot10^{18}$. Pour des doses supérieures, le cristal est si perturbé que les largeurs du domaine angulaire de réflexion augmentent beaucoup et les mesures de pouvoir réflecteur n'ont plus grand sens. On n'atteint pas la valeur maximale donnée par la théorie cinématique qui est de $7\cdot10^{-4}$. Quand le cristal est recuit, on constate que son pouvoir réflecteur diminue de moitié après une heure de chauffage à 370 °C, ce qui rend le cristal d'une couleur rouge alors qu'il était complètement noir après irradiation. Après un recuit à 450 °C, qui le décolore complètement, le pouvoir réflecteur diminue encore et retrouve sensiblement la valeur qu'il avait avant irradiation. Cela ne veut pas dire d'ailleurs que la courbe de réflexion (rocking curve) retrouve la même forme. Il semble en effet que le traitement de guérison reforme des domaines assez grands pour que l'extinction devienne considérable, mais néanmoins laisse entre ces domaines des désorientations assez grandes; on dit qu'il y a *polygonisation* [10]. Ces mesures représentent un effet moyen des radiations sur le cristal; on n'a pas encore essayé, en faisant l'image d'un cristal irradié, de voir s'il existe une répartition irrégulière de déformations qui serait intéressante à connaître.

3. – Défauts de périodicité.

Les défauts que nous avons considérés dans le paragraphe précédent sont rares ou tout au moins les déformations sont extrèmement progressives de façon qu'il subsiste des domaines cohérents d'assez grandes dimensions. La limite vers laquelle on tend, c'est ce qui correspond au modèle du cristal « idéalement imparfait » subdivisé en petits domaines incohérents entre eux. Ce que nous allons maintenant étudier, c'est ce qui se passe quand l'intérieur même d'un « domaine cohérent » est perturbé par des défauts de périodicité du réseau affectant des atomes à petite distance les uns des autres. Autrement dit, nous partons du cristal dont la figure de diffraction peut être calculée par la théorie cinématique et nous allons chercher quelles modifications sont apportées à cette figure par les défauts de périodicité.

Ces défauts peuvent être créés, d'une part par le déplacement des atomes à partir du réseau moyen idéal, et d'autre part, en plaçant en deux nœuds homologues des atomes de natures différentes. Dans le premier cas, la géométrie du réseau est affectée. Dans le second, les translations possibles du réseau géométrique remplacent un atome par un autre de nature différente. On dit qu'il s'agit de défauts de déplacement d'une part, de substitution de l'autre; évidemment les deux types peuvent se superposer quand les substitutions d'atomes dans un cristal produisent en même temps des déformations du réseau. C'est le principe du calcul des interférences pour un tel cristal à périodicité imparfaite que nous avions donné dans l'article déjà cité de *Il Nuovo Cimento* [2]. Nous ne rappellerons ici que les conclusions.

La différence capitale entre cristal parfait et imparfait est la suivante: pour le cristal parfait, les interférences annulent rigoureusement les ondes diffusées par les différents atomes, *sauf si* le cristal se trouve dans les conditions de diffraction de Bragg. Pour le cristal imparfait au contraire, il n'y a pas annulation complète de l'amplitude totale pour une direction quelconque d'observation. Cela signifie que la figure de diffraction d'un cristal imparfait comprend en plus des taches de diffraction correspondant au réseau idéal moyen, et prévues par la théorie cinématique classique, une diffusion généralisée (diffuse scattering): *cette diffusion est caractéristique de l'imperfection cristalline.* Les expériences ont pour but de déterminer la répartition en l'espace de la diffusion et on demande à la théorie de relier cette répartition à la nature des défauts de périodicité.

D'une façon générale, l'information maximale tirée d'expériences aussi complètes que possible, est la détermination d'une certaine « fonction de désordre », φ_m, que l'on définit de la façon suivante:

$$\varphi_m = \overline{F_n \cdot F^*_{n+m}} \, .$$

C'est la moyenne du produit des facteurs de structure de deux mailles du cristal réel, de rangs n et $n+m$, séparées par un vecteur donné du réseau moyen $\boldsymbol{x}_m$. Le facteur de structure d'une maille donnée dépend de la nature des atomes effectivement présents dans la maille considérée ainsi que des déplacements de ces atomes par rapport à la maille du réseau moyen.

Nous insisterons sur deux conséquences importantes de cette formule.

D'abord ce que l'on détermine, c'est une moyenne, autrement dit une valeur statistique; et c'est là un caractère général des résultats des techniques de rayons X. On obtient une statistique de l'emplacement des atomes par rapport à un atome quelconque du cristal (c'est la généralisation de ce que l'on appelle la fonction de Patterson dans les structures cristallines).

Un bon exemple est fourni par la mesure des paramètres d'un cristal. Il est évident, à cause des mouvements d'agitation thermique, à cause aussi de l'existence d'atomes de diamètres différents quand il s'agit d'une solution solide, que les distances individuelles entre atomes homologues peuvent fluctuer de façon importante, mais néanmoins, les rayons X nous permettent de mesurer la valeur du paramètre avec une grande précision. Cela vient de ce que ce paramètre est une grandeur statistique moyenne qui conditionne la diffraction des rayons X.

Ensuite, ce qu'on peut connaître, ce n'est pas la valeur moyenne du désordre dans une maille, mais bien une fonction qui dépend de la valeur du désordre dans *deux mailles* données, c'est-à-dire qui fait intervenir la *corrélation* entre les désordres dans ces deux mailles. L'effet d'une distorsion d'un cristal est complètement différent suivant que la distorsion est répartie au hasard de maille à maille, ou bien que la distorsion est la même pour les voisins jusqu'à des distances plus ou moins grandes.

Expérimentalement, cela se traduit de la façon suivante: quand il n'y a aucune corrélation dans le désordre, c'est-à-dire que le désordre d'une maille n'influe aucunement sur celui des mailles voisines du cristal, on obtient une diffusion continue et s'étendant sans variations brusques dans tout l'espace réciproque. Au contraire, s'il y a une très forte corrélation entre les mailles voisines de façon que les atomes soient déplacés ou substitués en bloc dans des domaines assez grands, la diffusion est concentrée autour des positions de réflexions sélectives. Cela revient alors tout simplement à un élargissement des taches de diffraction. Le remplacement des taches nettes de diffraction par des taches élargies est un des effets possible du désordre.

Enfin, outre la diffusion continue, ou bien l'élargissement des taches de diffraction, les imperfections cristallines peuvent produire un autre effet: la décroissance de l'intensité des réflexions sélectives. Une partie de l'intensité qui, pour le cristal parfait, se trouve concentrée dans les directions de réflexions sélectives est répartie dans la diffusion continue en dehors des directions prévues par les lois simples de Laue et Bragg.

Pour illustrer la façon dont on peut effectivement déterminer la « fonction de désordre » φ_m à partir de l'expérience et dont on peut utiliser φ_m pour trouver la structure des imperfections cristallines, nous nous contenterons de donner dans la deuxième partie un exemple de ces méthodes dans le cas particulier du fluorure de lithium irradié aux neutrons. Mais ce que nous voudrions surtout pour le moment, c'est mettre en évidence les facteurs principaux qui gouvernent les possibilités d'application des rayon X. De ce point de vue, le fait le plus important, c'est que l'intensité diffusée dans une direction donnée par un cristal imparfait dépend d'une statistique portant sur *tous* les atomes du cristal. Il s'ensuit que les rayons X sont aptes à mettre en évidence des imperfections, *si* elles atteignent l'ensemble des atomes ou au moins une proportion notable. Par contre, la technique est très mal adaptée à l'étude de défauts isolés. C'est cette simple idée qui souvent permet de décider si une expérience avec les rayons X vaut la peine d'être tentée pour résoudre un problème. Remarquons qu'il se trouve que pour le microscope électronique c'est le contraire qui se produit, c'est-à-dire que ce sont les accidents isolés, bien marqués, que mettra naturellement en évidence l'instrument, même s'ils sont rares; tandis que des défauts de périodicité étendus à toutes les mailles ne se voient absolument pas, même si les perturbations sont assez notables.

Donnons deux exemples contradictoires: d'une part, l'agitation thermique des atomes dans le cristal provoque les vibrations de tous les atomes: par conséquent il y a homogénéité du point de vue statistique: de fait, la diffusion des rayons X permet d'étudier de façon très détaillée les modes de vibration de l'agitation thermique. Au contraire, il n'y a aucun phénomène perceptible au microscope électronique qui corresponde à cette vibration des atomes individuels.

Par contre, une dislocation est un défaut qui intéresse un petit nombre d'atomes; mais sur le long de la ligne de dislocations les atomes subissent des déplacements non négligeables par rapport aux paramètres de la maille cristalline. Or, on sait que la dislocation est bien visible sur les images au microscope électronique mais donne lieu à une diffusion de rayons X imperceptible avec les moyens dont nous disposons actuellement [11].

Un autre exemple sera tiré de l'étude des alliages à l'état d'ordre partiel. Par la diffusion des rayons X, on peut déterminer de façon précise les divers degrés d'ordre à petite distance, c'est-à-dire les paramètres qui définissent statistiquement l'entourage d'une atome donné [12]. Par contre, il n'est pas possible, avec le microscope électronique, de distinguer une solution désordonnée d'une solution solide dans laquelle il y a ou un ordre parfait, ou un ordre partiel. Néanmoins, ce que des études récentes on montré, c'est que l'existence des domaines « antiphase » pouvait être révélée [13]. On voit apparaître des séparations entre domaines, parce que ces accidents localisés provoquent sur l'image, par un mécanisme d'ailleurs encore un peu obscur, un contraste suffisant pour être enregistré. Il est plus difficile, au contraire, avec les rayons X de définir la forme des domaines antiphase de façon précise.

Un facteur qui limite la sensibilité des méthodes de rayons X pour les détections des défauts, c'est l'existence de l'agitation thermique. Comme nous l'avons déjà signalé, tous les atomes y sont soumis et à toute température, même voisine du zéro absolu. Par conséquent, *à priori*, on conçoit que, pour qu'un désordre particulier soit sensible, il faut qu'il soit nettement plus important que le désordre provenant de l'agitation thermique. Si le défaut n'intéresse qu'une petite fraction des atomes, cela implique que l'effet des déplacements de ces quelques atomes sera noyé dans le phénomène global de l'agitation thermique. En tout cas, on prévoit que les études du désordre devront être conduites à température aussi basse que possible pour minimiser l'agitation thermique, ou encore à différentes températures pour distinguer la part de la diffusion qui est fonction de la température.

Nous insistons particulièrement sur cette comparaison du microscope électronique et de la technique des rayons X parce que, tout dernièrement, le microscope électronique a obtenu des succès remarquables dans l'étude des défauts cristallins et les expérimentateurs songent naturellement à recourir à cette technique pour l'étude de leurs problèmes sur les imperfections cristallines. Mais cela ne devrait pas les amener à négliger systématiquement l'emploi des rayons X. En réalité, les deux méthodes ne mettent pas en évidence les mêmes choses et il n'est pas possible de comparer d'une façon générale leur sensibilité. Soit, par exemple, le problème de la recherche des défauts qui peuvent expliquer certaines modifications de propriétés physiques, par exemple les propriétés mécaniques; le microscope électronique montrera l'existence de certains défauts rares et de diamètre assez considérable (> 50 Å). Il n'est pas certain que ces accidents localisés aient une influence sur les propriétés mécaniques. Ce qui est déterminant peut-être, ce sont des imperfections bien plus petites mais bien plus réparties que pourraient mettre en évidence seuls les rayons X. Signalons d'ailleurs que, quand on a essayé dans des cas particulièrement favorables, d'étudier par les deux méthodes les mêmes phénomènes, on est arrivé à un accord très satisfaisant, ce qui donne confiance dans les théories employées dans l'un et l'autre cas (images des zones G.P. mises en évidence d'abord par le rayons X et retrouvées ensuite par le microscope électronique [14]).

Enfin dans cette comparaison entre les deux techniques, il faut signaler les différences qui proviennent des formes d'échantillons qu'on emploie. Pour le microscope électronique, il est absolument indispensable d'opérer sur des feuilles extrèmement minces (épaisseur inférieure à quelques centaines d'Å) et, à cette échelle, le rôle considérable des surfaces modifie d'une façon notable les propriétés de la matière. On ne peut pas dire que des feuilles aussi minces soient vraiment représentatives de ce qui se passe à l'intérieur du solide. Au contraire, pour les rayons X, on n'est pas gêné par cet inconvénient, bien qu'on utilise de petits échantillons. C'est d'ailleurs la nécessité de préparer ces échantillons minces qui empêche quelquefois d'utiliser le microscope électronique dans des cas où il rendrait certainement des services. Nous verrons par exemple dans le cas du fluorure de lithium que l'on n'a pas encore pu recouper avec le microscope électronique les résultats obtenus avec les rayons X, à cause probablement de la difficulté de la préparation des échantillons convenables.

II. — **Etude de la structure du fluorure de lithium irradié aux neutrons.**

Nous allons examiner en détail les méthodes d'étude aux rayons X qui on été employées avec le fluorure de lithium irradié, parce que c'est un exemple où les rayons X ont pu apporter des renseignements que les autres méthodes n'avaient pas donnés. Nous donnerons des indications rapides sur les méthodes expérimentales et nous insisterons surtout sur le principe des interprétations, qui peut être étendu à d'autre cas.

Indiquons d'abord comment se présentait le problème quand nous avons abordé son étude. Les défauts produits dans le fluorure de lithium avaient déjà été souvent étudiés car c'est un exemple particulièrement avantageux. En effet, le lithium naturel comprend une proportion notable de ^{6}Li (7 %) qui donne une réaction de désintégration avec les neutrons thermiques, libérant une particule α, d'énergie 2.1 MeV, et un noyau de tritium, d'énergie 2.7 MeV. Les défauts sont créés dans le réseau par la particule α et le noyau de tritium, qui perdent leur énergie en provoquant l'ionisation puis le déplacement des atomes qu'ils rencontrent avec un libre parcours moyen de quelques centièmes de mm.

Par contre, le libre parcours moyen des neutrons thermiques est environ 2.5 mm, si bien que, dans les échantillons que nous utilisons, d'épaisseur voisine de 0.5 mm, l'irradiation était homogène. Le nombre d'atomes déplacés pouvait être assez considérable pour des temps d'exposition en piles qui ne sont pas prohibitifs. D'après les prévisions théoriques de Seitz [15], chaque fission de lithium correspondrait à un nombre d'atomes déplacés, de l'ordre de 1 900, et, d'après la section efficace du lithium, on trouve que, pour un flux intégré de $1.5 \cdot 10^{19}$ neutrons/cm^2, tous les atomes du cristal peuvent être déplacés une fois. Un autre avantage du fluorure de lithium, c'est que les dommages subis par le cristal sont stables à la température ordinaire, ce qui évite les complications des expériences qui doivent obligatoirement se faire à basse température.

L'irradiation colore le cristal LiF et le rend complètement noir pour des doses de l'ordre de 10^{16} neutrons/cm^2. Un des sujets d'étude a donc été l'étude des centres *F*. D'autre part, on a suivi la dilatation du cristal sous l'influence du rayonnement. Les rayons X avaient été utilisés avec quelques méthodes classiques [16-18]. D'abord, on avait mesuré le changement de paramètre en relation avec la densité et on avait mis en évidence que pour les faibles doses (jusqu'à 10^{17} n/cm^2) il y avait augmentation du paramètre, qui correspondait d'ailleurs à la diminution de la densité; les raies de diffraction restent fines, c'est-à-dire que le réseau ne semble pas perturbé. Pour les doses très fortes au contraire ($> 10^{18}$ n/cm²), le paramètre retrouve sa valeur normale, mais les mesures précises sont difficiles parce que les raies deviennent très larges. Il y a donc perturbation notable du réseau sans changement appréciable de la valeur moyenne du paramètre.

De ces deux résultats, on avait conclu qu'au début de l'irradiation, il se produit des défauts ponctuels qui restent répartis dans le réseau. C'est analogue à l'introduction d'un atome étranger dans un métal pur. Tant qu'il y a solution solide, les raies de diffraction restent fines et le paramètre du cristal varie proportionnellement à la concentration des additions. Au contraire, quand les défauts deviennent trop nombreux, ils sont expulsés du réseau probablement en formant des gros défauts qui produisent des distortions locales. Les raies sont élargies à cause des tensions internes ainsi introduites, mais le réseau étant à peu près débarassé des éléments introduits, le paramètre revient à sa valeur initiale. C'etait l'hypothèse des rassemblements des interstitiels qui avait été émise par KEATING [17].

Mais il restait beaucoup à faire pour préciser la structure des imperfections dans le fluorure de lithium irradié et c'est ce que, dans notre laboratoire, M. LAMBERT [9] a cherché à faire en employant differentes techniques des rayons X non encore appliquées à ce problème et dont nous avons donné le principe dans la première partie de cet exposé. Il s'agit d'étudier systématiquement les diffusions observées en dehors des directions de réflexions sélectives de façon à trouver comment sont répartis les atomes dans les régions perturbées. Deux méthodes ont été employées avec succès et ont donné deux séries de résultats complémentaires. C'est l'étude de la *diffusion aux petits angles* en particulier et l'étude de la *diffusion en général.* Nous suivrons en détail, dans ce qui va suivre, le processus des expériences et de leur interprétation. Tous les résultats utilisés ici sont tirés de la thèse de M. LAMBERT [9]. En ce qui concerne la diffusion aux petits angles, SMALLMAN et WILLIS [27] ont obtenu des résultats en bon accord avec les nôtres.

1. – La diffusion aux très petits angles des cristaux de fluorure de lithium irradiés.

Soit un faisceau de rayons monochromatiques traversant un échantillon. On dit qu'il y a diffusion aux petits angles, quand on observe autour du rayon transmis des rayons diffusés d'intensité en général décroissant avec l'angle et s'annulant à 1° ou 2° de la direction des rayons incidents. Cette diffusion est *caractéristique d'une hétérogénéité de densité électronique dans l'échantillon* [19]. Ainsi, un échantillon composé de particules bien distinctes, comme des micelles colloïdales dans un liquide ou bien encore un échantillon homogène dans lequel sont incluses de nombreuses petites cavités produit ce phénomène de diffusion centrale.

Pour observer le phénomène, la condition est de prendre toutes précautions pour que, en l'absence d'échantillon, il n'y ait pas de diffusion parasite. Ceci nécessite des systèmes d'écrans et il est très recommandé de monochromatiser les rayons primaires par réflexion sur un cristal. La diffusion peut être enregistrée, ou bien sur un film photographique, ou bien avec un compteur G.M. On trouvera dans une monographie [19] la description des dispositifs expérimentaux.

Avec le fluorure de lithium irradié, l'expérience a été faite d'abord par méthode photographique et il est apparu que le fluorure irradié produisait une très forte tache de diffusion autour du centre. Les premiers essais aussi ont montré que cette tache ne variait pas sensiblement ni de forme ni d'intensité quand on faisait varier l'orientation du cristal échantillon par rapport au faisceau direct.

Une fois le phénomène mis en évidence par photographie, on en a fait l'étude quantitative avec le compteur. Notons que c'est la méthode qui doit être employée en général. En effet, la photographie est nécessaire pour explorer le phénomène dont, *à priori*, on ne connaît rien. Il aurait pu se faire, par exemple, que les diffusions se présentent sous forme, non pas d'une tache isotrope, mais de traînées dont les directions dépendaient de l'orientation du cristal. Or, si on avait étudié le phénomène dès le début par le compteur, il aurait été très difficile de reconstituer la position de ces traînées dans l'espace par les seules mesures d'intensité.

Dans les cas des cristaux de fluorure de lithium, le premier fait observé est que l'intensité de diffusion ne dépend que de la distance angulaire par rapport au faisceau direct. Autrement dit, dans l'espace réciproque, la répartition de cette intensité diffusée est très sensiblement à symétrie sphérique par rapport à l'origine de cet espace.

Le deuxième résultat des expériences préliminaires est l'ordre de grandeur de l'étendue de cette diffusion. La loi générale est que la diffusion s'étend angulairement d'autant plus que l'hétérogénéité qui lui donne naissance est plus petite. Si la diffusion cesse d'être observable à l'angle ε, les dimensions de l'hétérogénéité sont de l'ordre de λ/ε, la formule ne donnant qu'un simple ordre de grandeur. Or, avec la radiation CuKα ($\lambda = 1.54$ Å), ε est égal pour les cristaux de FLi irradié à 2° à 3°. D'où un diamètre d'hétérogénéités évalué à 30 à 50 Å.

Cet ordre de grandeur est très important parce que c'est de lui dont dépend la visibilité du phénomène. Si les hétérogénéités sont trop petites, la diffusion est très faible et difficile à détecter. Si, au contraire, les hétérogénéités sont de volume considérable, la diffusion est très intense mais tellement près du faisceau direct que l'on ne peut expérimentalement l'en séparer qu'avec de très grandes difficultés et des montages tout à fait spéciaux. Donc le succes de notre expérience vient de ce que le FLi irradié contient des hétérogénéités de l'ordre de grandeur favorable.

En nous bornant encore à une interprétation qualitative, nous pouvons déjà nous demander quelle peut être l'origine de cette diffusion d'après ces premiers résultats. Dans un cristal aussi compact que le fluorure de lithium, ne contenant aucune impureté, il est très difficile d'imaginer des domaines où la densité électronique soit notablement supérieure à la densité normale. On est donc logiquement conduit à l'idée que cette diffusion centrale est due à l'existence de régions moins denses, ou même de cavités. Or, l'on sait que l'un des effets primaires des chocs contre les atomes est de créer les lacunes. On peut donc imaginer que les cavités sont formées par la coalescence des lacunes initialement dispersées.

La théorie des effets de l'irradiation fait beaucoup usage des lacunes isolées mais est fort peu avancée au sujet des groupements de lacunes. Il est donc très intéressant d'avoir des données expérimentales: c'est pourquoi une étude a été faite de façon systématique en fonction du taux d'irradiation et, pour un cristal irradié donné, en fonction du traitement thermique de guérison.

Il nous faut maintenant examiner comment nous allons pouvoir de l'expérience tirer des renseignements quantitatifs sur ces systèmes de cavités. Il existe plusieurs théories qui permettent d'interpréter quantitativement l'intensité diffusée aux petits angles. La plus simple est celle qui s'applique dans le cas de particules identiques ou de tailles très voisines et assez loin les unes des autres pour qu'il n'y ait pas interférence entre les particules. Dans ces conditions, si ϱ est la densité de la particule, ϱ_0 la densité du milieu dans laquelle elle baigne, le pouvoir diffusant (*) s'écrit sous la forme approchée suivante:

$$I(s) = N(\varrho - \varrho_0)^2 V^2 \exp\left[\frac{-4\pi^2 R^2 s^2}{3}\right]. \tag{1}$$

s est égal a ε/λ, ε est l'angle de diffusion, V est le volume de la particule et N le nombre de particules. Le paramètre de longueur, R, est le *rayon de giration* de la particule. L'approximation n'est valable que si l'angle ε n'est pas trop grand. On reconnaît qu'une courbe expérimentale d'intensité peut s'interpréter par cette formule seulement si la croissance de l'intensité pour les ε très petits n'est pas trop grande, puisque $I(s)$ doit tendre paraboliquement, d'après la formule (1), vers un maximum pour $s=0$:

$$I(0) = NV^2(\varrho - \varrho_0)^2 . \tag{2}$$

(*) Le pouvoir diffusant est égal au nombre d'électrons libres et indépendants qui, placés dans les mêmes conditions que l'échantillon, produiraient la même intensité diffusée.

D'autre part, d'après (1), la courbe de coordonnées $\log I$ et ε^2 doit être rectiligne. Or, on constate dans notre problème que les courbes expérimentales ne satisfont pas à cette condition. En effet, la courbe $(\log I, \varepsilon^2)$ a une pente croissante au voisinage de l'origine, mais tout de même la croissance de l'intensité n'est pas tellement grande qu'on ne puisse espérer obtenir la valeur diffusée à l'angle nul par extrapolation. M. Lambert [5] a remarqué qu'on obtient une droite si l'on adopte les coordonnées $(\log I, \varepsilon)$. Ceci peut s'interpréter en admettant que les cavités présentes dans le cristal ne sont pas de taille homogène. Si on suppose qu'elles sont semblables, on peut chercher la répartition des rayons de giration qui explique la fonction intensité diffusée trouvée expérimentalement. Soit $g(R)$ la proportion de particules dont le rayon de giration est compris entre R et $R+\mathrm{d}R$, et supposons toujours qu'il n'y ait absolument aucune interférence entre particules, c'est-à-dire que les intensités diffractées s'ajoutent, on obtiendra la formule:

$$I(s) = (\varrho - \varrho_0)^2 \int_0^\infty \exp\left[-\tfrac{4}{3}\pi^2 R^2 s^2\right] V^2(R)\cdot g(R)\,\mathrm{d}R\,, \tag{3}$$

$V(R)$ est le volume de la particule de rayon de giration R. Puisque nous avons supposé que les particules étaient semblables, le volume $V(R)$ est proportionnel à R^3, soit $V(R) = AR^3$. Donc

$$I(s) = (\varrho - \varrho_0)^2 \int \exp\left[-\tfrac{4}{3}\pi^2 s^2 R^2\right]\cdot(A^2 R^6)\,g(R)\,\mathrm{d}R\,. \tag{4}$$

Faisons le changement de variable

$$\tfrac{4}{3}\pi^2 s^2 = p\,, \qquad R^2 = u\,,$$

la formule (4) est une transformation de Laplace

$$I(p) = \int_0^\infty \exp\left[-pu\right]\varphi(u)\,\mathrm{d}u\,,$$

avec

$$\varphi(u) = \frac{(\varrho - \varrho_0)^2 A^2 g(R) R^5}{2}\,.$$

Pour aller plus loin, il faut maintenant faire une hypothèse sur la forme des particules. Nous savons qu'elles doivent être approximativement équiaxes, sinon il serait très probable que la diffusion centrale n'aurait pas une symétrie sphérique et serait dépendante de l'orientation de l'échantillon. Nous ne commettrons pas d'erreur considérable, en admettant que les cavités sont sphériques, ce qui détermine le rapport entre le volume et le rayon de giration

$$V(R) = AR^3 = \frac{20\pi}{9}\sqrt{\frac{5}{3}}\,R^3\,.$$

Connaissant A, on peut par l'inversion de Laplace trouver la fonction $g(R)$ et le nombre total de particules $N = \int_0^\infty g(R)\,\mathrm{d}R$ à partir de la fonction expérimentale $I(s)$.

Résumons-nous:

1) Les mesures relatives d'intensité permettent, sans hypothèse autre que la similitude des particules, de trouver leur rayon de giration le plus probable et leur fonction de répartition autour de cette valeur: on peut ainsi calculer les diverses moyennes.

2) Si on fait des mesures absolues d'intensité d'une part et si, d'autre part, on fait des hypothèses sur la forme des particules et leur nature, de façon à fixer la valeur du contraste des densités électroniques $(\varrho - \varrho_0)$ (par exemple, on suppose que ce sont des cavités vides et sphériques), on peut déterminer leur nombre total. D'où, par combinaison avec les premiers résultats, le volume total des cavités, leur surface, etc....

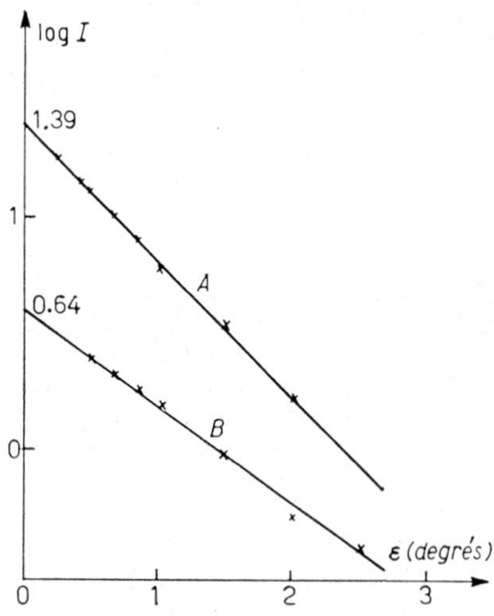

Fig. 1. – Variation de log I en fonction de l'angle ε pour deux échantillons irradiés: A) dose $2 \cdot 10^{18}$ n/cm²; B) dose $5 \cdot 10^{18}$ n/cm².

Pour passer à l'interprétation des résultats expérimentaux, il faut encore transformer un peu les formules que nous avons écrites [19, 9]. En effet, ces formules supposent que le faisceau direct a une section ponctuelle et qu'on fait la mesure de l'intensité également en un point. Ceci n'est pas possible en réalité. Le faisceau direct a une section linéaire en forme d'une droite plus ou moins haute: c'est ce que par exemple donne un monochromateur cristallin; l'on fait la mesure, soit avec le microphotomètre sur un film, soit avec le compteur avec une fente parallèle à la trace du faisceau. On montre que la transformation est assez simple dans les cas où l'intensité varie de façon exponentielle avec l'angle [9].

Les échantillons qui ont été étudiés le

plus en détail sont deux cristaux de fluorure de lithium ayant respectivement les doses de $5 \cdot 10^{18}$ et $2 \cdot 10^{18}$ neutrons par cm^2. Pour les deux échantillons (désignés respectivement par A et B) la courbe de l'intensité mesurée en fonction de l'angle est bien représentée par une droite dans le diagramme ($\log I$, ε) (Fig. 1) et les formules rappelées plus haut, corrigées du fait de la forme du faisceau, conduisent aux deux résultats suivants: dans les deux cas, la répartition des rayons de giration des cavités autour de la valeur la plus probable est donnée par la courbe de la Fig. 2 et la valeur la plus probable de ce rayon est respectivement de 6.7 Å et 8·5 Å pour les échantillons le moins et le plus irradiés. La faible valeur des rayons trouvés montre que l'approximation exponentielle pour l'intensité diffusée était justifiée.

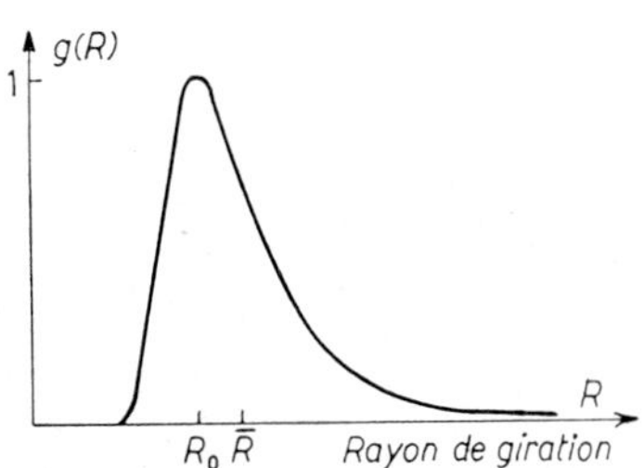

Fig. 2. – Répartition des rayons de giration des cavités dans les cristaux LiF irradiés (échantillons A et B); R_0, valeur la plus probable; $\bar{R}$, valeur moyenne arithmétique.

Mais ceci n'est plus le cas avec un troisième échantillon ayant reçu une dose plus forte de $2 \cdot 10^{19}$ neutrons par cm^2 (échantillon C). Dans ce cas, la diffusion est très intense et, d'autre part, la courbe ($\log I$, ε) n'est plus rectiligne, elle a une pente qui croît à mesure que ε devient plus petit. Ceci prouve qu'il y a de grosses particules en plus des petites particules et la méthode d'interprétation qui a été exposée tombe en défaut. Très grossièrement, on peut dire que le rayon de giration moyen est de l'ordre de 50 Å, mais il y a certainement des particules de rayon bien plus grand que nous ne pouvons atteindre. Ceci est caractéristique de beaucoup d'expériences de diffusion aux petits angles. Les résultats ne sont sûrs que si le diamètre des hétérogénéités recherchées est inférieur à une certaine limite.

Sur les deux premiers échantillons, les mesures absolues ont été faites par M. Lambert et ont abouti aux résultats suivants:

Le nombre totale des cavités trouvées est égal à

$$2.2 \cdot 10^{16} \text{ pour l'échantillon } B$$

et

$$3.3 \cdot 10^{16} \text{ pour l'échantillon } A\,.$$

Les mesures qu'on pourrait faire sur l'échantillon très irradié, C, sont trop incertaines pour qu'elles aient une signification. En plus, M. Lambert a évalué la surface spécifique des cavités; 0.37 m^2/cm^3 pour l'échantillon B, 0.88 m^2/cm^3 pour l'échantillon A; et la concentration en volume des défauts: $1.8 \cdot 10^{-4}$ pour B, $5.2 \cdot 10^{-4}$ pour A.

Une partie intéressante de l'étude a consisté à suivre les variations des différents paramètres mesurés avec le traitement de recuit qui amène la guérison du cristal. On a chauffé le cristal 1 h successivement à 250°; 300°; 350°; 400°; 450°; 500 °C. Le cristal se décolore à partir de 400° et redevient transparent après chauffage à 500°. Le résultat des mesures aux rayons X est que, d'une part, le rayon de giration moyen croît (Fig. 3), d'autre part, le nombre de particules passe par un maximum après un recuit à 300° et décroît ensuite (Fig. 4). Une variation analogue avec passage par un maximum pour la même température se retrouve pour la concentration totale des défauts (Fig. 5). Il est essentiel de signaler que cette décroissance du nombre de cavités ou de la concentration totale des défauts est due en grande partie à notre méthode expérimentale. En effet, la conséquence du recuit est la disparition de petites particules et l'apparition de cavités plus grandes. Or, *ces cavités plus grandes échappent complètement à notre méthode d'analyse*, puisqu'elles produiraient une diffusion centrale qu'on ne peut atteindre expérimentalement parce que trop près du faisceau direct. Aussi il ne faut pas conclure que le recuit fait disparaître toutes les cavités, mais simplement que celles qui subsistent sont trop grandes pour être détectées par la diffusion aux petits angles. Des expériences faites sur des échantillons très irradiés et recuits à de hautes températures montrent qu'il existe des cavités qui sont devenues de taille microscopique (voir plus loin).

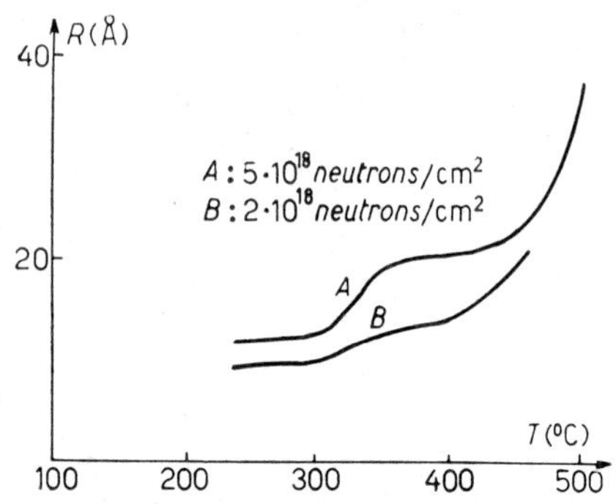

Fig. 3. – Variation du rayon de giration en fonction de la température de recuit (durée du traitement à chaque température: 1 h).

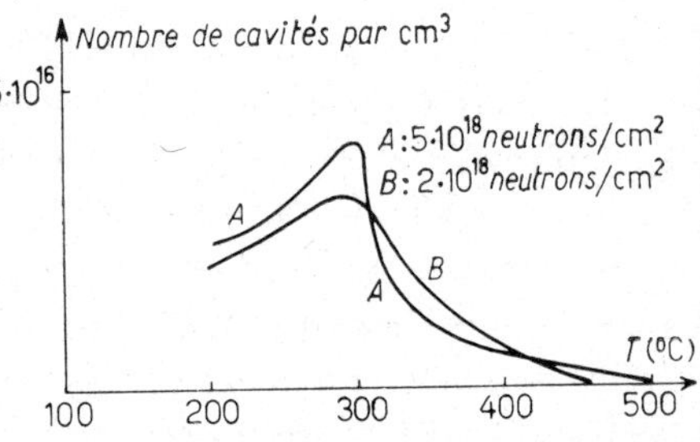

Fig. 4. – Nombre de cavités par cm³ en fonction de la température de recuit.

Pour l'échantillon C ayant reçu une dose supérieure, de 10^{19} neutrons/cm², il a été essayé une autre methode d'interprétation, puisque la première est impraticable. C'est celle qui est basée sur la loi de Porod [19] qui définit la décroissance de l'intensité diffusée quand l'angle augmente (c'est-à-dire les ailes de la courbe de diffusion aux petits angles) en fonction de la surface totale des particules diffusantes, ici des cavités. Le calcul n'exige pas, comme les calculs reposant sur les rayons de giration, que les cavités soient de tailles homogènes et elles peuvent être proches les unes des autres.

La relation de Porod est

$$I(s) = \frac{(\varrho - \varrho_0)^2}{8\pi^3} \cdot \frac{S}{s^4}, \tag{5}$$

S étant la surface totale des particules, et $s = \varepsilon/\lambda$.

Cette relation est valable à la condition qu'aucune des dimensions des particules ne soit trop faible vis-à-vis des autres (la particule ne doit pas être un disque ou une aiguille).

Dans ce cas encore la substitution d'un faisceau à section linéaire au faisceau à section ponctuelle change la forme de la loi (5). $I(s)$ est alors proportionnel à s^{-3} [19].

M. Lambert a essayé d'utiliser la loi de Porod avec l'échantillon C, le plus irradié. Cette loi n'est pas très bien vérifiée. On évalue S à 40 m²/cm³, résultat très supérieur à la surface déterminée par la première méthode sur les échantillons moins irradiés, ce qui est vraisemblable; mais il est difficile de juger de la valeur du résultat obtenu.

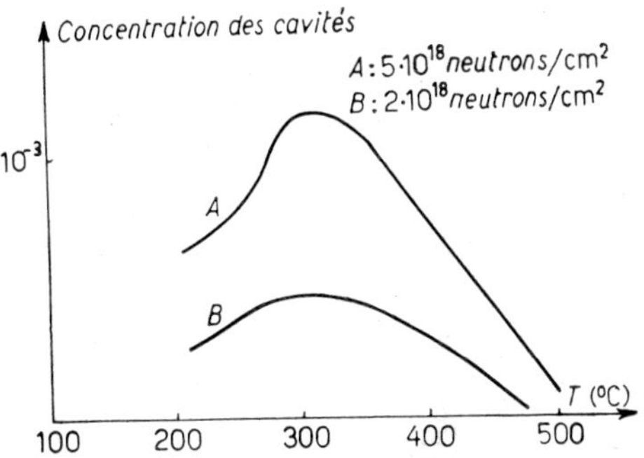

Fig. 5. – Concentration de cavités en fonction de la température de recuit.

Pour tirer parti des résultats de cette étude spéciale aux rayons X, il faut faire appel aux données que nous fournissent d'autres méthodes et qui soient susceptibles d'étayer nos hypothèses. Le premier fait, c'est que, comme nous l'avons signalé, l'existence de cavités formées par la coalescence des lacunes, produites par l'irradiation, a été mise en évidence par Gilman [20] par observation au microscope après un recuit à très haute température (700 °C). En effet, les résultats des rayons X laissent entrevoir que les cavités les plus grosses peuvent se développer aux dépens des cavités de faible taille au cours des recuits après irradiation. Quand la température de recuit est suffisante, il est compréhensible qu'il puisse se créer des cavités de l'ordre de plusieurs µm. Ces cavités ont des formes parallépipédiques en relation évidemment avec la structure du cristal de fluorure de lithium. Ceci ne contredit pas nos hypothèses sur la forme sphérique qui, en réalité, n'ont été faites que pour exprimer le fait que la cavité était à peu près équiaxe. Ainsi les rayons X ont mis en évidence le commencement de la formation de ces cavités que le microscope ne pouvait voir à cause de son pouvoir de résolution et que le microscope électronique n'a pas encore mis en évidence à cause de la difficulté de préparation des échantillons convenables.

Une autre observation très importante est que, par irradiation, le fluorure de lithium laisse échapper du gaz fluor. Ceci est mis en évidence par l'expérience suivante: on enferme, dans un tube de quartz scellé et vidé, des fragments de cristaux de fluorure de lithium et on les soumet à une longue irradiation. Après irradiation, on trouve que l'ampoule est remplie de fluor à une pression supérieure à la pression atmosphérique. D'autre part, il y a du fluor qui reste dans le cristal: ainsi quand on dissout le fluorure de lithium irradié dans l'eau on obtient une solution qui a un fort pouvoir oxydant [18].

On peut donc imaginer que ce sont les vides laissés par le départ des atomes de fluor qui provoquent les cavités. Ces cavités pouvant garder quelques atomes de fluor à l'état gazeux en même temps que les produits de fission, tritium ou hélium.

Pourquoi le fluor peut-il s'échapper? C'est parce que l'atome neutre du fluor a un diamètre notablement inférieur à celui de l'ion négatif fluor: puisque $R_F = 0.7$ Å et $R_{F^-} = 1.40$ Å. Il n'est donc pas difficile pour les atomes neutres de se déplacer par insertion dans le réseau et, sous l'influence de la pression croissante, certains sont chassés à l'extérieur. Mais s'il est vrai que le fluorure de lithium laisse échapper du fluor à l'état neutre, cela veut dire qu'il reste du lithium en excès, à l'état neutre aussi, pour que l'équilibre électrique soit conservé. Or il est facile de comprendre que les atomes de lithium ne peuvent pas s'échapper. En effet, contrairement à ce qui se passe dans le fluor, l'atome neutre de lithium a un diamètre bien plus considérable ($R_{Li} = 1.60$ Å) que l'ion positif ($R_{Li^+} = 0.60$ Å). Par conséquent, l'atome neutre restera dans le cristal irradié. Que deviendra-t-il? C'est ce que nous montrera la seconde série d'expériences, qui sera décrite dans la section suivant.

L'expérience montrant l'influence considérable de la température de recuit sur la formation et le développement de ces cavités, il est certain que ce que nous avons observé résulte en partie du fait que l'irradiation a été faite dans le réacteur sans que la température soit contrôlée. Il y a par conséquent, pendant l'irradiation même, un phénomène de revenu non contrôlé. Il sera donc très intéressant de reprendre cette étude avec des échantillons irradiés à basse température. On pourra alors déceler si les cavités se forment immédiatement par irradiation à très basse température ou bien si elles se forment seulement au-dessus d'une certaine température: dans les conditions où nous avons fait l'irradiation, la température pouvait être de l'ordre de 100 °C. D'autre part, des revenus à des températures étagées pourront permettre de déterminer la chaleur d'activation du processus de coalescence des lacunes.

2. – Rassemblement des atomes interstitiels de lithium dans le fluorure de lithium irradié.

C'est l'étude de la répartition des diffusions des rayons X dans l'ensemble de l'espace réciproque qui a permis de découvrir le processus de rassemblement des atomes interstitiels de lithium restant en excès par suite du départ des atomes de fluor.

Décrivons brièvement le dispositif expérimental: le cristal de fluorure de lithium irradié est placé sur un faisceau de rayons X (CuKα) monochromatisé. L'épaisseur du cristal est de l'ordre de $\frac{1}{2}$ mm, de façon que l'absorption des rayons ne soit pas trop grande. On commence, comme dans le cas de l'étude de la diffusion centrale, par une étude photographique: le cristal est placé au centre d'une chambre cylindrique sur laquelle on reçoit les rayons diffusés par l'échantillon.

Il est essentiel que le faisceau primaire soit strictement monochromatique, sinon la partie la plus intense du diagramme observée serait le diagramme de Laue qui pourrait masquer certaines des diffusions anormales que l'on cherche. Pour que l'expérience soit pratique, il est indispensable de disposer d'un faisceau de grande intensité, sinon non seulement les temps de pose nécessaires seraient très longs, mais surtout dans l'exploration d'un phénomène il se pourrait que l'on n'ait pas la patience de faire des poses suffisantes pour découvrir les très faibles diffusions intéressantes. Quand le cristal est immobile, une exposition donne sur le film la section de l'espace réciproque par la sphère d'Ewald. Souvent il est plus avantageux de faire osciller le cristal autour d'un axe simple, de façon à enregistrer la superposition d'une série de coupes de l'espace réciproque: on ne peut le faire que si les diffusions sont réparties de façon simple, car évidemment les figures obtenues ne pourraient pas être interprétées si les diffusions étaient répandues dans de larges portions de l'espace réciproque.

Dans le cas du fluorure de lithium, en faisant des diagrammes où le cristal oscillait autour de l'axe [100], il est apparu dès les premiers essais que les cristaux irradiés, quand la dose dépassait $5 \cdot 10^{17}$ neutrons/cm^2, présentaient des « trainées » de diffusion. Ces trainées de diffusion sont dirigées suivant les axes $\langle 100 \rangle$ du réseau réciproque. On connaît d'autres exemples de figures de diffusion analogue. Notamment, on en rencontre dans l'étude des structures caractérisant le durcissement des alliages légers. Dans un alliage aluminium-cuivre, ce durcissement est dû à l'apparition de ce qu'on appelle les zones Guinier-Preston [21], ou amas d'atomes de cuivre qui se rassemblent sur des plans (100) du cristal de solution solide.

D'une façon générale, quand les diffusions sont concentrées suivant les axes $\langle 100 \rangle$ du réseau réciproque, cela signifie que dans le cristal il y a un désordre dit *planaire*: les plans (100) gardent leur structure périodique intacte, mais sont désordonnés les uns par rapport aux autres, soit que certains d'entre eux soient occupés par des atomes de pouvoir de diffusion différent, soit que l'écartement entre ces plans, qui restent parallèles, ne soit pas égal à la distance interréticulaire normale du cristal.

Les diffusions observées dans le fluorure de lithium laissent donc penser qu'il doit y avoir des rassemblements d'atomes suivant les plans (100) provoquant éventuellement des distorsions locales.

Le simple aspect des diffusions donne déjà des renseignements sur ces zones distordues. Nous avons déjà indiqué que ces zones doivent être en forme de plaquettes parallèles à {100}. On peut déduire leurs diamètres approximatifs de la netteté des trainées le long des axes ⟨100⟩. En effet, s'il s'agit de très petites zones, la diffusion n'est pas exactement concentrée sur les axes, mais il y a un certain flou autour de ces axes; d'une façon plus précise, on peut dire que l'ordre de grandeur de la largeur de la traînée dans l'espace réciproque est $1/L$, si la zone a un diamètre de longueur L. Sur les cristaux juste après irradiation, la largeur déterminée à l'aide de cette formule donne une valeur de l'ordre de 100 Å pour le diamètre de la zone. Quand les cristaux ont été recuits après un chauffage vers 400°, on atteint des dimensions supérieurs à 300 Å.

La perturbation dans la zone qui cause des diffusions anormales peut être due, soit à un déplacement des atomes hors de leurs positions normales, soit à la substitution aux atomes du cristal régulier d'atomes de pouvoir de diffusion différent. L'examen qualitatif des photographies permet déjà d'éliminer l'hypothèse du simple déplacement. En effet, la théorie générale montre que, dans ce cas, il ne peut pas y avoir de diffusion intense au voisinage du centre du réseau réciproque, mais que les diffusions deviennent de plus en plus marquées à mesure que l'on s'éloigne du centre. Ainsi elles peuvent exister autour des nœuds du réseau réciproque, sauf autour du nœud central (d'indices 000). Or, l'observation montre que les traînées sont visibles le long des axes ⟨100⟩ *à partir du centre*, ainsi qu'au voisinage des nœuds, comme par exemple 200 etc. Par conséquent, on peut éliminer une hypothèse qui pourrait être suggérée par des résultats du microscope électronique sur les métaux irradiés. On a observé en effet des anneaux de dislocation [22] qui seraient formés par le rassemblement de lacunes en disque sur un plan réticulaire suivi d'un effondrement de plans voisins. Une telle irrégularité, si le plan de lacunes était (100), donnerait des diffusions du type planaire suivant les axes ⟨100⟩ mais on ne pourrait pas rendre compte d'une diffusion autour du centre aussi intense que celle qui est observée.

Par conséquent, on doit admettre qu'il y a des couches d'atomes différents de ceux du cristal. D'autre part si ces plans de pouvoir diffusant anormal étaient intercalés dans le cristal sans que la position des plans soit perturbée, on ne pourrait pas expliquer les variations de l'intensité diffusée observées le long de l'axe [100]. Donc nous devons conclure que les zones responsables des diffusions comprennent des atomes différents de ceux du cristal, soit F+Li, et que la présence de ces atomes anormaux provoque des distortions du réseau. Or, nous savons que le fluorure de lithium irradié contient en excès des atomes de lithium. Par conséquent, on peut imaginer que les plaquettes provoquant ces diffusions planaires sont dues à des *rassemblements sur les plans* (100) *d'atomes de lithium.*

Pour pousser plus loin l'interprétation, on doit disposer de mesures de l'intensité diffusée. A cet effet, il faut employer le compteur G.M. et explorer l'axe [100] dans l'espace réciproque: cela revient expérimentalement à placer sur le porte-échantillon d'un goniomètre le fluorure de lithium en position de réflexion et à faire varier l'angle d'incidence de façon continue. Le résultat est donné par la Fig. 6 pour différentes doses d'irradiation. On voit que la caractéristique est qu'il y a un maximum de diffusion avant la tache de diffraction 200 aux environs des $\frac{3}{4}$ de la distance. Puis après cette tache, la diffusion tombe à peu près à zéro et reste nulle quand on s'éloigne vers la tache 400, etc.

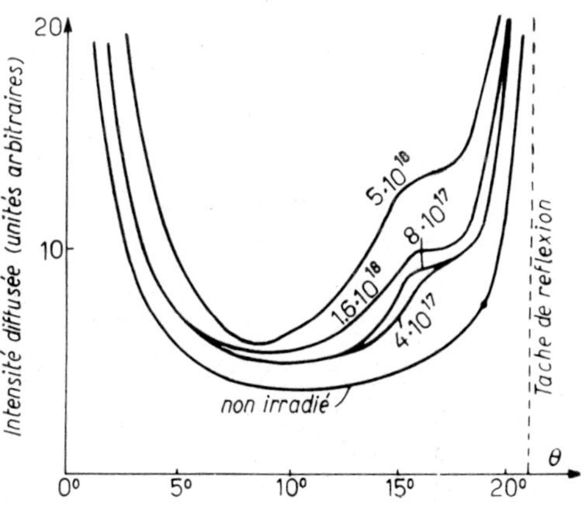

Fig. 6. – Variation de l'intensité diffusée le long de l'axe pour différentes doses d'irradiation.

De même que pour la diffusion aux petits angles, on a comparé au cristal après irradiation le cristal ayant subi des traitements thermiques de guérison.

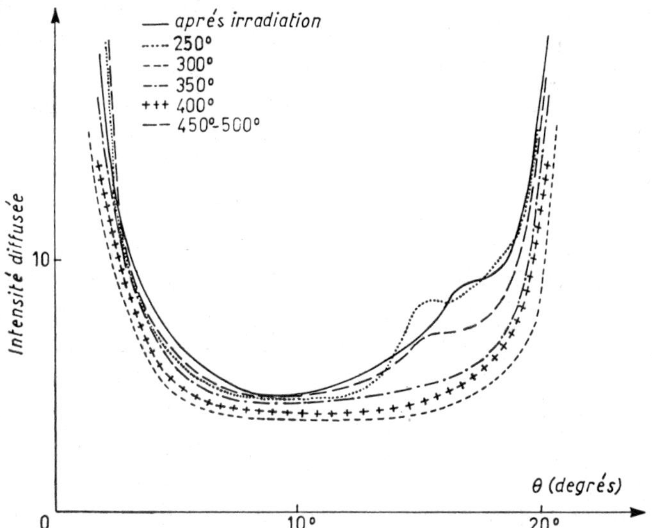

Fig. 7. – Courbes d'intensité diffusée le long de l'axe [100] pour le même échantillon (dose $2 \cdot 10^{18}$ n/cm²) après différents recuits de guérison.

Le résultat est le suivant (Fig. 7): le maximum de la traînée se précise jusqu'à des températures de recuit de l'ordre de 300°. Mais quand le recuit est poussé à une température telle que le cristal est guéri, c'est-à-dire qu'il se décolore, et, à condition que l'irradiation primitive n'ait pas été trop forte (de l'ordre de 10^{18} neutrons/cm^2), les diffusion disparaissent complètement.

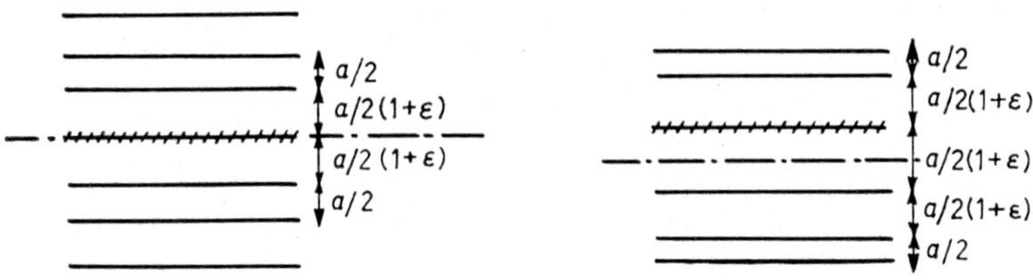

Fig. 8. – Modèles de zones de rassemblement d'atomes de lithium à 1 et à 2 plans de lithium.

Il est difficile de déduire de la courbe expérimentale la répartition des plans réticulaires dans la zone perturbée. En effet, il y a deux paramètres dont les influences se mélangent: la valeur du facteur de diffusion du plan, c'est-à-dire la nature des atomes qui l'occupent, et le déplacement du plan par rapport à sa position normale dans le réseau. Il est plus simple de chercher des modèles dont on calcule la diffusion et qui rendent compte aussi approximativement que possible de l'observation. Ce modèle peut être fondé sur l'observation qu'il y a un maximum pour une distance inférieure à la distance de la tache 200 dans l'espace réciproque. Cela veut dire qu'il y a des plans dans la zone perturbée qui doivent se trouver à une distance plus grande que l'intervalle normal. Le modèle qu'a essayé M. Lambert est formé d'une ou deux couches d'atomes de lithium insérées dans le fluorure de lithium, de façon que la distance entre les plans anormaux soit plus grande que la normale, puisque les atomes de lithium ont un diamètre supérieur à la moyenne des ions F^- et Li^+. On peut prendre un plan unique d'atomes de lithium entouré de plans de LiF, ou une suite de 2 plans de lithium écartés de 3 Å insérés dans le fluorure de lithium (Fig. 8). Si on mélange les 2 types de zones dans la proportion de 80 % et 20 %, on arrive à une courbe théorique (Fig. 9) qui reproduit assez fidèlement les trois faits fondamentaux des courbes expérimentales: il y a diffusion aux petits angles, il y a un maximum à la place observée et la diffusion après la tache 200 devient d'intensité très faible. Si après le chauffage

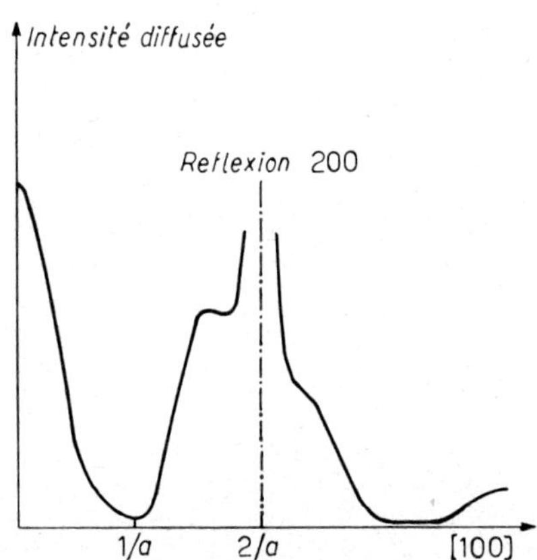

Fig. 9. – Intensité diffusée calculée pour un mélange de 80 % de modèles à 1 plan et 20 % à 2 plans.

le maximum de diffusion devient plus net, cela signifie probablement que les couples de plan de Li deviennent plus nombreux, alors qu'au début les plans isolés sont plus fréquents. Ensuite, ces zones distordues doivent disparaître quand le cristal est chauffé à une température plus élevée, ce qui est naturel car de telles formations incluses dans un réseau sont dans un état assez peu stable.

Le problème qui se pose ensuite est de savoir ce qu'il advient quand les atomes de lithium sont plus nombreux par suite d'une irradiation plus intense ou bien que les chauffages prolongés à une température assez élevée font tendre le cristal vers un état d'équilibre.

3. – Formation de lithium métallique par irradiation.

Si le cristal subit une dose d'irradiation supérieure à $5 \cdot 10^{18}$ neutrons/cm^2, on observe qu'en plus des diffusions précédentes apparaissent sur le diagramme de nouvelles taches de diffraction cristalline. Ces taches sont situées à proximité des taches de réflexion 200 et 111 du fluorure de lithium. On observe accessoirement un autre système de traînées de diffusion qui sont dirigées suivant les axes $\langle 111 \rangle$ du réseau réciproque, elles sont d'intensité plus faible que celles des axes $\langle 100 \rangle$ et leur intensité est assez uniforme depuis le centre jusqu'à la tache 111 où elles s'arrêtent. Les taches de diffraction révèlent la présence d'une *nouvelle phase cristalline* dont les grains doivent être de dimensions assez grandes, au moins plusieurs centaines d'angström d'épaisseur, sinon l'effet de taille élargirait les taches de diffraction. Etant donné que ces taches sont voisines de celles du fluorure de lithium, on peut les interpréter comme venant d'une phase cubique à faces centrées dont les axes seraient parallèles à ceux du fluorure de lithium. On peut aisément calculer le paramètre de la maille et l'on trouve 4.30 Å.

Nous avons interprété cette phase comme étant formée de *lithium métallique* cristallisant sous une forme anormale, *cubique à faces centrées.* On sait en effet que le lithium cristallise sous forme cubique centrée, mais il existe une autre forme, cubique à faces centrées, qui normalement n'est stable qu'à très basse température, la transformation se faisant sous l'influence d'une action mécanique (BARRETT [23]). Le paramètre qui avait été trouvé est 4.40 Å, donc très voisin de celui que nous avons mesuré.

Dans ce cas, on peut se représenter la formation de ce lithium de la façon suivante; les petites plaquettes dans lesquelles se rassemblent les atomes de lithium, telles que nous les avons décrites, ne peuvent croître sans prendre une structure plus stable. Ce sera celle de lithium métallique, mais l'influence du réseau LiF dans lequel les particules sont insérées est si forte que la structure de moindre énergie est la structure ordinairement instable, cubique à faces centrées, en épitaxie avec le réseau de LiF.

C'est là une interprétation qu'il est nécessaire de justifier et c'est ce que nous avons fait de différentes façons. S'il est vrai que nous sommes en présence de lithium métallique à température ordinaire et si nous chauffons le cristal à une température supérieure à 200 °C, et que nous prenons le diagramme de diffraction à cette température, on ne devra plus voir les taches de diffraction attribuées au lithium, puisque le métal doit être fondu. L'expérience a pleinement vérifié ce point: *au-dessus de* 200°, *les taches de* Li *disparaissent des diagrammes.* Si ensuite on fait refroidir le cristal et qu'on prend un nouveau diagramme de diffraction, on voit apparaître de nouvelles taches mais *celles-ci ne sont pas identiques aux taches visibles avant chauffage.*

L'analyse de la position de ces nouvelles taches a été faite par M. Lambert qui a reconnu qu'elles peuvent être identifiées avec des taches de diffraction de la *forme normale du lithium, cubique centrée.* Les taches les plus visibles sont les taches correspondant à la distance 2.48 Å, c'est-à-dire les taches d'indices (110) du lithium normal. Ces nouveaux cristaux sont aussi orientés par rapport au cristal de fluorure de lithium, c'est-à-dire aussi par rapport au cristal de lithium cubique à faces centrés initial. M. Lambert a vérifié les relations d'orientation qui correspondent à la transformation martensitique du fer γ en fer α (relation de Nishiyama)

(110) Li parallèle à (111) LiF ,

[110] Li parallèle à [211] LiF .

Barrett [23] avait trouvé des relations d'orientation entre les deux phases cubiques centrés et cubiques faces centrées un peu différentes

(110) Li c.c. parallèle à (111) Li c.f.c. ,

[110] Li c.c. formant un angle de 3° avec [111] Li c.f.c.

A température de 200°, les traînées de diffusion suivant [111] disparaissent immédiatement alors que celles suivant [100] subissent l'évolution lente que nous avons décrite dans le paragraphe précédent. Cela laisse penser que ces traînées sont relatives aux cristaux de lithium puisqu'elles disparaissent avec ceux-ci. On peut imaginer que ces diffusions sont dues à des défauts d'empilement des plans (111) qui doivent exister dans ces cristaux à cause des fortes interactions entre eux et la matrice du fluorure de lithium qui les entoure.

Si après refroidissement, on réchauffe de nouveau le fluorure de lithium au-dessus de 200 °C, on constate que les nouvelles taches de diffraction disparaissent comme les anciennes. Il y a donc encore fusion du lithium, mais quand on laisse maintenant refroidir le cristal, *les taches réapparaissent à la même place.* Nous sommes donc en présence d'un état stable qui passe de façon reversible de l'état solide à l'état liquide. Ainsi, après la première fusion, il y a recristallisation du lithium. Cette recristallisation se fait de façon à faire apparaitre la forme stable du lithium, le cristal de Li étant maintenant incohérent vis à vis de la matrice.

On retrouve ainsi dans cette évolution les stades que l'on trouve dans l'évolution d'une solution solide sursaturée. Au début du revenu, il y a une formation des « zones » puis un précipité métastable cohérent avec la matrice et enfin un précipité stable plus ou moins incohérent avec la matrice, mais souvent avec des relations d'épitaxie. Le processus de la formation du lithium dans les cristaux irradiés suit donc des lois qui semblent générales dans les réactions à l'état solide.

4. – Analyse thermique différentielle du fluorure irradié.

Si le fluorure irradié après une dose suffisante d'irradiation contient du lithium, les transformations du lithium et la fusion du lithium doivent pouvoir être mises en évidence par l'analyse thermique différentielle (A.T.D.). Certes, la proportion de lithium est assez faible mais un appareil construit par Ch. Mazières [24] pour l'étude de microéchantillons est d'une sensibilité suffisante. Nous donnerons ici les résultats de l'étude de Ch. Mazières [25].

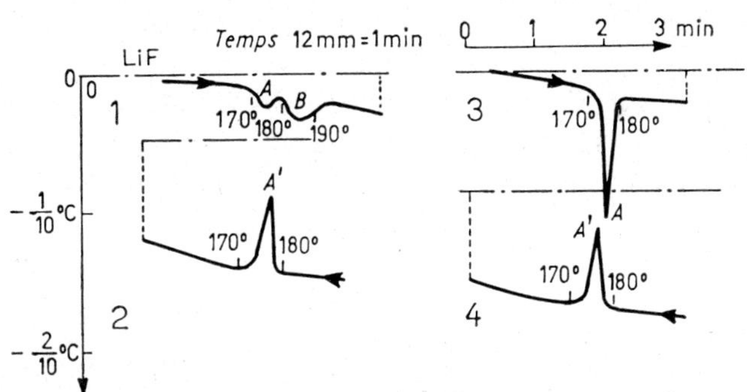

Fig. 10. – Courbes d'analyse thermique différentielle pour un échantillon de LiF irradié (dose $6 \cdot 10^{18}$ n/cm²); 1-2: 1er chauffage et refroidissement; 3-4: 2ème chauffage et refroidissement.

Quand un échantillon de fluorure de lithium irradié est soumis à un premier chauffage, la courbe de l'A.T.D. présente deux pics successifs correspondant à une absorption de chaleur aux températures de 179° et 186° (Fig. 10). Au refroidissement, on n'observe plus qu'un seul pic à la température de 179°. Si maintenant on soumet le même échantillon à un nouveau chauffage il n'y a plus qu'un pic à 179 °C, tant à la montée qu'à la descente. Or, cette température de 179° est la température de fusion du lithium métallique normal. Ces résultats confirment donc bien les conclusions que nous avions déduites des expériences de diffraction de rayons X. Au début, après irradiation, il y a du lithium sous forme anormale, puisqu'il y a un double pic, et, après le premier chauffage, il reste le lithium sous forme normale. On peut d'ailleurs, de façon plus précise, grâce à la hauteur du pic, évaluer la proportion de lithium métallique. On trouve ainsi, pour un échantillon donné, une proportion de l'ordre de 5 % qui est tout à fait comparable à ce qu'on peut déduire de l'intensité relative des taches de diffraction du fluorure de lithium et de celles du lithium métallique. L'apparition des deux pics dans le prenier chauffage doit s'expliquer par la présence des deux formes du lithium. Or le pic qui se maintient dans les fusions ultérieures est celui qui correspond à la plus basse température, il n'y a pas de doute qu'il est dû au lithium normal (c.c.). Donc la forme métastable (c.f.c.) fond à une température supérieure à celle du lithium normal. Ce résultat est peut-être un peu surprenant parce que c'est une forme métastable mais il n'est contredit par aucune considération thermodynamique.

La présence du premier pic correspondant au lithium cubique centré, concurremment à celui du lithium cubique faces centrées, montre que, au cours du chauffage, il y a transformation partielle à l'état solide de la forme métastable vers la forme stable, mais la transformation n'est pas complète. D'ailleurs, on constate que si le cristal est maintenu un long temps à une température voisine de 160 °C, le premier pic est bien plus important que le second. Au contraire, quand le chauffage est rapide, la transformation n'est que très partielle et le premier pic est plus faible.

Outre cette preuve directe de l'existence du lithium métallique, la méthode A.T.D. donne quelques autres renseignements intéressants. D'abord, les échantillons moins irradiés, ne comportant que des zones perturbées correspondant aux traînées diffuses sur les diagrammes de diffraction, ne donnent aucun signal perceptible dans la courbe A.T.D. Ceci signifie que les plaquettes d'atomes de lithium ne constituent pas une véritable phase solide distincte du réseau dans lequel elles sont insérées. Ensuite on remarque que les formes des pics correspondant à la fusion du lithium varient suivant le traitement thermique. Il s'affinent et ne deviennent semblables à ce que donne un morceau de lithium pur qu'après un chauffage à température élevée (500 °C). Au début, ils sont plus larges comme si les petites particules de lithium avaient des points de fusion moins bien définis à cause des distorsions superficielles provoquées par l'interaction du réseau de fluorure de lithium.

5. – Résonance magnétique nucléaire.

Une autre expérience a donné également confirmation de l'existence de lithium dans les cristaux irradiés, c'est la résonance magnétique nucléaire [26]. On sait qu'il est nécessaire pour pouvoir observer le signal donné par un métal, que ce métal soit en très petits grains, étant donné que les ondes H.F. ne peuvent pénétrer profondément dans un milieu conducteur. Or, il est difficile de donner à un métal alcalin une granulométrie assez fine sans provoquer des oxydations superficielles. C'est pourquoi les signaux de métaux alcalins étaient rarement observés. Or, avec le fluorure de lithium, irradié suffisamment (10^{19} neutrons/cm^2) et recuit à une température assez élevée, on a obtenu des signaux extrêmement nets car le lithium se présente sous forme de grains de taille voulue; il a été observé que la largeur de ces signaux était très faible. On peut donc utiliser la méthode d'irradiation du fluorure de lithium pour produire du lithium métallique sous une forme très convenable pour l'étude de la résonance magnétique et cela permet des expériences qui n'étaient pas possibles dans d'autres conditions.

On n'observe pas de signal dans le stade qui correspond au rassemblement de lithium en plaquettes ayant une épaisseur de quelques plans atomiques au maximum. De même que l'A.T.D., cette expérience nous montre encore qu'on ne peut pas parler à cet état d'une phase métallique séparée du cristal de LiF.

6. - Destruction du crystal.

Quand on produit l'irradiation jusqu'à des doses très élevées (10^{19} neutrons/cm^2) et que l'irradiation se fait dans l'air comme il est usuel, des profondes perturbations apparaissent pour le cristal. D'abord il devient extrêmement fragile et, quand il se casse, il ne se clive plus mais présente une cassure conchoïdale analogue à celle d'un corps vitreux. D'autre part, on voit à l'intérieur de ce cristal des traces d'une poudre blanche. En réalité, les distorsions ont été tellement fortes que le cristal n'a presque plus de cohésion. Les rayons X montrent que de nombreuses nouvelles taches, ou même des raies, de poudre cristalline apparaissent sur les diagrammes. Il y a formation de nouvelles phases et nous en avons identifié certaines. On trouve notamment la phase LiOH et Li_2CO_3. Ce sont les principaux composés d'ailleurs que l'on observe quand on fait le diagramme d'un morceau de lithium qu'on a laissé à l'air libre un certain temps. Cela signifie que le cristal de fluorure de lithium après cette dose d'irradiation est fissuré et que l'air humide et chargé de CO_2 vient attaquer les particules de lithium qui s'oxydent et donnent des carbonates.

Quand on essaye de guérir des cristaux irradiés à ce taux, on constate qu'on n'arrive jamais à revenir au cristal intact primitif. Généralement d'ailleurs le chauffage provoque la rupture du cristal. Il ne blanchit que partiellement, restant grisâtre à cause des produits de décomposition qu'il contient. En somme, à ce stade, on a depassé la dose intéressante puisqu'il y a une véritable destruction du cristal et attaque chimique par le milieu ambiant. L'existence de ces produits d'oxydation et de carbonatation du lithium sont encore une preuve de la formation de lithium métallique par l'action des neutrons. Car évidemment il n'y a pas d'action de l'air sur le fluorure sain.

7. – Conclusion.

Ainsi, l'étude du fluorure de lithium a donné un exemple d'une véritable réaction chimique de décomposition, provoquée par l'irradiation aux neutrons, et nous avons pu suivre le processus de cette réaction, qui se poursuit à l'état solide dans un cristal qui maintient à très peu de choses près sa forme extérieure inchangée malgré les profonds bouleversements de structure interne.

La réaction qui aboutit à la formation de lithium est rendue possible du fait que le fluor s'échappe du cristal à cause, comme nous l'avons dit, de la petite taille de l'atome fluor, ce qui favorise sa diffusion dans le réseau. D'autres sels de lithium d'ailleurs se décomposent de la même manière, c'est le cas de l'hydrure de lithium, duquel l'atome hydrogène peut également s'échapper facilement et il se produit du lithium à peu près dans les mêmes conditions que dans le fluorure [11].

D'autre part, cette étude est un bon exemple de ce que peuvent donner les rayons X pour élucider les structures de cristal imparfait. Là où les rayons X donnent les renseignements les plus précis et les plus importants, c'est dans le cas où il se produit des défauts d'une taille d'un ordre de grandeur compris entre 10 et 100 Å. Ces limites expriment les conditions essentielles: il faut que les défauts ne soient ni trop gros car ils seraient trop rares, ni trop petits parce que l'intensité de diffusion qu'ils provoquent est trop faible.

C'est particulièrement intéressant parce que l'on trouve ainsi, d'une façon plus ou moins précise, la structure de formations qu'il serait extrèmement difficile de prévoir de façon théorique. Tels sont ces défauts « planaires » parallèles à (100) qu'on retrouve à la fois dans les solutions solides en voie d'évolution (zones G.P.), dans les solutions solides qui s'ordonnent de façon partielle (domaine antiphase, cuivre-or) et enfin dans ces cristaux ioniques soumis aux neutrons. Une explication théorique du rôle particulier du plan (100) dans le cristaux cubiques à faces centrées n'a pas encore été donnée.

Par contre, les défauts vraiment ponctuels ou à peu près ponctuels (lacunes, interstitiels isolés) qui font intervenir un très petit nombre d'atomes sont encore difficiles à déceler par les rayons X. Des expériences préliminaires ont montré que dans le fluorure de lithium il y avait un fond continu de diffusion qui pouvait être dû à des lacunes ou interstitiels dispersés, mais ce fond continu de diffusion est d'un ordre de grandeur d'intensité inférieur à celui qui est provoqué par l'agitation thermique ou encore la diffusion Compton qui est absolument inévitable. Une étude précise sera donc difficile.

Quand on tient compte des limitations des possibilités des rayons X, on est à même de bien les utiliser et de découvrir par cette méthode des phénomènes d'imperfections cristallines qui seraient très difficiles de mettre en évidence par d'autres méthodes physiques.

BIBLIOGRAPHIE

[1] P. B. Hirsch: ce volume, p. 39.

[2] A. Guinier: *Suppl. Nuovo Cimento*, **7**, 444 (1957).

[3] A. Guinier: *Théorie et Technique de la Radiocristallographie* (Paris, 1956).

[4] R. W. James: *The Crystalline State*, vol. II (London, 1948); W. H. Zachariasen: *Theory of X-Ray Diffraction by Crystals* (New York, 1945).

[5] C. S. Barrett: *Structure of Metals* (New York, 1952).

[6] J. B. Newkirk: *Journ. Appl. Phys.*, **29**, 995 (1958).

[7] A. R. Lang: *Journ. Appl. Phys.*, **29**, 597 (1958).

[8] P. B. Hirsch: *Journ. Inst. Metals*, **87**, 406 (1959).

[9] M. Lambert: *Etude des imperfections de structure du fluorure de lithium irradié*, Rapport C.E.A. n. 180 (1959), C.E.N. Saclay France.

[10] R. W. Cahn: *Progress in Metal Physics*, vol. II (London, 1950).

[11] A. J. C. Wilson: *Nuovo Cimento*, **1**, 277 (1955).

[12] B. E. Warren et B L. Averbach: *Modern Research Techniques in Physical Metallurgy*, A.S.M. 93 (1953).

[13] D. W. Pashley et A. E. B. Presland: *Journ. Inst. Metals*, **87**, 419 (1959).

[14] R. Castaing: *Rev. Met.*, **52**, 669 (1955); R. B. Nicholson, G. Thomas, J. Nuttings: *Journ. Inst. Metals*, **78**, 929 (1959).

[15] F. Seitz et J. Koehler: *Solid State Physics*, vol. II (New York, 1956).

[16] D. Binder et W. J. Sturm: *Phys. Rev.*, **96**, 1519 (1954).

[17] D. Keating: *Phys. Rev.*, **97**, 832 (1955).

[18] P. Pério, M. Tournarie et M. Gance: *Action des rayonnements de grande énergie sur les solides* (Paris, 1956), p. 116.

[19] A. Guinier et G. Fournet: *X-Ray Small Angle Scattering* (New York, 1954).

[20] J. J. Gilman and W. G. Johnston: *Journ. Appl. Phys.*, **29**, 877 (1958).

[21] A. Guinier: *Solid State Physics*, vol. IX (New York, 1955).

[22] P. B. Hirsch, J. Silco, R. E. Smallman et K. H. Westmacott: *Phil. Mag.* **3**, 897 (1958).

[23] C. S. Barrett: *Phase Transformation in Solids* (New York, 1951), p. 351.

[24] Ch. Mazières: *Compt. Rend. Acad. Sci.*, **248**, 2990 (1959); **249**, 540 (1959).

[25] M. Lambert, Ch. Mazières et A. Guinier: *Journ. Phys. Chem. Solids*, **18**, 129 (1961).

[26] M. Guéron et C. Ryter: *Phys. Rev. Lett.*, **3**, 338 (1959).

[27] R. Smallman et B. Willis: *Phil. Mag.*, **20**, 101 (1957).

Influence of Local Irregularities on Lattice Vibrations.

G. F. NARDELLI

Gruppo per la Fisica dello Stato Solido - CNEN, Ispra

1. – Preliminary remarks.

The dynamics of the atomic nuclei in a perfect crystal can be analysed in terms of lattice waves. This fact follows directly from the translational symmetries of Bravais lattices and from the Born adiabatic theorem.

In fact, the adiabatic theorem gives the proof that, up to the second order of approximation, the total wavefunction of the coupled nuclei-electrons system is of a quasi separable type, in the sense that the nucleus-nucleus interactions take place by means of an effective potential which depends only on the nuclear co-ordinates. If the potential is approximated by its harmonic term, it is well known that the quantum frequencies of the system are equal to the classical characteristic frequencies, so that the small vibrations of the lattice may be studied in the scheme of classical mechanics.

Let $\boldsymbol{u}(\boldsymbol{g}, \boldsymbol{r}; t)$ be the displacement vector of the nucleus at the $\boldsymbol{g}$ position in the lattice cell located at the site $\boldsymbol{r}$ of the Bravais lattice; the general solution of the classical equations of motion may be written as

$$\boldsymbol{u}(\boldsymbol{g}, \boldsymbol{r}; t) = \sum_{s=1}^{3p} \sum_{k} C_{s,k} \boldsymbol{\chi}_{s,k}(\boldsymbol{g}, \boldsymbol{r}) \exp[-i\omega_{s,k} \cdot t] . \tag{1}$$

Both $\boldsymbol{g}$ and $\boldsymbol{r}$ are discrete vectors: $\boldsymbol{g} = \boldsymbol{g}_1, \boldsymbol{g}_2, ..., \boldsymbol{g}_p$, where p is the number of atoms in the unit cell of the Bravais lattice; $\boldsymbol{r} = r^i \boldsymbol{a}_i$, where $\boldsymbol{a}_i$ are the principal translations of the lattice ($i = 1, 2, 3$) and r^i are integer numbers. $\chi^i_{s,k}(\boldsymbol{g}, \boldsymbol{r})$ are the scalar amplitudes of the normal modes of vibration and $\omega_{s,k}$ are their characteristic frequencies ($s = 1, 2, ..., 3p$).

$C_{s,k}$ are arbitrary scalar (*complex*) constants. The equation for the amplitudes of the normal modes is

$$\sum_{i'=1}^{3} \sum_{(\boldsymbol{g}',\boldsymbol{r}')} A_{ii'}(\boldsymbol{g}, \boldsymbol{g}' | \boldsymbol{r} - \boldsymbol{r}') \chi^{i'}(\boldsymbol{g}', \boldsymbol{r}') = m_g \omega^2 \chi^i(\boldsymbol{g}, \boldsymbol{r}) , \tag{2}$$

where $A_{ii'}(\boldsymbol{g}, \boldsymbol{g}' | \boldsymbol{r} - \boldsymbol{r}')$ are the coupling coefficients of the interaction between the nuclei and m_g ($\boldsymbol{g} = \boldsymbol{g}_1, \ldots, \boldsymbol{g}_p$) are the masses of the atoms in the unit cell.

For a perfect crystal subjected to periodic boundary conditions, the translation symmetries of the lattice make it possible to write the solutions of eq. (2) as

(3)
$$\chi_{s,\boldsymbol{k}}(\boldsymbol{g}, \boldsymbol{r}) = \frac{1}{\sqrt{N}} \boldsymbol{v}_{s,\boldsymbol{k}}(\boldsymbol{g}) \exp\left[i\boldsymbol{k} \cdot \boldsymbol{r}\right],$$

where $\boldsymbol{v}_{s,\boldsymbol{k}}(\boldsymbol{g})$ are complex versors, and the significant values of $\boldsymbol{k}$ are confined to the first Brillouin zone.

$1/\sqrt{N}$ is the normalization constant, N being the total number of unit cells in the crystal. The vibrational frequencies are grouped into $3p$ partially overlapping bands (Fig. 1)

$$\omega^2 = \omega_s^2(\boldsymbol{k}) \quad s = 1, 2, \ldots, 3p;$$

three of these begin with $\omega = 0$ at $k = 0$ (the acoustic branch); for the other bands (optical branch) $\omega_{s>3}(0) \neq 0$. Eq. (2) represents a generalized discrete analog of the differential equation for the eigenstates of an electron in the periodic field.

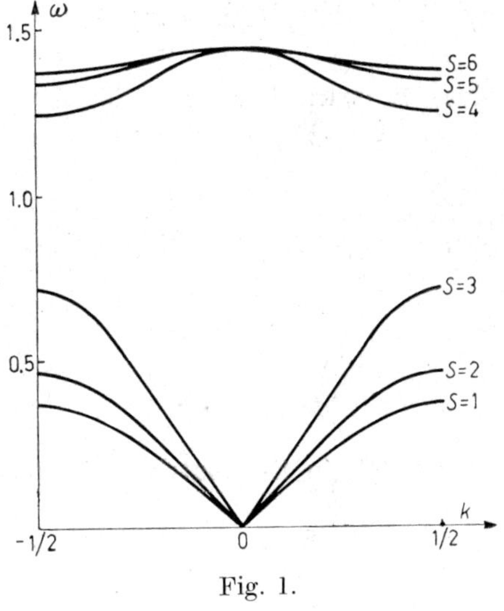

Fig. 1.

Taking into account that the variable $\boldsymbol{g}$ characterizes the co-ordinate inside the cell, while $\boldsymbol{r}$ is the cell co-ordinate, the normal mode of vibration appears as a modulated plane wave, and thus corresponds to the Bloch wave of a zone electron.

Let $\hat{A}$ be the operator corresponding to the (square) matrix of the coupling coefficients, and χ the $3pN$-dimensional vector defined by the $3pN$ scalar amplitudes of vibration; in matrix notation eq. (2) becomes

(2 *bis*)
$$(\hat{A} - \omega^2 \hat{M})\chi = 0,$$

where $\hat{M}$ is defined by $M_{ii'}(\boldsymbol{g}, \boldsymbol{g}' | \boldsymbol{r} - \boldsymbol{r}') = \delta_{i,i'} \cdot \delta_{g,g'} \cdot \delta_{r,r'} \cdot m_g$.

When point imperfections are present, they affect both $\hat{A}$ and $\hat{M}$. In the case of a single point imperfection, the rank of the perturbation $\delta\hat{A}$ or $\delta\hat{M}$ does not depend upon the size of the crystal, so that, in the limit of large crystals, one may use the theory of local perturbations.

2. – Influence of a local irregularity on the lattice dynamics.

For the sake of simplicity we consider a monatomic lattice with all the oscillations polarized in a given direction, and we assume that the local perturbation consists in a change of mass of the atom at the origin of the Bravais axis.

The approximations implicit in the scheme of polarized vibrations may be very important for the reliability of numerical computations, but they do not affect the fundamental features of the problem.

Choosing one of the co-ordinate axes parallel to the polarization direction, the equation for the amplitudes of the polarized vibrations in the perturbed cystal is

$$\sum [A(\boldsymbol{r}-\boldsymbol{r}') - m\omega^2\cdot(\delta_{r,r'} - \varepsilon\cdot\delta_{0,r}\cdot\delta_{0,r'})]\,\chi(\boldsymbol{r}') = 0\,, \tag{4}$$

where m is the mass of a generic atom in the perfect unperturbed crystal, and $\varepsilon = (m - m')/m$ is the fractional change of mass; $\delta_{r,r'}$, $\delta_{0,r}$ are the Kronecker symbols.

If we let

$$L(\boldsymbol{r}-\boldsymbol{r}') \equiv \frac{A(\boldsymbol{r}-\boldsymbol{r}')}{m}\,,$$

$$\Delta(\boldsymbol{r},\boldsymbol{r}') \equiv \delta_{0,r}\cdot\delta_{0,r'}\,,$$

$$z \equiv \omega^2\,,$$

the eq. (4), in the matrix notation, becomes

$$(\hat{L} - z(\hat{I} - \varepsilon\hat{\Delta}))\,\chi = 0\,, \tag{4 bis}$$

where $\hat{I}$ is the identity operator.

We shall not impose any restrictions on the magnitude of ε; its value ranges from $-\infty$ to $+1$.

Equation (4 *bis*) is equivalent to

$$(\hat{L} - z)\chi = -z\varepsilon\hat{\Delta}\chi\,. \tag{5}$$

$\hat{L}$ may be considered as the unperturbed operator and $z\varepsilon\hat{\Delta}$ as the local perturbation. The eigenvalues of the perturbed operator are the roots of the secular equation

$$\det\{\hat{L} - z(\hat{I} - \varepsilon\hat{\Delta})\} = 0\,. \tag{6}$$

Provided the roots of eq. (6) are determined, the eigenvectors of the perturbed operator are obtained, in principle, by solving the linear system (4*bis*) with the addition of the orthonormality relations between the perturbed eigenvectors. The eigenvectors of the unperturbed operator $\hat{L}$ are the plane waves (*)

$$\chi^0_{\boldsymbol{k}}(\boldsymbol{r}) = \exp[i\,\boldsymbol{k}\cdot\boldsymbol{r}]\,; \tag{7}$$

in the limit of large crystals, $\hat{L}$ has a continuous spectrum, ranging from zero to a finite value z^0_L. $\boldsymbol{k}$ plays then the role of a continuous quantum number and the eigenvalues $z=\omega^2$ are given by

$$z \equiv \omega^2 = \omega^2(\boldsymbol{k}) = \sum_{\bar{\boldsymbol{r}}} L(\bar{\boldsymbol{r}}) \exp[i\,\boldsymbol{k}\cdot\bar{\boldsymbol{r}}]\,, \tag{8}$$

where $\boldsymbol{k}$ assumes values inside the first Brillouin zone.

The presence of a local perturbation leads to two kinds of effect: first, the elastic waves propagating in the crystal are scattered, and then the perturbed waves are given by the superposition of the incoming and a diffusing wave; secondly, new modes of oscillation may be possible, in the sense that wave packets, localized around the irregularity, could have standing character.

According to the above picture, the frequencies inside the continuous range are only slightly affected; however, if there are localized modes, the maximum frequency is shifted by a finite amount outside the continuous range.

The general theory has been developed by many authors [2-5]; in what follows we discuss some of the most important points.

2·1. *Appearance of discrete frequencies.* – The perturbed spectrum can be obtained, in principle, solving the secular eq. (6). Assuming that z is outside the continuous interval of the unperturbed operator, the determinantal eq. (6) may be factorized as

$$\det\{\hat{L}-z\}\cdot\det\{\hat{I}+(\hat{L}-z)^{-1}\varepsilon z\hat{\Delta}\} = 0 \tag{9}$$

so that the discrete frequencies are the roots of

$$\det\{\hat{I}+\varepsilon z(\hat{L}-z)^{-1}\hat{\Delta}\} = 0\,. \tag{9 bis}$$

The inverse operator $(\hat{L}-z)^{-1}$ is defined in the usual way

$$(\hat{L}-z)^{-1} = \frac{1}{(2\pi)^3}\int\limits_{(\text{B.Z.})} \mathrm{d}\boldsymbol{k}\,\frac{1}{\omega^2(\boldsymbol{k})-z}\,\chi^0_{\boldsymbol{k}}\times\chi^{0\dagger}_{\boldsymbol{k}}\,, \qquad (z>z^0_L)\,, \tag{10}$$

(*) Hereafter we neglect the normalization constant $1/\sqrt{N}$.

where d$\boldsymbol{k}$ is the element of volume in the $\boldsymbol{k}$ space, and the integration extends over the first Brillouin zone, *i.e.* the unit cell of the reciprocal lattice (the volume of the unit cell of the direct lattice is assumed to be unity).

$\chi_k^{0\dagger}$ is the adjoint to the N-dimensional vector χ_k^0; by $\chi_k^0 \times \chi_k^{0\dagger}$ we mean the direct product of the two N-dimensional vectors. In the simple case discussed here, $\hat{\Lambda}$ is a first-rank operator, so that (9 *bis*) may have a single root which is the solution of the scalar equation:

$$1 = \varepsilon z \int_{(\mathrm{B.Z.})} \mathrm{d}\boldsymbol{k} \frac{1}{z - \omega^2(\boldsymbol{k})}; \qquad z > z_L^0 . \tag{11}$$

In a three-dimensional lattice, the zone integral in the r.h. member of (11) remains finite when z is on the border z_L^0 of the continuous spectrum, while outside this interval it decreases gradually with z going away from the border. It then follows that for sufficiently small ε the discrete frequency cannot exist (*).

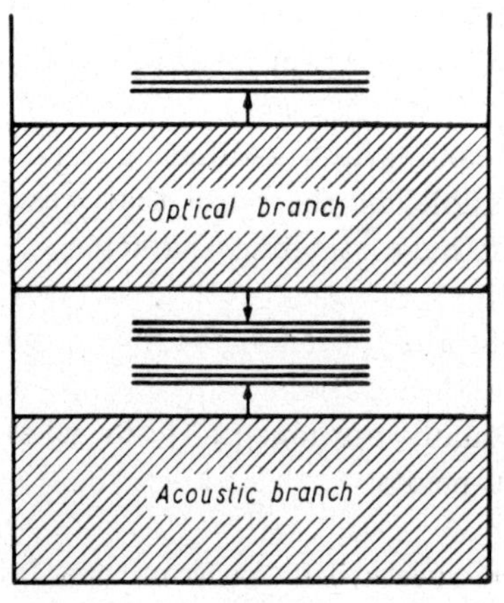

Fig. 2.

For a monoatomic lattice, the frequency spectrum begins with zero ($\omega(0)=0$), and the discrete frequency appears only for sufficiently large and positive $\varepsilon > \varepsilon_{\mathrm{cr}}$, where

$$\varepsilon_{\mathrm{cr}} = \frac{1}{z_L^0 \int_{(\mathrm{B.Z.})} \mathrm{d}\boldsymbol{k}\, 1/(z_L^0 - \omega^2(\boldsymbol{k}))} . \tag{12}$$

The above result can be easily extended to the more realistic case of nonpolarized lattice vibrations. Let $\hat{\Lambda}$ be the local perturbation operator, and let J be the rank of the corresponding matrix; the discrete-frequencies' equation is then

$$\det\{\hat{I} + [(\hat{L} - z)^{-1}]^{(J)}\hat{\Lambda}\} = 0 , \qquad z_{\mathrm{ext}}(0, z_L^0) , \tag{11 bis}$$

where $[(\hat{L}-z)^{-1}]^{(J)}$ is the square matrix of rank J formed by those elements of $(\hat{L}-z)^{-1}$ which are connected by the perturbation.

In the case of a many-component lattice, the inverse operator $(\hat{L}-z)^{-1}$ is represented by

$$(\hat{L} - z)^{-1} = \frac{1}{(2\pi)^3} \sum_{s=1}^{3p} \int_{(\mathrm{B.Z.})} \mathrm{d}\boldsymbol{k} \frac{1}{\omega_s^2(\boldsymbol{k}) - z} \chi_{sk}^0 \times \chi_{sk}^{0\dagger} , \tag{10b}$$

(*) In the one-dimensional case, the corresponding integral in (11) diverges at $z = z_L$, and the discrete frequency appears for an arbitrarily small ε.

where the summation is extended over the $3p$ vibrational bands. If there are two or more nonoverlapping branches, discrete frequencies may arise from each branch (see Fig. 2): the maximum number of discrete frequencies coming from a given branch does not exceed the rank of the perturbation.

2·2. *Localized modes of vibration.* – If there are $J' \leqslant J$ discrete frequencies, there are also J' linearly independent solutions of the eq. (5). Let $\{\psi_j\}$, $(j = 1, 2, \dots, J')$ be the set of J-dimensional vectors representing linearly independent solutions of the equation,

$$(\hat{I} + [(\hat{L} - z)^{-1}]^{(J)} \hat{\Lambda})\psi_j = 0\,, \tag{13}$$

(as before, $[(\hat{L} - z)^{-1}]^{(J)} \hat{\Lambda}$ is a J-rank operator.)

The J' solutions of (5) are then seen to be

$$\{\chi_j = -(\hat{L} - z_j)^{-1} \hat{\Lambda} \psi_j\}_{j=1,2,\dots,J'}\,, \tag{14}$$

The localized modes of vibration are then given in terms of J' nontrivial solutions of a linear system of order J. The dependence of the amplitude of the localized modes on lattice co-ordinates, far from the irregularity, is determined by the behavior, at the same lattice points, of the elements of the matrix corresponding to the inverse operators $(\hat{L} - z)^{-1}$. This, for instance, in a simple cubic lattice with nearest-neighbors interactions, has an asymptotic expression [5],

$$(\hat{L} - z)^{-1}_{\bar{r}\to\infty} \sim \frac{\exp[-\alpha\sqrt{z}R]}{R}\,; \qquad \begin{cases} \bar{\boldsymbol{r}} \equiv \boldsymbol{r}' - \boldsymbol{r} \\ R \equiv \{\gamma_i(\bar{r}^i)^2\}^{\frac{1}{2}}\,, \end{cases} \tag{15}$$

where α is a positive quantity, and γ_i, $(i = 1, 2, 3)$, are the force constants.

The above example suggests that, also in the general case, the amplitude of localized modes undergoes a fast attenuation as one moves away from the local irregularity.

2·3. *Perturbation of the continuous spectrum.* – It has been suggested by LIFSCHITZ, that the eigenvalues problem for a given operator $\hat{L} + \hat{\Lambda}$, when the unperturbed operator $\hat{L}$ has a continuous spectrum and the perturbation $\hat{\Lambda}$ is a finite-rank operator, may be studied successfully by the following method. Let us introduce the sequence of operators $\hat{L}_\alpha$ defined by the same set of eigenvectors $\{\chi^0_{s,k}\}$ of the original operator $\hat{L}$, and by eigenvalues $\lambda_n \equiv n\alpha$, where $n = [\omega^2_s(\boldsymbol{k})/\alpha]$. By $[p]$ we mean the entire part of any number p. Each eigenvalue λ_n of the operator $\hat{L}_\alpha$ for the infinite crystal has infinite degeneracy. One can discuss the eigenvalues problem for the perturbed operator $\hat{L}_\alpha + \hat{\Lambda}$ at an arbitrary value of α; the results for the original operator $\hat{L} + \hat{\Lambda}$ are then obtained when we go to the limit $\alpha \to 0$. Because the operator $\hat{L}_\alpha$ has a discrete spectrum the inverse operator $(\hat{L}_\alpha - z)^{-1}$ can be still defined.

This operator shows N_α poles at points $z = \lambda_n = n\alpha$ of the real axis; α is the distance between two neighboring poles (see fig. 3).

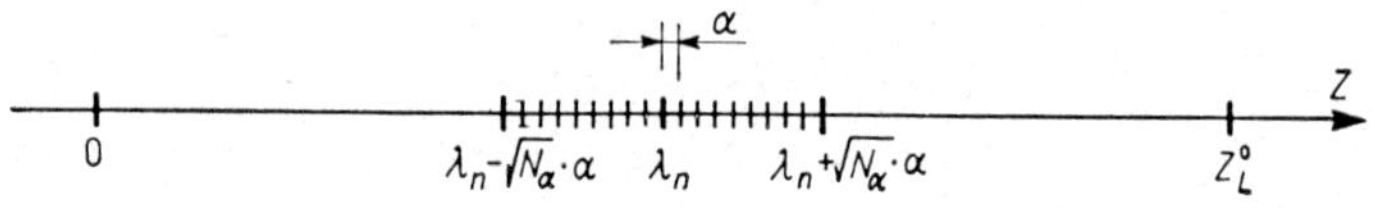

Fig. 3.

If z lies in the interval $\lambda_{n-1} < z < \lambda_{n+1}$, let us write $z = \lambda_n + \alpha\xi$, with $|\xi| < 1$. It follows

$$(16) \qquad (\hat{L}_\alpha - z)^{-1} = \sum_{n'=0}^{N_\alpha} \frac{1}{\lambda_{n'} - \lambda_n - \alpha\xi} \frac{1}{(2\pi)^3} \sum_s \int\limits_{(\lambda_{n'} \leq \omega_s^2(\boldsymbol{k}) < \lambda_{n'+1})} \mathrm{d}\boldsymbol{k}\, \chi_{s\boldsymbol{k}}^0 \times \chi_{s\boldsymbol{k}}^{0\dagger} .$$

We note that in the limit $\alpha \to 0$, N_α is infinite of the first order. The summation in the r.h. member of (16) may be split into two partial summations, the first extending to the poles inside the interval $(\lambda_n - \sqrt{N_\alpha}\cdot\alpha,\ \lambda_n + \sqrt{N_\alpha}\cdot\alpha)$, while the second extends over all the other poles. The number of poles inside the interval around λ_n is then $N'_\alpha = 2N_\alpha^{\frac{1}{2}}$ and diverges as $1/\alpha^{\frac{1}{2}}$ in the limit of $\alpha \to 0$; however, the amplitude of the above interval in the z-scale is

$$|\Delta\lambda| = \{[z_L^0/\alpha]\}^{\frac{1}{2}}\cdot\alpha ,$$

and vanishes as $\alpha^{\frac{1}{2}}$ in the same limit (see Fig. 3).

When $\alpha \ll z_L^0$, the integral in the r.h. member of (16) can be written

$$\int\limits_{(\lambda_n \leq \omega^2 < \lambda_{n+1})} \mathrm{d}\boldsymbol{k} = \alpha \cdot \int\limits_{(\omega^2 = \lambda_n)} \frac{\mathrm{d}S}{|\nabla\omega^2|} ,$$

where $\mathrm{d}S$ is the differential area on the constant frequency surface $\omega_s^2(\boldsymbol{k}) = \lambda_n$. We have

$$(17) \qquad (\hat{L}_\alpha - z)^{-1} = \sum_{\bar{n}=-N_\alpha^{\frac{1}{2}}}^{+N_\alpha^{\frac{1}{2}}} \frac{1}{(\bar{n} - \xi)} \frac{1}{(2\pi)^3} \sum_s \int\limits_{(\omega_s^2(\boldsymbol{k}) = \lambda_{n+\bar{n}})} \frac{\mathrm{d}S}{|\nabla\omega_s^2(\boldsymbol{k})|} \chi_{s\boldsymbol{k}}^0 \times \chi_{s\boldsymbol{k}}^{0\dagger} +$$

$$+ \left\{ \sum_{n'=0}^{(n-N_\alpha^{\frac{1}{2}})} + \sum_{n'=n+N_\alpha^{\frac{1}{2}}}^{N_\alpha} \right\} \frac{1}{\lambda_{n'} - \lambda_n - \alpha\xi} \frac{\alpha}{(2\pi)^3} \sum_s \int\limits_{(\omega_s^2(\boldsymbol{k}) = \lambda_{n'})} \frac{\mathrm{d}S}{|\nabla\omega_s^2(\boldsymbol{k})|} \chi_{s\boldsymbol{k}}^0 \times \chi_{s\boldsymbol{k}}^{0\dagger} .$$

If one remembers that $\sum_{\bar{n}=-\infty}^{+\infty} 1/(\xi-\bar{n}) = \pi \operatorname{ctg} \pi\xi$, taking the limit for $\alpha \to 0$, we may write

$$(18) \qquad (\hat{L}-z)^{-1} = \lim_{\alpha\to 0}(\hat{L}_\alpha - z)^{-1} = -\pi \operatorname{ctg}(\pi\xi)\cdot\frac{1}{(2\pi)^3}\sum_s \int\limits_{(\omega_s^2(\boldsymbol{k})=z)} \frac{\mathrm{d}S}{|\nabla\omega_s^2(\boldsymbol{k})|}\chi^0_{s\boldsymbol{k}}\times\chi^{0\dagger}_{s\boldsymbol{k}} + P\int_0^{z_L^0}\frac{\mathrm{d}z'}{z'-z}\,\frac{1}{(2\pi)^3}\sum_s\int\limits_{(\omega_s^2(\boldsymbol{k})=z')}\frac{\mathrm{d}S}{|\nabla\omega_s^2(\boldsymbol{k})|}\chi^0_{s\boldsymbol{k}}\times\chi^{0\dagger}_{s\boldsymbol{k}}.$$

By $P\int_0^{z_L^0}\mathrm{d}z'$ we mean the principal value of the integral.

In the expression (18), ξ is regarded as a real parameter ranging from -1 to $+1$. When $\alpha\neq 0$, the determinantal equation for the perturbed operator may be factorized into two distinct equations; for the sake of simplicity we consider again a monoatomic lattice with polarized oscillations, and the perturbation $\hat{\Lambda}$ is assumed to be a first-rank operator.

Thus, the determinantal eq. (6) can be factorized as

$$(19) \qquad \det\{\hat{L}_\alpha - z\}\cdot\det\{\hat{I}+(\hat{L}_\alpha - z)^{-1}\hat{\Lambda}\} = 0\,.$$

The first factor in the left-member of (19) shows N_α zeros, located at the points $z=\lambda_n$ on the real axis; for a large, but finite, crystal, there is a

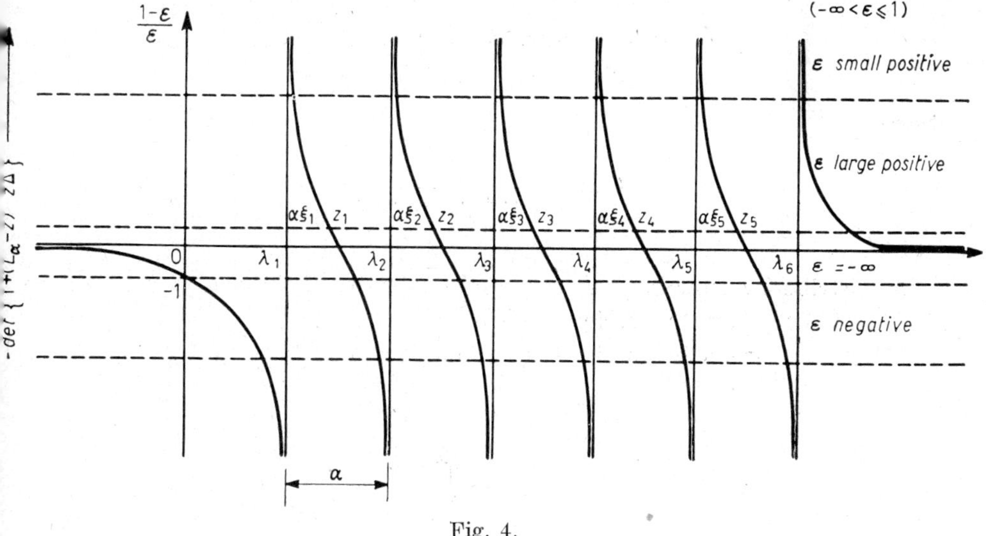

Fig. 4.

$\mathcal{N}\cdot G_0(\lambda_n)$-fold zero at every $z=\lambda_n$, where $\mathcal{N}$ is the total number of atoms in the crystal, and $G_0(\lambda_n)$ is the degeneration fraction. Moreover, the second factor in (19) shows on the real axis both single-poles and single-zeros; the poles are located just at $z=\lambda_n$, while the zeros are located at intermediate point $z=\lambda_n+\alpha\xi_n$ between the poles. The existence of single zeros and poles follows immediately from (18) if one remembers that $\hat{\Lambda}$ is a first-rank operator (see Fig. 4).

From the above considerations one can see that the addition of a one-dimensional operator to an operator with a degenerate spectrum decreases by one the multiplicity of each eigenvalue of the spectrum; the degenerate eigenvalues remain in the former place, and the new ones settle between the neighboring eigenvalues λ_n and $\lambda_{n\pm1}$. The equation for the new eigenvalues of the operator $\hat{L}_\alpha+\hat{\Lambda}$ reads

$$\det\{\hat{I}+(\hat{L}_\alpha-z_n)^{-1}\hat{\Lambda}\}=0\,, \tag{20}$$

where $z_n=\lambda_n+\alpha\cdot\xi(\lambda_n)$.

When the perturbation corresponds to a local change of the atomic mass, the eq. (20) becomes, in the limit $\alpha\to0$,

$$\det\{\hat{I}+\varepsilon z(\hat{L}-z)^{-1}\hat{\Delta}\}=0\,, \tag{20 bis}$$

where ε and $\hat{\Delta}$ are defined in Section **2** and $(\hat{L}-z)^{-1}$ is defined by [18].

Remembering (18) the above determinantal equation is equivalent to the scalar equation

$$1-\varepsilon z G_0(z)\pi\,\mathrm{ctg}\,\pi\xi+\varepsilon z P\int_0^{z_L^0}\mathrm{d}z'\,\frac{G_0(z')}{z'-z}=0\,, \tag{21}$$

where

$$G_0(z)=\frac{1}{(2\pi)^3}\int_{\omega^2=z}\frac{\mathrm{d}S}{|\nabla\omega^2(\mathbf{r})|}\,,$$

is the distribution function, *i.e.* the spectral density, of the square of the vibrational frequency for the perfect lattice.

From (21) one may obtain ξ as a function of z (in the range $(0,z_L^0)$):

$$\xi(z)=\frac{1}{\pi}\,\mathrm{arctg}\,\frac{\pi\varepsilon z G_0(z)}{1+\varepsilon z P\int_0^{z_L^0}\mathrm{d}z'\,G_0(z')/(z'-z)}\,. \tag{22}$$

We note that ξ is a pure number. The perturbation of the continuous spectrum is then given in terms of the function $\xi(z)$ of the continuous eigenvalue z.

In order to illustrate the practical use of $\xi(z)$, we report the expression derived by LIFSCHITZ of the spectral density $G(z)$ for an isotopic solution, at low concentration c, in a simple lattice with one direction of polarization:

$$G(z) = \frac{G_0\big(z - c\cdot(\xi/G_0(z))\big)}{1 + \mathrm{d}\big(\xi/G_0(z)\big)/\mathrm{d}z}; \tag{23}$$

z ranges from zero to a new maximum

$$z_L = z_L^0\left(1 + \frac{c\cdot\varepsilon\cdot\varepsilon_{\text{cr}}}{\varepsilon_{\text{cr}} - \varepsilon}\right).$$

One can see from (23) that the perturbation consists substantially of a local shift of the nonperturbed density: at any point the shift is proportional to ξ.

2·4. *Scattering of lattice waves by local irregularities.* – The last point to discuss in this section is the solution of eq. (5) in the region of the continuous spectrum. The determination of the eigenvectors of a given perturbed operator is more difficult than that of the corresponding eigenvalues. Owing to the fact that the irregularity is localized in a small portion of the crystal, the problem can be solved in terms of scattering processes. When the wavelength of the incoming wave is very large as compared to the linear dimensions of the irregularity, so that the simple law of dispersion $\omega^2 \sim k^2$ may also be valid, the solutions of (5) are substantially equivalent to waves scattered by single scattering centers in the elastic theory of continuum.

It has been stressed by LIFSCHITZ that this picture changes considerably with the transition to a discrete crystalline lattice, when the wavelengths become comparable to the atomic dimensions, *i.e.* to the linear size of the irregularity. LIFSCHITZ himself developed a detailed analysis of the rigorous solutions of the eq. (5); the most interesting result is the asymptotic expression which describes incoming and scattered waves for $|\boldsymbol{r}| \to \infty$:

$$\left\{\begin{aligned} &(\chi(\boldsymbol{r}))_{|r|\to\infty} = \exp[i\boldsymbol{k}\cdot\boldsymbol{r}] - \frac{\varepsilon\tau\omega^2}{r}\sum_\nu \frac{\exp[i\varkappa_\nu r]}{|\nabla\omega^2(\boldsymbol{k}_\nu)|\cdot\sqrt{|\mathscr{K}_\nu|}} \\ &\frac{1}{\tau} = 1 + \varepsilon\omega^2\int\left(\frac{\mathrm{d}\boldsymbol{k}}{\omega^2(\boldsymbol{k}) - z}\right)_{z=\omega^2+i0}; \quad \begin{cases}\boldsymbol{r} = r\boldsymbol{n};\\ \varkappa_\nu = \boldsymbol{k}_\nu\cdot\boldsymbol{n}.\end{cases}\end{aligned}\right. \tag{24}$$

Here $\boldsymbol{k}_\nu = \boldsymbol{k}_\nu(\boldsymbol{n})$ is the radius-vector which is drawn to the contact point of the surface $\omega^2(\boldsymbol{k}) = \omega^2$ with the plane normal to the direction $\boldsymbol{n}$ (see Fig. 5). $\mathscr{K}_\nu$ is the Gauss curvature of the surface $\omega^2(\boldsymbol{k}) = \omega^2$ in this point; the summation is extended over all points of contact for which

$$(\mathrm{d}\varkappa_\nu/\mathrm{d}z)_{z=\omega^2} > 0 .$$

In the long waves region, the sign of $\varkappa_\nu$ and $d\varkappa_\nu/dz$ is the same, becau $|\boldsymbol{k}|$ increases with the fequency; then, in the expression (24), only terms the type $\exp[i\varkappa_\nu r]/r$ with $\varkappa_\nu > 0$ occur, which correspond to diverging wav On the contrary, in the case of sufficiently short waves there may be difference in the signs; if $\varkappa_\nu \cdot (d\varkappa_\nu/dz)_{z=\omega^2} < 0$, the summation in (24) must

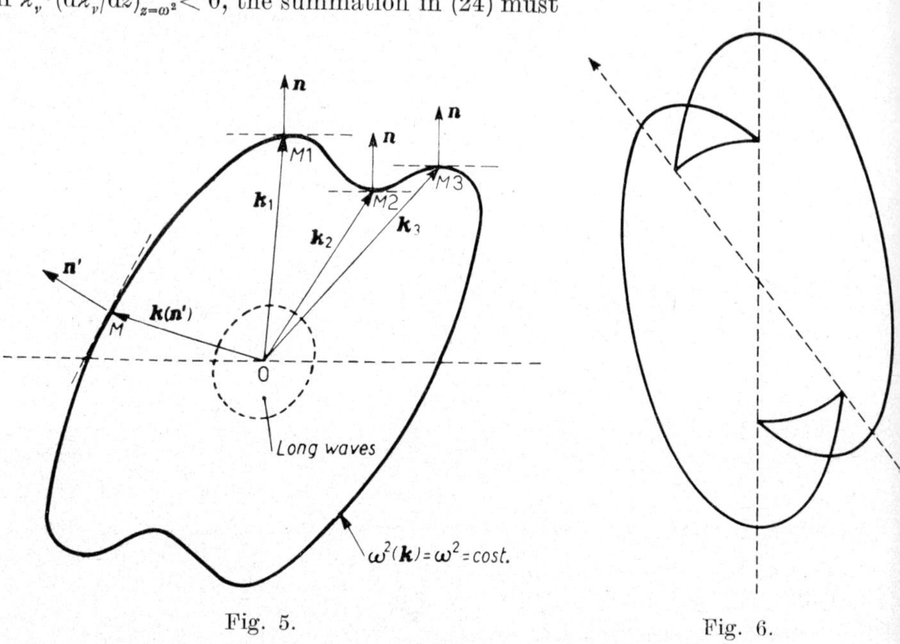

Fig. 5.

Fig. 6.

contain terms with $\varkappa_\nu < 0$, *i.e.* apparently converging waves. However, the wav vector $\boldsymbol{k}$ is determined up to a vector $\boldsymbol{K}$ of the reciprocal lattice, so that th negative quantity $\varkappa_\nu = -\alpha$ is equivalent to the positive quantity

$$\varkappa'_\nu = -a + \boldsymbol{K}\cdot\boldsymbol{n} > 0.$$

The shape of the wavefront is determined by equating the phase $\boldsymbol{k}_\nu \cdot \boldsymbol{r}$ to a constant value. In the simplest case $\omega \sim k$, (Debye scheme), the diffused waves are of spherical type $\sim \exp[i\varkappa r]/r$; however, when the surface $\omega^2(\boldsymbol{k}) = \omega^2$ ceases to be convex, and hyperbolic points appear on the surface, there are some directions ($\boldsymbol{n}$, in Fig. 5) in which we shall have the propagation of three waves, and other directions ($\boldsymbol{n}'$, in Fig. 5) in which we shall have the propagation of a single wave. In this case, a section of the wave front should appear as plotted in Fig. 6.

For a more detailed discussion we refer the reader to the original papers of LIFSCHITZ and co-workers [2].

3. – Influence of local irregularities on the free energy of the lattice.

The vibrational free energy is an additive function of the characteristic frequencies of the lattice:

$$F = \sum_n \varphi(\omega_n^2) . \tag{25}$$

Here, φ is a well defined function; for the Helmholtz free energy

$$\varphi(z) = \tfrac{1}{2}\hbar\sqrt{z} + \beta^{-1}\ln\left(1 - \exp[-\beta\hbar\sqrt{z}]\right) , \qquad \beta \equiv (kT)^{-1}, \tag{26}$$

where k is the Boltzmann constant, and T is the absolute temperature.

For a large but finite perfect crystal, we have

$$F_0 = N\int_0^{z_L^0} dz\, \varphi(z) G_0(z) = \mathrm{Sp}\,\varphi(\hat{L}) , \tag{27}$$

where N is the total number of unit cells. $G_0(z)$ is the distribution function for the square of the frequency (*i.e.* the spectral density), and z_L^0 is the maximum frequency of the spectrum. The last expression means the « diagonal sum » of the operator $\varphi(\hat{L})$.

Let $\hat{\Lambda}$ be the perturbation operator; according to (27), the free energy of the distorted lattice will be

(27 *bis*) $$F = \mathrm{Sp}\,\varphi(\hat{L} + \hat{\Lambda}) .$$

Thus, the free energy suffers a change

$$\Delta F \equiv F - F_0 = \mathrm{Sp}\,\{\varphi(\hat{L} + \hat{\Lambda}) - \varphi(\hat{L})\} . \tag{28}$$

In the case of an infinite crystal, the spectrum of the operator $\hat{L}$ is continuous, and $\mathrm{Sp}\,\varphi(\hat{L})$ is meaningless; however the difference (28), *i.e.* the change of free energy caused by the irregularity, remains finite.

3·1. *Local change of mass.* – Here we shall calculate the change of free energy corresponding to the replacement of one atom by another which differs only in mass, in the limiting case of an infinite crystal. As before, we consider monoatomic lattices in the simplified scheme of polarized oscillations. The principal equation is then given by (6); this equation does not appear in the familiar form, and it would be somewhat ambiguous to assume $\varepsilon z\hat{\Delta}$ as the perturbation operator in the above expression (28). This ambiguity may be avoided if one multiplies the initial eq. (4 *bis*) by $(\hat{I}-\varepsilon\hat{\Delta})^{-1}$ from the left; we obtain

$$(29)\qquad (\hat{L}+\varepsilon'\,\hat{\Delta}\hat{L})\chi = z\chi\,;\qquad \varepsilon' = \frac{\varepsilon}{1-\varepsilon}\,.$$

Thus the square of oscillation frequencies $z=\omega^2$ in the presence of the impurity atom are the eigenvalues of the operator $\hat{L}+\varepsilon'\hat{\Delta}\hat{L}$. Moreover, by a similiarity transformation, the last operator is seen to be equivalent to the hermitian operator $\hat{L}+\varepsilon'\hat{L}^{\frac{1}{2}}\hat{\Delta}\hat{L}^{\frac{1}{2}}$. The perturbation operator in (28) may be assumed

$$(30)\qquad \hat{\Lambda} = \varepsilon'\hat{L}^{\frac{1}{2}}\hat{\Delta}\hat{L}^{\frac{1}{2}}\,,$$

and any ambiguity disappears.

In the general case the change of free energy is given by the sum of two terms: the first term corresponds to the perturbation of the continuous spectrum, while the second term arises from the discrete frequencies. The first term may be calculated following the line of Section 2'3.

Consider the sequence of operators $\hat{L}_\alpha$ previously defined; the separate eigenvalues of $\hat{L}_\alpha+\hat{\Lambda}$ are then $z_n=\lambda_n+\alpha\xi(\lambda_n)$, so that, up to terms small compared to α,

$$(31)\qquad \varphi(\lambda_n+\alpha\xi(\lambda_n))-\varphi(\lambda_n) = \varphi'(\lambda_n)\alpha\xi(\lambda_n)\,.$$

Therefore, in the limit $\alpha\to 0$, we obtain

$$(32)\qquad \Delta F = \mathrm{Sp}\,\{\varphi(\hat{L}+\hat{\Lambda})-\varphi(\hat{L})\} = \int_0^{z_L^0} \mathrm{d}z\,\varphi'(z)\xi(z)+\varphi(z_1)-\varphi(z_L^0)\,,$$

where $\xi(z)$ is given by (22), and z_1 is the real root of the eq. (11), outside the continuous interval. In the literature, the above expression is referred to as the « trace formula ». Formulae (32), (22) and (11) are the exact solutions of the problem.

3'2. *Extension to the general case.* – Here we shall extend the above results to a monoatomic lattice with no polarized oscillations, and to a general type of local irregularity. Let $\hat{\Lambda}$ be the perturbation operator; if $\hat{\Lambda}$ is a J-rank operator, let $[(\hat{L}-z)^{-1}]^{(J)}$ be the operator represented by the J-dimensional matrix formed by those elements of $(\hat{L}-z)^{-1}$ which are connected by the perturbation itself. When z lies inside the continuous interval $(0, z_L^0)$, $[(\hat{L}-z)^{-1}]^{(J)}$

can be represented as

$$(33)\qquad [(\hat{L}-z)^{-1}]^{(J)} = -\pi \operatorname{cotg}(\pi\xi)\,\hat{G}_0(z) + \hat{\tilde{G}}_0(z)\,,$$

where the J-rank operators $\hat{G}_0(z)$ and $\hat{\tilde{G}}_0(z)$ are defined by

$$(34)\qquad \begin{cases} \hat{G}_0(z) = \dfrac{1}{(2\pi)^3}\displaystyle\sum_{s=1}^{3}\int\limits_{(\omega_s^2(\boldsymbol{k})=z)} \dfrac{\mathrm{d}S}{|\nabla\omega_s^2(\boldsymbol{k})|}\,[\chi^0_{s,\boldsymbol{k}}\times\chi^{0\dagger}_{s,\boldsymbol{k}}]^{(J)}\,,\\[2ex] \hat{\tilde{G}}_0(z) = P\displaystyle\int_0^{z_L^0}\mathrm{d}z'\,\hat{G}_0(z')/(z'-z)\,. \end{cases}$$

Therefore, in the limit of a large crystal, the determinantal eq. (20) may be written

$$(35)\qquad \det\{\hat{I} + \hat{\tilde{G}}_0(z)\hat{\Lambda} - \pi\operatorname{cotg}(\pi\xi)\,\hat{G}_0(z)\hat{\Lambda}\} = 0\,,$$

where z is a real parameter.

If

$$\det\{\hat{G}_0(z)\hat{\Lambda}\}\neq 0 \qquad \text{for } z\notin(0, z_L^0)\,,$$

(35) is equivalent to

$$(35\ bis)\qquad \det\left\{\hat{G}_0(z)\hat{\Lambda}(\hat{I}+\hat{\tilde{G}}_0(z)\,\hat{\Lambda})^{-1} - \frac{1}{\pi}\operatorname{tg}\pi\,\xi\right\} = 0\,.$$

This determinantal equation defines a set of J functions $\xi_j(z)$ ($j = 1, 2, \ldots, J$) which may be written, formally (*),

$$\xi_j(z) = \frac{1}{\pi}\operatorname{arctg}\pi K_j(z)\,; \qquad j = 1, 2, \ldots, J\,,$$

where $K_j(z)$ are the eigenvalues of $\hat{G}_0(z)\hat{\Lambda}(\hat{I}+\hat{\tilde{G}}_0(z)\hat{\Lambda})^{-1}$.

From (11 *bis*), (35 *bis*) it follows that the exact solution of the perturbed problem is given, in terms of the eigenvalues of an operator of a rank J, equal to the rank of the perturbation, which depends on a continuous real parameter z. (32) becomes now:

$$\Delta F = \int_0^{z_L^0}\mathrm{d}z\,\varphi'(z)\sum_{j=1}^{J}\xi_j(z) + \sum_{j'=1}^{J}\{\varphi(z_{j'}) - \varphi(z_L^0)\}\,.$$

(*) Here we consider only the branch of arctg which includes the zero.

4. – Methods of approximation.

The general theory of local perturbations is very useful for it gives a rigorous picture of the physical situation in crystals when point imperfections are present. Unfortunately, practical applications of the above theoretical results in realistic lattices and for the more common lattice imperfections, lead to very hard numerical problems. An exceptional case is represented by the local change of mass in monoatomic crystals of cubic symmetry, because the determinantal eq. (11 *bis*), and (35 *bis*) reduce always to simple scalar equations [7].

If the local perturbation is small, so that there are not discrete frequencies, and provided the eigenvalues $K_j(z)$ of $\hat{G}_0\hat{\Lambda}(\hat{I}+\hat{\tilde{G}}_0\hat{\Lambda})^{-1}$ are always smaller than unity (in absolute value), the change of an extensive property ΔF can be evaluated by a perturbative expansion. One obtains

$$\text{(36)}\qquad \begin{cases} \sum_{j=1}^{J} \xi_j(z) \simeq \operatorname{Sp} \hat{G}_0(z)\hat{\Lambda}(\hat{I}+\hat{\tilde{G}}_0)\hat{\Lambda})^{-1}+\ldots \\ \qquad\qquad \simeq \operatorname{Sp}\hat{G}_0\hat{\Lambda} - \operatorname{Sp}\hat{G}_0\hat{\Lambda}\hat{\tilde{G}}_0\hat{\Lambda}+\ldots\,. \end{cases}$$

Therefore, ΔF may be expanded as

$$\text{(37)}\qquad \Delta F = \Delta F^{(1)} + \Delta F^{(2)} + \ldots$$

where

$$\text{(38)}\qquad \begin{cases} \Delta F^{(1)} = \int_0^{z_L^0} \mathrm{d}z\,\varphi'(z)\,\Phi^{(1)}(z)\,, \\ \Delta F^{(2)} = -\int_0^{z_L^0} \mathrm{d}z\varphi'(z)\cdot P\int_0^{z_L^0}\mathrm{d}z'\,\dfrac{1}{z'-z}\,\Phi^{(2)}(z,z')\,, \\ \ldots\ldots\ldots\ldots\ldots \end{cases}$$

where

$$\text{(39)}\qquad \Phi^{(1)}(z) = \operatorname{Sp}\hat{G}_0(z)\hat{\Lambda} = \sum_{s=1}^{3}\frac{1}{(2\pi)^3}\int_{(\omega_s^2(\boldsymbol{k})=z)}\frac{\mathrm{d}S}{|\nabla\omega_s^2(\boldsymbol{k})|}\,(\chi^0_{s,\boldsymbol{k}}|\hat{\Lambda}|\chi^0_{s,\boldsymbol{k}})\,,$$

$$\text{(40)}\qquad \Phi^{(2)}(z,z') = \operatorname{Sp}\hat{G}_0(z)\hat{\Lambda}\hat{G}_0(z')\hat{\Lambda} =$$

$$= \sum_{s=1}^{3}\frac{1}{(2\pi)^3}\int_{(\omega_s^2(\boldsymbol{k})=z)}\frac{\mathrm{d}S}{|\nabla\omega_s^2(\boldsymbol{k})|}\sum_{s'=1}^{3}\frac{1}{(2\pi)^3}\int_{(\omega^2_{s'}(\boldsymbol{k}')=z')}\frac{\mathrm{d}S'}{|\nabla\omega_{s'}^2(\boldsymbol{k}')|}\,|(\chi^0_{s,\boldsymbol{k}}|\hat{\Lambda}|\chi^0_{s',\boldsymbol{k}'})|^2$$

As an application, consider a vacancy in a monoatomic crystal; if the inter-omic forces arise from a two-body potential of central type, the matrix cor-sponding to the perturbation operator in the unrelaxed lattice is found to be

$$\Lambda_{x,x'}(\boldsymbol{r},\boldsymbol{r}') = \sum_{\bar{r}\neq 0}^{(H)} \delta_{r,\bar{r}}\delta_{r',\bar{r}} L_{x,x'}(\bar{\boldsymbol{r}}) - \sum_{\bar{r}\neq 0}^{(H)} \delta_{0,r}\delta_{r',\bar{r}} L_{x,x'}(\bar{\boldsymbol{r}}) - \sum_{\bar{r}\neq 0}^{(H)} \delta_{r,\bar{r}}\delta_{0,r'} L_{x,x'}(\bar{\boldsymbol{r}}) \,. \tag{41}$$

The hole is assumed to be at the origin of the crystallographic axes. By H) we mean the set of neighbors which initially were coupled with the atom the origin; the decoupled atom is thought to remain on its lattice site. In the normal-modes representation, we have

$$\begin{aligned}(\chi^0_{s,\boldsymbol{k}}|\hat{\Lambda}|\chi^0_{s',\boldsymbol{k}'}) = \sum_{s''} \boldsymbol{v}^*_s(\boldsymbol{k})\cdot\boldsymbol{v}_{s''}(\Delta\boldsymbol{k})\,\omega^2_{s''}(\Delta\boldsymbol{k})\,\boldsymbol{v}_{s''}(\Delta\boldsymbol{k})\cdot\boldsymbol{v}_{s'}(\boldsymbol{k}') - \\ - \omega^2_s(\boldsymbol{k})\boldsymbol{v}^*_s(\boldsymbol{k})\cdot\boldsymbol{v}_{s'}(\boldsymbol{k}') - \omega^2_{s'}(\boldsymbol{k}')\boldsymbol{v}^*_s(\boldsymbol{k})\cdot\boldsymbol{v}_{s'}(\boldsymbol{k}') + \omega^2_E\boldsymbol{v}^*_s(\boldsymbol{k})\cdot\boldsymbol{v}_{s'}(\boldsymbol{k}') \,,\end{aligned} \tag{42}$$

here ω^2_E is the Einstein frequency for the uncoup-d lattice and $\Delta\boldsymbol{k} = \boldsymbol{k}' - \boldsymbol{k}$, so that $\Phi^{(1)}(z)$ is eadily obtained

$$\Phi^{(1)}(z) = (\omega^2_E - 2z)\,G_0(z) \,. \tag{43}$$

On the other hand $\Phi^{(2)}(z, z')$ involves in a com-licated way both the frequencies and the com-onents of the polarization versors of the lattice vaves, and cannot be represented by simple expres-ions [6]. Up to the first order term, the exten-ive properties of a lattice are changed, by the resence of a vacant site, by an amount

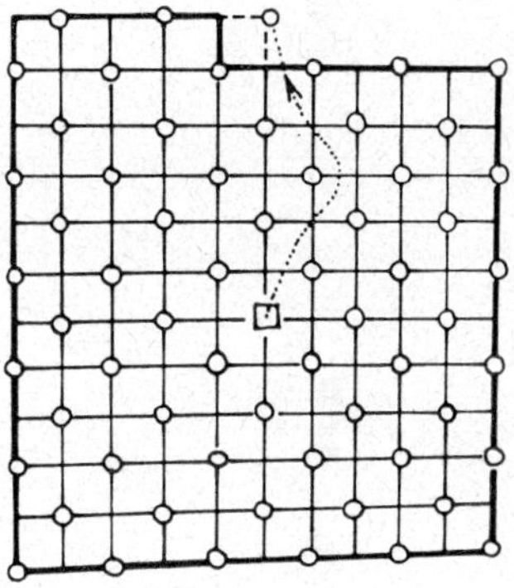

Fig. 7.

$$\Delta F^{(1)}_h = \int_0^{z^0_L} \mathrm{d}z\,\varphi'(z)(\omega^2_E - 2z)\,G_0(z) - 3\,\varphi(\omega^2_E) + \int_0^{z^0_L} \mathrm{d}z\,\varphi(z)G_0(z) \,. \tag{44}$$

The above expression is normalized to the same number of atoms as in the perfect crystal; the last two terms in the r.h. member of (44) correspond to the rearrangement of the decoupled atom on the surface of the crystal (see Fig. 7).

The self-entropy of a vacancy, to the first order, is found to be

$$\Delta S^{(1)}_h = \frac{3}{2}k + \frac{k}{2}\int_0^{z^0_L} \mathrm{d}z\left(1 - \frac{\omega^2_E}{z} + \ln\frac{\omega^2_E}{z}\right) G_0(z) \,. \tag{45}$$

From the definition, $G_0(z) \equiv \sum_s G^{(s)}(z)$; if every $G^{(s)}(z)$ is approximated by a Debye distribution function, and we assume $z_D^{(1)} = z_D^{(2)} = f z_D^{(3)}$, $(z_D^{(3)} \equiv z_L^0)$, then $z_L^0 \equiv z_D^{(3)}$ may be evaluated in terms of ω_E^2 and f, from the well-known relation $\mathrm{Sp}\,\hat{L} = 3N\omega_E^2$. With the choice $f = \frac{1}{2}$, one obtains

$$(\Delta S_h^{(1)})_{\text{Debye}} = \tfrac{3}{2}\,k - 0.184\,k\,,$$

and, for $f = 9/16$,

$$(\Delta S_h^{(1)})_{\text{Debye}} = \tfrac{3}{2}\,k + 0.245\,k\,.$$

It then follows that, in the Debye scheme, the self-entropy depends very critically upon the choice of f [6].

We note that, in the Einstein scheme, $(\Delta S_h^{(1)})_{\text{Einstein}} = \frac{3}{2}\,k$.

As a general remark, we may conclude that practical applications of the above theoretical expressions require detailed information about both the spectral density of the vibrational spectrum and the polarization of the lattice waves. Moreover, we are not able to prove the convergence of the expansion (36) in the case of a vacant lattice site, so that the above perturbative expansion might not to be applicable to this kind of defect.

REFERENCES

[1] M. BORN and HUANG: *Dynamical Theory of Crystal Lattices* (Oxford, 1950).

[2] I. M. LIFSCHITZ: *Journ. Phys. U.S.S.R.*, **7**, 211 (1943); **7**, 249 (1943); *Žurn. Ėksp. Teor. Fiz.*, **18**, 293 (1943); *Journ. Phys. U.S.S.R.*, **8**, 89 (1944); *Dokl. Akad. Nauk. S.S.S.R.*, **48**, 83 (1945); *Žurn. Ėksp. Teor. Fiz.*, **17**, 1017 (1947); **17**, 1076 (1947); *Usp. Math. Nauk*, **7**, 170 (1952).

[3] G. F. KOSTER and J. C. SLATER: *Phys. Rev.*, **95**, 1167 (1954).

[4] M. LAX: *Phys. Rev.*, **94**, 1391 (1954).

[5] E. W. MONTROLL and R. B. POTTS: *Phys. Rev.*, **100**, 525 (1955).

[6] K. F. STRIPP and J. G. KIRKWOOD: *Journ. Chem. Phys.*, **22**, 1579 (1954).

[7] G. F. NARDELLI and N. TETTAMANZI: to be published on *Phys. Rev.*

The Observed Nature of Primary Damage.

M. W. THOMPSON

Metallurgy Division, A.E.R.E., Harwell - England

1. – Evidence for momentum focussing from high-energy sputtering experiments.

1·1. *Introduction.* – In an irradiated solid atoms recoil from nuclear collision with energies up to 10^5 eV. In substances having medium or large atomic weight ($A > 20$) the energy loss from such a particle is predominantly due to interatomic collisions. The primary recoil energy is thus rapidly dissipated into a cascade of atomic collisions and it is the detailed mechanisms within this cascade which determine the nature of primary radiation damage.

In order to study such dynamic effects experimentally the atoms ejected from the surface of an irradiated crystal have been observed. The momentum characteristics of such atoms may be then related to the momentum distribution in those cascades which terminate at the surface.

« Sputtering » was a term originally applied to the disintegration of the cathode in a gas discharge. The effect was shown to be due to the positive ion bombardment and WEHNER [1] demonstrated that atoms left the surface of a metal crystal cathode preferentially along the close-packed crystal directions. Unfortunately the ion energies in his experiments were insufficient (~ 100 eV) to preclude the possibility that the phenomenon was due to a surface effect.

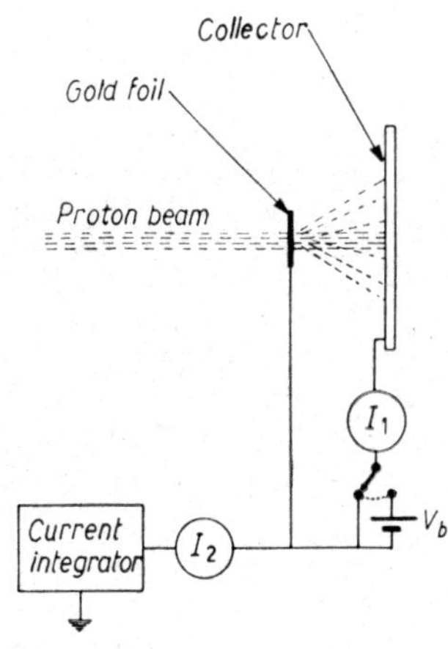

Fig. 1. – The proton sputtering experiment.

1·2. *Experiments and results.* – High-energy sputtering experiments have now been performed [2] which also show directional ejection. In Fig. 1 a proton beam passed from a Van de Graaf accelerator through a thin gold target into a 10^{-6} mm Hg vacuum, emerging from the target's rear surface at 0.3 MeV. In the course of an irradiation with

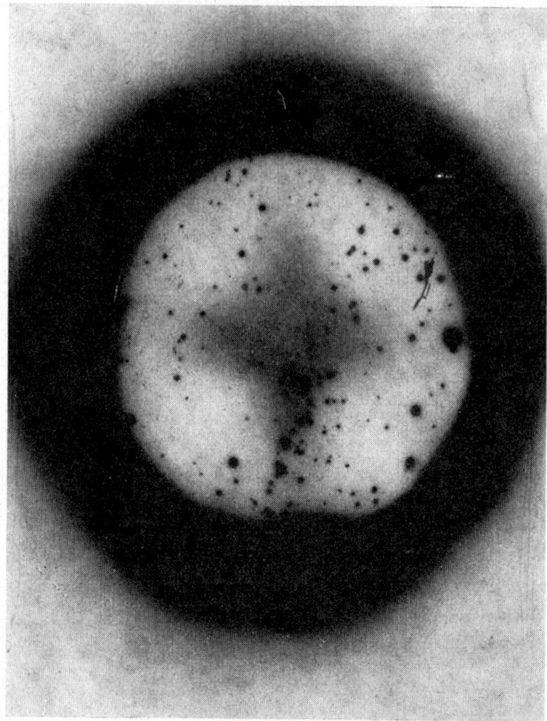

Fig. 2. – An autoradiograph of the deposit from the {100} surface of a gold crystal.

10^{17} protons some 10^{14} ejected gold atoms were deposited on an aluminium coated silica collector plate. In order to observe this deposit the collector was irradiated in a thermal neutron flux of 10^{12} cm$^{-2}\cdot$ $\cdot$s^{-1} for 3 days after which the gold, which has a long half-life (2.7d) relative to the collector, was detectable by its radioactivity.

Fig. 2 is an autoradiograph of an activated collector showing the deposit from a gold crystal with the {100} plane parallel to the collector. The four maxima indicate preferential ejection in the ⟨110⟩ crystal directions. The pair of deposits shown in Fig. 3 were obtained from a polycrystalline gold foil with twin crystallite orientations having {111} planes in the surface. The second deposit was obtained with a potential difference of +120 V applied between collector and target.

The six maxima again indicate preferential ejection in the ⟨110⟩ directions and the displacement of the maxima in the second deposit suggests that the ejected particles are positive ions. An estimate of their energy from the mag-

Fig. 3. – Autoradiographs of the deposit from a twinned {111} surface of gold showing the effect of a retarding potential of 120 V on the collector.

tude of the displacement leads to a figure of 350 eV. This energy is sufficiently high relative to surface potentials (10 eV) to rule out the possibility that preferred directions of ejection are due to surface effects. It is therefore considered that this experiment is evidence for momentum transfer along selected directions in the atomic collision cascade.

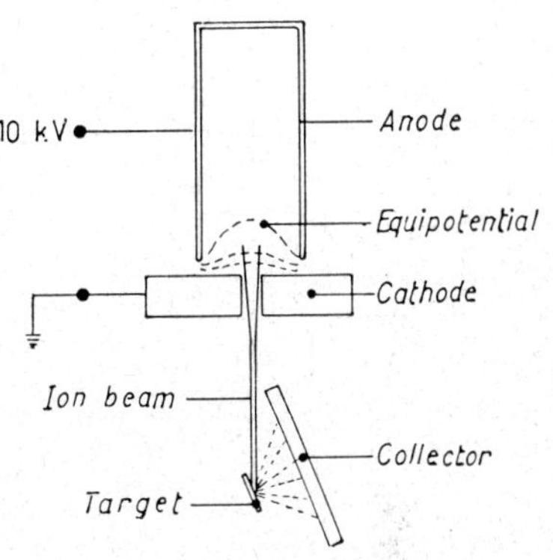

Fig. 4. – The ion gun, target and collector used for heavy ion bombardment.

Bombardment with 10 keV argon ions rather than protons gave an increased deposit intensity and resolution and thus permitted a more detailed investigation, the penetration of argon ions at 10 keV is about 100 Å [3], sufficiently large for cascades to be initiated below the surface. Fig. 4 shows the ion gun and target-collector assembly used in these experiments [2] while Fig. 5 to 9 show deposits from targets of Cu, Pd, Ag and Au. These targets were polycrystalline with strongly preferred crystal orientations. Each contained a principal orientation, to which experimental results are referred, and four subsidiary orientations which were twins of the principal. In Fig. 10, *a*, *b*, *c* the crystal directions of the orientations are shown in gnomonic projection for each of three types of foil: *i.e.* {100}, {110} and {111} planes of the principal orientation in the surface. In these figures, also, the observed deposit maxima are compared in diagrammatic form with the crystal directions. It is immediately obvious that in addition to the ⟨110⟩ ejection there is also present ⟨100⟩ and ⟨111⟩ ejection whose relative intensity decreases on ascending the series Cu-Ag-Au. Here then is evidence for further correlation of momentum transfer into ⟨100⟩ and ⟨111⟩ directions in the collision cascade.

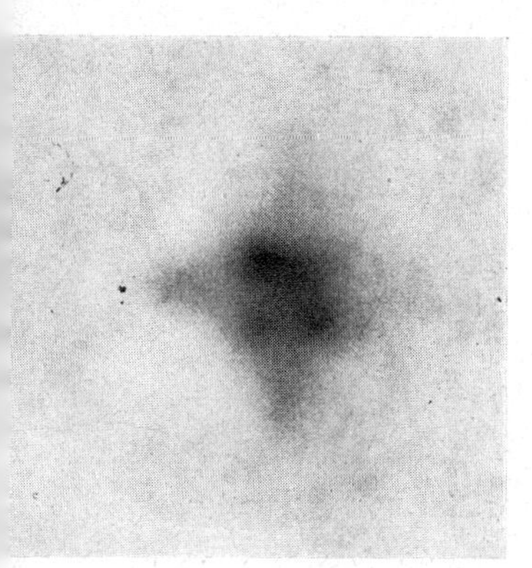

Fig. 5. – Deposit from a gold target, having a principal {100} plane in the surface, under 10 keV ion bombardment, *i.e.*, A^+-Au {100}, 10 keV.

As important experimental condition which must be known, if such experiments are to be interpreted in this way, is the state of the surface from which ejection occurs. Clearly, if a thick oxide layer or a film of organic contamination is present, then the momentum characteristics of the ejected atoms will bear little relation to those in the cascade.

One solution is to perform experiments on freshly prepared surfaces of noble metals in a clean vacuum with efficient cold-trapping around the spec-

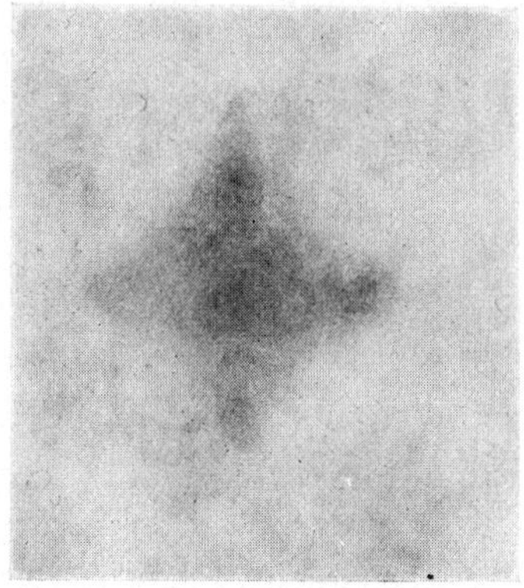

Fig. 6. – A^+-Ag $\{100\}$, 10 keV.

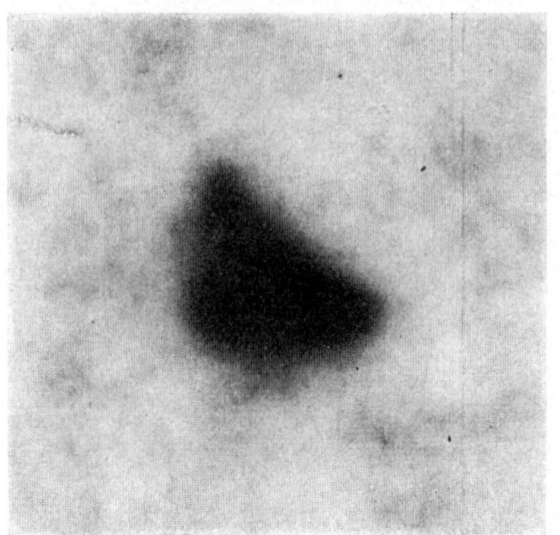

Fig. 7. – A^+-Pd $\{100\}$, 10 keV.

imen. This was done in the proton irradiation experiment described above where the gold target was cleaned by argon ion bombardment before each irradiation and surrounded by a baffle cooled to liquid nitrogen temperature.

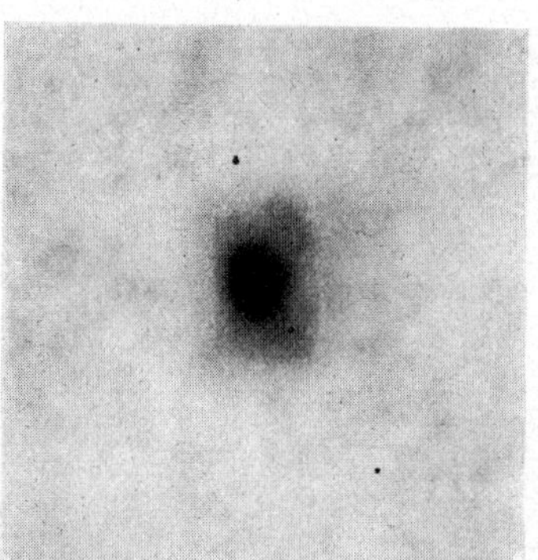

Fig. 8. – A^+-Au $\{110\}$, 10 keV.

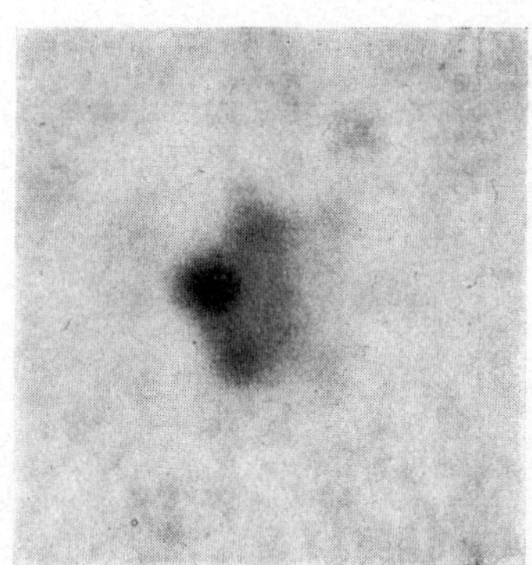

Fig. 9. – A^+-Ag $\{111\}$, 10 keV.

Alternatively the rate of removal of material by sputtering may be made greater than the rate of arrival of oxygen molecules when a dynamically clean surface will be maintained. In the case of heavy ions causing sputtering from a very reactive surface in a vacuum of 10^{-8} mm a current density of 10 $mA \cdot cm^{-2}$ will fulfil this condition for sputtering ratios down to 10^{-2}.

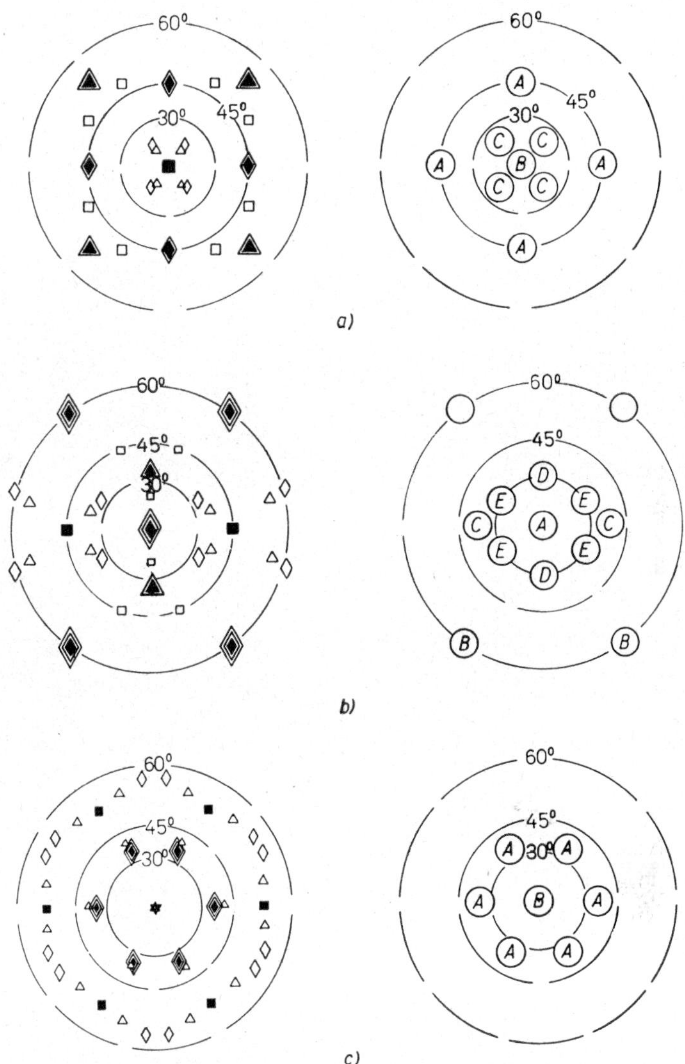

Fig. 10. – *a*), *c*), *b*). The location of observed deposit maxima produced by ion bombardment relative to the low index crystal directions of the three types of target foil. The solid symbols indicate crystal directions in the principal orientation. Open symbols refer to directions in subsidiary orientations. The number of symbols encircling a point represents the number of contributing orientations.

1·3. *Interpretation.* – First let us consider the ⟨110⟩ ejection effect. SILSBEE [4] has shown that under certain conditions the momentum in a sequence of collisions along a line of hard spheres may be focused into the line. When this occurs, momentum transfer is by direct impact and is therefore highly efficient. In a metal crystal atoms are thought to repel one another according to a two-body Born-Mayer potential $A \exp[-r/a]$. SILSBEE show the effective hard sphere radius R of an atom in collision to be given l

$$\tfrac{1}{2}E = A \exp[-2R/a]\,, \tag{1}$$

where E is the kinetic energy of a moving atom. If the separation of atoms along a line satisfies $D < 4R$, SILSBEE showed by simple mechanics that th angle between the momentum of any atom and the line decreases in successi collisions; that is, momentum focusing will occur. The energy limit E_f belo which focusing operates is given by $R = D/4$ and $E = E_f$ in relation (1). Th effect will be strongest in crystal directions for which D is least, and in th f.c.c. metals these are the $\langle 110\rangle$ close-packed directions.

It is interesting to notice that the condition for the incident atom to com to rest closer to the struck atom's equilibrium position than to its own, an therefore to replace it, is $D > 4R$. Therefore, in this simple model momentu focusing and replacement cannot occur together; there is no mass transfe involved in the collision sequence which is simply a *focused energy packet*. I a more refined calculation [5] using the actual Born-Mayer potential rathe than the hard-sphere approximation, the struck atom starts to move befor the incident atom comes to rest, and replacement is therefore possible eve though focusing operates. Such a collision sequence involves mass transfe and because of its configuration has been called a *dynamic crowdion*. Thi defect can only be produced at the upper end of the energy range over whic focusing operates.

Both SILSBEE [4] and LEIBFRIED [6] have assumed the attenuation of th focused energy packet and suggest a maximum range n_f in copper of the orde of 100 collisions for a sequence starting with the focusing energy of 60 eV

From an extension of Leibfried's calculation it is possible to derive tw relations giving N/P, the number of atoms ejected per proton in the first ex periment, as a function of either n_f and E_f or the Born-Mayer constants A and a. Substituting the experimental estimates of N/P and E_f into the firs relation the implied value of n_f is 170 collisions. Alternatively, the secon relation together with (1) taken at the focusing limit allows the Born-Maye constants to be evaluated for gold, giving $V(r) = 9\cdot 10^5 \exp[-15r/D]$ eV. The compressibility of gold calculated from this potential is within 20% o the observed value.

The calculations (5) referred to above have recently followed the spread of momentum from a recoiling atom in a f.c.c. crystal model using an iterative computing method. The crystal was simulated by a f.c.c. array of $5\times5\times4$ unit cells. Each atom was assigned co-ordinates of position and velocity and a two-body Born-Mayer interaction with its neighbours. The cohesive energy was represented by a constant force on the outermost atoms. It was found that the momentum of a recoiling atom was transmitted by collision sequences of the type illustrated in Fig. 11 along ⟨110⟩, ⟨111⟩ and ⟨100⟩ directions. It is clear that the ⟨110⟩ sequences are just the focused packets discussed above.

A simple analytical treatment [2] of the ⟨100⟩ and ⟨111⟩ focusing has been based on a glancing collision approximation in which the rings of atoms

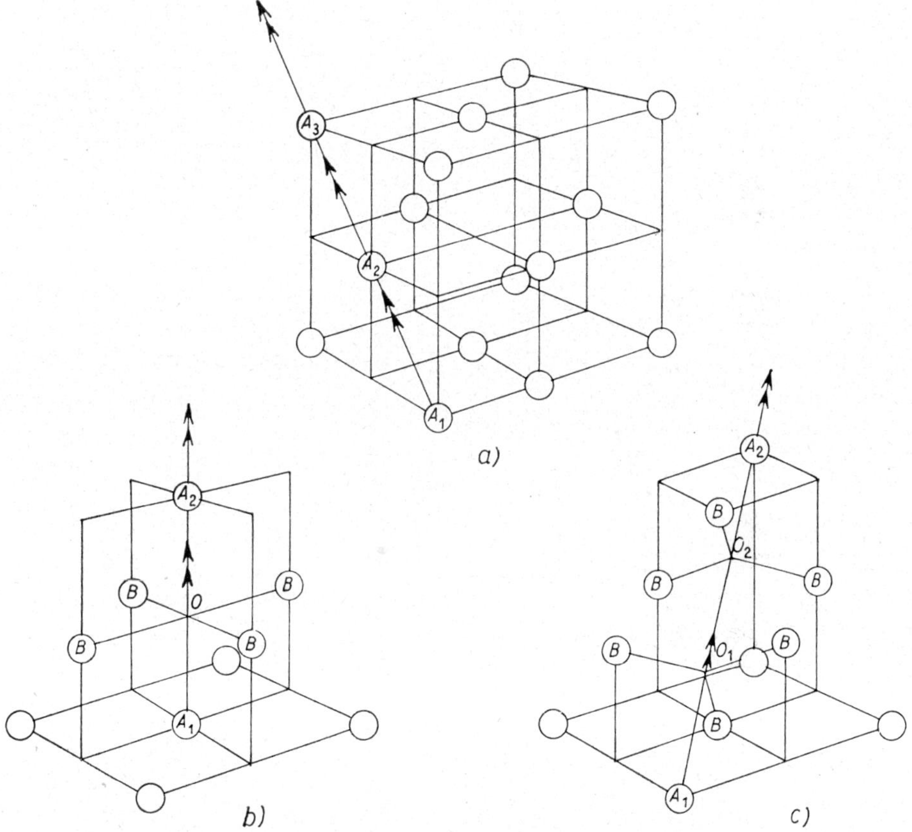

Fig. 11. – The three focused sequences.

B exert a focusing effect on the motion of A_1 in transit to A_2. If this trajectory deviates from the line A_1A_2 then the atom A_1 passes closer to one side of the ring than to the other and interatomic repulsion induces a momentum transfer perpendicular to the trajectory in such a way as to produce focusing. The magnitude of the momentum transfer depends on the interaction time and hence inversely on the velocity. The angular deviation of the trajectory $\mathrm{d}(mv)/mv$ is therefore inversely proportional to energy $\frac{1}{2}mv^2$. The ring may be shown to be formally equivalent to a thin lens in optics with focal length f

proportional to the energy of the incident atom. In the ⟨100⟩ case the condition for focusing is $D^{100} > 4f$ and focusing thus occurs below a limit E_f^{100} given by the equality. D^{100} is the ⟨100⟩ interatomic separation.

In a similar way the ⟨111⟩ focusing was shown to be due to two rings of atoms in successive ⟨111⟩ planes with an upper energy limit E_f^{111}. In each of these sequences it is easy to show that $D > 4R$ and thus focusing is always accompanied by replacement and mass transfer. A very crude calculation of the lower energy limit E_1 at which penetration of the ring just occurs has also been made.

The calculated values of E_1, E_f and n_f are shown in the table using the gold potential derived from ⟨110⟩ focusing experiments and the copper potential used by LEIBFRIED.

We observe that the predicted maximum range of ⟨110⟩ and ⟨111⟩ sequences is less than that for ⟨110⟩ sequences. This is in accord with the observation that 10 keV xenon ions, with a penetration of only 10 Å, excite more ⟨100⟩ and ⟨111⟩ ejection relative to ⟨110⟩ than do 10 keV argon ions.

TABLE I. – *Energy limits and ranges in copper and gold.*

	E_f eV		E_1 eV		n_f	
	Cu	Au	Cu	Au	Cu	Au
110	60	<u>800</u>	1	1	90	<u>170</u>
100	65	700	10	9	9	13
111	490	7300	44	500	17	45

(underlined values are experimentally determined)

Potentials: Cu, $V = 2 \cdot 10^4 \exp[-13r/D]$ eV,
Au, $V = 9 \cdot 10^5 \exp[-15r/D]$ eV,

2. – Other evidence for focusing.

In addition to the high-energy sputtering experiments certain observations can at present only be explained by invoking focused collision sequences. Under neutron irradiation at 20 °K it was found at Oak Ridge [7] that the internal friction of copper crystals was drastically reduced. Although the irradiation was carried out at a temperature where all point defects are thought to be immobile, the magnitude of the effect suggested that many more defects were near dislocations than could be expected from a model in which they were randomly produced.

LEIBFRIED suggested [9] that when a focused energy packet entered the distorted lattice near a dislocation, a Frenkel pair would be produced which would pin the dislocation. Furthermore, he showed that a range of 100 collisions in copper was sufficient to explain the observed effect.

A further consequence of Leibfried's calculation is that the rate of damage, measured for instance by resistivity increase, should be higher in samples with high dislocation density. An experiment at Oak Ridge to test this prediction [8] produced a positive result when the resistance increase of a heavily cold-worked specimen was found to be greater than that of an annealed specimen after an identical irradiation.

3. – Experimental information about spikes.

The term «spike» in radiation damage is generally applied to the region of local heating which is thought to occur as the energy of a primary recoil atom is dissipated into the lattice. Several types of spikes have been postulated. The thermal spike [10] is a heated region associated with a recoil which has insufficient energy to become displaced; the effect is purely one of heating. The displacement spike [11] is a heated region associated with the collision cascade initiated by an energetic recoil. In this case displaced atoms are also present. The fission spike is associated with the passage of a fission fragment, but space does not permit discussion of this type. Estimates [10] based on macroscopic thermodynamic concepts suggest the duration of a spike to be of the order 10^{-11} s. Direct observation of the transient event is therefore difficult and experiments have so far investigated permanent residual effects due to the heating.

3·1. *Electron microscopy*. – The direct observation of dislocations in thin metal foils has become a standard technique of electron microscopy. (See lectures by Dr. HIRSCH.) Recently, observations have been made [12] of foils prepared from irradiated metals, and although this work is at an early stage certain conclusions can be drawn.

Two types of defect are observed (Fig. 12), the first being dislocation loops some 10^2 Å across; the second, blobs less than 30 Å in diameter. The indications are that the loops are present after irradiation at -196 °C whereas the blobs only appear after subsequent heating. A very significant fact is that the density of loops or blobs is almost two orders of magnitude less than the density of energetic recoil atoms (*i.e.*, than the expected density of spikes).

There seems little chance, therefore, that observations so far have revealed primary damage directly attributable to spikes.

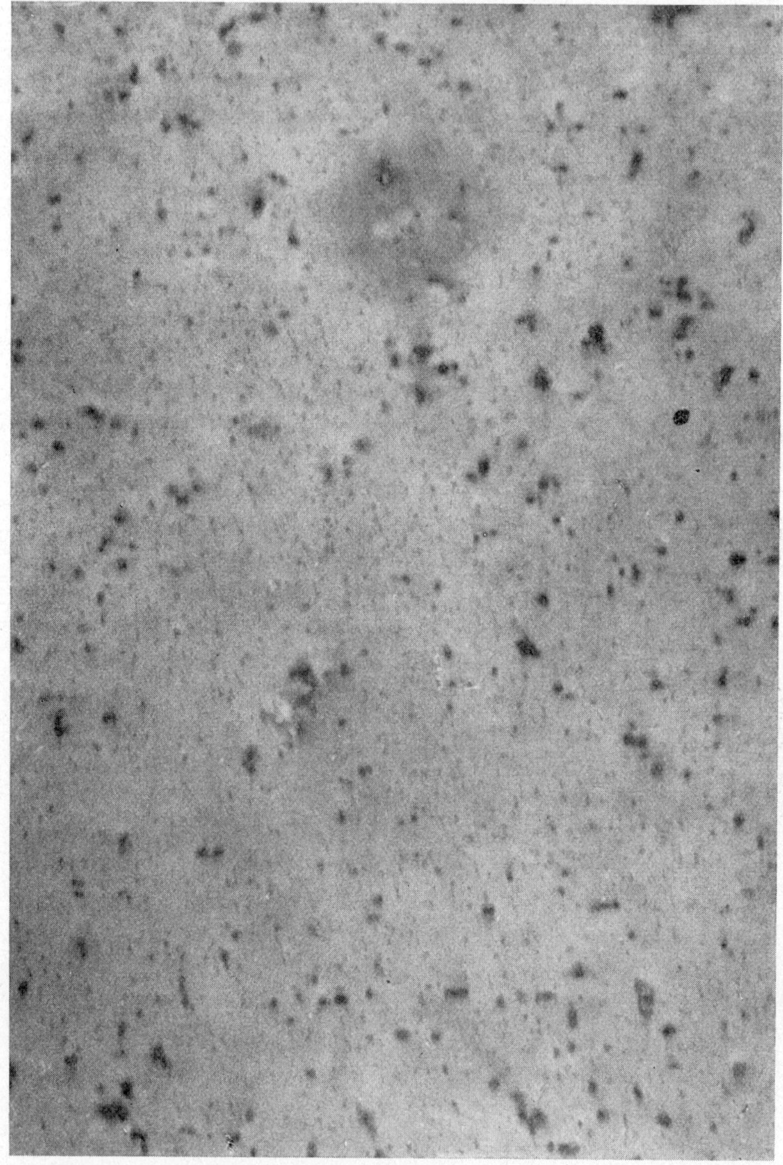

Fig. 12. – Electron micrograph of a foil prepared from copper irradiated with 10^{19} neutron cm^{-2} at 30 °C and subsequently annealed at 300 °C (by courtesy of Dr. M. J. MAKIN and Dr. A. WHAPHAM).

3·2. *Experiments using phase transformations.* – An early demonstration of spike heating was given by DENNEY [13] who prepared an alloy Cu 2.4 wt. % Fe containing a ferromagnetic precipitate which turns paramagnetic on heating. This was irradiated with 9 MeV protons and a reduction in ferromagnetism occurred which was attributed to the local heating of spikes.

Perhaps the most striking experiments on spikes are due to GONSER, OKKERSE and FUJITA [14-16] who utilized the unusual properties of gallium antimonide to reveal their presence. GaSb has a greater density as a liquid than as a solid; consequently, by the Clausius-Clapeyron relation the melting point must decrease with decreasing pressure. A melting region caused, say, by a spike would contract and therefore experience a reduced pressure and hence a lowered melting point. Cooling of this region, in the liquid phase, to the temperature of the surrounding matrix might then be possible.

After 12 MeV deuteron irradiation it was found that there was a net contraction of the sample accompanied by a diffuse X-ray diffraction pattern, typical of a liquid. Low-angle scattering of X-rays revealed the presence of regions with a different electron density some 30 Å in diameter. The density of such regions corresponded to the density of recoil atoms with energies in excess of 10^4 eV. The evidence strongly suggests the presence of regions transformed to the liquid phase by the heating action of spikes.

3·3. *Metastable systems.* – The resistance increment of a metal undergoing irradiation at a temperature at which at least one defect is mobile normally exhibits a negative curvature with respect to dose. This is thought to be due to two causes, first the so-called radiation annealing, which represents the probability that an interstitial will be produced sufficiently close to a preexisting vacancy that annihilation will occur. The second, which will be dealt with in a subsequent lecture, is due to the accumulation of a mobile defect on traps. If the number of traps is finite, saturation must occur according to a $(1-\exp[-t/T])$ law.

In the case of heavily cold-worked tungsten, however, it has been observed that the rate of increase of resistance *increases* with dose. (See Fig. 13 of lecture III.) It is generally accepted that cold-work produces defects in metastable arrays and the action of local heating might well be to produce local rearrangements with a consequent reduction in resistivity. (For example, strings of vacancies might be condensed into small dislocation loops.) This effect would show an exponential decrease with dose as overlapping of heated regions occurred, and the time constant of the process would not necessarily be the same as that for trapping. Thus such a mechanism occurring in competition with the normal processes of accumulation could produce a positive curvature in the resistance-dose graph, and calculations show that a heated region of 10^5 atoms associated with each cascade is sufficient to explain the observed effect in tungsten. (See Fig. 12*D* of lecture III.)

4. – The current picture of primary damage.

One of the longest standing discrepancies in radiation damage is that between the calculated and observed numbers of defects produced by a cascade. For the small cascade initiated by electron bombardment the discrepancy is slight, but in the case of energetic recoils in heavy metals the observed number may be two orders of magnitude less than that calculated. The method of calculation neglected the periodicity of the lattice and was based on the idea that a moving atom will continue to produce new displaced atoms until its energy falls below $2E_d$ [10, 18], where E_d is the displacement energy (25 eV). Thus, KINCHIN and PEASE [18] gave the number of atoms displaced by a recoil of energy E as $E/2E_d$.

In the light of momentum focusing a new basis of calculation must be found, since a recoil atom moving in a direction favourable for focusing will be unable to increase the number of displaced atoms if its energy lies below the focusing limit. The number of displaced atoms should perhaps be expressed by $E/2\gamma\bar{E}_f$, where $\bar{E}_f$ is an effective focusing energy and γ is an unknown parameter of the order of but less than unity. Then in the case of gold, where $\bar{E}_f$ would appear to be of the order of 1000 eV, the predicted number of displaced atoms would be at least an order of magnitude less than the older theories would suggest.

As regards the spatial distribution of primary damage the existence of long-range replacement sequences implies that the interstitial is deposited up to ten interatomic spacings from its associated vacancy. Thus, in the wake of a cascade we might expect a core of vacancies surrounded by an outer region of interstitials.

A very important modification to the older theories arises when the heating effect of a cascade is considered. The range of a 10^4 eV recoil atom in a substance of medium or high atomic weight is some ten interatomic spacings and it was assumed that a cascade was of this order of size. Thus the heated region was expected to contain some 10^3 to 10^4 eV; this represents a considerable effective temperature. When one takes momentum focusing into account, the linear extent of the affected region increases by an order of magnitude and the number of affected atoms by three orders. Thus in this case the energy per atom is of the order of 10^{-2} eV and the predicted temperature rise is less significant.

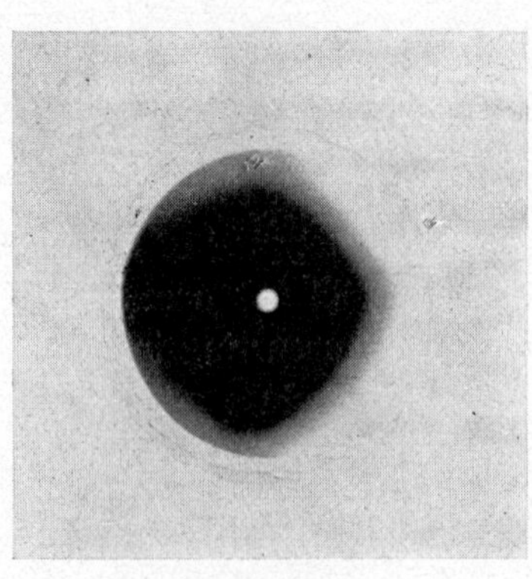

Fig. 13. – A^+-Ge {100}, 60 keV.

An interesting point is that GeSb has a ZnS structure with no close-packed directions and in which one would expect focusing to be weak. This is borne out by the sputtered deposit from a Ge crystal (Fig. 13), with a similar lattice, which shows little directional ejection. It is perhaps significant that one of the best experimental demonstrations of high-temperature spikes was performed in such a crystal lattice.

REFERENCES

[1] G. K. WEHNER: *Phys. Rev.*, **102**, 3, 690 (1956).
[2] R. S. NELSON and M. W. THOMPSON: *Proc. Roy. Soc.*, A **259**, 458 (1961).
[3] R. A. SCHMITT and R. A. SHARP: *Phys. Rev. Lett.*, **1**, 12 (1958).
[4] R. H. SILSBEE: *Journ. Appl. Phys.*, **28**, 11, 1246 (1957).
[5] J. B. GIBSON, A. N. GOLAND, M. MILGRAM and G. VINEYARD: *Journ. App. Phys.*, **30**, 8, 1322 (1959), and private discussion with G. VINEYARD.
[6] G. LEIBFRIED: *Journ. App. Phys.*, **30**, 9, 1388 (1959).
[7] D. O. THOMPSON, T. H. BLEWITT and D. K. HOLMES: *Journ. App. Phys.*, **28**, 742 (1956).
[8] R. R. COLTMAN, T. H. BLEWITT, C. E. KLABUNDE and J. K. REDMAN: *Bull. Am. Phys. Soc.*, **4**, 3, 135 (1959).
[9] G. LEIBFRIED: *Journ. App. Phys.*, **31**, 1, 117 (1960).
[10] J. S. KOEHLER and F. SEITZ: *Progress in Solid State Physics*, **2**, 305 (1956).
[11] J. BRINKMAN: *Journ. App. Phys.*, **25**, 961 (1954).
[12] M. J. MAKIN and A. WHAPHAM: (1960), private discussion.
[13] J. M. DENNEY: *Phys. Rev.*, **94**, 1147 (1954).
[14] U. GONSER and B. OKKERSE: *Phys. Rev.*, **105**, 757 (1957).
[15] F. E. FUJITA and U. GONSER: *Journ. Phys. Soc. Jap.*, **13**, 9, 1068 (1958).
[16] U. GONSER and B. OKKERSE: *Journ. Chem. Phys. Sol.*, **7**, 1, 55, (1958).
[17] M. THOMPSON: *Phil. Mag.*, **5**, 51, 278 (1960).
[18] G. H. KINCHIN and R. S. PEASE: *Rep. Prog. Phys.*, **48**, 1 (1955).

Radiation Damage Theory.

Terms and Concepts in Radiation Damage Theory.

D. K. HOLMES

Solid State Division, Oak Ridge National Laboratory (*) - *Oak Ridge, Tenn.*

1. – History and motivation.

The original stimulus for the beginning of serious studies of the damage to solid materials caused by energetic radiation came from the sudden growth of nuclear technology during the Second World War; thus a convenient date which may be regarded as the starting point for the field of radiation damage is 1943. Of course, there had been a great deal of work before that involving the interaction of radiation and matter. In fact, from the discovery of X-rays and natural radioactivity just before the turn of the century the most important work in physics involved the study of radiation and materials leading to the modern theories of the atom and of crystal structure. However, these studies were concentrated on the scattered radiation and little notice was taken of the material which had suffered the irradiation, which was generally only slightly affected in any case because of the low intensity and energy of the incident radiation. It should be noted, however, that there was some attention given to the effects of radiation on the chemistry of some materials.

There is one interesting set of investigations, which are not directly relevant to present-day radiation damage, but which have been going on for some 150 years. In 1815 WOLLASTON and BERZELIUS observed a very large release of stored energy when the natural mineral, gadolinite, was heated. Further study showed that this and other similar crystals, while retaining their crystalline form, were essentially non-crystalline in structure. For example, they had lost their optical anisotropy. In 1895, BROEGGER created a special classification for such crystals, terming them « metamict ». When it was established that these minerals all contained uranium or thorium, di-

(*) Operated by Union Carbide Corporation for the U.S. Atomic Energy Commission, Oak Ridge, Tennessee, U.S.A.

rectly as primary constituents or as important impurities, HAMBERG in 1914 concluded that the effects observed were due to α-particle bombardment from natural radioactive decay over geologic times. In 1939, in what was certainly one of the first radiation damage experiments, two investigators, STACKELBURG and ROTTERBOCH, tried to simulate this effect by external α-particle bombardment; the results were not conclusive, presumably due to the small total bombardment they were able to give.

During the Second World War nuclear reactors came into use, and the direct effects of radiation on materials were felt as a practical hazard. As a specific example, graphite, which is widely used as a moderator material, suffers considerably from fast neutron damage. Two important effects on external properties are:

1) The expansion upon long-term irradiation, which can lead to significant changes in dimensions in a large block of graphite, which must, of course, be seriously considered in the design of graphite reactors.

2) The energy stored in graphite under certain conditions can be very significant. For example, a heat excursion during operation may initiate the release of the stored energy and lead to a dangerous rise in the temperature of the graphite.

Of course, these are only examples. Many other effects may be as important or more important in other types of reactors. Fission fragment damage is always present in solid fuel elements, and damage to structural and control elements of the reactor design may not be negligible.

Such considerations as these led to the initiation and development of a long-term program designed to investigate the technologically important results of irradiation, particularly in reactors and on reactor materials, and thus establish the basic principles of radiation damage. Since 1945, this field has been of ever-increasing importance. It was soon found convenient to use many other sources of energetic radiation besides nuclear reactors, such as nuclear particle accelerators and radioactive isotopes, with which more specific information could, in some cases, be obtained.

The greatest cause of the development of this field, however, was the value, quickly recognized, of radiation damage as a means of studying the solid materials themselves. In particular, radiation in many cases affords a very convenient means for introducing defects, in a controlled manner, into solids, so that their effects on externally observable properties can be studied. This, then, is the basic motivation for the study of radiation damage theory, so that we may, eventually, predict the quantity and arrangement of the defects produced in a given solid under given conditions of irradiation, and thus assist in the advancement of the field of defect solid state.

2. – The basic elements and concepts of radiation damage.

2·1. *Experimental parameters.* – There are two extreme types of experiments in this field: irradiation of a piece of solid material by 1) a well-collimated beam and 2) an isotropic flux, though any actual experimental arrangement will very likely involve a distribution of incident radiation which is somewhere between these two. In a radiation-damage experiment, the important parameters somewhat at our disposal are:

1) the material;

2) the property (measured either before and after completion of irradiation or during irradiation);

3) the type of radiation;

4) the amount of radiation; both the instantaneous rate and the accumulated total exposure may be varied;

5) the energy of the radiation;

6) the temperature or internal state of material;

7) the direction of radiation with reference to some axis. (This is a very minor parameter at present.)

2·2. *The «flux» of radiation.*

1) Flux: In the case of the beam experiment, the flux, φ, is defined as the number of particles crossing unit area normal to the beam in unit time. In the case of the isotropic experiment, the flux is defined as the product $\varphi = n \cdot v$, where n is the particle density and v (for simplicity taken as constant) is the velocity (speed) of the particles (*).

2) The total exposure is given by the integrated flux,

$$\int_0^t \varphi(t')\,\mathrm{d}t' = \varphi t = nvt\,, \tag{2.1}$$

if φ is constant in time. Thus, experimental results are often seen plotted against the integrated fast flux, denoted by «nvt».

(*) Note that in an isotropic flux the number of particles striking one side of unit test area per unit time is $\varphi/4$.

3) If $\varphi(E)\,\mathrm{d}E$ is the flux of particles having kinetic energies between E and $E+\mathrm{d}E$, then the total flux of all particles is

$$\int_0^\infty \varphi(E')\,\mathrm{d}E' = \Phi\,. \tag{2.2}$$

2'3. *Types of radiation.* – While any type of moving particle or electromagnetic radiation may be used in radiation-damage studies, the following have been principally used in the field:

1) heavy charged particles: protons, deuterons, α-particles, and fission fragments;

2) fast electrons;

3) neutrons;

4) gamma rays.

The extent and scope of the field of radiation damage to materials is enormous. Table I indicates some of the complexity by a partial listing of some of the elements which may enter a radiation-damage experiment. It is apparent that it would be quite impossible to explore one-by-one all the possible combinations of radiation, energy, interactions, materials, and properties. Consequently, it is of primary importance, even from the purely technological viewpoint, to find the basic principles upon which an understanding and ultimate predication of results may be based. Thus, the importance of knowledge of the theoretical background can be seen.

At present the theoretical basis for the whole field of radiation damage is only very incompletely established. The present discussion will be largely confined to the theory of the *production of radiation damage*, *i.e.*, the « interactions » of Table I and their immediate consequences. In particular, atomic displacements will be of the greatest concern; but we will not, for example, enter here into such questions as that of the atomic configuration in the neighborhood of displaced atoms, nor the calculation of the effects of such defects on the various properties of the many types of solids.

3. – Interaction of radiation and matter.

3'1. *The density of interaction events.* – The incident radiation may interact with the

1) electrons of the solid;

TABLE I. – *Some examples of the various parameters in radiation damage experiments.*

Radiation	Energies	Interactions	Materials	Properties altered
			Standard materials	*Mechanical*
	0.01 eV ↓	Excitation		
Electron (positron)			Wood Concrete Steel	Elastic moduli Internal friction Yield point Brittle fracture Creep
	1 eV ↓			*Electrical* Conductivity
Neutron		Ionization	Plastics and polymers	Hall effects Magneto-resistanc High-frequency propertie
Proton	100 eV ↓	Atomic displacement	Glasses	*Magnetic*
Deuteron	10 000 eV ↓	Transmutation	Semiconductors	*Optical*
Alpha	1 MeV ↓	Fission	Ionic crystals	*Thermal* Conductivity Specific heat
Heavy atoms (fission fragments)	1 GeV	Spallation	Organic crystals	*Chemical reactivity* Especially at surface
γ rays (X-rays)		Heating (local)	Metals and alloys	*Diffusion rate*

2) atoms of the solid as a whole, through the electron cloud;

3) nuclei, either through the charge of the nucleus or the nuclear forces.

The quantity which is usually of the greatest interest is the number of interactions between the incident radiation and elements of the solid occurring per cm³ per second. This is calculated according to the formula:

(3.1) $$\text{number of events (collisions) per cm}^3 \text{ per s} = \sigma v n N\,,$$

where: v = the velocity of the incident particles (neglecting the velocity of elements of the solid);

n = the density of incident particles. If there are, for example, particles of many velocities, n is taken to be the density of particles in a small velocity range about a given velocity; and the total number of events is obtained by summing over all velocities;

N = the density of those elements of the solid which are involved in the particular interaction considered;

σ = the « cross-section » for the particular type of event. For example, if point incident particles are moving through an array of hard spheres of radius R, in a classical calculation σ is just given by the target area:

(3.2) $$\sigma = \pi R^2 .$$

Eq. (3.1) may also be seen sometimes written as

(3.3) $$(\text{number of events per cm}^3 \text{ per s}) = \Sigma\varphi ,$$

where

(3.4) $$\varphi \equiv n \cdot v ;$$

and

(3.5) $$\Sigma \equiv N\sigma$$

is called the « macroscopic » cross-section and distinguished from σ, which is called the « microscopic » cross-section.

Since, for most irradiation experiments, the radiation is incident upon the specimen from the outside, it is usually of interest to know the distribution of events along the path of the radiation from the surface of the solid inward. Not only may this distribution not be uniform, it may even occur that the radiation fails to penetrate at all into the interior of the specimen. In general terms, some of the more important considerations of this type may be presented using the concept of the macroscopic cross-section introduced above. The probability that a particle penetrates into the solid a distance x without any collision is

(3.6) $$p(x) = \exp[-\Sigma x] .$$

Thus, the average penetration depth, $\bar{x}$, denoted by the symbol λ, is given by

(3.7) $$\lambda \equiv \bar{x} = \Sigma \int_0^\infty x \exp[-\Sigma x] \, dx = \frac{1}{\Sigma} .$$

λ is called the « mean free path » to a collision, *i.e.*, an interaction. Notice that this average is taken over a « broad » distribution, and actually more particles have their first interaction near the beginning of the path than later on. To give an idea of typical orders of magnitude: for thermal neutrons, the average velocity is $v_{th} \approx 2\,200$ m/s. In a reactor having a thermal neutron flux, $\varphi_{th} \approx 10^{13}$ neutrons/cm²·s. For nuclei having an absorption cross-section of one barn (*) for thermal neutrons, $\sigma_a \approx 10^{-24}$ cm²; and if these nuclei are arranged in a solid with a typical atomic density of $N = 10^{23}$ nuclei/cm³, then the number of capture events (nuclei-capturing thermal neutrons) per cm³ per s is $\Sigma_a \varphi_{th} \approx 10^{12}$. The mean free path of a thermal neutron to an absorption is $\lambda_a = 1/\Sigma_a \simeq 10$ cm.

3·2. *The differential cross-section, especially for elastic collisions.* – One important class of interactions in radiation damage is that of *elastic* collisions between incident radiation and elements of the solid. Such collision events are inadequately described by the total scattering cross-section, σ_s. The differential cross-section, $d\sigma(\theta)$, which gives the angular distribution of scattered particles, is related to σ_s by

$$\sigma_s = \int_{\text{all possible } \theta} d\sigma(\theta) \,. \tag{3.8}$$

The most complete information on the scattering process would consist of *an exact knowledge* of $d\sigma(\theta)$.

For radiation-damage purposes it is important to know the kinetic energy, T, given the struck particle (mass M), which depends directly on the angular deflection of the incident particle. If the kinetic energy of the incoming particle (mass m) is E, the following relation holds for purely elastic scattering (see Fig. 1):

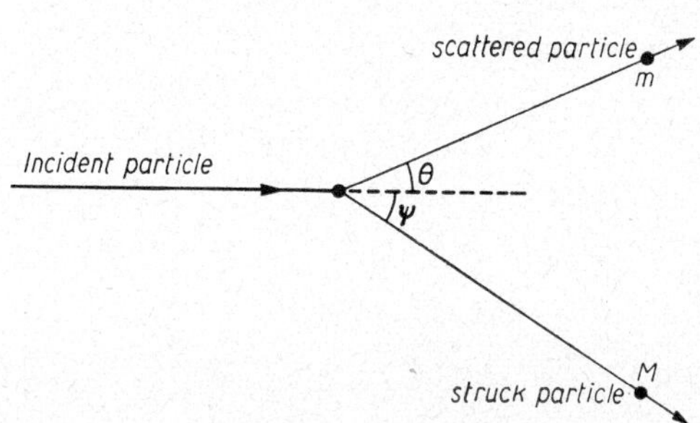

Fig. 1. – An elastic scattering collision.

$$\frac{T}{E} = 2\frac{M}{m}\frac{1-\eta(\theta)}{(M/m+1)^2}\,, \tag{3.9}$$

where η is the cosine of the scattering angle (Θ) in the center-of-mass system. $\eta(\theta)$ is regarded here as a function of θ, the scattering angle in the laboratory system, and may be defined by

$$\frac{1+(M/m)\eta(\theta)}{\sqrt{1+2(M/m)\eta+(M/m)^2}} = \cos\theta \,. \tag{3.10}$$

(*) A convenient unit for neutron-nucleus cross-sections is the « barn ». One barn $= 10^{-24}$ cm².

The maximum energy transfer is

$$\left(\frac{T}{E}\right)_{max} = 4\,\frac{M/m}{(M/m+1)^2}\,. \tag{3.11}$$

Using this relation between θ and T we may derive the differential cross-section, $d\sigma(E, T)$, from the cross-section, $d\sigma(E, \theta)$. If we introduce the distribution function, $f(E, \theta)$, defined by

$$d\sigma(E, \theta) \equiv \sigma_s(E)\, f(E, \theta)\sin\theta\, d\theta\,, \tag{3.12}$$

with the normalization condition

$$\int f(E, \theta)\sin\theta\, d\theta = 1\,, \tag{3.13}$$

to be integrated over all possible scattering angles, then we may write down the differential cross-section

$$d\sigma(E, T) = \sigma_s(E) f(E, \theta)\sin\theta \left(\frac{d\theta}{dT}\right) dT\,, \tag{3.14}$$

where $(d\theta/dT)$ is obtained from the relation between θ and T. This may be rewritten as

$$d\sigma(E, T) = \sigma_s(E)\, K(E, T)\, dT\,; \tag{3.15}$$

and $K(E, T)$ gives the distribution in kinetic energy of the struck particles, T, for an incident particle of energy, E. This can be calculated only with knowledge of the interaction potential. Examples:

I) Particles of equal mass, $M/m = 1$ (collisions between atoms of the lattice):

$$\frac{T(\theta)}{E} = \sin^2\theta \quad \text{and} \quad 0 \leqslant \theta \leqslant \pi/2\,. \tag{3.16}$$

II) Light incident particle, $M/m \gg 1$ (collisions between neutrons and atoms of the lattice):

$$\frac{T(\theta)}{E} = \frac{2m}{M}(1-\cos\theta) \quad \text{and} \quad 0 \leqslant \theta \leqslant \pi\,. \tag{3.17}$$

In this last case the center-of-mass and laboratory systems are essentially equivalent.

3·3. *An example of the calculation of the differential cross-section. The hard-sphere model.* – In order to calculate the differential cross-section for scattering through various angles, it is necessary to specify the inter-particle potential function. Of course, it is also necessary to have sufficient information to be able to decide whether the calculation must be based on relativistic mechanics, quantum mechanics, or both. For the present we shall use classical mechanics, which turns out to be very useful in radiation damage work. Of course, the two-body problem with central forces specified is completely solved in classical mechanics [1]; however, in a survey of the present type, we wish mainly to illustrate the principles. A very easy example is the collision between two rigid spheres, which has been used with some success as a model for atom-atom collisions at higher energies. This is called the « hard-sphere » or « billiard-ball » model. Consider the instant of impact as shown in Fig. 2 in a case in

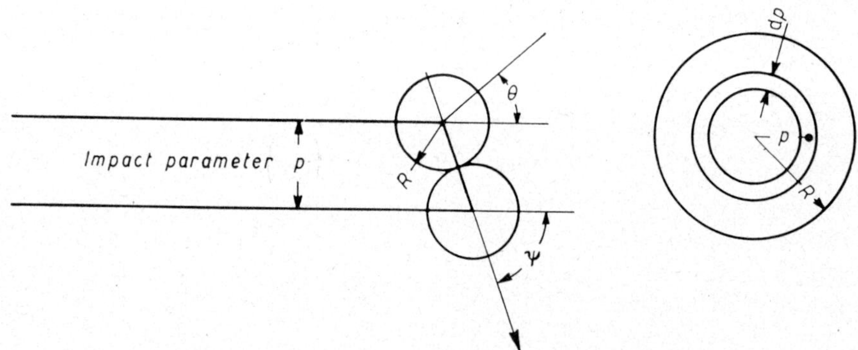

Fig. 2. – The impact between two rigid spheres.

which the incident sphere (radius R) is so directed that its center would miss the center of the struck sphere (also of radius R) by a distance, p, called the « impact parameter » if the incident particle were to continue undeflected along its initial path. It is clear from the figure that the impact parameter completely determines the final deflection angle, θ; in fact,

$$\frac{p}{2R} = \cos\theta \,. \tag{3.18}$$

Thus, the cross-section for deflection through an angle θ is directly related to the cross-section for striking with an impact parameter, p. From Fig. 2 it is seen that

$$\mathrm{d}\sigma = 2\pi p\,\mathrm{d}p = 2\pi p\left(\frac{\mathrm{d}p}{\mathrm{d}\theta}\right)\mathrm{d}\theta \,. \tag{3.19}$$

Then the scattering function, $f(E, \theta)$, of eq. (3.12) is seen to be

$$f(E, \theta) = 2 \cos \theta \, , \tag{3.20}$$

$$\sigma_s(E) = 4\pi R^2 \, ; \tag{3.21}$$

and from eq. (3.15)

$$K(E, T) = \frac{1}{E} \, . \tag{3.22}$$

Note that in this case the details of the collision are independent of the initial kinetic energy, E, except insofar as the range of possible values of T is from $T=0$ to $T=E$; thus, the E in eq. (3.22) is essentially a normalization factor. Eq. (3.22) shows the feature of hard-sphere collisions that makes their use as a collision model so popular. Mathematically, it is the simplest of all, since the two particles, incident and struck, simply share the original kinetic energy of the incident particle in such a way that all manners of sharing the energy are equally probable.

3·4. *Range of radiation in solids.*

1) Charged particles. When a charged particle (heavy or light) strikes the solid material, it immediately begins to lose energy to the electrons of the solid through excitation and ionization. Thus, it slows down and finally comes to rest if the dimensions of the solid are sufficiently great. In the case of heavy charged particles it is convenient to speak of the *range*, R, *i.e.*, the distance traveled in the solid before coming to rest, since this does not vary greatly between particles of the same type and same energy moving in a given solid medium.

Examples: *a*) 1 MeV electrons in Cu: $R \sim 0.1$ cm.
b) 2 MeV deuterons in Cu: $R \sim 0.001$ cm.
c) 80 MeV fission fragments in Cu: $R \sim 0.0006$ cm.

To obtain uniform damage, it is important to use samples which are thin compared to R; otherwise, the damaged region will only be a surface layer of thickness R.

2) Neutrons. The mean free path λ is a more important quantity than the range, since neutrons do not slow down along each flight path.

Examples: *a*) 1 MeV neutrons in Cu: $\lambda_s \sim 2$ cm.
b) Thermal neutrons (0.025 eV) in B: $\lambda_{abs} \sim 0.01$ cm.
(λ_s is mean free path for scattering, λ_{abs} for absorption.)

3) Gamma rays. In this case the attenuation distance x_0 is important. If $E(x)$ is the intensity (energy) of the beam at a depth x in the solid, then

$$E(x) = E(0) \exp[-x/x_0] \,. \tag{3.23}$$

Example: 1 MeV γ-rays in Cu: $x_0 \sim 3$ cm.

3·5. *Effects of radiation in the solid.*

1) Heating. All forms of radiation in passing through solids deposit some fraction of their energy as heat in certain regions of the solid; this is, of course, a *transient effect*, since the heat will quickly be removed by conduction. However, there may be semipermanent effects due to the localized nature of the original source of the heat, and the relatively high temperatures which may be achieved under certain conditions.

2) Excitation of the (nearly free) electrons. Only neutrons, of our basic list of bombarding particles, fail to excite electrons directly. In many cases such energy transfer to the electrons of the solid is a transient effect; however, in other cases, semipermanent effects may remain. In particular solids, the electronic excitation may break chemical bonds which may not be re-established. These effects are clearly most important in biological tissues, polymers, organic crystals, ionic crystals, and other chemically and structurally complex materials, but are not important in metals or elemental semiconductors. It should be pointed out that if such effects can occur they are likely to be the predominant results of the radiation, since so many more low-energy ionized electrons are formed than any other disturbance to the solid.

3) Production of chemical impurities, either through transmutation of lattice atoms (as by slow neutrons) or if the incident particles themselves remain in the lattice as impurities.

As a specific example, consider the case of germanium in a thermal flux of 10^{13} neutrons/cm^2 s. The specimen has 20.55 per cent ^{70}Ge:

$$^{70}\text{Ge} + \text{n} \Rightarrow {}^{71}\text{Ge} \Rightarrow {}^{71}\text{Ga} \,, \tag{3.24}$$

the final step being due to orbital electron capture. The absorption cross-section for neutrons of the ^{70}Ge nucleus is $\sigma_a = 3.3$ barns. Thus, a calculation of $\sigma_a \varphi_{\text{th}} t$ reveals that after one day's bombardment the germanium sample would have an atomic fraction of gallium $3 \cdot 10^{16}$. These gallium atoms may be on lattice sites or may be in interstitial positions. We shall discuss this question later.

4) Production of highly energetic moving charged ions. This is transient in itself but, again, may leave semipermanent effects. Two predominant examples are *a*) nuclear fission, *e.g.*, in ^{235}U total kinetic energy for two fission fragments ~ 160 MeV; *b*) nuclear reactions, *e.g.*, $^{6}Li(n, \alpha)^{3}H$, $E_{\alpha} = 2.1$ MeV.

5) Displacement of lattice atoms. As a result of a direct encounter with the incident radiation or as an indirect result due to the action of secondary particles (*e.g.*, fission fragments), atoms may be directly ejected from their lattice sites with such energies (and under such lattice conditions) that they may have practically zero chance of ever returning. Thus, the lattice is damaged, imperfect, due to the presence of a vacant lattice site, or a « vacancy », and to the presence of an interstitially lodged lattice atom, an « interstitial ». For many purposes, and especially for solid state research, this is the most interesting effect of the bombarding radiation and it will be given most attention here.

4. – Slowing of heavy charged particles by ionization.

4·1. *The stopping power.* – Though the displacement of lattice atoms will require the greatest attention, we must first clarify one important aspect of the behavior of particles moving through solid materials. Although atomic displacement may occur near the end of the path of an incident charged particle, most of the slowing down of that charged particle is caused by ionization in the solid, *i.e.*, energy transfer to the electrons of the solid due to the Coulomb field interaction. The rate of energy loss may be written in terms of the differential cross-section:

$$-\frac{\mathrm{d}E}{\mathrm{d}x} = N_e \int\limits_{T_{\text{lower}}}^{T_{\max}} T\,\mathrm{d}\sigma(E, T)\,. \tag{4.1}$$

The quantity, $(-\mathrm{d}E/\mathrm{d}x)$, is called « the stopping power » of the solid (*), and N_e is the density of « available » electrons,

$$T_{\max} = E\,\frac{4(M/m_e)}{(M/m_e+1)^2} \simeq 4E\,\frac{m_e}{M}\,, \tag{4.2}$$

(*) Note that the *range* of a particle of original energy E_0 discussed previously may be directly calculated from the stopping power by

$$R(E_0) = \int\limits_0^{E_0} \frac{\mathrm{d}E}{(-\,\mathrm{d}E/\mathrm{d}x)}\,.$$

is the maximum energy transferable to an electron of mass m_e by an incident particle of mass M and energy E, and T_{lower} is some lower limit yet to be specified.

4·2. *Illustrative calculation using the momentum approximation.* – As a very approximate calculation of $d\sigma(E, T)$, introduced here primarily to illustrate the principles, use is made of the *momentum approximation*, in which the struck electron is assumed to remain quite stationary while the incident particle passes by without deviating from its course. The velocity of the incident particle must be large compared with the orbital velocity of the valence electron if this approximation is to be valid.

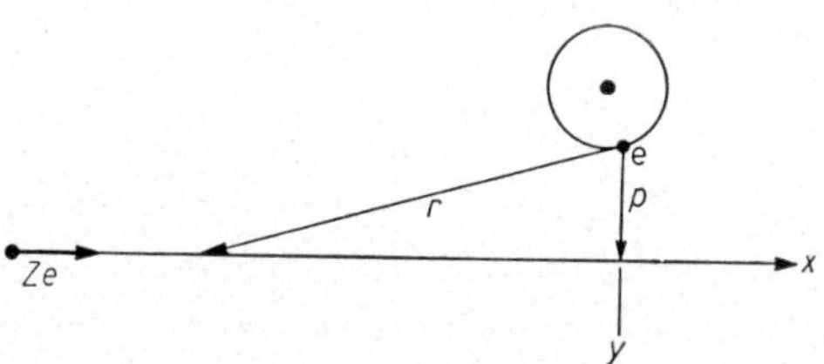

Fig. 3. – The interaction between a moving ion and an orbital electron.

The geometry of the collision is depicted in Fig. 3, in which the path of the moving ion (charge Ze, kinetic energy E) is along the x axis and has an impact parameter, p, with respect to the position of the electron in its orbit. Assuming that the ion moves by so rapidly that the electron does not move appreciably during the passage, the forces on the electron in the x direction before and after the ion passes the point $x = 0$ effectively cancel; but the forces in the y direction add and give an impulse to the electron, which may be calculated:

$$\text{impulse} = m_e v_e = \int_{-\infty}^{\infty} F_y(t)\, dt\,. \tag{4.3}$$

($t = 0$ is taken at the time the ion passes $x = 0$.) The interaction field, F_y, is given by

$$F_y = \frac{Ze^2}{r^2}\frac{p}{r}, \tag{4.4}$$

and the electron kinetic energy may be written (using the classical form in this low-energy case)

$$T = \frac{1}{2} m_e v_e^2 = \frac{1}{2m_e}(\text{impulse})^2\,. \tag{4.5}$$

Thus,

$$T = \frac{Z^2 e^4}{Ep^2}\cdot\frac{M}{m_e}, \tag{4.6}$$

and the required differential cross-section becomes

$$(4.7) \qquad \mathrm{d}\sigma(E, T) = 2\pi p\,\mathrm{d}p = 2\pi p \frac{\mathrm{d}p}{\mathrm{d}T}\,\mathrm{d}T = \frac{\pi Z^2 e^4}{E}\left(\frac{M}{m_e}\right)\frac{\mathrm{d}T}{T^2},$$

which is the well-known Rutherford scattering law.

In passing, it may be noted that this law greatly favors low energy transfers to the electrons, as seen through the $1/T^2$-dependence, and that the cross-section increases in magnitude as the ion slows down (note the $1/E$-dependence).

Note that not only does this give the energy transfer cross-section (in this case the momentum approximation gives the accurate result) but also the spectrum of kinetic energies of the electrons along the path of the charged particle.

From this equation, the stopping power can be calculated (using eq. (4.7) in eq. (4.1)).

Approximate stopping power:

$$(4.8) \qquad -\frac{\mathrm{d}E}{\mathrm{d}x} = N_e \int_I^{4(m_e/M)E} T\,\frac{\pi Z^2 e^4}{E}\left(\frac{M}{m_e}\right)\frac{\mathrm{d}T}{T^2} = N_e \frac{2\pi Z^2 e^4}{m_e v^2} \ln \frac{2m_e v^2}{I}\,.$$

In arriving at the final result of eq. (4.8), T_{lower} has been taken to be equal to I, the ionization energy of an electron from its atom. This choice is based upon the thought that energy transfers to the electrons, which are smaller than the ionization energy, do not contribute appreciably to the slowing-down of the moving ions. The calculation given here is not intended to be precise but to illustrate the principles involved so that, actually, eq. (4.8) is not an accurate result. A more careful examination of the lower limit [2] shows that the result above is incorrect by a factor of two, so that

Accurate stopping power:

$$(4.9) \qquad -\frac{\mathrm{d}E}{\mathrm{d}x} = N_e \frac{4\pi Z^2 e^4}{m_e v^2} \ln \frac{2m_e v^2}{I}\,.$$

In any case, the quantity I does enter into the stopping power formula. In our naive picture this is the ionization energy of the electron; but, of course, the atoms have many electrons of different I's. A general approach is to regard the ionization energy $\bar{I}$ as some appropriate average over all the electrons, defined, for example, by

$$(4.10) \qquad \sum_i N_i \ln \frac{c}{I_i} = NZ \ln \frac{c}{\bar{I}}\,.$$

As the energy of the charged particle decreases along its path, some high-binding-energy electrons will be nonionizable; and some terms must be cut out from the sum. This is a complicated procedure and little has been done along this line.

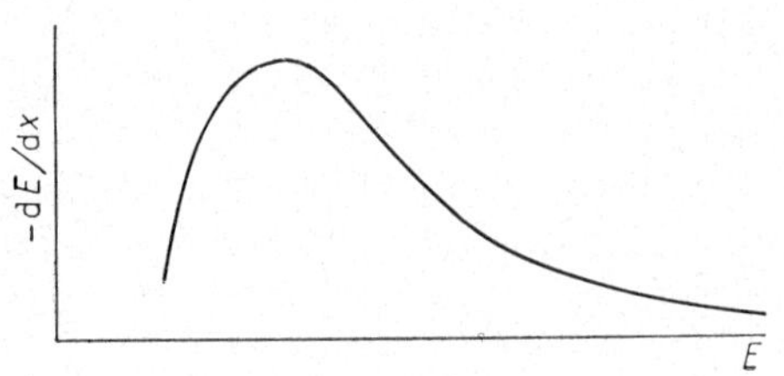

Fig. 4. – Schematic representation of the variation of the stopping power with the energy of a moving ion.

The formula for $-\mathrm{d}E/\mathrm{d}x$ must also be corrected for small E, *i.e.*, when the velocity of incident particle is small (of the order of the electron velocity in its orbit), since 1) the struck electrons then have time to adjust to the varying electric field of the moving ion and so do not leave their orbits and 2) the moving particle may be partly neutralized by picking up electrons as it moves through the lattice. This results in the curve for $-\mathrm{d}E/\mathrm{d}x$ falling rapidly at low E (see Fig. 4).

Representative values of stopping power in copper are:

1 MeV protons	1350 MeV/cm
2 MeV deuterons	1350 MeV/cm
4 MeV α-particles	5460 MeV/cm .

Note that, since the average energy transferred to each electron is small, this implies enormous numbers of ionized electrons along the path of the moving atom.

5. – The production of primary displaced atoms.

5·1. *The cascade process.* – In any solid the atoms are effectively bound to their lattice sites; however, any of the principal types of radiation under discussion here can deposit enough energy at the atomic site and in such a way as to knock the atom out of its normal position. In fact, in general, it will be given a kinetic energy of its own as a result of the action of the radiation. This latter kinetic energy may vary anywhere from a few eV up to many MeV. The atom which is first produced as an energetic displacement directly by the incident radiation is called a *primary displaced atom*, or simply a *primary*. And it is clear that it may go on acting itself as a destructive bombarding particle, producing further displaced atoms with kinetic energy, called *secondaries*, which may produce in their turn *tertiaries*, and so on, in a cascade process. Much time will be spent in discussing these cascades, but first let us take a closer look at the primaries.

In general, there is little interest in special *directions* of ejection of the primary; and it is usually assumed that the initial momentum of the lattice atom is isotropically distributed. However, the quantity of great interest is the total energy given to the primary. This is a good example of a nonunique event as implied in a differential cross-section. None of the types of incident radiation discussed here give, on a direct collision, a unique energy to the atom.

Now it must be asked whether the energy transfer leads to a displaced atom. This is a complicated, and as yet very imperfectly understood matter. Certainly the atom is in some sense bound to its lattice site so that, unless considerable energy is given to the atom, no displacement will result; but the energy transferred will be eventually dissipated as heat in the lattice. Further, it is clear that, if a high enough kinetic energy is given to the atom, it will certainly tear away from its lattice site and move on through the lattice with considerable kinetic energy of its own. At the present time it is thought that, for a close-packed lattice, such as copper (f.c.c.), 25 eV of kinetic energy represents a satisfactory choice for an energy which divides these two extremes; *i.e.*,

for $T \gg 25$ eV, the atom certainly leaves its lattice site;

for $T \ll 25$ eV, the atom certainly remains bound.

5'2. *The « sharp threshold » model.* – One mathematically convenient model which has been widely used in calculations of atomic displacements is the « sharp threshold » model, in which it is assumed that

$$\left\{\begin{array}{l}\text{for } T \geqslant 25\text{ eV, the atom certainly leaves its lattice site;}\\ \text{for } T \leqslant 25\text{ eV, the atom certainly remains bound.}\end{array}\right. \tag{5.1}$$

Such sharply differentiated behavior is, of course, not realistic. This may be most easily seen through consideration of the consequences of various original « directions » of projection of the primary atom; if the atom is initially directed toward one of its nearest neighbors, it is surely harder (*i.e.*, requires more energy) for it to leave its lattice than if it is initially directed toward the center of the triangle formed by three nearest neighbors. Thus, the probability for leaving the lattice site, if the atom is given a certain kinetic energy, is obtained by adding up the various directions through which escape is possible at that kinetic energy. It is expected that the probability curve will actually look like the solid curve of Fig. 5 rather than the dashed curve which represents the « sharp threshold » model. Here the symbol « E_d » is introduced as the « displacement threshold energy » in general. It is, of course, not necessarily true that E_d should be taken at the $p(T)=\frac{1}{2}$ position of the true displacement curve, even if that were known. Nor is there any reason to suppose that there is any particular symmetry of $p(T)$ about E_d. The difficulty in achieving a correct, basic calculation of $p(T)$ results from the lack of knowledge of the proper interatomic potential used to predict the movement of one atom, with kinetic energy of the order of 5 to 50 eV, near an originally stationary atom. For a given, selected form of the potential function, small adjustment of the parameters (especially the distance scaling parameter) result in large changes in the predicted energy required for pushing through. For example, a calculation by HUNTINGTON [3] for copper gave values from 18 to 43 eV for getting a lattice atom out of its lattice position, using a Born-Mayer-type potential function and allowing a reasonable range of values for the constants.

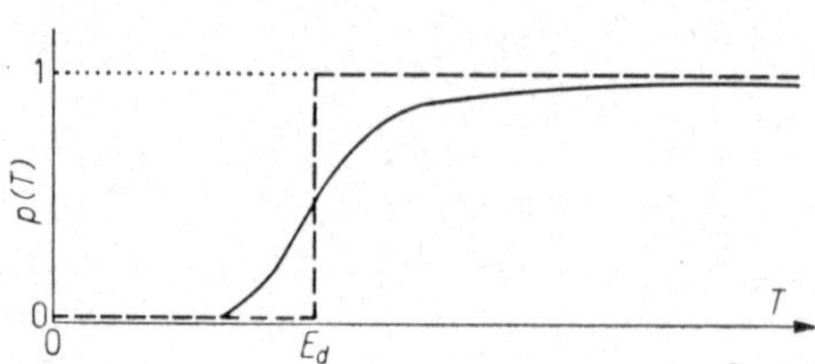

Fig. 5. – The displacement probability as a function of the kinetic energy transferred to a lattice atom.

It should perhaps be mentioned here that the choice of 25 eV is really separate and distinct from the energy required to form a vacancy-interstitial pair. Or, to put it another way, if a vacancy and interstitial wander together, at an appropriately high temperature, and annihilate, a certain energy is released (~ 5 eV in copper) which is considerably lower than the E_d which would be used for that lattice. This is because the displacement process, essentially a recoil from an energetic collision, takes place before the neighboring atoms have a chance to relax from their normal positions. This is to be contrasted with the slower process of formation of a pair by thermal activation, in which the lattice relaxes to make the process as easy as possible.

We consider separately the displacement of an atom by either heavy charged particles, fast electrons, or γ-rays.

5·3. *Primaries from heavy charged particles.* – If E is the energy of the incident charged particle (mass m, charge ze) and T is the kinetic energy transferred to the lattice atom (mass M, charge Ze), then the differential cross-section for transfer of energy to the nucleus of the lattice atom is

$$\text{(5.2)} \qquad \mathrm{d}\sigma_{\text{atom}}(E, T) = \frac{\pi z^2 Z^2 e^4}{E} \frac{m}{M} \frac{\mathrm{d}T}{T^2} \quad \text{(Rutherford scattering)}.$$

Note that this result is based on the interaction of the charged particle with the Coulomb field of the nucleus; thus, screening by the orbital electrons is neglected and eq. (5.2) cannot be expected to hold for low-energy transfers (small T), in which the charged particle does not penetrate very far into the atom. However, for the calculation of atomic *displacements* this form is quite adequate, since the values of T below which it is invalid are far below displacement threshold energies. Compare this with the transfer of energy to electrons of bound atoms (ionization) (from eq. (4.7)):

$$\mathrm{d}\sigma_{\text{elec}}(E, T) = \frac{\pi Z^2 e^4}{E} \frac{m}{m_e} \frac{\mathrm{d}T}{T^2}. \tag{5.3}$$

The energy loss by the moving charged particle to the electrons by ionization and to the atoms as a whole may be roughly compared by taking the ratio of these cross-sections, weighted with the appropriate atomic and electronic densities:

$$\frac{N_a \,\mathrm{d}\sigma_{\text{atom}}}{N_e \,\mathrm{d}\sigma_{\text{elec}}} = Z \frac{m_e}{M} \text{ for Cu (*) } \simeq \frac{1}{4\,000}. \tag{5.4}$$

Note the predominance of the ionization losses in the range in which they can occur.

5·4. *Primaries from fast electrons.* – For atomic displacement, we must use energetic electrons (~ 1 MeV), for which relativistic corrections are necessary. The maximum energy transferred to an atom of mass M by an electron E_e is then

$$T_{\max} = \frac{2(E_e + 2m_e c^2)E_e}{Mc^2}. \tag{5.5}$$

This relationship may be regarded another way. In the sharp threshold model we may calculate the lowest energy $E_e^{(t)}$, the « threshold energy », with which an electron could just displace an atom as

$$E_d = \frac{2}{Mc^2}(E_e^{(t)} + 2m_e c^2)E_e^{(t)}. \tag{5.6}$$

In copper the minimum energy an incoming electron must have in order to displace an atom is $E_e^{(t)} \simeq 0.5$ MeV (assuming $E_d = 25$ eV). An appropriate form for the differential cross-section for energy transfer to an atom has been given by MOTT [4] and by MCKINLEY and FESHBACH [5] as

$$\mathrm{d}\sigma(E_e, T) = \frac{2\pi Z^2 e^4}{m_e^2 v_e^4} \frac{E_e(E_e + 2m_e c^2)}{Mc^2}(1-\beta^2)\cdot \left[1 - \beta^2 \frac{T}{T_{\max}} + \pi\alpha\beta\cdot\left\{\left(\frac{T}{T_{\max}}\right)^{\frac{1}{2}} - \frac{T}{T_{\max}}\right\} + \dots\right]\frac{\mathrm{d}T}{T^2}, \tag{5.7}$$

where $\beta = v_e/c$, $\alpha = Z/137$, and $T_{\max}$ is given by eq. (5.5).

(*) Or for any substance for which $A \simeq 2Z$.

The approximate formula (using only the terms explicitly shown) holds only for medium and light elements. (The quantity α is the expansion parameter for the approximate result.) Note that this is a modified Rutherford law, which still retains the feature of greatly favoring low-energy transfers.

Consider an 0.8 MeV electron in copper, here in the sharp threshold model; with $E_d = 25$ eV, the maximum energy transfer to displaced atoms is 50 eV and the minimum 25 eV. Thus, we do not expect secondary displacements, and the form of the damage may be conveniently simple.

The atomic displacement cross-section, $\sigma_d(E_e)$, in terms of the above expression for $d\sigma(E_e, T)$ is

$$\sigma_d(E_e) = \int_{E_d}^{T_{max}} d\sigma(E_e, T) . \tag{5.8}$$

Calculations of these cross-sections have been performed [6], and the general form of the results is shown in Fig. 6. Generally speaking, the cross-section rises essentially linearly from $E_e = E_e^{(t)}$ and later levels off at some asymptotic value. However, it may go through a low maximum before reaching its asymptotic value.

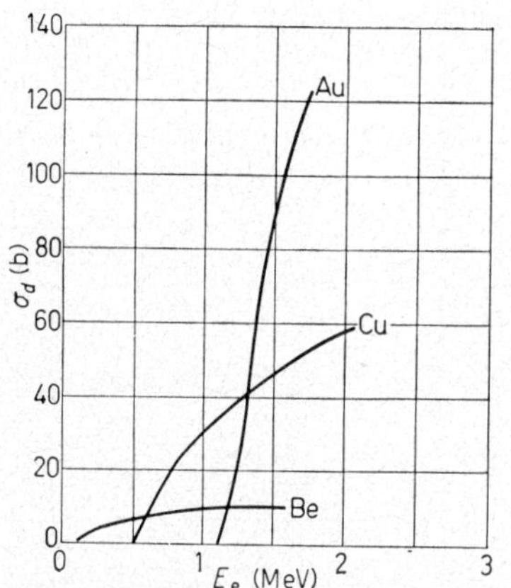

Fig. 6. – The displacement cross-section for various solids by energetic electrons (schematic).

For high energies the asymptotic expression for σ_d is (*)

$$\sigma_d \simeq 2\pi r_0^2 Z^2 \left(\frac{m_e}{M}\right)\left(\frac{m_e c^2}{E_d}\right) . \tag{5.9}$$

Note that these cross-sections for displacement are calculated for a particular electron energy and, thus, apply most exactly to bombarded samples which are sufficiently thin that very little energy loss by ionization occurs in passage through the samples. For electrons slowing down inside a solid, the cross-section (for displacement) changes continuously along the path due to the ionization losses to the electrons of the solid. (The stopping power is given by an equation somewhat more complicated than eq. (4.9) for heavy charged particles.) The very low mass of the electrons means that the electrons « bounce around » as they slow down; *i.e.*, there are several collisions (with atoms) of significant angular deflection during

(*) $r_0 \simeq e^2/m_e c^2$ = the classical radius of the electron.

the slowing-down history as well as, perhaps, one collision sufficiently large to displace an atom. Of course, as in the case of the heavy charged particles, the predominant share of the energy is lost by ionization.

5·5. *The displacement probability curve.* – The properties of fast electrons also allow for a critical examination of the displacement probability curve. Since adequate numbers of electrons of the appropriate energies, in this range, can be obtained, and since almost continuous variation of the energy is possible, one may bombard samples with the same number of electrons but with ever increasing energies and measure some property which should depend sensitively on the number of displaced atoms and so get a measure of how the displacement curve looks. If the sharp threshold model is correct, a sharp rise in the number of displacements should be seen in the region of $E_e^{(t)}$ as given above (eq. (5.6)). This type of work has been going on for some time now, with results as given by BILLINGTON and CRAWFORD (Table II) [7].

TABLE II. – *Experimentally determined displacement energies for a number of solids.*

Solid	Property	Displacement energy (eV)	Reference
Graphite	resistivity	25	(*a*)
Germanium	resistivity	31	(*b*)
Germanium	minority carrier lifetime	13	(*c*)
Silicon	minority carrier lifetime	13	(*c*)
Copper	resistivity	24	(*d*)
Fe in Cu-Fe alloy	saturation magnetization	27	(*e*)
Cu_3Au	resistivity (ordering)	~ 10	(*f*)
InSb	resistivity	~ 6	(*g*)

(*a*) Unpublished work of D. T. EGGEN quoted by G. R. HENNIG and J. H. HOVE: *Proc. Conf. on Peaceful Uses of Atomic Energy*, Vol. 7 (Geneva, 1956), p. 666.
(*b*) E. E. KLONTZ and K. LARK-HOROVITZ: *Phys. Rev.*, **82**, 763 (1951); **86**, 643 (1952). See also E. E. KLONTZ: *Thesis* (1953).
(*c*) P. RAPPAPORT and J. J. LOFERSKI: *Phys. Rev.*, **100**, 1261 (1955); **98**, 1861 (1955).
(*d*) D. T. EGGEN and M. J. LAUBENSTEIN: *Phys. Rev.*, **91**, 238 (1955).
(*e*) J. M. DENNEY: *Phys. Rev.*, **92**, 531 (1953).
(*f*) R. A. DUGDALE: *Rept. of the Bristol Conf. on Defects in Crystalline Solids* (London, 1956), p. 246.
(*g*) F. EISEN: private communication.

It must be pointed out that other types of radiation are not well suited to this kind of study:

1) Heavy charged particles (from eq. (3.11)):

$$T_{\max} = \frac{4mM}{(m+M)^2}\,E; \qquad \text{so,} \qquad E^{(t)} = \frac{(M+m)^2}{4mM}\,E_d\,. \tag{5.10}$$

Thus, for protons in copper, with $E_d = 25$ eV, $E^{(t)} \sim 400$ eV, and the range of such protons is far too small for practical experiments.

2) Neutrons: Again, say, in copper, $E^{(t)} \sim 400$ eV; and neutrons cannot as yet be obtained in sufficient intensity at such energies to make a threshold experiment feasible.

3) γ-rays: Here the pertinent threshold energies are like those of electrons, and the penetration is adequate, but the gammas cannot be obtained in anything like a continuous and controlled array of energies over the required range.

5·6. *Primaries from* γ*-rays.* – There are many possible interactions of γ-rays with the electrons and nuclei of a solid; however, for purposes of arriving at probabilities for atomic displacement only three interactions are sufficiently important to merit consideration for γ-ray energies in the range 0.1 MeV to 10 MeV. These are:

1) Compton scattering (C).

2) The photoelectric effect (P.E.).

3) Pair production (P.P.).

In none of these cases is an atom directly ejected by the γ-ray, but an energetic electron (or positron) is produced which may subsequently displace atoms by the type of collision discussed above. Of these three interactions, the Compton scattering process predominates in an important area of investigation, namely, solids of light elements bombarded with γ-rays of energies less than 3 MeV but greater than 0.5 MeV. As an example of the type of considerations which enter into calculations of the pertinent cross-sections, we examine briefly the Compton scattering case. γ-rays (of some one energy; *e.g.*, $E_\gamma \simeq 1.25$ MeV for ^{60}Co radiation) incident upon a sample (light elements) whose dimensions are of the order of a centimeter or less will generate fast electrons fairly uniformly throughout the specimen. These electrons will have a range very short in comparison with the dimensions of the sample and will slow down to rest inside the sample, producing displaced atoms as they travel. For the Compton scattering case we first require the differential cross-section, $d\sigma^{(C)}(E_\gamma, E_e)$, for the production of an electron of energy E_e (in dE_e) by a γ-ray of energy E_γ. Then the differential cross-section, $d\sigma^{(C)}(E_\gamma, T)$, for the transfer of kinetic energy T (in dT) to an atom from the γ-ray, may be calculated by

$$d\sigma^{(C)}(E_\gamma, T) = \int_{E_e^{(t)}(T)}^{E_e^{\max}} d\sigma^{(C)}(E_\gamma, E_e)\overline{n(E_e, T)}\,. \tag{5.11}$$

In eq. (5.11), $\overline{n(E_e, T)}$ is the average number of atoms given a kinetic energy T during the entire slowing-down history of an electron starting at E_e.

(5.12) E_e^{max} is the maximum energy which can be given an electron by the γ-ray of energy E_γ. (This is slightly smaller than E_γ for the Compton process.)

(5.13) $E_e^{(t)}(T)$ is the lowest electron energy which can transfer T to an atom (given by eq. (5.6) with T replacing E_d).

The calculation of the average number, $\bar{n}$, involves the stopping power for electrons; and the cross-section for kinetic energy transfers by electrons (eq. (5.7)); thus,

$$\overline{n(E_e, T)} = \int_{E_e^{(t)}(T)}^{E_e} \frac{dE_e'}{(-dE/dx)_{E_e'}} N\,d\sigma^{(C)}(E_e', T)\,. \tag{5.14}$$

The cross-section for atomic displacement is then calculated by

$$\sigma_d^{(C)}(E_\gamma) = \int_0^{T_{max}^{(C)}} p(T)\,d\sigma^{(C)}(E_\gamma, T)\,, \tag{5.15}$$

where $p(T)$ is the displacement probability function, and $T_{max}^{(C)}$ is the maximum kinetic energy which can be transferred to an atom from an incident γ-ray of energy E_γ by Compton scattering. Since $p(T)$ is not at present well known, progress is made by using the sharp threshold model; thus,

$$\sigma_d^{(C)}(E_\gamma; E_d) = \int_{E_d}^{T_{max}^{(C)}} d\sigma^{(C)}(E_\gamma, T)\,. \tag{5.16}$$

It can be easily shown that, if such sharp threshold cross-sections are calculated for various assumed values of E_d, then the true value, eq. (5.15), may be calculated if $p(T)$ is known by

$$\sigma_d^{(C)}(E_\gamma) = \int_0^{T_{max}^{(C)}} \left(\frac{dp}{dT}\right)_{T=E_d} \sigma_d^{(C)}(E_\gamma; E_d)\,dE_d\,. \tag{5.17}$$

Finally, this computation must be repeated for all important γ-ray interactions:

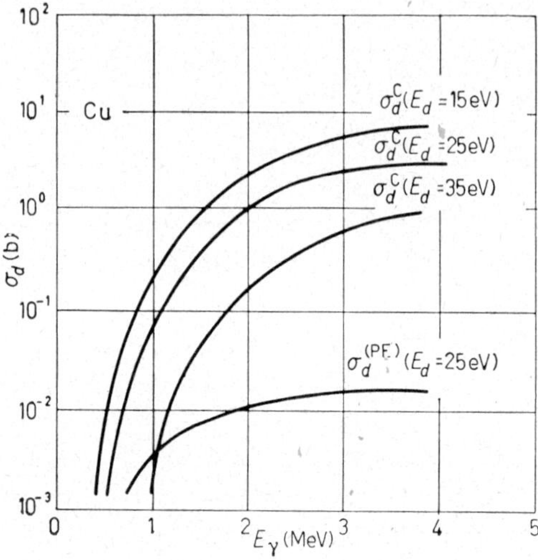

$$\sigma_d^{(\gamma)}(E_\gamma) = \sigma_d^{(C)}(E_\gamma) + \sigma_d^{(P.E.)}(E_\gamma) + \sigma_d^{(P.P.)}(E_\gamma) + \dots \tag{5.18}$$

Some examples of γ-ray displacement cross-sections (based on the sharp threshold model) are given in Fig. 7, after OEN and HOLMES [8].

Fig. 7. – Displacement cross-sections by γ rays through Compton scattering (C) and the photoelectric effect (PE) (schematic)

5·7. *Primaries from recoils.* – The nuclei of lattice atoms may become radioactive as a result of nuclear interactions with the bombarding particles, especially neutrons and γ-rays. As a result of the subsequent emission of radiation, the lattice atom will be given a certain amount of recoil kinetic energy. This may be sufficient to displace the atom from its lattice site. As examples of such reactions, we have:

1) Irradiation of cobalt with thermal neutrons produces radioactive ^{60}Co. ^{60}Co decays with the emission of γ-rays whose average energy is ~ 1.25 MeV. The mechanics of the process show that the cobalt atom will be given a recoil kinetic energy of about 30 eV.

2) Irradiation of copper with γ-rays having energies ~ 20 MeV leads to a (γ, n) reaction in copper, such that the ejected neutron has an energy of ~ 2 MeV. The recoil energy of the copper atom is $\sim 60\,000$ eV. Thus, this copper atom is surely displaced and by further collisions forms secondary, tertiary, and so on, displacements.

6. – Simple cascade theory.

6·1. *The expected number of displaced atoms.* – We now center our attention on the number of displaced atoms (vacancy-interstitial pairs) produced in a given lattice by a primary ejected lattice atom of a given initial kinetic energy, T, as imparted to it by some form of incident energetic radiation. The particular quantity which is most easily calculated is

$$(6.1)\qquad \nu(T) = \left[\begin{array}{c}\text{the average (or expected) number of displaced atoms}\\ \text{produced by a primary of kinetic energy } T.\end{array}\right].$$

Notice that this is the « average » value. If the same kinetic energy, T, is imparted to lattice atoms many different times, in different lattice directions, it can be expected that each resultant cascade will have a somewhat different total number of displaced atoms. However, it turns out as shown by LEIBFRIED [9] that this distribution in total number is sharply peaked, so that the average value, $\nu(T)$, is all we really require. Notice further that the calculation of $\nu(T)$ does not include any information as to the spatial distribution of vacancies and interstitials in the final damaged region resulting from one energetic primary. This topic is left for later discussions. Finally, it should be noted that in consideration of these quantities we are thinking of a lattice at the absolute zero of temperature (and with no zero point vibration) so that a vacancy-interstitial pair once formed (and stable under the assumption of the calculation) cannot be annihilated or disappear to sinks by thermal diffusion. (Also, for convenience, we will neglect the low-probability event that a slowly moving lattice atom encounter a previously created vacancy.)

Even after these assumptions we still have to make further, and much more limiting, approximations to permit a final calculation. These are:

1) Hard-sphere scattering collisions between lattice atoms is assumed.

2) The sharp threshold model for the displacement probability curve is assumed.

For the moment let us just regard these as accepted and examine their effects on the final results later. Because of the hard-sphere scattering assumption (*), the kinetic energy of a moving lattice atom is shared with a stationary lattice atom (equal mass) in such a way that any two final energies of the two atoms which add up to T are equally probable. This may be expressed analytically in terms of the differential cross-section (see eq. (3.15)) that an incident atom of kinetic energy T transfers kinetic energy T' in $\mathrm{d}T'$ to the struck atom:

$$(6.2)\qquad \mathrm{d}\sigma(T, T') = \sigma_s(T)K(T, T')\,\mathrm{d}T' = \begin{cases}\sigma_s(T)\,\dfrac{\mathrm{d}T'}{T} & 0 \leqslant T' \leqslant T\,.\\[2ex] 0 & T' > T\,.\end{cases}$$

(*) Note that the radius of the assumed atomic sphere is not important for this calculation, since we are not interested in the spatial distribution of displacements.

Thus, the distribution of final energies of either atom is flat, as represented in Fig. 8. Some energy is essentially lost if one of the atoms falls into the region below E_d, as shown; but this can be neglected when we are considering high-energy primaries.

As a simple, intuitive approach (*) to the calculation of $\nu(T)$, consider the successive stages in the cascade process, with the use of the over-simplified model in which the energy at each collision is exactly equally shared between the two atoms (see Fig. 9):

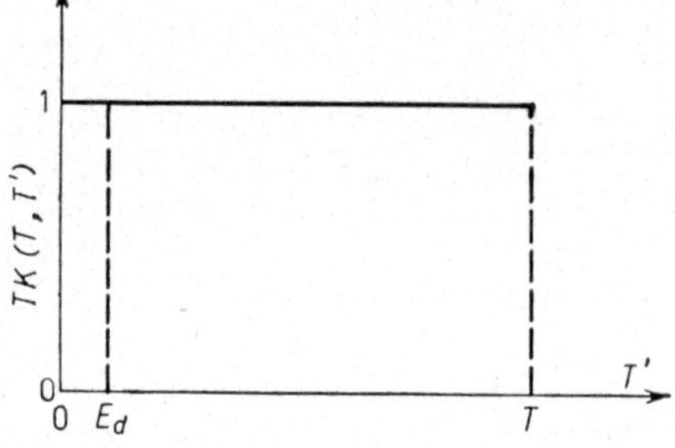

Fig. 8. – The hard-sphere energy transfer cross-section.

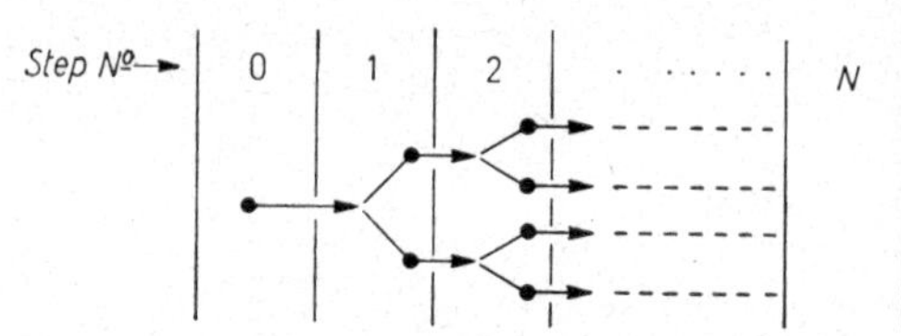

Fig. 9. – Simplified model of the cascade process.

Step number	0	1	2 ...	N,
Number of displaced atoms	1	2	4 ...	2^N,
Energy of each atom	T	$\frac{T}{2}$	$\frac{T}{4}$ ...	$\frac{T}{2^N}$.

Now suppose that we choose N such that

$$T/2^N \lessapprox 2E_d \,. \tag{6.3}$$

then each atom in the N-th step will be unable to cause further displacement and must lose its kinetic energy in nonproductive collisions. So the cascade ends. Then our quantity of interest, $\nu_a(T)$, the average number of displaced atoms, is just

$$\nu_a(T) = \frac{T}{2E_d} \quad \text{(approximate form)} \,. \tag{6.4}$$

This is very much like the accurate result which can be obtained under these assumptions.

(*) For a more accurate calculation, see Appendix I.

One of the most convenient forms of the more accurate result is

$$(6.5)\qquad \nu(T) = \begin{cases} 0 & T < E_d\,, \\ 1 & E_d \leqslant T \leqslant 2E_d\,, \\ \dfrac{T}{2E_d} & T \geqslant 2E_d\,. \end{cases} \qquad \text{(more accurate form)}$$

The approximate form, $\nu_a(T)$, is very convenient for use in calculations of high-energy primaries; but for electrons and γ-rays of one MeV or so, the « structure » in $\nu(T)$, when T is of the order of a few E_d, can be quite important. As an example, suppose a two-MeV neutron transfers 100 000 eV to a copper atom in copper, then the expected number of vacancy-interstitial pairs which will eventually be produced when the motion of all secondaries, tertiaries, etc., has ceased is

$$\nu = \frac{100\,000}{2\cdot 25} = 2000\,.$$

The calculation, as noticed previously, does not tell us where these 2 000 displaced atoms are, though some estimate of this can be made separately. For the present we may use the result that these 2 000 atoms will be included in a region about 100 lattice spacings in diameter. It can also be seen that essentially all of the initial kinetic energy of the primary also appears in this volume in some way among all the 10^6 atoms. How this energy is dissipated and how its presence affects the defect structure of the cascade are difficult and as yet poorly understood problems.

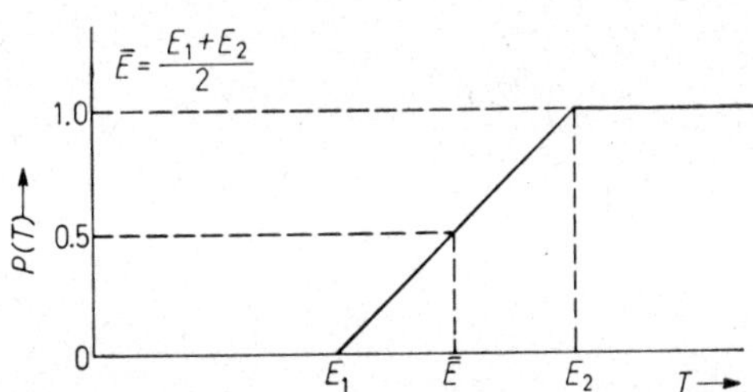

Fig. 10. – The linear displacement probability curve.

However, the result for $\nu(T)$ is of great value if we can believe that critical approximations involved in the calculation have not destroyed its validity. Recent investigations, particularly by LEHMANN [10], have howsn that the sharp threshold assumption gives acceptable results as long as the energy region over which the displacement probability curve is rising from zero to unity is small in comparison with T, the kinetic energy of the primary of interest. For example, if the displacement probability curve rises linearly between E_1 and E_2 as shown in Fig. 10, then it can be shown that for $T \gg \bar{E}$ and $(E_2/E_1) - 1 \ll 1$

$$(6.6)\qquad \nu(T) \simeq \frac{T}{2\bar{E}}\,.$$

Until further knowledge is obtained for $p(T)$, we must be satisfied with this, fully realizing that if $p(T)$ varies over 100 eV or so, the results for the low-energy primaries, such as in electron or γ-irradiation, will not be very accurately given by the sharp threshold model (*).

As far as the hard sphere scattering assumption is concerned, recent work, again by LEIBFRIED, seems to indicate that the form given here for $\nu(T)$ is quite acceptable, again for high-energy primaries, as long as the scattering law is not extreme, in the sense of greatly exaggerating the low-energy transfer.

6·2. *Replacement collisions.* – There is one assumption in the calculation of $\nu(T)$ as yet unmentioned concerning the « replacement collisions ». In the full treatment of the calculation of $\nu(T)$ given in the Appendix, it is shown that this assumption is not critical for the result. However, the various possible assumptions give greatly differing ratios of displacement collisions to replacement collisions, and while this is unimportant for the resultant total number of displaced atoms, it may be very important for ordering changes in lattices of more than one atomic species. The question is essentially this: suppose a primary of kinetic energy T collides with a lattice atom, and transfers to the latter most of its energy. Then with the primary now essentially at the lattice site of the struck atom (note: in collisions between equal masses a head-on collision results in a complete stop for the originally moving mass), and having an energy somewhere around E_d or below, will the primary fall into the now vacated lattice site? If this does happen, the process is called a replacement collision. Note that no new displacement is produced; in a single element lattice, it is just as if the primary went on after the collision, with some small loss of energy, since the atoms are indistinguishable. However, if such collisions are possible, in, say, an alloy, atom A may be replaced by atom B, and the state of order of the alloy may be altered. At the present time, it seems that replacement collisions very probably do occur; but little can be said theoretically about the number of such collisions, especially in the important cases where there are two atomic species of different atomic sizes.

7. – Average and total number of displacements.

7·1. *Formalism.* – The differential cross-section, $d\sigma(E, T)$, for primaries may now be seen to have also an interpretation as a differential cross-section for the production of various-sized groups of displacements. If $d\sigma(E, \nu)$ is the

(*) Note that the trick of performing the calculation for various assumed values of E_d and the averaging appropriately as (presented above for the γ-ray calculations, eq. (5.17)) will not work here because the threshold is involved in every step of a multistep process.

differential cross-section for radiation of energy E to produce a group of displaced atoms (all resulting from one primary) having a number of displacements between ν and $\nu+\mathrm{d}\nu$, then

$$\mathrm{d}\sigma(E,\nu)=\sigma(E)\,K(E,\,T(\nu))\,\frac{\mathrm{d}T}{\mathrm{d}\nu}\,\mathrm{d}\nu\,, \tag{7.1}$$

and it is seen that because of the linear dependence (for high energy radiation, eq. (6.5)), the two cross-sections, $\mathrm{d}\sigma(E,T)$ and $\mathrm{d}\sigma(E,\nu)$, have the same functional form. Thus a type of radiation, such as heavy charged particles, which has a spectrum of primaries going as $1/T^2$, will have a spectrum of groups of displaced atoms going as $1/\nu^2$, so that in a solid suffering such irradiation there will be far more groups having a small number of defects than those having a larger number.

It is usually more important to deal with the cross-section for producing one displaced atom than to deal with the cross-section for producing a primary. The cross-section for producing one displaced atom can be calculated using the average number of displacements per primary; thus,

$$\sigma_d(E)=\int_{E_d}^{T_m}\nu(T)\,\mathrm{d}\sigma(E,\,T)\,. \tag{7.2}$$

If, as for electrons and γ-rays in the 1 MeV range, T_m is sufficiently low that $\nu(T)$ does not deviate significantly from unity over the range of integration, this is essentially the same as the expression

$$\sigma_d^{(p)}(E)=\int_{E_d}^{T_m}\mathrm{d}\sigma(E,\,T)\,, \tag{7.3}$$

which was used previously and is just the cross-section for production of primaries alone (see eq. (5.8)). However, for more energetic radiation the integral with $\nu(T)$ as a weighting function must necessarily be used. Another quantity of interest is the average number of displaced atoms, *i.e.*, the average size of the various groups produced by the primaries of various energies. This may be seen to be given by

$$\overline{\nu(E)}=\frac{\sigma_d(E)}{\sigma_d^{(p)}(E)}\,. \tag{7.4}$$

We now consider some specific cases of these quantities.

7·2. *Heavy charged particles (high energy).* – Using the approximate form for $\nu(T)$ (*)

(7.5) $$\nu^{(0)}(T) = \begin{cases} \dfrac{T}{2E_d} & T \geqslant 2E_d\,, \\ 0 & T < 2E_d\,, \end{cases}$$

and (eq. (5.2))

(7.6) $$\mathrm{d}\sigma(E, T) = \frac{2\pi z^2 Z^2 e^4 m}{EM} \frac{\mathrm{d}T}{T^2}\,,$$

we find

(7.7) $$\sigma_d(E) = \left(\frac{2\pi z^2 Z^2 e^4 m}{EM}\right) \frac{\ln (T_m/2E_d)}{2E_d} \qquad \text{with} \qquad \frac{T_m}{E} = \frac{4mM}{(m+M)^2}\,,$$

(7.8) $$\bar{\nu}(E) = \frac{1}{2} \ln \frac{T_m}{2E_d}\,.$$

7·3. *Fast neutrons.* – In this case the quantities above must be averaged over the energy distribution of the neutrons. We consider two different distributions.

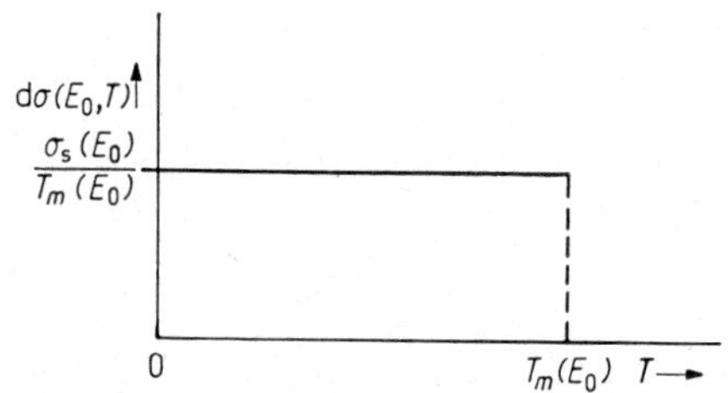

Fig. 11. – The differential cross-section for energy transfer to an atom from a neutron of energy E_0 (assuming isotropic scattering).

1) Neutrons all of one high energy, E_0 (a simplified model for fission spectrum neutrons, with $E_0 \sim 2$ MeV).

If we assume also that these neutrons are scattered isotropically (in the center-of-mass system) from the nucleus of the type of atoms we are considering, and if we further assume that these atoms are sufficiently heavy that the laboratory system is essentially equivalent to the center-of-mass system, the differential scattering cross-section (see Fig. 11) is

(7.9) $$\mathrm{d}\sigma(E_0, T) = \sigma_s(E_0) \frac{\mathrm{d}T}{T_m(E_0)}\,; \qquad T_m(E_0) = \frac{4A}{(A+1)^2} E_0 \sim \frac{4}{A} E_0\,,$$

(7.10) $$\sigma_d(E_0) = \frac{\sigma_s(E_0)}{4T_m(E_0)E_d}(T_m^2 - 4E_d^2) \simeq \sigma_s(E_0) \frac{T_m(E_0)/2}{2E_d}\,,$$

(7.11) $$\overline{T(E_0)} = \frac{T_m(E_0)}{2} = \text{the average energy transferred by a neutron of energy } E_0\,.$$

(7.12) $$\bar{\nu}(E_0) = \frac{T_m(E_0)/2}{2E_d} = \frac{\overline{T}(E_0)}{2E_d}\,.$$

(*) The form given really means that for the more energetic radiation we neglect the integral $\int_{E_d}^{2E_d} \mathrm{d}\sigma(E, T)$ when added to the integral $\int_{2E_d}^{T_m} \nu(T)\, \mathrm{d}\sigma(E, T)$.

2) Neutrons having a $1/E$ spectrum up to some high energy E (and above some low energy E_{th}). This is a simplified model for the low-energy portion of the neutron flux in a well-moderated reactor, where E_0 = fission-neutron energy, and E_{th} is the energy of completely thermalized neutrons. This energy distribution is specified by the neutron flux per unit energy range, $\varphi(E)$,

$$\varphi(E) = \begin{cases} \dfrac{c}{E} & E_0 \geqslant E \geqslant E_{th}\,, \\ 0 & \text{otherwise}\,. \end{cases} \tag{7.13}$$

Again assuming isotropic scattering of all neutrons from the atoms (nuclei) of a specimen placed in this flux, we note that, if

$$\mathrm{d}\sigma(E, T) = \sigma_s(E)\,\frac{\mathrm{d}T}{T_m(E)}\,, \tag{7.14}$$

then we may conveniently define an average differential cross-section, $\mathrm{d}\sigma(T)$, that any neutron produce a primary of kinetic energy T, by

$$\mathrm{d}\sigma(T) = \frac{\int_{E^{(t)}(T)}^{E_0} \varphi(E)\,\mathrm{d}\sigma(E, T)\,\mathrm{d}E}{\int_{E_{th}}^{E_0} \varphi(E)\,\mathrm{d}E}\,, \tag{7.15}$$

where

$$E^{(t)}(T) = \text{the lowest energy of a neutron which permits the transfer of kinetic energy } T = \frac{(A+1)^2}{4A}\,T \simeq \frac{A}{4}\,T\,. \tag{7.16}$$

In order to demonstrate the general trend of these expressions, let us take

$$\sigma_s(E) \simeq \sigma_s^{(0)} \quad \text{(a constant)} \tag{7.17}$$

over the range considered. This may actually not be bad for some cases of neutron-nucleus elastic scattering cross-section in the few-eV to the few-MeV range. Then

$$\mathrm{d}\sigma(T) = \frac{\sigma_s^{(0)}}{\ln\,(E_0/E_{th})}\left(\frac{1}{T} - \frac{1}{T_m(E_0)}\right)\mathrm{d}T\,. \tag{7.18}$$

The atomic displacement cross-section then may be obtained from (*)

$$\sigma_d = \int_{E_d}^{T_{\max}(E_0)} \nu(T)\,\mathrm{d}\sigma(T)\,, \tag{7.19}$$

$$\sigma_d \simeq \frac{\sigma_s^{(0)}}{\ln(E_0/E_{th})}\,\frac{T_m(E_0)/2}{2E_d}\,, \tag{7.20}$$

$$\bar{\nu} \simeq \frac{T_m(E_0)/2}{2E_d \ln\left(T_m(E_0)/E_d\right)}\,. \tag{7.21}$$

For comparison with the monoenergetic neutrons considered above, if the E_0 are taken to be the same, it is observed that the average number of displaced atoms, in the case of moderated neutrons, is lower by a factor of $\ln\left(T_m(E_0)/E_d\right)$. For $E_0 \sim 2$ MeV,

$$A = 64\,, \qquad E_d = 25\ \text{eV}\,, \qquad \ln\frac{T_m}{E_d} \sim 8.5.$$

To calculate the total number of displacements, N_d, produced per unit time per unit volume, in a reactor flux, consider the simplified model of fission neutrons all of energy E_0, slowing down in an infinite medium (**) of good moderator (absorption cross-section for neutrons negligible). N_d is made up of two contributions: 1) from the virgin fast neutrons (E_0) before they begin to slow down by making their first collision, and 2) from the $1/E$ flux (with displacement cross-section denoted simply as σ_d). With N_a as the atomic density of the specimen, we have

$$N_d = N_a\varphi(E_0)\,\sigma_d(E_0) + N_a\,\Phi_T\,\sigma_d\,. \tag{7.22}$$

If S_0 neutrons of energy E_0 are produced per unit volume per unit time, then (with superscript « M » referring to moderator quantities)

$$\varphi(E_0) = \frac{S_0}{\Sigma_s^M(E_0)}\,, \tag{7.23}$$

(*) Note that the σ_d of eq. (7.19) is to be used with the *total flux* of eq. (2.2). This results from the definition of eq. (7.15). The average $\mathrm{d}\sigma(T)$ could be taken only over that part of the flux *above* the displacement threshold energy, $E^{(t)}(E_d)$, [eq. (5.10)], but, then, σ_d would be used only with that part of the total flux.

(**) This neglects the spatial variation of the neutron flux across a reactor. For a large, thermal reactor the results given here are quite acceptable, and will still give the general trend, in any case.

and

$$\varphi(E) \simeq \frac{S_0}{E\xi^M \Sigma_s^M(E)}, \quad \text{where} \quad \xi^M = 1 + \frac{\alpha \ln \alpha}{1-\alpha}, \qquad \alpha = \left(\frac{A^M - 1}{A^M + 1}\right)^2, \tag{7.24}$$

$$\Phi_T = \int_{E_{\rm th}}^{E_0} \varphi(E)\,\mathrm{d}E \simeq \frac{S_0}{\xi^M \Sigma_s^M(E_0)} \ln \frac{E_0}{E_{\rm th}}, \tag{7.25}$$

if the scattering cross-section of the moderator is taken to be constant in energy. Then

$$N_d = S_0 \frac{T_m(E_0)/2}{2E_d} \frac{N_a \sigma_s^{(0)}}{N_a^M \sigma_s^M} + \frac{S_0}{\xi^M} \frac{T_m(E_0)/2}{2E_d} \frac{N_a \sigma_s^{(0)}}{N_a^M \sigma_s^M}, \tag{7.26}$$

$$N_d = S_0 \frac{T_m(E_0)/2}{2E_d} \left(1 + \frac{1}{\xi^M}\right) \frac{N_a \sigma_s^{(0)}}{N_a^M \sigma_s^M}. \tag{7.27}$$

For graphite, $\xi^M \sim 0.16$, so in a graphite reactor, on this very simple model the fission neutrons, before they start slowing down, produce about one-sixth as many displaced atoms as the whole spectrum of moderated neutrons, in spite of the fact that the total fission neutron flux (7.23) is less than 1/100 of the total slowing-down flux (eq. (7.25)).

8. – Ionization losses.

8·1. *The ionization threshold.* – Such a result as the one just obtained showing the much greater displacement-producing effectiveness of the higher-energy particles is directly due to the linear rise of $\nu(T)$ with T in our simple model. Since this rise cannot continue indefinitely, some care must be taken in applying this kind of result. Specifically, if the primary ejected atom is sufficiently energetic it may be suffering ionization losses to the electrons of its own lattice just as discussed above for energetic charged particles. In fact, if it is moving fast enough, the primary itself may actually be charged.

Now, we have discussed previously the fact that while ionization losses rise along the path of the moving atom as its energy decreases, there is a turnover point, and the ionization losses decrease rapidly as the velocity of the atom falls below the velocities of the slowest electrons in the solid. However, elastic collision losses continue to rise with decreasing energy (*). Choose E_i as an energy somewhere in the region of the crossing of these two curves (see

(*) The loss by displacement is shown as a rising curve with descending energy. Actually, it may level off at low energies or even fall with decreasing energy.

Fig. 12); then a primary produced at an energy much greater than E_i will very quickly slow down by ionization losses (since the stopping power is so great) without producing any significant number of displaced atoms. After the atom is well below E_i in energy, ionization is over and our previous mode, for the cascading displacement applies well. The region around E_i is difficult and it must be noted that treatments of the problem at these energies are lacking at the present time. This problem is a bothersome one in the case of energetic radiation, particularly reactor neutrons, since a proper accounting for the number of displaced atoms must take ionization losses into account, for they surely predominate at least in the high end of the spectrum. The generally accepted scheme at present is to say that a primary loses all its energy above E_i by ionization and at E_i immediately enters into the simple cascade process. This is the « sharp ionization threshold » model, and E_i is called the ionization threshold energy.

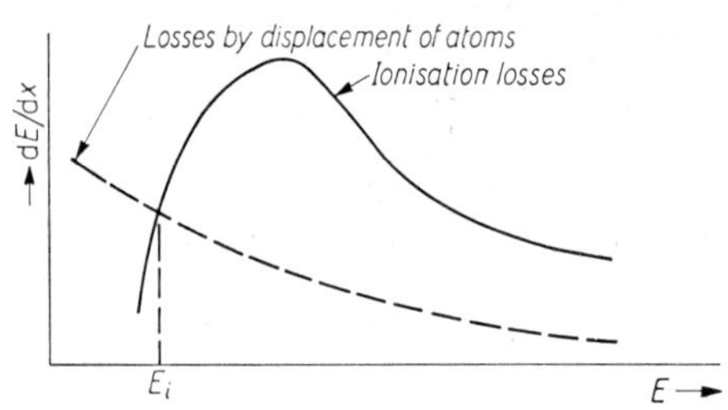

Fig. 12. – The ionization and atomic displacement stopping power (schematic).

SEITZ has suggested the following values for E_i:

$$(8.1)\quad \begin{cases} (a)\ \text{Insulators:}\quad E_i = \dfrac{M}{m_e}\dfrac{E_G}{8} & \text{where } E_G = \text{the optical width of the forbidden gap;} \\ (b)\ \text{Metals:}\quad E_i = \dfrac{M}{m_e}\dfrac{\zeta}{16} & \text{where } \zeta = \text{the Fermi level.} \end{cases}$$

These formulas arise essentially from velocity matching. Note that, if ζ is the kinetic energy of a « free » electron in a metal, then the threshold velocity, v_i, for the moving atom, from the equation above, is

$$(8.2)\qquad v_i = \frac{v_e}{4}\,.$$

Thus, when the atom is moving as slowly as $\frac{1}{4}$ the velocity of the electrons, it can no longer excite them. DIENES and VINEYARD [11] have assumed as a rough approximation for all materials

$$(8.3)\qquad E_i \sim \frac{1}{2}\frac{M}{m_e}\ \{\text{eV}\}\,.$$

Using eq. (8.3), we construct the following Table (Table III), showing clearly why this problem is of importance for reactor irradiations.

TABLE III. – *Threshold energies.*

Substance	Average energy transferred to the atom by collision with a 2 MeV neutron	$E_i = \frac{1}{2}\frac{M}{m_e}$ (eV)
Be	360 000	2 700
Al	150 000	24 300
Cu	85 000	57 600
Ag	40 000	100 000
Au	20 000	180 000

These results indicate that in reactor bombardment ionization effects vary from being quite unimportant for heavy elements to being of primary importance for light elements. Actually, the effects are not so enormous as would appear from the table. In order to calculate the effect, we must use a better form for the reactor flux than the simple model discussed above. In a large graphite reactor, for example, the fast flux (actually, $E\varphi(E)$ is plotted) might look like the solid line in Fig. 13, whereas the dotted line is the simplified model. (The simplified model is the sum of two fluxes: 1) $1/E$, the flat portion, and 2) the sharply peaked part which represents the virgin fission neutrons.) Of course, the simplified model is quite useless for this case, since the result would be essentially the same as long as $E_i < E_0$.

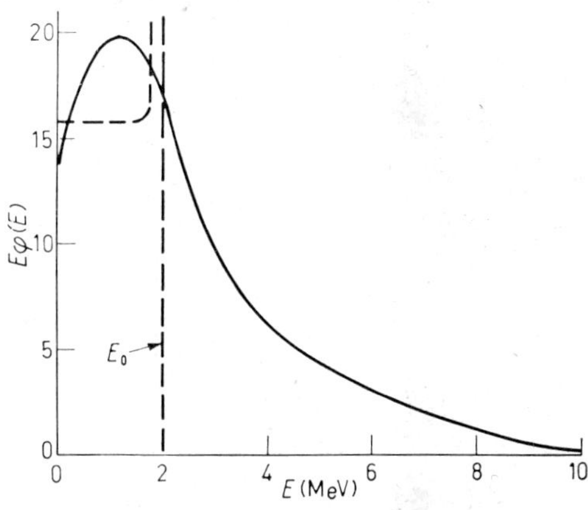

Fig. 13. – The high energy neutron flux in a graphite reactor, solid curve (schematic) compared with simplified model (dashed curve).

8'2. *Reactor case, using the ionization threshold.* – In our standard notation we have

$$N_d = \int_0^\infty \nu(T) \int_0^\infty \Sigma_s(E)\varphi(E)\,\mathrm{d}E\,K(E,T)\,\mathrm{d}T\,. \tag{8.4}$$

Manipulating the integrals, dropping negligible terms and using the sharp ionization threshold model, *i.e.*,

$$\nu(T) = \begin{cases} \dfrac{T}{2E_d} & T \leqslant E_i\,, \\[2ex] \dfrac{E_i}{2E_d} & T > E_i\,, \end{cases} \tag{8.5}$$

then (also assuming constant scattering cross-sections)

$$N_d \simeq \frac{4}{A}\frac{\Sigma_s^{(0)}}{4E_d}\int_{AE_d}^{AE_i/4} E\varphi(E)\,\mathrm{d}E + \frac{\Sigma_s^{(0)}}{4E_d}\int_{AE_i/4}^{\infty} E_i\varphi(E)\,\mathrm{d}E\,, \tag{8.6}$$

if $E_i \to \infty$

$$N_d(\infty) = \frac{4}{A}\frac{\Sigma_s^{(0)}}{4E_d}\int_{AE_d/2}^{\infty} E\varphi(E)\,\mathrm{d}E\,, \tag{8.7}$$

as before.

From the actual flux plots (*) we obtain, for various assumed threshold energies, Table IV.

TABLE IV. – *Effects of various assumed threshold energies.*

E_i (eV)	$N_d(E_i)/N_d(\infty)$
100 000	0.75
60 000	0.58
30 000	0.37

9. – The effects of the deviation from isotropic of the angular distribution of neutron scattering.

In the calculations we have so far considered for reactors, one important approximation has not been discussed in detail. We have always assumed that the neutron scattering is isotropic in the center-of-mass system (and,

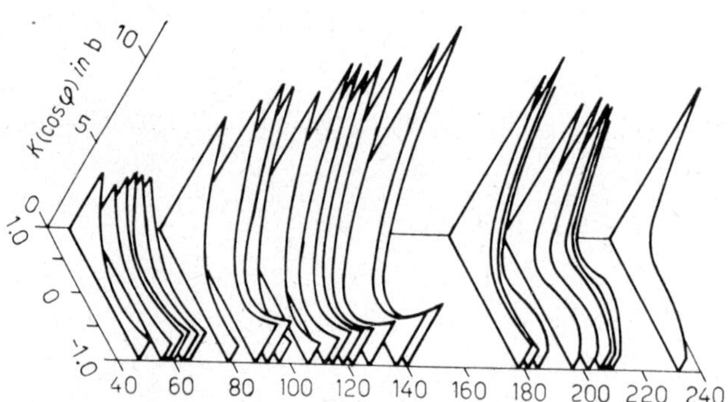

Fig. 14. – The angular distribution of scattering neutrons (1 MeV) from various nuclei.

(*) See Appendix II for a better discussion of the energy-dependence of the neutron flux.

thus, in the laboratory system for heavy nuclei). However, this assumption does not fit with the experimental data. The accompanying curves from WALT and BARSCHALL [12] (Fig. 14) show the angular distribution of scattered neutrons of energy 1 MeV from various nuclei. In our previous notation (see eq. (3.12)) the curves show essentially $f(E, \theta)$ (except for numerical factors) where

$$d\sigma(E, \theta) = \tfrac{1}{2}\sigma_s(E)\, f(E, \theta) \sin\theta \, d\theta \,. \tag{9.1}$$

For the relationship between the energy transferred to the nuclei and the scattering angle we have (see eq. (3.17))

$$\frac{T}{T_m} = \sin^2\frac{\theta}{2}, \qquad 0 \leqslant \theta \leqslant \pi, \qquad T_m = \frac{4A}{(A+1)^2}\, E \,, \tag{9.2}$$

and it is then seen that a plot of $f(E, \theta)$ (against $\cos\theta$ as shown) is also a plot $K(E, T)$ against T/T_m, except for numerical factors, with the abscissa running from 0 (at $\cos\theta = 1$) to 1 (at $\cos\theta = -1$). Then for isotropic scattering, we would look for horizontal straight lines, so it is immediately seen that the deviations are very significant. It is also observed that the most outstanding direction of the deviation is to favor « forward scattering », *i.e.*, low values of T/T_m. This reduces the estimate of the average energy transferred (as compared with the estimate from assumed isotropic scattering) and would tend to reduce the estimate of the total number of displacements, and reduce the importance of ionization effects. An examination of more extensive data indicates that this effect is found (in a significant way) in the entire energy range from somewhat below 1 MeV up. Though there are not yet sufficient data on angular distributions for an accurate calculation, it has been estimated that in the region of the fission spectrum the average energy transferred to nuclei might actually be $\frac{2}{3}$ to $\frac{3}{4}$ that calculated for isotropic scattering.

10. – Comparison of the calculated total number of displacements with experiment.

In general it may be said that the methods we have discussed for calculating numbers of displaced atoms yield higher values than would be consistent with experimental results. As an example, using the equations given above for the graphite moderated reactors and applying to the ORNL Graphite Reactor, we may calculate the total number of displaced atoms produced in a copper sample in one week. Using a nominal figure for the resistivity of vacancy-interstitial pairs, as $\Delta\varrho \simeq 2\cdot 10^{-6}$ ohm·cm per atomic per cent vacancy-interstitial pairs, it is found that one week's bombardment would yield

$$\Delta\varrho_{\text{theor}} = 35\cdot 10^{-9} \text{ ohm}\cdot\text{cm} \,.$$

BLEWITT and co-workers [13] have found experimentally (bombarding at 20 °K)

$$\Delta\varrho_{\text{exp}} = 4.5\cdot10^{-9}\ \text{ohm}\cdot\text{cm}\ .$$

It is of significance that the theoretical values are more in line with experiment in the case of electron bombardment. This perhaps indicates that ionization effects and « forwardness » of fast neutron scattering may be very important in the neutron case. However, it is entirely possible that there is an important effect from the fact that the primary in the neutron case deposits its energy in a small region of the crystal, just where the vacancies and interstitials are clustered. Just what this effect would amount to in terms of annealing defects is impossible to say, at the present time. It should be noted, however, that BLEWITT has also irradiated many good metals in the periodic table, and it does not seem possible to bring the results into line by use of the ionization threshold, as might be expected from the table given previously.

11. – The range of the primary atoms.

This immediately brings up the question as to just what is the size of the region in which the displacement atoms from one primary are spread out. Some measure of this is given by the « range » of the primary atom itself. The range is not so easily defined in this case as in the case of charged particles, since we are dealing here with atoms interacting through their screened Coulomb fields. The actual path of a primary atom might look as shown in Fig. 15. Here each turning point represents a collision with a lattice atom, and at these points the secondary displaced atoms are created. It is apparent that the final resting place of the primary will have a quite broad distribution with respect to the starting position; thus the difficulty in defining the range. It has been pointed out by LEIBFRIED that the first free flight path (λ_1 of the figure) can act as a fair estimate of the range.

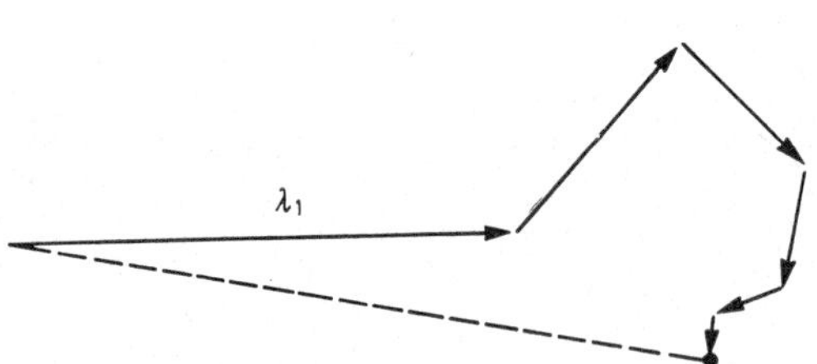

Fig. 15. – The path of an energetic primary in a solid.

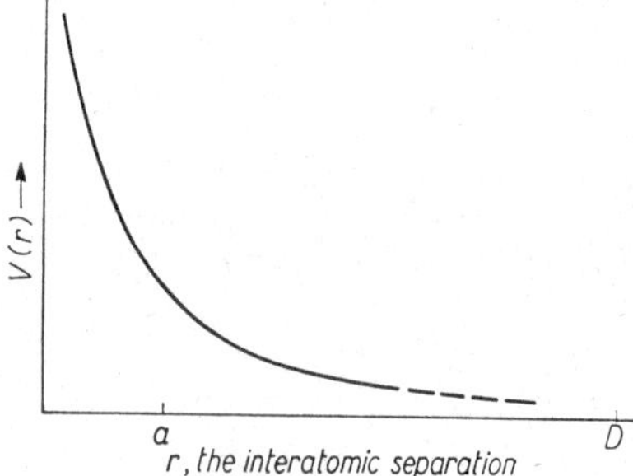

Fig. 16. – The interatomic potential (schematic).

This is essentially because the first mean free path is much the largest of all; subsequent flights are at lower kinetic energies and the cross-section for collision is higher.

The solution of this entire problem may be regarded as resting on knowledge of the interatomic potential, sketched in Fig. 16. The scattering problem in this case can be shown to be essentially classical, so that if $V(r)$ were really known over its full extent, the complete solution would follow easily. However, it is not known. For illustration of the type of consideration which has been given to this problem, let us use the « Bohr potential » (for like atoms)

$$V_B(r) = \frac{Z^2 e^2}{r} \exp[-r/a] , \tag{11.1}$$

and Bohr has taken the screening parameter « a » to be

$$a_B = \frac{a_h}{\sqrt{2} \cdot Z^{\frac{1}{3}}}, \quad a_h = \text{the Bohr radius of the hydrogen atoms.} \tag{11.2}$$

This potential has the right form for small values of r, just the Coulomb interaction when the atoms are very close together, and there is even some justification for the exponential fall-off with increasing separation. However, at the moment, it is just a guess. Note that the screening parameter is surely much less than D, the interatomic spacing, by a factor of 10 or so, as indicated in the figure. Even with this relatively simple form for the potential, further progress is not trivial. The classical scattering theory shows that the differential cross-section for a given kinetic energy transfer has the form shown by the solid curve in Fig. 17. For comparison, the «hard sphere » cross-section is shown as a dotted curve. (E is the kinetic energy of the primary, T is the energy transferred to the secondary.) The solid curve is known only numerically, not analytically. These matters are still under investigation, but for illustration, again we will simplify and use the hard sphere scattering approximation. Thus we say the primary « sees » the lattice as balls of radius $R(E)$. To determine $R(E)$, we take the classical distance of closest approach between two particles having an interatomic potential V and a relative energy $E/2$; thus

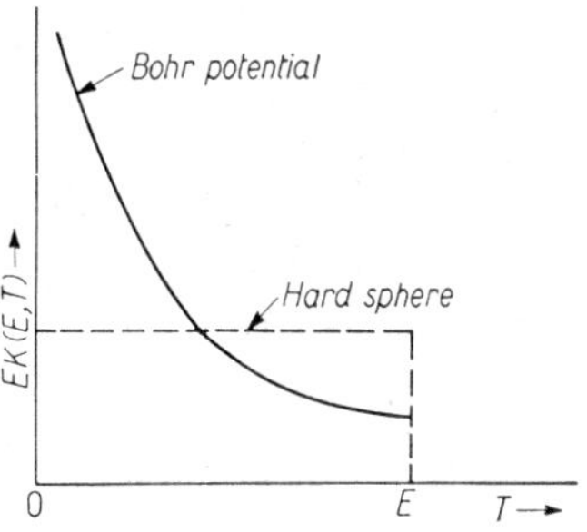

Fig. 17. – The differential cross-section for energy transfer for two interatomic potentials (schematic).

$$\frac{E}{2} = \frac{Z^2 e^2}{R(E)} \exp\left[-\frac{R(E)}{a}\right]. \tag{11.3}$$

Then the mean free path will be given by

$$\lambda_1(E) = \frac{1}{\Sigma_s(E)} = \frac{1}{N\pi R^2(E)} . \tag{11.4}$$

LEIBFRIED and HOLMES [14] have considered this problem in detail, and observing that it is important to allow variation in the screening parameter, a, have defined a as

$$a = \alpha a_B , \tag{11.5}$$

with the parameter α adjustable to fit experimental results. For a copper primary in copper of kinetic energy 40 000 eV, they find that

$$\frac{R(E)}{a} \sim 1 , \qquad \lambda_1(E) \sim 0.61 \cdot 10^{-6}\ \text{cm} , \tag{11.6}$$

and they conclude that the range is of the order of

$$\text{range} \simeq 1.6 \cdot 10^{-6}\ \text{cm} . \tag{11.7}$$

(Notice that the first mean free path makes up more than $\frac{1}{3}$ of the range.) In comparison with experiment [15] a value of

$$\alpha \simeq 2$$

was found to be the best, leading to the value quoted above.

Finally, it must be noted that a great deal needs to be done in this entire area of the interaction potential and all its implications in terms of range and distribution of damage.

12. – Lattice effects.

As long as the moving atoms have energies in excess of 1 keV, it may be expected that the problem may as well be treated as if the crystal were a « gas » of atoms. However, when the energies get down in the range of 100 eV, more or less, there are special « lattice effects ». These will, of course, be important in all damage by displaced atoms, since the final stages of a high-energy cascade are always low-energy collisions. In the treatment of problems such as these, the significant portion of the interatomic potential is at low energies, out at separations somewhat less than D, the interatomic spacing. It is possible that more realistic potential forms (such as the Born-Mayer

$A \exp[-r/a]$) may be chosen in this range. In any case, while the potential is important, it is also important that the atoms sit in a known geometrical array. This is an area which is now under intensive investigation, so that we must be satisfied with the introduction of a few elementary concepts, under the general heading of « focusing along close-packed lines of lattice atoms. » SILSBEE [16] first pointed out that energy may be passed from atom to atom down a close-packed line, without displacing atoms, and with relatively small losses to neighboring lines of atoms. The « focusing » effect is that the initial impulse need not be directed exactly down the line; even if it is « off center », under certain conditions, the line of atoms itself will focus the momentum along the lines.

This has two possible important effects:

a) energy may thus be removed rapidly from a region of damage (far more energy per transfer than carried by a phonon, for example);

b) displaced atoms may be produced relatively far from the initiation point of the focused energy; for example, when the pulse of energy reaches a « bad » lattice region, as near a dislocation line, it may « kick out » an atom.

LEIBFRIED [17] has also shown that matter may be transmitted down a line of atoms. In this effect, sometimes called a « dynamic condition », the atoms just replace each other down the line, until a final one is ejected from its lattice site, off to one side. This also has the effect of producing displacements rather farther away from the starting point than would be expected for energies of a few hundred eV.

13. – Spikes.

Finally, we must mention the various « spike » concepts that have been introduced into radiation damage theory. All of these have in common the deposition of energy by rapidly moving particles or lattice atoms somewhat along their tracks (and thus having the form of a spike). This energy must be dissipated by the lattice, and the question is as to what happens in the lattice in that local region during the time of dissipation. In none of these has the nature of these events been clearly shown at the present writing.

13·1. *The thermal spike.* – This is essentially the problem mentioned previously, that the primary deposits its energy in a fairly localized region. This energy is initially all given to the lattice atoms themselves, and so must soon appear as *heat*. The suggestion is, then, that this heat may cause atomic rearrangement, ordering, or disordering, or phase transformations in more complex solids such as alloys. Just for example, if a primary of 50 000 eV deposits its entire energy in a spherical region, 100 atoms across, in copper, then simply using ordinary heat conduction theory, with the table value for the thermal conductivity of copper, we find that the temperature might be initially 3 000 °K, and would cool down to, say, 300 °K in something like $3 \cdot 10^{-11}$ s; and the time actually spent in the range between, say 500 °K and 300 °K might even be a factor of two or so longer than this crude estimate. But this time is very short on a heat conductivity scale and brings up the question as to whether or not simple heat conduction theory applies; *e.g.*:

1) Can the lattice atoms exchange energy with the electrons in such a time; if not, one would have to use the lattice conductivity only, which is much lower (for a good metal).

2) But, more important, can we really speak of phonon equilibrium under these conditions, and will not very significant portions of the energy be carried away very quickly by escaping phonons.

3) Further, may not some energy be carried away by lattice focusing effects as discussed above.

All of these questions lead one to doubt that decisive statements can be made at this time on the thermal spike theory. And experimentally the situation is not clear.

13·2. *The ionization spike.* – Energetic charged particles, as shown above, deposit a lot of energy with the electrons of the lattice along their paths. The question here is whether much of this energy gets to the lattice atoms before it is dissipated by the electrons. These effects are also in doubt, though it does seem that important effects might be expected in complex crystals of very low electron mobility.

13·3. *The displacement spike.* – The concept here is a bit different, since it involves gross atomic motion as well as heat. BRINKMAN [18] has suggested that near the end of a cascade process (from a fairly high-energy primary) the mean free paths fall to essentially one interatomic distance. Thus in a small region practically all the atoms are in fairly energetic motion; the threshold for displacement does not mean much, because the lattice is locally highly disordered. Then the question, how does this region recover?

The suggestion by BRINKMAN is that it does not recover just as a group of separated vacancies and interstitials in an otherwise perfect lattice, but that there may be essentially a micro-recrystallization. There will be regions of mismatch and possibly regions of new lattice orientation. It has even been suggested that there will be dislocation loops locally formed. Again we must conclude that this effect has not been established completely at this time.

APPENDIX I

The average number of displaced atoms produced by a primary of kinetic energy T.

In this Appendix will be presented some of the considerations involved in calculating the number of displaced atoms in a cascade, on the basis of the simplifying assumptions:

1) The displacement probability curve is the sharp-threshold type, characterized by E_d.

2) The atom-atom collisions are of the hard-sphere type.

Further, the energy loss at each productive collision may be retained, in general by

3) If a (new) displaced atom is produced at a collision, there is an energy loss ΔE. This is based on the schematic potential well of Fig. 18.

Fig. 18. – Schematic potential well for a lattice atom.

The definition of $\nu(T)$ is taken here to be:

(A-I.1) $\nu(T)$ = the average number of displaced atoms which will result from the transfer of energy T to a lattice atom at its lattice site.

Thus, by assumption (1),

$$\nu(T) = 0\,, \qquad T < E_d\,. \tag{A-I.2}$$

Further, after leaving the lattice site the moving atom must have a *kinetic energy* of at least $2E_d$ if it is to displace another atom. Thus,

$$\nu(T) = 1\,, \qquad 2E_d + \Delta E > T > E_d\,. \tag{A-I.3}$$

The calculation is, then, based also on the «replacement collision» assumption:

4) If *either* of the atoms after collision has a kinetic energy less than E_d, it remains bound to the lattice site. (However, if both atoms have less than E_d, one must leave the lattice site.)

The basic physical argument by which $\nu(T)$ is constructed is that, if a moving primary makes a collision, the $\nu(T)$ for the primary must be just the sum of the two ν's of the incident and struck atoms after collision, *averaged over all possible energy distributions.* The integral equation which may be constructed on this model is

$$\text{(A-I.4)}\qquad \nu(T) = \int_{E_d}^{T-\Delta E} \nu(E'+E_d)\frac{\mathrm{d}E'}{T-\Delta E} + \int_0^{T-\Delta E} \nu(T-\Delta E - E')\frac{\mathrm{d}E'}{T-\Delta E},$$

which may be as well written

$$\text{(A-I.5)}\qquad (T-\Delta E)\nu(T) = \int_{E_d+\Delta E}^{T} \nu(E')\,\mathrm{d}E' + \int_0^{T-\Delta E} \nu(E')\,\mathrm{d}E' .$$

This equation must be solved by proceeding upward in T from the two forms given in eqs. (A-I.2) and (A-I.3); in each interval of ΔE above $T=2E_d+\Delta E$, the $\nu(T)$ has a different analytical form. However, it is much more convenient to start with the forms (A-I.2) and (A-I.3) and continue to higher values of T by numerical integration, observing that, from (A-I.5)

$$\text{(A-I.6)}\qquad \frac{\mathrm{d}\nu(T)}{\mathrm{d}T} = \frac{\nu(T-\Delta E)}{T-\Delta E},$$

which shows that, for any ΔE, for large values of T, $\nu(T)$ has an asymptotic form,

$$\text{(A-I.7)}\qquad \nu_{\text{asymptotic}} = cT ,$$

for large T.

The constant, c, is essentially determined from the starting conditions at low T. Writing (A-I.7) in the alternate form,

$$\text{(A-I.8)}\qquad \nu_{\text{asymptotic}} = \alpha\frac{T}{E_d}$$

direct integration (*) shows that α has the following typical values:

ΔE	α
0	0.5
$\frac{E_d}{2}$	0.41
E_d	0.36

(*) The numerical integration shows that the function approaches the asymptotic form *very* rapidly, so that only a few moments with a desk calculator are needed to obtain α, for various assumptions.

Appendix II

It has been found [19] that, to a good approximation, the neutron flux in a large graphite reactor (low fuel density) may be represented by the following form:

$$\text{(A-II.1)} \qquad \varphi(E) = \frac{s_0}{E\xi^M \Sigma_s^M(E)} \int_0^\infty s(E')\, dE' + \left(\frac{s_0\, s(E)}{\Sigma_s^M}\right) \qquad \xi^M = 1 + \frac{\alpha^M \ln \alpha^M}{1-\alpha^M}\,, \quad \alpha^M = \left(\frac{A^M+1}{A^M-1}\right)^2,$$

(with superscript M referring to quantities calculated for the moderator). Here s_0 = the number of fission neutrons produced per unit volume per unit time and $s(E)$ is the fission spectrum, well represented for ^{235}U by

$$\text{(A-II.2)} \qquad s(E) = \frac{2}{\sqrt{\pi}}\, \alpha\left[(aE)^{\frac{1}{2}} \exp\left[-\alpha E\right]\right] \qquad \text{(with } E \text{ in MeV);}$$

and $a = 0.7751\ \text{MeV}^{-1}$. In the flux plot shown (Fig. 13), the function $E\varphi(E)$ has been smoothed out over the « bumps » due to variations with energy of

$$\sigma_s^{(C)}(E)\,.$$

References

[1] See, for example, H. Goldstein: *Classical Mechanics* (New York, 1960), p. 81.
[2] See, for example, notes on lectures on *Nuclear Physics*, by E. Fermi.
[3] H. B. Huntington: *Phys. Rev.*, **93**, 1414 (1954).
[4] N. F. Mott: *Proc. Roy. Soc. (London)*, A **124**, 425 (1929).
[5] W. A. McKinley and H. Feshbach: *Phys. Rev.*, **74**, 1759 (1948).
[6] R. Fuchs: unpublished.
[7] D. S. Billington and J. H. Crawford, jr.: *Radiation Damage in Solids* (Princeton, 1961).
[8] O. S. Oen and D. K. Holmes: *Journ. Appl. Phys.*, **30**, 1289 (1959).
[9] G. Leibfried: *Nukleonik*, **1**, 57 (1958).
[10] C. Lehmann: *Nukleonik*, **3**, 1 (1961).
[11] G. J. Dienes and G. H. Vineyard: *Radiation Effects in Solids* (New York, 1957).
[12] M. Walt and H. H. Barschall: *Phys. Rev.*, **93**, 1062 (1954).
[13] T. H. Blewitt, R. R. Coltman and J. K. Redman: *Dislocations and Mechanical Properties of Crystals* (ed. by Fisher, Johnston, Thomson and Vreeland), (New York, 1957), pp. 179-214.
[14] D. K. Holmes and G. Leibfried: *Journ. Appl. Phys.*, **31**, 1046 (1960).

[15] R. A. Schmitt and R. A. Sharp: *Phys. Rev. Lett.*, **1**, 445 (1958).
[16] R. H. Silsbee: *Journ. Appl. Phys.*, **28**, 1246 (1957).
[17] G. Leibfried: *Journ. Appl. Phys.*, **30**, 1388 (1959).
[18] J. A. Brinkman: *Journ. Appl. Phys.*, **25**, 961 (1954).
[19] M. T. Robinson, O. S. Oen and D. K. Holmes: *Fast neutron spectra in graphite moderated reactors*, to be published.

BIBLIOGRAPHY

General, on radiation damage:

D. S. Billington and J. H. Crawford, jr.: *Radiation Damage in Solids* (Princeton, 1961).
F. Seitz and J. S. Koehler: *Displacement of atoms during irradiation*, in *Solid State Physics*, Vol. II (New York, 1956), p. 305.
G. J. Dienes and G. H. Vineyard: *Radiation Effects in Solids* (New York, 1957).
G. H. Kinchin and R. S. Pease: *Rep. Prog. Phys.*, **18**, 1 (1955).

Passage of radiation through matter:

H. A. Bethe and J. Ashkin: *Experimental Nuclear Physics* (ed. by O. E. Segrè) (New York, 1953), p. 166.

Radiation Damage Theory.

G. Leibfried

Technische Hochschule Aachen und Kernforschungsanlage Jülich

1. – Introduction.

It is useful to discuss the effects of irradiation in solids in two parts. *First*, one considers the collisions of irradiation particles with the constituents of the solid, nuclei and electrons. These processes may be called primary processes. The most commonly employed types of radiation are

irradiation with charged particles, as electrons, protons, deuterons, α-particles up to heavy fission fragments,

irradiation with uncharged particles, particularly γ-rays and neutrons.

Such encounters can induce nuclear reactions, for instance fission or nuclear transmutation in neutron irradiation or pair production by γ-rays, or they can simply transfer energy to the constituents of the crystal lattice. We will confine our discussion to effects of the second type where only energy is transferred from radiation to the crystal and no new particles are produced. These processes are symbolically shown in Fig. 1 where radiation particle R of energy E transfers energy T to a nucleus N or an electron e. The particle R itself loses the energy T and moves on with the energy $E' = E - T$. Of course, the electrons and nuclei of the crystal lattice cannot be treated as completely independent unless the transferred energy is so large that binding effects become unimportant. The particles to which energy is transferred in primary processes are called primary particles, primary electrons, primary nuclei or atoms or simply primary knock-ons.

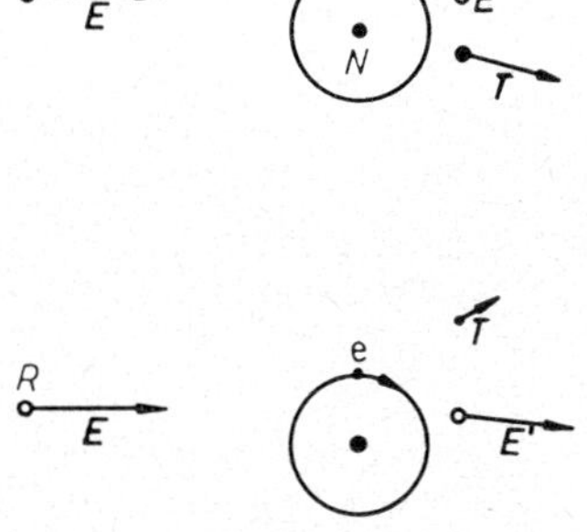

Fig. 1. – The transfer of energy T to a nucleus or an electron as the primary event in radiation damage.

Secondly, one has to investigate the effects of primary knock-ons upon the other constituents of the crystal. If the energy transfer is « large » the primary knock-on moves through the lattice, encounters other electrons or nuclei, produces secondary, tertiary, etc., knock-ons and induces in this way a kind of internal irradiation effect in the crystal. These processes one may call secondary processes. The minimum energy to displace an atom from its lattice site (threshold energy for displacement E_d) is of the order of 25 eV; for electrons in insulators, some eV (the distance between conduction and valence band) are required, whereas in metals the most loosely bound electrons are essentially free to move through the lattice even with very small transferred energies.

The distinction between primary and secondary effects is particulary useful if the range of the primary knock-on is small as compared with the distance between two subsequent primary events produced by the same radiation particle. By range we mean roughly the average distance traversed by the primary from its original lattice site to its eventual position which is about the same as the linear dimensions of the volume where the primary introduces structural changes in the crystal (primary region). Details depend very sensitively on the energy and the character of the primary and on the material. The distance between two subsequent primary events is given by the mean free path of the radiation particle for the process in question. With these assumptions the primary regions do not overlap and different primary zones can be treated as independent, as shown in Fig. 2.

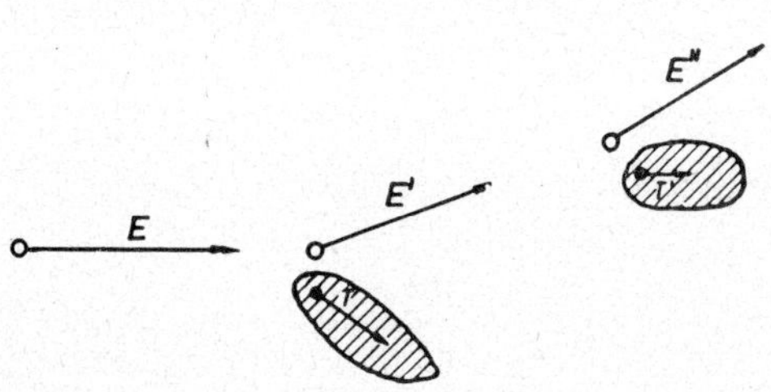

Fig. 2. – Primary regions T and T' which do not overlap.

The physical properties of the solid are changed by irradiation. This change is essentially determined by the eventual structure of the primary zones. Primary events which lead to structural changes affect the physical properties. From this point of view those primary events can be disregarded in which all the transferred energy is eventually transformed into heat and consequently does not change the physical state of the solid (if direct effects of locally increased temperatures can be neglected). A simple example of such an ineffective primary particle is a low-energy primary electron in a metal which comes to rest after having lost its energy by exciting lattice vibrations. This ineffectiveness of low-energy primary electrons holds only for metals and elemental semiconductors such as Ge and Si. In ionic and organic crystals the displacement of an electron may well result in structural changes, *e.g.* if bonds of an organic crystal are broken by removing an electron. Another simple example is the energy transfer to an atom or nucleus of the lattice. For primary energies smaller than a threshold value E_d the primary atom is set into motion about its equilibrium position. This motion is eventually transformed to irregular heat motion (via the interactions of lattice vibrations) and the primary event gives rise to a small temperature increase without leaving any permanent structural change. For primary energies larger than E_d the primary atom is displaced, leaves its lattice site and settles down in an interstitial position. Thus, the simplest defect consists of a vacancy-interstitial pair (Frenkel pair). If the energy is only slightly above E_d, the primary does not go very far and presumably settles at the closest possible stable interstitial position (close pair, Fig. 3*a*); with increasing energy the distance between the vacancy and the interstitial may increase, too (Fig. 3*b*). For larger energies the primary may encounter other stationary atoms and produce secondary Frenkel pairs (Fig. 3*c*), thus leading to a cascade of vacancies and interstitials. This picture roughly applies to metals where electronic excitation is not important.

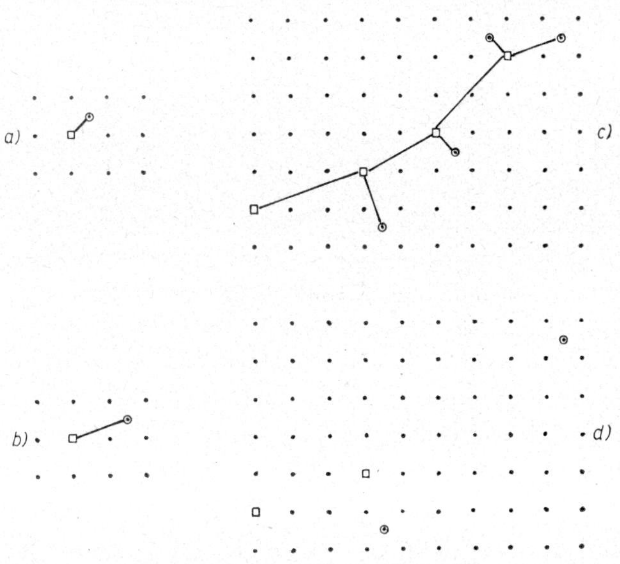

Fig. 3. – Schematic representation of possible primary effects: *a*) close Frenkel pair; *b*) Frenkel pair of somewhat larger distance; *c*) small cascade containing four Frenkel pairs; *d*) the same cascade after annealing of two pairs.

The defect structure of the primary zone is determined by the primary energy and by its direction with respect to the lattice. The change in physical properties is given in turn by the structure of the primary region. For instance, a primary zone contains a certain amount of stored energy; or it scatters electronic or lattice waves to a certain extent and this changes electrical and heat resistivity.

If one wants to calculate the physical changes produced by irradiation one has to know:

the distribution of primary events with energy and direction, *and*

the physical properties of the primary zones depending on energy and direction.

Then one can calculate the change in physical properties in most cases by simple addition, if the primary events are independent and if the radiation dose is so small that primary zones do not overlap appreciably. A simple example may illustrate this: Let us take a metal where only primary atoms lead to structural changes. Now let us assume that the stored energy of a primary atomic event $E_s(T)$ depends only on the transferred energy T. Then we can calculate the stored energy per unit volume $\varepsilon_s(\boldsymbol{x})$ from the distribution of primary atoms $F(\boldsymbol{x}, T)$ per unit volume and energy

$$\varepsilon_s(\boldsymbol{x}) = \int E_s(T) F(\boldsymbol{x}, T)\, \mathrm{d}T \,.$$

Here $F(\boldsymbol{x}, T)\,\mathrm{d}T$ is the number of primary atoms per unit volume at position $\boldsymbol{x}$ with energies in the interval $(T, T+\mathrm{d}T)$. The stored energy is always much smaller than the transferred energy $\int TF(T)\,\mathrm{d}T$. Only a small fraction is stored, most of the energy being transferred to heat.

The calculation of the primary distribution requires a thorough knowledge about the collision process between the radiation particles and the constituents of the crystal, and also details about the intensity and spectral distribution of the radiation. The first problem will be dealt with in Section **2**, and the radiation part will also be treated briefly, in Section **3**. There are two sides to look at in the problem of interaction of radiation with the solid. First, from the point of view of radiation-induced changes in the solid, the primary distribution is the most essential part; here only transferred energies above the threshold are important. On the other hand, the fate of the radiation particle itself is also completely determined by the collisions within the crystal. Here all the collisions change the energy and direction of the radiation particle and determine the «range» of radiation particles in the material. In most experimental setups, homogeneity of the radiation within the test piece is provided so that range effects are unimportant, and the structural changes are homogeneous also. But the change of radiation by interaction with the material is of utmost importance in reactor physics. The next step in radiation damage theory is an investigation into secondary effects. Since the primary zones come about by collisions between lattice particles, the interaction between atoms and electrons in the solid has to be treated, which is qualitatively also done in Section **2**. Knowing the interaction within the lattice, one can give a very simple and qualitative theory of primary events containing a large number of structural defects. This is done in Section **4**, primarily applying to simple metals and semiconductors. Since an exact knowledge of atomic interaction potentials in the solid is of central importance for the primary zone structure, this question is dealt with in more detail in Section **5**. Methods for deriving collision data from the potential are described in Section **6**.

Copper is given as a numerical example. More detailed information about atomic interaction results in more detailed knowledge about the structure of the primary zones. This is treated in Section **7**. For primary atoms with energies much larger than the threshold, the lattice structure is irrelevant for the collision history. However, for smaller energies the lattice structure is important and may give rise to correlated collisions along crystallographic directions with very long ranges. These focusing effects are treated briefly in Section **8**; they are important for the structure of a primary zone. All the effects mentioned in this paragraph are solid state problems related to energies large as compared with the binding energies and to the question of how structural changes are built up by fast moving lattice particles. These problems are far from being solved and we can only give hints as to the most important questions.

The last step then would be the theory of the physical properties of primary zones provided the zone structure is known and understood. These questions belong to the general class of solid state problems concerning the physical properties of defects in crystals. Here also our knowledge is fragmentary, and only a brief discussion is given in view of the fact that property changes will be discussed in detail in many other lectures given here. Also, the effects of annealing will only be mentioned briefly for the same reason. The annealing effect describes the change of structure and consequently of physical properties with temperature. An example is shown in Fig. *3d* where one can imagine that the increased mobility of defects with temperature may lead to the recombination of Frenkel pairs, thus reducing the structural change of irradiation at low temperature. At the same time this illustrates the fact that low temperature investigations are important for a basic understanding of radiation damage, because one should investigate a structure where none of the originally introduced change has been annealed out already.

It is not intended here to give a comprehensive review of radiation damage theory. Rather, we try to give a general outline in order to understand the physical problems and then we try go to into more detail on a few problems related to most recent experimental and theoretical work.

2. – Interaction of radiation with matter.

2·1. *The description of collisions by cross-sections.* – To introduce the commonly used description of collision processes we discuss the collision between two particles in classical terms. The two particles have masses M_1 and M_2; particle 1 is the incident particle moving with velocity $\boldsymbol{v}_1$, whereas particle 2 rests initially ($\boldsymbol{v}_2 = 0$). The final velocities after the collisions are marked by a prime ($\boldsymbol{v}_1'$, $\boldsymbol{v}_2'$). For a given potential $\varphi(r)$ depending on the distance r between 1 and 2 the final velocities can be calculated from the initial velocities and the impact parameter p (Fig. 4). Details about the path traversed during the encounter are not of interest. One wants the distribution of the final velocities for a given initial velocity where the impact parameter is not specified but one deals rather with a homogeneous current of incident particles with density n_1 and also many particles of 2 density n_2, in which problem only statistical aspects of the collision process come into play. The interaction ranges are so small that inhomogeneities over these distances can always be disregarded.

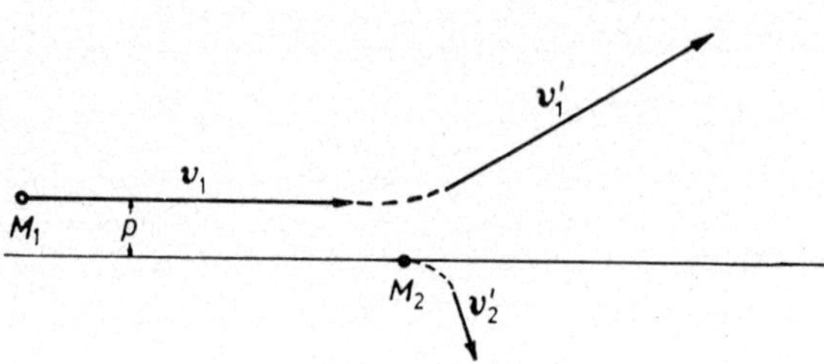

Fig. 4. – Collision between two atoms.

The required information can be expressed by the differential cross-section

$$d\sigma = K(\boldsymbol{v}_1; \boldsymbol{v}_1', \boldsymbol{v}_2')\, d\boldsymbol{v}_1'\, d\boldsymbol{v}_2' \tag{2.1}$$

with the following meaning: « Imagine various initial impact parameters with initial velocities aiming through an infinitesimal area $d\sigma$ perpendicular to $\boldsymbol{v}_1$ (Fig. 5). The final velocities will then show a spread according to the different impact parameters belonging to $d\sigma$. Now $d\sigma$ in (2.1) is that area where the final velocities are in the range $(\boldsymbol{v}_1', \boldsymbol{v}_1'+d\boldsymbol{v}_1')$ and $(\boldsymbol{v}_2', \boldsymbol{v}_2'+d\boldsymbol{v}_2')$ »

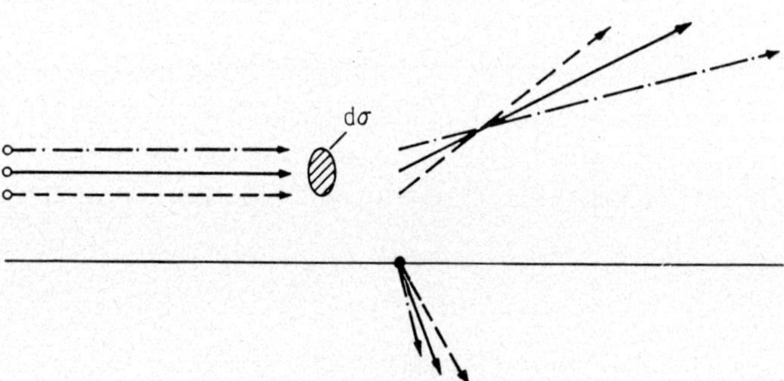

Fig. 5. – Definition of the differential cross-section $d\sigma$.

The function K often abbreviated symbolically by $d\sigma/d\boldsymbol{v}_1' d\boldsymbol{v}_2'$ gives the most detailed information about the collision process. Specifically the quantity

$$n_1 v_1\, dt\, d\sigma\, n_2 \tag{2.2a}$$

is the number of collisions per unit volume during the time interval $\mathrm{d}t$ leading to final velocities in $\mathrm{d}\boldsymbol{v}_1'\mathrm{d}\boldsymbol{v}_2'$ (more exactly in a statistical sense this is the average number). Further

$$v_1 \mathrm{d}t \mathrm{d}\sigma n_2 \tag{2.2b}$$

and

$$n_1 v_1 \mathrm{d}t \mathrm{d}\sigma \tag{2.2c}$$

are the number of collisions into $\mathrm{d}\boldsymbol{v}_1'\mathrm{d}\boldsymbol{v}_2'$ in $\mathrm{d}t$ for *one* particle 1 and for *one* particle 2 respectively (more exactly the probability for those processes).

Other differential cross-sections can be derived from (2.1) if the required information about the final data is specified otherwise. If, for instance, one only wants information about the transferred energies, then the differential cross-sections for energy transfers into $(T, T+\mathrm{d}T)$ is obtained by integrating (1.1) over all velocities with the condition $T \leqslant (M_2/2)v_2'^2 \leqslant T + \mathrm{d}T$. The result for radially symmetric potentials depends only through $E = (M_1/2)v_1^2$ on the initial velocity and can be written

$$\mathrm{d}\sigma = K(E, T)\,\mathrm{d}T; \qquad \frac{\mathrm{d}\sigma}{\mathrm{d}T} = K(E, T)\,. \tag{2.3}$$

This function is closely related to the primary distribution $F(T)$ mentioned in Section **1**. If 1 is the radiation particle and 2 is the primary then one has

$$F(T) = n_1 v_1 t n_2 K(T)\,, \tag{2.4}$$

where t is the irradiation time, and otherwise time-independence has been assumed. This follows immediately from (2.2*a*) which definition holds, of course, for any $\mathrm{d}\sigma$ which specifies any particular final result of the collision. If one knows the relation $p(T)$ then one has obviously

$$K(T) = \left| \pi p \frac{\mathrm{d}p}{\mathrm{d}T} \right| . \tag{2.3a}$$

The same nomenclature as in (2.1) can be used because the variable T and the differential $\mathrm{d}T$ tell what kind of differential cross-section is really meant.

Cross-sections are obtained when allowing for finite intervals of the final data. We give two examples:

The total cross-section σ is obtained by integrating over all possible final states, *e.g.* either (2.1) over all $\boldsymbol{v}_1'$ and $\boldsymbol{v}_2'$ or (2.3) over all T.

The displacement cross-section σ_d, defined by the cross-section for energy transfers larger than the displacement threshold E_d, is obtained by integrating with the condition $T \geqslant E_d$.

For instance one would have

$$(2.5) \qquad \sigma = \int_{\text{all } T} K(T)\, \mathrm{d}T\,; \qquad \sigma_d = \int_{T \geq E_d} K(T)\, \mathrm{d}T\,.$$

Sometimes it is convenient to factorise the differential cross-section into a cross-section and a normalized distribution function, denoted by $\varkappa$, *e.g.* (*)

$$(2.6) \qquad K(T) = \sigma\varkappa(T) \qquad \text{or} \qquad K_d(T) = \sigma_d\varkappa_d(T)\,.$$

The quantities $\varkappa$ can now be considered as probability distributions, $\varkappa(T)\,\mathrm{d}T$ being the probability that after a collision the transferred energy is in $(T,\ T+\mathrm{d}T)$. Introducing that into (2.4), $n_1 v_1 t\sigma n_2$ gives the density of primary events and $\varkappa(T)$ the distribution of energies. With the subscript d these quantities would refer to the primary events leading to structural changes by displacements.

The final velocities are not completely independent because conservation of energy and momentum establish a direct relation between initial and final data. This has the following consequences:

K after (2.1) is to vanish for values of the velocities which violate energy and momentum conservation, *i.e.* K contains as factors four δ-functions expressing energy (one condition) and momentum (three conditions) conservation.

Because of these four conditions, four of the six final variables can be expressed by the initial values. This means that there are only two really independent variables, for instance the direction of $\boldsymbol{v}_1'$ or $\boldsymbol{v}_2'$. If one direction is given, one can then construct $\boldsymbol{v}_1'$ and $\boldsymbol{v}_2'$ from the initial data using energy-momentum conservation. These two independent variables are reduced to a single one for radially symmetrical potentials, because then K can only depend on the angle between $\boldsymbol{v}_1'$ and $\boldsymbol{v}_1$ because $\boldsymbol{v}_1$ is the only specified direction in the scattering problem.

There are various possible choices for the one independent variable. One may choose, for instance, T. Then one can obtain $K(\boldsymbol{v}_1', \boldsymbol{v}_2')$ from $K(T)$ by introducing as factors the above mentioned δ-functions. Other choices would be the angle ϑ_1 between $\boldsymbol{v}_1'$ and $\boldsymbol{v}_1$ or the angle ϑ_2 between $\boldsymbol{v}_2'$ and $\boldsymbol{v}_1$. However, there are restrictions to these variables caused by energy and momentum conservation. We mention only the restriction for the transferred energy

(*) Because in the differential displacement cross-section K_d only energies larger than E_d are considered, K_d is obtained from K by cutting off for $T \leqslant E_d$.

which has to be smaller than a maximum value T_m

$$T_m = \eta E ; \qquad \eta = \frac{4 M_1 M_2}{(M_1 + M_2)^2} , \tag{2.7}$$

an equation easily obtained from energy and momentum conservation in case of a head-on collision. Since T_m is the maximum lost energy of the incident particle one has the corresponding condition $E - T_m \leqslant E' \leqslant E$.

One of the most convenient choices for the independent variable is the scattering angle θ in the center-of-mass system which is not restricted but varies over its natural range $0 \leqslant \theta \leqslant \pi$. Since most of the neutron scattering data use this variable and since, from a theoretical point of view, this is the only distinguished variable, we have to explain its meaning.

The center of mass moves with velocity

$$\boldsymbol{V} = M_1 \boldsymbol{v}_1 / (M_1 + M_2) . \tag{2.8}$$

An observer moving with the center of gravity (center-of-gravity system CGS) observes velocities

$$\boldsymbol{w} = \boldsymbol{v} - \boldsymbol{V} . \tag{2.9}$$

This is the transformation from the velocities $\boldsymbol{v}$ of the laboratory system (LS) to the CGS. In the CGS the description of the collision is particularly simple.

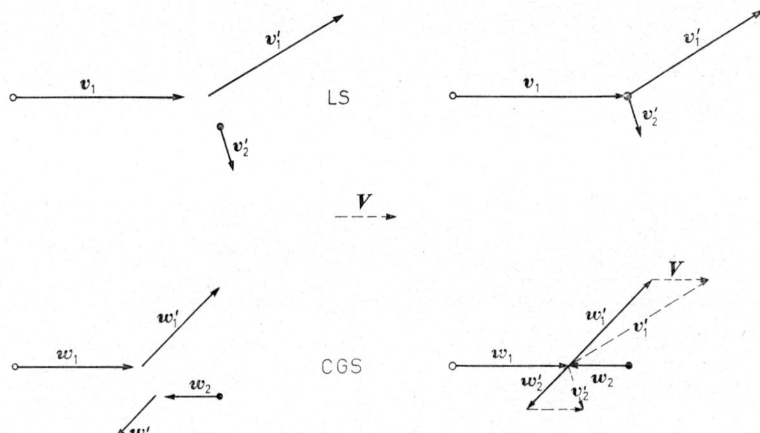

Fig. 6. – Relation between the center of gravity system (CGS) and laboratory system (LS).

The total momentum vanishes and the conservation of energy and momentum insures that only the direction of the velocities is changed by the collision, their magnitude being unchanged. This is shown in Fig. 6. The angle θ between

$\boldsymbol{w}_1'$ and $\boldsymbol{w}_1$ or between $\boldsymbol{w}_2'$ and $\boldsymbol{w}_2$ is not restricted. In the construction of the figure M_2 has been taken as twice M_1. To the picture in the CGS one simply adds $\boldsymbol{V}=-\boldsymbol{w}_2$ to obtain the LS quantities, as is also shown in the figure.

The velocities in the CGS have to be on a sphere of radius w_2 and w_1 respectively. This is demonstrated in Fig. 7. The distribution in the LS is

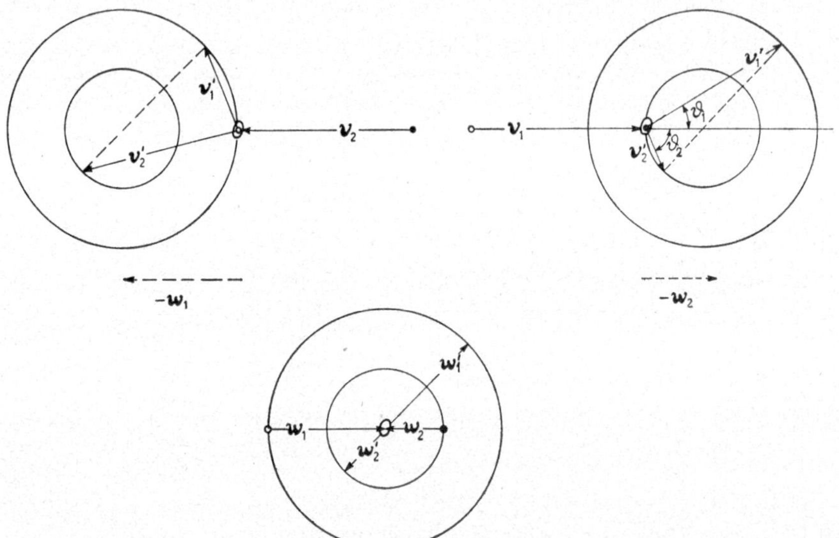

Fig. 7. – The velocity distribution in the center of gravity and laboratory systems.

obtained by shifting these spheres by $\boldsymbol{V}=-\boldsymbol{w}_2$ so that particle 2 is at rest initially ($\boldsymbol{v}_2=0$). In this picture one can immediately see that the angle ϑ_2 is restricted to the interval $(0, \pi/2)$. Further, one can easily recognize that the maximum final velocity of particle 2 is $2V$ and that, therefore, T_m is given by (2.6). As easily, one obtains by adding $-\boldsymbol{w}_1$ to the CGS picture the case in the LS where the heavier particle 1 is at rest initially. Here both angles are restricted.

Mostly, $\cos\theta$ is used as the variable and values are given for (*)

$$\mathrm{d}\sigma/\mathrm{d}\cos\theta = K_c(\cos\theta)\,. \tag{2.10}$$

Since the cross-sectional areas do not change when transforming between LS and CGS, one can obtain immediately the differential cross-sections for all those quantities which are directly determined by θ.

(*) Often one finds in the literature the differential cross-section $\mathrm{d}\sigma/\mathrm{d}\Omega$ referring to the solid angle element $\mathrm{d}\Omega=\mathrm{d}\cos\theta\,\mathrm{d}\varphi$ in the CGS which only depends on $\cos\theta$. Here one has the relation $\mathrm{d}\sigma/\mathrm{d}\Omega=(2\pi)^{-1}\cdot(\mathrm{d}\sigma/\mathrm{d}\cos\theta)$.

As an example let us consider the transferred energy

$$T = \frac{M_2}{2} v_2'^2 = \frac{M_2}{2} (\boldsymbol{w}_2' - \boldsymbol{w}_2)^2 = M_2 w_2^2 (1 - \cos\theta) = T_m (1 - \cos\theta)/2 \, .$$

Then one has

(2.11) $$d\sigma = K_c(\cos\theta)\,|d\cos\theta| = K(T)\,|dT|$$

or

(2.11a) $$K(T) = K_c\,(\cos\theta) \left| \frac{d\cos\theta}{dT} \right| = K_c \left(1 - \frac{2T}{T_m}\right) \frac{2}{T_m} \, .$$

Therefore the distribution K_c is, apart from trivial factors and displacements, the same as the distribution of transferred energies. Another example of relating differential cross-sections would be the connections between $K_2(T)$ and $K_1(E')$ which is calculated by means of $E' + T = E$:

(2.12) $$K_1(E') = K_2(E - E') \, .$$

In the theory of the collision process between two particles usually the motion of the center of mass is separated, and this is exactly the description of the CGS. Thus, the introduction of the CGS saves one co-ordinate and simplifies the theoretical treatment. Since the dynamics of the center of mass is independent of the scattering process, physical conditions are to be expressed in the CGS or, what is the same, in quantities referring to relative motion. This applies, for instance, to the criterion of applicability of classical mechanics. There is no basic difference between classical and quantum mechanics in the general description of scattering by cross-sections, but the methods of calculation and the results are quite different. We will give a rough criterion here for repulsive potentials $\varphi(r)$. Here one can define first a distance of closest approach R which is reached in head-on collisions and can be calculated by equating the potential energy at distance R with the energy of relative motion $E_{rel} = \mu v_1^2/2$

(2.13) $$\varphi(R) = E_{rel} \, .$$

Here μ is the reduced mass $1/\mu = 1/M_1 + 1/M_2$. This equation gives R as a function of E_{rel}. Now classical theory can be applied if R is large as compared to the de Broglie wavelength $\lambda\!\!\!^- = \hbar/\mu v_1$ in the CGS

(2.14) $$\frac{R}{\lambda\!\!\!^-} \gg 1 \, ,$$

and the classical treatment holds approximately down to angles of the order

$\lambda\!\!\!^{-}/R$ (*). If (2.14) is satisfied, one can almost forget about the small angle quantum-mechanical corrections because small angles mean small energy losses of the incident particle and small energy transfers to the stationary particle. But these corrections give usually a finite total cross-section, whereas in classical theory the cross-section is exactly determined by the range of the potential, this being infinite for potentials extending to infinity.

Until now we have only discussed the unrelativistic behavior which for our problem is in general sufficient when discussing irradiation with neutrons, protons and heavier particles. For γ and electron irradiation, however, relativity theory comes into play and introduces some changes. Most important is the relativistic expression for maximum transfer of kinetic energy

$$T_m = \eta E_1 \frac{1 + E_1/2M_1c^2}{1 + \eta E_1/2M_1c^2}\,. \tag{2.15}$$

Here c is the velocity of light and E_1 is the kinetic energy (total energy minus rest energy) of the incident particle; η is given by (2.7).

Two examples will be given to illustrate (2.15):

Collisions of an electron ($M_1 = M_e$) *with a nucleus* ($M_2 = M_N$). – Here $\eta \approx 4M_e/M_N$ is small (of the order of 10^{-3}) and for electrons with energies in the MeV-range ($E_e \sim M_e c^2$) the denominator in (2.15) can be dropped. Introducing the atomic weight $M_N = AM_p$ (M_p = proton mass) one gets

$$T_m = \frac{C}{A}\frac{E_e}{2M_e c^2}\left(1 + \frac{E_e}{2M_e c^2}\right). \tag{2.16}$$

Here C is given by

$$C = \frac{4M_e}{M_p}\, 2M_e c^2 \sim 2\,000 \text{ eV}\,.$$

Formula (2.16) is illustrated in Figs. 8*a* and *b*. Fig. 8*a* shows T_m *vs.* E_e and Fig. 8*b* gives the relations between E_e and A for given T_m. Since $2M_e c^2$ is about 1 MeV the 1 on the energy scale corresponds to 1 MeV. It is easily

(*) More exactly the condition for classical theory is [1] $(r_m(\theta)/\lambda\!\!\!^{-})\, 2\sin\theta/2 \gg 1$ where $r_m(\theta)$ is the minimum distance of the classical path leading to a scattering angle θ. For $\theta = \pi$, corresponding to a head-on collision, this is equivalent to (2.14) because $r_m(\pi) = R$. In most cases one can approximately neglect the variation of r_m with θ as compared with that of $\sin\theta/2$ and can consequently substitute R for r_m. This would mean that for small angles classical mechanics always fails. But for slowly decreasing potentials, *e.g.* the Coulomb potential $\varphi \sim 1/r$, this is not true and the criterion for classical theory can hold for all angles. In this case the total cross-section is infinite as for every classical scattering if the potential extends to infinity.

seen that for transferred energies of the order of 25 eV relativistic energies of the electron are required.

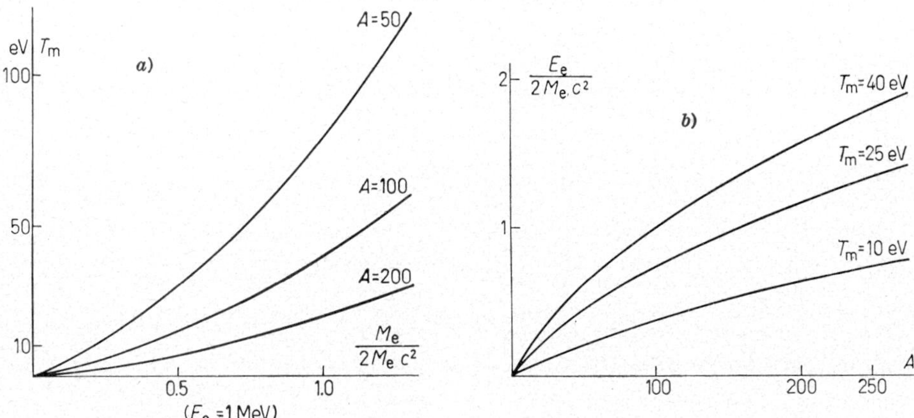

Fig. 8. – Energy transfer by electrons to atoms of atomic weight A: *a*) plot of the maximum transferred energy T_m *vs.* electron energy E_e; *b*) plot of E_e *vs.* A for given T_m.

Collision of a γ quantum ($M_1 = 0$, $E_1 = E_\gamma$) *with an electron* (*Compton effect*). Here (2.15) changes into

$$T_m = \frac{2E_\gamma^2}{M_e c^2 + 2E_\gamma}. \tag{2.17}$$

This behavior is shown in Fig. 9. If E_γ is appreciably larger than $M_e c^2 \sim 0.5$ MeV almost the whole γ energy can be transferred to the electron.

The description in the CGS is the same as in unrelativistic theory but the transformation to the LS involves Lorentz transformations. It is convenient here not to use the velocities but the momenta. In the CGS the momenta of particle 1 and 2 are equal

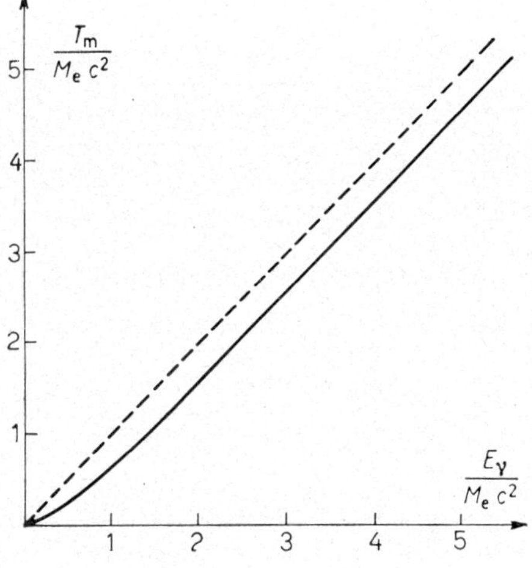

Fig. 9. – Relation between the maximum transferred energy T_m and the γ energy E_γ for the Compton effect.

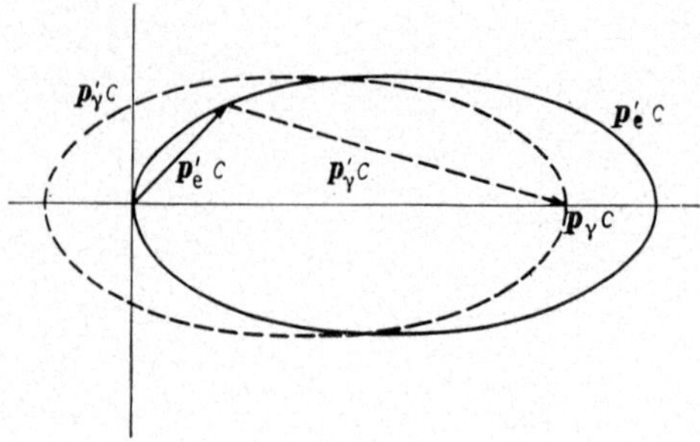

and opposite, they are distributed on the same sphere. This sphere changes into two ellipsoids as shown for the Compton effect with $E_\gamma = 1$ MeV in Fig. 10.

Fig. 10. – The momentum ellipsoids in relativistic scattering.

2'2. *Quantitative discussion of cross-sections for various types of irradiations.*

2'2.1. Neutron irradiation. – The collision of neutrons with the electrons of the solid can be neglected since there is only a very weak magnetic interaction. Neutrons affect solely the nuclei of the materials. We discuss here only so-called elastic collisions where the internal state of the encountered nucleus does not change.

Since the nuclear forces decrease very strongly with distance the dimensions of the scattering potential are given approximately by the nuclear radius,

$$R_N \sim A^{\frac{1}{3}} \times 1.5 \cdot 10^{-13}\ \text{cm}\,. \tag{2.18}$$

For neutrons scattering generally classical reasoning does not hold and wave mechanics has to be applied. The critical quantity here is the ratio of nuclear dimensions to the de Broglie wavelength $R_N/\lambda\!\!\!^{-} = \mu v_1 R_N/\hbar$ which is also the angular momentum in units $\hbar$ of incident neutrons aiming just at the nuclear surface. If $\lambda\!\!\!^{-}$ is large as compared to R_N (low energies), one gets so-called s-scattering where only zero angular momentum is involved. In this case the scattering in the CGS is isotropic, independent of θ. The distribution is constant over the scattering spheres in Fig. 7. For isotropic scattering one has

$$K_c(\cos\theta) = \frac{\sigma}{2}; \qquad \varkappa_c(\cos\theta) = \frac{1}{2}\,, \tag{2.19}$$

$$K(T) = \frac{\sigma}{T_m}; \qquad \varkappa(T) = \frac{1}{T_m} \quad \text{for} \quad 0 \leqslant T \leqslant T_m\,. \tag{2.19a}$$

The differential cross-section is plotted in Fig. 17.

The same behavior is obtained in classical « hard core » scattering between two impenetrable spheres. The potential describing this behavior is infinite for distances smaller than the hard core radius R and vanishes outside. R is the sum of the radii of the two spheres. In classical theory (condition $R \gg \lambda\!\!\!^{-}$) the cross-section is obviously $\sigma = \pi R^2$. But even in the limit $\lambda\!\!\!^{-} \to 0$, the criterion for classical theory does not apply to small angles and quantum mechanics gives $\sigma = 2\pi R^2$. But the quantum-mechanical deviations leading to the factor 2 in the cross-section are only appreciable for very small angles ($\theta \sim \lambda\!\!\!^{-}/R$). In the extreme wave-mechanical case ($R \ll \lambda\!\!\!^{-}$) one again obtains iso-

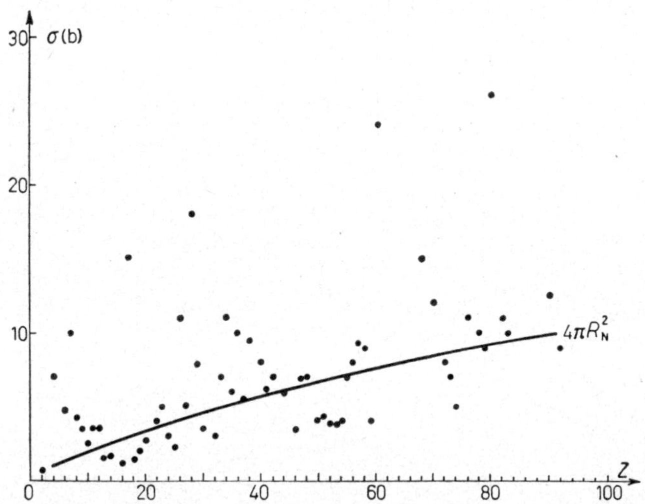

Fig. 11. – Low energy neutron cross section after A. M. WEINBERG and E. P. WIGNER: *The Physical Theory of Neutron Chain Reactors* (Chicago, 1958) (Copyright 1958 by the University of Chicago).

tropic s-scattering but for an entirely different reason. Here one finds no deviation from (2.19) and one has $\sigma = 4\pi R^2$.

Very loosely, the cross-section for low energy neutron scattering should be of the order of $4\pi R_N^2$. In Fig. 11 the cross-sections are shown and can be compared with $4\pi R^2$ given by the solid line. The deviations can be very large because the cross-section is very sensitive to peculiarities of the potential and is not solely determined by its dimensions.

For larger energies one gets contributions from higher angular momenta and one can show [2] that the second appreciable term in K_c is

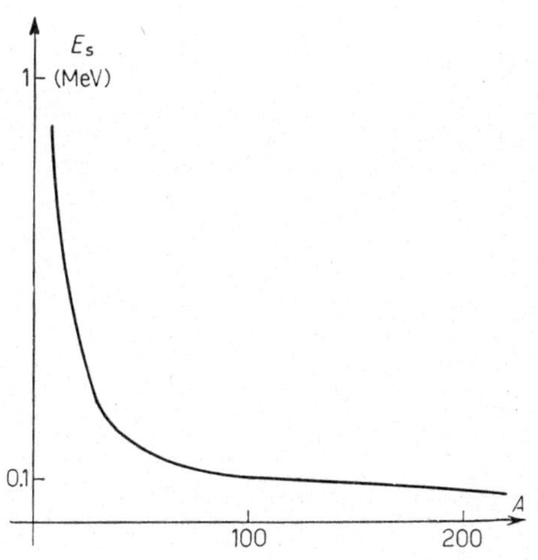

Fig. 12. – The limiting energy $\hat{E}_s$ for isotropic scattering of neutrons *vs.* atomic weight A.

proportional to $\cos\theta$

$$K_c(\cos\theta) \sim 1 + C\cos\theta\,, \tag{2.20}$$

where C is of the order $R_N^2/\lambda\!\!\!^-{}^2$. The third term would be proportional to $\cos^2\theta$. If one permits 20% deviations ($R_N^2/\lambda\!\!\!^-{}^2 \simeq \frac{1}{5}$) this defines an upper limit E_s of neutron energies giving isotropic scattering ($E_s \sim A^{-\frac{2}{3}} \times 2$ MeV). This energy is plotted *vs.* the atomic weight A in Fig. 12. One sees that for medium weight elements 0.1 MeV is about the limit for isotropic scattering. Roughly, the total cross-sections do not depend too much on energy so that the low energy cross-sections of Fig. 11 can be used qualitatively up to E_s.

In a reactor the neutron energies are distributed from about 10 MeV down to zero energy. Hence one has to expect rather large deviations from the simple isotropic behavior (2.19). Details depend quite sensitively on the reactor type and the irradiated material.

For neutron energies around 1 MeV, corresponding to the most probable neutron energy in fission, one expects quite appreciable deviations from isotropic scattering. This is illustrated in Fig. 13 showing $K_c(\cos\theta)$ for 1 MeV neutrons and for various atomic weights [3]. One recognizes strong deviations from (2.19) and even from (2.20). Striking is the preferred forward scattering ($\cos\theta = 1$). These plots can be read also as plots of $K(T)$ *vs.* T, $\cos\theta = 1$ corresponding to $T=0$ and $\cos\theta = -1$ to $T = T_m$. The trend to forward scattering then can be expressed also as preference for small energy transfer. The cross-sections are of the same order of magnitude as shown in Fig. 11 for low energies. The general behavior is a decrease of σ with increasing energy. Though the deviation from isotropic scattering, where K is constant, is appreciable, one should keep in mind that K does not change by many orders of magnitude in $0 \leqslant T \leqslant T_m$. Consequently, often the isotropic distribution is assumed for want of better knowledge. This may be correct qualitatively, but is certainly misleading quantitatively.

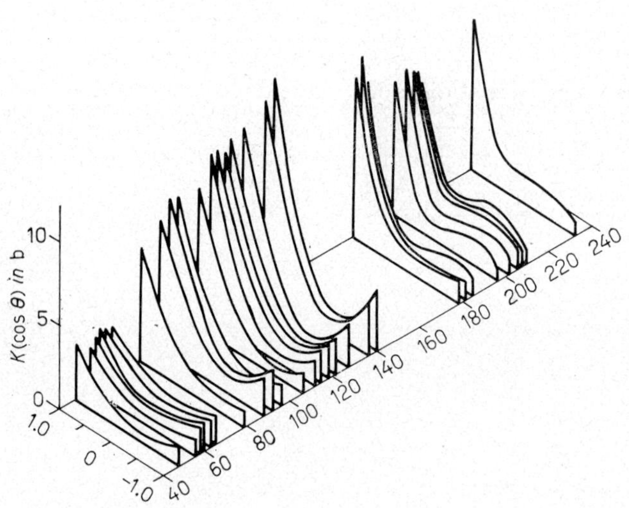

Fig. 13. – Neutron cross-sections for 1 MeV, after N. WALT and W. H. BARSHALL: *Phys. Rev.*, **93**, 1062 (1954).

An example for the dependence of differential and total cross-section on energy is given in Fig. 14 for Cu and Au. The energy dependence of $K(T)$ is rather marked (*). The cross-section for Cu and Au is about the same, decreasing from about 1 barn at 1 eV to about 0.21 barn between 1 and 10 MeV.

The cross-section σ is generally about 1 barn (10^{-24} cm^2). Corresponding to (2.2b), $v_1 \mathrm{d}t\,\sigma n_2$ is the number of collisions of the incident particle in dt.

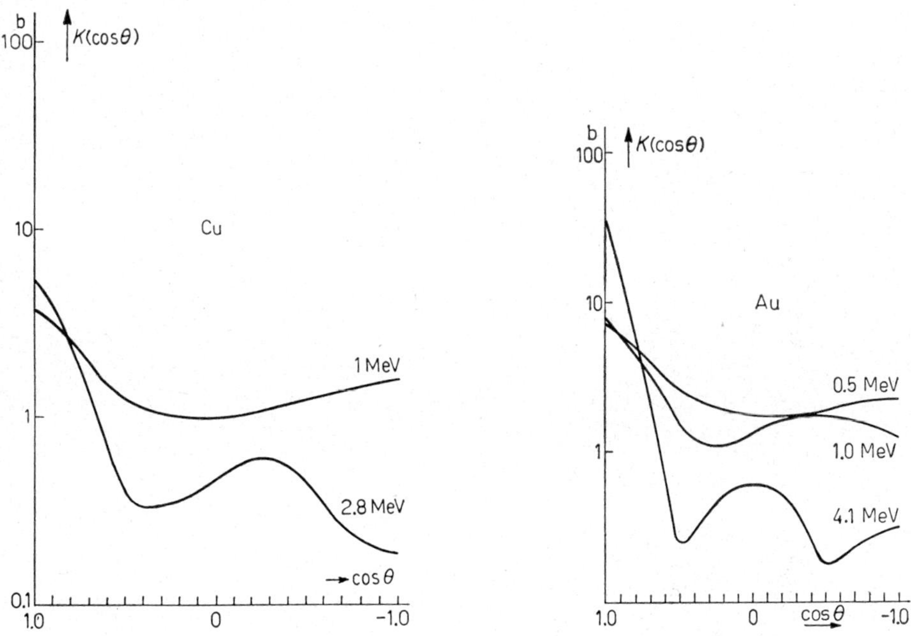

Fig. 14. – Neutron cross-sections for Cu and Au [4].

If this number is set equal to 1, then $v_1 \mathrm{d}t = \lambda$ is the path traversed by the incident particle until it has made one collision (in the average). The « mean free path » λ is thus given by

$$\lambda = \frac{1}{n_2 \sigma}. \tag{2.21}$$

For $n_2 = 10^{23}$ cm^{-3} and $\sigma = 10^{-24}$ cm^2 the mean free path or the average distance between subsequent collisions is 10 cm. The average distance λ_d between displacement collisions would be even larger:

$$\lambda_d = \frac{1}{n_2 \sigma_d}, \tag{2.21a}$$

where

$$\sigma_d = \sigma \left(1 - \frac{E_d}{T_m}\right),$$

(*) General information about neutron cross-sections can be found in [4].

assuming s-scattering. If the nuclear mass M_N is much larger than the mass of the neutron M_n one has

$$T_m \simeq \frac{4M_n}{M_N} E = \frac{4E}{A}. \tag{2.22}$$

For neutron energies E with $T_m \leqslant E_d (E \geqslant AE_d/4)$ no more displacements can be produced. Consequently, only neutrons above $AE_d/4$ can introduce structural damage in solids by elastic collisions. The characteristic energy depends on the material and varies between $E_d \sim 25$ eV ($A = 1$ where (2.22) does not apply) and $60\,E_d \sim 1500$ eV ($A = 240$).

The range of the neutron is roughly the path traversed by the neutron until it has lost most of its energy. The average energy transferred per collision is given by

$$\overline{T} = \int T\varkappa(T)\,\mathrm{d}T = \frac{T_m}{2} = \frac{\eta E}{2}, \tag{2.23}$$

for s-scattering. Very approximately, the range P can be expressed by

$$P \simeq \lambda \frac{E}{\overline{T}} = \lambda \frac{2}{\eta}. \tag{2.24}$$

$E/\overline{T}$ is the approximate number of collisions until the neutron comes to rest and consequently the range is the product of this number and the distance λ between subsequent collisions. Energy variations have been neglected.

Often the energy losses are described by a differential equation. Traversing the distance $\mathrm{d}x$ the neutron suffers $\mathrm{d}x/\lambda$ collisions and the energy loss $\mathrm{d}E$ is given obviously by $\overline{T}\,\mathrm{d}x/\lambda$.

Hence one has

$$-\frac{\mathrm{d}E}{\mathrm{d}x} = \frac{\overline{T}}{\lambda} = n_2 \sigma \overline{T}. \tag{2.25}$$

The factor multiplying n_2 in this equation is $\int T K(T)\,\mathrm{d}T = \int T\,\mathrm{d}\sigma$. If s-scattering is assumed and if σ does not depend on energy (λ = const) then (2.25) can be solved: $E(x) = E \exp[-(x\eta/2\lambda)]$, where E is the initial energy for $x = 0$. Here one would define the range as that x-value where $E(P) = E/2.71$ which also yields (2.24). One sees that the simple formula (2.24) is rather correct, at least in order of magnitude. The range for heavier nuclei is much larger than λ because the neutron loses only a small fraction of its energy per collision. In very light solids ($\eta \sim 1$) the range would be about λ.

2.2.2. **Irradiation with charged particles (Coulomb interaction).** – When irradiating with charged particles, the Coulomb interaction between electrical charges is predominant. The scattering between two free charges e_1 and e_2 can be applied to almost all problems occuring in charged-particle irradiation. Consequently, we treat this simple problems first ($\varphi(r) = e_1 e_2 / r$).

Classical and quantum mechanics give the same result

$$K_c = \frac{\pi R^2}{8 \sin^2(\theta/2)}; \qquad K(T) = \frac{\pi R^2 T_m}{4T^2}, \qquad \text{with } R = e_1 e_2 / \tfrac{1}{2}\mu v_1^2. \tag{2.26}$$

For repulsive potentials ($e_1 \cdot e_2 > 0$) R is the distance of closest approach. The total cross-section diverges. The displacement cross-section is

$$\sigma_d = \frac{\pi R^2}{4}\left(\frac{T_m}{E_d} - 1\right). \tag{2.27}$$

In Fig. 17 one finds a plot of $K(T)$ *vs.* T. In contrast to neutron scattering small energy transfers prevail and the ratio between low- and high-energy transfer can be very large, *e.g.* for $T_m = 10^5$ eV and $E_d \sim 25$ eV one has

$$\frac{K(E_d)}{K(T_m)} = \frac{T_m^2}{E_d^2} \simeq 10^7 .$$

In relativistic Coulomb scattering one can only give approximate solutions. We give only one example which can be used for scattering of electrons by nuclei ($M_2 \gg M_1$) where recoil effects of the nucleus can be disregarded in zero approximation. One obtains [5] for

$$\begin{cases} \mathrm{d}\sigma/\mathrm{d}x = T_m K(T); \qquad (x = T/T_m), \\ \dfrac{\mathrm{d}\sigma}{\mathrm{d}x} = \pi \left\{\dfrac{e_1 e_2 (E + M_e c^2)}{E^2 + 2EM_e c^2}\right\}^2 \dfrac{1}{x^2}\left\{1 - \dfrac{v_1^2}{c^2}x - \dfrac{\pi e_1 e_2 v_1}{\hbar c^2}(\sqrt{x} - x)\right\}. \end{cases} \tag{2.28}$$

Because of the assumption $M_2 \gg M_1$ this formula passes to the nonrelativistic formula (2.26) only when μ is replaced by M_1. The behavior is plotted in Fig. 15. It shows the same general trend as unrelativistic Coulomb scattering.

It will be explained later to what extent Coulomb scattering can be applied when irradiating with charged particles. Usually the formulae are valid if one considers displacement collisions ($T \geqslant E_d$) with the nuclei. If $T_m \gg E_d$, which most commonly holds, then one obtains

$$\sigma_d = \frac{\pi R_2 T_m}{4E_d} = \frac{\pi M_1 Z_1^2 Z_2^2 e^4}{M_2 E_1 E_d} = 4\pi a_{\mathrm{H}}^2 Z_1^2 Z_2^2 \frac{M_1}{M_2}\frac{I_{\mathrm{H}}^2}{E_1 E_d}. \tag{2.29}$$

Z_1 and Z_2 are the atomic numbers, a_H is the Bohr radius of hydrogen ($a_H \sim 5 \cdot 10^{-9}$ cm) and I_H is the ionization energy of hydrogen. As an example we will give the σ_d value for irradiation of Cu ($Z_2 = 29$) with deuterons ($Z_1 = 1$) of 10 MeV. Here σ_d is about 10^{-20} cm^2 and λ_d, the distance between subsequent primary displacement events, is approximately 10^{-3} cm, much smaller than in the neutron case. The range of the deuterons is not given by these collisions but rather by ionization which will be discussed later.

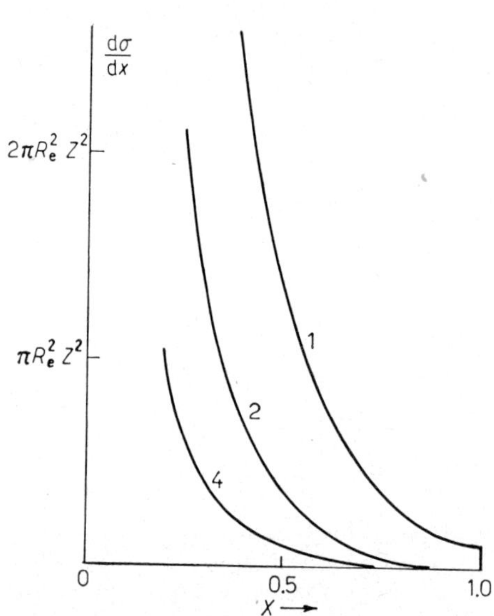

Fig. 15. – Differential cross-sections for scattering of electrons by nuclei of atomic number Z; $R_e \simeq 3 \cdot 10^{-13}$ cm (1) 0.5 MeV; 2) 1 MeV; 4) 2 MeV electrons).

2'2.3. Irradiation with γ-rays.

– γ-rays interact primarily with the electrons of the material, the cross-sections for direct interactions with the nuclei being much too small to be relevant. In metals structural damage can be produced by γ-rays via production of fast electrons which can displace the nuclei by Coulomb scattering. The scattering of γ-rays by electrons is called the Compton effect. In the γ energy range of interest around 1 MeV the Compton effect prevails. For low γ energies the absorption (photoeffect) is predominant, but here the transferred energies are too small to be of importance for subsequent atomic displacement. For large γ energies pair production is predominant but these large energies are not of interest in reactors.

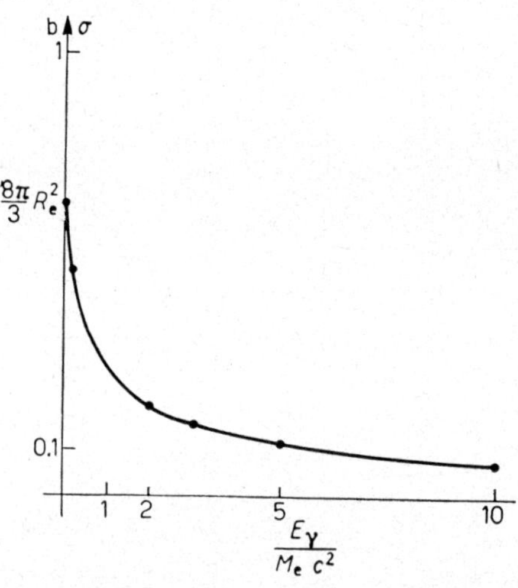

Fig. 16. – Compton cross-section.

The Klein-Nishina formula [5] gives

$$\text{(2.30)} \qquad \frac{d\sigma}{dx} = \pi R_e^2 \frac{2(\gamma-1)}{\gamma} \cdot \left\{\frac{\gamma}{\gamma - x} - \frac{x}{\gamma} + \left(1 - \frac{2(\gamma-1)}{\gamma - x}\, x\right)^2\right\};$$

$$\gamma = 1 + \frac{M_e c^2}{2E\gamma}.$$

Here R_e is the classical radius of the electron ($R_e \simeq 3 \cdot 10^{-13}$ cm). The total cross-section is about πR_e^2 and of the same order of magnitude as the neutron cross-sections. In Fig. 16 σ is plotted *vs.* the γ energy E_γ, In Fig. 17 the dependence on T/T_m is shown. For $E_\gamma \sim 1$ MeV one has pronounced large energy transfers in contrast to Coulomb scattering. Thus it is quite probable in large-energy Compton scattering that energies near T_m are transferred, which means that the γ quantum loses a large fraction of its energy to the electron.

Since σ is about 10^{-24} cm² the mean free path is of the order of centimeters and because a large fraction of E_γ is lost through collision the range is comparable to λ.

In Fig. 17 the differential cross-sections for Coulomb, neutron and Compton scattering can be compared. The differences are quite striking, in particular the trend in Coulomb scattering to favor small energy transfers.

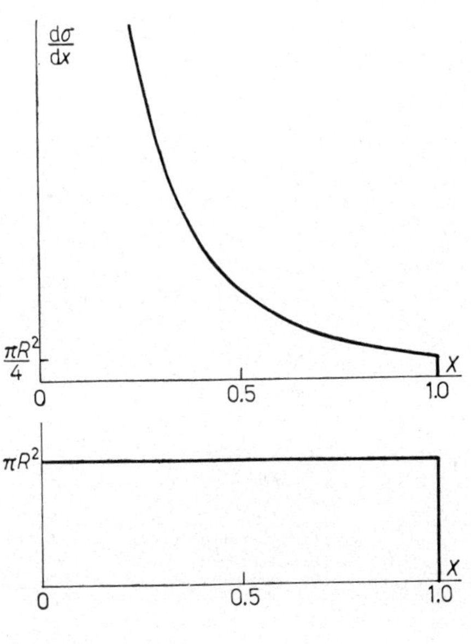

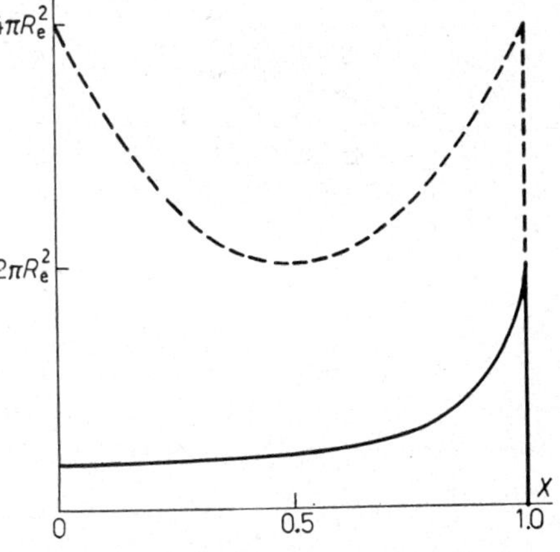

Fig. 17. – Comparison of Coulomb, isotropic and Compton scattering. The dashed line is Compton scattering for low energies, the full line corresponds to $E_\gamma = 1$ MeV.

2'2.4. Coulomb scattering and ionization. – There is a simple way to discuss ionization in terms of Coulomb scattering. Consider an electron bound to an atom with energy I. This electron collides with a charged particle and obtains the energy T. If $T \geqslant I$, the electron is freed and moves off with kinetic energy $T - I$. If $T \gg I$, the whole scattering process can be treated as though the electron were free and the Coulomb formulae apply. If $T_m \gg I$ then Coulomb scattering prevails over most of the energy range and consequently small energy transfers are very much preferred.

One may get a rough approximation

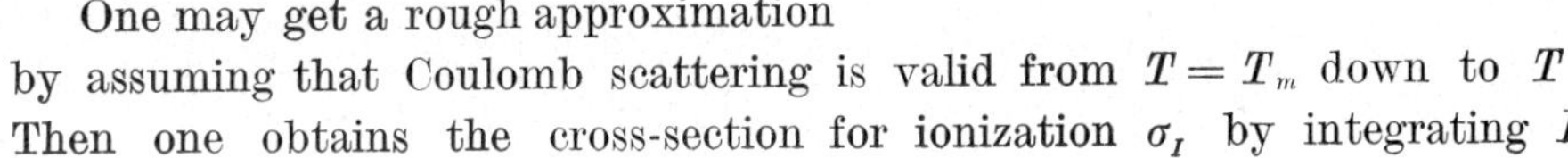

by assuming that Coulomb scattering is valid from $T = T_m$ down to $T = I$. Then one obtains the cross-section for ionization σ_I by integrating $K(T)$

after (2.26) with $T \geqslant I$:

$$\sigma_I = \frac{\pi R^2}{4}\left(\frac{T_m}{I} - 1\right), \tag{2.31}$$

with $R^2 = (2Z_1 e^2/\mu v_1^2)^2$.

If $T_m \gg I$ this changes into

$$\sigma_I \simeq \frac{\pi R^2 T_m}{4I}. \tag{2.31a}$$

The energy loss of the incident particle is then given as in (2.25) by

$$-\frac{\mathrm{d}E}{\mathrm{d}x} = n_2 \frac{\pi R^2}{4} T_m \ln \frac{T_m}{I}, \tag{2.32}$$

where n_2 is the density of electrons in question. Consequently, one would obtain when considering all electrons with different excitation and ionization energies:

$$-\frac{\mathrm{d}E}{\mathrm{d}x} = n_{\mathrm{At}} Z_2 \frac{2\pi Z_1^2 e^4}{M_e v_1^2} \ln \frac{2M_e v^2}{\bar{I}}. \tag{2.33}$$

For heavy particles ($M_1 \gg M_e$; $\mu \simeq M_e$) T_m is about $2\,\mathrm{M_e} v_1^2$. Further the density of electrons is given by the density of atoms n_{At} times the atomic number. $\bar{I}$ is some suitable average energy of ionization and excitation.

This formula has to be corrected somewhat [5]. First there has to be added a factor of 2 which stems from the small-energy transfer processes where free Coulomb scattering is invalid. Further instead of Z_1, Z_2 we introduce effective atomic numbers $Z_1(v)$ and $Z_2(v)$ and also an $\bar{I}(v)$, depending on the relative velocity $v = v_1$. $Z_2(v)$ is the number of electrons likely to be excited at all, for large energies $Z_2(v)$ passes to the real atomic number because then all electrons come into play. $\bar{I}(v)$ is a suitable average over the energies of the $Z_2(v)$ excitable electrons. $Z_1(v)$ is the effective charge of an atom with atomic number Z_1 moving with velocity v through the lattice. For low velocities the incident atom may not be completely ionized and this is taken into account by $Z_1(v)$.

Eventually one has

$$-\frac{\mathrm{d}E}{\mathrm{d}x} = \frac{4\pi n_{\mathrm{At}} Z_2(0) Z_1^2(v) e^4}{M_e v^2} \ln \frac{2M_e v^2}{\bar{I}(v)}. \tag{2.34}$$

As a rule of thumb one has $\bar{I}(v) \simeq Z_2(v)\cdot 10$ eV, where errors do not matter much because of the logarithmic dependence. Even free conduction electrons can be described in the same way if T_m is much larger than the Fermi energy.

We will discuss $Z_2(v)$ only in two simple limiting cases. Above a certain energy limit E_I^m all electrons will be capable of being excited; then $Z_2(v)$ is just the atomic number Z_2 independent of v. Approximately this energy can be obtained by equating the maximum transferred energy T_m to the ionization energy of the most tightly bound electron, which is about $Z_2^2 I_H$ (I_H being the ionization energy of hydrogen):

$$E_I^m \simeq \frac{M_1}{4M_e} Z_2^2 I_H . \tag{2.35}$$

For Cu ($Z_2 = 29$) one has $Z_2^2 I_E \sim 10^4$ eV and for deuteron irradiation ($M_1 = 2M_p$) one has $M_1/AM_e = 10^3$; therefore E_I^m is about 10 MeV in that case. Hence, in irradiation of Cu by 10 MeV deuterons, virtually all electrons can be excited ($Z_2(v) = Z_2$ and $\bar{I}(v) = Z_2 \cdot 10$ eV $\simeq 300$ eV). For very low energies when T_m is smaller than the smallest excitation energy I_{min} no excitations can occur and Z_2 is zero. The energy limit E_I for this will be approximately

$$E_I \simeq \frac{M_1}{4M_e} I_{min} \simeq 500\, A I_{min} , \tag{2.36}$$

where A is the atomic weight of the incident particle. It must be mentioned that both (2.36) and (2.35) are conditions for the velocities rather than for energies because $T_m = 2M_e v^2$; for instance, (2.36) can be written as $2M_e v^2 = I_{min}$. In non-metals I_{min} is essentially the energy difference between valence and conduction band. In metals one can take the Fermi energy for I_{min} though the picture used here does not apply, because in metals even very small energies can be transferred to the electrons. The reason that one obtains a kind of ionization limit in metals is that if T_m becomes much smaller than the Fermi energy then only a small fraction of collisions can take place, namely only those collision which do not lead to occupied states in the Fermi sphere. By the same reasoning one can use the Fermi energy as a cut-off energy in the treatment leading to (2.32). I_{min} is thus of the order of some eV. As a rule of thumb one may take $I_{min} \sim 2$ eV, hence

$$E_I \simeq A \text{ keV} . \tag{2.37}$$

Of course this is only an order of magnitude relation and should not be taken too seriously.

The ionization state of the moving particle also depends on its energy or its velocity. The incident particle collides continuously with the lattice particles its electrons being stripped off. Now seen from the incident particle, the lattice particles move against it also with velocity v_1, the maximum energy transfer to the electron of the incident particle also being $2M_e v^2$. If one equates this value of T_m to the smallest excitation energy of the incident atom, then one gets the energy limit below which the incident atom is neutral. When we use the above value of 2 eV of $I_{\min}$ then (2.37) not only defines the energy of the incident particle where its ionizing power stops but also the energy where its own effective charge drops to zero. Again one has to be cautious when making quantitative statements.

In Fig. 18 E_I is plotted *vs.* A. If one now considers a primary atom in its own solid with energy larger than E_I then it ionizes and is itself ionized partly. It slows down by ionization processes and atom-atom encounters until it reaches the energy E_I. From then on only atom-atom collisions are remaining for the slowing down process. Generally, above E_I the ionization is overwhelming so that one may disregard the atomic encounters in a first approximation. In Fig. 18 one finds further the average transferred energy ($T_m/2$ for s-scattering) for an incident neutron of 2 MeV, the average fission energy ($T_m/2 = 4$ MeV$/A$). For low A the energy transfer is large and larger than E_I. Much energy will be spent in ionization and only a small part in atomic collisions. For large A the energy transfer is small and smaller than E_I. Here one only has collisions between the neutral atoms of the solid. Because ionization in metals mostly does not lead to structural damage one may conclude that just for medium atomic weights the largest fraction of energy per neutron hit is available for structural damage.

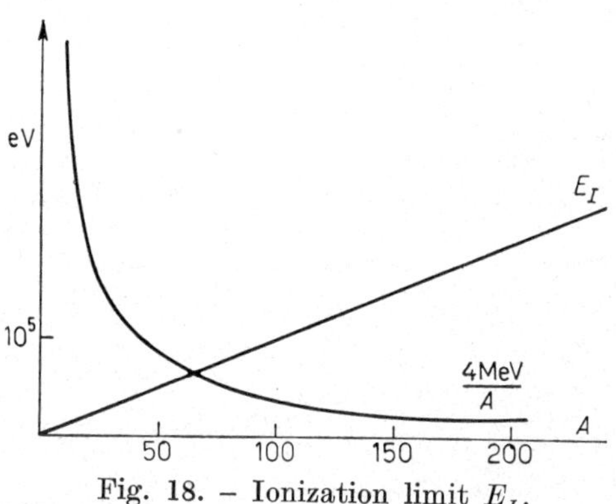

Fig. 18. – Ionization limit E_I.

To give an example we discuss the range for 10 MeV deuteron irradiation of Cu ($Z_1(v) = Z_1 = 1$, $Z_2(v) = Z_2 = 29$, $\bar{I}(v) = 1 \times Z_2$ eV $= 300$ eV). According to (2.34) the energy loss $-\mathrm{d}E/\mathrm{d}x$ is about $5\cdot10^8$ eV/cm and the approximate range $-E/(\mathrm{d}E/\mathrm{d}x)$ becomes $2\cdot10^{-2}$ cm. For electrons of 1 MeV the loss would be in the order 10^7 eV/cm and the range about 10^{-1} cm. These ranges are rather small and this shows that in charged-particle irradiations one has to use thin foils to produce homogeneous damage. It shows further that in investigation of displacement thresholds by charged-particle irradiation only electrons can be used. The ranges of 1 MeV electrons required for transferring about 25 eV are 1 mm and can be handled easily. The range for heavy particles of about 1000 eV, required to transfer E_d, are in the order of some lattice distances and are essentially determined by collision with the atoms themselves.

To get the order of magnitude for subsequent ionization events one may use (2.31a) with $I \simeq I_{\min} \sim 2$ eV because the small energies give the largest contributions. This yields

$$\sigma_I \simeq \frac{\pi Z_1^2(v) M_1 e^4}{M_e E_1 I_{\min}} = 4\pi a_H^2 \frac{M_1}{M_e} \frac{I_H^2}{E_1 I_{\min}} Z_1^2 ,$$

where $a_H = 0{,}5 \cdot 10^{-8}$ cm, is the hydrogen radius. For the example given above on deuteron irradiation of copper, σ_I is about 10^{-17} cm² and the mean free path for ionization is of the order of 10^{-6} cm. The same cross-sections and mean free paths would hold for electrons with energies of some keV.

2·2.5 Atom-atom interaction. – In irradiation with charged particles the incident particle does not interact directly with the charged stationary nuclei by Coulomb interaction because the nucleus is more or less neutral and its Coulomb potential is screened by its electrons. The calculation of the potential of a neutral atom is rather difficult. The results given here are due to approximations which are open to objection. BOHR [6] has assumed the following form

$$\varphi(r) = \frac{Z_1 Z_2 e^2}{r} \exp\left[-r/a\right] , \tag{2.38}$$

with

$$a = \frac{a_H}{\{Z_1^{\frac{2}{3}} + Z_2^{\frac{2}{3}}\}^{\frac{1}{2}}} , \tag{2.38a}$$

for more or less neutral atoms of atomic numbers Z_1 and Z_2 and with

$$a = \frac{a_H}{Z_2^{\frac{1}{3}}} , \tag{2.38b}$$

if the incident particle is merely a « point charge », *e.g.* an electron or a completely ionized atom. In the primary process we have to deal mainly with (2.38b) whereas in the secondary events (2.38a) is to apply with $Z_1 = Z_2$

$$a = \frac{a_H}{\sqrt{2} Z_2^{\frac{1}{3}}} . \tag{2.38c}$$

For want of better knowledge we will use this screened Coulomb potential. Though the shape of the potential may be qualitatively all right, the magnitude of the screening radius as given by BOHR is certainly open to doubt. Various authors have used different values of a and because a enters exponentially into φ the results are quite sensitive to assumptions about the value of a. Later on we will discuss a method to determine a experimentally.

If one wants to know whether or not classical theory can be used one has to discuss the ratio $R/\lambda\!\!\!^-$ given by

$$\frac{\exp[-R/a]}{R/a} = \frac{E_{\text{rel}}}{E_a}; \qquad E_a = \frac{Z_1 Z_2 e^2}{a}, \tag{2.39a}$$

$$\frac{\lambda\!\!\!^{-2}}{a^2} = \frac{E_a}{E_{\text{rel}}} \frac{M_e\, a_{\text{H}}}{2\mu a Z_1 Z_2}. \tag{2.39b}$$

In Fig. 19, R/a and $\lambda\!\!\!^-/a$ are plotted *vs.* E_{rel}/E_a for $\lambda\!\!\!^-/a$ one finds two curves, one for the deuteron-copper case and one for the copper-copper case. Between the two points of intersection of $\lambda\!\!\!^-/a$ and R/a is the classical range. If one defines the classical limits by $R \simeq 10\,\lambda\!\!\!^-$ then one obtains roughly 2 MeV, 5 eV for D-Cu and 10^{11} eV, 0.4 eV for Cu-Cu.

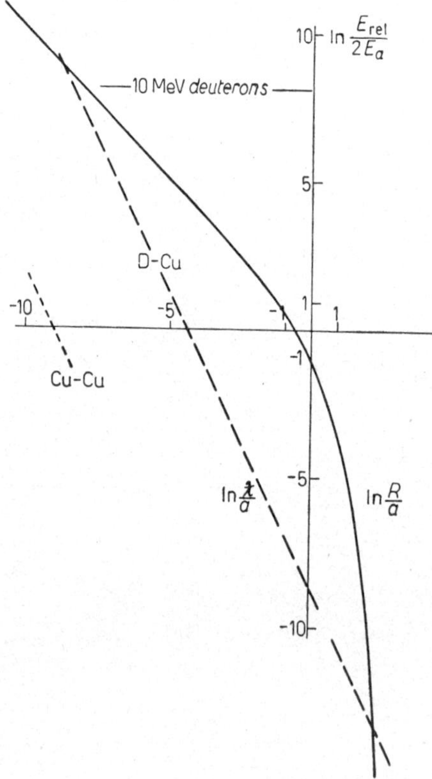

Fig. 19. – Diagram to determine the limits of classical theory.

If $R \ll a$ the screening effect is small and the Coulomb potential will strongly contribute to the cross-section, If, further, $R \gg \lambda\!\!\!^-$, then classical Coulomb scattering applies down to energies corresponding to impact parameters $p \simeq a$; if $R \ll \lambda\!\!\!^-$, then one has to use quantum mechanics but can apply the well-known Born approximation. This again gives Coulomb scattering down to energies corresponding to an angle $\theta \simeq \lambda\!\!\!^-/a$. Thus one can calculate a lower limit for Coulomb scattering if $R \gg \lambda\!\!\!^-$ or $R \ll \lambda\!\!\!^-$ and $R \ll a$. Generally, this lower limit in charged-particle irradiation is well below E_a, which means that the Coulomb formulae can be used for the physically relevant displacement processes. On the other hand, just for the often cited example of irradiation of Cu by 10 MeV deuterons, R is about $\lambda\!\!\!^-$ and neither theory applies. To my knowledge, this intermediate range has never been investigated. One can prove the applicability of the Coulomb formulae over a large energy interval for both $R \gg \lambda\!\!\!^-$ and $R \ll \lambda\!\!\!^-$ and may take it as plausible that when passing through $R \simeq \lambda\!\!\!^{-}$ this statement still would hold.

It may be mentioned that the form (2.38) for the interaction between two atoms should be valid only for relatively small distances and does not apply to distances of the order of the lattice distance. This screening effect is essentially due to the behavior of the most tightly bound electrons. For larger distances the external structure (ionic radii) comes into play and gives deviations. This will be discussed later.

3. – The primary distribution.

3·1. *General methods of calculation.* – For the sake of simplicity we discuss here only the energy distribution $F(T)$ mentioned in Section **1** and do not consider the distribution of directions. The methods are the same. For a simple case $F(T)$ has already been given in (2.4),

$$F(T) = n_1 v_1 t n_2 K(E; T) . \tag{3.1}$$

In this formula the direction of the incident radiation of energy E does not come into play; only the so-called flux density $\Phi = n_1 v_1$, the irradiation time t and the differential cross-section matter. Φ can be visualized as the path traversed by the irradiation particles per unit time and unit volume.

The formula (3.1) can be applied if the irradiation is monoenergetic, regardless of the angular distribution,

$$F(T) = \Phi t n_2 K(T) . \tag{3.2}$$

Consequently, it would apply to the common irradiation by charged particles with essentially unique energy. This means that the curves for Coulomb scattering give $F(T)$ already.

But in reactors the neutrons are distributed over a very large energy range and this has to be taken into account when calculating $F(T)$. In this case one has to know the distribution of the flux with energy $\varphi(E)$, where $\varphi(E)\,\mathrm{d}E$ is the contribution of radiation particles in $(E, E+\mathrm{d}E)$ to Φ:

$$\Phi = \int \varphi(E)\,\mathrm{d}E . \tag{3.3}$$

If $\varphi(E)$ is known then one obviously gets

$$F(T) = \int \varphi(E)\,\mathrm{d}E t n_2 K(E; T) . \tag{3.4}$$

Only K_d, taking the displacement threshold E_d into account, is of physical significance in neutron irradiation:

$$F_d(T) = \Phi t n_2 \sigma_d \varkappa_d(T) \tag{3.2a}$$

for monoenergetic irradiation and

$$F_d(T) = \int \varphi(E)\,\mathrm{d}E t n_2 \sigma_d(E) \varkappa_d(E;\,T)\,, \tag{3.4a}$$

for a distribution of energies. The first factor in (3.2a) is the number of displacement events per unit volume and the last factor is their energy distribution. One can write (3.4a) also as

$$F_d(T) = \Phi_d t n_2 \overline{\sigma}_d \cdot \overline{\varkappa}_d(T) \tag{3.5}$$

with

$$\Phi_d = \int\limits_{\eta E \geq E_d} \varphi(E)\,\mathrm{d}E\,; \qquad \overline{\sigma}_d = \frac{\int \varphi(E)\,\mathrm{d}E \sigma_d(E)}{\Phi_d}\,, \qquad \overline{\varkappa}_d = \frac{\int \varphi(E) \sigma_d(E) \varkappa_d(E;\,T)\,\mathrm{d}E}{\sigma_d}\,.$$

Here Φ_d is the displacement flux density, where only those energies are contributing which can displace an atom ($E \geqslant E_d/\eta$). The quantities $\overline{\sigma}_d$ and $\overline{\varkappa}_d$ are suitable averages.

3·2. *Qualitative comparison between charged-particle and neutron irradiation.* We are going to discuss here the energy distribution $\varkappa_d(T)$, resp. $\overline{\varkappa}_d(T)$ for charged particles and neutron irradiation. For charged particles of unique energy this is given by the Coulomb formulae. In neutron irradiation we give two simplified examples:

Fission neutrons approximately given by a unique energy E_f of 1.5 MeV and assumed s-scattering, corresponding to irradiation in a converter.

Pile neutrons (*) with an energy distribution $\varphi(E) \sim 1/E$ which approx-

---

(*) The displacement flux Φ_d is then proportional to

$$\int\limits_{\eta E = E_d}^{E_f} \mathrm{d}E/E = \ln \eta E_f/E_d = \ln T_m/E_d\,.$$

This depends on the irradiated material through T_m and E_d, but only logarithmically. Though η changes by a factor 50 in the periodical system, the change of the logarithm is not very important for qualitative discussions. Because E_d does not vary too much either, qualitatively, Φ_d is independent of the material. But different authors seem to use quite different fluxes and this should be taken into regard in quantitative statements.

imately should hold for reactors with relatively high atomic weight of the moderator (graphite reactors), assuming *s*-scattering again and energy-independent cross-section.

These examples are very qualitative and are only given to point out the essential differences between different kinds of irradiation. The results are shown in Table I.

TABLE I.

	$\bar{\varkappa}_d(T)$	$\int_{E_d}^{T} \bar{\varkappa}_d(T')\,\mathrm{d}T'$	$\bar{T}_d$	$\int_{E_d}^{T} T'\bar{\varkappa}_d(T')\,\mathrm{d}T' \Big/ \int_{T_d}^{T_m} T'\bar{\varkappa}_d(T')\,\mathrm{d}T'$
Charged particles	$\frac{T_m E_d}{T_m - E_d}\frac{1}{T^2} \simeq \frac{E_d}{T^2}$	$1 - E_d/T$	$E_d \ln T_m/E_d$	$\frac{\ln T/E_d}{\ln T_m/E_d}$
Pile neutrons	$\frac{1/T - 1/T_m}{\ln T_m/E_d - 1 + E_d/T_m} \simeq \frac{1}{T \ln T_m/E_d}$	$\frac{\ln T/E_d}{\ln T_m/E_d}$	$\frac{T_m}{2 \ln T_m/E_d}$	$\frac{T - E_d}{T_m}$
Fission neutrons	$\frac{1}{T_m - E_d} \simeq \frac{1}{T_m}$	$\frac{T - E_d}{T_m}$	$T_m/2$	$\frac{T^2 - E_d^2}{T_m^2}$

The table contains first $\bar{\varkappa}_d(T)$; one recognizes that the trend to small energy transfers decreases when changing from charged particles to pile neutrons and then to fission neutrons. This is shown qualitatively in Fig. 20*a* for $F(T)$. To get a clearer picture of the meaning of the distribution, $\int_{E_d}^{T} \bar{\varkappa}_d(T')\,\mathrm{d}T'$ is calculated and plotted in Fig. 20*b*. This quantity is the fraction of primary displaced atoms with energies below T. The different energetic behavior with energy can clearly be seen in Fig. 20. For the sake of simplicity T_m has been chosen the same (about 10^5 eV) for all irradiations, corresponding to Cu and deuterons of 0.75 MeV energy. If one determines the value of T for a fraction of 50% then one gets: $T \simeq 2E_d \simeq 50$ eV for charged particles, $T \simeq 50 E_d \simeq$ $\simeq 1250$ eV for pile neutrons and $T \simeq T_m/2 \simeq 50\,000$ eV for fission neutrons. Consequently, most of the primary events in charged-particle irradiation are low-energy events. This is also expressed by calculating the average energy of the displaced primaries $\bar{T}_d = \int T \bar{\varkappa}_d(T)\,\mathrm{d}T$. Although 50% of the primaries in charged particle radiation have energies below $2E_d$ this does not necessarily mean that only low-energy events are physically important. Let us assume that the physical property in question is proportional to T (the stored energy for example); then the last column in the table gives the fraction of physical property change which is produced by primary events below T. For charged particles this quantity is given by the pile neutron curve in Fig. 20, which means that 50% of the change is made by energies above 1250 eV, which is quite a high energy.

For electron irradiation the primary distribution is given by (2.28) (Fig. 15). It shows the same qualitative behavior as heavy-particle irradiation except for the lower values of T_m near E_d. But here really only low energies between T_m and E_d come into play, whereas in all the other irradiations mentioned above the primary energies show a tremendous spread from E_d to T_m. Except in electron damage one invariably has to do with a mixture of primary events of very different energies with possibly also very different defect structures. One would anticipate that a given T always leads to a certain defect without much variance. Because in heavy-particle irradiation T is spread out, one cannot investigate by these means the property of defects caused by a given large T. The only way to transfer a more or less unique T to a stationary atom seems to be by nuclear processes and will be discussed later. In the most common kinds of irradiation one produces a mixture of very different energies.

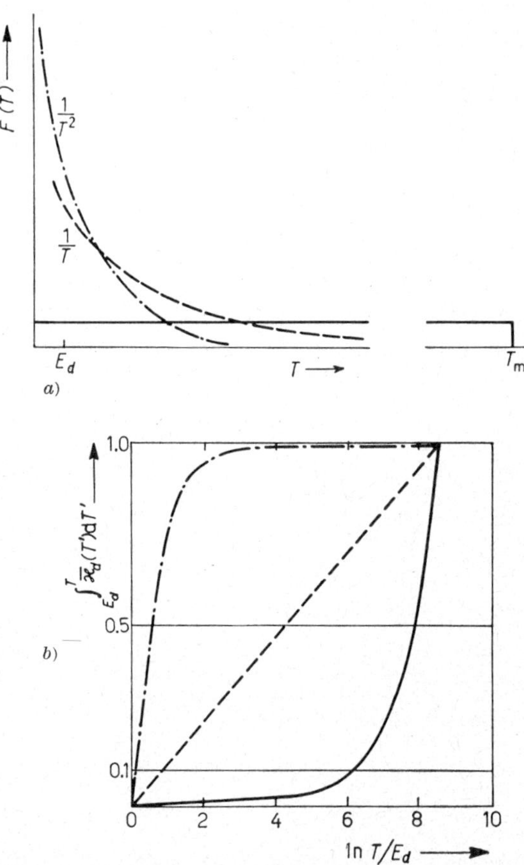

Fig. 20. – Comparison of primary distributions for heavy charged particle (–·–·–), pile neutron (– – –) and fission neutron (——) irradiation: *a*) the energy distribution; *b*) the fraction of primary events with energies between E_d and T.

Because the primary electrons are mainly produced by Coulomb scattering, small primary energies are very much preferred and those electrons cannot introduce structural damage except by direct heating effects which seem to be unimportant. The primary distribution due to γ irradiation is shown for the Compton effect in Fig. 17 where high energies are preferred. These high-energy Compton electrons can displace atoms. This will not be discussed here.

Details about the energy distribution of primary atoms induced by γ irradiation via Compton electrons are discussed in the lecture of D. K. HOLMES. Because of the long γ range this effect can be used very conveniently to replace electron irradiation. In photo-absorption the electron takes over practically all the γ energy. But for γ energies about 1 MeV the Compton effect is predominant. For smaller energies the electrons do not displace atoms any more, except light atoms. In photo-absorption the atom has to take over a recoil which may be important for light atoms. The recoil depends on the angle between the electron velocity and the incident direction. As an example we will give values for $E_\gamma = 1$ MeV. Here one gets 100 eV/A and 2 500 eV/A as recoil energies (2 to 50 eV for Cu) for forward, respectively, backward emission of the electron. In general forward emission prevails but experimental and theoretical investigations are sparse.

4. – Simple theory of irradiation effects.

4·1. *The displacement threshold.* – In metals and homopolar semiconductors the simplest defect is a vacancy-interstitial pair (Frenkel pair), as mentioned in the introduction. There is a threshold energy E_d for this process which can be determined by studying property changes in electron irradiation of variable energy. This threshold energy is of the order of 25 eV.

It has already been mentioned that only electron irradiation is useful for

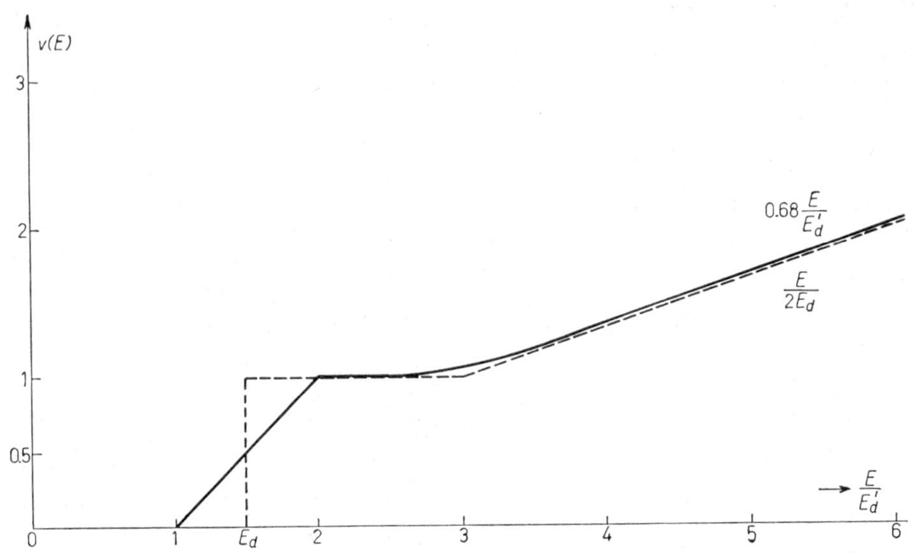

Fig. 21. – The number of Frenkel pairs *vs.* primary energy: *a*) for sharp threshold energy E_d; *b*) for linearly varying displacement probabilities in $(2E_d/3,\ 4E_d/3)$.

determining E_d. The ranges of heavy charged particles of about 1000 eV in solids are far too small, and neutrons of about 1000 eV energy are not easy to handle. Irradiations with γ-rays could be used, however.

In general, there will be only a certain probability $W_d(T)$ of producing a defect, when transferring the energy T to a stationary atom, and the threshold will not be sharp (for sharp threshold: $W_d=0$ for $T\leqslant E_d$; $W_d=1$ for $T\geqslant E_d$). On simple models one can demonstrate [7] that a reasonable effective threshold value can be defined by $W_d(E_d)\simeq\frac{1}{2}$. In Fig. 21 it is shown how good this assumption really is if one calculates the number $\nu(E)$ of Frenkel defects produced by a primary of energy E. The full line gives the result for $W_d(E)$ varying linearly from $E/E_d'=1$ to $E/E_d'=2$ whereas the dashed line shows the result assuming a sharp threshold at $E_d=3E_d'/2$, where $W_d(E_d)=\frac{1}{2}$. The agreement for $E\gg E_d$ is seen to be very good. For the sake of simplicity we will assume a sharp threshold value in the following.

4·2. *Simple cascade theory.* – The simplest approach to calculating irradiation effects is the attempt to resolve the whole damage into the simplest basic point defect of irradiation, the Frenkel pair. If one can assume that the single pairs do not interfere with each other, then one needs only the number of pairs per unit volume and the physical properties of one pair. One may as well assume that the vacancies and interstitials behave as independent, and then the physical properties can be obtained additively from vacancy and interstitial densities, which are of course equal to the pair densities. The evidence in electron damage, available at present, seems to support the view, that the change of physical properties by one Frenkel pair does not sensitively depend on its distance, which means that vacancies and interstitials can also be treated as independent.

In this simple approach one would have to calculate the number of pairs $\nu(T)$ produced by one primary of energy T. Then one can calculate the density of pairs

$$n_{\text{pair}}=n_{\text{At}}t\Phi_d\bar{\sigma}_d\cdot\bar{\nu} \tag{4.1}$$

with

$$\bar{\nu}=\int\limits_{E_d}^{T_m}\nu(T)\bar{\varkappa}_d(T)\,\mathrm{d}T\,.$$

The first factor in (4.1) is the density of primary displacement events, the second is the average number of pairs per primary event. Knowing then the energy E_{pair} for one pair, one gets the stored energy per unit volume

$$\varepsilon_s=n_{\text{pair}}E_{\text{pair}}\,, \tag{4.2}$$

or knowing the resistivity change per pair one can calculate the total resistivity change.

Although there are serious objections to that oversimplified picture it is quite instructive to discuss it.

Now $\nu(T)$ is wanted. This calculation requires information about the collisions between the atoms of the solid and details about the process by which a stationary atom is displaced. Various models for both have been discussed. Again one can demonstrate [7] that details of the models do not matter much. We discuss only some of these models with sharp threshold E_d.

If a primary of energy E encounters a stationary atom its energy after the collision will be E' and it will have transferred an energy T to the stationary atom. If after the collision both atoms can be treated as independent then one can compose $\nu(E)$ out of the contributions $\nu(E')$, $\nu(T)$ after the collision:

$$\nu(E) = \nu(E') + \nu(T)\,. \tag{4.3}$$

First we discuss the simple model of Kinchin and Pease [8]. (4.3) holds only if the energies E' and T are sharp. Actually there is a distribution. Further, one has to assume a certain model for the displacement process, which is simply this: « If the energy of an atom after a collision is larger than E_d it moves off with just its energy; if the energy is smaller it remains at the collision site ». The physical interpretation for this model can be given as follows. It will be shown later that the collisions between two atoms can be described approximately as hard-core collisions with a radius R given by the distance of closest approach. The radius R decreases with energy. A moving atom will see the stationary atoms as spheres of radius R impeding its motion. Through the open space it can move freely. The displacement energy may be visualized now as that energy where the radii are so small that the moving atom can escape its surroundings easily, and if so it takes its full energy (compare Fig. 28). In that model one has

$$\nu(E) = 0 \qquad \text{for } E \leqslant E_d, \tag{4.4}$$

and

$$\nu(E) = 1 \qquad \text{for } E_d \leqslant E \leqslant 2E_d. \tag{4.5}$$

(4.5) is due to the fact that a primary in that energy interval can only displace another atom if it stays behind with energy less than E_d and replaces the displaced stationary atom. Consequently we can confine ourselves to $E \geqslant 2E_d$. The energies T and E' have distributions $\varkappa(E;T)$ and $\varkappa'(E;E')$ which are related by $\varkappa'(E') = \varkappa(E-T)$. Now $\nu(E)$ is expressed by the average values after the collision

$$\nu(E)=\int_{E_d}^{E}\nu(T)\varkappa(T)\,\mathrm{d}T+\int_{E_d}^{E}\nu(E')\varkappa'(E')\,\mathrm{d}E'\,, \tag{4.6}$$

or

$$\nu(E)=\int_{E_d}^{E}\nu(T)\{\varkappa(T)+\varkappa(E-T)\}\,\mathrm{d}T\,. \tag{4.6a}$$

Most commonly one uses the hard core distribution $\varkappa=1/E$. The resulting equation

$$\nu(E)=\frac{2}{E}\int_{E_d}^{E}\nu(T)\,\mathrm{d}T\,, \tag{4.7}$$

can be easily solved with the result

$$\nu(E)=\frac{E}{2E_d}\quad\text{for}\quad E\geqslant 2E_d\,. \tag{4.8}$$

This result is not very sensitive to even drastic changes in $\varkappa$ because $\varkappa$ appears only in the symmetrized form $\varkappa(T)+\varkappa(E-T)$ [7]. If, for instance, one only allows energy transfers smaller than $E/2$ with equal probability then $\varkappa(T)=2/E$ for $T\leqslant E/2$ and $\varkappa'(T)=2/E$ for $T\geqslant E/2$ and the integral in (4.6a) does not change at all leading again to (4.8). Also linear behavior of $\varkappa(T)$ with T would give exactly (4.7). $\nu(E)$ is in fact an average value but one can show that deviations are usually small.

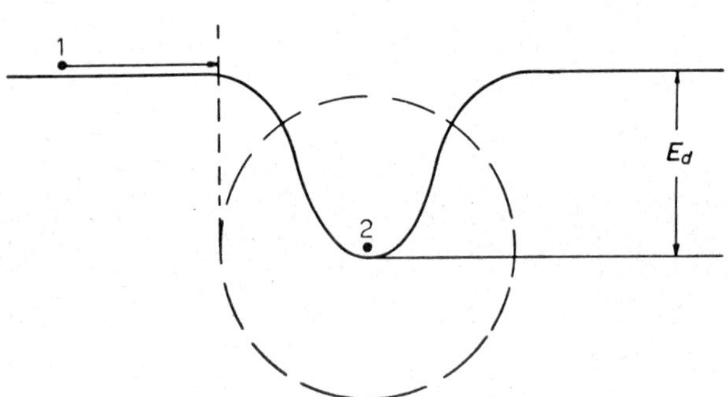

Fig. 22. – Model for a displacement process.

Other models of the liberation process change the basic equation but do not change the results appreciably. An example for another liberation process is demonstrated in Fig. 22. The potential trough is the potential exerted by the lattice on the incident primary and the atom to be displaced. If one assumes hard-core collisions, then the quantitative details depend on the radius. In any case the energy E_d is lost in the process. If the radius is of the size of the trough the displaced atom loses E_d. This is the model of Snyder and Neufeld [9]. If the radius is small then the collision occurs at the bottom of the trough and the incident particle first gains and then loses E_d, the displaced atom loses E_d in any case. This is a more symmetrical model. As mentioned before, the results are essentially unchanged [7] and it is therefore convenient to use the simplest description.

The energy E_F of a Frenkel pair should be about 5 eV. The stored energy for a primary of energy T is $\nu(T)E_F$. One can easily see that the ratio of stored to primary energy $\nu(T)E_F/T \simeq E_F/2E_d = 1/10$ is quite small so that only a small percentage ($\sim 10\%$) of the transferred energy can be stored, most of it being transferred to heat.

It is interesting to compare the values of $\bar{\nu}$ for various irradiations. In electron irradiation $\bar{\nu}$ is about 1. For neutron and deuteron irradiation it is much larger than 1 and one can replace approximately $\nu(T)$ by $T/2E_d$ which gives $\bar{\nu} = \overline{T}/2E_d$. The values for $\overline{T}$ are generally given in table I page 255, and for Cu in particular one obtains: in 10 MeV deuteron irradiation $\overline{T} \simeq 250$ eV; $\bar{\nu} \simeq 5$, in pile neutron irradiation $\overline{T} = 5\,000$ eV; $\bar{\nu} \simeq 10^2$ and for fission neutrons $\overline{T} \simeq 5000$ eV; $\bar{\nu} \simeq 10^3$.

Theory and experiment do not agree too well, theoretical values generally giving too much damage, particularly in neutron irradiation up to about a factor of 10. The disagreement becomes worse with increasing $\overline{T}$. If our simple model really applies, this would mean that $\nu(T)$ is overestimated for large T (for instance, by not accounting for self-annealing in the large T events) or the whole model of independent Frenkel pairs does not make sense for large T, which is quite plausible. Consequently, the development and the structure of a high-energy primary zone is of especial interest. This point will be discussed later.

But in electron damage of metals this simple picture seems to be fairly consistent. Essentially single pairs are produced there. The vacancy and the interstitial attract each other with short-range forces. Consequently, outside the attraction range the pair consists of a « single » vacancy and a « single » interstitial. Inside this range the structure of the vacancy and the interstitial is changed. Near the vacancy there are different lattice sites available for the interstitial which interact differently. These may be called close pairs if they show an appreciable interaction. For more distant pairs vacancy and interstitial can be treated as independent.

The distances between the vacancy and the interstitial of one pair produced by an electron hit should not be too large, usually from about one lattice distance (close pair) to ten lattice distances. But there may also be larger distances due to special collision series along close-packed directions in the lattice which are discussed later.

It must be recognized that the investigation of these point defects is rather difficult. The structure and the properties of a single vacancy are fairly well known, but information about the interstitial is fragmentary. One does not even know for sure the approximate structure and symmetries of the interstitial. Fig. 23 shows some possible structures for a f.c.c. lattice:

Fig. 23. – Interstitial configuration in f.c.c. lattices. Left upper corner: normal lattice; right upper corner: symmetrical interstitial; left lower corner: crowdion; right lower corner: dumbbell configuration.

— the symmetrical position in the position with maximum available space and small relaxation (arrows); the crowdion structure where the interstitial is quenched into the position with the least available space. The relaxation is large and centered around the 110 direction;

— the position with dumbbell symmetry with relaxation in 100.

All these structures have different properties. In the case of Cu there have been numerous theoretical investigations on the stability of those structures. The results show that the energy difference between these structures is small; they are very sensitive to small changes in the potentials used in the calculation. Since the potentials are not very well known it is difficult to decide the interstitial structure on purely theoretical reasons. There may even exist more than one stable structure. Naturally the structure of a close pair is even more complicated. Consequently one has to rely on experiment in deciding this, but here also our information is far from being complete. These questions are dealt with in more detail in the lecture of G. H. VINEYARD.

The pair structure shows up in the annealing of damage, *e.g.* in the annealing of radiation-induced resistivity. There should be several temperature stages in this annealing. The first stages in the annealing at low temperatures are due to the annealing (vacancy-interstitial annihilation) of close pairs, the closest ones annealing out at the lowest temperatures. Then pairs with larger distance anneal out by diffusion, for instance of the mobile interstitial to its vacancy. Further, there is a possibility that the interstitial does not diffuse to its own vacancy but diffuses over a large distance to the vacancy of another pair, which leads to another annealing stage.

In electron irradiated Cu such stages have been found and interpreted along the above lines. This will be discussed in another lecture given here by R. M. WALKER.

This would be the picture in an ideal crystal containing no defects other than those induced by radiation. There are quite strong interactions with the defects already present in the crystal before irradiation, particularly with dislocations and impurity atoms. Even in the simple picture of vacancies and interstitials, given above, there is the possibility of building up defects during the annealing stage, *e.g.* vacancy clusters beginning with the divacancy, etc.

5. – Atomic interaction potentials.

5·1. *General discussion.* – In Section 2·2.5 we discussed the potential between two atoms which has been assumed by BOHR. It was mentioned that this screened Coulomb potential essentially only accounts for the inner electrons and does not properly take into account the outer electrons. For distances which are of the order of the distance between neighbors in the lattice one uses more commonly a repulsive potential of purely exponential type, Born-Mayer potential, ($\varphi(r) = A \exp[-r/a']$), where a' is closely related to the ionic core radius. This description is thought to apply particularly to closed ionic shells and has been used often for the repulsive short-range potentials in the alkali halides and in metals. Consequently, for smaller distances one has reason to use a screened Coulomb potential which changes to purely exponential behavior for larger distances (*).

Besides the central repulsive potentials there are other contributions partly corresponding to central attractive potentials and partly corresponding to many-body forces. It is generally assumed that for distances which are essential in high-energy atomic collisions one can disregard the many-body and the central-attractive part and can confine oneself to the central, repulsive potentials discussed in the first paragraph.

5·2. *Determination of the potential at large distances.* – By large distances, where the Born-Mayer potential should be valid, we understand $r \sim D$ where D is the neighbor distance in the lattice. The parameters of the Born-Mayer potential

$$\varphi(r) = A \exp[-r/a'] \tag{5.1}$$

can be determined from the elastic behavior of the solid, *e.g.*, from the elastic moduli, their dependence on pressure and shock waves. This may be illustrated for a f.c.c. lattice where every atom has $Z = 12$ neighbors. We assume a central potential throughout and a *known* attractive potential $\varphi_a(r)$. To sim-

---

(*) The potential of a hydrogen atom

$$V_{\mathrm{H}}(r) = \frac{e}{r}(1 + r/a_{\mathrm{H}}) \exp[-2r/a_{\mathrm{H}}],$$

is quite an instructive example.

plify things further we assume short-range potentials where only the potential of neighbors has to be taken into account. Then the energy per atom is given by $\varepsilon(r) = (Z/2)(A\exp[-r/a'] + \varphi_a(r))$, where r is the neighbor distance. The first derivative of ε gives the equilibrium distance D: $\varepsilon'(D) = 0$ or $A/a' \cdot \exp[-D/a'] = \varphi'_a(D)$. Because D is given experimentally and therefore $\varphi_a(D)$ is given too, this establishes one relation to determine A, a'. In fact, since $\varepsilon(D)$, the lattice energy, can also be measured, $\varepsilon(D)$ and D are sufficient to determine A and a'. Mostly it is more convenient for several reasons to determine A, a' by the compressibility which is given by $\varepsilon''(D)$ or even higher-order derivatives.

Thus one can use different methods to calculate A', a'. If the results for A, a' do not agree, this means that either the «known» part of the potential, used in the calculation, is not really known too well and disagrees with reality or that the repulsive part is not well described by the ansatz of Born-Mayer or both. Therefore one will not be surprised if the data for A, a' scatter when using different elastic properties for the calculation. Here I will only mention an investigation of Cu [10] where the extreme values were given by $A = 7 \cdot 10^3$ eV, $D/a' = 11$ and $A = 6 \cdot 10^6$ eV; $D/a' = 27$. Both values are very much different and give also a quite different physical picture, essentially if one tries to interpolate from $r \simeq D$ to smaller values of r. Later on we will use for purposes of demonstration the values $A = 2 \cdot 10^4$ eV, $D/a' = 13$ given by HUNTINGTON [11] which seem to give a physically reasonable picture, at least near $r \simeq D/2$, which we will discuss later on. But this discussion should show how unreliable our information really is.

5.3. *Determination of the potential at small distances.* – At small distances $r \simeq a \simeq a_H/\sqrt{2}\,Z^{\frac{1}{3}}$ (for equal atoms of atomic number Z) the screened Coulomb potential is generally assumed. We will use it in our discussion, too although it must be pointed out that there might be quite strong deviations not only in the screening radius given by BOHR but also in the form of the potential. Again we will take Cu as an example. For $R = a$ one has $E_{rel} = E/2 = E_a e^{-1}$, and because $E_a = Z^2e^2/a \simeq 10^5$ eV the energy to penetrate to a is about 10^5 eV. This is just at the upper limit of energies transferred to Cu atoms in neutron irradiation. To explore the potential in this region one has to have atoms of about 10^5 eV. This could be done by investigations into the scattering of high-energy Cu atoms in a Cu gas. Actually this experiment has been proposed, but because of experimental difficulties it will take some more time to perform it (*).

Up to now there is only one experiment for exploring the potentials with

(*) Recently potentials for some rare gases were derived from ion-atom scattering data [G. H. LANE and E. EVERHART: *Phys. Rev. Lett.*, **5**, 391 (1960) (A)].

such energies namely the range experiments by SCHMITT and SHARP [12]. They have measured the ranges of high-energy primaries in various substances and since the range is determined by a series of subsequent atom-atom collisions this range gives information about the atomic potential. If one assumes the screened Coulomb potential

$$\varphi(r) = \frac{Z^2e^2}{r} \exp\left[-r/a\right], \tag{5.2}$$

but regards the screening radius a only as a parameter and not given by Bohr's value (2.38c) and if one can calculate the range $P(a)$ properly for given initial energy, then one gets a by equating the experimental range P_{exp} and the theoretical result $P_{\text{th}}(a)$. This procedure gives as the most reasonable value for Cu

$$a \simeq \sqrt{2}\, a_{\text{H}}/Z^{\frac{1}{3}}, \tag{5.3}$$

which is twice the value of Bohr, and this factor may well apply generally to other substances.

We are first going to discuss the range experiments briefly and will then give an outline of the theory leading to an «experimental» value of a.

In the experiment material is irradiated with γ-rays up to about 20 MeV. For these energies resonance (γ, n) processes are quite frequent, the cross-section being comparable to 1 barn. During the (n, γ) reaction the nucleus absorbs the γ energy, which is used to heat the nucleus to high temperatures, and then evaporates a neutron with practically equal probability in all directions. The energy of the evaporated neutrons seems not to depend very much on the nuclear mass but rather on the γ energy absorbed. For 20 MeV γ-rays the neutron energy is about 2 MeV. The emission of the neutron gives a recoil to the nucleus of magnitude 2 MeV/A which is about 50 000 eV for Cu. Also the γ absorption leads to a transfer of kinetic energy to the compound nucleus (about $E_\gamma^2/A\cdot 2M_{\text{p}}c^2$) but this energy is small as compared with the recoil energy (3 000 eV as compared with 50 000 eV in Cu). The recoil nuclei become radioactive and can easily be detected by their radioactivity.

The principle of the measurement is quite easy. If one irradiates a plane foil of thickness T, then one obtains a certain number n_γ of (γ, n) events per cm in the direction of the normal to the foil. Those recoil atoms which are nearer to the surface than the range will have a chance to leave the plate, can be sampled on a target and their number can be measured by observing their radioactive decay. The recoil atoms stopped inside the foil can be measured by the same means. Now it is easy to prove that by measuring the activity outside the foil N_{out}, the activity in the foil N_{in} and the thickness T one can determine the range by

$$P = 2T \frac{N_{\text{in}}}{N_{\text{out}}} . \tag{5.4}$$

This can be seen by means of Fig. 24, where the range P is supposed to be the distance to where the recoil atom moves straight forward and settles down. Every recoil atom nearer to the surface than P will have a certain probability to escape. At the distance P from the surface this probability will drop to zero; in the surface itself the probability will be $\frac{1}{2}$ because half of the recoil atoms produced at the surface are directed toward the interior. This probability varies linearly with the distance, its average value being $\frac{1}{4}$. Now the number emitted through one surface will be $n_\gamma \cdot P/4$ because $n_\gamma \cdot P$ is the number of recoil atoms produced within the range from the surface and every atom has the chance $\frac{1}{4}$ to escape. Taking into account the two surfaces one has

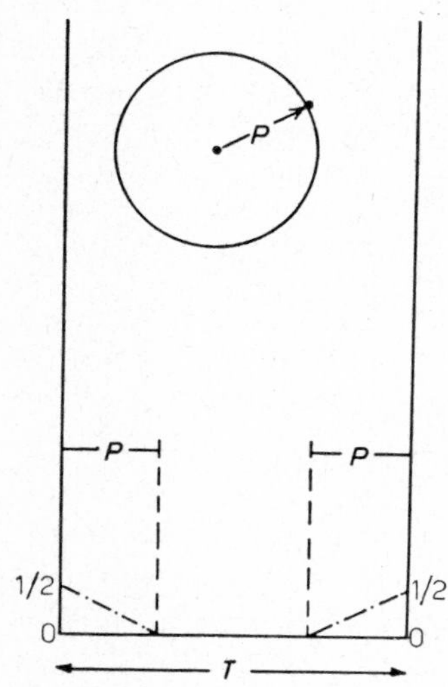

Fig. 24. – Sketch for the determination of the range P. The dash-and dot line shows the probability for escape.

$$N_{\text{out}} = n_\gamma \cdot P/2 . \tag{5.5}$$

Evidently one gets

$$N_{\text{in}} = n_\gamma T - N_{\text{out}} \simeq n_\gamma T , \tag{5.6}$$

where $T \gg P$ or $N_{\text{in}} \gg N_{\text{out}}$ has been assumed. Dividing (5.6) by (5.5) n_γ drops out and the result is (5.4).

The experimental ranges for some metals are given in the Table II. They are generally very small, of the order of 10^{-6} cm. Consequently, the range refers to a very thin surface layer and is affected by oxidation and other surface phenomena. One can give reasons, however, to sustain that the ranges in the bulk material should not be very much different from those obtained at the surface.

Generally the recoil atom does not move straightforward to its final position but it collides with other atoms and its path is a polygon connecting the collision points of the recoil atoms with the stationary atoms of the lattice.

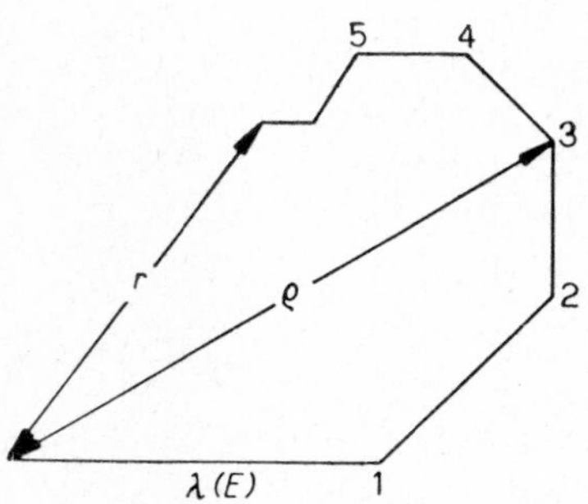

Fig. 25. – Collision series of a primary knock-on.

TABLE II. – *Comparison of experimental ranges with theory.*

Element	$\bar{E}$	E_B	$\bar{E}^3 E_B$	λ_a	R/a	P_{th}	P_{exp}	$\bar{L}$	
		10.4	0.51	3.3	0.85	10.4		10.6	1
Ti	5.28	7.38	0.715	1.6	0.70	7.4	3.1	7.3	$\sqrt{2}$
		5.28	1.0	0.81	0.55	5.51		5.5	2
		15.5	0.31	2.35	1.1	4.8		5.2	1
Fe	4.8	10.9	0.44	1.17	0.91	3.3	5.6	3.4	$\sqrt{2}$
		7.74	0.62	0.58	0.75	2.3		2.3	2
		20.0	2.2	2.5	1.3	3.5		4.1	1
Cu	4.0	14.3	0.28	1.25	1.1	2.3	1.6	2.6	$\sqrt{2}$
		10.0	0.4	0.61	0.95	1.6		1.65	2
		21.1	0.19	3.3	1.35	4.5		5.2	1
Zn	4.0	15.4	0.26	1.7	1.15	2.9	1.37	3.35	$\sqrt{2}$
		10.8	0.37	0.83	1.0	2.1		2.1	2
		47.4	0.054	4.3	2.15	2.6		3.4	1
Mo	2.56	33.2	0.077	2.15	1.9	1.6	0.71	2.0	$\sqrt{2}$
		23.3	0.11	1.1	1.7	1.0		1.2	2
		60.5	0.037	5.1	2.45	2.5		3.3	1
Ag	2.24	43.1	0.052	2.5	2.2	1.5	0.71	1.9	$\sqrt{2}$
		30.7	0.073	1.27	1.95	0.9		1.15	2
		205.7	0.007	7.1	3.65	1.8		2.7	1
Au	1.44	144	0.01	3.5	3.4	1.0	0.27	1.5	$\sqrt{2}$
		103	0.014	1.8	3.1	0.58		0.84	2

The energies are given in units of 10 000 eV and the lengths in units of 10^{-6} cm.

This is shown qualitatively in Fig. 25. The first section is in the average the mean free path of the recoil primary with energy E. After the first collision the primary moves off with changed energy and angle until it collides a second time. This goes on until the recoil atom comes to rest at a distance r from the starting point. This distance is of course not deciding for the range, but the range is rather given by the maximum distance ϱ from the starting point. The whole collision story of the recoil atom obeys statistical laws. Consequently, one has a distribution function for ϱ and the range then is given by the average

$$P = \bar{\varrho} \,. \tag{5.7}$$

An attempt has been made in [13] to calculate P for a screened Coulomb potential of the form (2.38). We know that we can use classical scattering throughout (compare Section 2·1), and to discuss the collision history of the recoil atom one has to calculate scattering cross-sections to determine the mean free paths, and differential cross-sections to obtain the distribution of energy and angles after each collision. These quantities have to be determined as a function of the energy of the primary.

We will discuss briefly the method of calculation and the results. Since the calculation of the classical differential cross-section, even for a simple screened Coulomb potential, is difficult and certainly does not give simple expressions, the attempt has been made to describe the scattering by hard-core scattering where the hard-core radius is determined by the distance of closest approach R. The general condition for hard-core scattering would be that the potential falls off very rapidly from the value $\varphi(R)$ at the distance of closest approach. One can express this somewhat more quantitatively in the following way: « If the potential $\varphi(R)$ in R is extrapolated linearly the line will intersect the axis at $r=R'>R$. The condition for hard-core scattering would be $R/(R'-R)\gg 1$ ». If one now calculates $R'-R$ from the potential the condition for hard-core scattering is

$$\left|\frac{R\varphi'(R)}{\varphi(R)}\right| \gg 1 . \tag{5.8}$$

For a screened Coulomb potential this gives

$$1+R/a \gg 1 \tag{5.9}$$

and for a Born-Mayer potential

$$R/a' \gg 1 . \tag{5.10}$$

In the above attempt hard-core scattering has been used throughout even for values $R/a\simeq 1$ where the hard-core condition is certainly not satisfied too well. In one of the next sections we will give some results of classical scattering theory, particularly for screened Coulomb potentials, which seem to support the use of hard-core scattering.

The required quantity is $\bar{\varrho}$. Even in the hard-core approximation the calculation of $\bar{\varrho}$ is very difficult and it could not be calculated. But one can place it between certain limits. One has obviously $\varrho \geqslant r_{(n)}$ for every collision point $n=1, 2, 3$ along the collision series, the same holds for the average $\bar{\varrho}\geqslant \bar{r}_{(n)}$. The average of the distance to the first collision point is just the mean free path by definition: $\bar{r}_{(1)}=\lambda(E)$. Thus, $\lambda(E)$ establishes a lower limit to P. It is difficult already to calculate $\bar{r}_{(2)}$, which would establish a better lower limit for P. An upper limit would be clearly given by the total path traversed L: $\bar{\varrho}\leqslant \bar{L}$. There are certain averages which can be easily calculated in the hard core-approximation; one of them is

$$\bar{L} = \lambda(E) + \int_0^E \lambda(\xi) \frac{\mathrm{d}\xi}{\xi} . \tag{5.11}$$

This gives for the screened Coulomb potential

$$\bar{L} = \lambda(E) \left\{ \frac{3}{2} + \frac{R}{a} \right\} . \tag{5.12}$$

Another average which can be expressed by an integral over $\lambda(\xi)$ is $\overline{r^2}$. The discussion shows that $\sqrt{\overline{r^2}}$ can be used as a theoretical estimate of P

$$P \approx \sqrt{\overline{r^2}} . \tag{5.13}$$

In Fig. 26, the results of the theory are plotted.

In the table experimental and theoretical results are given. The first column gives the average recoil energy $\bar{E}$; it must be mentioned that only the recoil

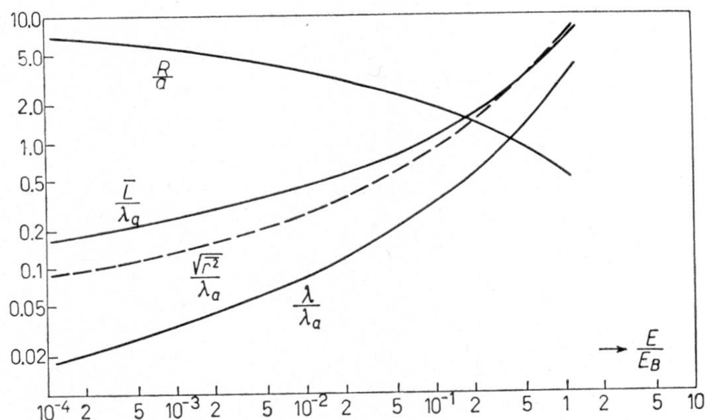

Fig. 26. – Averages for the screened Coulomb potential at the hard-core approximation.

energy of Cu has been measured by observing the neutron evaporation spectrum. All the other energies are obtained by assuming that the nuclear evaporation temperature depends only on the absorbed energy. This is qualitatively true but there might be differences when discussing the effect in a quantitative way. The second column gives $E_B = 2E_a$ depending on the choice of a, $\lambda_a = 1/n_{\mathrm{At}}\pi a^2$ is the mean free path for $R = a$, R/a is given for $E = \bar{E}$, and α is the ratio of a to Bohr's value (2.38c): $a = \alpha a_{\mathrm{H}}/\sqrt{2}\,Z^{\frac{1}{3}}$. The best value for Cu is given by $\alpha \simeq 2$. Since P is rather near the upper limit, a lower value of P is indicated and this would mean that α would be somewhat lower, say between $\sqrt{2}$ and 2.

It may be mentioned that in Cu the influence of the ionic shell potential should not matter much because the main contribution comes from high energies where the inner electrons are decisive. This can be seen also from the result (5.12) where $\bar{L}$ is about $\lambda(E)$ for $R/a \simeq 1$ but much larger if $R \gg a$; in the latter case the subsequent collisions play a much more important role. This may not be true for Au with about 10^4 eV recoil energy which may account for the low value of P_{obs}. For the lighter elements the hard-core approximation is likely to break down ($R \leqslant a$). At the moment it does not seem worth-while to discuss the deviation more in detail because of the uncertainty of the recoil energies.

These experiments were the first to give information about primaries of almost unique energy. Although the γ irradiation produced by an electron accelerator has a continuous spectrum down from about 20 MeV maximum γ energy, the γ absorption is due to a giant resonance with absorption at a preferred energy and therefore preferred temperature. Also the neutron evaporation spectrum shows some spread about an average energy. But in contrast to irradiation with charged particles or with neutrons the recoil atoms have distributions with a pronounced maximum at energies of about 50000 eV in Cu. There is, of course, some energy spread but one really can treat the problem in a first approximation as though the primaries would have unique energies. This is not possible in the more common irradiations. If sufficient intensity could be obtained one could investigate in this way the physical property changes effected by primaries of large energy alone. Further experiments are in progress where the primary energy is changed. This would give details about the r-dependence of the potential. The change in energy can be made either by changing the energy within the resonance region [23] or by utilizing other nuclear processes. Also, one would get some information about the ionization limit for primaries with $E > E_I$.

5·4. *A potential for copper* [14]. – The way to determine the atomic interaction potentials between the atoms of a solid at large and small distances has been discussed in the last two paragraphs. Again we will use Cu as an example to illustrate an attempt to derive a potential which holds for small *and* large distances or for large *and* small energies. For the Born-Mayer potential we take the values $A = 2 \cdot 10^4$ eV, $D/a' = 13$. The screening radius of the Bohr potential is estimated according to the methods of the last paragraph to be slightly less than $D/10$. For the sake of simplicity we choose the same value $a = D/13 = 0.2$ Å for Bohr's potential; then E_a is about $75 \cdot 10^3$ eV. That a and a' are close to each other is merely accidental and cannot be generalized, remembering that a should decrease and a', as ionic radius, should increase with atomic number. If one compares both potentials one sees that at small distances the screened Coulomb potential would prevail and that at large distances only the Born-Mayer potential would be important. Consequently, it seems reasonable just to add these potentials. Then one has at small distances practically the Bohr potential alone and for large distances the Born-Mayer potential. Because the whole potential should reproduce the original elastic data it makes sense to adjust the A in the complete potential so, that the value of the potential for $r \simeq D$ is the same as for the Born-Mayer potential itself. It can be shown that the low-order derivatives of the complete potential at $r = D$ agree quite well with the corresponding derivatives of the Born-Mayer potential alone. Consequently, this potential reproduces the elastic data as well as the Born-Mayer potential. Eventually this potential has the form

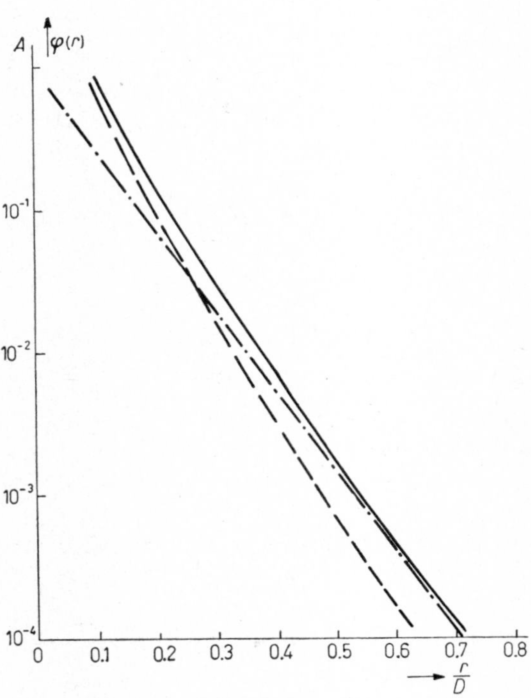

Fig. 27. – Potential for Cu: – – – screened Coulomb potential; –·–·– Born-Mayer potential; —— interpolation potential.

$$(5.14) \qquad \varphi(r) = E_a\left(\frac{1}{4} + \frac{a}{r}\right)\exp\left[-r/a\right],$$

with

$$E_a \simeq 75\cdot 10^3\ \text{eV} \qquad \text{and} \qquad a \simeq D/13 \simeq 2\cdot 10^{-9}\ \text{cm}.$$

This potential gives the experimental ranges (high energy, small r) as well as the experimental elastic data (low energy, $r \sim D$). Fig. 27 serves to illustrate this potential. The Fig. 28 show how a primary of energy E sees the lattice in the hard-core approximation. The primary is drawn as a point in the origin; around the stationary atoms circles with radius $R(E)$ are drawn to demonstrate the space into which the primary cannot penetrate. Fig. 28*a* corresponds to the energy of the range experiment where λ should be of the order of the range. The mean free path becomes of the order of one lattice distance D at energies of the order of E_d which is also quite sensible. In Fig. 28d for $E = 30$ eV $= E_d$ the spheres of neighbor atoms just begin to over-

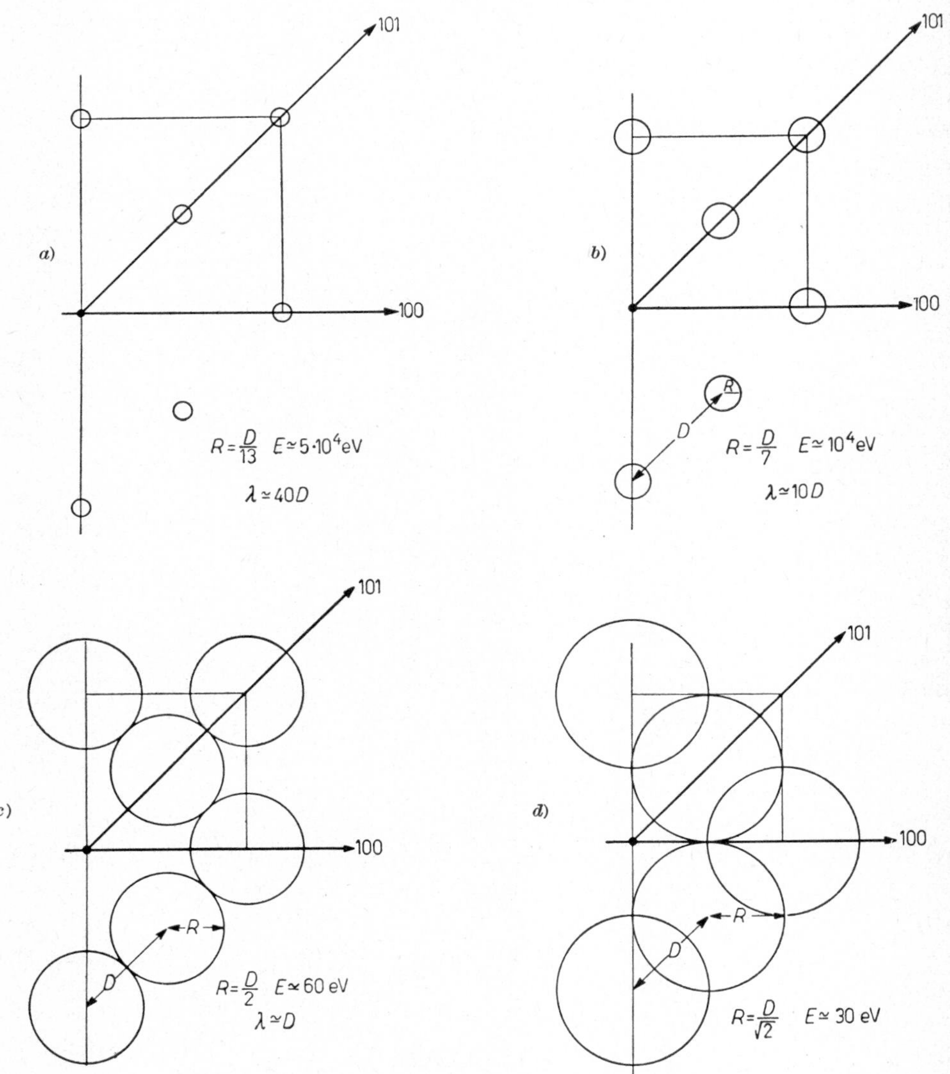

Fig. 28. – Illustration of the potential for Cu.

lap, leaving no chance for the primary to escape its surroundings. This potential will be used later to calculate approximately the spatial distribution of defects in a high-energy primary event.

6. – Classical scattering theory.

6·1. *General remarks.* – In classical scattering theory the relation between scattering angle θ and impact parameter p is given by an integral containing $\varphi(r)$, [15]:

$$\theta = \pi - \int_{r_m}^{\infty} \frac{2p\,\mathrm{d}r}{r^2\{1 - \varphi(r)/E_{\mathrm{rel}} - p^2/r^2\}^{\frac{1}{2}}}, \tag{6.1}$$

r_m is the distance of closest approach for given p where the square root in (6.1) vanishes. Elementary solutions are known only for $\varphi(r) = \text{const}$ (no scattering at all), $\varphi(r) \sim 1/r$ (Coulomb scattering), $\varphi(r) \sim 1/r^2$ and r^2, hard-core potentials and combination of these cases. The Coulomb scattering was discussed in Section **2**; the result for $1/r^2$ scattering is elementary but complicated. Both cases, by the way, have infinite cross-sections not only classically but also in quantum mechanics. Consequently, in general one has to rely on numerical or approximate methods to calculate the differential cross-section over the whole range of transferred energies. Fairly good approximations can be given near $T = T_m$ and for $T/T_m \ll 1$ (see the discussion in [16]). In the following we will discuss a method which gives quite a good approximation over a large energy range, including $T = T_m$, but which fails at very low transferred energies. It is an extension of the hard-core approximation which also gives the wrong behavior at small energies where classically K should tend to infinity. But, since we are not very interested in low-energy transfers because they are not effective, this method is quite valuable for an approximate description of scattering.

6·2. *Approximate differential cross-section by matching potentials.* – One natural method to calculate differential cross-sections with fair accuracy near T_m is to approximate the potential $\varphi(r)$ by another, simpler, potential $\varphi_{\mathrm{aD}}(r)$ which fits well for $r \geqslant R(E)$. For every energy E another adjustment is required. The hard-core approximation is the simplest approximation of this kind:

$$\varphi_{\mathrm{aD}}(r) = \begin{cases} \infty & \text{for } r < R\,, \\ 0 & r > R\,. \end{cases} \tag{6.2}$$

As a matter of fact, for $r < R$ the potential can be chosen arbitrarily except for $\varphi_{\mathrm{aD}}(r) > \varphi(R)$ because then in classical scattering the distance $r < R$ cannot be reached and does not influence the result. This is an approximation where $\varphi(R) = \varphi_a(R)$ but where the slopes at R do not fit. A better method would be one where the potential and the slopes agree at $r=R$

$$\varphi(R)=\varphi_{ap}(R)\;;\qquad \varphi'(R)=\varphi'_{ap}(R)\;. \tag{6.3}$$

There are various possibilities to construct approximative potentials. The potential one thinks of first, namely the linear extrapolation of the slope in R to $\varphi=0$, does not give an elementary solution of (6.1).

Here we discuss only one special φ_{ap} which seems to give the simplest result, another kind of screened Coulomb potential

$$\varphi_{ap}=\begin{cases} A'\left(\dfrac{R'}{r}-1\right) & r\leqslant R'\,,\\ & \text{for} \\ 0 & r\geqslant R'\,. \end{cases} \tag{6.4}$$

This potential corresponds to the screening of a charge by a charged spherical surface of radius R' and it has been used very often because of its simplicity to demonstrate screening effects in scattering. The differential cross-section is very simply

$$K_{ap}(T)=\frac{\pi R'^2}{T_m}\left(\frac{A'}{2E_{rel}}\right)^2\left\{\frac{1+A'/2E_{rel}}{(1+A'/E_{rel})(T/T_m)+(A'/2E_{rel})^2}\right\}^2. \tag{6.5}$$

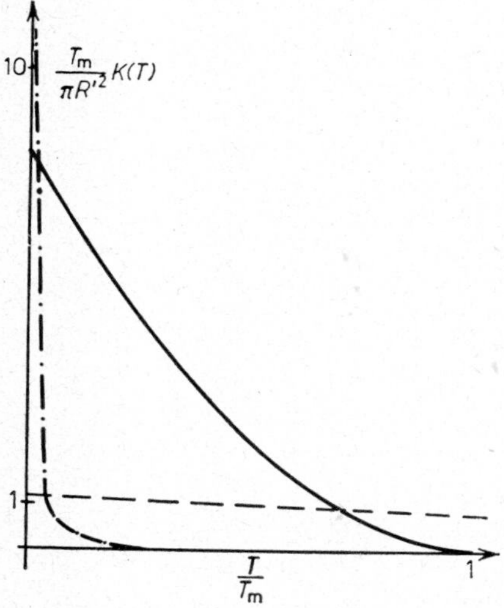

Fig. 29. – Differential cross section for the cut-off Coulomb potential (6.4): $E_{rel}/A'=10$ —·—·—; $E_{rel}/A'=1$ ——; $E_{rel}/A'=\frac{1}{10}$ – – –.

The total cross-section is always $\pi R'^2$ because R' is the range of this potential. The differential cross-section (6.5) is quite instructive. For very small energies ($E_{rel}\ll A'$) the T term in the denominator can be dropped and one has $K_{ap}(T)\simeq\pi R'^2/T_m$, which is hard-core scattering with hard-core radius R'. At very large energies ($E_{rel}\gg A'$) one gets practically Coulomb scattering ($K_{ap}\sim 1/T^2$) down to energies of the order $T/T_m\simeq A'^2/4E^2_{rel}$. This behavior is plotted in Fig. 29.

By means of (6.3), A' and R' can be expressed by $\varphi(R)$ and $\varphi'(R)$:

$$\begin{cases} A'=-\{\varphi(R)+R\varphi'(R)\}\,,\\ R'=\dfrac{R^2\varphi'(R)}{R\varphi'(R)+\varphi(R)}\,. \end{cases} \tag{6.6}$$

6·3. *Results and discussion for the screened Coulomb potential.* – If one evaluates A', R' for the screened Coulomb potential (2.38) one obtains

$$A' = E_a \exp[-R/a]\,, \qquad R' = R + a\,. \tag{6.7}$$

In Figs. 30 and 31 $\varphi(r)$ and $\varphi_{ap}(r)$ are plotted,

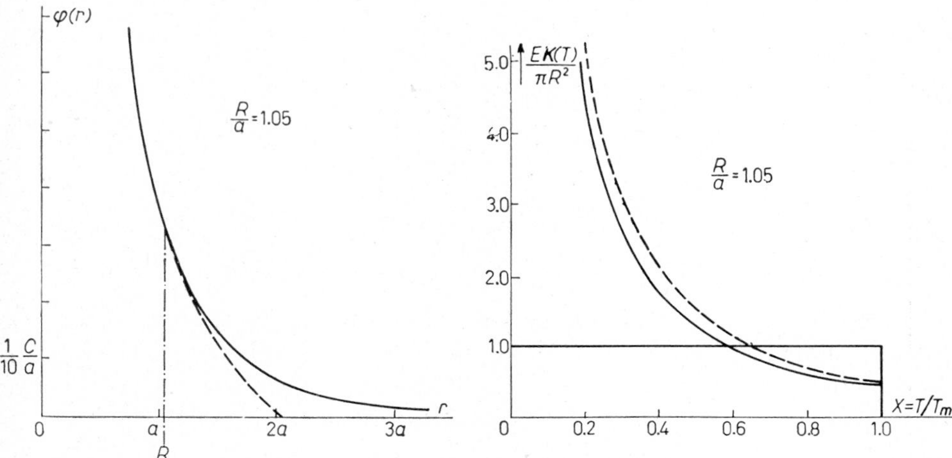

Fig. 30. – Approximate cross sections of the screened Coulomb potential (2.38) by matching potentials ($R/a=1.05$): *a*) potential (——) and matching potential (– – –); *b*) exact (——) and approximate (– – –) cross-sections.

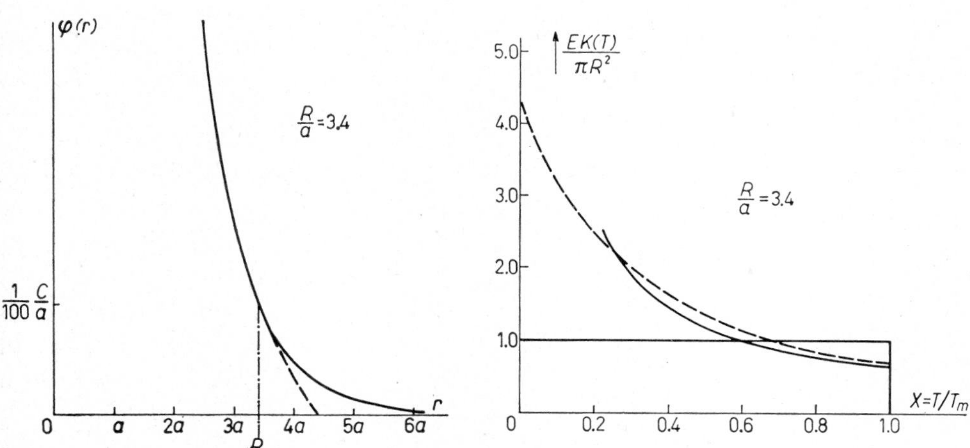

Fig. 31. – The same as Fig. 30, only $R/a=3.4$.

Because R is defined by

$$E_{rel} = E_a \frac{a}{R} \exp[-R/a]\,, \tag{6.8}$$

one can replace A'/E_{rel} in (6.5) by R/a with the result

$$K_{\text{ap}}(T) = \frac{\pi R^2}{T_m}\left\{\frac{\frac{1}{2}(1+R/a)(1+R/2a)}{(1+R/a)(T/T_m)+(R/2a)^2}\right\}^2 . \tag{6.9}$$

This now is an approximation for the screened Coulomb potential with R given by (6.8). The first factor is the hard-core approximation, the second takes care of the deviations. For $R \gg a$ one has hard core scattering, for $R \ll a$ practically Coulomb scattering.

To illustrate the quality of this approximation K_{ap} after (6.9) is plotted in Figs. 30 and 31 for two values of R/a. Further, there are plotted the exact results from machine calculations [16] and the corresponding hard-core distribution. One recognizes that the agreement is surprisingly good. Of course, this agreement fails for small T because the real classical cross-section of the screened Coulomb potential must tend to infinity for $T \to 0$. This is not shown in the figures. There are several reasons, however, to disregard this singular behavior of the classical scattering cross-section. First, there is a natural cut-off for the impact parameter at about half the distance between the atoms ($p \leqslant D/2$), secondly there are quantum mechanical corrections at small energies which presumably are not important here (for $p \leqslant D/2$). Finally even if $K(T)$ diverges the energy loss $\int TK\,\mathrm{d}T$ remains finite and is not much affected by the behavior for small T. And that is what counts. In Fig. 32 the ratio of the energy loss between the screened Coulomb potential which should be well approximated by (6.9) and the hard-core approximation is given. One seens that they agree well for $R \gtrsim a$. That means that the energy loss is about the same, but that in the real distribution small energy transfers are somewhat preferred. Small energy transfers correspond to small angular deviations. The picture of the motion of the recoil atom in Fig. 25 has to be corrected in the sense that, before changing the path by a large angle as shown in the Fig. 25, the primary undergoes some collisions with small energy loss and practically no change of the direction. But since the total energy loss for the hard-core approximation and the real potential are about the same, the result for the range due to the hard-core approximation should be rather correct.

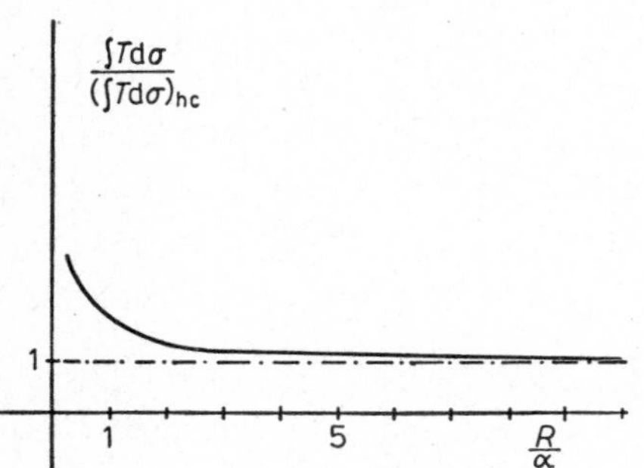

Fig. 32. – Energy losses in the hard-core approximation as compared to true losses.

Another point must be mentioned. The exact solution at $T = T_m$ is lower than the hard-core approximation. This corresponds to another effective hard-core radius R_{ef} for $T=T_m$ given by

$$T_m K(T_m) = \pi R_{ef}^2 \, . \tag{6.10}$$

This effective radius has the following meaning. For small-angle scattering (nearly head-on collisions) the scattering angles can be determined as though the scattering were hard-core scattering but with the smaller effective radius R_{ef}. Even for $R=10a$ the deviation would be appreciable, using (6.9): $R_{ef}=11R/12$, in the order of 10%.

7. – The structure of large-energy primary events.

7·1. *General remarks.* – In Section **6** we have discussed the experimental ranges. Further, we have seen how one can use these ranges and measurements of elastic behavior to derive a potential for Cu. It must be admitted that the experimental evidence for that potential is not very strong, particularly in view of the fact that the large distance part of it has been extrapolated from $r \simeq D$. But the potential matches the range measurements, certain elastic data and from the various available parameters, A, a' those have been chosen where $\lambda \simeq D$ for $E \simeq E_d$, which seems to be the most sensible procedure.

In a primary event with large primary energy many Frenkel pairs are produced in the simple picture discussed in Sect. **4**, and the spatial distribution of the vacancies and interstitials is a question of primary interest. The development of a primary cascade can be pictured as a series of collisions between essentially two atoms if the mean free path is always larger than about the atomic distances for energies above some E_d. If, on the other hand, the mean free path for large energies is of the order or smaller than D then one has to deal with « collisions » where many atoms are taking part. There are many authors who take this standpoint (*e.g.* [17]). This means that one would have to treat a primary zone in a more collective way. We emphasize that there is evidence from the range measurements, which seems to support the view adopted here. Nonetheless, this is only one side of the story and the other side will be touched upon in many other lectures here (compare the lecture of J. BRINKMAN). The results show anyhow that the density of defects in a primary zone becomes so large (in Cu) that the development of the end stage after the collisions are finished would need a collective treatment. Further, there are direct effects of the energy transferred to the primary event which is very concentrated in the beginning and excites vibrations corresponding to high local temperatures, which won't be discussed here either. It is only attempted here to discuss a possible treatment of one large-energy primary event.

7·2. *The spatial distribution of a collision cascade in* Cu. – It has been explained already how one gets information about the final distribution of the primary atom $W(\boldsymbol{r})$ in the Schmitt and Sharp experiment using the hard-core approximation. The distribution $W(\boldsymbol{r})$ of the endpoints $\boldsymbol{r}$ of the primary recoil atom could not be calculated, only certain averages were discussed to obtain an expression for the range.

The use of the hard-core approximation has the following very important advantages. After the first collision of the primary recoil atom the secondary knock-on atom and the primary are completely indistinguishable. Each atom has the same energy and angular distribution. The distribution of the two atoms is only correlated by energy-momentum conservation. This, of course, applies then to all interstitials produced in the cascade and this means that all the interstitials have the same distribution $W(\boldsymbol{r})$. The density ϱ of interstitials produced in the cascade would then be

$$\varrho(\boldsymbol{r}) = \nu W(\boldsymbol{r})\,, \tag{7.1}$$

where ν as well as W depend on the primary energy E.

Although the distribution $W(\boldsymbol{r})$ can not be calculated there are certain averages which can help to give an idea of the distribution. Particularly, linear averages $\overline{X}_i = \int X_i W \, \mathrm{d}\boldsymbol{r}$ and quadratic averages $\overline{X_i X_k}$ are easily calculated. The linear average gives the center of the distribution, the quadratic averages give the approximative extension. The calculation is tedious and details cannot be given here.

The results for Cu with the potential (5.14) are given in Fig. 33 which shows the density ϱ of interstitials, averaged over a volume near the center of the cascade, containing about 50% of all the interstitials. The interstitial density

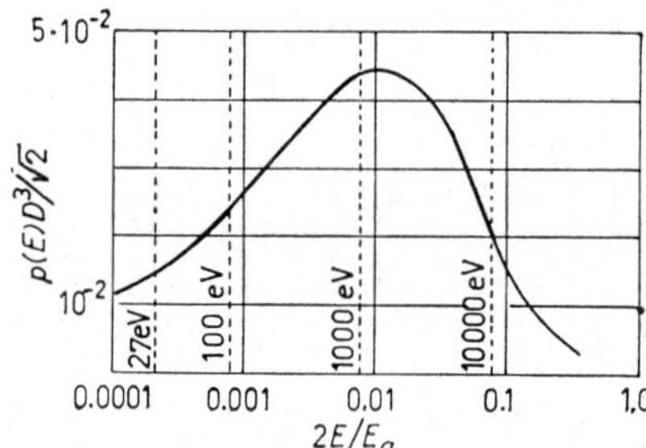

Fig. 33. – Interstitial density (in atomic %) *vs.* primary energy.

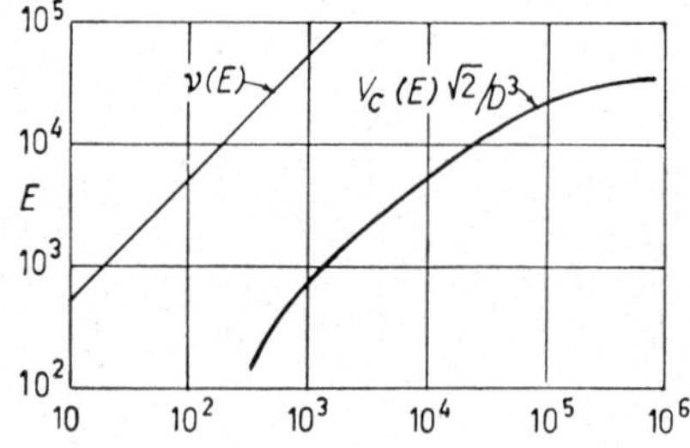

Fig. 34. – Number of pairs $\nu(E)$ and volume of the cascade V_c *vs.* primary energy.

shows a maximum of about 5 at.% for energies near 1300 eV. This cascade would contain about 25 interstitials and the same number of vacancies. This is a very high density from an atomistic point of view; it corresponds to an average distance between interstitials of about 2.5 interatomic distances. The linear dimensions of this region of high density are about 5 atomic distances and the affected volume with such a high density would contain about 100 atoms. The absolute extension of this cascade would be considerably larger.

To get and idea about the absolute dimension of the cascade, one may assume a homogeneous elliptical distribution of interstitials where the volume is matched with the quadratic averages. The result of this assumption is shown in Fig. 34, where the volume of the cascade V_c is plotted *vs.* energy. The average densities of the cascade are roughly decreased by a factor of 2. The total affected volume for $E \simeq 1300$ eV would be about 1000 atomic volumes. It may be mentioned that the distribution is spherical rather than elliptical in the energy range discussed here.

At first it seems surprising that the density shows a maximum. For an initial energy above the maximum, it is known that the cascade can be resolved into a superposition of smaller subcascades belonging to smaller energies. These have partly higher densities than those resulting for the total cascade. But the subcascades have a distribution which altogether gives an average density for the total cascade which is less than that for the subcascades themselves. (This behavior is quite analogous to the small average density of a gas consisting of drops with relatively high density.) If, on the other hand, the initial energy is at or below the maximum, the subcascades have smaller densities than that calculated for the total cascade. In this case there must be an essential overlap between the substances in order to increase the total density above the smaller densities of the subcascades. This behavior is sketched in Fig. 35 for various initial energies. Here it is assumed that the primary causes two subcascades, each possessing half the primary energy. The elliptical content of the subcascades has been taken using the homogeneous elliptical distribution. The numerical values have been chosen such that the volume of all ellipsoids is the same. It has to be imagined that this distribution rotates about the primary direction and that the origin of the production of the subcascades is distributed along the primary direction according to a mean free path law. This altogether would then give the corresponding elliptical distribution of the total cascade.

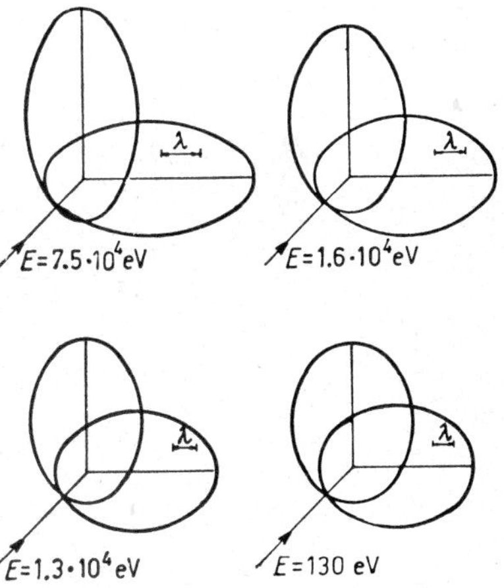

Fig. 35. – Overlap between subsequent cascades.

According to Fig. 35 the overlap increases with decreasing energy. For the energy corresponding to the maximum in the density the overlap just begins to reach the central regions. But also for relatively high energies the overlap is not negligible. Altogether one gets the impression that the sub-cascades cannot be treated as more or less independent, that is, as not overlapping structures. It might be possible for higher energies where the central regions are not affected, but would certainly be a bad approximation for energies less than 1300 eV.

It must be mentioned that the introduction of the Born-Mayer potential is rather essential with regard to the numerical values. The Bohr potential alone would qualitatively show the same behavior of density with energy, but the maximum density would be smaller by a factor of about 5 and the corresponding energy would be lower by a factor of about 2. The introduction of the additive Born-Mayer potential makes the mean free path smaller than that of the Bohr potential itself, and this effect is more pronounced at lower energies, giving a mean free path of the order of the atomic spacing for energies near E_d.

Since the high density obtained for copper is to a large extent due to the influence of the Born-Mayer potential which describes the closed-shell repulsion, this implies that for a material such as germanium, where the closed-shell repulsion is not important and where the Bohr potential is approximately the same, the densities are substantially less (by about a factor of 5). On the whole the effect should be largest for the noble metals with big ionic cores.

So far the vacancies have not been discussed, and only the interstitial distribution has been treated. But for cascades with large ν the vancancy distribution should be similar to that of the interstitials, and the error when assuming the same distribution should not be great.

The high defect densities, especially for intermediate energies, should result in an interaction between the defects produced by one primary. It is possible that the structure can be changed by low-energy effects, such as crowdion motions (see the next section) which tend to shoot out interstitials over distances larger than the dimensions of the cascade. This would show up especially for intermediate primary energies for which the linear dimensions of the cascade are small (of the order of 10 atomic distances). This could lead to cascades with an excess of vacancies, and would essentially lead to Brinkman's description of a cascade (displacement spike) [17] consisting of a depleted internal zone which is surrounded by a zone of higher density.

It is by no means clear that the cascade structure discussed above is a stable structure for intermediate and high energies. The primary energy which is set free in the cascade and the close distance between defects may well lead to an appreciable self-annealing, drastically reducing the damage expected on account of the simple theory. But it should be mentioned that the time for the development of the cascade is very short. This means that the cascade as pictured here can be taken as a first step, whereas annealing effects require much longer times and can be treated separately, with the picture developed here taken as initial configuration. Of course it is possible also that this very heavily distorted structure changes to another structure not coherent with the basic lattice. Since the densities in the cascade are largely influenced by the ionic cores one would anticipate less drastic changes in materials where the ionic core effect is small, *e.g.* Ge, Si and the alkali metals.

8. – Influence of the lattice structure.

8·1. *General remarks.* – In the foregoing we have operated with mean free paths to obtain the ranges and the spatial structure of displacement cascades. This statistical concept can only be used if the mean free path is large compared with the lattice distance. For small energies, however, where in the hard-core approximation an appreciable fraction of space is covered by the hard-core spheres (compare Fig. 28) one has to consider correlated collision series which are travelling along chains of atoms in lattice directions by consecutive, nearly head-on, collisions. At first one would think that this cannot occur because the probability for obtaining *exactly* a head-on collision would be zero; further, the thermal motion of atoms would destroy the sequence. SILSBEE [18] has shown that, nevertheless, under certain circumstances head-on collision sequences are induced with finite probability. This is because even if one starts with a finite angle to the lattice direction the angle can decrease by «focusing», eventually leading to zero angle, forming thereby a head-on collision sequence.

This effect is important in many respects. First of all there are then directions where energy can travel in a fairly concentrated way, which means that the range of the physical effectiveness of a primary event can be enlarged very much. This does not mean that the primary itself obtains a larger range, because along the atomic chains there are travelling essentially structures transporting the energy, whereas the atoms themselves move only by one lattice distance at most. The physical ranges measured in irradiation of Cu are about 100 lattice distances [19], probably also for very low energies, where primary ranges are of the order of one lattice distance.

This can be explained by head-on collision sequences. In this way an appreciable part of the energy can be shot out of the primary region along lattice directions, thus reducing the energy content capable of «heating up» the primary zone. Further, there are possible interactions of these correlated collisions with other defects of the lattice.

The discussion will be kept short because in this course there are two more lectures on such collision sequences, one by G. H. VINEYARD giving results of machine calculations, the other one by M. W. THOMPSON stressing more the experimental point of view. Nevertheless we try to give the basis for a quantitative analysis in order to make clear what kind of effects are to be expected.

8·2. *Collision sequence in a linear chain of atoms (billiard ball model with constant* R) (*). – In the following we will discuss a collision series in a row of atoms of equal distance D in equilibrium position. The theory will be applied particularly to Cu (**). The hard-core approximation will be used in first approximation. Since it will become clear soon that the most interesting cases are given by $R(E) \simeq D/2$ we use the Born-Mayer potential (5.1) for more quantitative discussions.

Fig. 36 shows the construction of the scattering anges for a single collision. Because momentum is only transferred in the direction of the radius vector between the center of the two spheres, the knocked-on second sphere moves off in direction PD, whereas the incident atom goes off perpendicularly (equal masses!). Out of the triangle OPD one can easily get the relationship between the angle ϑ_1 of the knocked-on to the angle ϑ_0 of the incident atom,

$$\sin\vartheta_1 = \sin\vartheta_0\{\alpha\cos\vartheta_0 - (1-\alpha^2\sin^2\vartheta_0)^{\frac{1}{2}}\} \tag{8.1}$$

with $\alpha = D/R$. The relation between the energies of the incident (E_0) and of the knocked-on atom (E_1) is

$$E_1 = E_0(1-\alpha^2\sin^2\vartheta_0)\,. \tag{8.2}$$

One can distinguish between two kinds of collisions (Fig. 37).

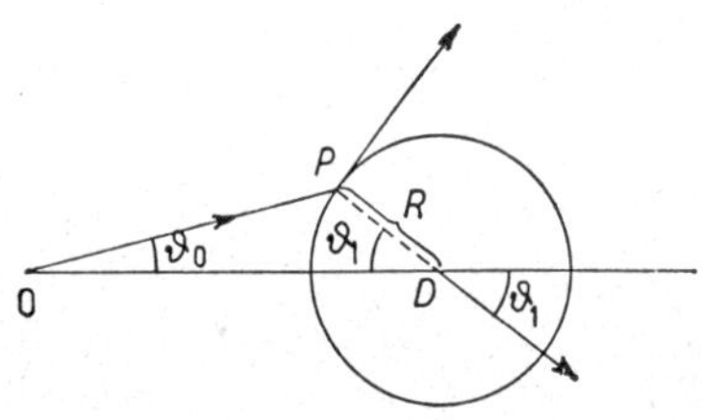

Fig. 36. – Angular relations for a single collision in the hard core approximation.

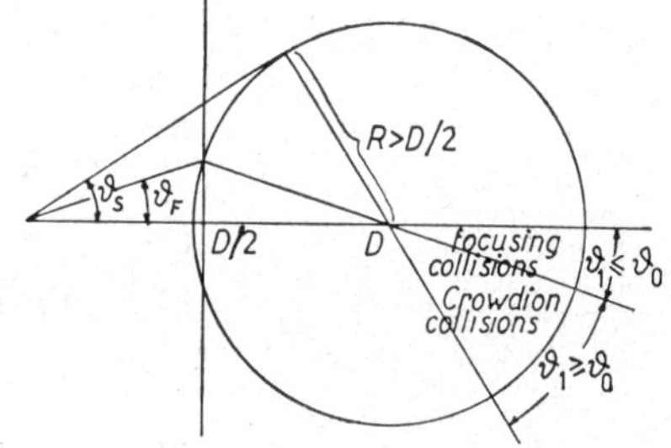

Fig. 37. – Definition of focusing and crowdion collisions.

(*) In the collision between two billiard balls with radii R_1 and R_2 only $R = R_1 + R_2$ is decisive. To simplify the description we always treat the incoming atom as a mass point and the stationary atom as a ball of radius R.

(**) On the whole the effects to be discussed here are only important if the « ionic core radii » are equal to about the lattice distance. Consequently the considerations apply primarily to the noble metals and not to Ge, Si or the alkali metals.

$\vartheta_1 < \vartheta_0$ (P to the left of half the distance OD): These we will call focusing collisions with SILSBEE; they can only occur for $R > D/2$ or $\alpha < 2$. If one treats a collision sequence along a row of atoms of equal separation D the collision angles become smaller with every hit and eventually one has a series of central collisions with angle zero propagating along the chain if one neglects the variation of R with energy in a first approximation (Fig. 38). Here the collision point is nearer the original position of the incident atoms. All the atoms will eventually fall back to their original positions. Thus no interstitial transport occurs.

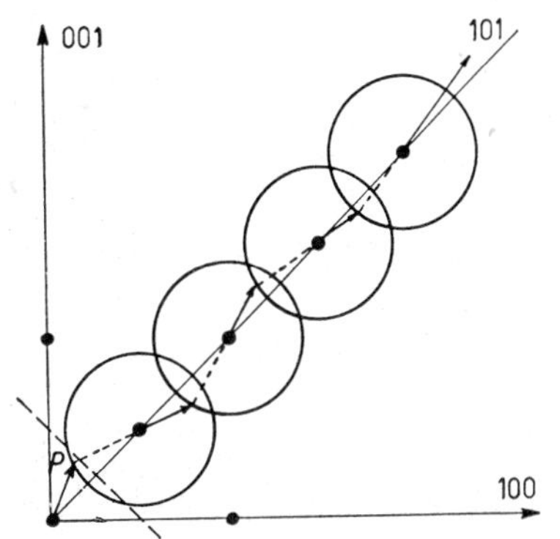

Fig. 38. – Focusing collision series.

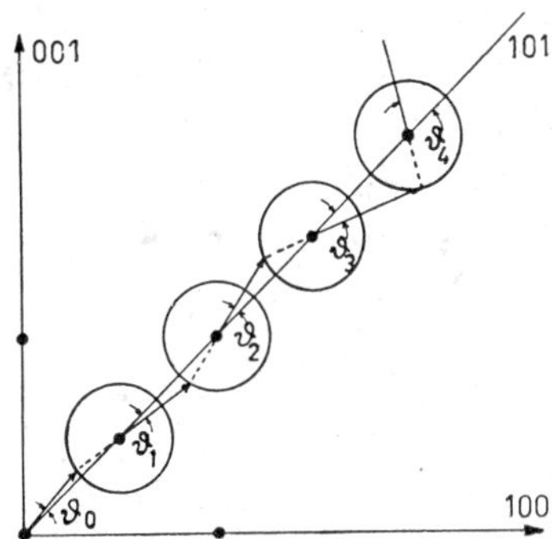

Fig. 39. – Crowdion collision series.

$\vartheta_1 > \vartheta_0$ (P to the right of $D/2$). These we will call crowdion-collisions (Figs. 37 and 39). In this case the collision point is nearer to the equilibrium position of the struck atom. There is a fair chance that in such a collision a vacancy will be left behind at the origin and a crowdion-like interstitial motion will occur along the row, especially if the incident angle is small and one has essentially a central collision along the chain over quite a large distance. In this case the crowdion motion has a range which depends strongly on the incident angle, the smaller the angle the larger the range. The motion along the row stops when the angles become too large.

The focusing condition is $D/R = \alpha < 2$. It can be shown that long-range crowdion collisions are possible only when $\alpha \sim 2$. These condition show that rows with small D values are especially adapted for the focusing effect. Thus one only needs to take into regard relatively densely packed rows. In the f.c.c. lattice which will be discussed in the following, all but the close-packed 110 rows can be disregarded. D is then the distance between nearest neighbors in the lattice. The second favored lattice rows are 100 rows with a distance $D\cdot\sqrt{2}$. The focusing condition for 100 is then $\alpha < \sqrt{2}$. For $\alpha = \sqrt{2}$ the collision spheres of the nearest neighbors in 110 directions just begin to overlap so that no direct 100 focusing hit can occur. Thus only 110 focusing is important.

Such collision sequences have been treated [20] *assuming* R to be constant in zero approximation. This means that one neglects the energy change during the collision. This is qualitatively correct for focusing collisions which lead to head-on collisions with eventually no energy change. For crowdion collisions the change of R may be important and will be discussed later.

In this approximation the range of focusing collisions is infinite and the range of crowdion collisions is given by the initial angle. All long range effects are only of importance for energies near $E = E_F$, corresponding to $R = D/2$. For Cu one has $E_F \simeq 60$ eV. The range of the collision sequence is mainly given by interaction with the neighboring rows. The potential energy difference between an atomic site and half its distance to one neighbor due to all other atoms except this neighbor itself is about 0.5 eV. Since for $\alpha \simeq 2$ every atom in the sequence has to spend that energy before colliding with its neighbor this means a loss of about 0.5 eV per collision. Because $\alpha \simeq 2$ corresponds to 60 eV energy the range is roughly 100 D, that is the distance where the whole energy is used up by the neighboring chains. Using this simple assumption one can treat the problems more quantitatively for primary events with large energies $E \gg E_d$, E_F with the following results.

The number of focusing collisions with ranges larger than 10 D is about the same as the number of Frenkel pairs in the simple theory, whereas the number of corresponding crowdion collisions is about 1/10 of this number, indicating that crowdion motion is less important for long range effects. About 30% of the primary energy is travelling away in long range focusing collisions. This is a rather drastic change in energy content travelling away without being capable of contributing to the «temperature» in the cascade. This temperature is decreased by focusing roughly by 30% also, and this is very large for processes, considered to be important, which depend exponentially on reciprocal temperature. When a focusing collision meets a surface the last atom will leave the surface. Consequently, at the surface of a material where focusing collisions are produced by irradiation one expects to see the close-packed directions in the emission pattern. This is discussed in detail by M. W. THOMPSON [21] who first investigated this effect in Au. If a focusing collision meets an internal surface, *e.g.* a stacking fault of an extended dislocation, the same effect occurs. The last atom of the sequence does not find a partner, but moves to an interstitial position if it has sufficient energy, thus creating a Frenkel pair. This effect can be used to explain the pinning of dislocations by these Frenkel pairs at low temperatures where no mobile effects are thought to exist and a range of about 100 D is required to explain the experimental data. Further, it may be used to explain the enhancement of damage in materials with high dislocation concentration. In both cases the theory gives qualitative agreement with the experimental data [22].

It should be mentioned that crowdion collisions in alloys change the order by replacing one kind of atom by another. Further, the focusing as well as the crowdion collisions are largely inhibited in an alloy with very different interchanging masses because the energy transport does not work any more then on account of the mass difference.

8'3. *More refined theory of collision series, taking into regard changes of energy.* – We will give now a discussion of the effects of energy change which should be particularly important for crowdion collisions. It will be shown that the energy range where correlated collisions are focused eventually extends to much higher energies than could have been anticipated along the lines of the last section. For want of better knowledge we can only give an approximate treatment being supported by the results of some exact calculations.

The atoms in the chain shall be numbered by $n=0, 1, 2, \ldots$. Then one obtains the relations

$$F_{n+1} = F_n\{\alpha_n(1-F_n)^{\frac{1}{2}} - (1-\alpha_n^2 F_n)^{\frac{1}{2}}\}, \tag{8.3a}$$

$$\alpha_{n+1} = \frac{\alpha_n}{1-(a'/D)\alpha_n \ln(1-\alpha_n^2 F_n)} . \tag{8.3b}$$

eq. (8.3*a*) is evidently obtained by squaring (8.1) and introducing $F=\sin^2\vartheta$. Eq. (8.3*b*) is obtained by taking the ln of (8.2) and substituting R, respectively, α for E using the Born-Mayer potential (5.1).

Because an exact analytical treatment of the recurrence formulae (8.3) seems to be difficult we attempt an approximate treatment by assuming that: F and $\alpha-2=\eta$ are small quantities (because $\alpha=2$ is the most interesting case) and that F and α are slowly varying with n:

$$F_n = F(n); \qquad F(n+1) = F(n) + \frac{dF}{dn} .$$

and similarly for $\alpha(n)$.

By these assumptions the recurrence formulae change to a set of two coupled differential equations:

$$\frac{dF}{dn} = 2F(F+\eta) , \tag{8.4a}$$

$$\frac{d\eta}{dn} = -\frac{16a'}{D}F . \tag{8.4b}$$

Eq. (8.4*b*), shows that η decreases monotonically. If one discusses (8.4*a*) in the F, η plane it means that the angle increases for $F+\eta>0$ and decreases for $F+\eta<0$ (excluding the trivial case $F=0$, *i.e.* head-on collision right from the beginning). When $F+\eta=0$ one has a maximum in F; this case is given just when for $R>D/2$ the collision occurs without change of angle.

To give the solutions of (8.4) as functions of n is not so easy. But one can easily find a description which demonstrates the general behavior very nicely by considering $\mathrm{d}F/\mathrm{d}\eta$ the quotient of (8.4a) by (8.4b),

$$\frac{\mathrm{d}F}{\mathrm{d}\eta}=-\frac{D}{8a'}\,(F+\eta)\,, \tag{8.5}$$

with the solution (*)

$$F(\eta)=\left\{F_0+\eta_0-\frac{8a'}{D}\right\}\exp\left[-\frac{D}{8a'}\,(\eta-\eta_0)\right]-\eta+\frac{8a'}{D}\,. \tag{8.6}$$

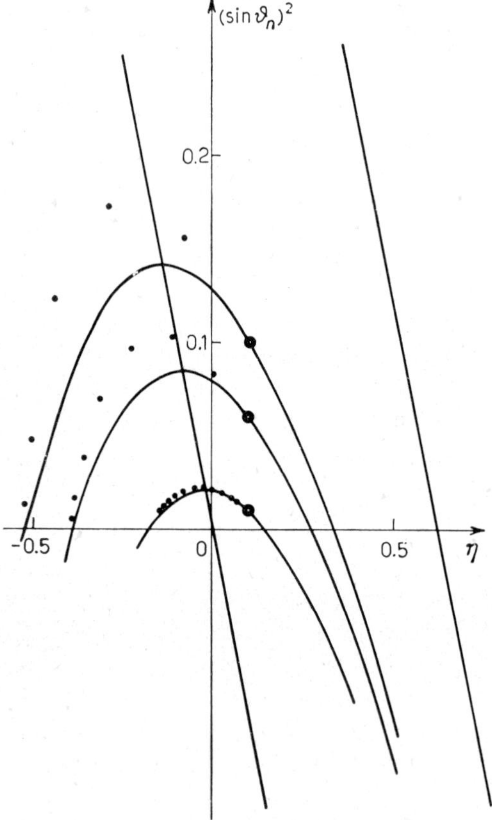

Fig. 40. – Comparison of exact calculations of a collision series with the approximation (8.6).

$F(\eta)$ according to (8.6) is a curve passing through the point F_0, η_0 in the F, η plane and it describes the behavior of F with η when starting at F_0, η_0 and moving toward decreasing η. Of course the part of the F, η plane with $F<0$ has no physical meaning; the case « $F=0$, η arbitrary » is a singular case. It is not contained any more in (8.5); this singular solution has been singled out when dividing (8.4a) by (8.4b).

The general behavior of $F(\eta)$ is the following: For large η all curves asymptotically join the line $F=-\eta+(8a'/D)$; this is the straight line in Fig. 40 intersecting the axis at $\eta=8a'/D=8/13=0.62$ ($F(\eta)\to-\infty$ for $\eta\to\infty$). If the initial values F_0, η_0 are left of this straight line, the factor of the exponential is negative; $F(\eta)$ then passes through a maximum and tends again to $-\infty$ for $\eta\to-\infty$. If $F_0+\eta_0>8a'/D$ then

(*) The complete solution could be obtained by introducing (8.6) into (8.4b) and integrating this equation.

$F(\eta)$ continuously increases with decreasing η and tends to $+\infty$ with $\eta \to -\infty$.

In the approximation with constant energy used in the foregoing section one would only have to discuss (8.4*a*) with constant $\eta = \eta_0$. In this simple case one has to distinguish qualitatively between the following regions of initial conditions (excluding again $F = 0$).

$F_0 + \eta_0 > 0$; $\mathrm{d}F/\mathrm{d}n$ is positive and stays positive, because F increases continuously. These are the crowdion collisions of Section **8**·2. The discussion is not very well based in this case because in defocusing collisions one cannot well neglect the energy change.

$F_0 + \eta_0 < 0$: This is only possible for $\eta_0 < 0$. $\mathrm{d}F/\mathrm{d}n$ is negative and stays negative, F decreases continuously; these are the focusing collisions of Section **8**·2.

Now we have to distinguish 3 different regions:

$F_0 + \eta_0 > 8a'/D$: Continuously increasing F, crowdion-like collisions.

$0 < F_0 + \eta_0 < 8a'/D$: Increasing F and crowdion-like collisions until $F + \eta = 0$ where maximum angle is reached and further on focusing collisions. The eventually focused energy is found where $F(\eta)$ intersects the axis. According to the simple concept used in Section **8**·2 an interstitial is produced when $(F + \eta \simeq 0)$.

$F_0 + \eta_0 < 0$: F decreases continuously, this is the focusing effect of the foregoing section.

The new effect introduced by taking into account the energy variation is thus a set of initial conditions where defocusing (crowdion) motion changes to focusing motion. In Fig. 40 there are plotted some curves corresponding to various initial conditions ($\eta_0 = 0.1$; $F_0 = 0.1$; 0.06; 0.01) according to (8.6); drawn are also the straight lines $F + \eta = 0$ (separation line between focusing and defocusing) and $F + \eta = 8a'/D$ (the asymptotic line). The dots are exact values using the recurrence formulae (*) (8.3). The agreement is quite good in view of the drastic approximations having been made. As also seen from (8.4*b*) the spacing of the dots becomes increasingly smaller with $F \to 0$; the angle zero is only reached after an infinite number of collisions. In Fig. 41 one finds a plot of F_n for these initial conditions and Fig. 42 should give a direct demonstration of the collision sequence beginning with $F_0 = 0.1$.

Thus, it seems that the qualitative behavior is described quite well. Of course, one would have to discuss the limiting angles for F which are lost when changing to the small-angle expansion. But this does not influence the description too much. Consequently it appears that one may obtain collision series which are eventually going to focus at still appreciable energies (crowdion-focusing collisions). The energy below which this effect occurs should

(*) Calculated by Ch. LEHMANN.

be of the order of $5E_F \simeq 300$ eV. Quantitative details of this effect have not been worked out yet but it seems fairly consistent to say that a focusing condition can start at appreciably higher energies than hitherto has been assumed.

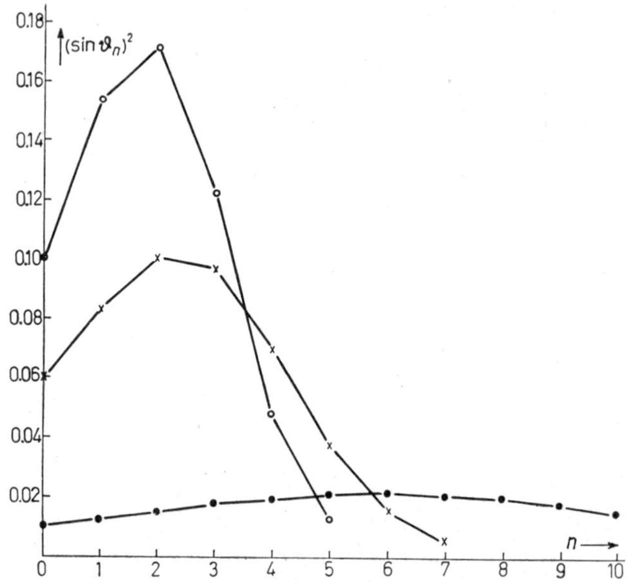

Fig. 41. – Dependence of angle on collision number for the three events in Fig. 40.

The foregoing discussion should really be confined to α near 2 and relatively small angles. But one has the impression that this is really the relevant region. If one starts, for instance, with too large α or F, the eventual focused energy will be too small to be important. Consequently the approximations are really valid for the values of physical interest.

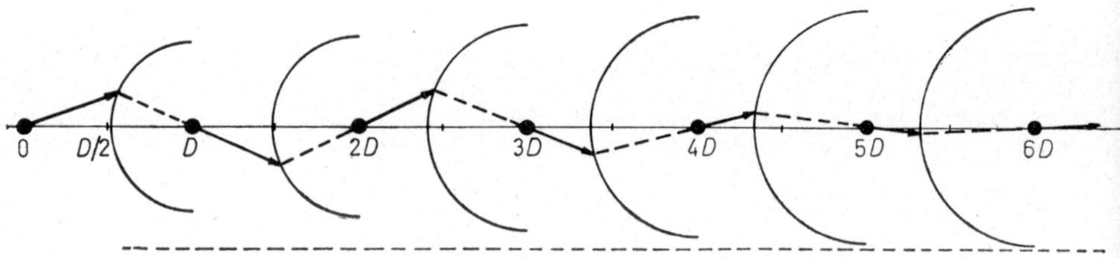

Fig. 42. – Representation of a collision series where defocusing changes into focusing.

8·4. *Other effects to be observed in focusing.* – For a quantitative theory one has to consider two more effects:

a) Deviations of the hard-core approximation. As has been discussed in Section **6**, there are deviations from hard-core scattering because the effective radius determining the angles is smaller than the hard-core radius used here to calculate the angular change. This is a defocusing effect as compared with the hard-core approximation. According to Section **6** one can estimate that for $E \simeq E_F$ the effective radius is about 10% smaller than the hard-core radius. This would shift roughly the original focusing condition from $\alpha \simeq 2$ to $\alpha \simeq 1.8$ and this leads to lower focusing energies. Further, the eventual position, of the incident particle is also not given correctly in the hard-core approximation.

b) The effect of neighboring chains. The neighboring chains have been discussed very qualitatively in Section **8**·2. They were only taken into regard as causing an energy loss for every collision. Now, the repulsive forces from neighboring chains not only change the energy but also change the angle and obviously in the sense that the angle decreases. Consequently, this supports focusing, tending to keep the angles small. The effect is more pronounced the nearer the neighbor rows or the less close-packed the lattice direction under consideration, *i.e.*, small for 110, larger for 100 and even larger for 111 in the f.c.c. lattice. On the other hand, the energy loss due to neighbor chains increases when passing from 110 over 100 to 111, thus keeping the range down. Consequently, focusing may exist along other than close-packed directions with energies certainly larger than the focusing energy E_F of the 110 direction but with presumably smaller ranges. This behavior will be treated more quantitatively in the lectures of G. H. Vineyard and M. W. Thompson.

REFERENCES

[1] G. Wentzel: *Handb. d. Phys.*, **24**/1 (1930).
[2] E. Wigner and A. Weinberg: *Physics of Neutron Chain Reactors* (Chicago, 1958).
[3] M. Walt and H. H. Barshall: *Phys. Rev.*, **93**, 1062 (1954).
[4] D. F. Hughes and R. B. Schwartz: *Neutron Cross Sections* (Brookhaven, 1958) 2nd ed. (BNL 325).
[5] Article by F. Sauter in W. Heisenberg: *Kosmische Strahlung* (Berlin, 1953).
[6] N. Bohr: *Kgl. Dan. Widenskab. Selskab. Mat. fys. Medd.*, **18**, no. 8 (1948).
[7] Ch. Lehmann: *Thesis* (Aachen, 1960).
[8] G. H. Kinchin and R. S. Pease: *Rep. Progr. Phys.*, **18**, 1 (1955).
[9] W. S. Snyder and I. Neufeld: *Phys. Rev.*, **97**, 1636 (1955); **99**, 1326 (1955).
[10] E. Mann and A. Seeger: *Journ. Phys. Chem. Solids*, **12**, 314 (1960).
[11] H. B. Huntington: *Phys. Rev.*, **93**, 1414 (1954).
[12] R. A. Schmitt and R. A. Sharp: *Phys. Rev. Lett.*, **1**, 445 (1958); R. A. Schmitt and V. A. F. Van Lint: General Atomic Report GA-1193 (Jan. 1960).
[13] D. K. Holmes and G. Leibfried: *Journ. Appl. Phys.*, **31**, 1046 (1960).

[14] G. Leibfried: Oak Ridge Nat. Lab., Solid State Division, Annual Report (1959).
[15] H. Goldstein: *Classical Mechanics* (Cambridge, Mass. 1950).
[16] D. K. Holmes, G. Leibfried and O. S. Oen: Oak Ridge Nat. Lab., Solid State Division, Annual Report (1959).
[17] F. A. Brinkman: *Am. Journ. Phys.*, **24**, 246 (1956).
[18] R. H. Silsbee: *Journ. Appl. Phys.*, **28**, 1246 (1957).
[19] D. O. Thompson, T. H. Blewitt and D. K. Holmes: *Journ. Appl. Phys.*, **28**, 742 (1957).
[20] G. Leibfried: *Journ. Appl. Phys.*, **30**, 1388 (1959).
[21] M. W. Thompson: *Phil. Mag.*, **4**, 139 (1959).
[22] G. Leibfried: *Journ. Appl. Phys.*, **31**, 117 (1960).
[23] V. A. J. Van Lint, R. A. Schmitt and C. S. Suffredini: Report GA-1671.

Dynamic Stages of Radiation Damage.

G. H. VINEYARD (*)

Brookhaven National Laboratory, Physics Department - Upton L. I., N. Y.

1. – Introduction.

The initial event in the damaging of a crystal lattice by high-energy radiation is the sudden transfer of a rather large amount of kinetic energy (10 to perhaps 10^5 eV) to a single atom. The energized atom then ploughs through the lattice knocking other atoms from their sites and leaving a damaged region behind. From a theoretical standpoint this damaging event is a complex many-body problem, and it has been treated in the past only by making drastic approximations [1]. Generally it has been considered as a cascade of independent, two-body collisions between knock-on atoms and stationary atoms. The knock-on atoms have been assumed to move freely between collisions. The stationary atoms have been assumed to behave as though randomly located, and their binding in the lattice has been taken into account by the very much simplified assumption that they will be displaced and enter the group of freely moving knock-ons if and only if endowed with energy above a certain threshold, generally in the neighborhood of 25 eV. On this cascade model the damage is predicted to be a set of interstitial atoms and an equal number of vacant lattice sites, distributed randomly over a small region. Other models have been proposed in which many-body effects are given prominence. Thermal spike and displacement spike models are of this character. In the former, the region around the site of a knock-on is assumed to behave as if suddenly heated, and its subsequent cooling is treated by the classical laws of heat conduction in a homogeneous medium. In the displacement spike

(*) Based on work performed by J. B. GIBSON, A. N. GOLAND, M. MILGRAM, and the author and supported by the U. S. Atomic Energy Commission.

models, qualitative arguments about the character of damage are advanced on the assumption that a kind of miniature « explosion » occurs around the site of the knock-on. These models are difficult to harmonize with one another, and each has obvious shortcomings. Patchwork attempts at improving the models in individual details have not yet been very impressive. It has seemed to us that analytical methods are inadequate and that numerical treatment with the aid of a high-speed computing machine is required.

Our procedure [2] is to consider a crystallite containing a reasonably large number of atoms which interact with realistic forces. Atoms on the surface of the crystallite are supplied with extra forces simulating the reaction of atoms outside, as though the crystallite were embedded in an infinite crystalline matrix. A radiation damage event starts with all atoms on their lattice sites and all but one at rest. That one atom is initially endowed with arbitrary kinetic energy and direction of motion, as though it had just been struck by a bombarding particle. A high speed computer then integrates the classical equations of motion for the set of atoms, showing how the initially energized atom (the knock-on) transfers energy to neighboring atoms, how the dynamic stages evolve, and how the kinetic energy finally dies away and the atoms of the set come to rest in a damaged configuration. A series of « runs » are made, corresponding to a representative variety of initial conditions.

The computer program can also be used to study the stability, energy, equilibrium configuration, and other properties of lattice defects permitted by the model. One guesses the positions of the atoms in the defect and uses these as initial conditions, with zero initial velocities (actually a very small kinetic energy may be imparted to one atom to spoil the symmetries of the starting configuration).

All computations have been made for metallic copper. This material has been chosen because it is a reasonably simple metal and because more radiation damage experiments at low temperatures have been performed on it than on any other substance [3].

A further important limitation of the calculations must be pointed out. Because of the speed and the size of memory of the computing machine available, the fundamental crystallite dealt with has been of modest size. Most of the computations reported were on crystallites containing about 500 atoms; a few computations have been done more recently on crystallites of about 1000 atoms.

A detailed discussion of the model and the force laws is given in Section **2**. Section **3** outlines the numerical methods used in the calculation. Section **4** describes the results of some static calculations on the defects supported in the model. Section **5** reports the principal dynamic results achieved to date, and Section **6** summarizes the conclusions reached.

2. – The model.

As stated, computations have been made on a model designed to represent metallic copper. The atoms are allowed to interact with two-body, central repulsive forces. For these a Born-Mayer form is assumed, the interaction energy of a pair of atoms at separation r being

$$\varphi = B\exp[-\beta r]\,. \tag{2.1}$$

This interaction describes the repulsion of atoms at close approach. The choice of the constants in this law will be discussed below. A cohesive tendency is also needed, and for this a constant inward force is applied to each atom on the boundary of the crystallite. In the equilibrium configuration this force just balances the Born-Mayer repulsions of neighboring atoms. The equilibrium configuration, of course, is a face-centered cubic array with the normal lattice spacing of copper. Since all crystallites considered are rectangular parallelepipeds, for an atom in a face the surface force is normal to the face, for an atom in an edge the force is normal to the edge (along $\langle 110\rangle$) and for an atom in a corner it is along the inwardly directed cube diagonal. In any distortion involving small displacement of surface atoms these surface forces give an increment of total binding energy proportional to the increment of volume of the crystallite. The forces can thus represent any binding energy that is a function only of volume of the crystallite and which varies at the right rate with volume to equilibrate the Born-Mayer repulsions. In a monovalent metal the conduction electrons are the major source of binding, and their cohesive energy is, to a certain approximation, dependent only on volume. Thus the constant surface forces employed here represent, in first approximation, the cohesive effect of the conduction electrons. Since it is not a purely central-force model, it does not require the Cauchy relation for the elastic constants.

Since the crystallite is supposed to behave as a set of atoms in the interior of an infinite perfect crystal, it is necessary to have additional forces on the surface atoms to represent the reaction forces of atoms beyond the surface caused by any displacement of atoms in the microcrystallite. For small displacements an elegant expression for these reactions can be written in terms of a Green's function and an integral over the history of the motions in the crystallite. It does not seem feasible to use this expression in an actual calculation, however, both because of the difficulty of finding the Green's function explicitly and because of added requirements on storage of information during the computation. Instead, the additional surface forces were simply taken to be a spring force, proportional to the displacement of the surface atom, and a viscous force, proportional to the velocity of the surface atom (further information on these forces is given in ref. [2]). These are only approximations to the true reaction forces, but with judicious choice of the spring and viscosity constants, they are thought to be adequate for the accuracy required. The spring forces represent the tendency of material just outside the crystallite to resist slow or static deformation of the crystallite by a system of forces proportional to the deformation.

Results have not proved very sensitive to boundary effects, as is demonstrated by cases where the same dynamic event has been run twice, starting at a different point in the crystallite, and where the same event has been run both in a large and in a small crystallite. Except for a few special trials all runs to date have been made in three fundamental microcrystallites, which will be referred to as sets A, B, and C. All were rectangular parallelepipeds bounded by $\{100\}$ planes. Set A was made up of $5\times4\times4$ unit cells, and contained 446 atoms. Set B was $2\times6\times7$ unit cells, and contained 488 atoms (Fig. 1). Set C was $2\times9\times10$ unit cells, and contained 998 atoms.

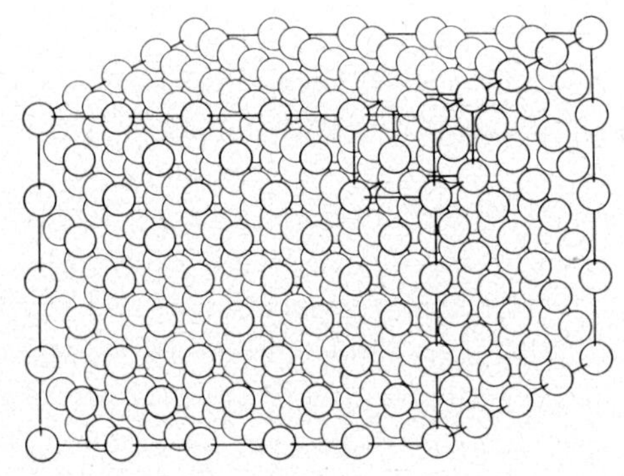

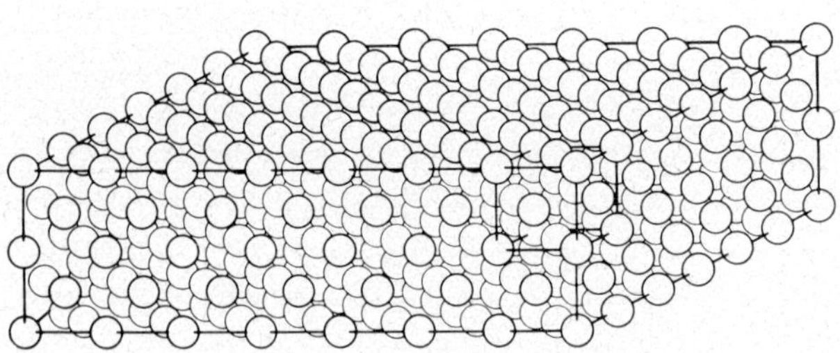

Fig. 1. – Two of the sets of atoms used in the calculations. Set A is above, Set B is below.

The Born-Mayer form of repulsive potential, eq. (2.1), was chosen largely after the lead of HUNTINGTON and SEITZ [4] in work on point defects and self-diffusion in face-centered cubic metals. It is admittedly an approximation, but it is hoped that it may be an adequate approximation over the range of distances important to the present problem if the constants B and β are properly chosen. At very close approach potentials of interaction can be established on theoretical grounds, and at separations near the equilibrium separation in the crystal some information is available from considerations of elastic constants and from atom-atom scattering experiments that have been conducted in gases. The radiation damage problem, unfortunately, demands knowledge of the potential at intermediate separations, where no reliable information exists. We have attempted to bridge this gap in the following way: We have three Born-Mayer potentials, which will be referred to simply by number, all of which give a moderately good account of the elastic constants and their variation with pressure when employed near equilibrium separations, and which are plausible as extrapolations to large separations of the theoretical repulsive potentials at small separation. The difference between the three potentials shows most strongly in the threshold energy for permanent displacement of an atom by irradiation, and the choice among the three is ultimately made by comparison between the calculated and measured threshold energy.

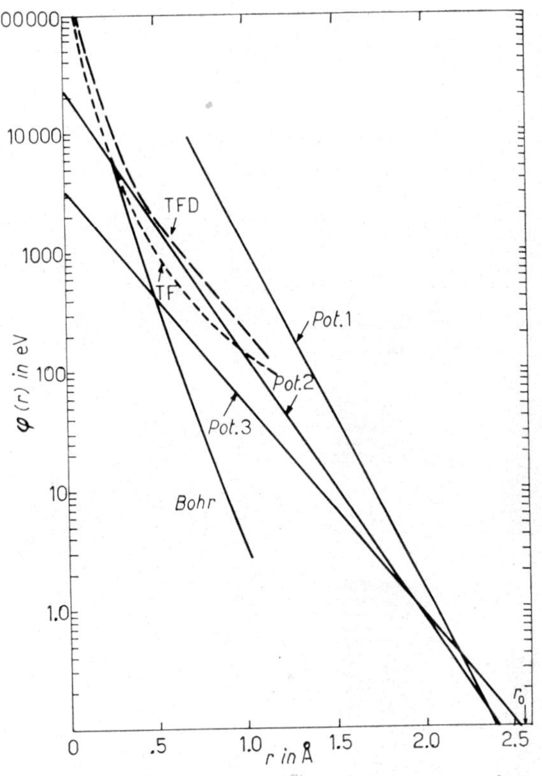

Fig. 2. – Various forms of repulsive energy for a pair of copper atoms. Potentials 1, 2 and 3 were used in the calculations. r_0 is the equilibrium separation in the crystal.

Fig. 2 shows various curves of repulsive potential energy between a pair of copper atoms plotted against the separation of the pair. At separations smaller than 0.1Å the screened Coulomb potential suggested by BOHR [1], $\varphi = Z^2e^2r^{-1}\exp[-r/\alpha]$, where $\alpha = a_0 2^{-\frac{1}{2}}Z^{-\frac{1}{3}}$, Z being the atomic number, e the charge of the electron, and a_0 the Bohr radius, is a good representation. At larger separations the Bohr potential is undoubtedly too small [5]. Theoretical potentials which should be better than the Bohr potential at moderately small separations and which agree with the Bohr potential at very small separations have been found by ABRAHAMSON [6], using the Thomas-Fermi and the Thomas-Fermi-Dirac approximations (labeled TF and TFD, respectively in Fig. 2). The TFD curve is probably the more accurate of the two. Both these become unreliable at about 1 Å, and so the curves are terminated a little beyond this point. The three Born-Mayer potentials employed in the present work are the three straight lines, labeled Pot. 1, Pot. 2, and Pot. 3. Potentials 1 and 2 are close to those suggested by HUNTINGTON for copper. For energies in the range 1 to 100 eV potential 2 represents a smaller atom than potential 1. Potential 3 was chosen arbitrarily to give the same bulk modulus as potential 1 and to give, at intermediate energies, the smallest atom of the three. It is seen from Fig. 2 that any of the three potentials might be joined to the TFD curve between 100 and 1000 eV by moderate alterations in the range 10 to 100 eV, although this would require the least alteration if done with potential 2, and would produce a more complex curve if done with potential 1. Allowing for a considerable uncertainty in the TFD result, no one of the potentials 1 to 3 is immediately ruled out for the low and moderate energy range, although potential 2 looks best. It will be shown subsequently that all three potentials give qualitatively similar results, both for the static configurations of lattice defects and for dynamic damage events, but that the threshold energies for producing a permanently displaced atom are very different for the three, being too high for potential 1, too low for potential 3, and approximately right for potential 2. The majority of our calculations have been made with potential 2.

To specify the potentials it is convenient to recast eq. (1) into a commonly used form

$$\varphi = A \exp[-\varrho(r - r_0)/r_0]\,, \tag{2.2}$$

where r_0 is the near-neighbor distance at zero pressure and absolute zero of temperature. Taking r_0 for copper to be 2.551 Å, the constants A and ϱ for the potentials employed in the present work are given in Table I.

TABLE I. – *Constants in the Born-Mayer potentials employed* [*see eq.* (2.2)].

Potential	A (eV)	ϱ
1	0.0392	16.97
2	0.0510	13.00
3	0.1004	10.34

3. – Method of computation.

Integrating the equation of motion. – Let the i-th atomic co-ordinate at time t be $x_i(t)$ and let the associated velocity be $v_i(t)$, where $i = 1, 2, ..., N$, and N is three times the number of atoms in the crystallite. The force in the i-th degrees of freedom depends, in general, on the positions of all atoms. In the case that x_i refers to a boundary atom the force depends in addition on the velocity in the i-th degree of freedom (because of the viscous damping). Thus the force may always be written $F_i[x_1(t), ..., x_N(t); v_i(t)]$. Letting m be the mass of an atom, the classical equations of motion of the system are

$$\dot{v}_i(t) = m^{-1}F_i[x_1(t), ..., x_N(t); v_i(t)] , \tag{3.1}$$

$$i = 1, 2, ..., N.$$

$$\dot{x}_i(t) = v_i(t) , \tag{3.2}$$

Our procedure is to replace time derivatives by finite differences with arbitrary interval Δt:

$$\dot{v}_i(t) \simeq [v_i(t + \Delta t/2) - v_i(t - \Delta t/2)]/\Delta t , \tag{3.3}$$

$$\dot{x}_i(t + \Delta t/2) \simeq [x_i(t + \Delta t) - x_i(t)]/\Delta t . \tag{3.4}$$

In eq. (3.2) t is replaced by $t+\Delta t/2$, then (3.3) and (3.4) are inserted in (3.1) and (3.2). Rearrangement gives

$$v_i(t + \Delta t/2) \simeq v_i(t - \Delta t/2) + \Delta t m^{-1} F_i[x_i(t), ..., x_N(t); v_i(t - \Delta t/2)] , \tag{3.5}$$

$$x_i(t + \Delta t) \simeq x_i(t) + \Delta t\, v_i(t + \Delta t/2) , \qquad (i = 1, 2, ..., N) \tag{3.6}$$

Starting with a complete set of positions $x_i(t)$ at arbitrary time t, and corresponding velocities $v_i(t - \Delta t/2)$, the machine essentially employs (3.5) to compute the new velocities $v_i(t+\Delta t/2)$ and (3.6) to compute new co-ordinates $x_i(t+\Delta t)$. The process is then iterated to generate coordinates at $(t+2\Delta t)$, $(t+3\Delta t)$, etc., together with the corresponding velocities. The optimum size for Δt depends on the maximum velocity of any atom. Thus in the early stages of a calculation Δt must be small; after the velocities of moving atoms have diminished, Δt may be increased to hasten the computation. The calculation is stopped whenever the configuration is judged to have stabilized sufficiently. The program itself will be described in detail in a forthcoming Brookhaven National Laboratory report. Further information on the computation is also given in ref. [2].

The co-ordinates and velocities of all atoms at alternate time steps are stored on magnetic tape and can be printed out as desired . The positions of selected atoms can also be displayed as dots on a cathode ray screen. Displays are presented sequentially, and multiflash pictures can be taken on stationary film; by advancing the film after each display, moving pictures have been made.

It should also be noted that in all the work reported below the unit of length is $1.804 \cdot 10^{-8}$ cm, the unit of time is $3.273 \cdot 10^{-15}$ s, and the unit of energy is the electron volt. These units are convenient in the problem because the (cubic) lattice constant of copper becomes 2 and the velocity of a copper atom with 1000 V of kinetic energy becomes unity.

4. – Static results.

It is desirable to know the configuration and stability of various lattice defects that can be housed in our model. Accordingly a number of « static » calculations have been run. In these the equilibrium configuration of a defect is estimated from simple considerations, and the atoms are given these coordinates at the beginning. All the atoms are started from rest, except that in cases where the configuration has symmetry one atom is given a very small initial velocity in such a way as to spoil the symmetry without introducing appreciable kinetic energy. False equilibria corresponding to « dead center » positions are thus avoided. The machine calculates the motions of the atoms from these initial conditions, until a static, equilibrium configuration is reached. Artificial damping (in which the kinetic energies of all atoms are set equal to zero each time the total kinetic energy reaches a maximum) is usually employed to hasten the attainment of equilibrium.

The vacancy seems entirely normal. The relaxation of three shells of neighbors after the creation of a vacancy is shown in Fig. 3. In the beginning all neighbors were on their lattice sites, and the radial displacements are plotted

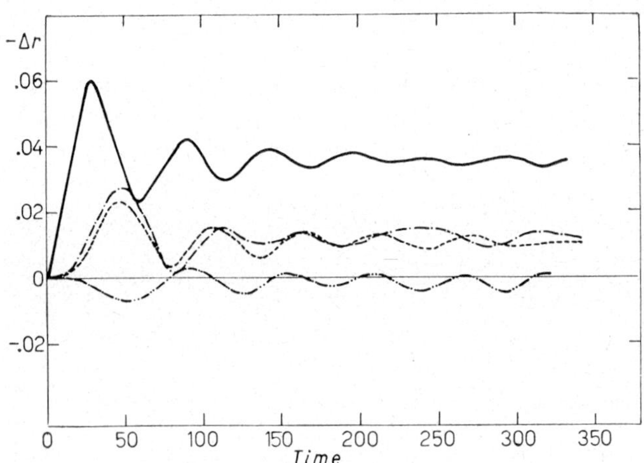

Fig. 3. – Dynamic relaxation of neighbors around a vacancy. Inward component of displacement is plotted against time (here and elsewhere the length unit $= 1.8 \cdot 10^{-8}$ cm, the time unit $= 3.27 \cdot 10^{-15}$ s). Upper line is for 1st neighbor, bottom line for 2nd neighbor, and middle lines are for two atoms in set of 3rd neighbors. Difference in 3rd neighbor lines is a boundary effect. Calculation made with potential 2.

against time. Oscillations, followed by stabilization around relaxed positions can be seen. The calculation shown in Fig. 3 employed potential 2. Other calculations were made with potentials 1 and 3. The behavior is qualitatively similar in all three cases, with the amount of relaxation being largest in the case of potential 3 and least with potential 1. The nearest neighbors relax radially inward by a small amount—about 1.5% of the equilibrium distance in the case of potential 1; 2.5% in the case of potential 2; and 3.2% in the case of potential 3. The second neighbors, and more distant neighbors in or near the cubic axial directions, relax slightly outward. In the case of second neighbors, the percentage outward relaxation is about one twentieth the inward relaxation of near neighbors. Such apparently anomalous relaxation has already been found by others [7] and is easily understood by considering the geometry of the lattice. An immediate consequence is that the strain field at a distance from the vacancy cannot be very well fitted to the field of a point singularity in an *isotropic* elastic continuum. A cubic elastic continuum is required and the outward relaxation along cubic directions can be considered as a manifestation of the anisotropic character of the medium.

The interstitial has been investigated carefully with potential 2, and is found not to reside at the center of the cubic unit cell. Instead, the interstitial has what may be termed a split configuration, in which it shares a lattice site symmetrically with another atom, the axis of the pair being along a cubic axis of the lattice. Fig. 4 shows a split interstitial in the face-centered lattice. For potential 2 the separation of the two atoms is very nearly 1.2 (in units in which the lattice constant is 2). The possibility of this configuration of the interstitial in copper was pointed out by HUNTINGTON and SEITZ [4], although its stability was not settled at that time. More recently, JOHNSON *et al.* [8] have also demonstrated its stability in a lattice model rather similar to ours. It should be noted that there are three possible orientations of this interstitial on each lattice site. Its symmetry is only tetragonal, and it should thus give rise to resonant anelastic effects.

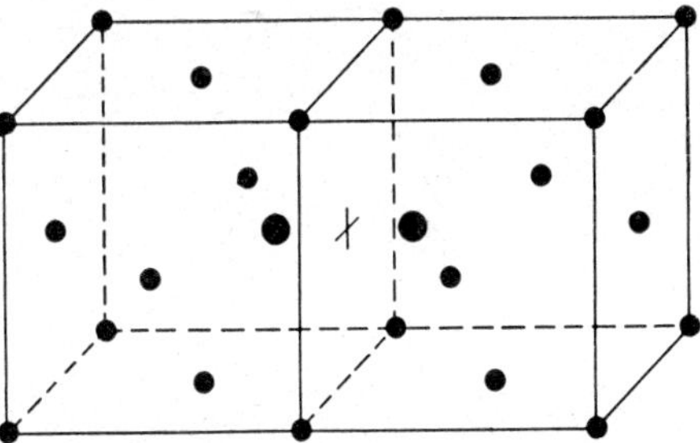

Fig. 4. – The split configuration of the interstitial that is found to be stable. Relaxation of neighbors is not shown.

The stability of this interstitial has been demonstrated in two calculations. First an interstitial was set up in the cube center, with relaxation of its neighbors, according to our first estimate of the stable position of the interstitial. The machine calculation showed that this atom rapidly moved away from the cube center toward a neighoring atom, in a direction determined by minor asymmetries in the starting conditions, and settled down in the split configuration with this atom. This behavior is shown in Fig. 5. Later, as a check,

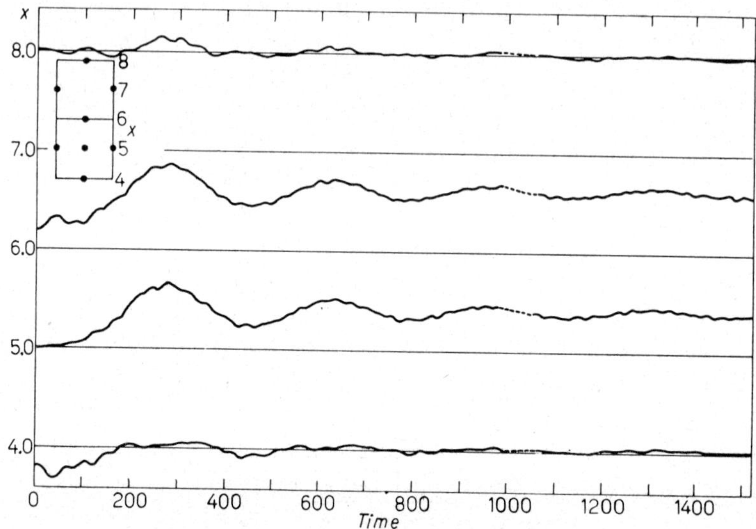

Fig. 5. – Showing relaxation of body-centered interstitial into split configuration. x-co-ordinates of 4 atoms in a line are plotted against time. Body-centered interstitial starts at $x=5$ and moves upward to share lattice site at $x=6$.

the split configuration, with minor perturbations, was set up as an initial condition, and a long machine run was made. This demonstrated the complete stability of the split configuration and gave accurate values of the re-

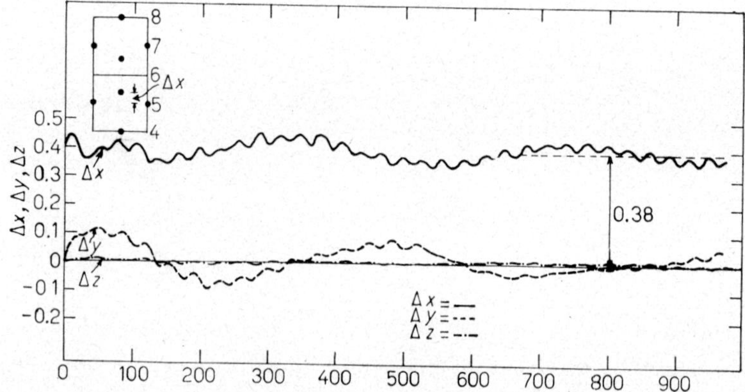

Fig. 6. – Oscillation of an atom in the split interstitial configuration. The high-frequency component which damps only slowly is due to localized vibrational modes associated with the defect.

laxations of surrounding atoms. The Cartesian components of displacement of one member of the pair during this run are shown in Fig. 6. As will be seen in the following section, a number of dynamic events have also produced interstitials, and in all cases these are seen to settle down in the split configuration.

The foregoing calculations do not demonstrate fully that there are no other stable configurations of the interstitial, and indeed experimental evidence has occasionally been interpreted as requiring that the crowdion be stable in copper (see Fig. 7). We have tested the stability of the crowdion in our model by

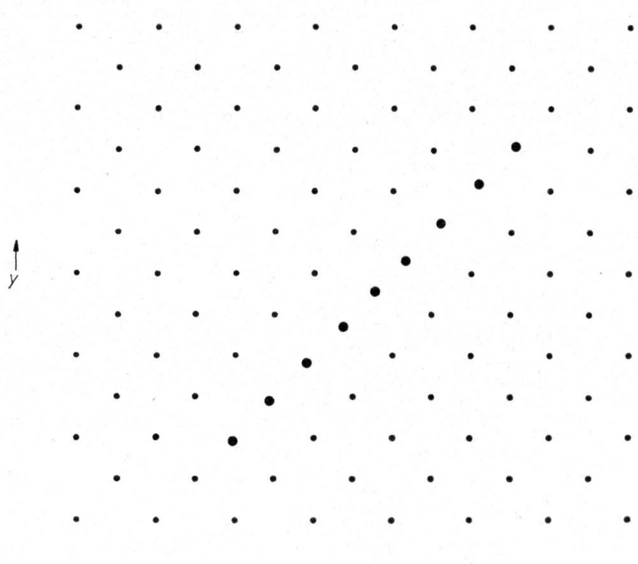

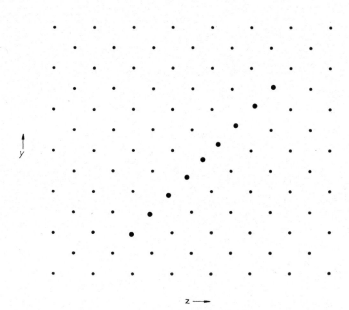

Fig. 7. – The crowdion, in a face-centered cubic lattice.

two static calculations, both employing potential 2. In both of these a crowdion was formed by inserting an interstitial atom in a ⟨110⟩ line ad moving three atoms on either side of the inserted atom outward along the line by diminishing amounts. A total of eight neighbors on adjoint ⟨110⟩ lines were also relaxed away from the interstitial, in each case, to obtain the lowest energy configuration possible. In one calculation the extra atom was inserted halfway between two neighboring lattice sites and the relaxation along the line was made symmetrical about this point. This might be called a space-centered crowdion. In the second calculation, which might be called a site-centered crowdion, the extra atom was placed on one side of a lattice site and the pattern of relaxation was made symmetrical about this site. Both crowdions proved to be unstable, and decayed into a split interstitial by simple rotation of a pair of atoms near the center. The results of the second calculation are shown in Fig. 8. The decay occurred rather slowly, which demonstrates that

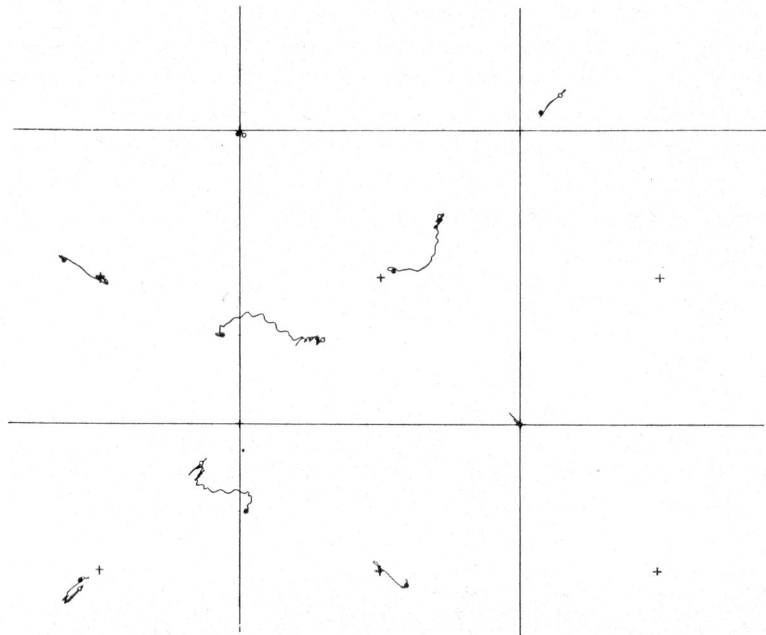

Fig. 8. – Decay of crowdion into split interstitial. This calculation indicates that crowdion is not stable in our model.

potential energy is fairly flat near these crowdion configurations. We conclude that the crowdion is not stable in our model; nevertheless rather modest changes in the force laws might make it stable.

It is also necessary to know which Frenkel pairs are stable. Accordingly a series of static runs on Frenkel pairs at various separations were made with potential 2. The results for pairs in the {100} plane are shown in Fig. 9. Here the split interstitial is shown at a fixed position in the lower left corner of the figure. Lattice sites around this interstitial at which a vacancy yielded a

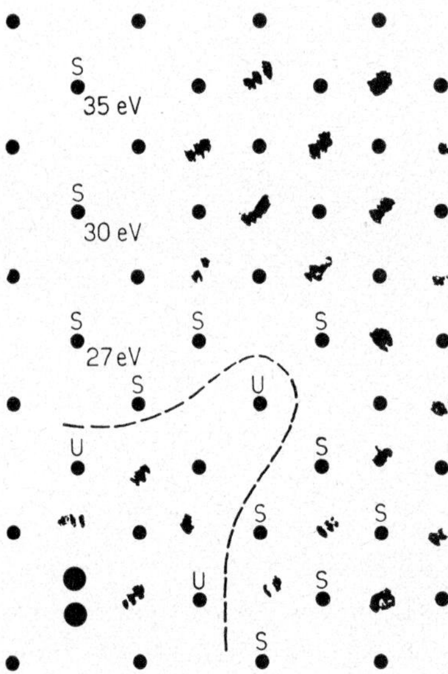

Fig. 9. – Stability of Frenkel pairs in (100) plane of copper. Split interstitial is at lower left. Dashed line separates stable from unstable sites for a vacancy. Approximate threshold energies for dynamic production of three particular pairs are indicated.

stable Frenkel pair (by actual calculations) are indicated by S. Sites for the vacancy which yielded an unstable Frenkel pair are indicated by U. All sites inside the dotted line are unstable, all sites outside it are judged to be stable. It is seen that a surprisingly large separation of the pair is needed to produce stability, particularly for a pair on a close-packed line. The size of instability has obvious implications for near-threshold damage events, and also for the annealing process in which a migrating interstitial recombines with a vacancy.

5. – Dynamic results.

5·1. *Some typical events.* – Fig. 10 shows the trajectories resulting in the y-z plane when an atom (A) is set in motion with 40 eV of kinetic energy in a direction in this plane making an angle of 15° with the $-y$ axis. The initial

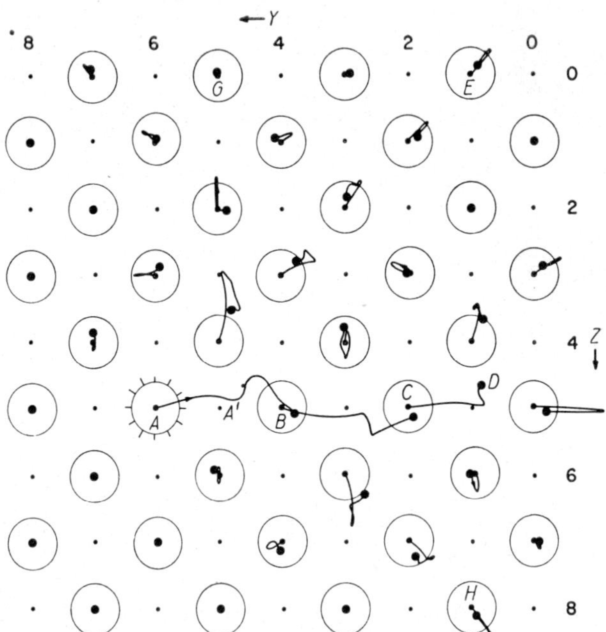

Fig. 10. – Atomic orbits produced by shot in (100) plane at 40 eV. Knock-on was at A and was directed 15° above $-y$ axis. Large circles give initial positions of atoms in plane; small dots are initial positions in plane below. Vacancy is created at A, split interstitial at D. Run to time 99.

positions of atoms in the planes immediately above and below the plane of major action are shown by small black dots. Large open circles show the

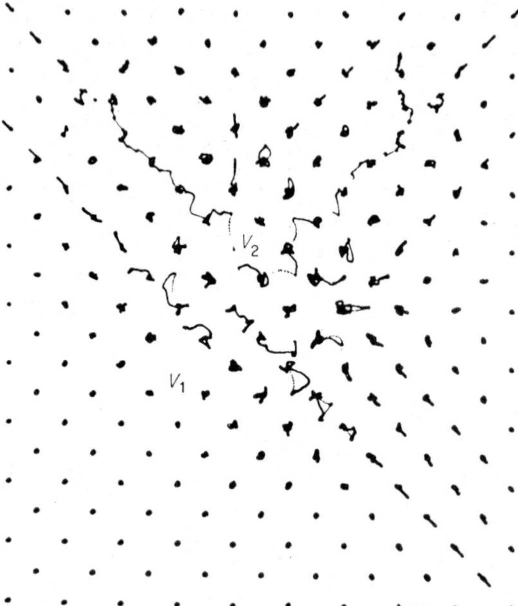

Fig. 11. – Shot in (100) plane at 100 eV, 10° away from [011]. Orbits in plane to time 200 (approximately) are shown. Knock-on started at V_1.

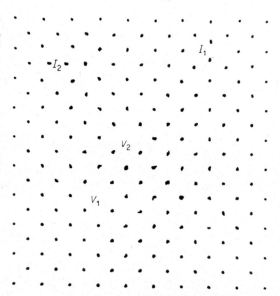

Fig. 12. – Same event shown in Fig. 11, orbits from time 200 to 703. Two vacancies, V_1 and V_2, and two stable interstitials, I_1 and I_2 have formed.

atoms in the plane of major action at time 0, large black dots show the positions of these atoms at time 99 (one time unit is $3.27 \cdot 10^{-15}$ s). The large open circles give the sizes of the atoms, as determined by the distance of closest approach in a head-on collision between a 40 eV atom and a stationary atom. Atoms for which no trajectory is shown suffered negligible displacements. Replacement collisions can be seen at B and C, a vacancy is left at A, and an interstitial is formed at D. This appears to be the usual split configuration (see Fig. 4) in which the atom at $y=1$, $z=4$ is displaced upward from its lattice site, the site being shared by D. Also notable are the chains of strongly focused collisions along $\langle 110 \rangle$ and $\langle 100 \rangle$ directions, including the chains AD, AB, FG, BH, etc. The $\langle 110 \rangle$ focusing is essentially that predicted by SILSBEE [9], but the $\langle 100 \rangle$ focusing occurs only because of the influence of neighboring lines of atoms, and had not been anticipated. Atoms along all lines other than AD are in the process of relaxing back to the vicinity of their original positions. Although the relaxation has not been entirely completed by time 99, experience with this and other events convinces us that the further relaxation will not change the topology of the final configuration from that which is evident in Fig. 10. The net result of this event is two replacements and one Frenkel pair. Although velocities are not given in Fig. 10, it should be noted that a great range of velocities occurs. The original knock-on which had 40 eV at A, has slowed to 19 eV just before A' (where it is in nearly head-on collision with B), and has dropped to only 0.1 eV just beyond the point A'.

The next four figures show results of some shots above threshold in a direction well away from symmetry axes, namely 10° away from [011] in the plane $x = 2$. In all of these the large atomic set C (see Section **2**) was used. Orbital plots of the plane $x = 2$ are shown. In all cases the interatomic potential was number 2. Fig. 11 shows a 100 eV shot which, because of the

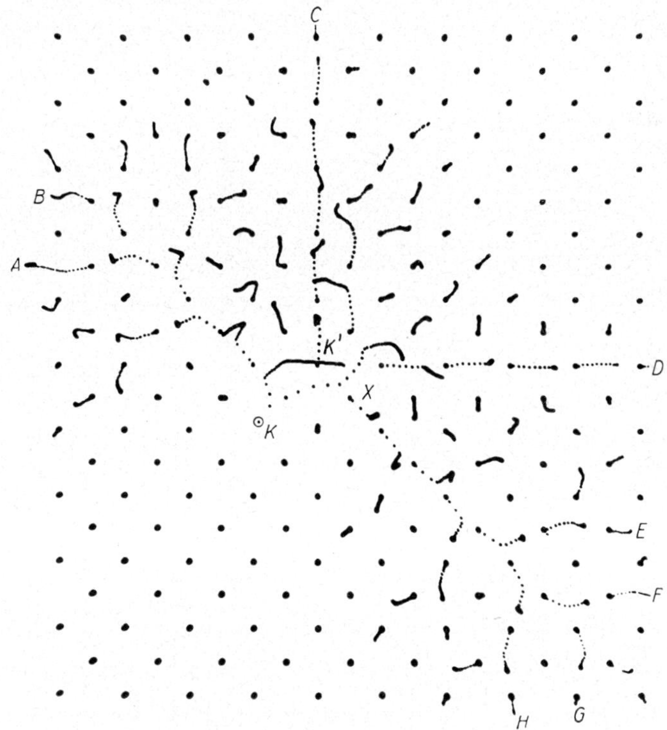

Fig. 13. – Shot in (100) plane at 400 eV, 10° away from [011]. Orbits in plane to time 45 are shown. Knock-on started at K, moves to K'. At end of run collision chains A, B, ..., H are still active.

large set in which it was run, is completely contained. Time runs up to about 200 units in this figure. The knock-on atom was at V_1. Two vacancies are created, at V_1 and V_2, and two interstitials, at the somewhat distant points

I_1 and I_2. Twelve replacements are seen. Fig. 12 shows the same plane, from the time where Fig. 11 was terminated up to time 703. The effect pattern is now well established and the atomic vibrations are all quite restricted. Vacancies and interstitials are marked by the same symbols as in Fig. 11. Fig. 13 shows orbits produced by a 400 eV knock-on atom, directed initially 10° away from [011]. The knock-on atom started at K and goes to K'. This shot runs to time 45, at which time large motions have reached the boundary and the configuration is still rather far from equilibrium.

The 400 V event in Fig. 13 really exceeds the capabilities of our present computing methods. It is presented, however, as a suggestive example of intermediate-energy damage events. By looking at the energies of key orbits at the end of this run and drawing on experience gained with lower-energy shots, it is possible to estimate the final configuration. This estimate is no more than a plausible guess, and many of its particular features are likely to be revised when more powerful computing methods become available. The general character of the damage may, however, be correctly assessed. The action remaining at the end of the calculation is analysed into a number of collision chains. $\langle 100 \rangle$ chains are still active at A, B, C, D, E, F, G, and H. Looking at the kinetic energies at these points and using the rule that a focused $\langle 100 \rangle$ chain loses about 7 eV per step, one estimates that 8 interstitials would eventually be formed at sites outside the fundamental set, as indicated in Fig. 14. In addition 3 interstitials appear to be forming inside the set, at sites also indicated in Fig. 14. A total of 11 vacancies must also have been produced; the sites of some of these are obvious, others are found by extrapolation, and these location are indicated by open circles in the figure. About 39 replacements are estimated to occur. It is quite possible that some of these closely spaced vacancies will immediately rearrange themselves (as, for example

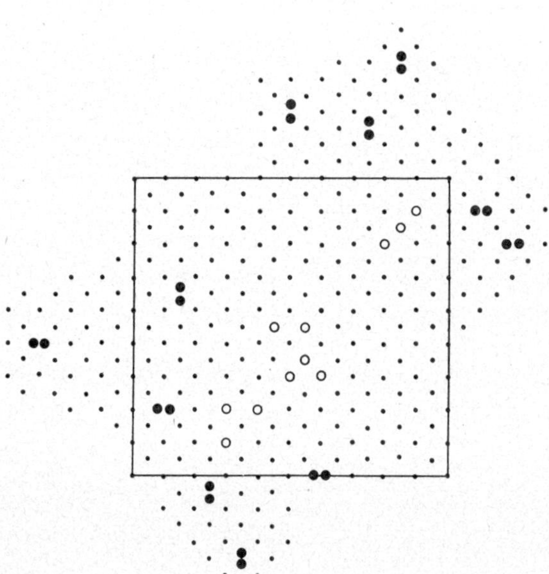

Fig. 14. – Estimated array of 11 vacancies (circles) and 11 interstitials (double dots) that could result from shot in Fig. 13. Set used in Fig. 13 indicated by rectangle. Indicated vacancy arrangement may not be stable.

in the case of a closely spaced trivacancy), but it is not possible to make any reliable statements about this yet.

The configuration of vacancies and interstitials produced is noteworthy for several reasons. The vacancies are near the site of the original knock-on, the interstitials are farther away. ⟨110⟩ collision chains have not played as prominent a role in this event as in some of the lower energy events discussed earlier. This can be attributed to the fact that the energies here are far above the focusing limit for ⟨110⟩ chains, causing these to spray out into ⟨100⟩ chains which are near or below their focusing threshold. An especially clear example is the chain which starts at X and moves toward the lower right corner of the figure (Fig. 13). The kinetic energy at X is 125 eV. The action along this line is reminiscent in many ways of Brinkman's displacement spikes, although there is nothing like the melting and turbulent mixing that he predicted. Note especially the 3 vacancies in a line and the 5 interstitials outside them. It seems clear that, at this energy, almost every kind of stable cluster of vacancies and interstitials will be produced, at least when there is even the slightest annealing.

A series of shots in or near the close-packed direction ⟨110⟩ have also been made. At low energies pronounced focusing in this direction has been found, at high energies defocusing occurs, followed by focusing when the chain has lost enough energy. When directed close to ⟨110⟩ these chains lose energy only very slowly, at a rate of about $\frac{2}{3}$ eV per collision for energies from 3 to several hundred eV. Consequently their range is so long that they cannot be stopped inside our set of atoms. Contrary to early expectations, the threshold energy for producing permanent displacements in ⟨110⟩ is rather low. Because of the difficulty with the long range of these chains, we have not been able to obtain an accurate value for this threshold, but the best estimate is that, for potential 2, it is less than 35 eV and probably is in the neighborhood of 25 eV. Since the ⟨100⟩ threshold is also around 25 eV, this mean that both of these directions are important in near-threshold bombardments. Also it is clear that the interstitials produced by a ⟨110⟩ chain will be far from the beginning of the chain—at least 10 atomic spacings near threshold and as much as 150 spacings at 100 eV. Fig. 15 gives the z-displacements *vs.* time for successive atoms in a chain initiated at 25 eV exactly along ⟨011⟩. Each atom moves just slightly past the midpoint ($\Delta z = \frac{1}{2}$) between it and its neighbor, before being brought to rest, and the relaxation thereafter is extremely slow. The first atom, unlike the others, relaxes back toward its original site and will clearly return there. The anomalous behavior of this atom is explained by the fact that the atom preceding it has not moved much, and thus an unbalanced restoring force is supplied by the second atom in the chain. The second and neighboring atoms are lingering near saddle points, and it is impossible to tell for certain from this calculation whether their relaxation will finally be forward or back. In any case, a slightly higher initial energy should insure the forward relaxation, and if this occurs an interstitial must be produced some distance down the chain and a vacancy will be left at the site of

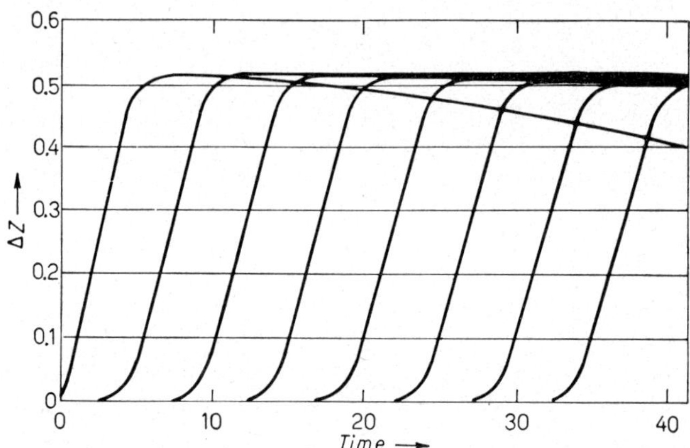

Fig. 15. – z-displacement (Δz) *vs.* time for series of atoms in [011] chain. Knock-on, starting at time zero, had 25 eV kinetic energy, directed along [001].

the *second* atom in the chain. In some other events that have been run, it would appear that the vacancy may even form at the site of the third atom in the chain.

A higher-energy event which clearly does produce a permanently displaced atom is shown in Fig. 16. This event is exactly like that of Fig. 15 except

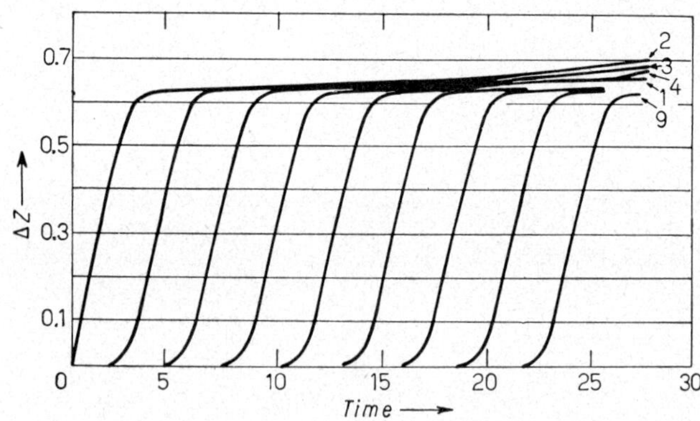

Fig. 16. – Similar to Fig. 15 but with initial kinetic energy of 100 eV. Curves belonging to consecutive atoms are identified by numbers at upper right.

that the initial atom was given a kinetic energy of one hundred eV. Now each atom moves well past the mid-point in its first strong collision, and subsequent relaxation is proceeding in a forward direction. This time the vacancy is being formed at the site of the first atom. The interstitial should be formed about 150 atomic distances away.

Shots with initial velocity vector near a cube axis will be considered next. One run was at 35 eV, with atom 2, 2, 6 directed initially 1° away from the y-axis in the plane $x=2$ (see Fig. 17). This seems clearly to make a Frenkel pair after 3 replacements, the vacancy being left at 2, 2, 6 and the split interstitial, oriented along y, being centered on 2, 10, 6. Assisted focusing down the cubic axis is clearly evident in this run, and Fig. 17 may be considered to

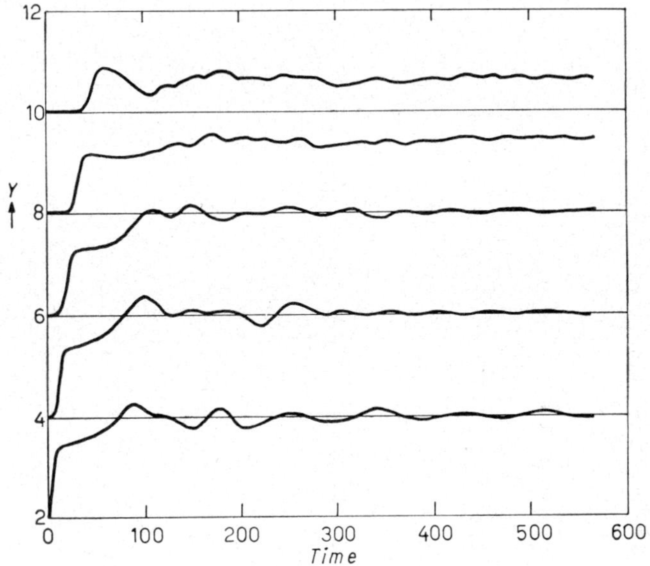

Fig. 17. – y-co-ordinate *vs.* time for line of atoms in ⟨100⟩ chain. Knock-on (bottom curve) was shot at 35 eV, 1° away from y-axis. Split interstitial is created at $y=10$.

demonstrate the transport of both matter and energy in ⟨100⟩ chains. Similar action along ⟨110⟩ has been termed a « dynamic crowdion », and it is now seen that the dynamic crowdion, if this is to be the name adopted, can indeed act along the ⟨100⟩ axes as well. The energy loss in the ⟨100⟩ case is at a greater rate than in ⟨110⟩. In these runs the attenuation of energy in well-focused ⟨100⟩ chains occurs at the rate of 7 to 8 eV per collision. Atoms other than those in the direct path of the knock-ons in these events are not moved very far and return to the vicinity of their original sites. Fig. 18 gives a summary of all dynamical events that have been run with potential 2. The co-ordinates in the figure are the initial energy and the initial direction of motion of the knock-on atom. Each event is represented by a dot. The number of stable Frenkel pairs produced in the shot is given by the first figure near the dot, and the number of replacements occurring is given

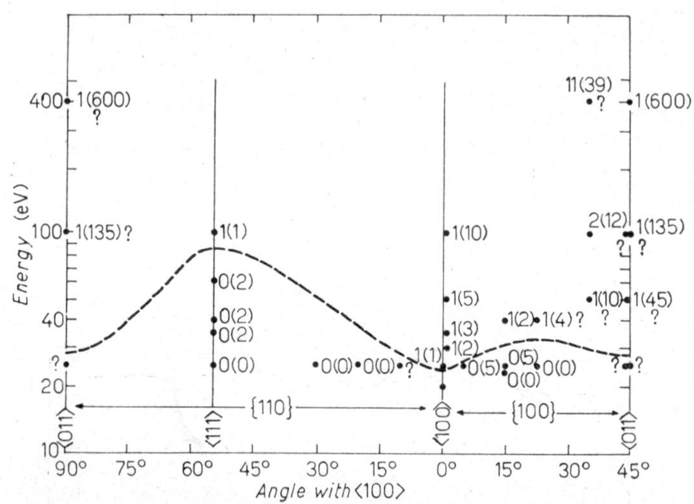

Fig. 18. – Diagram showing all dynamic events calculated with potential 2. A dot is shown for each event and indicates kinetic energy and direction of knock-on atom. First figure attached gives number of stable Frenkel pairs created, figure in parentheses gives number of replacements. Dashed line is estimated threshold for creation of at at least one stable Frenkel pair.

by the figure in parentheses. The dashed line shows the estimated threshold energy for making a stable Frenkel pair at each direction. Further information on the dynamical events is given in ref. [2].

5·2. *Collision chains.* – One of the most striking features of the orbital plots reported here is the strong tendency of energy to propagate along two preferred lines of atoms, the close-packed ⟨110⟩ lines, and the cubic ⟨100⟩ lines. As mentioned before, the ⟨110⟩ effect was anticipated by SILSBEE, who first pointed out that focusing occurs in an isolated, uniformly spaced, straight line of hard spheres. If the first sphere is projected toward the second at an angle θ_1 with the line of centers, the second will be driven away at an angle θ_2 given by

$$\theta_2 = \sin^{-1}\left(\frac{S}{D}\sin\theta_1\right) - \theta_1 \, , \tag{5.1}$$

where S is the separation of centers and D is the diameter of a sphere. If the spheres are sufficiently closely spaced θ_2 will be less than θ_1, and in general

θ_{i+1} will be less than θ_i. If θ_1 is small, eq. (5.1) reduces to

$$\theta_2 = \left(\frac{S}{D} - 1\right)\theta_1 , \tag{5.2}$$

and focusing occurs if $S/D < 2$. For atoms that are soft spheres, a first approximation is obtained if an equivalent hard-sphere diameter is defined, equal to the distance of closest approach of the atoms in a head-on collision. Considering a moving atom with kinetic energy E to be in collision with a stationary atom of equal mass, and using the exponential repulsive potential $\varphi = B \exp[-\beta r]$, one finds the hard-sphere diameter for energy E to be

$$D = (1/\beta) \ln 2B/E . \tag{5.3}$$

The strength of the focusing can be conveniently described by a focusing parameter Λ defined as the ratio of angles θ_2 and θ_1:

$$\Lambda = \theta_2/\theta_1 . \tag{5.4}$$

For small angles, one has from (5.2) $\Lambda = (S/D) - 1$, with D given by eq. (5.3).

In a more realistic model, as employed in the present calculation, the row of atoms is not isolated, but is imbedded in adjoining rows of atoms. Also a moving atom is in continuous interaction with its next neighbor in the line, and it is not possible to make a rigorous separation of the collision into before and after stages: the moving atom pursues curved trajectory, losing speed continuously, and the struck atom moves away on a curved trajectory as it gradually picks us speed. It is thus of considerable interest that the calculation produced collision sequences having such close qualitative resemblances to the Silsbee chains. In order to check more closely on the resemblance, and also in order to see if the focused chains observed can be easily characterized so that complex damage events can be resolved into simple elements, a quantitative study has been made of the chains appearing in our calculations. A chain was characterized in the i-th stage ($i = 1, 2, 3, \ldots$) by a kinetic energy E_i and by the angle θ_i between the axis of the chain and a tangent to the orbit of the moving atom. E_i was always chosen as the kinetic energy of one atom, at the point of its maximum kinetic energy, and θ_i was also defined at this point; this seemed to be the best compromise between the requirements that the preceding collision be ended and the next collision not yet begun. If the angle in the chain at its next stage is θ_{i+1} it is convenient to define a focusing parameter $\Lambda(E_i)$ as

$$\Lambda(E_i) = \frac{\theta_{i+1}}{\theta_i} . \tag{5.5}$$

Examining the major $\langle 110 \rangle$ focusing chains occurring in all of our calculations with interatomic potential 2, and limiting attention to cases where θ_i was less than 20° and did not belong to a boundary atom, values of $\Lambda(E)$ for a large variety of energies E were found. These points are plotted in Fig. 19, and

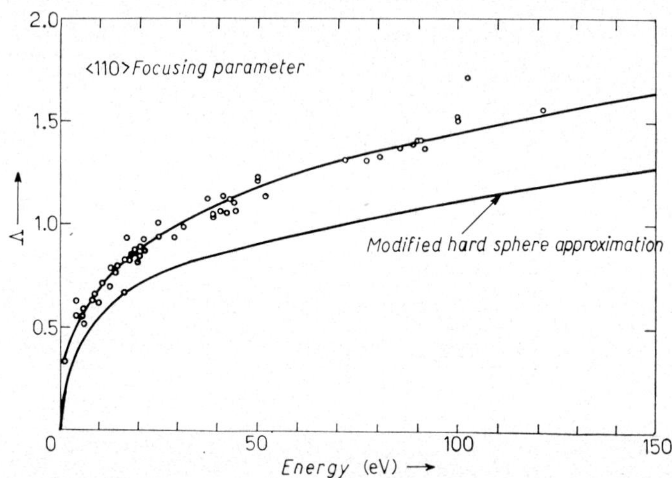

Fig. 19. – Focusing parameter $\Lambda = \theta_2/\theta_1$ as found from $\langle 110 \rangle$ chains in various runs (open circles), plotted against kinetic energy in the chain.

are seen to lie on a rather well-defined curve. Very little dependence of Λ on θ was observed, and most of the scatter of the points in the figure can be attributed to the somewhat arbitrary attempt to characterize chains initiated in a variety of ways by only two parameters, θ and E, and also, to a minor extent, to truncation error. From Fig. 19 it is seen that $\Lambda = 1$ at $E \simeq 30$ eV, so that chains above 30 eV are defocused, chains below 30 eV are focused. A defocused chain increases its angle and causes a more rapid loss of energy. In $\langle 110 \rangle$ chains, the energy lost at each stage is found to be approximately

$$\Delta E_i = \tfrac{2}{3}\,(\text{eV}) + E \sin^2 (\theta_i + \theta_{i+1}) \,. \tag{5.6}$$

As the angle increases, the attrition of energy increases until the chain drops into the focusing range. Its angle then rapidly approaches zero and the chain continues for a distance determined by the first term in eq. (5.6). This term arises because even the perfectly focused chain must force its way between neighbors and lose some energy to them. The value $\frac{2}{3}$ eV per step was found to be a fairly good approximation for repulsive potential 2 at small angles and for chain energy E between about 3 and 400 eV.

The $\langle 100 \rangle$ lines are more widely spaced than the $\langle 110 \rangle$ lines by a factor $\sqrt{2}$. A modified hard-sphere theory for these lines would predict defocusing at all energies above 5.5 eV. Much stronger focusing effects are actually observed in these lines, and examination of Fig. 10 shows that this occurs because of the confining action exerted by neighboring lines; it is quite insufficient to consider a ⟨100⟩ line to be isolated. Focusing in a variety of ⟨100⟩ chains in our calculations (all for interatomic potential 2) was examined, and characterized at each stage by a parameter Λ, defined exactly as for the ⟨110⟩ chains. The results are presented in Fig. 20. Again there is some scatter of points, attributable to the same causes. Focusing occurs, in general, when

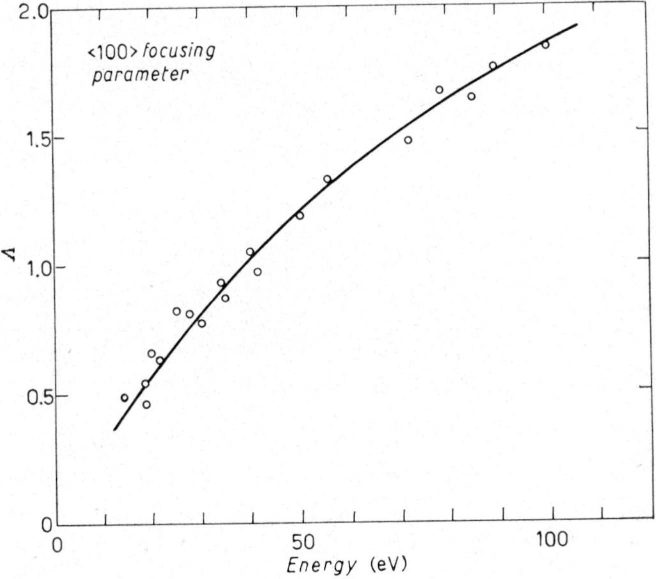

Fig. 20. – Focusing parameter $\Lambda = \theta_2/\theta_1$ as found from ⟨100⟩ chains in various runs (open circles), plotted against kinetic energy in the chain.

the kinetic energy is less than about 40 eV, and defocusing occurs at energies above this. As energy increases above the focusing threshold, Λ grows more rapidly in the ⟨100⟩ case than in the ⟨110⟩ case. The angles θ range up to 20° for the events represented in Fig. 20, but the majority of angles are below 3°. As with ⟨110⟩ chains, no systematic dependence of Λ on θ could be found within the range examined.

5·3 *Replacement collisions.* – The number of replacements occurring in a chain that starts with energy E_1 and angle θ_1 can now be calculated. Taking $\Lambda(E_1)$ from the solid line through the « experimental » points in Fig. 19, one finds the second angle in the chain, θ_2, from $\theta_2 = \Lambda(E_1)\theta_1$. Then using eq. (2.6) to find the energy loss ΔE_1, one has the second energy in the chain

$$E_2 = E_1 - \Delta E_1 .$$

The process is now repeared, starting with E_2 and θ_2, to find energy and angle in the third stage of the chain; by iteration, energy and angle at each successive stage is found. From the dynamic events run to date it is estimated that a well-focused chain produces an interstitial (and thus ceases to transport matter) when its energy falls to about 3 or 4 eV. This energy is subject to rather wide limits of error, in the present stage of our computation, but will be assumed to be 3.5 eV for the present purpose. A quantity $N(E, \theta)$ is defined as the number of collisions required for the energy of a chain that starts at energy E and angle θ (assuming $E \geqslant 30$ eV and $|\theta| < 15°$) to drop to 3.5 eV. This quantity, $N(E, \theta)$, is the number of replacements in the chain, and also it is the distance (in atomic spacings) between the vacancy at the start of the chain and the interstitial at its end. Contours of constant $N(E, \theta)$ are shown on a plane of E and θ in Fig. 21. It is seen that the length of a chain initiated at low energies (around 50 eV) diminishes rather slowly as θ increases, while the length of a higher-energy chain drops very rapidly as θ increases. Along the line $\theta = 0$, $N(E, \theta) = \frac{3}{2}(E - 3.5)$. This predicts that a 100 V chain with $\theta = 0$ travels 146 atomic spaces, while a 100 V chain with $\theta = 1°$ travels only 22 spaces. It is obvious that the considerations leading to Fig. 21 are quite crude, but it is felt that the figure represents a better approximation than earlier work based on a hard-sphere model. The contours in Fig. 20 are terminated at 30 eV because the assumptions in their derivation do not apply to chains initiated at energies lower than this.

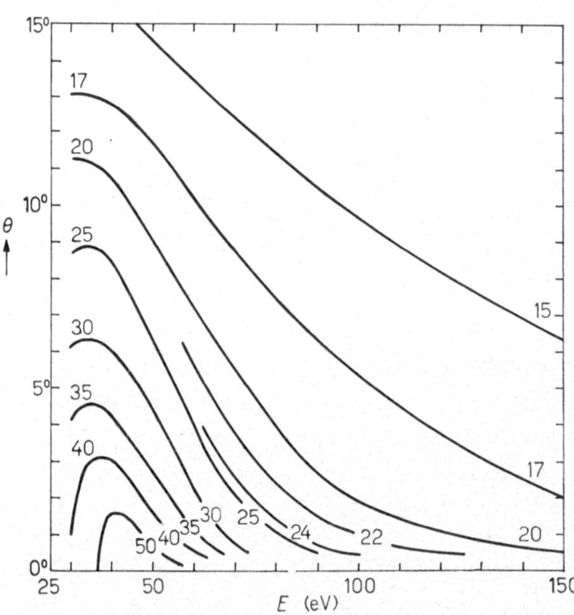

Fig. 21. – Calculated lengths, N, of ⟨100⟩ collision chains started at various angles and energies. Lines give contours of constant N.

6. – Summary and conclusions.

The calculations presented here give a more intimate view of radiation damage events at low and moderate energies in a face-centered cubic metal than has been obtained before. It should be remembered, however, that all results are based on a simple model of metallic copper which is plausible, but whose accuracy has not been finally established. With this reservation, the following conclusions concerning radiation damage and lattice defects in copper have been reached:

1) Damage at low energies consists of vacancies ad interstitials. This point is only confirmation of what has been commonly supposed.

2) Vacancies are of the conventional character, but interstitials reside in the split configuration (Fig. 4); no other configuration of the interstitial has been found to be stable.

3) The regular arrangement of atoms on a lattice has an important influence on the character of damage events. Collision chains occur in both $\langle 110 \rangle$ and $\langle 100 \rangle$ directions, propagating with especially low loss of energy in the former direction, as anticipated by SILSBEE [9]. Chains in $\langle 110 \rangle$ focus at kinetic energies below approximately 30 eV, chains in $\langle 100 \rangle$ focus below 40 eV; all chains defocus at higher energies. These threshold are surprisingly low.

4) A chain with energy above 25 or 30 eV carries matter, as well as energy, somewhat in the fashion of the « dynamic crowdion » [10-12], and produces an interstitial atom near its terminus. The ranges of various $\langle 110 \rangle$ chains have been estimated (Fig. 21).

5) Because of the « dynamic crowdion » action, interstitials tend to be produced at a distance from the site of a primary knock-on, while the vacancies, having no mechanism of propagation, remain behind in fairly compact groups. At moderate energies a variety of clusters of vacancies, and possibly more complex configurations resulting from the collapse or rearrangement of such clusters, can be expected. The present calculations have not yet been able to follow such rearrangements in detail. The question of the existence of amorphous zones at the site of a damage event, as suggested by SEEGER [12] is not yet settled.

6) Another result of the collision chains is the production of many more replacements than displacements. In compounds or alloys of nearly homogenous mass this effect would produce many more disordered atoms than displaced atoms [13].

7) The threshold energy for producing a single Frenkel pair is lowest (about 25 eV) in or near ⟨100⟩ and probably is almost as low in or near ⟨110⟩. The threshold is much higher, probably 85 eV, around ⟨111⟩. Experiments on the directional dependence of the threshold are clearly indicated.

8) The closest Frenkel pairs are not stable, in the present model, and pair along ⟨110⟩ directions must be separated to 4th neighbor positions in order to be stable (see Fig. 9). These conclusions are probably rather sensitive to the details of the force law employed.

9) Knock-on with energy near threshold produce a variety of Frenkel pairs. The explanation advanced by CORBETT, SMITH and WALKER [14] for the substages that they observed in the lowest temperature annealing of electron irradiated copper are consistent with results reported here, except that the interstitial is not in the position assumed by CORBETT *et al.*, and the present calculations are not far enough advanced to identify particular Frenkel pairs with all of the particular annealing substages.

10) Agitations following damage events of moderate energy are seen to bear some resemblance to thermal spikes, but the transport of energy is far from isotropic, as would be predicted by thermal-spike models in a cubic material. Localized vibrational modes associated with interstitials are prominently excited, and retain their energy longer than other modes. Localized annealing appears to be promoted by the excitation that lingers in these modes.

11) It would appear that these calculations have proved the feasibility of simulating events of radiation damage by mathematical models on high speed computers. Limitations on the size of the set of atoms that can be treated are still a matter of concern, and practical means of increasing this size are under study. Further checks and improvements on the force laws are needed. Work in these areas is continuing.

REFERENCES

[1] For reviews see F. SEITZ and J. S. KOEHLER, in *Solid State Physics*, vol. **2** (New York, 1956), p. 305; also G. J. DIENES and G. H. VINEYARD: *Radiation Effects in Solids* (New York, 1957).

[2] J. B. GIBSON, A. N. GOLAND, M. MILGRAM and G. H. VINEYARD: *Phys. Rev.*, **120**, 1229 (1960).

[3] *Proceedings of the Conference on Lattice Defects in Noble Metals*, North American Aviation Report NAA-SR-3250 (available from Office of Technical Services, Department of Commerce, Washington 25, D. C.).

[4] H. B. Huntington: *Phys. Rev.*, **91**, 1092 (1953); H. B. Huntington and F. Seitz: *Phys. Rev.*, **61**, 315 (1942).

[5] J. A. Brinkman: *Journ. Appl. Phys.*, **25**, 961 (1954). Measurements of ranges of knock-on atoms also confirm this conclusion. See R. A. Schmitt and R. A. Sharp: *Phys. Rev. Lett.*, **1**, 445 (1958); D. K. Holmes and G. Leibfried: *Journ. Appl. Phys.*, **31**, 1046 (1960).

[6] A. A. Abrahamson: *Thesis* (New York University, 1960), unpublished; A. A. Abrahamson, R. D. Hatcher and G. H. Vineyard: *Bull. Am. Phys. Soc.*, **5**, 231 (1960) and also *Phys. Rev.*, **121**, 159 (1961).

[7] H. Kanzaki: *Journ. Phys. Chem. Solids*, **2**, 24 (1957); G. L. Hall, *Journ. Phys. Chem. Solids*, **3**, 210 (1957); A. Seeger and E. Mann: *Journ. Phys. Chem. Solids*, **12**, 326 (1960); L. A. Girifalco and V. G. Weizer: *Journ. Phys. Chem. Solids*, **12**, 260 (1960).

[8] R. A. Johnson, G. H. Goedecke, E. Brown and H. B. Huntington: *Bull. Am. Phys. Soc.*, **5**, 181 (1960).

[9] R. H. Silsbee: *Journ. Appl. Phys.*, **28**, 1246 (1957).

[10] G. Leibfried: *Journ. Appl. Phys.*, **30**, 1388 (1959).

[11] G. Leibfried: *Journ. Appl. Phys.*, **31**, 117 (1960).

[12] A. Seeger: *Second International Conference on Peaceful Uses of Atomic Energy* (Geneva, 1958) paper no. 998.

[13] G. H. Kinchin and R. S. Pease: *Rep. Progr. Phys.*, **18**, 1 (1955).

[14] J. W. Corbett, J. M. Denney, M. D. Fisk and R. M. Walker: *Phys. Rev.*, **108**, 954 (1957); J. W. Corbett, R. B. Smith and R. M. Walker: *Phys. Rev.*, **114**, 1452, 1460 (1959).

Radiation Damage in Semiconductors.

Introductory Lectures on Semiconductors.

E. GERMAGNOLI

Laboratori C.I.S.E. - Milano
Istituto di Fisica del Politecnico - Milano

1. – In these lectures a qualitative discussion of the properties of the most extensively investigated semiconducting crystals will be given.

It is not the purpose of this review to cover the field of semiconductors in any detail, so we will consider only germanium and silicon, under the hypothesis that the atoms of these elements are assembled to form nearly perfect crystals, namely crystals containing small and, to some extent, controllable concentrations of defects. Neither surface properties of these crystals nor phenomena taking place near the boundary between differently doped pieces of a semiconducting material (barriers) will be considered. Consequently, only the bulk properties of a typical semiconductor will be discussed.

Some elements of valence 4 (Ge, Si), 5 (Bi), 6 (Se, Te), a number of inorganic compounds (ZnO, Cu_2O, PbS, InSb, ...) and some organic compounds are usually considered as belonging to this class of solids. The conditions which a compound must obey to be a semiconductor have been discussed by several authors, for instance by BUSCH [1]. A definition of semiconductors is somewhat arbitrary: referring to electrical conductivity, we may classify as semiconductors those crystalline solids which in a pure state are insulators near the absolute zero and display an electronic-type conductivity at high temperature, the temperature coefficient being opposite to that of metals. If the crystal lattice is distorted with respect to its ideal structure, or if impurity atoms are added, the conductivity may change by many orders of magnitude and is attributable sometimes to negative carriers, sometimes to positive carriers. Actually, many kinds of behavior are possible near room temperature.

The most striking peculiarity of semiconductors is the enormous influence of impurities and lattice disorder on their electrical properties.

A typical behavior of semiconductors is suggested by the study of germanium and silicon. In many materials the semiconducting behavior is much less evident, and some substances are considered to be semiconductors only because of the peculiarity of some properties (for instance some organic compounds). The predominant bond is homopolar in typical semiconductors. The crystals show the diamond structure: each atom has four valence electrons which it shares with its nearest neighbors in such a way that four covalent bonds are formed, each one consisting of two electrons. While the nature of the structure itself shows rather clearly the difference between semiconductors, metals and ionic crystals, the situation is less clear as far as the difference between semiconductors and insulators is concerned; it is more quantitative than qualitative (for instance, diamond has the same structure but it is a well known insulator), though Van der Waals bonds predominate in many insulators.

2. – The peculiar behavior of semiconductors when impurities are added or when the crystal lattice is distorted due to cold-work or radiation damage is related to the fact that these operations are effective in introducing empty or filled electronic energy levels into the forbidden band which is located between the valence band and the conduction band. The forbidden band is large enough in germanium (0.73 eV) and in silicon (1.13 eV) to prevent transitions of electrons directly from the valence band to the conduction band under the influence of usual electric fields or thermal agitation, if temperature is not too high. The situation is completely different if levels due to defects of whatsoever origin exist within the forbidden band; their practical effect is similar to that produced by a drastic reduction of the width of the forbidden band. A calculation of the electronic energy band structure is, generally speaking, a very difficult problem. A solution giving the energy of electrons as a function of the wave number $\boldsymbol{K}$ can be obtained easily only in extremely idealized cases, such as for a simple array of similar atoms. In the case being considered, some data can be derived by combining general symmetry arguments with experimental data which can be obtained from the measurement of optical properties, from cyclotron resonance experiments, from magnetoresistivity measurements ...; in any case an extensive theoretical work is needed.

The simplest method of calculation is the one-electron approximation, which considers one single electron within the average potential which is created by other electrons; the crystal is assumed to be perfect and at the absolute zero, the atoms staying consequently fixed at their lattice sites. Lattice disorder is neglected and eventually taken into account later as a perturbation, just as lattice vibrations are. Then the electronic eigenfunction can be deduced in the Bloch form $\psi_k = \exp[i\,\boldsymbol{k}\cdot\boldsymbol{r}]U_k(\boldsymbol{r})$, where U_k is a function showing the same periodicity as the crystal lattice; $\exp[i\boldsymbol{k}\cdot\boldsymbol{r}]$ is simply a plane wave eigenfunction whose wave number is k. For each $\boldsymbol{k}$ different solutions for U exist, each one corresponding to a different energy; in this way, by varying $\boldsymbol{k}$, a series of energy bands is obtained and each one of the bands covers an energy interval. While the energy bands corresponding to lower eigenvalues are narrow and widely spaced, the bands corresponding to higher eigenvalues are enlarged and overlap, giving place to a continuum.

This follows from general principles of quantum mechanics.

The electrons which are available within the crystal arrange themselves in the energy bands, each state being occupied by one electron according to the Pauli principle. The material is a semiconductor or an insulator whenever the electrons fill completely one band and leave the next one totally empty; this band is separated from the preceding one by a forbidden band where no possible electronic energy levels can be found (see Fig. 1). The practical result can be described in the present case by saying that the electrons which are accomodated in a filled band cannot give any contribution to conduction. There is no transport of electricity through the crystal by migration of bound electrons from atom to atom. In fact, an electric field cannot be responsible for any change in the energy distribution of electrons within a filled band: if an electron jumps towards a direction another one must necessarily acquire the same speed in the opposite direction and no current arises. In the most usual situations only thermal agitation can change the population of a band raising electrons above the forbidden band. This is energetically possible at not too high temperatures in the most typical semiconductors, in which the forbidden band is about 1 eV wide, but it is not possible if the forbidden band is as wide as 5 eV, as happens in several insulators.

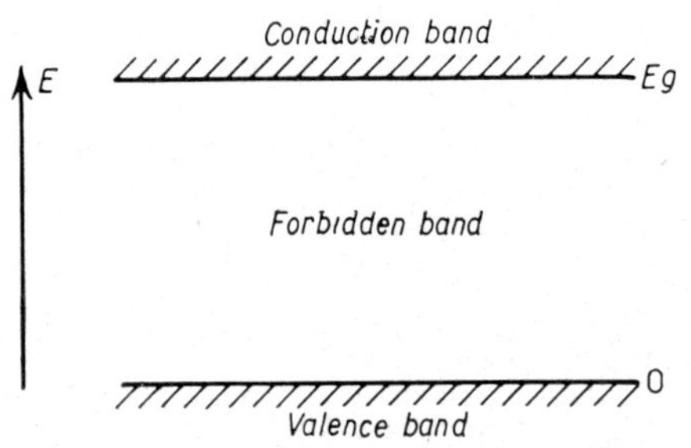

Fig. 1. – Energy bands in a typical semiconductor.

If temperature is raised, thermal vibrations are effective in breaking bonds and electrons become free to migrate through the lattice. Each freed electron leaves behind a hole, or unpaired electron in the valence band. The hole is able to migrate, by changing its position in the lattice. Electrons and holes are responsible of conduction and are called the charge carriers.

By studying how a charge carrier modifies its momentum under the influence of an electric field $\boldsymbol{E}$ we are led to the concept of effective mass. From the definition of the group velocity v of an electronic wave packet ($v = \mathrm{d}\omega/\mathrm{d}k = (1/\hbar)\,\mathrm{d}\varepsilon/\mathrm{d}k$), where ω is the circular frequency of the De Broglie wave and ε is the energy of the electron, we get

$$\frac{\mathrm{d}k}{\mathrm{d}t} = \frac{eE}{\hbar}\,.$$

The acceleration of the electron is then

$$\frac{\mathrm{d}v}{\mathrm{d}t} = \frac{eE}{\hbar^2}\frac{\mathrm{d}^2\varepsilon}{\mathrm{d}k^2},$$

and this relationship suggests that it is possible to represent the inertial properties of the charge carrier by means of its effective mass

$$m = \hbar^2\left(\frac{\mathrm{d}^2\varepsilon}{\mathrm{d}k^2}\right)^{-1},$$

which in the general case of a periodic potential in a three-dimensional space can be written as

$$\frac{1}{m_{ij}} = \frac{1}{\hbar^2}\frac{\partial^2\varepsilon}{\partial k_i \partial k_j}.$$

Every simple model giving the dependence of ε on $\boldsymbol{k}$ shows that m is positive near the bottom of a band and negative near the top of it: the electrons which are missing in a filled band usually have energy states near the top of it and are consequently associated with negative effective masses. That means that from the point of view of their contribution to conduction they are equivalent to positive particles with positive effective masses: this explains the behavior of holes.

If the energy bands are known, the electric behavior of a semiconductor can be studied. Accurate information for this purpose is lacking, but a usual situation is that the few conduction electrons are located near the bottom of the conduction band and the holes are near the top of the valence band. In order to predict the behavior of the material it is then sufficient to know the shape of the band in a rather narrow energy interval. This is usually described by simple quadratic forms in which the linear terms in the components of $\boldsymbol{k}$ are missing. This is reasonable in the proximity of a maximum or a minimum of the $\varepsilon = \varepsilon(k)$ function, though the solution is more complicated in general because it is impossible to choose co-ordinates in such a way that only the quadratic term is present.

3. – The previous general considerations suggest that semiconductors are materials in which conduction takes place through those electrons which for some reason are raised to energy states within the nearly empty conduction band, and through the holes which are created within the valence band. From Fermi statistics, if the density of electronic states in the system is known, the concentration n of electrons in the conduction band and the concentration p

of holes in the valence band are easily calculated:

$$n = 2\left(\frac{2\pi m_e kT}{h^2}\right)^{\frac{3}{2}} \exp\left[\frac{E_F - E_g}{kT}\right], \tag{1}$$

$$p = 2\left(\frac{2\pi m_h kT}{h^2}\right)^{\frac{3}{2}} \exp\left[-\frac{E_F}{kT}\right], \tag{2}$$

provided the concentrations of carriers are sufficiently small, which is true, for instance, for a low temperature $T((E-E_F)/kT \gg 1)$. Here m_e and m_h are the effective masses of the two kinds of charge carriers, E_F is the Fermi level, E_g is the width of the forbidden band. It is important to point out that the following equilibrium relationship holds:

$$np = 4\left(\frac{2\pi kT}{h^2}\right)^3 (m_e m_h)^{\frac{3}{2}} \exp\left[-\frac{E_g}{kT}\right], \tag{3}$$

showing that the product of the carrier concentrations is constant for a given semiconductor at a given temperature, and does not change if impurities are added, provided the distance of the Fermi level from the boundaries of the forbidden band is $\gg kT$.

For an « intrinsic » semiconductor

$$n = p = 2\left(\frac{2\pi kT}{h^2}\right)^{\frac{3}{2}} (m_e m_h)^{\frac{3}{4}} \exp\left[-\frac{E_g}{2kT}\right], \tag{4}$$

and comparing (1) and (4)

$$E_F = \frac{E_g}{2} + \frac{3}{4} kT \log \frac{m_h}{m_e}.$$

So E_F is usually near the middle of the forbidden band, at least if m_h and m_e are not too different.

In the intrinsic range the conductivity is

$$\sigma_i = |e|(n\mu_e + p\mu_h) = 2|e|\left(\frac{2\pi kT}{h^2}\right)^{\frac{3}{2}} (m_e m_h)^{\frac{3}{4}} (\mu_e + \mu_h) \exp\left[-\frac{E_g}{2kT}\right], \tag{5}$$

μ_e and μ_h being the mobilities of electron and holes.

Mobilities depend on temperature according to a $T^{-\frac{3}{2}}$ law, as shown by calculations of Seitz and of Bardeen-Shockley, if lattice scattering predominates. In this case σ_i is proportional to $\exp[-Eg/2kT]$.

This is observed for intrinsic semiconductors and in general for all semiconductors at high temperature, in which case the contribution to conduction by intrinsic charge carriers predominates. According to this law the width of the forbidden band can be measured and is found to be in agreement with results from measurements of the optical absorption edge.

4. – The above picture is valid at temperatures higher than 400 °K in the case of germanium and 600 °K in the case of silicon. Below these temperatures conductivity shows a different behavior because mobility is strongly influenced by impurity atoms. Moreover, impurities contribute to the production of charge carriers, and at low temperature trapping of carriers plays an important role. The purer the material, the wider the range in which the simple intrinsic law is valid, but it is worth mentioning how few impurity atoms or other defects are enough to influence electrical properties, conductivity, Hall coefficient, and lifetime of carriers in particular. Concerning this last parameter, we recall that it is strongly affected by the density of dislocations. It is comparatively easy to grow germanium and silicon simple crystals with a small concentration of dislocations. The best available crystals usually contain 10^3 dislocations/cm^2, but recently silicon crystals have been grown with no more than 10 dislocation lines/cm^2; this is an extremely small density of dislocations if it is compared with the one typical for a carefully annealed metal specimen $((10^6 \div 10^7)$ dislocations/$cm^2)$.

Among lattice defects, the most typical one is an atom of impurity. Its influence can be described by saying that it introduces electronic energy levels within the forbidden band. These levels are either donor or acceptor type. A donor defect in an otherwise perfect crystal makes an electron appear within the conduction band, or in a localized state within the forbidden band just below the conduction band. In this way the crystal acquires one positive charge. On the contrary, an acceptor produces a hole within the valence band or an empty localized state within the forbidden band just above the valence band, acquiring a larger charge.

For instance, a semiconductor which contains donor impurities has conduction electrons in excess with respect to holes, according to the electric neutrality condition. Moreover, (3) requires that there are more electrons in the conduction band than would be present intrinsically at the same temperature in a purer sample. Similarly, a semiconductor containing negatively charged acceptor centers must have more holes than electrons.

In the former case the semiconductor is extrinsic, and n-type; in the latter case, extrinsic and p-type.

It is difficult to say *a priori* which is the effect of an atom of a given impurity. Only in particularly simple cases is an answer possible. If a pentavalent impurity is substitutionally added, we may conclude that it has one electron in excess with respect to the germanium or silicon atom. This electron is raised towards the conduction band, being rather loosely bound near the impurity atom due to the large dielectric constant of the medium. A calculation can be made which is similar to the one giving the energy eigenvalues of electrons in the Bohr atom. The radius of the orbit is equal to several lattice constants and the energy of the considered bound state is small. Consequently, a small ionization energy ($\simeq 0.01$ eV) is calculated for a donor state.

For a trivalent impurity a similar calculation can be formally developed, and the result is that the ionization energy of the resulting acceptor state is also very small.

In other cases the positions of levels which are introduced within the forbidden band by many impurities are well known from experimental data, but it is difficult to perform satisfactory calculations. The behaviour of lithium is easily explained because a lithium atom introduces a donor level by giving up its valence electron and assuming a noble gas (helium) configuration. Concerning impurities like Zn, Fe, Ni, Co, Mn (two acceptor levels), Cu and Au (three acceptor levels), it is believed that such substitutional impurities complete their valence bonds by sharing electrons with the four nearest atoms of the semiconductor lattice. In such cases the atoms having a S^2 configuration would act like double acceptors, and the atoms having a S^1 configuration would act like triple acceptors. This explanation is, however, only partial and not too satisfactory.

5. – The effect of impurities, as far as the introduction of excess carriers is concerned, is readily calculated by making use of the condition of electrical neutrality of the whole crystal. If $n \gg p$, one gets immediately in two remarkable limiting cases:

$$a) \qquad n = 2\left(\frac{2\pi m_e kT}{h^2}\right)^{\frac{3}{2}} \exp\left[\frac{E_F - E_g}{kT}\right],$$

with

$$E_F \simeq E_g + kT \log \frac{N_D}{2\,(2\pi m_e kT/h^2)^{\frac{3}{2}}}\,.$$

This gives

$$n \simeq N_D \tag{6}$$

if T is high and N_D is small.

$$b) \qquad n = (2N_D)^{\frac{1}{2}} \left(\frac{2\pi m_e kT}{h^2}\right)^{\frac{3}{4}} \exp\left[-\frac{E_g - E_2}{kT}\right], \tag{7}$$

if T is low and N_D is large.

Here N_D is the concentration of added impurity atoms.

(6) means that practically all the impurities are ionized and each one of them supplies a conduction electron; in (7) the ionization energy of donors $E_g - E_2$ is included, E_2 being the energy of the donor level, measured from the top of the valence band.

As $E_g - E_2 \ll E_g$, electrons can be found within the conduction band much more easily than in the intrinsic case. It is then immediately understood why so few atoms of a suitable impurity are effective in controlling the electrical properties of a semiconductor. Similar considerations hold with acceptor levels introduced by impurities.

Both for research and for technological purposes extremely pure semiconductors are needed, and some methods have been successfully used in order to purify materials and to grow single crystals.

The Czochralski method is convenient for the production of very pure single crystals. To this end a seed is lowered to the surface of the molten material and then slowly withdrawn so that the crystal grows continuously. Very perfect crystals can be grown if the vertical gradient of temperature is properly established and axial symmetry of temperature with respect to axis of the crucible is achieved. The purification is obtained because most impurities remain in the molten material as their solubilities in germanium or silicon are much smaller in the solid phase than in the liquid phase.

PFANN developed the zone refining method, which is based on the same principle as far as purification is concerned; however, single crystals cannot be produced. In this case a heating coil is moved along a rod of the material to be purified, always in one direction; in such way impurities are concentrated in the proximity of one end of the rod. After a rather small number of passages a saturation is reached in the purification effect, the limit corresponding to residual concentrations of impurities of about 10^{-9} or 10^{-10}.

The floating zone method is a modification of the zone refining method and is very useful for silicon, which easily reacts with crucibles. A vertical geometry is adopted and the molten zone is gradually raised, being held in position by surface tension. This method is somewhat complicated but compares favorably with the zone refining methods, because it makes it possible to grow single crystals during purification and no contact between silicon and crucible is needed.

6. – Impurity atoms can be quantitatively introduced into semiconductors with the help of several procedures:

a) chemically, during the growth of the crystals,

b) by diffusion at high temperature,

c) by nuclear reactions, mainly induced by slow neutrons.

Other defects are equally effective in modifying the properties of semiconductors: Schottky defects (lattice vacancies), which can be produced by quenching at high temperature, and Frenkel defects, which are introduced by irradiation with nucleons, electrons and γ-rays.

The behavior of irradiated semiconductors will be discussed in detail by J. H. CRAWFORD. The aim of the present considerations is to clarify some basic facts in the physically simplest situations. As long as sufficiently intense fluxes of neutrons having energies in the range of a few keV are not available, the simplest kind of radiation damage is presumably obtained with γ-rays or electrons whose energy is 1 MeV or less. In this case the ionization tracks are long, and therefore the production of several Frenkel defects in a small region is unlikely. Consequently, practically no association of defects will be expected.

If, also, Frenkel defects are effective in introducing donor and acceptor levels within the forbidden band, semiconductors must be extremely sensitive to radiation damage. This fact is actually shown by the close qualitative similarity between the results which are obtained by gradually adding impurities to a semiconductor and the results which are obtained by introducing Frenkel defects.

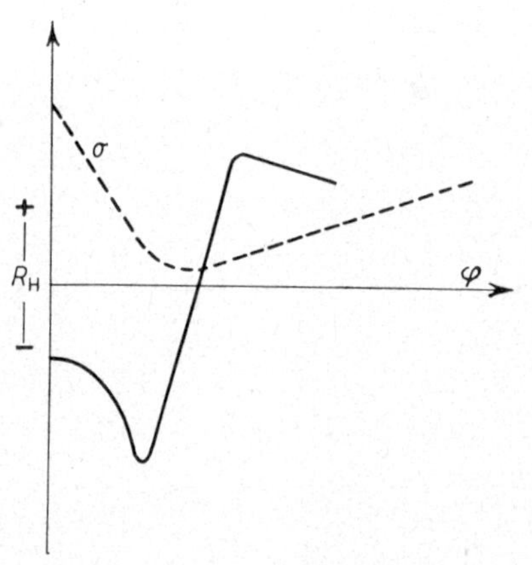

Fig. 2. – Typical behavior of conductivity and Hall coefficient under irradiation in initially n-type germanium.

Very clear examples of the influence of irradiation have been published by many authors. Fig. 2 shows the typical changes in conductivity and Hall coefficient which have been observed under irradiation of an n-type germanium specimen. These two properties are very sensitive to bombardment; in particular, the Hall coefficient is given by

$$R_{\rm H} = \frac{1}{ec}\,\frac{p\mu_{\rm h}^2 - n\mu_{\rm e}^2}{(p\mu_{\rm h} + n\mu_{\rm e})^2}\,,$$

and is consequently sensitive to the sign of charge carriers. The change of the sign of $R_{\rm H}$ indicates that after a rather short time of irradiation the specimen is converted from n- to p-type.

Also, optical properties of irradiated specimens are very interesting, as they allow one to study the location of energy levels within the forbidden band [2]. The most sensitive property is probably the lifetime of carriers in non-equilibrium conditions. LOFERSKI and RAPPAPORT [3] took advantage of this fact to measure the threshold energy for the production of atomic displacements in germanium and silicon.

7. – Curves shown in Fig. 2 demonstrate that Frenkel defects are responsible for the production of acceptor centers. Moreover, the fact that after the maximum the conductivity rises much more slowly than it decreased before the minimum suggests that the introduced acceptor centers are less effective in removing electrons from the valence band than they are in removing them from the conduction band. From an early experiment BRATTAIN and PEARSON [4] concluded that one acceptor center is created for every displaced atom. This followed from a comparison between the number of atomic displacements due to one α-particle in germanium, which was calculated by SEITZ, and the number of electrons which were experimentally found to be removed from the conduction band.

This picture is certainly oversimplified because it does not explain quantitatively the trend shown by conductivity in irradiated germanium and does not give any reason for the substantial difference in behavior between germanium and silicon.

The theory which was proposed by JAMES and LARK-HOROVITZ [5] assumes that vacancies introduce acceptor centers while interstitials introduce donor centers. What is to be explained is why the simultaneous effect of both donor and acceptor centers results in a predominating introduction of acceptors. We summarize briefly the arguments by JAMES and LARK-HOROVITZ concerning germanium; the case of silicon is different, the conductivity decreasing in both initially n- and p-type specimens, but the theory can be developed along conceptually similar lines.

They suggest that if one electron is removed from an interstitially situated germanium atom, it will remain bound in a localized state, the binding energy being 0.05 eV or thereabout. Consider now the Ge^{+} ion; if one electron is removed from it the electron will be attracted by the residual Ge^{++} ion with a much larger energy. The energy of second ionization of Ge is believed to be comparable in magnitude to the width of the forbidden band. The third and fourth ionization potentials are much larger, the corresponding levels being well within the filled band of the crystal. In equilibrium conditions they are filled and do not need to be considered. Consequently a germanium interstitial can be represented in terms of band structure by means of two levels lying below the conduction band, their distance from the bottom of it being equal to the first and second ionization energies. Such levels act as donors and the first one in particular can easily give up an electron to any low-lying trap within the forbidden band. A germanium vacancy, on the contrary, is supposed to introduce two acceptor levels. If a Ge^{++++} ion is removed from the lattice, the number of states in the lowest-energy filled band is reduced by four. Concerning the filled valence bands, their structure is perturbed due to the removal of four positive charges from the ion site. Such a large perturbation cannot be analysed accurately and only a few alternative situations can be envisaged. For instance, if four localized states are removed from the valence band, they remain occupied in the hypothesis of an adiabatic removal of the ion. The electronic density in proximity to the vacancy remains the same as before, but four holes are added to the filled band and are attracted to the vacancy, so that the electric neutrality of the crystal is preserved, and they are neutralized here by the electrons from the four localized states. These states will consequently become empty.

Not only a Ge^{++++}, but also four electron charges will be missing at the vacancy. An electron can be pushed into the vacancy (and a hole removed) with some expense of energy; the same operation can be repeated (and a second hole removed) with a much bigger expense of energy due to the Coulomb repulsion by the electrons. It is then almost impossible energetically to force a third and a fourth electron into the vacancy.

Speaking in terms of holes, a first and a second ionization energy for removal of holes from a vacancy are defined, but the third and fourth ionization energies are too big and therefore of no interest. A vacancy can be thought of as responsible for two energy levels which are located above the top of the valence band, their distances from it being equal to the above defined first and second ionization energies for holes. Both states are empty at low temperature and act as acceptor levels.

The final conclusion is that each Frenkel pair introduces two donor and two acceptor levels (see Fig. 3). Their efficiency in removing electrons from the conduction band depends on the position of the Fermi level within the crystal. If the Fermi level is above all four levels, each Frenkel defect removes

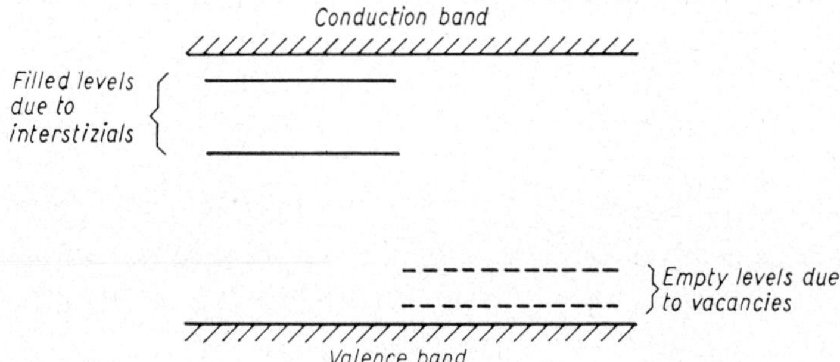

Fig. 3. – Levels introduced by irradiation in germanium, according to JAMES and LARK-HOROVITZ.

two conduction electrons from the crystal; if the Fermi level is between the second and the third level, the irradiation is almost ineffective; if the Fermi level is below all four levels, each Frenkel pair removes two holes from the crystal.

The above sketched model gives a qualitative agreement with experimental data, its basic idea being that each interstitial and each vacancy gives more than just one donor or acceptor level. Of course, the theory should be accepted with reservation, but no alternative and more satisfactory scheme has been put forward to date. In a recent paper, BLOUNT [6] proposed a somewhat different explanation, but it is hard to say whether it gives a better agreement with experimental results or not. Moreover, it should be recalled that the JAMES and LARK-HOROVITZ proposal is valid under the hypothesis that isolated vacancies and interstitials are present within the crystal. This is approximately true if the bombarding particles are electron or γ-rays but certainly a very poor approximation if heavier particles are used as projectiles.

The experimental search for levels introduced by radiation damage is performed with the help of different experimental methods: the rate of carrier removal can be studied in several specimens as a function of the location of Fermi level [7], changes in conductivity and Hall coefficient, can be observed at several temperatures [8], photoconductivity can be measured [9]. The first of these methods has been discussed in some detail in a paper by the author [10]: it is based on the fact that the number of carriers being removed from the conduction band by one impinging particle changes remarkably whenever the Fermi level in its shift during irradiation crosses one of the levels which are introduced within the forbidden band. Fig. 4 shows qualitatively the trend of experimental curves.

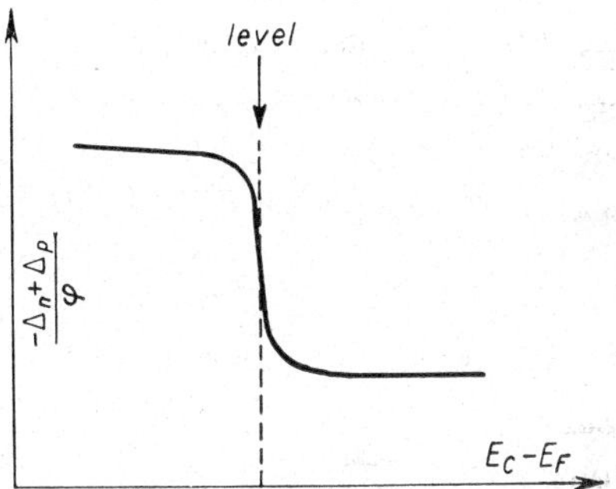

Fig. 4. – Typical results obtained in an investigation of levels introduced into semiconductors by irradiation.

A detailed discussion of levels being created by irradiation of silicon is given in a recent paper by KLEIN [11].

8. – Annealing experiments performed at several temperatures are a useful source of information about the nature of defects. Only a few data concerning semiconductors irradiated with monoenergetic electrons at room temperature will be considered here. It is expected that electrons give a rather uniform distribution of defects within the specimen. In such conditions an investigation of the annealing kinetics gives an interesting picture of the behavior of defects and, moreover, suggests reasonable values of migration energies of some defects. The physical situation is nevertheless more confused than it is in the case of metals: the features of annealing seem to depend also on the state of charge of defects and the simple direct annihilation of vacancy-interstitial pairs is complicated by impurity-lattice defects interactions.

Evidence for motion of defects has been found even at very low temperatures ($(30 \div 40)$ °K): about 50 % of the defects disappear in this range of temperature. We consider here simply Waite's interpretation [12, 13] of the annealing of germanium specimens after irradiation with 3 MeV electrons at room temperature.

An investigation of the fraction, f, of defects being annihilated at different temperatures, carried out by means of conductivity measurements, points out that two annealing states are present. In the lower temperature stage, which typically lasts a few minutes at 200 °C, f is proportional to the square root of annealing time; in the higher temperature stage, around 300 °C, defects obey a second order law.

The former stage is interpreted as due to preferential recombination of vacancies with their own interstitials. A satisfactory agreement with experimental curves is obtained if the interstitial-vacancy distance r_0 is supposed to be distributed according to a Gaussian law, the most probable r_0 being around a few Å. The theoretical result for $4Dt \ll (\lambda r_0)^2$, λ being near to unity, is

$$\frac{\mathrm{d}C_A}{\mathrm{d}t} = -\,4\pi r_0^2 D C_A^0 N \exp\left|-\frac{1}{\lambda^2}\right|\left(\frac{1}{\pi D t}\right)^{\frac{1}{2}},$$

which gives the above indicated $t^{\frac{1}{2}}$ law. C_A is the concentration of defects at time t, C_A^0 is the initial concentration of defects, D is the sum of the diffusion coefficients of both defects involved, N is the number of atoms in a unit volume.

After the disappearance of $(40 \div 50)$ % of defects according to this mechanism, the residual defects continue to annihilate each other but nonpreferentially. This gives rise to a second order process whose rate is controlled by diffusion of the most mobile defect. This type of recombination process predominates because the capture of defects at dislocations, owing to the low dislocation density, is negligible.

Similar results have been obtained by Airoldi *et al.* [14] with germanium specimens which were irradiated with 1.2 MeV electrons at room temperature. The density of carriers was obtained during annealing by means of conductivity and Hall coefficient measurements. In the range between 190 °C and 270 °C the second order process is controlled by an activation energy equal to 1.4 eV.

If this activation energy has any simple meaning, it should be identified with the migration energy of the most mobile defect. A comparison between the results of quenching experiments performed with germanium single crystals and the value of self-diffusion energy in germanium seems to suggest that the mobile defects are lattice vacancies; therefore 1.4 eV is expected to be the migration energy E_M of vacancies.

The self-diffusion energy in germanium is 3 eV according to LETAW *et al.* [15]. If self-diffusion involves single vacancies (this is accepted by most authors), we conclude that $E_F + E_M = 3$ eV, where E_F is the formation energy of vacancies which might be obtained from quenching experiments. In principle such measurements are quite interesting because only single vacancies are present at the equilibrium at high temperature. This, however, does not necessarily mean that the annealing mechanism reflects the behavior of single vacancies, because they could possibly congregate into more complex defects both during quenching and during annealing.

Several authors [16, 17] showed that quenching introduces acceptor levels into n-type germanium in a sufficient amount to cause its n-p conversion, and found E_F equal to about 2 eV. If this is combined with the result of self-diffusion measurements, it should be concluded that E_M is about 1 eV; this is approximately true according to the quoted annealing data.

It is not certain that these conclusions are correct. Actually, MAYBURG and LOGAN gave the same E_F value but the concentrations of vacancies which they found were different. Moreover the behavior of quenched specimens during annealing is different in the two cases; MAYBURG found complex kinetics and only a partial recovery, while LOGAN observed a more complete recovery. It may be that the quenching rate (larger in Logan's experiment) and the purities of the specimens are important.

HOPKINS and CLARKE [18] and Russian authors [19] performed similar experiments with special care in handling specimens as far as surface cleaning is concerned. They found much lower acceptor densities ((10÷100) times less). According to HOPKINS and CLARKE, most thermally-induced acceptors are due to copper impurities which diffuse very rapidly from the surface into the specimen; the subsequent recovery should be attributable at least partly to a redistribution of impurities through a precipitation process.

It is possible to conclude only that the quenching method has some disadvantages due to the extreme sensitivity of germanium to small amounts of some impurities and also because it is difficult to achieve fast quenching rates. Whatever the interpretation of quenching results, it is certain that a slow quenching makes clustering of defects and vacancy-impurity association easy. These effects are known to make the annealing kinetics complex in many materials.

REFERENCES

[1] G. A. BUSCH: *Suppl. Nuovo Cimento*, **7**, 698 (1958).
[2] See for instance: N. Y. FAN and A. K. RAMDAS: *Journ. Appl. Phys.*, **30**, 1127 (1959).
[3] J. J. LOFERSKI and P. RAPPAPORT: *Phys. Rev.*, **111**, 432 (1958).

[4] W. H. BRATTAIN and G. L. PEARSON: *Phys. Rev.*, **80**, 846 (1950).
[5] H. M. JAMES and K. LARK-HOROVITZ: *Zeits. Phys. Chem.*, **198**, 107 (1951).
[6] E. I. BLOUNT: *Journ. Appl. Phys.*, **30**, 1218 (1959).
[7] See for instance: N. Y. FAN and K. LARK-HOROVITZ: *Report of the Conference on Defects in Crystalline Solids* (Bristol, 1954), p. 232.
[8] See for instance J. W. CLELAND, J. H. CRAWFORD jr. and J. C. PIGG: *Phys. Rev.*, **98**, 1742 (1955).
[9] H. Y. FAN and K. LARK-HOROVITZ: *Irradiation Effects in Semiconductors*, in J. J. HARWOOD, H. H. HAUSNER, J. G. MORSE and W. G. RAUCH: *Effect of Radiation on Materials* (New York, 1958), p. 173.
[10] A. ASCOLI, M. ASDENTE and E. GERMAGNOLI: *Energia Nucleare*, **4**, 131 (1957).
[11] C. A. KLEIN: *Journ. Appl. Phys.*, **30**, 1222 (1959).
[12] T. R. WAITE: *Phys. Rev.*, **107**, 463 (1957).
[13] T. R. WAITE: *Phys. Rev.*, **107**, 471 (1957).
[14] G. AIROLDI, Z. FUHRMANN and E. GERMAGNOLI: *Nuovo Cimento*, **14**, 452 (1959).
[15] H. LETAW jr., W. PORTNOY and L. SLIFKIN: *Phys. Rev.*, **102**, 636 (1956).
[16] R. A. LOGAN: *Phys. Rev.*, **91**, 757 (1953); **101**, 1455 (1956).
[17] S. MAYBURG: *Phys. Rev.*, **91**, 1015 (1953); **95**, 38 (1954); **103**, 1130 (1956).
[18] R. L. HOPKINS and E. N. CLARKE: *Phys. Rev.*, **100**, 1786 (1955).
[19] V. G. ALEKSAEVA, B. N. ZOBNINA and I. V. KARPOVA: *Soviet Physics, Technical Physics*, **2**, 190 (1957).

Radiation Effects in Semiconductors.

J. H. CRAWFORD, Jr.

Oak Ridge National Laboratory, Solid State Division (*) - *Oak Ridge, Tenn.*

1. – Introduction.

The electrical properties of certain of the diamond lattice and zinc-blende semiconductors are among the most sensitive indices of radiation damage known. For example, as few as 10^{12} Frenkel defects per cm^3 can be detected with ease in high-purity Ge exposed to ^{60}Co γ-rays or electrons by means of changes in minority carrier lifetime, conductivity and Hall coefficient. The origin of this sensitivity, which has already been touched upon by GERMAGNOLI [1], lies in 1) the high purity of germanium, silicon and other semiconductors which is now possible, and 2) the fact that localized energy states of defects in these lattices can alter charge carrier concentrations through either donor or acceptor action. It is noted that, since the influence of added imperfections is felt only in the extrinsic or structure-sensitive range of behavior, the actual sensitivity depends on what degree the background contribution due to initial acceptor or donor impurity atoms can be reduced by purification techniques. Happily, zone refining methods have been capable of reducing the electrically active impurity content to less than one part in 10^{10} in both Ge and Si.

Radiation effects in semiconductors were first observed in 1947 by LARK-HOROVITZ, JOHNSON, and co-workers [2], who exposed Ge specimens to cyclotron particles (10 MeV deuterons) and fast neutrons in a nuclear reactor. Since that time much effort has been spent investigating radiation effects in a variety of elemental and compound semiconductors at a number of laboratories in

---

(*) Oak Ridge National Laboratory is operated by Union Carbide Corporation for the U. S. Atomic Energy Commission.

the U.S. and Europe [3]. Table I lists those materials which have received more than passing attention and the predominant effect of bombardment for each is indicated.

TABLE I.

Material	End result of irradiation
Ge	becomes p-type
Si	becomes intrinsic
InSb	becomes n-type (room temperature irradiation)
	becomes p-type (irradiation below 200 °K)
GaSb	becomes p-type
AlSb	becomes n-type
InAs	becomes n-type
CdTe	becomes n-type

The major aim of these studies is to obtain a quantitative description of the lattice damage sustained by these materials when exposed under various conditions to different types of energetic particles. Of almost equal importance to semiconductor physics is the inverse view, namely, the use of energetic radiation as a technique for the introduction of lattice defects in order that their properties might be studied in detail. Although much progress has been made, neither goal has been attained. The primary obstacles to a better understanding are: *a*) the lack of a good theoretical model for the energy levels of lattice defects, *b*) extensive interactions between defects and imperfections already present (impurity atoms and perhaps dislocations) which alter the energy-level structure of the defects both during and subsequent to bombardment, and *c*) relaxation of electronic effects (trapped minority carriers) after low-temperature irradiation which obscure relaxation processes involving the defects. The last two factors prevent unequivocal evaluation of low-temperature investigations of defect production and annealing which have been so fruitful in the study of metals [4].

In the following discussions I would like first to deal with the problem of defect energy states and their determination; secondly, to proceed to an examination of recent experimental results; and, finally, to summarize the present state of knowledge of radiation-induced disorder in diamond-lattice and zinc-blende structure semiconductors with particular attention to disordered regions expected to result from fast neutron bombardment. In view of the more complex defect structures possible in the binary III-V compounds and the smaller amount of experimental information on these structures, we shall restrict attention primarily to Ge and Si.

2. – Models of defect-energy level.

As mentioned above, a good quantitative theory of the electronic states of defects in germanium and silicon is not available. The only first-principle calculation for defects in covalent crystals that has been made is that by COULSON and KEARSELY [5] for vacancies in diamond. Unfortunately, it is not amenable to generalization for the materials of interest here. Therefore, at present one must be satisfied with more qualitative models based on more general arguments. Two such with quite different foundations have been proposed: one by JAMES and LARK-HOROVITZ [6] and one by BLOUNT [7]. We shall briefly consider each of these.

2·1. *The model of James and Lark-Horovitz.* – This description of defect states was devised to explain the observation that several energy levels were observed in irradiated Ge. Proceeding on the assumption that only isolated Frenkel defects were produced by bombardment, the interstitials and vacancies were examined separately. It was pointed out that in a crystal of high dielectric constant each component of the Frenkel pair might undergo multiple ionization. The interstitial was treated as a donor center which might successively lose two or even three electrons before the ionization energy exceeds the forbidden energy gap. In the hydrogenic approximation the ionization energy is

$$E_i = Z_i^2 E_{\mathrm{H}} M_e^* / \varkappa_{\mathrm{eff}}^2 , \tag{1}$$

where E_i is the i-th ionization energy, Z_i is the excess charge of the core after removal of the i-th electron, E_{H} is the ionization energy for the hydrogen atom (13.6 eV), M_e^* is the ratio of the effective mass of an electron in the conduction band to the electronic rest mass, and $\varkappa_{\mathrm{eff}}$ is the effective dielectric constant experienced by the i-th electron. An effective dielectric constant is required for all but the first ionization because the higher core charge reduces the orbit of the remaining electrons so that they do not experience the full dielectric constant of the lattice. Unfortunately, it is not possible to calculate $\varkappa_{\mathrm{eff}}$, and one can only obtain lower limits for the E_i's. Taking $M_e^* \simeq 0.2$ and $\varkappa = 16$, one obtains $E_1 = 0.01$ eV, $E_2 \simeq 0.4$ eV, and $E_3 \simeq 0.10$ eV, for the first, second, and third ionization energies respectively. E_2 and E_3 are expected to be considerably larger than these lower limits.

Alternatively, the vacancy was considered only as an acceptor, and it was concluded that two or perhaps three electrons could be placed into its incomplete orbitals before the energy required exceeded the band gap. This is not an unreasonable view, since three successive acceptor levels have been observed for copper impurity in both Ge and Si.

The situation just described may take the form as indicated schematically in Fig. 1. When interstitials and vacancies are present in equal concentration, there will be a redistribution of electrons over available sites as shown in

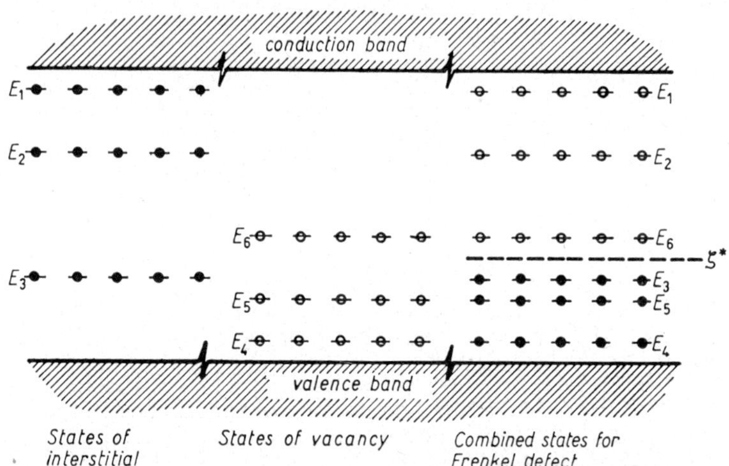

Fig. 1. – A schematic representation of the James-Lark-Horovitz energy-level model.

Fig. 1. Electrons from states associated with the 1-st or 2-nd ionizations of the interstitial will gravitate to the lower-lying vacant states of the vacancy, so that the role of the defects as acceptors or donors becomes reversed. The upper states of the interstitial, being empty, can remove electrons from the conduction band and the lower states of the vacancy, being occupied, can remove holes from the valence band. It is also evident from Fig. 1 that the net effect of Frenkel defect introduction depends sensitively on the spacing and distribution of the various defect states in the band gap. Whether the net effect is acceptor or donor action depends on the « center of gravity » of the levels or the limiting position of the Fermi level ζ^*. This point will be considered in more detail below.

In summary, it is seen that the James–Lark-Horovitz model provides for a number of defect states for a Frenkel pair. However, it is unable to give any quantitative information about either the total number or the positions of these energy levels in the band gap. Its main value lies in that it provides a basis for understanding the different behavior of different systems, *i.e.*, why n-type Ge, for example, can be converted to p-type, whereas both n- and p-type Si become intrinsic on bombardment.

2·2. *The model of Blount.* – Blount [7] has proposed a model to explain the observed energy-level structure of Ge and perhaps Si on the basis of properties of atomic and molecular orbitals He considers that both interstitials and vacancies may either gain or lose electrons depending on the position of the Fermi level ζ. Therefore, each component of the Frenkel pair may exhibit « amphoteric » action. The line of argument is as follows. The defects are treated as atomic systems with characteristic atomic orbitals. The s^2p^2 atomic orbitals require an energy δ for promotion into the sp^3 molecular orbitals necessary for binding in the diamond structure. Aside from δ, the atomic orbitals of the defects are expected to lie midway in energy between the bonding orbitals which form the valence band and the antibonding orbitals which give rise to the conduction band. The orbitals of the vacancy which are split-out of the valence band require demotion from sp^3 to s^2p^2, and these will have an energy $\Delta/2-\alpha\delta$ above the bonding orbitals (valence band) of the crystal. Δ is the energy separation between bonding and antibonding orbitals in the crystal, and α is an adjustment parameter slightly less than unity. Similar arguments applied to the interstitial place atomic orbitals associated with it an energy $\Delta/2+\beta\delta$ below the conduction band where again β is slightly less than unity.

An extra electron in the conduction band can lower its energy by falling into one of the orbitals of either the interstitial or the vacancy, the relative energy decrease being $(\Delta/2+\alpha\delta)$ and $(\Delta/2-\beta\delta)$, respectively. Similarly, the energy of an extra hole is lowered by localization in atomic orbitals by $(\Delta/2-\alpha\delta)$ for the vacancy and $(\Delta/2+\beta\delta)$. Hence each component of the Frenkel pair can act as either an acceptor or a donor. These energy values apply only to the relative energies of an electron or hole in the atomic orbitals of a given defect. In order to position these states within the forbidden energy gap, the problem must be solved for the entire crystal, which is an exceedingly difficult undertaking. However, BLOUNT has used arguments based on the band structure of Ge to show that the states associated with the vacancy lie lower in the band gap than the corresponding ones of the interstitial. Hence, in Ge a net acceptor action of Frenkel defects might be expected. It is interesting to note that in contrast to the James–Lark-Horovitz model, Blount's model does not predict multiply charged defects.

3. – Determination of defect-energy levels.

Before considering defect-energy level structures, it should be emphasized that, if a number of states arise from the multiple ionization of a defect, these do not have independent existence. Clearly, the state representing the second ionization of an interstitial is not available unless it is already singly ionized and, alternatively, the level representing single ionization is meaningless if the interstitial is already doubly ionized. Similar remarks apply to the vacancy. For most purposes, however, one may take advantage of the large energy separation (relative to kT) between levels of the same defect and treat them as independent states. This is possible because any one of a set of successive levels will not be statistically important unless the next adjacent ones are either essentially filled or empty. The problem of states of successive ionization has been treated by SHOCKLEY and LAST [8].

Let us now consider in more detail the « center of gravity » of defect states, or more precisely, the limiting position of the Fermi level ζ^* which determines the response of semiconductors to the introduction of lattice defects. By ζ^* we mean the value of ζ attained when the concentration of defects is much greater than the concentration of chemical donors or acceptors initially present. Consider a set of levels such as shown in Fig. 1. If all of these states are present in equal concentration as implied in the James–Lark-Horovitz model, to a good approximation ζ^* lies at the median position between the highest filled state (E_3) and the lowest empty one (E_6). The basis for this conclusion is the significance of ζ; namely, it is the energy at which the probability of occupancy of a nondegenerate quantum state is one-half (*), *i.e.* the probability of occupancy of a state ΔE above ζ is equal to the probability that a state ΔE below ζ will be vacant, provided the states have the same statistical weights. Therefore, if ζ^* lies in the upper half of the gap, the end result of bombardment is an n-type specimen with a limiting electron concentration of

$$n^* = N_C \exp[-(E_C - \zeta^*)/kT] \tag{2}$$

and for ζ^* in the lower half of the gap, a p-type specimen results, with

$$p^* = N_V \exp[-(\zeta^* - E_V)/kT]\,. \tag{3}$$

Here E_C and E_V are the positions of the edges of the conduction and valence bands respectively, $N_C = 2(2\pi m_e kT)^{\frac{3}{2}}/h^3$ and $N_V = 2(2\pi m_h kT)^{\frac{3}{2}}/h^3$. Therefore, one might expect that the carrier type and concentration after saturation would give information about levels such as E_3 and E_6. However, because of possible preferential annealing of one type of defect, one cannot be at all certain that the different levels are present in equal concentration, which is the requirement for this definition of ζ^*.

(*) Because of a change in spin degeneracy which may occur on ionization, this statement is not entirely general. For example, a donor with a statistical weight $w_i = 2$ because of spin orientation is converted to a nondegenerate center $w_f = 1$ on ionization. The Fermi-Dirac distribution function for occupation of this donor is

$$f = 1 + \gamma \exp[(E_D - \zeta)/kT]^{-1}\,,$$

where $\gamma = w_f/w_i = \frac{1}{2}$. Therefore, when $\zeta = E_D$, the probability of occupation is $\frac{2}{3}$. For most calculations γ is customarily taken as unity.

There is an alternative approach, namely the use of the initial rate of change of carrier concentration and its dependence on the initial Fermi level ζ^0, which avoids this difficulty to some extent. Clearly, for $\zeta^0 > \zeta^*$ a decrease in n (an increase in p) will occur, the reverse holding for $\zeta^0 < \zeta^*$. Moreover, the dependence of initial rate on ζ^0 can be functionally related to the positions of the two levels fixing ζ^* so that these levels can be located by fitting the data. Consider the situation in which ζ^* lies in the lower half of the band gap being fixed by states E_a and E_b ($E_a > E_b$) which are introduced in equal concentration by bombardment. It can be shown [9] that

$$\left(\frac{\mathrm{d}p}{\mathrm{d}N}\right)_{N=0} = \frac{p_a'}{p_0 + p_a'} - \frac{p_0}{p_0 + p_b'}, \tag{4}$$

where

$$p_i' = N_V \exp\left[-(E_i - E_V)/kT\right] \tag{5}$$

and p_0 is the initial hole concentration. An analysis [9] of this type has been performed for p-type Ge exposed to fast neutrons at 195 °K. The results are shown in Fig. 2, where the points are experimental and the curve is calculated

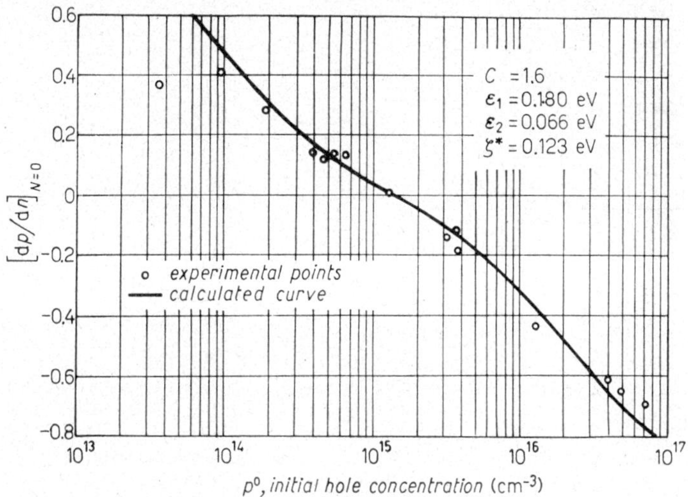

Fig. 2. – The initial rate of change of hole concentration *vs.* initial hole concentration for p-type Ge during fast-neutron bombardment at 195 °K (after CLELAND, CRAWFORD and PIGG, ref. [9]).

according to relation (4). The rate $(\mathrm{d}p/\mathrm{d}N)_{N=0}$ was related to the initial slopes of conductivity *vs.* bombardment curves by an assumed defect production rate per incident fast neutron $C = 1.6$ and the assumption that the mobility was not appreciably affected during the early part of the exposure. The best fit to the data yields the values $E_a - E_V = \varepsilon_1 = 0.18$ eV and $E_b - E_V = \varepsilon_2 = 0.066$ eV. It should be noted that these values are sensitive to the choice of C. More recent studies (see below) suggest that ε_1 lies nearer to 0.25 eV. In any event, ζ^*, which corresponds to the value of p_0 for which $(\mathrm{d}p/\mathrm{d}N)_{N=0} = 0$, is independent of C. The results of Fig. 2 give $\zeta^* = (0.123 \pm 0.003)$ eV. It is reassuring to note that initial slope determinations for room temperature irradiations yield the same value which would not occur unless the two states fixing ζ^* were present in the same concentration.

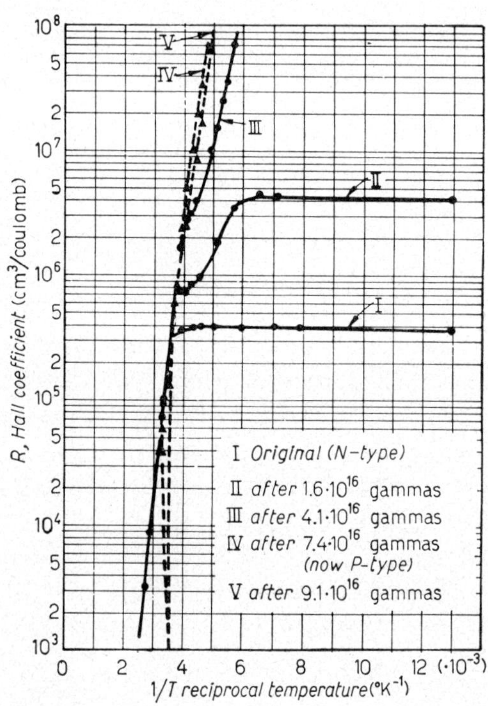

Fig. 3. – log Hall coefficient *vs.* reciprocal temperature for n-type Ge after successive exposures to ^{60}Co γ-rays (after CLELAND, CRAWFORD and HOLMES, ref. [10]).

There are somewhat more general methods of determining defect-energy levels. The one most extensively used is the temperature-dependence of the Hall coefficient. A typical [10] $\log R$ *vs.* $1/T$ curve for ^{60}Co γ-irradiated n-type Ge is shown in Fig. 3. After the first exposure (curve II) a step in the Hall curve centered near $5 \cdot 10^{-3}$ °K^{-1} indicates the presence of a vacant state in the upper half of the gap completely effective in removing electrons at lover temperatures and ionized at higher temperatures. In addition, a state or states much deeper in the gap which is effective in removing electrons up to temperatures at which the intrinsic process sets in can be observed. Comparison of the total decrease in n at low temperature with that at higher temperatures where the shallow state is empty reveals that the concentration of deep states is equal to that of the shallow level. This state of affairs is consistent with predictions of the James–Lark-Horovitz model and the Blount model provided interstitials and vacancies are present in equal concentration. On further exposure, essentially all of the conduction electrons are in equilibrium with the shallow vacant state (curve III) and the slope of this curve yields an ionization energy of $E_c - E_s \simeq 0.20$ eV. Further irradiation increases the concentration of deep states until this exceeds the initial electron concentration. The specimen has now been converted to p-type and the slope indicates that the deep acceptor state lies near a position 0.25 eV above the valence band. $\log R$ *vs.* $1/T$ curves have also given detailed information about the energy level structure in irradiated Si [11]. The $\log R$ *vs.* $1/T$ curves after several exposures [12] are shown in Fig. 4 for Si exposed to ^{60}Co γ-rays.

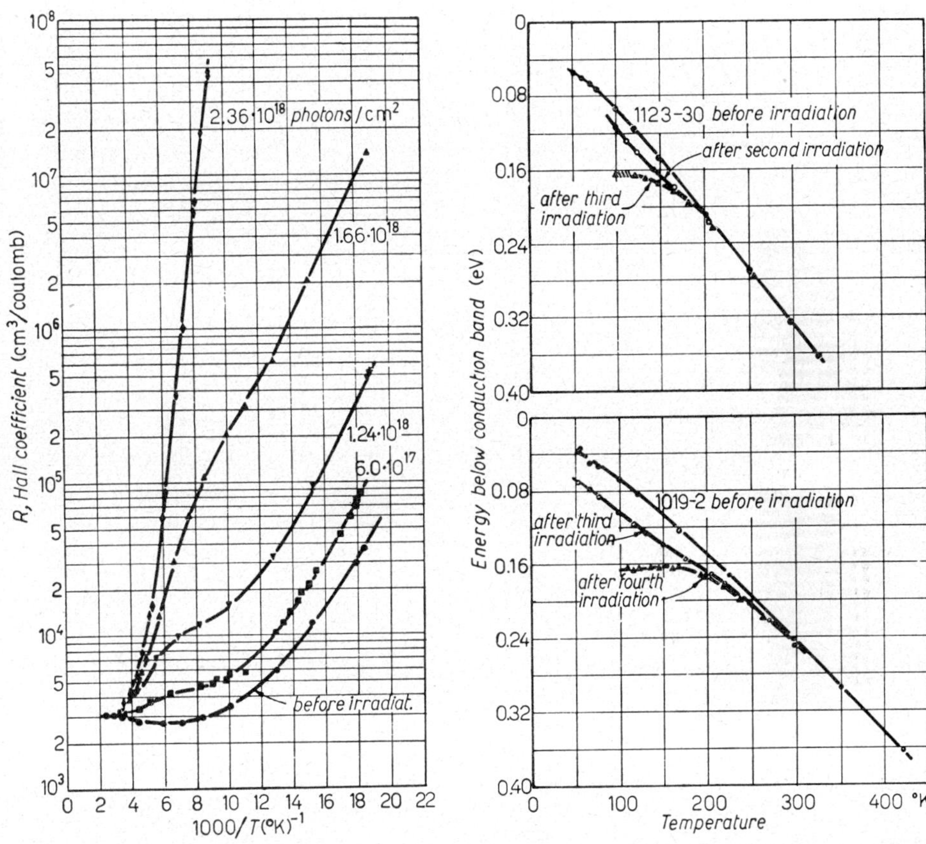

Fig. 4. – log Hall coefficient *vs.* reciprocal temperature for n-type Si after successive exposures to ^{60}Co γ-rays (after SONDER and TEMPLETON, ref. [12]).

Fig. 5. – Fermi level *vs.* temperature for the data of Fig. 4 (after SONDER and TEMPLETON, ref. [12]).

A Fermi level analysis of these data (Fig. 5) indicates the presence of a defect state at 0.17 eV.

The main drawback of $\log R$ *vs.* $1/T$ curves for locating energy levels is that one is restricted to a region well within the energy gap for readily accessible temperatures. FAN and LARK-HOROVITZ [13] have used a more general technique based on the rate of carrier concentration change during bombardment as a function of ζ. This method is based on the fact that the rate of electron removal will drop each time ζ is depressed through an acceptor level and the rate of hole removal will decrease when ζ is elevated through a donor level. In Ge they find a much enhanced removal rate for electrons and holes when ζ lies within 0.02 eV of the conduction band and valence band respectively. This suggests that the shallow states predicted by the James–Lark-Horovitz model (see Fig. 1) are indeed present in Ge. LONGO [14] has observed similar indications of shallow states in silicon using this method.

Another quite sensitive method is the temperature-dependence of minority carrier lifetime. This method requires that the energy level in question be a recombination center for excess electron-hole pairs. Moreover, it suffers the limitation that it gives the position of the level relative to a band edge and one cannot tell *a priori* whether this is in the upper half or lower half of the gap. However, from lifetime studies, CURTIS *et al.* [15] have observed the 0.20 eV state below the conduction band. Moreover, data obtained in p-type specimens indicate that multiple ionization of a given defect may indeed be occurring. WERTHEIM [16] has also determined the positions of two bombardment-produced levels in Si by means of this method.

Finally, optical detection of localized states deserves mention. For some reason not well understood the optical absorption spectrum of irradiated Ge shows no discrete band structure even though the spectral dependence of photoconductivity indicates the presence of localized defect levels [13]. In Si, on the other hand, certain of the defect states are readily detected by means of their optical absorption. FAN and RAMDAS [17] have made a study of the defect absorption bands in irradiated Si and find that several can be correlated with those detected by other means.

The various levels that have been located in Ge for different types of incident particles are summarized in Fig. 6. The absence of states near the band edges for neutron and ^{60}Co γ-ray bombardment does not mean that

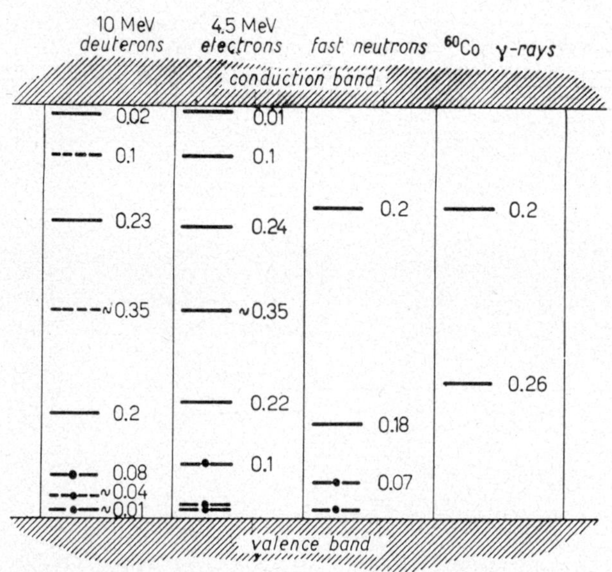

Fig. 6. – Defect energy levels that have been detected in bombarded Ge for various incident particles.

levels do not exist here but only that these portions of the band gap were not probed for these radiations.

A similar summary for irradiated Si is given in Table II. The second column indicates the character of the state, *i.e.* whether it is vacant (acceptor) or occupied (donor) after the redistribution of charge. The third column lists

TABLE II. – *Defect energy levels in silicon.*

Level location (eV)	Character of state	Irradiation employed	References
$E_C - 0.025$	A	4.5 MeV electrons 10 MeV deuterons	[14]
$E_C - 0.17$	A	4.5 MeV elec., 0.7 MeV elec., neutrons, ^{60}Co γ-rays	[11], [12], [14], [16]
$\sim E_C - 0.40$	A	4.5 MeV elec., neutrons, ^{60}Co γ-rays	[11], [18], [19]
$E_V + 0.30$	D	0.7 MeV electrons, neutrons	[11], [16], [18]
$E_V + 0.16$	D	neutrons	[11]
$E_V + 0.055$	D	4.5 MeV elec., 10 MeV deuterons, neutrons	[11], [14], [20]

A = acceptor state; D = donor state.

those radiations by means of which the levels were introduced and the final column lists the principal pertinent references.

Studies of irradiated III-V compound semiconductors are somewhat more scanty. Therefore, the energy level structures of these materials are not well documented. The available results for these and other compound semiconductors have been recently reviewed by AUKERMAN [21].

4. – Recent experimental results.

Thus far we have only presented possible models for the electronic structure of defects and summarized those energy level structures experimentally determined without attempting to justify the models or identify the defects responsible for the different observed energy levels. In this section, recent experimental results which have bearing on the identification of defects will be examined and their implications with regard to the choice of model will be discussed. For reasons which will become apparent in the next section, we shall confine our attention here primarily to electron and ^{60}Co γ-ray exposures.

Consider first the defect states in the upper half of the band gap of Ge. The 0.20 (0.23) eV state has been identified in the past with the first ionization state of the interstitial [10, 22]. In view of the very shallow state 0.02 eV below the conduction band [13] and the predictions of the James-Lark-Horovitz model, the second ionization state seems to be a better identification if the 0.20 eV state is indeed associated with the interstitial. This interpretation that the 0.70 eV state is associated with the interstitial is based on an interesting annealing behavior of the 0.20 eV state. It is found [23] that a mild anneal at 100 °C is able to remove almost completely this state and at the same time cause only a small reduction in the total number of electrons removed at low temperature for a number of specimens. This behavior is shown in Fig. 7, where it is evident that the step in $\log R$ *vs.* $1/T$ curve (curve II) caused by the 0.2 eV state is eliminated, this state apparently being replaced by one much deeper in the band gap. This behavior was explained on the framework of the James–Lark-Horovitz model. The interstitial, which is expected to be the most mobile component of the Frenkel pair, apparently migrates to and is annihilated at a dislocation jog or some other sink more readily than recombining with a vacancy. Removal of the interstitial also removes electrons which it had previously lost to lower vacant states of a vacancy. Hence, the removal of the interstitial and its 0.20 eV state makes a deeper state available for electron removal. The fact that this behavior was not

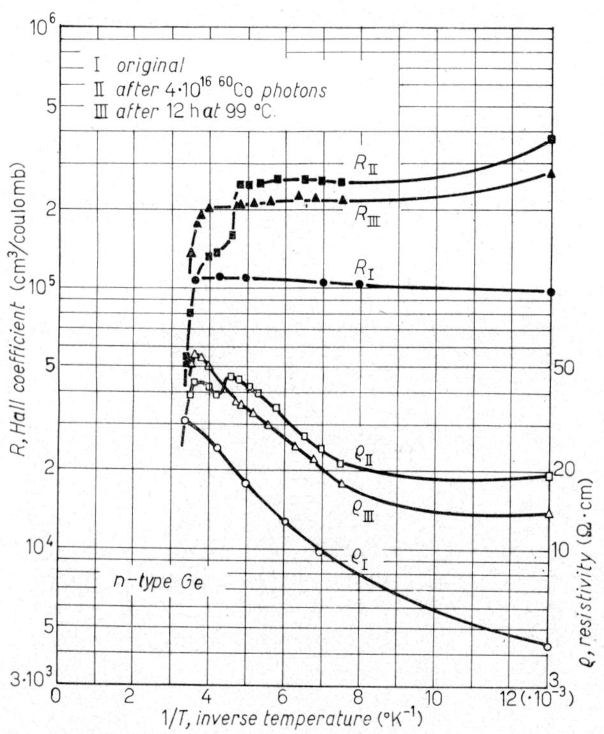

Fig. 7. – Effect of 100 °C annealing on the temperature dependence of the Hall coefficient of n-type Ge after exposure to ^{60}Co γ-rays (after CRAWFORD, ref. [21]).

shown by all specimens was attributed to the absence of a sufficient quantity of interstitial sinks.

This identification of the 0.20 eV state suggests that the responsible defect would bear a positive charge (one or two units, depending on whether it is the first or second ionization state) when empty, and this charge would be reduced by one unit when the state is filled. Mobility studies do not support this view [23]. Since an increase or decrease in the concentration of charged centers should be reflected in the ionized-center scattering, a decrease in mobility when the 0.20 eV state becomes occupied is expected. The curves [24] of Hall mobility μ_H *vs.* temperature after successive γ-ray exposures of Fig. 8

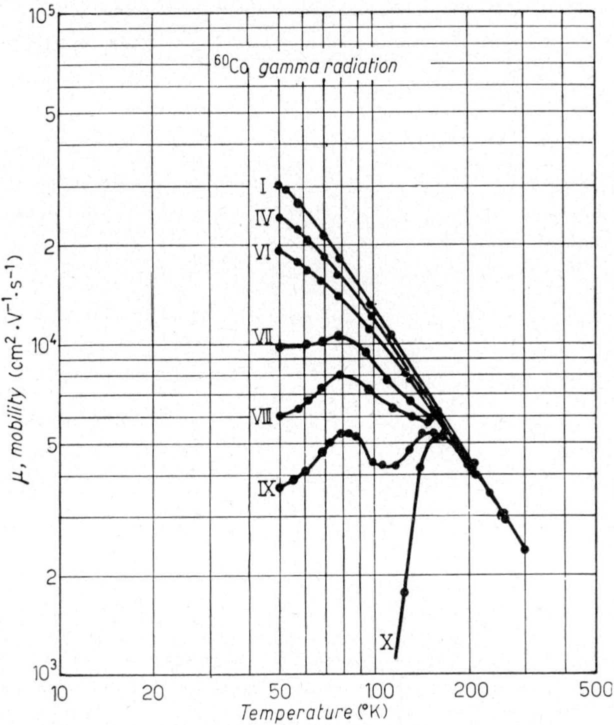

Fig. 8. – The temperature dependence of Hall mobility in n-type Ge after successive exposures to ^{60}Co γ-rays (after CLELAND and CONNELL, ref. [24]).

show that this is not the case. Indeed, the reverse is true. For the specimen in question, the 0.20 eV state begins to fill at an appreciable rate as the temperature drops below 180 °K, and in this temperature range the μ_H curves after irradiation show a significant drop below the curve for the unirradiated specimen. Hence, one must conclude that occupancy of the 0.20 eV state causes it to become negatively charged.

This is expected only if the 0.2 eV state can be described as associated with a vacancy in the James–Lark-Horovitz model, which is the interpretation given by FAN and LARK-HOROVITZ [13], or if it is an amphoteric state such as proposed in Blount's model [7]. However, assigning it to the vacancy would require the vacancy to be mobile near 100 °C to explain the annealing behavior of Fig. 7. There is another inconsistency, namely, the absence of appreciable ionized impurity scattering above 180 °K (Fig. 8); certainly, multiply charged defects, which scatter proportionally to the square of the charge, should have some influence in this temperature range, even though the cross-section for charge-center scattering is proportional to $T^{-\frac{3}{2}}$.

There is a way out of this dilemma. WERTHEIM [16], in his studies of carrier recombination and mobility in electron-bombarded Si, pointed out that an interstitial will not be driven more than a few atomic distances away from its parent vacancy during a primary collision with an incident electron for most energy transfers. These two defects might be oppositely charged but, provided their spacing is not greater than the wavelength of an electron (~ 50 Å), the electron will only see a dipole, which is not an efficient scatterer. Should the interstitial in such a pair now capture an electron, the overall charge of the composite center will increase by one negative unit and scattering can occur. This may well be the explanation of the discrepancy noted above and would permit the original identification to stand.

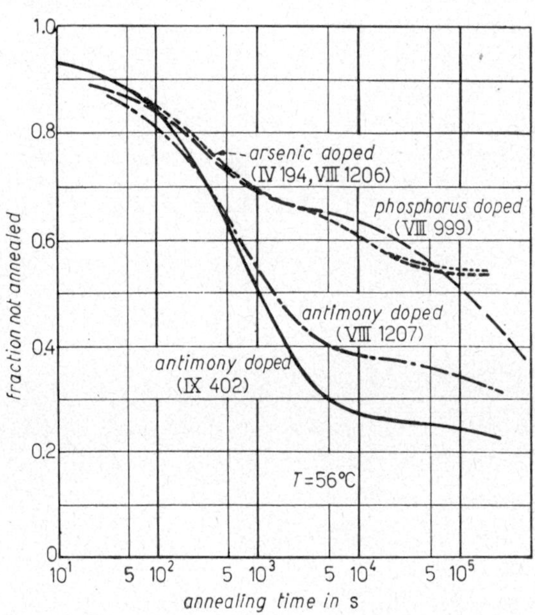

Fig. 9. – Isothermal recovery curves for the change of conductivity in n-type Ge bombarded with 0.5 MeV electrons at 79 °K. Curves for different donor impurities are shown (after BROWN *et al.*, ref. [25]).

BROWN and co-workers [25] have carefully investigated the annealing behavior of germanium bombarded with 0.5 MeV electrons at 79 °K. Aside from a minor annealing stage associated with the disappearance of minority carrier traps which occurs near 100 °K, essentially all of the annealing in n-type specimens occurs in the room temperature range or above. Since the extensive annealing, presumably due to close interstitial-vacancy pair recombination, observed in specimens exposed to electrons near 10 °K has occurred well below 79 °K, one may conclude that the damage introduced at liquid nitrogen temperature is relatively stable. The annealing above room temperature exhibited an unexpected impurity-dependence. The annealing behavior at 56 °C for several specimens doped to the same initial level ($\sim 10^{15}$ cm^{-3}) with different donor impurity is shown in Fig. 9. Antimony-doped specimens show a much more rapid recovery than do specimens containing arsenic or phosporous. All specimens indicate recovery by at least two stages, an initial rapid stage followed by a much slower stage (or stages). In the arsenic- and phosphorous-doped specimens the initial recovery stage is suppressed and the second one becomes dominant. One can understand this behavior on the basis of the trapping of a mobile defect by an impurity atom. Moreover, the trapping process must require more than a simple Coulomb interaction, since the different donors exhibit a different effect. The annealing of the Hall mobilities also shows significant differences, depending on the donor impurity. In antimony-doped specimens irradiated at 79 °K, both n and μ_H recover together, retracing to a good approximation their relative values during bombardment. On the other hand, in arsenic-doped specimens μ_H recovers almost completely to its γ-unirradiated value, while only about one-third of the decrease in n is restored. This behavior is shown in Fig. 10. Once again this suggests pairing between a mobile defect and an impurity atom, such that the total scattering charge is decreased but the number of vacant states for removal of electrons from the conduction band remains the same. Another interesting observation from these mobility studies can be made. The decrease of μ_H with acceptor introduction during low temperature bombardment is almost exactly what would be expected for the introduction of single-charged scattering centers rather than the multiply charged defects predicted by the James–Lark-Horovitz model.

Let us now return to the key problem raised by these annealing studies. The form of the annealing curves (Fig. 9) suggests that the first stage may be due to interstitial-vacancy recombination. It is not a first-order process, and it occurs with an activation energy of 0.8 eV. On the other hand, the second stage appears to proceed with a much higher activation energy and is drastically influenced by the type of donor impurity in the crystal. Consider various trapping processes. First, because of the specificity of the donor impurity, it is evident that the nature of binding must be other than Coulombic interaction. Secondly, the nearly complete recovery of μ_H during the anneal for As-doped specimens (Fig. 10) indicates that the defect being trapped was initially negatively charged when occupied. Moreover, the mobility data suggest that no multi-charged defects are introduced. One further point of evidence concerning the defect-donor pair comes from minority lifetime studies. CURTIS [26] finds that on annealing ^{60}Co γ-irradiated specimens the shallow recombination center, presumably due to the 0.20 eV state, is converted into one 0.3 to 0.35 eV from a band edge, and, moreover, that this behavior is much more pronounced for arsenic-doped specimens. This suggests that those specimens for which a similar conversion was observed in the $\log R$ *vs.* $1/T$ curves (Fig. 7) may have contained arsenic or perhaps phosphorus.

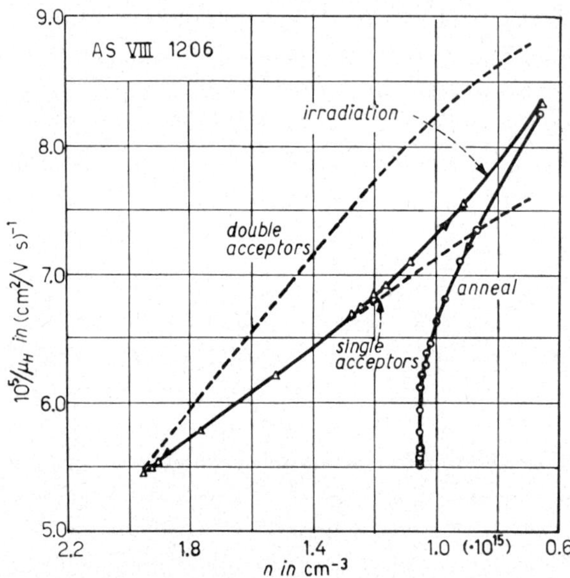

Fig. 10. – Comparison of the recovery of Hall mobility and electron concentration during the annealing of an arsenic-doped n-type Ge specimen subsequent to 0.5 MeV electron bombardment at 79 °K (after BROWN *et al.*, ref. [25]).

How can these points of evidence be resolved on the basis of existing models of defect-energy level structures? In order for these facts to conform to the James–Lark-Horovitz model, not only must the vacancy be responsible for the 0.20 eV state but it must also be the mobile defect in the annealing range considered above, *i.e.*, in the range from 40 to 100 °C. Moreover, to account for the observed decrease in μ_H during bombardment (Figs. 8 and 10) the vacancy must either bear a single negative charge or be located near a positively charged interstitial as suggested by WERTHEIM [16]. On the other hand, Blount's model, which predicts that both vacancies and interstitials are negatively charged when ζ is near the conduction band and which requires no multi-charged defects, seems to fit the observed behavior without extensive modification. The main advantage of this model is the fact that the interstitial can be the mobile entity. The reason for stressing this point is that measurements of self-diffusion [27] in Ge, which presumably occurs by a vacancy mechanism, together with quenching studies [28], suggest that the activation energy of motion of a vacancy is ~ 1 eV and, therefore, the vacancy should be quite immobile in the temperature range in question. However, the Blount model cannot account for the other defect states observed in Ge (Fig. 6) in terms of simple defects, whereas the James–Lark-Horovitz model can. For this reason, one is reluctant to discard the J-L-H model.

Recent investigation of defects in Si by BEMSKI [29] and WATKINS and co-workers [30] by electron-spin-resonance techniques strongly suggest that vacancies are mobile in the diamond lattice at room temperature and below. Two prominent defect states in irradiated Si have been identified with composite defects containing a vacancy and an impurity atom. The state 0.17 eV below the conduction band (see Figs. 4 and 5) appears to be associated with a vacancy which has come to rest near an oxygen atom bound interstitially in the lattice. This center is strongly developed in crystals produced by the usual growth technique (quartz crucible) and which contain $\sim 10^{18}$ oxygen atoms/cm³ but is not observed in floating-zone Si crystals which contain only a small concentration of oxygen impurity. The model for the center [29, 30] as determined from the anisotropy of the ESR signal and polarized optical absorption studies in the infrared is shown in Fig. 11. The second center which

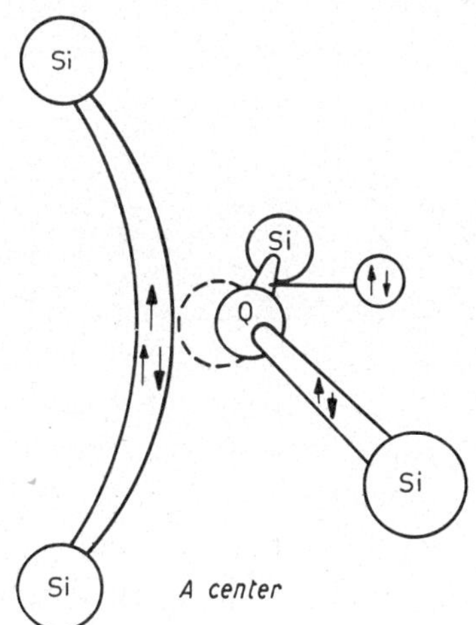

Fig. 11. – A model of the vacancy-oxygen center in irradiated Si as indicated by electron-spin resonance studies (after WATKINS *et al.*, ref. [30]).

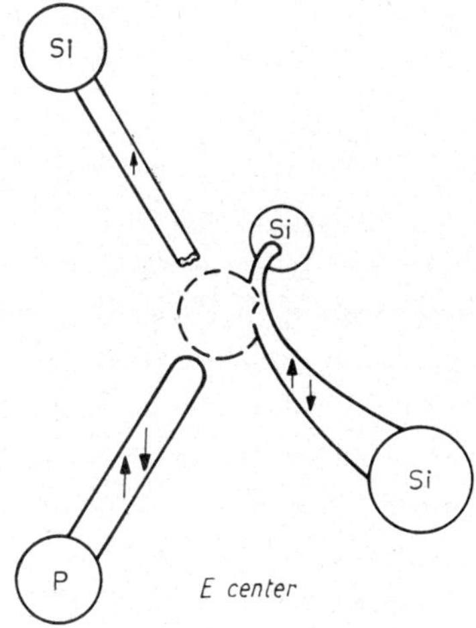

Fig. 12. – A model of the vacancy-phosphorus center in irradiated Si as indicated by electron-spin resonance studies (after WATKINS *et al.*, ref. [30]).

has been investigated by WATKINS and co-workers [30] is interpreted as a vacancy trapped adjacent to a phosphorus donor. This center is evidently the one responsible for the electron trapping state ~ 0.4 eV below the conduction band. The model for this composite defect as indicated by the g-tensor of the ESR absorption is shown in Fig. 12.

This excellent application of ESR techniques is unfortunately not possible in Ge, which for some reason does not give clearly resolved defect resonances. However, by analogy one might argue that, because of the similar crystal structure, vacancies might also be mobile in the Ge lattice and that the defect-impurity atom pairs indicated by the work of BROWN *et al.* [25] may be similar in nature to the vacancy-phosphorus center observed by WATKINS *et al.* [30]. If this is true, one may be able to retain the advantageous features of the James–Lark-Horovitz model. On the other hand, the difficulty of explaining the low motion energy of vacancies remains. It may be that the ionization state of the vacancy has an important influence on the activation energy of motion and that in the room temperature range this is quite different from the state of ionization in the temperature range where diffusion studies are conducted.

Annealing studies in p-type Ge have also been carried out [25]. These are complicated to a considerable degree by minority-carrier trapping centers which dominate the picture after exposure to electrons at 78 °K and which anneal in the interval between 78 °K and room temperature. The residual lattice damage anneals at a much higher temperature and with a greater activation energy (2.1 eV *vs.* 0.8 eV) than that in n-type specimens. Once again it appears that the ionization state of the defects which depends on the position of ζ is an important parameter in the recovery kinetics [13, 25]. Space does not permit a detailed discussion of the effects in neutron-bombarded p-type Ge. However, it appears that here it is even more difficult to reconcile experimental observation with energy-level models.

In summary, it appears that the existing models of defect-energy levels cannot account for the experimental results observed in Ge without considerable qualification. Moreover, interactions between defects and impurity atoms seem to play an important role in determining the response of Ge to bombardment in the room temperature range. Finally, since most of the observations on n-type Ge can be explained in terms of the behavior of the vacancy, one is left with the problem of the energy states and annealing behavior of the interstitial. On the whole we must conclude that our understanding of the electronic structure of defects in diamond-lattice semiconductors is not highly satisfactory.

5. – Disordered regions in neutron-bombarded semiconductors.

We now turn to quite a different aspect of the topic. Rather than considering effects due to isolated defects or pairs of imperfections, we shall examine the consequences of large local fluctuations in the concentration of lattice defects, such as might be encountered in fast-neutron bombardment. In earlier lectures it was shown that energetic recoils produced when a fast neutron collides with a lattice atom may have ranges as great as 100 to 200 Å in the lattice of the solid [31]. Since much of its energy is lost in creating secondary displacements, the linear dimensions of the affected region cannot be much greater, if as great, as the range of the primary. The concentration of defects in such a disordered region is expected to be quite high (the order of 0.1 to 1 per cent), provided recombination of defects is not extensive. Therefore, in a diamond-lattice semiconductor such as Ge one might expect the damage distribution to be characterized by highly disordered regions 100 to 200 Å in radius caused by the more energetic recoils, superposed on a more or less uniform background of isolated defects or small clusters produced by smaller energy transfers. Such an inhomogeneous defect distribution would have little effect on the changes in resistivity of metal because of the short wavelength of electrons at the top of the Fermi distribution. However, this is not the case for electrons in semiconductors, since potential fluctuations associated with the charged defects could have extensive consequences for the patterns of current flow.

We shall consider here a rather extreme case of potential fluctuations induced by disordered regions, namely neutron-bombarded n-type Ge, which has been treated by GOSSICK [32] and CLELAND and CRAWFORD [33]. Since the net effect of Frenkel defects in Ge is acceptor action, disordered regions will behave as p-type material imbedded in an n-type matrix and will be surrounded by a space-charge region (p-n junction) whose radial extent will depend principally on the concentration of electrons in the matrix. For a concentration of acceptors N_1 in the disordered region (radius $= r_1$) which is very much larger than the concentration of acceptors N_2 in the matrix, solution of Poissons' equation, under the assumption of spherical regions and neglecting the contribution of free carriers to the charge density, shows that essentially all of the potential drop occurs outside of the disordered region. Moreover, the total volume (assumed spherical) affected by the space charge is to a good approximation:

$$V_{sc} = 4\pi r_2^3/3 = \psi_p \varepsilon r_1/qN_2 , \tag{6}$$

where r_2 is the radius of the outer boundary of the space-charge zone, ψ_p the potential drop from the center of the disordered region to the matrix at point r_2, ε the dielectric constant, and q the absolute value of the electronic charge. For reasonably high purity Ge ($10^{13} \leqslant N_2 \leqslant 10^{15}$), r_2 is one to two orders of magnitude greater than r_1. The value of ψ_p is given by the differences in ζ within and without the disordered region, *i.e.*

$$\psi_p = \frac{1}{q}(\zeta_2 - \zeta_1) , \tag{7}$$

since this is the potential required to adjust the electrochemical potentials in the two regions to the same value. The defect level structure in the disordered region may be taken account of by setting $\zeta_1 = \zeta^* = (E_V + 0.123 \text{ eV})$ as discussed above. It can be shown that there is a critical value of r_1 below which not all of ψ_p will appear across the junction; rather, the potential gradient will extend through the disordered region. This critical radius, for $N_1^{\frac{1}{3}} \approx N_2^{\frac{1}{3}}$, turns out to be approximately

$$r_1\,(\text{crit}) \simeq (\varepsilon\psi_p/2\pi q N_1)^{\frac{1}{2}}\,. \tag{8}$$

Hence, for typical values of $\psi_p = 0.4$ V and $N_1 = 10^{19}$ cm^{-3}, $r_1\,(\text{crit}) \simeq 80$ Å. As the size of the disordered region decreases below r_1 (crit), there is a rapid decrease in both the radial r_2 extent of the space charge and the magnitude of the potential fluctuation. Large and small disordered regions are compared

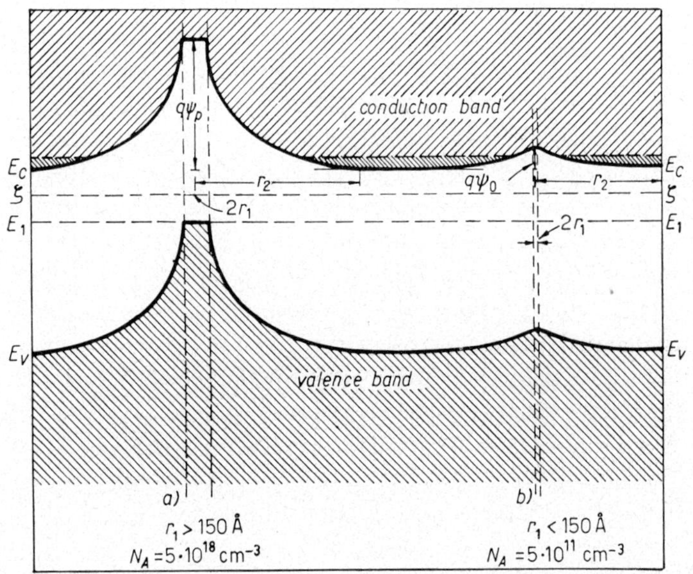

Fig. 13. – Schematic diagram of the space-charge zone for (*a*) a large disordered region and (*b*) one below the critical size (after CRAWFORD and CLELAND, ref. [33]).

schematically in Fig. 13. This behavior permits one to partition the damage into large disordered regions with an associated space charge and more or less isolated defects or small clusters.

Let us now consider the consequences of space-charge zones for the electrical behavior of n-type Ge. The region of the space charge is essentially a Schottky exhaustion region, *i.e.*, it has been denuded of conduction electrons by the electrostatic potential as shown in Fig. 13. Such regions should act as insulating voids for d.c. conductivity measurements. JURETSCHKE *et al.* [34] have shown that the measured conductivity σ_M of a crystal containing spherical voids is given by

$$\sigma_M = \sigma(1 - f)/(1 + f/2)\,, \tag{9}$$

where σ is the conductivity of the matrix and f is the fraction of the crystal occupied by voids. Hence, one expects fast-neutron bombardment to decrease the observed conductivity through the blocking of current by such space-charge zones as well as by a decrease of electron concentration caused by the isolated defects. For disordered region concentrations sufficiently small so that overlap of space-charge zones does not occur, we may define f as

$$f = \bar{v}_{sc} \Sigma_V \varphi_d t\,, \tag{10}$$

where $\bar{v}_{sc}$ is the average volume affected by space charge, Σ_V is the probability that an incident fast neutron creates a primary recoil sufficiently energetic to cause a disordered region, and $\varphi_d t$ is the integrated fast neutron flux.

The relative contributions of isolated defects and disordered regions to the decrease in σ_M are clearly quite sensitive to the energy spectrum of the bombarding neutrons. For a monoenergetic neutron source in the MeV range, the dominant effect would be the production of disordered regions. However, for a reactor spectrum in which the energies of neutrons capable of displacing atoms extend from a few kilovolts into the fission energy range (~ 2 MeV), isolated defects and defect clusters too small to form space-charge zones will be quite important. Recently, the energy spectrum of a facility in the Oak Ridge Graphite Reactor, a neutron converter employing a cylinder of enriched ^{235}U, has been probed. It was found by means of threshold detectors that the flux of neutrons with energy greater than 0.7 MeV was $\sim 2.7 \cdot 10^{11}$ cm^{-2} s^{-1}, whereas the total flux capable of producing damage has been estimated as $\sim 8 \cdot 10^{11}$ cm^{-2} s^{-1}. By happy accident, 0.7 MeV is the neutron energy which imparts 19 keV average recoil energy to a Ge atom, and consideration of the range of primaries as treated by HOLMES and LEIBFRIED [36] suggests that ~ 20 keV is not an unreasonable estimate of the energy needed for the primary to create a disordered region large enough to sustain a space-charge zone in the sense used in this discussion. Therefore, one may use this information to obtain a rough partition of the lattice damage into disordered regions and more or less isolated defects.

In earlier investigations [22] the entire conductivity decrease was attributed to removal of conduction electrons in the amount 3.2 electrons removed per incident fast neutron. The derivative of eq. (9) with respect to flux evaluated for initial behavior ($\varphi_d = 0$) is

$$[\mathrm{d}\sigma_M/\mathrm{d}\varphi_d]_{\varphi_d=0} = [\mathrm{d}\sigma/\mathrm{d}\varphi_d]_{\varphi_d=0} - \tfrac{3}{2}\sigma_0[\mathrm{d}f/\mathrm{d}\varphi_d]_{\varphi_d=0}\,. \tag{11}$$

Neglecting any small variation in electron mobility μ_n,

$$(12)\qquad [d\sigma/d\varphi_d]_{\varphi_d=0} = -\, q\mu_n[dn/d\varphi_d]_{\varphi_d=0} = -\, q\mu_n A\Sigma_d\,,$$

where A is the number of electrons removed per Frenkel defect and Σ_d is the probability per cm path of the neutron that a defect will be produced. Also, from eqs. (6) and (10)

$$(13)\qquad [df/d\varphi_d]_{\varphi_d=0} = \bar{v}_{sc}\Sigma_V = \psi_p\bar{r}_1\varepsilon\Sigma_V/2q\,,$$

where Σ_V is the probability that a disordered region will be produced.

Therefore, using $\sigma = q\mu_n n$, one has

$$(14)\qquad [dn_M/d\varphi_d]_{\varphi_d=0} = -\,[A\Sigma_d + 3\psi_p\bar{r}_1\varepsilon\Sigma_V/2q]\,,$$

which is the expression for the *apparent* electron removal rate. Σ_d and Σ_V may be placed on a relative basis by employing $\Sigma_s(=\sigma_s N_A)$, the macroscopic neutron scattering cross-section. Strictly, the microscopic cross-section σ_s is energy-dependent, but its variation over the range of interest is not great. We therefore assume it constant at $4\cdot10^{-24}$ cm^2, which gives $\Sigma_s = 0.18$ cm^{-1}. We now define $W_d = \Sigma_d/\Sigma_s$ and $W_V = \Sigma_V/\Sigma_s$. Since we assume every collision of a neutron with energy > 0.7 MeV leads to a disordered region of mean radius $\bar{r}_1$, $W_V = \varphi(E_n > 0.7)/\varphi_d$. This, together with eq. (14), may be used to find W_d; as used here W_d is the probability that a neutron of energy < 0.7 MeV will make a defect on colliding with a lattice atom multiplied by the average number of defects per collision.

For an n-type specimen with $n_0 = N_2 = 10^{14}$ electrons per cm^3, it can be shown that $\psi_p = 0.24$ V. If we take $\bar{r}_1 = 100$ Å and $[dn_M/d\varphi_d]_{\varphi_d=0} = 3.2$ per incident neutron, it can be shown that $AW_d = 4.5$, compared to $\bar{v}_{sc}W_V N_2 = 13.5$. Therefore, for this relatively arbitrary choice of $\bar{r}_1$ and the criterion used for partitioning the damage into isolated defects and disordered regions, the contribution of isolated defects to the decrease of σ_M is only one-third of that due to disordered regions. This model has also been applied to the monoenergetic neutron bombardment experiments of RUBY *et al.* [37]. They found that the apparent electron removal rates for 1.8, 3.2 and 4.8 MeV neutrons at 78 °K were 21, 12 and 12 per incident neutron, respectively. In the analysis we assume that all collisions produce disordered regions. At this temperature, their specimens are expected to have a $\psi_p = 0.58$ V. Hence, from eq. (14) using only the second term in the brackets and taking $\bar{r}_1 = 100$ Å one obtains an apparent electron removal rate of 17 per incident neutron, which is considered quite reasonable agreement with experiment [38].

These two correlations obviously are not sufficient evidence upon which to establish the validity of the model. They only show that the results of using such a model are not unreasonable. A more extensive test is afforded by the effect of bombardment on the Hall mobility. According to JURETSCHKE *et al.* [34]

$$\mu_H(M) = \mu_H(1 - f/4)/(1 + f/2)\,. \tag{15}$$

Writing $M = \mu_H(M)/\mu_H$, the initial variation with bombardment is

$$[\mathrm{d}M/\mathrm{d}\varphi_d]_{\varphi_d=0} = 3\psi_p\bar{r}_1\varepsilon\Sigma_V/4qN_2\,. \tag{16}$$

In deriving (16), as in (12), it is assumed that μ_H of the matrix is not appreciably affected during the early part of the bombardment. Employing the same criterion as above, namely that only neutrons of energy > 0.7 MeV produce disordered regions, eq. (16) when applied to the observed mobility change for a specimen with $N_2 = 1.3\cdot10^{14}\ \mathrm{cm}^{-3}$ yields $\bar{r}_1 = 120$ Å. This suggests that the choice of $\bar{r}_1 = 100$ Å used in the above correlations was a very good one.

As an alternative test we may use the temperature-dependence of M. This comes about because of the temperature-dependence of ψ_p. For small f

$$\mathrm{d}M/\mathrm{d}T \simeq (3\varepsilon\bar{r}_1\Sigma_V\varphi t/qN_2)(\mathrm{d}\psi_p/\mathrm{d}T)\,. \tag{17}$$

It can be shown that

$$\mathrm{d}\psi_p/\mathrm{d}T \simeq \frac{1}{q}\{\mathrm{d}E_g/\mathrm{d}T - k[\ln N_C/N_2 + \tfrac{3}{2}]\}\,, \tag{18}$$

where the band gap $E_g = 0.785 - 4.4\cdot10^{-4}T$ for Ge [39]. Eq. (17) cannot be used effectively at low temperatures because the assumption that μ_H of the matrix is not appreciably affected by bombardment is not valid below ~ 200 °K for most specimens studied. One series of irradiations on a specimen with $n_0 = 1.6\cdot10^{15}\ \mathrm{cm}^{-3}$ has been analysed according to (17) and $\bar{r}_1$ evaluated. For exposures of $1.4\cdot10^{14}$ and $2.8\cdot10^{14}$ fast neutrons per cm², the values of $\bar{r}_1$ were found to be 170 Å and 140 Å. In view of the contribution of ionized impurity scattering at the low temperature, which tends to increase $\mathrm{d}M/\mathrm{d}T$, this is considered to be good agreement with the value 120 Å found above.

The tests of the disordered region model for fast neutron damage in n-type Ge considered here cannot be taken as conclusive evidence of its validity. However, the reasonable values of parameters implicit in the model that have been obtained suggest that it is quite plausible. More conclusive evidence must come from a.c. rather than d.c. measurements. GOSSICK [40] has treated dipolar diffusion, hole storage and transient effects involving both minority and majority carriers associated with such regions theoretically. It is hoped that experimental tests of his theoretical results will soon be forthcoming.

REFERENCES

[1] E. GERMAGNOLI: this volume p. 318

[2] R. E. DAVIS, W. E. JOHNSON, K. LARK-HOROVITZ and S. SIEGEL: *Phys. Rev*,. **74**, 1255 (1948); W. E. JOHNSON and K. LARK-HOROVITZ: *Phys. Rev.*, **76**, 442 (1949). For a review of the early work in this field, the reader is directed to K. LARK-HOROVITZ: *Semiconducting Materials*, edited by H. K. HENISCH, (New York, 1951), p. 47.

[3] For a recent, comprehensive survey of developments in this field, see the *Proc. of the Conference on Radiation Effects in Semiconductors*, Gatlinburg, Tenn., *Journ. Appl. Phys.*, **30**, no. 8 (August issue, 1959).

[4] T. H. BLEWITT: this volume p. 630.

[5] R. A. COULSON apd M. J. KEARSLEY: *Proc. Roy. Soc.*, A **241**, 433 (1957).

[6] H. M. JAMES and K. LARK-HOROVITZ: *Zeits. Phys. Chemie*, **198**, 107 (1951).

[7] E. I. BLOUNT: *Phys. Rev.*, **113**, 995 (1959).

[8] W. SHOCKLEY and J. T. LAST: *Phys. Rev.*, **107**, 392 (1957).

[9] J. W. CLELAND, J. H. CRAWFORD and J. C. PIGG: *Phys. Rev.*, **99**, 1170 (1955).

[10] J. W. CLELAND, J. H. CRAWFORD and D. K. HOLMES: *Phys. Rev.*, **102**, 722 (1956).

[11] See for example C. A. KLEIN: *Journ. Appl. Phys.*, **30**, 1222 (1959).

[12] E. SONDER and L. C. TEMPLETON: *Journ. Appl. Phys.*, **31**, 1279 (1960).

[13] H. Y. FAN and K. LARK-HOROVITZ: *Semiconductors and Phosphors*, edited by M. SCHON and H. WELKER (New York, 1958) p. 113.

[14] T. A. LONGO: *Ph. D. Thesis* (Purdue University, 1957), unpublished.

[15] O. L. CURTIS, J. W. CLELAND apd J. H. CRAWFORD: *Journ. Appl. Phys.*, **29**, 1722 (1958).

[16] G. K. WERTHEIM: *Phys. Rev.*, **110**, 1272 (1958).

[17] H. Y. FAN and A. K. RAMDAS: *Journ. Appl. Phys.*, **30**, 1127 (1959).

[18] D. E. HILL and K. LARK-HOROVITZ: *Bull. Am. Phys. Soc.*, **3**, 142 (1958).

[19] E. SONDER and L. C. TEMPLETON: *Bull. Am. Phys. Soc.*, **5**, 196 (1960).

[20] D. E. HILL: *Bull. Am. Phys. Soc.*, **1**, 321 (1956).

[21] L. W. AUKERMAN: *Journ. Appl. Phys.*, **30**, 1239 (1959).

[22] J. W. CLELAND, J. H. CRAWFORD and J. C. PIGG: *Phys. Rev.*, **98**, 1742 (1955).

[23] J. H. CRAWFORD jr.: *Proc. of the Intern. Conference on Solid State Physics as Applied to Electronics and Telecommunications* (Brussels, 1958), to be published.

[24] Unpublished data of J. W. CLELAND and L. F. CONNELL: quoted by CRAWFORD in ref. [23].

[25] W. L. BROWN, W. M. AUGUSTYNIAK and T. R. WAITE: *Journ. Appl. Phys.*, **30**, 1258 (1959).

[26] O. L. CURTIS: private communication.

[27] H. LETAW, W. M. PORTNOY and L. M. SLIFKIN: *Phys. Rev.*, **102**, 636 (1956).

[28] R. A. LOGAN: *Phys. Rev.*, **101**, 1455 (1956).

[29] G. Bemski: *Journ. Appl. Phys.*, **30**, 1195 (1959).

[30] G. D. Watkins, J. W. Corbett and R. M. Walker: *Journ. Appl., Phys.* **30**. 1198 (1959); also work to be published in *Phys. Rev.*

[31] R. A. Schmitt and R. A. Sharp: *Phys. Rev. Lett.*, **1**, 445 (1958).

[32] B. R. Gossick: *Journ. Appl. Phys.*, **30**, 1214 (1959).

[33] J. H. Crawford and J. W. Cleland: *Journ. Appl. Phys.*, **30**, 1204 (1959).

[34] O. J. Juretschke, R. Landauer and J. A. Swanson: *Journ. Appl. Phys.*, **27**, 838 (1956).

[35] D. Binder: unpublished results.

[36] D. K. Hoimes and G. Leibfried: *Journ. Appl. Phys.*, **31**, 1046 (1960).

[37] S. L. Ruby, F. D. Schupp and E. D. Wolley: *Phys. Rev.*, **111**, 1493 (1958).

[38] This analysis, together with the following mobility correlation, was presented by J. W. Cleland and J. H. Crawford at the *International Conference on Semiconductors* (Prague, August 1960).

[39] F. J. Morin and J. P. Maita: *Phys. Rev.*, **94**, 1525 (1954).

[40] B. R. Gossick: *Proc. Intern. Conf. on Semiconductors* (Prague, August 1960)

Displacement Thresholds in Semiconductors.

R. Bäuerlein

Forschungslaboratorium, Siemens-Schuckertwerke AG - Erlangen

In this paper a review is given of the current status of displacement threshold determination in semiconductors. The discussion is divided into three sections. In Sect. **1** measuring methods are discussed for determining the threshold, special emphasis being given to the increase of the rate of production of Frenkel defects by fast electrons in the immediate neighborhood of the threshold. Sect. **2** deals with various experimental work on the determination of displacement energies in germanium, silicon, in III-V compounds and in cadmium sulphide. In Sect. **3** the relationship between displacement energy and bond energy in the diamond and zinc-blende lattice is considered. The displacement energies of the elemental semiconductors of Group IV in the Periodic Table are estimated from the known bond energies of the lattice and are compared with the measured values.

1. – Measuring methods for determining the threshold.

Lattice defects in semiconductors which result from fast particle collisions produce donor and acceptor states and recombination centers in much the same way as do impurity atoms. By reason of these properties it is possible to determine with a high degree of sensitivity defects present in semiconductor lattices. This high sensitivity of semiconductors to lattice distortion permits the variation of the production rate of defect formation due to fast electron collisions to be measured right into the immediate proximity of the threshold. This is the reason why accurate knowledge of the threshold energy of defect formation is at present restricted to semiconductors.

Of the many high-energy forms of radiation which can produce defects in solids, only accelerator electrons are suitable for the measurement of threshold energies, since these alone possess the two properties required for such measurements, namely a homogeneous and defined primary energy and an adequate penetration range in solids even in the neighborhood of the threshold.

In the various publications available two main methods are described for determining the threshold of defect formation in semiconductors. For the indication of defects the first method makes use of the change in conductivity produced by irradiation with fast electrons, *i.e.* of the property of the defects forming acceptor and donor states. The other method is based on the property of the defects forming recombination centers for the minority carriers. With the second method the change in lifetime of the minority carriers is observed.

If the first method is used, generally the measuring arrangement shown in Fig. 1 is chosen.

Thin samples of the substance under test are used. The measuring current flows in the longitudinal direction through the sample while the electron beam impinges in a perpendicular direction on the surface. The defects produced in the sample are distributed heterogeneously over the thickness of the sample, especially if the electron energy approaches the threshold energy. The concentration of the defects is at a maximum immediately below the irradiated surface and decreases towards the inside. This is due to the fact that the incident electrons are retarded by collisions with the electrons of the solid. They therefore possess energy sufficient for formation of defects only within a more or less thick surface range. The thickness of this layer decreases as the primary energy of the electrons approaches the threshold energy.

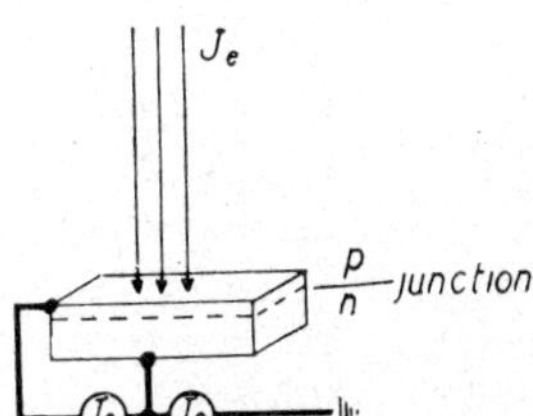

Fig. 1. – Schematic diagram of the experimental arrangement for determining the threshold by conductivity measurements.

The change in conductance of the sample, measured with that arrangement, is proportional to the total number of defects introduced by the bombardment. Let n_0 = carrier concentration before irradiation; d = thickness of the sample; j_e = beam current density; t = irradiation time; e = elemental charge; and $\Delta G/G_0$ = relative change in conductance. For the rate of defect formation, N_d/N_e, that is the total number of lattice defects introduced by one incident electron, one obtains

$$\frac{N_d}{N_e} = -\frac{n_0 \cdot d}{j_e \cdot t/e}\frac{\Delta G}{G_0}\,. \tag{1}$$

For the sake of simplicity we assumed that the change in conductivity only results from decrease in carrier concentration.

The variation of N_d/N_e due to the energy of bombarding electrons may be obtained by using the formula of the cross-section, $\sigma(E)$, of defect formation by SEITZ and KOEHLER [1]. This formula is calculated using homogeneous electron energies. As in our arrangement the incident electrons are retarded while traversing the solid, and therefore the energy decreases from the primary energy, E_0, to zero, we have to add up the cross-section from E_0 to E_t, the electron energy at the threshold [2, 3], for calculation of the total number of defects:

$$\frac{N_d}{N_e} = N_A \int_{E_t}^{E_0} \frac{\sigma(E)}{-\mathrm{d}E/\mathrm{d}x} \mathrm{d}E \,. \tag{2}$$

As the cross-section increases linearly from the threshold and the differential energy loss, $-\mathrm{d}E/\mathrm{d}x$, is nearly constant within the energy range considered here, in the summation over the entire range one obtains a parabolic increase of the total number of defects:

$$\frac{N_d}{N_e} \propto N_A (E_0 - E_t)^2 \,. \tag{3}$$

If consequently the total number of defects produced by one electron on its path through the solid is reflected in the measured value, as is the case with the conductivity measurement near the threshold (according to (1)), then it can be expected that from the threshold the carrier removal rate, N_d/N_e, will increase with the electron energy according to a square law. This applies, of course, only in so far as the assumed approximations hold, say within a range of 50 to 100 keV around the threshold.

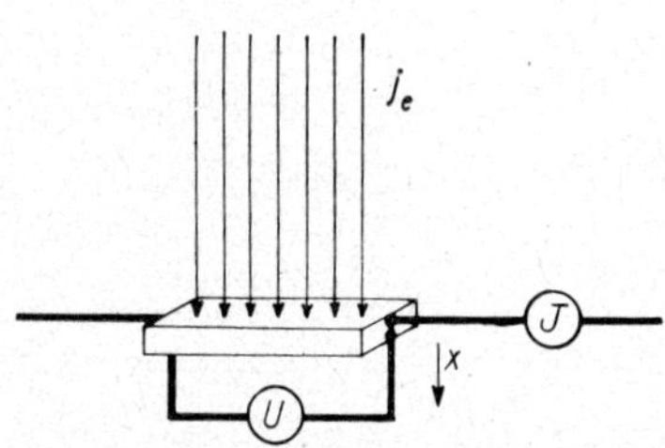

Fig. 2. – Schematic diagram of the experimental arrangement for determining the threshold using photodiodes.

In place of bulk material the second measuring method uses photodiodes with a diffused *pn*-junction as close as possible to the surface. See Fig. 2. If the *pn*-junction is irradiated with fast electrons, then as with light radiation, pairs of electrons and holes are produced on each side of the *pn*-junction. In the short-circuited photodiode a diffusion current, J_s, flows in the reverse direction and is proportional to the electron beam current, J_e.

The ratio J_s/J_e is proportional to the diffusion length, L, of the minority carriers as is known from photovoltaic theory:

$$\frac{J_s}{J_e} \propto L \,.$$

A prerequisite for this is, however, that the diffusion length be the determining factor, *i.e.*, that the range of the electrons and the remainder of the geometry be large as compared with the diffusion length. On the above assumptions the proportionality constant, which is not indicated, depends only to a lesser degree upon the energy of the incident electrons within the energy range under investigation.

The diffusion length is in turn a function of the lifetime, τ, of the minority carriers and of the diffusion constant, D:

$$L = \sqrt{D\tau}\,.$$

If limited by the presence of recombination centres, which is practically always the case, the lifetime of the minority carriers is inversely proportional to the concentration of the recombination centers.

The concentration of the newly produced recombination centers, n_{rd}, can be derived from the decrease in short-circuit current with respect to radiation time. As can be readily derived from the above relations:

$$n_{rd} \propto \Delta\left(\frac{J_e}{J_s}\right)^2. \tag{4}$$

If the range of formation of defects is less than the diffusion length, as is the case near the threshold, $\Delta(J_e/J_s)^2$ per dose unit can also be expected to vary in first order approximation with the square of the electron energy since in this case, too, the *total number* of recombination centers produced within the diffusion length is the decisive factor for the change in lifetime.

2. – Experimental work for determining the threshold for various types of semiconductors.

2·1. *Germanium and silicon.* – The experiments first published to determine the threshold energies for defect formation by high-energy irradiation were carried out in 1952 by KLONTZ and LARK-HOROVITZ [4] on Ge with fast electrons. Meanwhile, it has been established that the threshold energy of 630 keV obtained from these conductance measurements is too large. In 1956 the results of conductance measurements for the determination of the threshold energy for Ge were published by a group of Russian scientists, VAVILOV *et al.* [5], who obtained a threshold energy of 500 keV. The latest measurements, which were carried out with great care, are those of BROWN and AUGUSTYNIAK (1959) [6]. These will be used here to illustrate the method and the results.

Fig. 3 shows typical measurements of the change in conductivity per radiation dose, as a function of the energy of the incident electrons. The samples consisted of high-purity n-type germanium with an original carrier concentration of $3 \cdot 10^{-14}$ cm^{-3}. Their thickness was 15 and 63 μm. Owing to the fact that very thin samples were used the sensitivity of this method was increased considerably, but also the susceptibility to disturbances due to surface effects. The authors spared no pains to remove and eliminate such surface disturbances. The individual samples taken were single crystals which had different, well defined axial directions relative to the electron beam. The results of these measurements on the threshold energy as a function of the direction of the electron beam showed (Fig. 3) that the rate of defect formation, but not the threshold energy itself, depends on the orientation of the crystal. This agrees only partly with the predictions of KOHN [7] who believed that the threshold energy also varies with the direction.

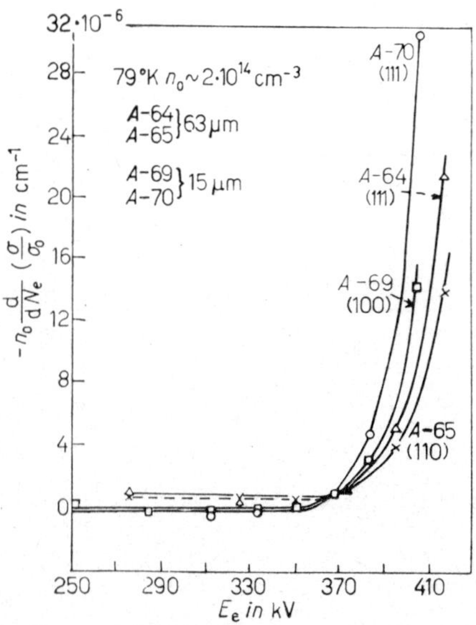

Fig. 3. – Acceptor introduction rate in the region of the threshold as a function of the energy of the incident electrons in germanium. The individual samples have different orientation to the electron beam. (BROWN and AUGUSTYNIAK [6]).

Another investigation referred to in the same paper deals with the threshold energy as a function of temperature. As a result of the thermal energy of the lattice atoms, the threshold energy should decrease with increasing temperature [6, 8]. This effect is considered to be much greater than that which would be expected from the ratio of the thermal energy to the displacement energy since not the energies but the corresponding velocities are added. In the case of Ge the decrease in the threshold energy due to the thermal motion of the lattice atoms at room temperature is roughly estimated at 1 eV. At liquid-nitrogen temperature it should, however, be negligible. The results from the measurements carried out by BROWN and AUGUSTYNIAK for the determination of this effect are shown in the following graph, Fig. 4. The three curves were obtained at 263, 78 and 21 °K, the corresponding threshold being 320, 355 and 420 keV. The variation with temperature and the shape of the curves cannot be explained simply by thermal motion of the lattice atoms. This problem requires further investigation.

The most recent determination of the threshold energy for Ge by conductance measurements is made by SMIRNOV and GLAZUNOV [9]. Contrary to the conventional arrangement the direction of the electron beam and the direction of the flow of current are parallel (Fig. 5). Therefore, it is possible to determine the distribution of the defects along the electron path by means of potential probes. The following graph, Fig. 6, shows the range of the defect formation in the crystal as a function of the electron energy. Extrapolation of this straight line to its point of intersection with the abscissa axis gives a threshold energy of 380 keV.

The second measuring principle described at the beginning of the paper, namely the determination of the rate of defect formation due to a decrease in lifetime of the minority carriers, was used for the first time by LOFERSKI and RAPPAPORT [8] in 1958 on Ge and Si. Fig. 7 shows the interrelationship between the irradiation dose and I_s^{-2}, the inverse square of the short circuit current, at various electron energies. The slope of the linear characteristic can be taken as a criterion for the rate of defect formation. The following graph (Fig. 8) shows this quality as a function of the electron energy for Ge (curve with measured points). The other curves are attempts to bring the curve through the measured points into line with theoretically calculated

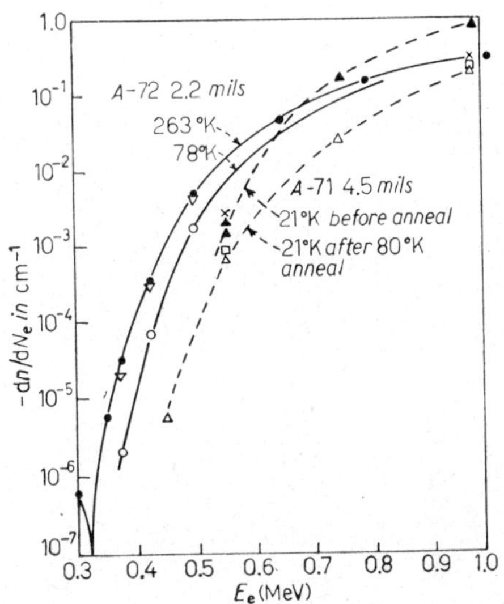

Fig. 4. – Temperature-dependence of acceptor introduction rate in germanium. The individual curves were obtained at 263, 78 and 21 °K. (BROWN and AUGUSTYNIAK [6]).

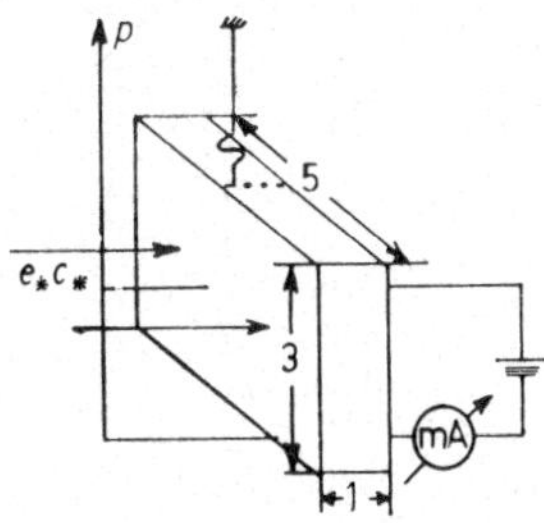

Fig. 5. – Schematic diagram of the experimental arrangement used by SMIRNOV and GLAZUNOV [9] for measurements of the depth of defect formation.

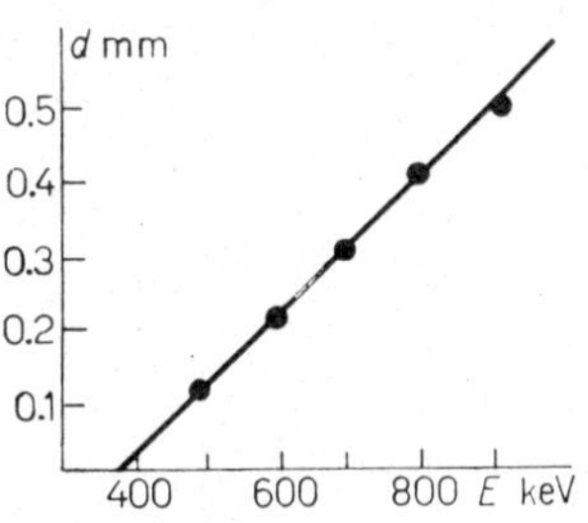

Fig. 6. – Range of defect formation in germanium as a function of the energy of the bombarding electrons. (SMIRNOV and GLAZUNOV [9]).

curves. Only two of these curves will be considered, namely: 1) the cross-section, $[\Delta(E_B)]$, for the production of Frenkel defects according to SEITZ, which rises linearly from the threshold and shows hardly any similarity to the meas-

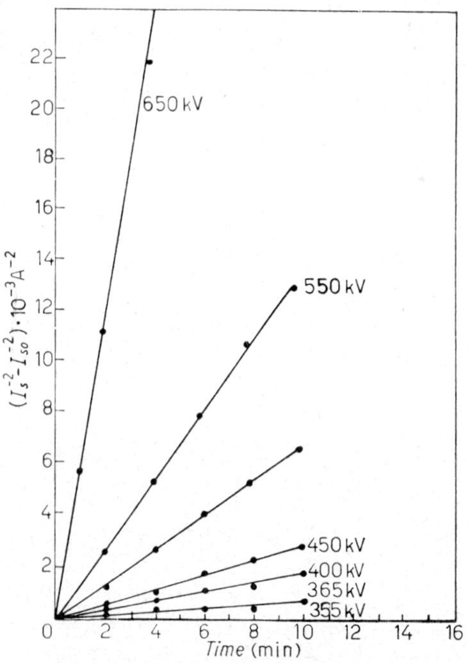

Fig. 7. – Change of the inverse square of the short-circuit current of a germanium photodiode as a function of the bombarding time. (LOFERSKI and RAPPAPORT [8]).

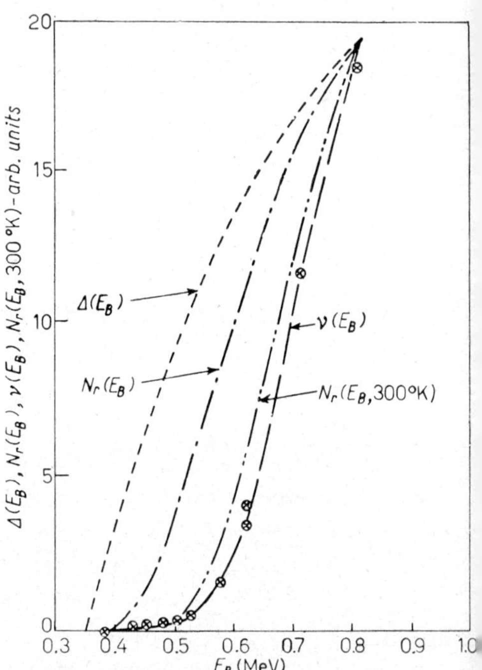

Fig. 8. – Rate of formation of recombination centers, $\nu(E_B)$, as a function of the energy of the bombarding electrons in germanium (curve with measured points). (LOFERSKI and RAPPAPORT [8]).

ured curve; 2) the total number of defects, $[N_r(E_B)]$, produced by one incident electron, which rises according to a parabolic law as we have already seen. Here too, there is no agreement with the measured curve over the entire length. The thresholds obtained by LOFERSKI and RAPPAPORT are 360 keV for germanium and 145 keV for silicon.

Table I lists all the threshold measurements for Ge known to date. In a head-on collision between an electron and a lattice atom the energy, E_d, which is transferred to the lattice atom, displacing it from its position can be computed from the electron energy, E_t, at the threshold in a very simple way by using the laws of impulse and energy conservation [1]:

$$E_d = 2\,\frac{m}{M}\,E_t\left(2+\frac{E_t}{mc^2}\right). \tag{2}$$

TABLE I. – *Measurement of the displacement energy of* Ge.

	Threshold energy (keV)	Displacement energy (eV)	Temperature (°K)	
KLONTZ and LARK-HOROVITZ [4]	630	30	80	1952
VAVILOV *et al.* [5]	500	23	300	1956
LOFERSKI and RAPPAPORT [8]	360	14.7	300	1958
BROWN and AUGUSTYNIAK [6]	420 355 320	18.0 14.5 12.7	20 80 260	1959
SMIRNOV and GLAZUNOV [9]	380	15.7	300	1959

m means the rest mass of the electron, M the mass of the knocked-on lattice atom and c the velocity of light. In this formula a relativistic correction has been taken into account, because in an usual material the electron energy required to displace an atom is in the relativistic range. The displacement energies for Ge to be calculated from the respective threshold are listed in Table I.

By definition the threshold energy is the lowest electron energy observable which is just sufficient to produce a displacement of an atom in the lattice. Therefore it may be taken for granted that the energy values which were observed in germanium by BROWN and AUGUSTYNIAK namely 12.7 eV at room temperature, and 14.5 eV at the temperature of liquid nitrogen, are corresponding best with the actual displacement energies.

From the experiments made by LOFERSKI and RAPPAPORT a value of 13.0 eV can be deduced for the displacement of Si at room temperature.

2·2. *Compound semiconductors.* – The compound semiconductors which are considered in the following section have a structure similar to that of semiconductors of Group IV. Of the III-V compounds the threshold energies for InP, InAs, InSb and GaAs have been determined [10, 11]. Except for InSb these measurements were carried out on photodiodes, whereby the variation of the short-circuit current upon irradiation was used as an index of defect formation. A typical curve is shown in Fig. 9. For InP the rate of formation of recombination centers is shown as a function of the electron energy. As already mentioned, see formula (3), the curve is expected to rise from the threshold according to a parabolic law. For this reason in Fig. 10 a square ordinate scale is used which causes the curve to turn into a straight line. This permits the threshold to be determined with a higher degree of reliability and accuracy. The threshold energy for InP is 111 keV. This energy is assumed

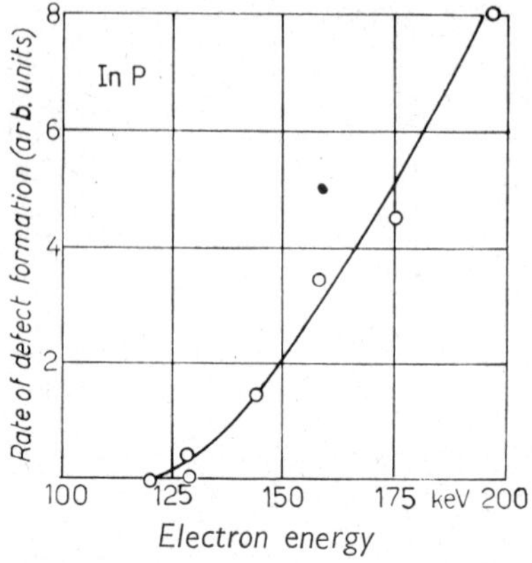

Fig. 9. – Rate of formation of recombination centers as a function of the energy of the bombarding electrons in an indium phosphide photodiode [10].

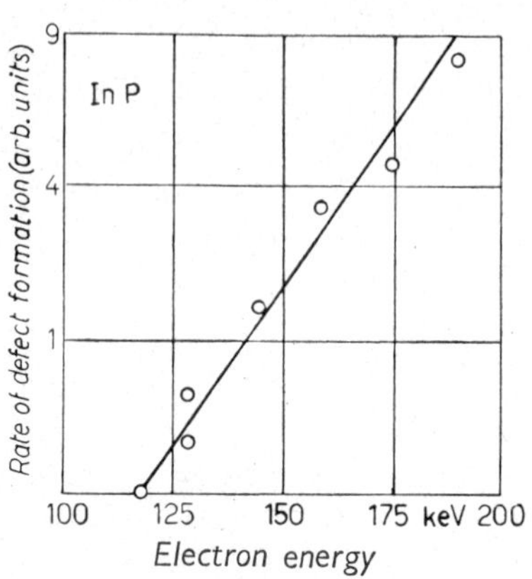

Fig. 10. – Rate of formation of recombination centers as a function of the energy of the bombarding electrons in an indium phosphide photodiode. Note the square scale of the ordinate [10].

to be such that an electron of this energy is just capable of displacing a P atom by central collision. The displacement energy is determined at 8.7 eV. At the same displacement energy the electron energy required for the production of an In-Frenkel-defect should be approximately 3 times greater since the In atom has a mass 3.6 times greater.

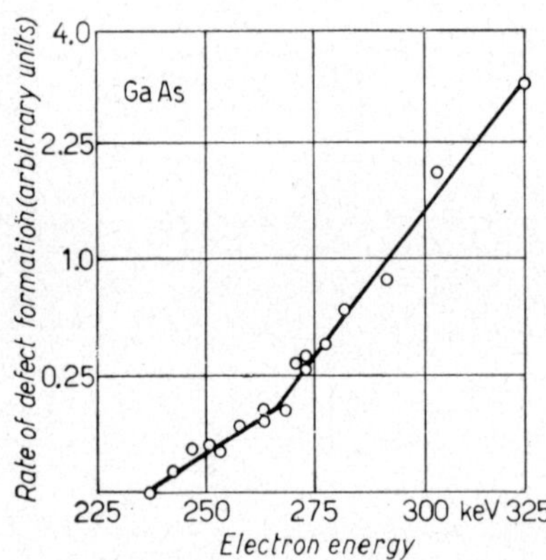

Fig. 11. – Rate of formation of recombination centers as a function of the energy of the bombarding electrons in a gallium arsenide photodiode. Note the square scale of the ordinate [10].

For GaAs the conditions are quite different. The atomic weights of the two elements are almost equal, so it can be expected that their thresholds are close together. In fact, the measuring results for GaAs (Fig. 11) can be interpreted to the effect that two thresholds are present which are indicated by the breaks in the straight-line characteristics. The squared ordinate scale should also be noted.

Similar results were obtained with InAs [10], but these will not be dealt with in detail. The results of measurements of InSb published by Eisen and Bickel [11] in 1959 should be included. Fig. 12 shows the original curve, namely the change in conductivity of the sample per dose unit as a function of the energy of the incident electrons. If in place of the linear scale a square ordinate scale is used as in the preceding graphs, then here, too, two thresholds can be made out at 240 and 285 keV (see Fig. 13). The portion of the curve below 245 keV shall not be considered. The associated threshold to be extrapolated is so low that it can be assumed that the effective mechanism for the production of defects below 240 keV is of a fundamentally different character than that occurring above this threshold energy.

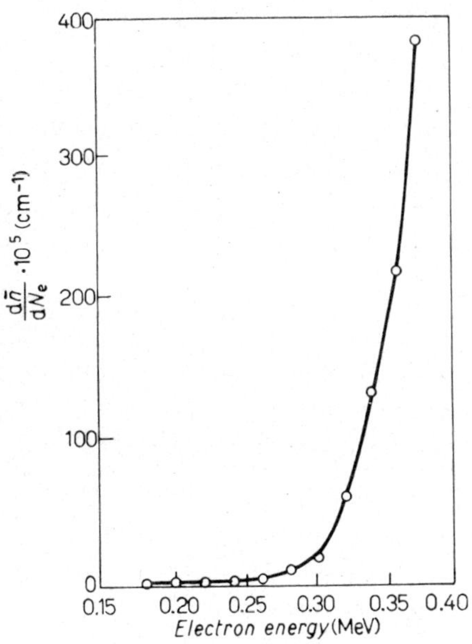

Fig. 12. – (Carriers removed per cm³)/(bombarding electrons per cm²), dn/dN_e, as a function of the energy of the bombarding electrons in indium antimonide. The thickness of the sample was .017 cm (EISEN and BICKEL [11]).

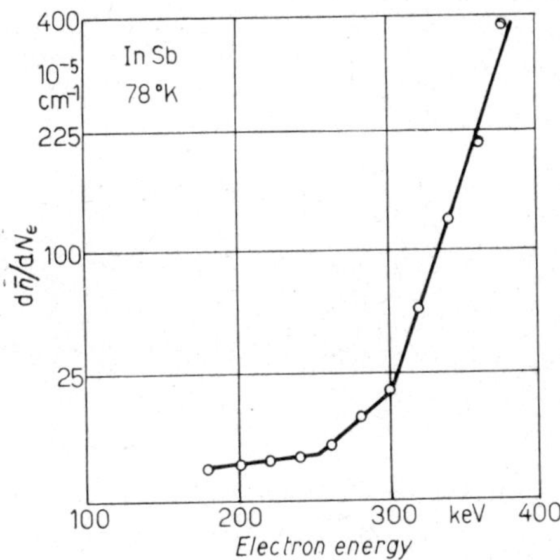

Fig. 13. – (Carriers removed per cm³)/(bombarding electrons per cm²), dn/dN_e, as a function of the energy of the bombarding electrons in indium antimonide. Note the square scale of the ordinate.

In accordance with the formula (5) the two threshold-energy values observed with III-V compounds are tentatively associated with the constituent elements on the basis of their atomic weights, namely the lower threshold with the lattice atom of lower mass. The displacement energies of III-V compounds to be computed under this condition are listed in Table II and are compared with the values of the semiconductors of Group IV in the Periodic Table.

In the first line are the substances to which these values refer. The second line indicates the lattice element with which the threshold energy listed in the third line is associated. The displacement energies computed from these values are shown in the fourth line. For comparison purposes the activation energy of self-diffusion is also indicated in as far as it is known [12, 13]. The

TABLE II. – *Displacement energy of semiconductors.*

Substance	Si	Ge	In P		Ga As		In As		Ga Sb		In Sb		Cd S		
Displaced atom	Si	Ge	In	P	Ga	As	In	As	Ga	Sb	In	Sb	Cd	S	
Threshold energy	145	320 (*) 355 (**)	274 (*)	111 (*)	233 (*)	256 (*)	274 (**)	231 (**)			240 (**)	285 (**)		115 (*)	keV
Displacement energy	12.9	12.7 14.5	6.7	8.7	9.0	9.4	6.7	8.3			5.7	6.6		8.7	eV
Activation energy of self-diffusion		2.98							3.15	3.45	1.82	1.94			eV

(*) Room temperature.
(**) Liquid-nitrogen temperature.

self-diffusion is connected with the displacement as in this case, too, lattice vacancies are formed, although in thermal equilibrium.

In addition to the elemental and the III-V compound semiconductors, a compound of Group II and VI elements, namely CdS, is represented. Briefly, this is how the displacement energy for sulphur could be determined. CdS shows a red fluorescence line which, as is assumed, depends on sulphur vacancies in the lattice. In order to solve this problem, CdS crystals that showed no red fluorescence were irradiated by KULP and KELLEY (1960) [14] with electrons having increasing energies. At 120 keV and above, a fluorescence glow occured suddenly. This phenomenon is explained by the fact that from about 115 keV upwards sulphur atoms are displaced by electron collision, and the sulphur vacancies required for activation of the fluorescence glow are thus produced.

A comparison between displacement energies of semiconductors shows the following: 1) the displacement energies of compound semiconductors are below those of the elements of Group IV; 2) in the same substance, the displacement energy of the constituent element of Group III is smaller than that of the element of Group V.

The final part of this paper deals with the problems connected with this effect.

3. – Displacement energy and bond energy.

3·1. *Elemental semiconductors of Group IV.* – In trying to find a relation between displacement energy and bond energy of the lattice it is necessary at first to occupy oneself with the lattice structure of semiconductors. As is known, semiconductors of Group IV of the Periodic Table crystallize in the diamond lattice. Concerning that type of lattice, according to its four valencies each atom is surrounded by four nearest neighbors having eight electrons together with them. This is the ideal case of homopolar binding.

The formation of a Frenkel defect by electron collision in that lattice may be seen in three stages:

1) The four bonds to the four nearest neighbors are broken. If E_v is the bond energy of the single valency the energy required to break the four bonds is $4E_v$.

2) The lattice atom released from its bond is pushed through between three nearest neighbors, an unimportant overlapping of the atomic shells taking place. The energy U required may be estimated from that overlapping of the atomic shells: in the case of the rather loosely packed diamond structure it amounts to some 1/10 eV.

3) The knocked-on lattice atom gets to an interstitial position where it generally must clear sufficient space by pushing aside the atoms in the neighborhood. That is not the case with the diamond lattice, so-called natural interstitial positions being there in a sufficient number. A natural interstitial position means a lattice site which normally is unoccupied, but has the same distances to nearest neighbors as a normal lattice site. In geometrical sense only half of the lattice points of the diamond lattice being occupied by atoms, there is an equivalent number of natural interstitial positions to the normal number of atoms: therefore no energy is required for that stage. Consequently, the displacement energy E_d in the diamond lattice is given by

$$E_d = 4E_v + U .$$

In proportion to the relatively high binding energy of the lattice, however, the energy U is negligible: calculating the displacement energy it is only necessary to know the bond energy of the single valency.

Consequently the next thing we have got to do is to determine the bond energy, E_v, of the single valency. In the diamond structure it is equal to half the bond energy, E_B, of the crystal lattice, as in the whole crystal there are only two valencies per lattice atom on the average.

Therefore the displacement energy is equal to double the bond energy

$$E_d \approx 4E_v = 2E_B .$$

Calculating the bond energy of the lattice it is necessary to go back: the bond energy of a crystal lattice is defined as the energy required to remove all the atoms of the crystal to infinity in just the same conditions in which the atoms had been in the crystal itself. In the case of an ionic crystal the atoms are to be removed as ions. The energy defined like that is generally not identical with the energy of sublimation E_{sub} of the crystal which can be measured thermodynamically. In sublimating, the lattice atoms generally are not evaporating in the same state as they were bound in the crystal lattice. There is again the example of the ionic crystal: at the sublimation in general not ions but molecules are evaporating, or, as in the case of AgBr, even Br atoms.

The consequences of that consideration to elemental semiconductors crystallizing in the diamond structure may be illustrated by the example of carbon [15]. The four valence electrons of the free carbon atom are in the state $2s^2 2p^2$. As the two s-electrons have an antiparallel spin, the carbon atom is bivalent in the ground state. Quadrivalent carbon atoms, however, are required to establish the tetrahedral bond in the diamond lattice. Therefore, the conclusion may be drawn that carbon atoms in diamond are in an excited quadrivalent state. Such a state, that is to say the state of the lowest excitation energy, is the state of $2s2p^3$. In order to reach that state of excitation, a transition of one of the two $2s$-electrons from the ground state to the state of $2p$ takes place while the spin is changing (as indicated in the following diagram). In that state ($2s2p^3$) of the carbon atom all the electrons have the same spin, consequently the carbon atom is quadrivalent. As is known from spectroscopic measurements the excitation energy required is 96 kcal/mole [15].

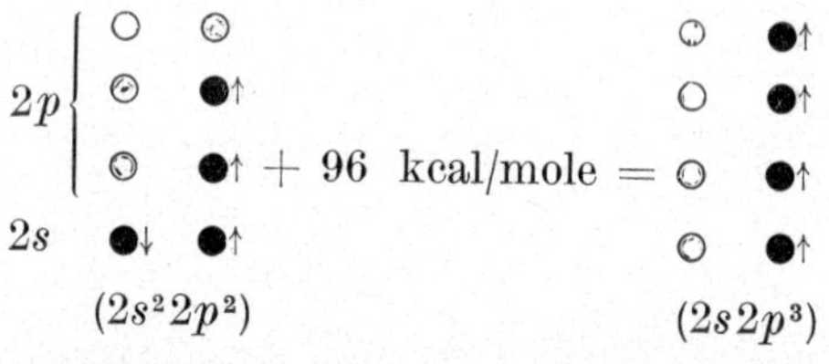

$2p$	○	○		○	●↑
	○	●↑		○	●↑
	○	●↑	+ 96 kcal/mole =	○	●↑
$2s$	●↓	●↑		○	●↑
	($2s^2 2p^2$)			($2s2p^3$)	

Legend: ○ = electron states unfilled
● = electron states filled
↑ = direction of spin.

The total binding energy, E_B, of the diamond structure consequently is composed of the energy of sublimation, E_{sub}, and of the energy of excitation, E_e, recovered at the sublimation of the atoms in the ground state,

$$E_B = E_{sub} + E_e \, .$$

In Table III these energy values for the Group IV elements are compared as far as those elements crystallize in the diamond lattice. The values for the energy of sublimation are borrowed from recent mass-spectrometrical work [16-17]. The values for the energy of excitation for Si, Ge, and Sn were obtained from analogical consideration of the atomic energy levels, as spectroscopical values for those elements are unknown.

In calculating the displacement energy we used the total binding energy because we believe that, contrary to the process of sublimation, a transition of the lattice atom from the excited $2s2p^3$ state to the ground state ($2s^22p^2$) will not be possible during the process of displacement. The available, time, of the magnitude of 10^{-13} s, is too short for that process especially when taking into consideration that the direct transition is forbidden. A comparison between calculations and measurements shows satisfactory agreement. For comparison purposes the known displacement energy of graphite [18] is listed in Table III, because it may be assumed that the bond energies of diamond and graphite are nearly the same.

TABLE III. – *Bond energies and displacement energies of the elements of Group IV.*

Substance	Heat of sublimation kcal/mole	Excitation energy kcal/mole	Bond energy		Displacement energy (eV)		
			kcal/mole	eV	calc.	80 °K meas.	300 °K meas.
C	179	96	275	12	24		25 (*)
Si	107	73	180	7.8_3	$15._7$		13.0
Ge	87.5	88	175.5	7.6_3	$15._3$	14.5	12.7
α-Sn	70.5	71	141.5	6.1_5	$12._3$		—

(*) Graphite.

3·2. *III-V compounds.* – III-V compounds usually crystallize in the zincblende lattice, a lattice type very similar to the diamond lattice. The geometrical arrangement of the atoms corresponds with that of the diamond lattice, only the lattice points are alternatively occupied by the two kinds of atoms of the compound. As the two constituent elements contribute respectively 3 and 5 electrons to the structure of the tetrahedral bond, that lattice type gets a certain slight asymmetry. Therefore, in addition to the pure homopolar bond of the diamond lattice, an appreciable heteropolar component appears. Because of this fact, calculations of the binding energy are relatively difficult. In the case of III-V compounds we will therefore confine ourselves to drawing a comparison between the displacement energies of the various compounds and will just refer to parallels to the binding energy.

The general conclusion may be drawn from measurements of the displacement energy of III-V compounds that the binding energy of these compounds is certainly lower than that of comparable elements of group IV. It seemed to us that the partly far lower displacement energies of that group of compounds cannot be explained in another way. An interpretation might be connected with the opinion occasionally to be heard that in III-V compounds only three electrons establish the tetrahedral bond, which is one electron less than in the case of the elements of Group IV in the diamond lattice.

In Table IV the displacement energies of III-V compounds are once again compared, in a slightly different way.

TABLE IV. – *Displacement energies of the III-V compound semiconductors in* eV.

	P	As	Sb	
Al				
Ga		9.4 (*) 9.2 9.0		E_{dV} E_d E_{dIII}
In	8.7 (*) 7.7 6.7	8.3 (**) 7.5 6.7	6.6 (**) 6.2 5.7	E_{dV} E_d E_{dIII}

(*) Room temperature.
(**) Liquid-nitrogen temperature.

Displacement energies of the corresponding compound are at the point of intersection of the two elements of which the compound is composed. From top to bottom the various numbers denote the displacement energy of Group V element, the average displacement energy, and the displacement energy of Group III element. Although a number of places are vacant, yet we will try to find out some regularities about the progress of displacement energy in that group of compounds.

Comparing the displacement energies separately among one another, it is found that the values decrease from left to right, and from top to bottom. In other words: when a compound element of a III-V compound is substituted for a higher homologous one, that is, an element of the same group of the Periodic Table but with a higher atomic number, then the displacement energy in that new compound has decreased. It is known from experience, however that a similar regularity is true also in regard to the bond energy of a group of compounds, that the bond energies in the Periodic Table decrease from top to bottom. We realize that concerning III-V compounds there also seems to be a close relation between displacement energy and bond energy of the lattice.

In Table V the difference $E_{d\text{III-V}} = E_{d\text{V}} - E_{d\text{III}}$ between the displacement energies of the two elements in a III-V compound is compared in a way similar to that in the table before. Comparing the table values, there is no difficulty in finding out that the difference between the displacement energies is smallest if both elements of the compound are as similar to each other as possible, that is, if the elements are in the same horizontal series of the Periodic Table, as is the case with GaAs and InSb. Elements of a compound which are very dissimilar from each other, as is the case with In and P in InP, cause the greatest difference observed so far. Therefore, the conclusion may be drawn that the different displacement energies of a compound result from the asymmetry being produced in the diamond lattice in consequence of the fact that the various lattice points are alternatively occupied by different elements. The cause might be bond energies of higher order, for example binding forces with second neighbors, energies of polarization, and so on.

TABLE V. – *Difference between the displacement energies of III-V compound semiconductors.*

	P	As	Sb	
Al				
Ga		0.4		eV
In	2.0	1.6	0.9	eV

The value (8.7 eV) of the displacement energy of sulphur in CdS (see Table II) gives very important particulars of the crystal structure of II-VI compounds. Hence, it seems to be very improbable that CdS should be a pure ionic crystal, which would mean that double positive charged Cd^{++} ions and double negative charged S^{--} ions should form a binding just by means of their Coulomb-forces. The bond energy of such a crystal and the presumable displacement energy ought to be far larger than actually is the case.

The problem which was raised in the last paragraph and the various considerations may demonstrate that the knowledge of displacement energy gives us valuable conclusions about the crystal structure of solids and the lattice forces being effective there. Still more intensive activity in just this field would help to solve many problems of solid state physics which are unsettled yet.

REFERENCES

[1] F. Seitz and J. S. Koehler: *Solid State Physics*, vol. **2** (New York, 1956), p. 305.

[2] O. S. Oen and D. K. Holmes: *Journ. Appl. Phys.*, **10**, 1289 (1959).

[3] J. H. Calm: *Journ. Appl. Phys.*, **10**, 1310 (1959).

[4] F. F. Klontz and K. Lark-Horovitz: *Phys. Rev.*, **86**, 643 (1952).

[5] V. S. Vavilov, L. S. Smirnov, G. N. Galkin, A. V. Spitsyn and V. M. Patskevich: *Journ. Tech. Phys. USSR*, **26**, 1865 (1956).

[6] W. L. Brown and W. M. Augustyniak: *Journ. Appl. Phys.*, **30**, 1300 (1959).

[7] W. Kohn: *Phys. Rev.*, **94**, 1409 (A) (1954).

[8] J. J. Loferski and P. Rappaport: *Phys. Rev.*, **111**, 432 (1958).

[9] L. S. Smirnov and P. A. Glazunov: *Fizika Tverdogo Tela*, **1**, 1376 (1959).

[10] R. Bäuerlein: *Zeits. f. Naturfor.*, **14***a*, 1069 (1959).

[11] F. H. Eisen and P. W. Bickel: *Phys. Rev.*, **115**, 345 (1959).

[12] W. M. Portnoy, H. Letwa jr. and W. L. Slifkin: *Phys. Rev.*, **98**, 1536 (1955).

[13] F. H. Eisen and C. E. Birchenall: *Acta Metall.*, **5**, 265 (1957).

[14] B. A. Kulp and R. H. Kelley: *Journ. Appl. Phys.*, **31**, 1057 (1960).

[15] L. Pauling: *Journ. Phys. Chem.*, **58**, 662 (1954).

[16] R. E. Honig: *Journ. Chem. Phys.*, **22**, 126 (1954).

[17] R. E. Honig: *Journ. Chem. Phys.*, **22**, 1610 (1954).

[18] Unpublished work of D. T. Eggen quoted by G. R. Hennig and J. H. Hove *Proc. Conference on Peaceful Uses of Atomic Energy*, vol. **7** (Geneva, 1956), p. 666.

Mobilité des défauts ponctuels dans le germanium.

P. Baruch

Laboratoire de Physique, Ecole Normale Supérieure - Paris

1. – Introduction.

Parmi les défauts du réseau cristallin, les plus simples, lacunes et interstitiels, peuvent être introduits par un grand nombre de moyens différents: traitements thermiques tels que trempe ou ségrégation contrôlée d'impuretés chimiques, déformation plastique ou irradiation. Ces défauts sont mobiles et susceptibles de se déplacer dans le cristal à des températures suffisantes sous l'action de champs électriques ou de gradients de concentration; cette migration, suivie ou non d'annihilation des défauts, constitue le principal mécanisme de «*revenu*» ou «*guérison*». L'étude de ces processus peut donc permettre l'identification de défauts, connus par leurs effets, de distinguer entre défauts simples et défauts complexes qui peuvent parfois être introduits simultanèment dans certaines expériences.

Dans cet esprit nous allons essayer de coordonner les résultats expérimentaux relatifs à la mobilité des défauts simples dans le germanium, et essayer d'obtenir par là une identification des défauts introduits par irradiation.

2. – Mobilité des défauts introduits par traitement thermique ou mécanique.

Nous groupons sous ce titre les expériences de self-diffusion, de ségrégation d'impuretés, de trempe, de déformation plastique. Une excellente vue d'ensemble de ces phénomènes a été fournie par Seeger [1] et Haasen et Seeger [2].

2·1. *Self-diffusion.* – Par mesure du coefficient de diffusion de ^{71}Ge, isotope radioactif du germanium, Letaw, Portnoy et Slifkin [3] ont mesuré entre 766 °C et 928 °C, le coefficient de self-diffusion D_s du germanium:

$$D_s = 7.8 \exp\left[\frac{-E_s}{kT}\right] \text{cm}^2/\text{s} ,$$

où $E_s = 3$ eV est l'énergie de self-diffusion du germanium.

La self-diffusion peut se produire soit par diffusion d'interstitiels, soit par diffusion substitutionnelle nécessitant la présence de lacunes, suivant les concentrations à l'équilibre de l'une ou de l'autre espèce. Divers arguments relatifs à la nature des accepteurs thermiques (cf. ci-dessous), à leur entropie d'activation permettent de conclure que le défaut responsable du désordre thermique dans ce domaine de température est la lacune. Dans ce cas le coefficient de self-diffusion est égal au coefficient de diffusion D_v des lacunes multiplié par la fraction des sites du réseau qu'elles occupent. Les densités de lacunes — accepteurs thermiques — ont été mesurées séparément. On en déduit

$$D_v = 1.2 \exp\left[\frac{-E_{\text{MV}}}{kT}\right] \text{cm}^2/\text{s}$$

où $E_{\text{MV}} = 1$ eV est l'énergie d'activation pour la migration des lacunes. L'énergie de formation des lacunes est alors: $E_{\text{FV}} = E_s - E_{\text{MV}} = 2$ eV.

2·2. *Précipitation du cuivre.* – Ces valeurs ont été brillamment confirmées par PENNING [4] utilisant des résultats de TWEET [5] sur le taux de précipitation du cuivre en sursaturation dans le germanium. Cette précipitation se produit par passage du cuivre de l'état substitutionnel à l'état interstitiel, réaction qui introduit une lacune, puis migration du cuivre interstitiel vers un noyau de précipitation. C'est le flux des lacunes qui contrôle la vitesse de réaction. Ce flux est proportionnel à la concentration et au coefficient de diffusion des lacunes, donc à D_s. Les valeurs de D_s obtenues ainsi sont en très bon accord avec celles obtenues par LETAW *et al.* [3], confirmant que la self-diffusion se produit effectivement par l'intervention des lacunes.

2·3. *Trempe. Déformation plastique.* – En trempant un cristal de germanium chauffé entre 900 °C et 930 °C on stabilise des défauts qui présentent des propriétés d'accepteurs [7]. La discussion par LETAW [5] et SEEGER [1] indique que l'on a affaire à des lacunes simples ou à des lacunes doubles, caractérisées par des énergies d'ionisation respectivement de 0.02 eV et 0.1 eV à partir du sommet de la bande de valence. Ces deux différents accepteurs disparaissent par recuit à des températures différentes: (350÷400) °C et (600÷750) °C. La structure du réseau du diamant rend difficile le mouvement de la lacune double, qui en revanche est facilement créée par déformation plastique. SEE-

GER [1] propose les valeurs suivantes pour les énergies caractéristiques de la lacune double: énergie de formation 2.5 à 3.3 eV; énergie de migration 1.5 à 1.6 eV.

La déformation plastique du germanium [8, 9] ne s'obtient qu'au dessus de 600 °C. A cette température, les lacunes simples sont guéries pendant l'expérience. Effectivement, les accepteurs qui restent, et ne disparaissent qu'à 800 °C, ont des propriétés qui permettent de les identifier comme les lacunes doubles décrites ci-dessus. En plus, la déformation crée des dislocations, qui jouent aussi un rôle d'accepteurs, mais sont beaucoup plus stables.

En conclusion, toutes les expériences décrites ci-dessus montrent qu'au-dessus de 300 °C, les défauts mobiles sont des lacunes simples ou doubles suivant les conditions. La lacune simple se montre relativement très mobile avec des coefficients de diffusion et des énergies d'activation bien déterminés. Il n'existe pas de mention de l'interstitiel dans ces expériences, surtout parce qu'elles sont réalisées dans des conditions où la concentration des interstitiels est faible devant celle des lacunes, particulièrement dans les expériences de trempe ou de précipitation. Il existe cependant des indications pouvant laisser croire à une création limitée d'interstitiels par déformation plastique [12].

3. – Effet des rayonnements.

L'effet des rayonnements se distingue de l'effet de la trempe, de la déformation plastique et autres traitements thermiques par deux points:

a) Les expériences peuvent être effectuées à des températures très basses. On aura donc des précisions sur l'état des défauts dans un tout autre domaine de température.

b) La création de lacunes est accompagnée de celle d'interstitiels en nombre égal (défauts Frenkel), tout au moins au stade primaire du phénomène.

Nous nous limiterons au cas des irradiations par des électrons (ou des rayons γ) d'énergie comprise entre 300 keV et 3 MeV. Les déplacements atomiques sont alors simples. Les défauts créés sont répartis de façon homogène à l'échelle microscopique, avec cependant une forte corrélation entre la lacune et l'interstitiel associés au même site.

Les différentes observations seront classées par ordre croissant de température.

3·1. *Guérison à très basse température* 4 °K *à* 78 °K. – Le groupe de Purdue University a irradié vers 10 °K du germanium dégénéré n ou p, avec des électrons [14]. Des centres donneurs dans Ge-p, accepteurs dans Ge-n, apparaissent mais avec des densités différentes. Dans Ge-n, les accepteurs sont peu stables, disparaissent par chauffage dans une proportion de 30 à 50% avec deux étapes marquées de guérison à 32 °K et 66 °K, correspondant à des énergies d'activation très faibles (0.04 eV et 0.07 eV); ces étapes de guérison seraient à attribuer à une recombinaison de paires Frenkel très voisines (premiers, puis seconds voisins) et n'exigeraient donc pas une grande mobilité des espèces se recombinant. Les très faibles énergies d'activation indiquent que ce n'est pas la diffusion qui contrôle le processus mais plutôt un phénomène de nature électronique; celà est d'ailleurs confirmé par une irradiation avec une énergie inférieure à celle du seuil, qui produit le même effet qu'un réchauffement: cette irradiation agirait par l'intense ionisation créée dans le cristal.

Dans le germanium *p*, la situation est différente; le taux d'introduction des donneurs est très faible à 4 °K, beaucoup plus faible que par une irradiation à 78 °K. Ceci laisse supposer que, pour que la paire lacune-interstitiel produise des effets électriques, il faut qu'il y ait une libération, c'est-à-dire que les défauts puissent se séparer avant de se recombiner.

Un phénomène analogue a été observé par Brown sur du germanium *n* de résistivité plus élevée [15] et attribué à l'existence d'une position métastable de l'interstitiel.

Nous voyons donc apparaître, dans ce type d'expérience, deux notions remarquables: l'influence de l'état d'ionisation du défaut sur sa mobilité, ou tout au moins sur la possibilité de recombinaison, et la nécessité d'une séparation des élements de la paire pour que les défauts soient détectables; l'un au moins des défauts est donc mobile dès 78 °K.

3·2. *Entre* 78 °K *et* 273 °K. – Dans le germanium *n*, les défauts sont stables dans ce domaine de température. Dans Ge-*p*, une étape de guérison très marquée a été observée vers (180÷200) °K [16, 17]; cependant vers cette température, les propriétés du centre en question dépendent très fortement de l'état d'ionisation, il n'a pas encore été possible de déterminer si l'on avait affaire à une vraie recombinaison de défauts ou seulement à un réarrangement électronique.

3·3. *Entre* 273 °K *et* 400 °K. – Le germanium *n* irradié à température plus basse (78 °K) recouvre une grande partie de ses propriétés (50 à 70%) au voisinage de la température ordinaire [16]. L'énergie d'activation pour ce processus est de 0.8 eV, mais la nature des impuretés chimiques présentes dans le cristal a une très grande importance. La guérison est plus complète dans un cristal dopé à l'antimoine tandis que dans un cristal dopé à l'arsenic, seule la mobilité retrouve sa valeur initiale, la concentration des porteurs restant diminuée. La guérison n'est donc pas une simple annihilation, mais elle met en jeu une association d'un défaut avec l'impureté chimique.

L'influence de ces impuretés (en concentration 10^{15} atomes/cm^3) signifie que le défaut qui disparait peut se déplacer sur des distances de l'ordre de 10^{-5} cm. Ceci, joint aux temps caractéristiques du processus, correspondrait à un coefficient de diffusion au moins égal à 10^{-13} cm^2/s à 56 °C, ce qui serait remarquablement élevé. Comme il n'y a pas d'apparence de guérison entre 78 °K et 300 °K, les lacunes et les interstitiels seraient restés en même nombre, mais l'un des deux types de défauts préfèrerait s'associer avec l'impureté chimique. Il faudrait donc, d'après BROWN, qu'existe une barrière à la recombinaison. De plus la nature de ce défaut mobile est inconnue: c'est un centre accepteur mais il n'est pas évident que ce soit la lacune.

D'autres expériences, à Oak Ridge [18, 19], confirment l'importance des impuretés chimiques et indiquent aussi que la guérison n'est pas une annihilation, mais une réorganisation du centre: un niveau à 0.2 eV de la bande de conduction disparait, remplacé par un niveau plus profond, après recuit à 100 °C. Dans le modèle de JAMES et LARK-HOROVITZ [11], ceci serait explicable par disparition de l'interstitiel.

3·4. *De* 420 °K *à* 550 °K. – La guérison a été étudiée en détail dans ce domaine, théoriquement et expérimentalement. WAITE [20] a proposé un modèle de recombinaison de deux espèces mobiles, la diffusion limitant le taux de réaction; on suppose une corrélation entre les deux espèces. Cette théorie est en bon accord avec les résultats expérimentaux [20, 13]. On trouve une énergie d'activation de 1.4 eV et un très long « transitoire » en $(Dt)^{\frac{1}{2}}$ qui correspond à la recombinaison de paires proches: 70 % des défauts. Il semblerait naturel de parler de recombinaison de lacunes et d'interstitiels; cependant, la considération des étapes précédentes à plus basse température, rend cela douteux: les paires proches semblent déjà s'être recombinées à 78 °K, et à température ordinaire, l'un des défauts a une mobilité suffisante pour s'être largement éloigné de l'autre élément de la paire.

3·5. *Mesure directe de la mobilité des défauts* [21]. – Dans le domaine $(0 \div 100)$ °C, nous avons tenté de mesurer directement la mobilité des défauts dans le germanium. Ces centres, ayant une action d'accepteur, sont chargés. Sous l'action d'un champ électrique, ils seront donc susceptibles de se déplacer. Nous avons mis au point une technique, voisine de la technique de « l'entrainement des ions » (ion drift) de PELL [22], où le champ électrique est celui d'un jonction *n-p* polarisée en inverse; la répartition des défauts chargés est mesurée par l'intermédiaire de la capacité de la jonction. Une description détaillée a été publiée ailleurs [21].

Les expériences ont été faites sur du germanium *n* dopé à l'antimoine irradié par des électrons de 1 MeV ou des γ du ^{60}Co, à -30 °C. Deux domaines distincts de température sont à considérer.

Entre 0 °C et 45 °C, aucun effet du champ électrique n'a pu être mis en évidence; cependant, les défauts accepteurs disparaissaient, comme dans les expériences décrites au paragraphe 3 précédent. Ceci semble paradoxal: les défauts sont chargés — sinon ils ne seraient pas visibles — et ils sont très mobiles, comme nous l'avons vu. Cependant il faut remarquer que l'expérience d'entrainement des ions mesure une mobilité effective, sur des déplacements de l'ordre de quelques microns, alors que la mobilité, supérieure ou égale

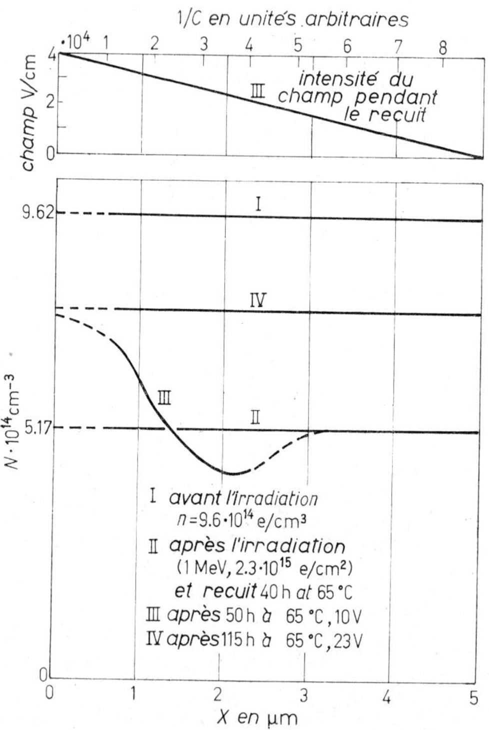

Fig. 1. – Répartition des centres chargés, dans la région n d'une jonction n-p, avant irradiation (I), puis, au cours de diverses étapes d'irradiation (II) et de guérison en présence d'un champ électrique (III, IV). La jonction est obtenue par alliage d'indium sur du germanium n de 2.3 Ω cm. La répartition des centres est mesurée par la variation de la capacité en fonction de la tension inverse (21). (Avec autorisation du *Journal of Applied Physics*.)

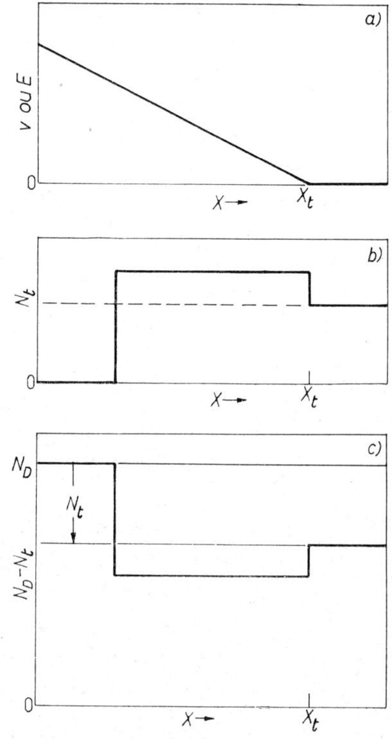

Fig. 2. – Interprétation de la figure précédente: (a) montre la répartition du champ électrique E et des vitesses d'entraînement v de centres chargés négativement, dans la partie n de la zone de charge d'espace; (b) montre leur distribution après un certain temps; les centres négatifs sont entraînés vers l'intérieur de la jonction, mais s'arrêtent à la limite x_t de la zone de charge d'espace; (c) représente la distribution obtenue expérimentalement (Fig. 1, III): les centres négatifs N_t compensent les centres positifs (donneurs chimiques N_D); on mesure $N_D - N_t$. (Avec autorisation du *Journal of Applied Physics*.)

à 10^{-13} cm²/s, qui correspond à l'association avec les impuretés, est une mobilité microscopique, mesurée sur des distances de 10^{-5} cm. Le centre diffusant n'aura donc pas le temps de subir le champ électrique, étant très rapidement piégé par un centre d'impureté fixe.

Au-dessus de 45 °C, après achèvement de l'étape précédente de guérison, une mobilité microscopique devient mesurable dans nos expériences. A cette température les centres qui se déplacent sont ceux qui disparaîtraient dans l'étape suivante du recuit, au-dessus de 120 °C. Le champ électrique peut les déplacer sur quelques μm (Fig. 1 et 2); on voit que ce sont des centres chargés négativement qui se déplacent avec une mobilité de $2.6\cdot10^{-14}$ cm²/V·s, à 65 °C. Si on suppose que les centres portent une charge unité, le coefficient de diffusion est $0.8\cdot10^{-15}$ cm²/s. L'énergie d'activation entre 45 °C et 70 °C est (0.95 ± 0.2) eV (Fig. 3).

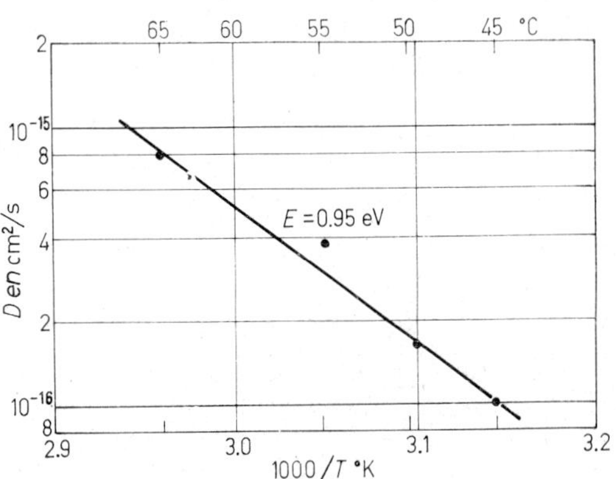

Fig. 3. – Variation du coefficient de diffusion du défaut mobile avec la température; on suppose que le centre a une charge $-|e|$. (Avec autorisation du *Journal of Applied Physics*.)

On remarquera la concordance de cette énergie d'activation avec celle signalée ci-dessus pour la migration des lacunes (**2**·1). Si on extrapole à 65 °C la valeur de D_v donnée par LETAW [3], on obtient 10^{-15} cm²/s, ce qui est assez remarquable. En plus, sans qu'on puisse déterminer dans cette expérience la position exacte du niveau d'énergie du centre, on peut montrer qu'il n'est observable que s'il se trouve voisin de la bande de valence.

Ceci nous conduit donc à proposer l'assimilation de ces centres mobiles avec des lacunes.

4. – Discussion.

Diverses questions se posent alors: quel est le rôle des interstitiels, quel est le centre « accepteur comme une lacune » qui disparait thermiquement dans l'étape 3, quelle est la nature du processus d'annihilation dans l'étape 4.

Supposer que l'interstitiel est, soit immobile, soit au contraire annihilé à très basse température soulève des objections. Dans un réseau ouvert comme celui du germanium, l'interstitiel devrait se déplacer très librement: le lithium interstitiel, à 50 °C, est 10^4 fois plus mobile qu'une lacune; un ion germanium serait évidemment, moins mobile, mais probablement plus que la lacune; par contre, pour assurer la disparition totale de l'interstitiel en dessous de 78 °K, il faudrait un coefficient de diffusion encore plus grand. D'ailleurs, dans ce cas, il ne resterait plus de lacunes. On peut aussi imaginer que l'interstitiel ne se manifeste pas par des effets électroniques, tout au moins dans les conditions expérimentales de Brown, et dans les nôtres, où toutes les mesures étaient effectuées à température de l'air liquide, température de référence. En raison de la position du niveau de Fermi à cette température, l'interstitiel n'est pas chargé si c'est un donneur; sa disparition ne serait donc pas remarquée. Des mesures en fonction de la température seraient nécessaires.

Une autre hypothèse est celle déjà signalée [16] de la barrière à l'annihilation des paires lacunes-interstitiels. Cette barrière permettrait vers 30 °C à une fraction importante des lacunes d'aller s'associer avec des impuretés chimiques sans faire la mauvaise rencontre d'un interstitiel. A une température plus élevée, la barrière serait moins efficace, on aurait de nouveau la recombinaison « bimoléculaire ». Dans tous les cas, l'hypothèse de Waite [20] de la forte corrélation entre lacunes et interstitiels doit être abandonnée, puisqu'on a vu qu'au moins un des éléments de la paire pouvait se déplacer sur des milliers de distances interatomiques, sans se recombiner.

L'hypothèse de la facile migration des lacunes, qui semble nécessaire pour expliquer ces différents phénomènes, a été pleinement justifiée dans le silicium, par différentes expériences de résonance de spin, où l'identification des centres est plus directe que dans les mesures électriques: les centres « A » (association oxygène-lacune) n'apparaissent, après une irradiation à basse température [23, 24] que si le cristal est suffisamment réchauffé pour rendre les lacunes mobiles; les résonances du manganèse ou du chrome substitutionnels n'apparaissent que si l'on a introduit des lacunes, par précipitation de cuivre ou par irradiation, à une température où elles sont mobiles [25]. Dans les deux cas, on trouve une mobilité notable à température ordinaire.

Des expériences analogues sur le germanium sont évidemment souhaitables, ainsi qu'une étude plus précise de l'influence des impuretés, de la répartition initiale des défauts, etc., dans les expériences de guérison thermique ou d'entrainement des ions, avant qu'on puisse conclure définitivement à la mobilité de la lacune à température ordinaire.

* * *

Une partie de ce travail a été effectuée durant un séjour d'un an aux Bell Telephone Laboratories et avec le soutien de la Wright Air Development Division of the U.S. Air Force. Je remercie W. L. Brown et P. Aigrani pour de nombreuses discussions.

BIBLIOGRAPHIE

[1] A. SEEGER: *Solid State Physics* (*Conference de Bruxelles*, 1958), vol. **1** (1960), p. 61.
[2] P. HAASEN et A. SEEGER: *Halbleiter Probleme*, **4**, 68 (1958).
[3] H. LETAW, W. PORTNOY et L. SLIFKIN: *Phys. Rev.*, **102**, 636 (1956).
[4] P. PENNING: *Phys. Rev.*, **110**, 586 (1958).
[5] A. G. TWEET: *Phys. Rev.*, **106**, 221 (1957).
[6] H. LETAW: *Journ. Phys. Chem. Solids*, **1**, 100 (1956).
[7] R. A. LOGAN: *Phys. Rev.*, **101**, 1455 (1956).
[8] A. G. TWEET: *Phys. Rev.*, **99**, 1245 (1955).
[9] E. S. GREINER, P. BREIDT, J. N. HOBSTETTER et W. C. ELLIS: *Trans. AIME*, **209**, 813 (1957).
[10] P. PENNING: *Phil. Res. Rept.*, **13**, 17 (1958).
[11] H. M. JAMES et K. LARK-HOROVITZ: *Zeits. Phys. Chem.*, **198**, 107 (1951).
[12] J. N. HOBSTETTER et P. BREIDT: *Journ. Appl. Phys.*, **28**, 1214 (1957).
[13] G. AIROLDI, Z. FUHRMAN et E. GERMAGNOLI: *Nuovo Cimento*, **14**, 452 (1959).
[14] J. W. MACKAY, G. W. GOBELI et E. E. KLONTZ: *Phys. Rev. Lett.*, **2**, 146 (1959); J. W. MACKAY et E. E. KLONTZ: *Journ. Appl. Phys.*, **30**, 9 (1959).
[15] W. L. BROWN et W. M. AUGUSTYNIAK: *Journ., Appl. Phys.*, **30**, 1300 (1959).
[16] W. L. BROWN, W. M. AUGUSTYNIAK et T. R. WAITE: *Journ. Appl. Phys.*, **30**, 1258 (1959).
[17] P. BARUCH: *Journ. Phys. Chem. Sol.*, **8**, 153 (1959)
[18] J. H. CRAWFORD et J. W. CLELAND: *Journ. Appl. Phys.*, **30**, 1204 (1959).
[19] O. L. CURTIS: communication personnelle.
[20] T. R. WAITE: *Phys. Rev.*, **107**, 471 (1957).
[21] P. BARUCH: *Journ. Appl. Phys.*, **32**, 653 (1961).
[22] E. M. PELL: *Journ. Appl. Phys.*, **31**, 291 (1960).
[24] G. WATKINS, J. W. CORBETT et R. M. WALKER: *Journ. Appl. Phys.*, **30**, 1198 (1959).
[25] H. H. WOODBURY et G. W. LUDWIG: *Phys. Rev. Lett.*, **5**, 98 (1960).

Transmutation Doping and Recoil Effects in Semiconductors Exposed to Thermal Neutrons.

J. W. CLELAND

Oak Ridge National Laboratory, Solid State Division - Oak Ridge, Tenn. (*)

The design and operation of a nuclear reactor depends greatly on the physical stability of the materials employed. The energetic particles present can produce drastic changes in the size, strength, electrical and mechanical properties of reactor materials. The effect of radiation on materials is therefore an important problem.

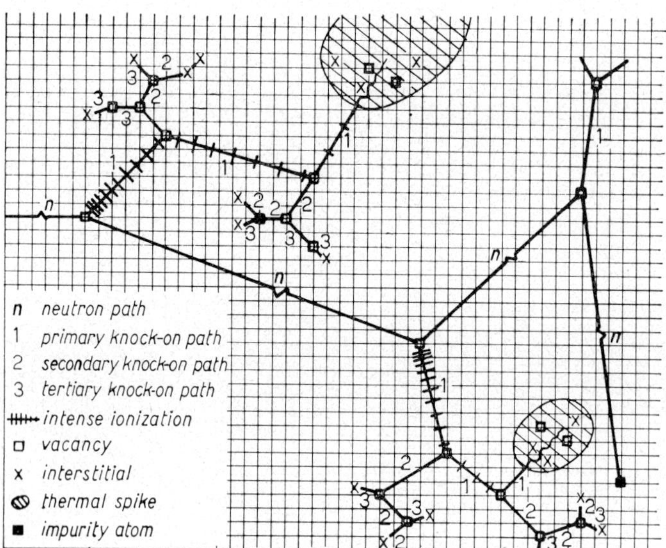

Fig. 1. – A schematic drawing of the various types of lattice damage produced by neutron bombardment.

(*) Oak Ridge National Laboratory is operated by Union Carbide Corporation for the U. S. Atomic Energy Commission.

Semiconductors are extremely sensitive to radiation effects. This sensitivity, plus a good fundamental knowledge of their physical structure, has made them of value in studies of radiation effects. J. H. CRAWFORD jr. [1], will discuss this general subject in detail; thus, it is my intention to concentrate on some recent experimental results on one phase of the overall problem.

The complexity of reactor irradiation effects is indicated in Fig. 1, where a single fast neutron has created interstitial atoms and vacancies, disordered regions or clusters (sometimes called thermal spikes), and finally, the fast neutron has been reduced to thermal energy and has produced a chemical impurity by trasmutation. Fig. 2 is a summary of these various processes.

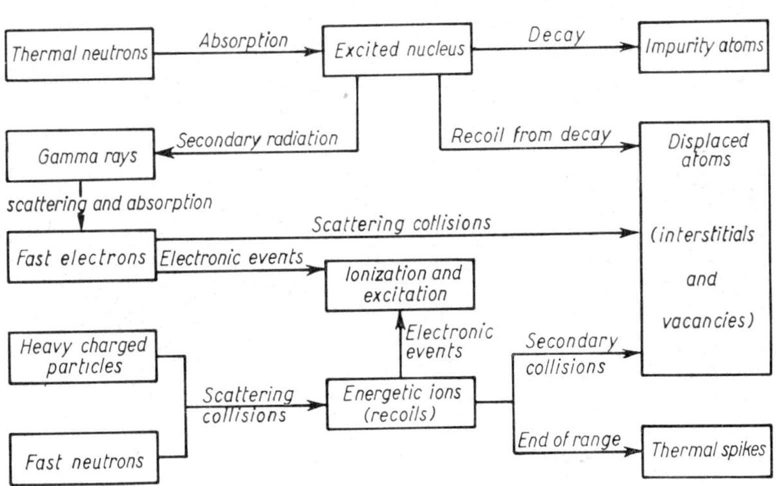

Fig. 2. – A « flow diagram » of radiation damage processes.

Note that an excited nucleus can recoil upon emission of secondary radiation and that γ-rays can produce fast electrons that can also produce displaced atoms.

The possibility of chemical impurity introduction into certain semiconductors by transmutation following thermal-neutron absorption has long been recognized [2]. n-type Ge can be converted to p-type material by this process, since the ^{71}Ge to ^{71}Ga transmutation effect exceeds the ^{75}Ge to ^{75}As effect; hence, acceptors are introduced. This technique has been employed in the past to produce material with a fixed compensation of chemical impurities, to study impurity banding phenomena and to investigate cross-sections, decay schemes and half-lives by Hall coefficient and conductivity measurements.

Chemical impurities, plastic deformation, quenching and radiation all serve to introduce defect states in semiconductors and these serve to alter the electrical, optical, chemical and mechanical behavior. Thus, the energy-level position and acceptor or donor action of such defects is a subject of considerable importance.

Transmutation doping, in principle, should provide a novel means of determining the energy-level position and acceptor or donor action of some of these defect states. The Fermi level or chemical potential may be defined as that energy position where the probability of occupancy of a particular energy state is exactly one-half. The Fermi level for normal n-type Ge lies in the region of the original donor states introduced by the n-type donor impurities. This is very near the top of the forbidden-energy band. The Fermi level for p-type Ge, however, lies very near the acceptor states introduced by the p-type acceptor impurities; and this is very near the floor of the forbidden-energy band.

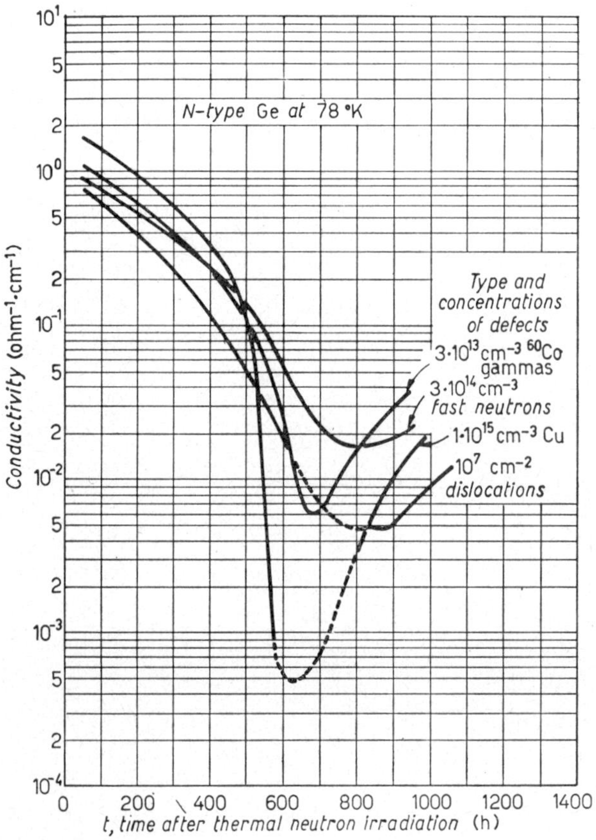

Fig. 3. – The change in conductivity of n-type Ge with time during radioactive decay of $^{71}Ge \rightarrow {}^{71}Ga$.

Consider a sample of n-type Ge, heavily irradiated with thermal-energy neutrons. The ^{75}Ge to ^{75}As transmutation, with an 84-minute half-life serves to make the sample more n-type; however, the ^{71}Ge to ^{71}Ga transmutation, which has a 12-day half-life, introduces p-type acceptor impurities; and the relative cross-sections are such that we obtain three Ga atoms for each As atom produced. The Fermi level, consequently, is swept across the forbidden energy gap as the electron concentration is reduced, and the sample is converted to p-type.

We have applied the technique of « Fermi level spectrometry » to material that contained defect states introduced by plastic deformation, chemical impurity diffusion, and irradiation [3]. It was hoped that the Fermi level would be held up or pinned as any of the localized defect states were forced to ionize or empty; however, Fig. 3 shows only a uniform reduction in carrier concentration or conductivity as the ^{71}Ga is introduced. It is believed that a slight attenuation in original impurity concentration may have masked any inflection that may have occurred. An attenuation of 0.1% at 10^{15} cm^3 original carrier concentration would be an attenuation of 100% at a concentration of 10^{12} cm^{-3}. Such an effect would produce a mixed n- and p-type material, for which electrical measurements would be essentially meaningless. We therefore intend to repeat these experiments with high-purity, zone-leveled material, with the hope that a more careful attention to homogeneity will enable us to observe the inflection that is expected as the Fermi level crosses these defect states.

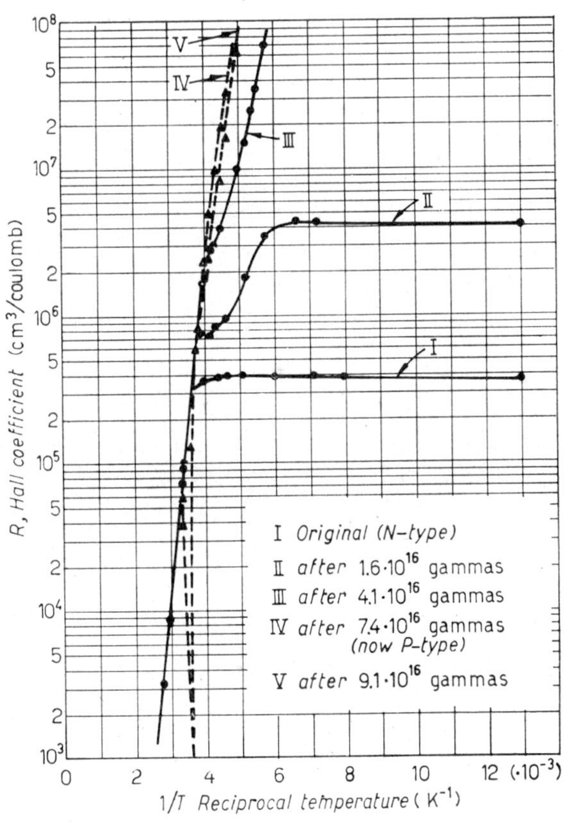

Fig. 4. – Log of Hall coefficient *vs.* reciprocal temperature of n-type Ge after successive γ-ray exposures.

Monoenergetic electron-irradiation experiments [4] on semiconductors have been employed to determine the displacement threshold, or the threshold energy required for the formation of a stable acceptor. This value is approximately 13 eV for both Ge and Si, which corresponds to an incident electron of about 0.4 MeV. The photons from a ^{60}Co γ source have energies of 1.17 and 1.33 MeV and these produce Compton electrons with a maximum energy of about 1 MeV. Fig. 4 shows the effect of ^{60}Co photon irradiation on n-type Ge, where the Hall coefficient is plotted *vs.* inverse temperature. This particular sample [5] had an original carrier concentration of about $1.8\cdot10^{13}$ electron/cm^3, which were introduced in the original melt by the addition of Sb impurity. The carrier concentration after irradiation by $1.6\cdot10^{16}$ photons has been reduced to about $2\cdot10^{12}$ electrons$\cdot$cm^{-3}, and the resultant step in the Hall coefficient curve indicates the presence of a deep-lying acceptor state and a shallow acceptor state that ionizes or empties at an intermediate temperature. Continued irradiation, and an analysis of the slope of curve III, places the shallow state at ~ 0.20 eV; and further irradiation converts the sample to p-type with an apparent energy-level position at ~ 0.26 eV above the valence band.

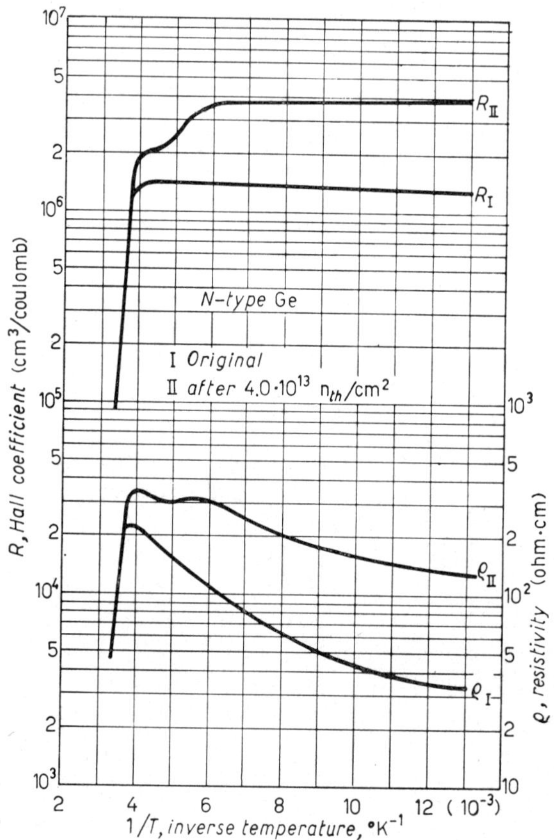

Fig. 5. – Log of Hall coefficient (upper curves) and log of resistivity (lower curves) *vs.* reciprocal temperature of n-type Ge before and after exposure to thermal neutrons.

Fig. 5 shows very similar data for n-type Ge that was irradiated with thermal-energy neutrons. Here the initial carrier concentration was about $6 \cdot 10^{12}$ electrons cm^{-3} and it was reduced to about $2 \cdot 10^{12}$ electrons cm^{-3} by a total integrated thermal neutron flux of $4.0 \cdot 10^{13}$ cm^{-2}. Note the step in the Hall coefficient curve that indicates the formation of two defect states. Further irradiation and an analysis of the slope places the shallow step at ~ 0.20 eV, and continued irradiation converts the material to p-type.

Let us examine the thermal-neutron absorption properties of normal isotopic Ge with the aid of Table I, where the isotopic abundance, absorption cross-section and relative absorptions are listed. These values indicate that 9.8% of the actual absorptions occur in ^{74}Ge, which later transmutes to ^{75}As; and 30.4% of the actual absorptions occur in ^{70}Ge, which later transmutes to ^{71}Ga.

TABLE I. – *A summary of the neutron absortion behaviour of the various germanium isotopes.*

Isotope	^{70}Ge	^{72}Ge	^{73}Ge	^{74}Ge	^{76}Ge
Abundance	20.45%	27.41%	7.77%	36.58%	7.79%
σ_a (10^{-24} cm^2)	3.4	0.98	14	0.62	0.36
Relative absorption	30.4 %	11.7 %	47.2 %	9.8 %	1.2 %

H. C. SCHWEINLER [6] recently considered the implications of thermal-neutron absorption in semiconductors and indicated that the recoil from capture γ-ray emission in an (n-γ) reaction may be sufficient to eject the atom undergoing neutron capture from its lattice site, thereby creating a Frenkel-type defect. This is essentially the Szilard-Chalmers process in the solid state.

The kinetic energy in eV of a recoiling atom of atomic weight A is equal to $537/A$ times the energy of the emitted γ-ray expressed in MeV. We have mentioned that the displacement threshold energy is about 15 eV for both

TABLE II. – *The calculated recoil energies of the various germanium isotopes on emission of capture γ-rays.*

$$\frac{(\text{K.E.})_A}{1\ \text{eV}} = \frac{537}{A}\cdot n\left(\frac{1}{n}\,\frac{bn}{1\ \text{MeV}}\right)^2 = \frac{537}{An}\left(\frac{bn}{1\ \text{MeV}}\right)^2$$

Target nucleus	^{70}Ge	^{72}Ge	^{73}Ge	^{74}Ge	^{76}Ge
bn = binding energy of neutron (MeV)	7.22	6.62	10.07	6.45	5.83
n = no. of γ-rays	2	2	4	2	2
K.E. of recoil (eV)	197	161	184	149	118
No. per 100 neutron captures in Ge	30.4	11.7	47.2	9.8	1.2
Average recoil energy = 182 eV					

TABLE III. – *A summary of the neutron capture behavior of the silicon isotopes.*

Isotope	^{28}Si	^{29}Si	^{30}Si
Abundance	92.28%	4.67%	3.05%
σ_a (10^{-24} cm^2)	0.08	0.27	0.12
Relative absorption	81.9%	14.0%	4.1%

Si and Ge. This would correspond to the emission of a γ-ray of 0.88 and 1.4 MeV for Si and Ge, respectively.

Unfortunately, the capture γ-ray emission spectrum of Ge has not been measured; however, we can estimate the recoil energy of a Ge nucleus from the known binding energy and an assumed number of γ-rays emitted per capture. This information is tabulated in Table II and indicates that the average recoil energy of a Ge atom undergoing thermal-neutron capture is approximately 180 eV.

Table III shows the principal isotopes of Si, the percentage abundance, the isotopic cross-section in barns and the relative absorption of the various isotopes. The capture γ-ray emission spectrum of Si is known in considerable detail. The nuclear energy level diagrams of the excited nucleus and the frequencies of the principal transitions per hundred neutron captures have been tabulated for a wide range of γ-ray energies [7]. Table IV summarizes this

TABLE IV. – *The recoil energy spectrum of silicon.*

Events per 100 neutron captures	Average K.E. of resulting Si
55.2	680
19.0	1050
9.0	835
6.5	990
6.5	555
4.0	380
2.0	1000
1.6	1330
0.7	1110

Summary: 100 *thermal-neutron captures in* Si *produce a*) 100 *recoiling* Si *nuclei, of average energy* 780 eV; *b*) 4 ^{31}P *with the net destruction of* 4 Si (*after several* $\times 2.6$ h).

data for Si and indicates that the average kinetic energy of the recoiling Si nucleus is about 780 eV.

The usual criterion [8] for the expected number of displaced atoms would be the total kinetic energy of the bombarding particle (which is 180 eV for Ge and 780 eV for Si) divided by twice the threshold energy of displacement, which has been determined as about 15 eV. Under these assumptions, one might expect 180 eV/30 = 6 and 780 eV/30 = 26 displacements in Ge and Si per actual thermal-neutron absorption and recoil.

Let us summarize the experimental conditions before returning to this particular result. The horizontal thermal column of the Brookhaven National Reactor has a thermal flux of $3.5\cdot10^{11}$ nvt/cm² s and a Cd ratio of 6000. The slant-animal tunnel of the Oak Ridge National Laboratory Graphite Reactor has a thermal flux of $1\cdot10^{9}$ nvt/cm²·s and a Cd ratio of 10^5. Cobalt-aluminium foil monitors were used to monitor the thermal-neutron flux; and boral shielding was employed on occasion to greatly reduce the thermal flux, thus providing an independent indication of the background effect of fast neutrons or, possibly, γ-rays.

A large number of *n*- and *p*-type samples of both Ge and Si were exposed in a series of experiments that were designed to investigate the recoil effect. The end result of these experiments was that the rate of electron removal in *n*-type Ge was almost identically « unity » per actual neutron absorption over a wide range of initial carrier concentrations and total dosages. Absolutely no evidence for the estimated six displacements per actual neutron absorption in Ge was observed. The rate of electron removal in *n*-type Si was approximately two per thermal neutron absorbed, again in sharp contrast with the ~ 26 displacements predicted.

Let me remind you of Fig. 5, which indicated a step in the Hall coefficient curve for thermal-neutron-irradiated *n*-type Ge. This would indicate that each recoil actually removes two electrons; hence, the rate of defect introduction may be only 0.5 per actual thermal-neutron absorption in Ge. Thus the experimentally observed conduction electron removal rate in *n*-type Ge and Si is approximately 1/10 that predicted by the above theory.

I do not want to dwell on this lack of agreement at present. The capture γ-ray spectrum in Ge has not been determined, and one does not know the extent of interstitial-vacancy recombination at the irradiation temperature of 40 °C. Low-temperature thermal-neutron irradiation experiments might help, but we do not have such a facility. Therefore, for the moment, one can only state that thermal-neutron absorption does result in the creation of Frenkel-

TABLE V. – *The decay-products induced into natural germanium by thermal neutron exposure.*

30.4% of neutron captures in germanium	$^{70}\text{Ge}\,(\text{n},\gamma)\,^{71}\text{Ge} \xrightarrow[K]{12\,\text{d}} {}^{71}\text{Ga}$
9.8% of neutron captures in germanium	$^{74}\text{Ge}\,(\text{n},\gamma)\,^{75}\text{Ge} \xrightarrow[\beta]{82\,\text{m}} {}^{75}\text{As}$
1.2% of neutron captures in germanium	$^{76}\text{Ge}\,(\text{n},\gamma)\,^{77}\text{Ge} \xrightarrow[\beta]{12\,\text{h}} {}^{77}\text{As} \xrightarrow[\beta]{38.8\,\text{h}} {}^{77}\text{Se}$

type defects; however, there is no evidence of any multiple defect production from the energetic recoil that results.

It should, perhaps, be emphasized that the above is an instantaneous process. Table V indicates the relative absorption, decay scheme, half-life and end products of those particular Ge isotopes that later transmute to other chemical impurities. The maximum recoil energy upon transmutation is only 2.2 eV for the ^{71}Ge and about 19 eV for the ^{75}As, where these values are much less than the original recoil energy of 182 eV.

If we thermal-neutron irradiate and then measure the carrier concentration, we observe an original decrease in electron concentration as a result of those defects introduced by recoil. We then observe an additional decrease in electron concentration of an amount and half-life of introduction that is predicted by the amount of ^{71}Ge to ^{71}Ga transmutation expected. If we thermal-neutron irradiate and then vacuum anneal the sample for twenty hours at 450 °C, we remove all lattice desorder or defects created by fast neutrons, γ-rays or recoil. This technique has long been employed to remove radiation-induced disorder in semiconductors. However, since the sample has been restored to its original order, the actual net effect is that one first observes an additional increase in electron concentration as produced by the relatively fast transmutation to ^{75}As and ^{77}Se. Approximately nine days are required for the amount of ^{71}Ga to compensate, after which we observe a further decrease in electron concentration of an amount and half-life of introduction that is predicted by the amount of ^{71}Ge to ^{71}Ga transmutation expected.

The main point of all this is that one would expect the ^{75}As and ^{71}Ga to be interstitial in the first experiment (no anneal), since Frenkel-type defects were created by the recoil and since the additional recoil on transmutation is very small. One would expect the ^{75}As and ^{71}Ga to be substitutional in the second experiment (after anneal), since the sample was restored to its original order and since the recoil energy on transmutation is very small. However, our experiments indicate an exactly identical behavior as regards donor or acceptor action by the ^{75}As and ^{71}Ga irrespective of whether these transmutation-produced impurities are evidently interstitial from the original recoil or substitutional as a result of vacuum anneal.

The absence of multiple displacements in Si and Ge from recoil and the apparently identical behavior of transmutation-produced donors or acceptors in Ge that are presumably interstitial compared with those that are substitutional must indicate that the recoil energy is absorbed in some other form than that of creating additional defects. These results may further indicate that the particular recoiling atom does not remain interstitial, since it is difficult to assume that interstitial and substitutional chemical impurities would exhibit identical properties. Some form of replacement collision process might be indicated, wherein the recoiling atom does not necessarily remain interstitial.

It has not been possible to examine the role of chemical impurity interstitial atoms in Si, since only 4.1% of the Si displacements are those of ^{30}Si, which transmutes to ^{31}P with a 2.6 hour half-life. Thermal-neutron radiation effects on the intermetallic semiconducting compound InSb are very extensive; however, recoil effects are somewhat difficult to determine. Extensive relaxation of lattice damage has been observed between 78 °K and room temperature in InSb, and the exact nature of the defect created by irradiation is apparently different for irradiation at these two different temperatures. Some evidence of recoil effects has been obtained following ambient-temperature thermal-neutron irradiation of this material, and the results appear to agree with expectations; however, low-temperature thermal-neutron irradiation and subsequent annealing studies would be of great value in any complete investigation of recoil effects in this material.

Table VI shows the isotopic content, absorption cross-section, fraction of

TABLE VI. – *Composition and end-products for thermal neutron exposure of the isotopically enriched Ge specimen. Isotopic enriched* ^{74}*Ge.*

Isotope	Fraction (f)	Cross-section σ_a (10^{-24} cm^2)	Fraction of neutrons absorbed	End-product
70	0.007	3.4	0.028	^{71}Ga
72	0.011	0.98	0.013	^{73}Ge
73	0.156	14.0	0.256	^{74}Ge
74	0.958	0.62	0.699	^{76}As
76	0.008	0.36	0.004	^{77}Se
	$(\bar{\sigma}_a) = 0.85 \cdot 10^{-24}$ cm^2			

thermal neutrons absorbed and transmutation end-product of isotopically enriched ^{74}Ge. The thermal-neutron recoil effect and subsequent transmutation effect of this material would seem of interest. The total absorption cross-section would be about 0.85 barns, and one would expect approximately 0.699 displaced ^{75}As atoms for each 0.256 displaced ^{74}Ge atom. Multiple defect creation by recoil would tend to make the material more p-type, since this process would again be expected to create Frenkel-type defects.

This material was only available, however, as impure GeO_2 at \$ 400/g from the Stable Isotopes Division of the Oak Ridge National Laboratory. I therefore want to give credit to T. H. GEBALLE and his associates at the Bell Telephone Laboratories, who obtained the total known supply of this material and were able to purify, zone refine and grow a single crystal from 17 g of GeO_2. This work has been published by GEBALLE and HULL in the May 1,

1958, *Physical Review*. I also want to thank Dr. WALTER BROWN, Dr. TED GEBALLE and their associates for the use of a portion of the original ingot.

Fig. 6 shows the Hall coefficient and resistivity *vs.* temperature of a high-purity, single-crystal n-type sample of 95.8 % enriched ^{74}Ge with an excess donor concentration of $1.2 \cdot 10^{13}$ electrons $\cdot$ cm^{-3}. Note that thermal neutron irradiation increases the donor concentration. Note also that evidence for two defect states is observed and that the net donor concentration is greatly enhanced by vacuum anneal at 450 °C.

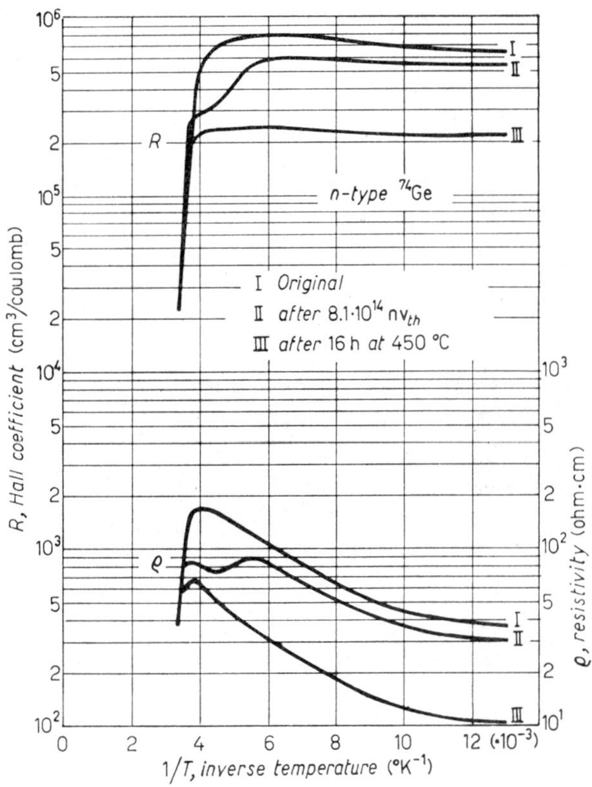

Fig. 6. – log Hall coefficient (upper curves) and log resistivity *vs.* reciprocal temperature for the enriched (^{74}Ge) specimen.

Table VII summarizes the experimental data that were obtained. Note that the actual increase in donor concentration after irradiation is only about 10 % of the expected amount of ^{75}As; however, the total change in carrier concentration after two irradiations and a vacuum anneal at 450 °C is almost identical with the expected increase in donor concentration. This latter result would indicate that the published values of absorption cross-section are correct, and that our experimental determination of thermal neutron flux values by cobalt-aluminium foils is also quite valid.

The very evident absence of those Frenkel-type defects that removed conduction electrons in normal isotopic Ge is perhaps the most important problem at the moment. There we observed the removal of two electrons for each actual thermal-neutron absorption and recoil. Under the same assumptions, and using the cross-section data just shown, one would expect that an irradiation of $8.1 \cdot 10^{14}$ nvt would produce $2.29 \cdot 10^{13}$ ^{74}Ge atoms $\cdot$ cm^{-3} that have transmuted to ^{75}As by the time of measurement, and $8.4 \cdot 10^{12}$ ^{73}Ge atoms $\cdot$ cm^{-3}

that do not transmute. The other three isotopes can be neglected. These values would indicate that $3.13 \cdot 10^{13}$ Frenkel-type defects would be created and would remove about $1.57 \cdot 10^{13}$ electrons$\cdot$cm^{-3} from conduction band. Instead, one observed the addition of $2.23 \cdot 10^{12}$ more donors$\cdot$cm^{-3} after irradiation and about ten times that number after anneal.

It has been suggested that the initial recoil upon thermal-neutron absorption may result in a series of lattice displacements, such that the original, recoiling atom is almost always left in a substitutional position, while some

TABLE VII – *Summary of experimental results on the enriched* (^{74}*Ge*) *specimen. n-type* ^{74}Ge.

Carrier concentration	Thermal flux	Change in carrier concentration	Expected donor increase
$n \cdot cm^{-3}$ at 77 °K	$n_{th} \cdot cm^{-2}$	$\Delta n \cdot cm^{-3}$ at 77 °K	^{74}Ge-^{75}As
$1.148 \cdot 10^{13}$	—	—	—
$1.279 \cdot 10^{13}$	$3.98 \cdot 10^{14}$	$1.31 \cdot 10^{12}$	$1.15 \cdot 10^{13}$
$1.375 \cdot 10^{13}$	$4.06 \cdot 10^{14}$	$0.92 \cdot 10^{12}$	$1.14 \cdot 10^{13}$
$3.444 \cdot 10^{13}$	0.00	$2.30 \cdot 10^{13}$ (*)	$2.29 \cdot 10^{13}$ (*)

(*) After 16 h at 450 °C vacuum anneal.

other lattice atom is placed in an interstitial position. This process might effectively dissipate the original recoil energy without the creation of multiple defects, and those atoms that later transmute would not be interstitial for the most part. This would explain the results on normal Ge, where two electrons were removed for each Frenkel defect produced, and where irradiated and irradiated-annealed material changed identically as the ^{71}Ga was introduced.

The addition of ^{75}As as a substitutional atom might essentially balance the removal of conduction electrons caused by the creation of some other Frenkel defect; however, about $\frac{1}{3}$ of the recoils in this material are those of ^{73}Ge that would not balance out the resulting defects. The fact that the sample is more n-type after irradiation would seem to indicate that this model of replacement collisions is not very adequate. It is therefore quite evident that additional experiments are necessary before the phenomena of recoil-defect introduction and transmutation doping experiments are well understood.

REFERENCES

[1] J. H. CRAWFORD jr.: this volume 333.
[2] J. W. CLELAND, K. LARK-HOROVITZ and J. C. PIGG: *Phys. Rev.*, **78**, 814 (1950).
[3] J. W. CLELAND and J. H. CRAWFORD: *Bull. Am. Phys. Soc.*, **5**, 196 (1960).
[4] See for example: J. J. LOFERSKI and P. P. RAPPAPORT: *Journ. Appl. Phys.*, **30**, 1296 (1959).
[5] J. W. CLELAND, J. H. CRAWFORD jr. and D. K. HOLMES: *Phys. Rev.*, **102**, 722 (1956).
[6] H. C. SCHWEINLER: *Journ. Appl. Phys.*, **30**, 1125 (1959).
[7] B. B. KINSEY, G. A. BARTHOLOMEW and W. H. WALKER: *Phys. Rev.*, **83**, 519 (1951); **93**, 1260 (1954).
[8] G. H. KINCHIN and R. S. PEASE: *Rep. Progr. Phys.*, **18**, 1 (1955).

Radiation Damage in Ionic and Covalent Crystals.

Introduction to Ionic Crystals.

G. Chiarotti

Istituto di Fisica dell'Università - Pavia

Introduction.

The study of ionic crystals has been very fruitful in understanding the defect properties of solids for a number of reasons:

i) In ionic crystals the lattice defects carry an electric charge and therefore contribute directly to the conductivity. Since ionic crystals are generally insulators or wide-gap semiconductors, very often such a contribution is by far the largest and the study of electrical properties yields direct information about the nature and concentration of defects. On the other hand, electrostatic interaction among the defects cause them to behave in a rather unique way as far as clustering and annealing properties are concerned [1].

ii) The existence of a wide gap between valence and conduction band allows a number of optical experiments to be done. The charged point defects create a field which at large distance is Coulombic; a well known theorem of quantum mechanics then states that there is an infinite number of levels in which a hole or an electron can be bound [2]. The optical transitions between such levels give rise to absorption bands, generally called color center bands, whose study provides considerable information on the defect pattern of the crystal [3].

iii) In ionic solids the main contribution to the cohesive energy comes from the interaction of closed-shell ions which may be treated as point charges; lattice calculations are therefore particularly simple and are expected to give reliable results [4].

1. – Point defects in ionic crystals.

The relative contribution of positive and negative ions to the electrical conductivity may be inferred from the knowledge of transport numbers (defined as the fraction of current carried by a given ion). In silver halides only positive ions are able to carry the current, whereas in alkali halides the negative ions give a small contribution just below the melting point. Table I

TABLE I. – *Transport numbers* [5].

Crystal	Temperature (°C)	t^+	t^-	$t_{\text{electronic}}$
NaCl	400	1.00	0.00	—
	500	0.98	0.02	—
	600	0.95	0.05	—
	625	0.93	0.07	
AgCl	20	1	—	—
	350	1	—	—
CuCl	18	0.00	—	1.00
	110	0.03	—	0.97
	232	0.50	—	0.50
	300	0.98	—	0.02
	366	1.00	—	0.00
PbI_2	255	0.39	0.61	—
	270	0.45	0.55	—
	290	0.67	0.33	—

shows some typical examples, taken from the experimental data of TUBANDT [5].

In alkali halides the lattice defects that cause conductivity and diffusion are the positive- and negative-ion vacancies (Schottky disorder), whereas in silver halides the equilibrium defect is the positive interstitial-vacancy pair (Frenkel disorder), the Ag^+ interstitial being the mobile unit [1].

The number of Schottky defects which are in thermal equilibrium at a given temperature is [6]:

$$n_s = N \exp[-g_s/2kT] , \tag{1}$$

where g_s is the free energy of formation of a pair of vacancies of opposite sign and N is the total number of ion pairs. Charge neutrality imposes that, in ideally pure crystals, the number of positive- and negative-ion vacancies are equal. In practice, however, aliovalent impurities introduce an excess of vacancies of a given sign, which become predominant at low temperatures where the number of defects given by (1) is very small. In alkali halides, for example, divalent cations are a very common impurity which go substitutionally into the lattice [7], thus giving rise to an excess of positive-ion vacancies.

The conductivity *vs.* temperature curve is therefore made up of two distinct regions clearly identifiable in Fig. 1 which shows the case of KCl containing different amounts of impurities [8]. In the high-temperature intrinsic range the number of vacancies is given by (1) and the activation energy for conductivity is $(E_s/2)+E_m$ (E_s = energy of formation of a pair of vacancies of opposite sign; E_m = energy of migration of the mobile defect); in the low temperature impurity range, on the other hand, the number of vacancies is essentially constant and the activation energy is simply E_m.

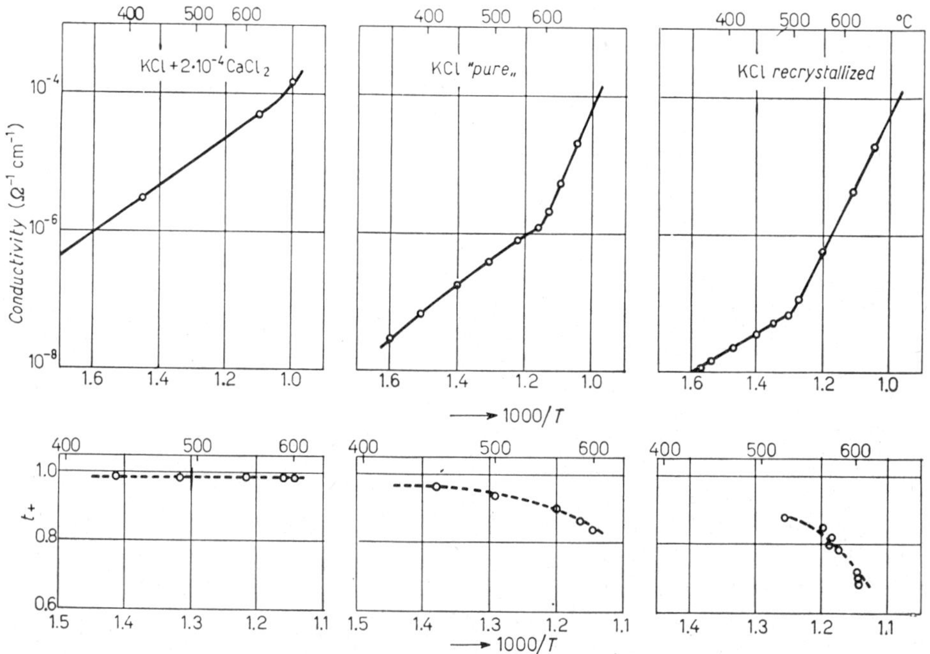

Fig. 1. – The electrical conductivity and transport numbers of positive ions (t_+) versus temperature for three crystals of KCl containing various amounts of impurities. (After KERKHOFF, ref. [8]).

Comparison between diffusion and conductivity is illuminating as to the nature of defects in ionic crystals; if both are due to the same mechanism, the ratio between the diffusion coefficient D and the electrical conductivity σ should be governed by the familiar Nernst-Einstein equation:

$$\frac{D}{\sigma} = \frac{kT}{Ne^2}, \tag{2}$$

where N is the total number of ion pairs per unit volume. On the other hand, deviations from (2) are expected when both ions contribute to conductivity or when diffusion takes place through an interstitialcy mechanism or through the migration of a neutral unit. Measurements of W. D. COMPTON [9] show, for example, that for AgCl in the intrinsic range the ratio between the diffusion coefficient of silver and the conductivity is about one half that given by (2). The discrepancy has been rationalized assuming that in silver halides diffusion takes place through an interstitialcy mechanism [10]. This is a process in which an interstitial ion (or atom) replaces an ion in a normal lattice site, pushing it into another interstitial position. It is clear that in this case the charge displacement is roughly twice the mass displacement. Considering correlations between successive jumps and the noncollinearity of collisions, MCCOMBIE and LIDIARD obtained satisfactory agreement between theory and experiments [10]. The occurrence of interstitialcy diffusion shows that in silver halides Frenkel disorder is predominant even at temperatures near the melting point.

Several types of experiments can be envisaged in order to establish which defect predominates in a given crystal. Combined measurements of density and lattice parameters at temperatures just below the melting point, where the concentration of defects is expected to be high, could be very valuable. In the case of Frenkel disorder the changes of density and of the elementary cell go together, whereas a net decrease of density is expected for Schottky disorder [11]. X-ray diffraction at high temperature shows conclusively that in silver halides Frenkel pairs are the predominant defect [12]. On the other hand, the conviction that positive- and negative-ion vacancies are the equilibrium defect in alkali halides is primarily based upon theoretical estimates, showing that the formation energy of a Frenkel pair is considerably higher (approximately three times) than that of a couple of vacancies of opposite sign [13]. In silver halides, on the contrary, the Van der Waals energy which gives a comparatively large contribution to the cohesive energy stabilizes the configuration of Ag^+ in interstitial position [14].

2. – Interaction among defects.

Elecrostatic interaction of charged defects cause them to agglomerate into clusters of various kind. It is customary to describe the equilibrium reactions which occur in a solid through the application of the mass-action law.

For the association of positive- and negative-ion vacancies in ionic crystals

$$(\boxed{+}) + (\boxed{-}) \rightleftarrows (\boxed{+}\boxed{-}) \,, \tag{3}$$

the mass-action law is written

$$\frac{n_{+-}}{n_+ n_-} = \frac{Z_{+-}}{Z_+ Z_-} = \sum_i z_{+-}^{(i)} \exp\left[-\varepsilon_{+-}^{(i)}/kT\right] , \tag{4}$$

where n_+, n_-, n_{+-} and Z_+, Z_-, Z_{+-} are respectively total numbers and partition functions of the defects participating in reaction (3), while $\varepsilon_{+-}^{(i)}$ and $z_{+-}^{(i)}$ are the energy and degeneracy of the i-th level of the vacancy pair. In eq. (4) the energy of the crystal when the vacancies do not interact has been taken as zero.

Table II shows the theoretical binding energies of a pair of vacancies in

TABLE II. – *Theoretical binding energy of a pair of vacancies (in* eV).

Crystal	Ground state [16]	First excited state [17]
KCl	0.72	0.38
NaCl	0.60	0.28

NaCl and KCl, for the fundamental and first excited states, according to calculations of FUMI *et al.* [15-17]. The excited states correspond to the vacancy pair having a separation larger than one atomic distance; in the first excited state the two vacancies sit at the two opposite positions along a cube diagonal.

The large energy difference between the fundamental and excited state make the contribution of the latter to the partition function of the pair negligible, so that in the intrinsic range where $n_+ = n_- = n$, (4) can be written

$$\frac{m}{n} = 6 \exp[E_0/kT] , \tag{5}$$

m being the fraction of associated pairs, and E_0 the binding energy of a pair in its fundamental state (sixfold degenerate since a pair of neighboring vacancies can be oriented in six ways in a cubic crystal). In the intrinsic range n is given by (1) and we obtain

$$m = A \exp\left[-\left((E_s/2) - E_0\right)/kT\right] , \tag{6}$$

E_s being the formation energy of two noninteracting vacancies. The fraction of associated pairs increases or decreases with temperature depending on the sign of $\left((E_s/2) - E_0\right)$. In alkali halides this quantity is generally positive so that the association is greater at high temperatures, which is just the contrary of what is found in a chemical dissociation reaction. Assuming for NaCl the theoretical values of E_s and E_0 (2.2 and .60 eV), FUMI and TOSI calculate values of m going from .08 at 500 °C to .24 at 700 °C. A considerable degree of association is therefore expected only just below the melting temperature.

O. THEIMER [18] has discussed the influence of entropy changes accompanying the association of vacancies, and has concluded that long range effects on the lattice frequencies of several rings of ions neighboring a dissociated vacancy may well produce a reduction of the estimated pair concentration of the order of 10.

Experimental evidence of association is rather poor. In principle, since the neutral pairs do not contribute to the conductivity, their presence should be detected in deviations from the Einstein relation (2). Deviations were in fact found in NaCl and NaBr [19] but are probably due to other effects [20]. It has been suggested recently by A. G. LIDIARD [21] that vacancy pairs might be responsible for the large diffusion coefficient found by MORRISON *et al.* [22] in the impurity range of NaCl. In fact in such a range the concentration of free negative-ion vacancies is expected to be depressed by the presence of a comparatively large amount of positive-ion vacancies, and one should not expect a large diffusion coefficient for the anion. On the other hand, the presence of pairs of vacancies which, according to calculations of DIENES [23], are rather mobile should help the diffusion of the negative ion. To check this point, LIDIARD suggested the study of anion diffusion in alkali halides contaning divalent cations; since doping does not change the concentration of pairs, the low temperature diffusion of Cl^- should be unaffected. Recent work of N. LAURANCE [24] on Ca-doped NaCl seems to provide some support for Lidiard's thesis, though the migration energy of the vacancy pair is found to be as high as that of isolated vacancies.

The experimental evidence of association of positive divalent impurities and positive-ion vacancies according to the quasi-chemical reaction

$$(7)\qquad (+\!\!+) + (\boxed{+}) \rightleftarrows (+\!\!+^{\boxed{+}}),$$

is, on the contrary, very good [1]. Table III shows few instances of the theoretical binding energies between divalent cations and positive ion vacancies [25, 17]. For Sr^{++} the binding energies are given for the fundamental as well as for the first excited state in which the two defects are collinear and

TABLE III. – *Theoretical binding energy between divalent cations and positive-ion vacancies (in* eV).

	Cd^{++} [25]	Ca^{++} [25]	Sr^{++} [17]	
			ground state	first excited state
NaCl	0.38	0.38	0.43	0.41
KCl	0.32	0.32	0.38	0.49

separated by a negative ion (Fig. 2). It must be noted that the two energies are indeed comparable. The ratio between the number of complexes in the fundamental and first excited state is

$$n_0/n_1 = 2 \exp[(E_0 - E_1)/kT] , \tag{8}$$

the pre-exponential factor being the ratio between the degeneracy of the two states.

G. D. WATKINS [26] has studied in great detail the electron spin resonance absorption of Mn^{++} in alkali halides and has been able to identify several different spectra arising from Mn^{++} ions in different environments. Two of them

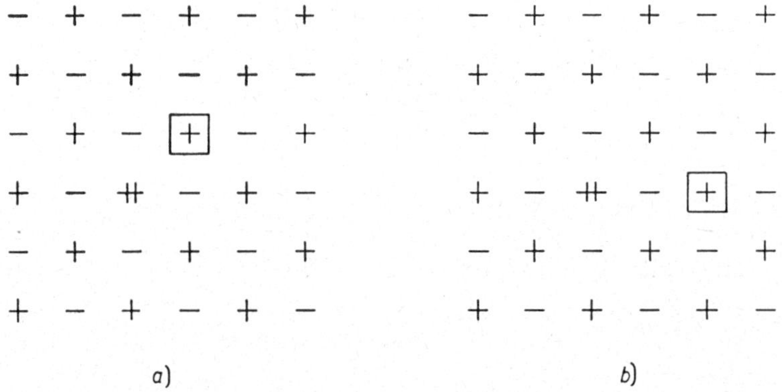

a)							b)					
−	+	−	+	−	+		−	+	−	+	−	+
+	−	+	−	+	−		+	−	+	−	+	−
−	+	−	[+]	−	+		−	+	−	+	−	+
+	−	++	−	+	−		+	−	++	−	[+]	−
−	+	−	+	−	+		−	+	−	+	−	+
+	−	+	−	+	−		+	−	+	−	+	−

Fig. 2. – The association of a divalent cation with a positive ion vacancy; *a*) fundamental state; *b*) first excited state.

have the symmetry corresponding to the configurations of Fig. 2. The knowledge of the relative intensities of these spectra at different temperatures allows then a direct determination (through eq. (8)) of the energy difference between the fundamental and the first excited state of the complex. The data obtained by WATKINS for Mn^{++} in KCl and NaCl are summarized in Table IV, where

TABLE IV.

Crystal	Mn^{++} (exp.) [26]		Sr^{++} (theor.) [17]
	n_0/n_1	$E_0 - E_1$ (eV)	$E_0 - E_1$ (eV)
NaCl	7.5	+ 0.034	+ 0.02
KCl	0.65	− 0.029	− 0.11

the theoretical results of TOSI and AIROLDI for Sr^{++} are also reported. Hovever, the two sets of results are not directly comparable, referring to different impurities. The excellent qualitative agreement is nevertheless worth mentioning.

The existence of several equally probable configurations of the complex could also explain the puzzling results obtained by several investigators who were concerned with the symmetry properties of the Z_2-center in KCl [27]. In fact it has been shown recently that the model of the Z_2-center proposed by F. SEITZ [28], namely the association of a complex with an F-center, accounts correctly for the data on thermal equilibrium of color centers in doped KCl [29]. However, assuming the planar structure of the Z_2-center shown in Fig. 3, several authors have unsuccessfully tried to detect anisotropic properties associated with the Z_2-band. In the light of what has been previously said for the complex, it seems reasonable to conclude that several configurations coexist also in the case of the Z_2 center whose symmetry is then considerably lowered.

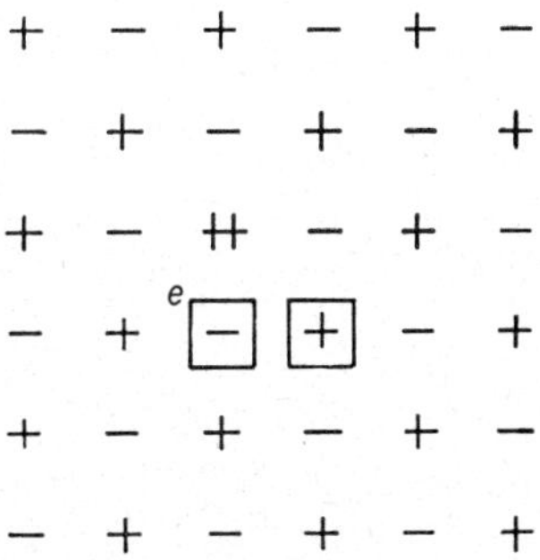

$$\begin{array}{cccccc}
+ & - & + & - & + & - \\
- & + & - & + & - & + \\
+ & - & ++ & - & + & - \\
- & + & {}^{e}\boxed{-} & \boxed{+} & - & + \\
+ & - & + & - & + & - \\
- & + & - & + & - & +
\end{array}$$

Fig. 3. – The model of the Z_2-center, according to SEITZ (ref. [28]).

3. – Lattice calculations in alkali halides.

3·1. *Cohesive energy.* – The cohesive energy of an ionic crystal is made up of four terms, namely: electrostatic, Van der Waals, repulsive and zero point energy.

The electrostatic potential at any lattice point of a NaCl-type crystal of constant r_0, is

$$\Phi = \pm \frac{e}{r_0}\left|\frac{6}{\sqrt{1}} - \frac{12}{\sqrt{2}} + \frac{8}{\sqrt{3}} - \frac{6}{\sqrt{4}} + \frac{24}{\sqrt{5}} - \dots\right] = \pm \alpha_M \frac{e}{r_0}\,.$$

α_M is called the Madelung constant and has the following values for the different structures [30]:

CsCl	b.c.c.	1.7627
NaCl	f.c.c.	1.7476
ZnS	Wurtzite	1.6410
ZnS	Zincblende	1.6381

The electrostatic interaction energy per ion is then

$$\varepsilon_{\text{el}} = -\frac{1}{2}\,\alpha_M\,\frac{e^2}{r_0}\,, \tag{9}$$

the factor $\frac{1}{2}$ entering so that each ion pair shall not be counted twice.

Several forms have been assumed for the repulsive energy of a pair of ions, namely:

Born potential [31]:

$$\varepsilon_{\text{rep}}(r) = a/r^n\,; \tag{10}$$

Born and Mayer potential [32]:

$$\varepsilon_{\text{rep}}(r) = bc_{12}\exp\left[\frac{r_1 + r_2 - r}{\varrho}\right]. \tag{11}$$

Verwey potential [33]:

$$\varepsilon_{\text{rep}}(r) = a + b/r^{12}\,; \tag{12}$$

r being the distance between two ions whose Goldschmidt radii are r_1 and r_2 [34]. The factor c_{12} appearing in (11) depends on the charges and electronic structures of the ions. PAULING [35] gives the formula:

$$c_{12} = 1 + \frac{z_1}{n_1} + \frac{z_2}{n_2}\,,$$

where z_1 and z_2 are the (algebraic) valences of the interacting ions and n_1 and n_2 the number of electrons in their outer shells. Each of the expressions (10), (11) and (12) contains two constants (a, b, n, ϱ) which, for a given crystal, can be determined imposing the following conditions:

$$\left(\frac{\mathrm{d}E}{\mathrm{d}r}\right)_{r=r_0} = 0\,; \qquad \beta = \frac{1}{V_0}\,\frac{1}{(\mathrm{d}^2E/\mathrm{d}V^2)_{V=V_0}}\,,$$

where E is the total (Coulomb plus repulsive) energy of the crystal, V its volume and β the experimental value of the compressibility.

An example of the contribution of the various terms to the theoretical cohesive energy of AgBr and NaCl is shown in Table V [36]. It is seen that, in the case of NaCl, which is typical of the alkali halides, Van der Waals forces give a small contribution and can be generally neglected in the calculations,

TABLE V. – *The various contributions to the cohesive energy per ion pair (in* eV) [36].

	AgBr	NaCl
Coulomb energy	8.64	8.86
Repulsive energy	1.37	1.02
Van der Waals energy	1.18	0.12
Zero point energy	0.04	0.07
Total energy	8.41	7.89
Experimental value	8.74	7.90

the lattice energy per ion pair being then simply

$$\varepsilon_L = -\alpha_M \frac{e^2}{r_0} + \varepsilon_{\text{rep}}(r_0) \; . \tag{13}$$

In silver halides, on the contrary, owing to the great polarizability of Ag^+, the Van der Waals energy is a substantial part ($\sim 15\%$) of the cohesive energy.

3·2. *Formation energy of a Schottky defect in alkali halides.* – To create a Schottky defect, one has to take out of the crystal two distant, noninteracting ions of opposite sign and put them back on the surface. Since the total surface energy is not changed by this addition, the work that should be done is

$$W = W^+ + W^- - \varepsilon_L \; . \tag{14}$$

$W^\pm$ is the work required to remove an ion of a given sign and ε_L the lattice energy per ion pair. W. JOST [37] first pointed out that $W^\pm$ can be considerably smaller than ε_L (which is simply the contribution of Coulomb and repulsive energies) because the lattice around a vacancy becomes polarized and the neighbouring ions move into new equilibrium positions. Both such effects decrease the value of $W^\pm$.

MOTT and LITTLETON [13] have evaluated the energy of polarization in the following way:

At large distance from the vacancy which bears a charge $\pm e$, a continuous approximation is justified and the polarization vector is

$$\boldsymbol{P} = \frac{e}{4\pi}\left(-1 \frac{1}{\chi_0}\right)\frac{\boldsymbol{r}}{r^3} \, , \tag{15}$$

χ_0 being the high-frequency dielectric constant, while the dipole moment induced on a single ion is simply

$$\boldsymbol{\mu} = r_0^3 \boldsymbol{P}.$$

μ is then set equal to the average of the dipole moments of positive and negative ions, whose value can be inferred from the known polarizabilities α_+ and α_-:

$$\mu = \tfrac{1}{2}(\mu_+ + \mu_-)\,; \qquad \mu_+/\mu_- = \alpha_+/\alpha_-\,; \tag{16}$$

and

$$\mu_\pm = \frac{2\alpha_\pm}{\alpha_+ + \alpha_-}\,\frac{er_0^3}{r^2}\,\frac{1}{4\pi}\left(1 - \frac{1}{\chi_0}\right). \tag{16}$$

As zero order approximation, MOTT and LITTLETON assume that (16) holds for *all* the ions of the crystal. The potential created at the vacant lattice site by the neighboring polarized medium is then simply

$$\Phi = -\sum_i \mu_i / r_i^2\,,$$

the sum being extended to all ions of the crystal; or substituting from (16)

$$\Phi = -\,er_0^3\,\frac{1}{4\pi}\left(1 - \frac{1}{\chi_0}\right)\left[\frac{2\alpha_-}{\alpha_+ + \alpha_-}\sum_{\text{neg. ions}} \frac{1}{r^4} + \frac{2\alpha_+}{\alpha_+ + \alpha_-}\sum_{\text{pos. ions}} \frac{1}{r^4}\right]. \tag{17}$$

The two lattice sums can be easily evaluated and, in case of a positive-ion vacancy, their values are

$$\sum_{\text{neg. ions}} \frac{1}{r^4} = \frac{10.1977}{r_0^4}\,; \qquad \sum_{\text{pos. ions}} \frac{1}{r^4} = \frac{6.3346}{r_0^4}\,.$$

As first order approximation, MOTT and LITTLETON take as unknown the six dipole moments, μ_1, nearest to the vacancy and postulate the validity of (16) for all the others. Eq. (17) becomes then

$$\Phi = -\frac{e}{r_0}\,\frac{1}{4\pi}\left(1 - \frac{1}{\chi_0}\right)\left[\frac{2\alpha_-}{\alpha_+ + \alpha_-}\cdot 4.1977 + \frac{2\alpha_+}{\alpha_+ + \alpha_-}\cdot 6.3346\right] - \frac{6\mu_1}{r_0^2}\,. \tag{18}$$

The field E_1 acting on any of the six neighbours to the vacancy is then found by direct summation and their moments obtained through the relation

$$\mu_1 = \alpha_- E_1\,.$$

A successive approximation would be to use (16) for all but nearest and next nearest neighbours, etc. The values of Φ are found to converge rapidly as shown by the following Table VI, which gives also, to first order, the potential

TABLE VI. – *Polarization potential* ($-\Phi$) *at a vacancy site* (*in* V) [13].

Order of approximation	NaCl		KCl	
	positive-ion vacancy	negative-ion vacancy	positive-ion vacancy	negative-ion vacancy
0 (from eq. (17))	4.67	—	3.26	—
1 (from eq. (18))	5.10	3.08	3.48	2.53
2	5.09	—	3.52	—
3	5.04	—	3.49	—

at a negative-ion vacancy site. The polarization created by a negative-ion vacancy is considerably smaller, owing to the smaller polarizabilities of the positive ions.

If we now let the lattice around the vacancy relax under the action of the new field (Fig. 4), another term should be added to (18), namely

$$-\frac{e}{r_0}\frac{6\xi}{1+\xi}, \tag{19}$$

where ξr_0 is the displacement from the equilibrium position, which should be determined by minimizing the total energy of the crystal in the new configuration. The expression (19) is simply the decrement of potential caused by the displacement of the nearest neighbors to the vacancy. A correction ought also to be made in the last term of eq. (18) and to the value of the repulsive energy of the neighboring ions.

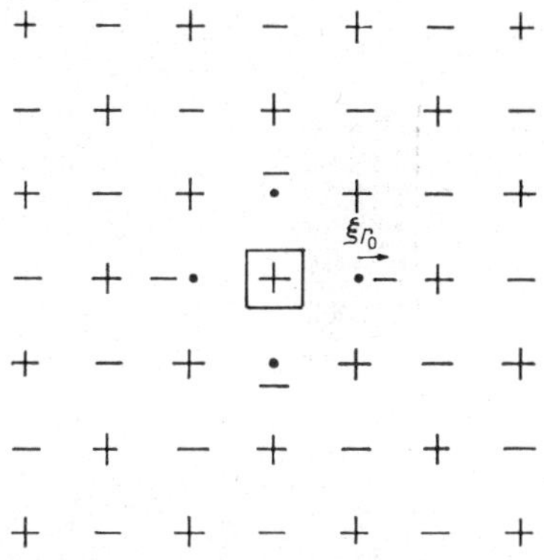

+ − + − + − +
− + − + − + −
+ − + − + − +
− + − [+] − + −   (ξr_0)
+ − + − + − +
− + − + − + −
+ − + − + − +

Fig. 4. – The relaxation of the nearest neighbors of a positive-ion vacancy.

The results of MOTT and LITTLETON for typical alkali halides are illustrated in Table VII.

In recent years several improvements have been introduced into the original calculations with the purpose of taking into account the elastic distortion [38] and the repulsive interaction between next nearest neighbors [25].

FUMI and TOSI [39] have discussed the effect of different types of repulsive potentials, while KUROSAWA [40] has introduced a more formal method in which the energy of the crystal is written as a function of the displacement and electronic polarizabilities of the ions round the defect.

TABLE VII. – *The various contributions to the formation energy of a Schottky pair* [13].

	NaCl	KCl	KBr
Work W^+ to remove a pos. ion	4.62	4.47	4.23
Work W^- to remove a neg. ion	5.18	4.79	4.60
Lattice energy per ion pair ε_L	7.94	7.18	6.91
$W^+ + W^- - \varepsilon_L$	1.86	2.08	1.92

Table VIII shows the various theoretical results along with experimental data obtained comparing the slopes of the conductivity *vs.* temperature curve in the intrinsic and impurity regions [41-43].

3·3. *Migration energy of the vacancies.* – The theoretical estimates of the energy of formation of a Schottky defect shown in Table VIII were found to be in good agreement with the experimental results. In particular, the values reported in the third column show that the energy of formation is not very sensitive to the choice of the repulsive potential. The contrary is true for the energy of migration as is shown by TOSI *et al.* in a recent paper which will be briefly summarized in the following part of this section [44].

TABLE VIII. – *Formation energies of Schottky defects* (*in* eV).

Crystal	Mott and LITTLETON [13]	BRAUER [38]	FUMI and TOSI (39)		KUROSAWA [40]	Experimental
			a	*b*		
NaCl	1.86	2.11	1.91	2.12	2.20	2.02 [41]
KCl	2.08	2.26	2.18	2.21	2.25	2.1 [43], 2.4 [42]

(*a*) Obtained using the Born and Mayer potential.
(*b*) Obtained using the Huggins and Mayer potential.

The migration energy of a defect is defined as the difference between the energy of the crystal in the saddle point configuration and that of the crystal containing a single defect. The configuration of the saddle point is shown in Fig. 5 for the jump of a cation vacancy in the NaCl structure.

If we hold the ions in their equilibrium position, the energy of the configuration of Fig. 5 relative to that of the perfect crystal contains, as usual, three terms, namely: the Coulomb, repulsive and polarization energies.

The Coulomb electrostatic interaction is simply

$$\varepsilon_{el} = \frac{e^2}{r_0}\left(2\alpha_M + \frac{1}{\sqrt{2}} - \frac{2}{\sqrt{2}/2}\right), \tag{20}$$

the first term being the work necessary to create the two vacancies, the second their interaction energy and the third the interaction energy of the ion in the saddle with the two vacancies. The interaction of the same ion with the perfect crystal is zero because of symmetry.

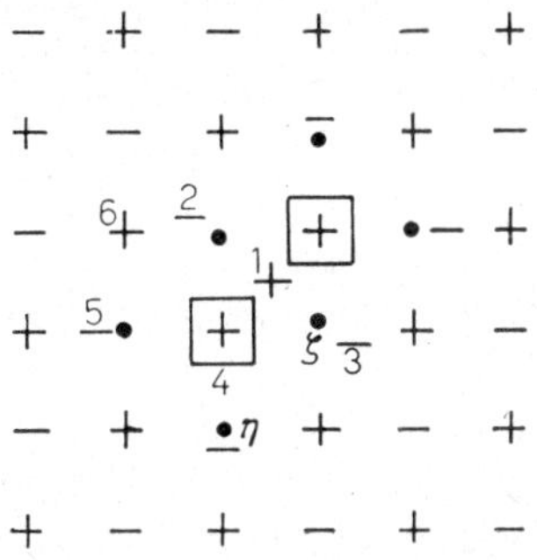

Fig. 5. – The saddle point configuration for the migration of a positive ion vacancy. (After GUCCIONE *et al.*, ref. [44]).

The repulsive energy is found to contain the following terms (with reference to Fig. 5):

$$2\varepsilon_{rep}(r_{12}) + 4\varepsilon_{rep}(r_{15}) + 4\varepsilon_{rep}[r_{16}] - 12\varepsilon_{rep}(r_{45}) - 23\varepsilon_{rep}[r_{46}] +$$

+ terms due to repulsion between couples of ions not lying in the plane of Fig. 5.

The negative terms originate from the lack of repulsive interaction for the neighbors of the vacancy. $\varepsilon_{rep}(r)$ and $\varepsilon_{rep}[r]$ are respectively the repulsive energies between like and unlike ions.

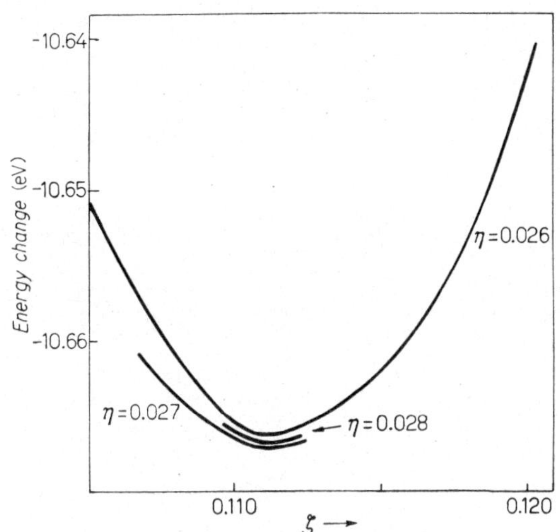

Fig. 6. – The total energy as a function of the displacements of the nearest neighbors of the ion in the saddle; the displacements are shown in Fig. 5 (After GUCCIONE *et al.*, ref. [44]).

The energy due to the polarization of the medium is obtained in a way similar to that outlined in the last section. The lattice distortion around the defect (Fig. 5) is evaluated by minimizing the total energy as a function of the displacement of the ions from their equilibrium position (Fig. 6), and the decrease in energy caused by such a distortion is then added to the other contributions mentioned before.

An important point to be stressed at this time is the form

of the repulsive energy. It is in fact evident that in the case of the interaction of ions 1, 2 and 1, 3 (Fig. 5), which have a separation considerably smaller than the equilibrium distance, the usual forms of repulsive potentials, whose constants are determined from the equilibrium properties of the crystals, might turn out highly incorrect. Tosi *et al.* use two forms of repulsive potential: Born and Mayer's expression (11) and the harder form (12) due to Verwey. The results shown in Table IX depend considerably upon the choice of the repulsive potential and set clearly the limits of the theory. Some experimental data are also listed for comparison in the last column of the same Table [22, 24, 41, 42, 45-48]. The experimental values of the migration energy of the anions have been evaluated by subtracting the value of $E_s/2$ (Table VIII) from the measured activation energies for the anion diffusion.

Table IX. – *Migration energies of vacancies* (*in* eV).

		Theoretical [44]		Experimental
		a	*b*	
NaCl	cation	0.08	0.87	0.85 [41]
	anion	0.48	1.11	1.1 [24], 1.2 [47], 1.3 [22]
KCl	cation	0.53	1.13	0.68 [45], 0.77 [46], 0.85 [42]
	anion	0.64	1.18	0.9 [47], 1.2 [48]

(*a*) Obtained using the Born and Mayer potential.
(*b*) Obtained using the Verwey potential.

4. – Optical properties of ionic crystals.

It has been recalled in the introduction that lattice defects introduce localized levels in the forbidden band of ionic crystals and that electrons and holes trapped into these levels give rise to characteristic absorbing centers. Since the entire subject of color centers will be extensively treated in Prof. Amelinckx's lectures [49], I shall limit myself here to mentioning the influence of defects upon the fundamental absorption of the ionic crystals [3].

According to the band picture of an insulator, when an electron is raised from the full valence band to the empty conduction levels, a state is obtained in which the electron and the hole are free to wander through the crystal. However, a nonconducting, positronium-like state in which the electron and the hole are bound together by means of their Coulomb fields is equally conceivable [50]. Nonconducting excited states were first introduced theoretically by FRENKEL [51], who called them excitons, and have been observed in many ionic crystals as well as in Ge and Si [52-56].

If the interaction potential between the electron and the hole varies slowly over the dimensions of a unit cell, *i.e.*, if the exciton dimensions are large compared with atomic distances, the effective mass approximation can be profitably used and the energy of the exciton, near the center of the Brillouin zone, is found to be [57, 58]

$$E_n(\boldsymbol{k}) = -\frac{\mu e^4}{2\hbar^2\chi_0^2}\frac{1}{n^2} + \frac{1}{2}\hbar^2(m_e^* + m_h^*)\,k^2\,, \tag{22}$$

where m_e^* and m_h^* are the effective masses of the electron and the hole, μ their reduced mass and $\boldsymbol{k}$ the wave vector of the exciton. The selection rule for optical absorption,

$$\boldsymbol{k} = \mathfrak{n}\,, \tag{23}$$

$\mathfrak{n}$ being the wave vector of the absorbed photon, singles out a very sharp transition to a state of $\boldsymbol{k}\sim 0$. A hydrogen-like absorption spectrum with the energy given by the first term of eq. (22) is therefore expected for optical excitons. Such a spectrum has been in fact found by E. F. GROSS [54], S. NIKITINE and others [55] in Cu_2O, CuI, CuCl, TlCl, CdS, etc.

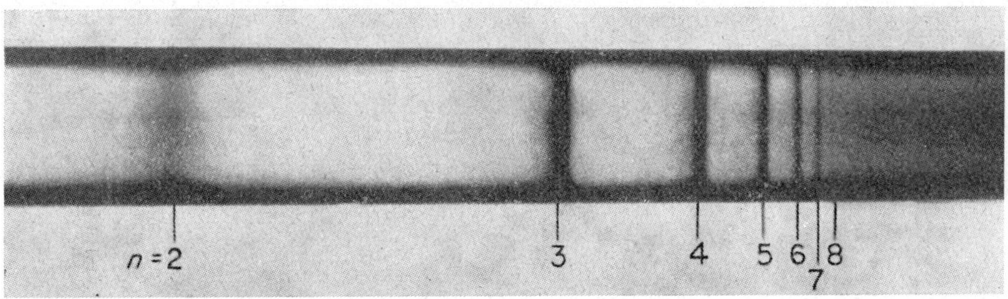

Fig. 7. – The absorption spectrum of Cu_2O at 1.3 °K (After GROSS, ref. [54]).

A typical example is shown in Fig. 7 for Cu_2O [54]. It is seen that the absorption lines exhibit sharp edges and narrow widths; their frequencies are given by

$$\nu = \nu_\infty - \frac{R_{exc}}{n^2} \qquad \begin{cases} n = 2, 3, 4 \ldots \text{ for } Cu_2O \\ n = 1, 2, 3 \ldots \text{ for CuI, CuCl, TlCl etc.} \end{cases} \tag{24}$$

where R_{exc} is the Rydberg constant of the exciton.

Eq. (22) and the knowledge of the experimental values of R_{exc} permit the calculation of the reduced mass and of the radius of the exciton. Gross finds for Cu_2O

$$\mu \simeq 0.25\, m_e\,; \qquad r_n = \left(\frac{\hbar^2}{\mu e^2}\right)\chi_0 n^2\,, \qquad r_2 \simeq 50\ \text{Å}\,.$$

On the other hand, crude estimates of the exciton radius in alkali halides give values of the order of the lattice parameter [59], showing that an approach which takes into account the details of the potential may turn out to be more convenient.

Let us consider as an example a system of N noninteracting atoms with a single electron of wavefunction φ_i^n ($n = 0,1,\ldots;\ i = 1, 2, \ldots, N$) [60]. The ground state of the system is represented by a Slater determinant of the φ_i^0's, while the n-th excited state is given by

$$\Psi_L^n = \frac{1}{\sqrt{N!}}\begin{vmatrix} \varphi_1^0(1) & \ldots & \varphi_1^0(N) \\ \cdot & \cdot & \cdot \\ \varphi_L^n(1) & \ldots & \varphi_L^n(N) \\ \cdot & \cdot & \cdot \\ \varphi_N^0(1) & \ldots & \varphi_N^0(N) \end{vmatrix}. \tag{25}$$

Ψ_L^n represents a state which is N-fold degenerate since any of the N atoms can be excited. If the atoms are brought together into a solid, (25) is no longer an eigenfunction of the total Hamiltonian, which now includes the interaction among the atoms, but must be substituted by the linear combination

$$\Psi_{\boldsymbol{k}}^n = \frac{1}{\sqrt{N}}\sum_L \exp\left[2\pi i \boldsymbol{k}\cdot\boldsymbol{R}_L\right]\Psi_L^n, \tag{26}$$

where $\boldsymbol{k}$ is a vector of the reciprocal lattice, and $\boldsymbol{R}_L$ a vector connecting the origin with the L-th cell. Clearly (26) represents an excited state which propagates through the crystal with a propagation vector $\boldsymbol{k}$ and a momentum $h\boldsymbol{k}$. The energy of state (26) depends upon $\boldsymbol{k}$ and we shall have a band of possible values. This is represented schematically in Fig. 8 which shows the results

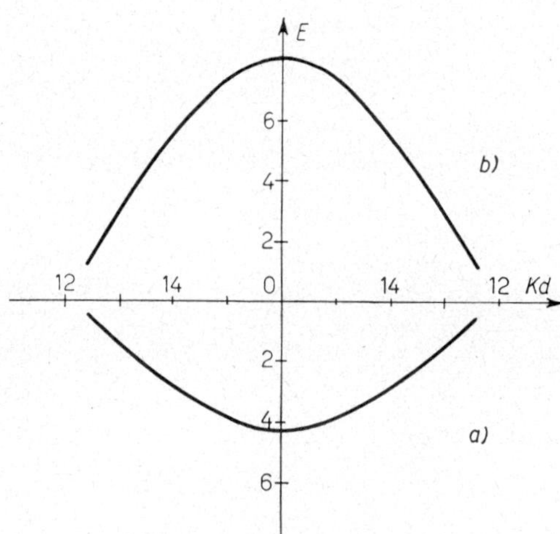

Fig. 8. – The dependence of the exciton energy on wave number; curve (*a*): dipole moment normal to the direction of propagation; curve (*b*): dipole moment parallel to the direction of propagation (After HELLER and MARCUS, ref. [61]).

of HELLER and MARCUS for an ideal cubic crystal of identical one-electron atoms [61]. The two curves represent the energy of an exciton whose dipole moment is *a*) perpendicular and *b*) parallel to the direction of propagation. The selection rule (23) and the fact that the electric field of an electromagnetic wave is perpendicular to its direction of propagation, show that only state *a*) can be reached optically in a perfect crystal. On the other hand, state *b*) may be important when phonons are simultaneously created or in case the excitation is caused by α or β particles.

The choice of the type of excitation in the elementary cell is important at this point for a theoretical treatment of the exciton problem. Two models have been extensively used in alkali halides: the excitation and the transfer model. In the former, which has been introduced by D. L. DEXTER [62] and further developed by T. MUTO and cow. [63], the unit excitation is sufficiently localized on the halogen to be somewhat characteristic of a free atom. In the transfer model, which was first used by VON HIPPEL [64] and recently taken up by OVERHAUSER and others [65, 66], the unit excitation involves the transfer of an electron from a halogen ion to a neighboring positive ion. Recently KNOX and INCHAUSPÉ [59] have investigated the exciton states of ionic crystals according to the group-theoretical analysis of the configurations allowed by cubic symmetry. They have been able to show that the two models yield the same results as far as the multiplicity of the absorption peaks is concerned, though they may give different values of the energy of the transition. Since the halogen atom left after the excitation of one of its electrons has a doublet fundamental state ($j=\frac{1}{2}, \frac{3}{2}$) [67], one must expect that the first line in the exciton spectrum of the alkali halides is a doublet. Fig. 9 shows the experimental results for KCl [53]. The first peak is clearly resolved in a doublet whose separation is in good agreement with the theory [59]. The shoulder appearing in the absorption curve at point *S* corresponds to the onset of band-to-band transitions. This has been pointed out first by TAFT and PHILLIP [68] who found photoemission upon irradiation with photons of energy higher than that of the shoulder. Recently K. TEEGARDEN has observed photoconductivity due to band-to-band transitions in KI crystals [69]. KI is a favorable case since its electron affinity is rather large (~ 1 eV) so that photoconductivity starts at a much lower energy than photoemission [70].

It has been pointed out by F. SEITZ that the presence of lattice defects, particularly dislocations, breaks the selection rule (23), allowing states with $\boldsymbol{k} \neq 0$ to be reached optically [71]. Should this be true, we expect that optical transitions with lower energy become allowed when a situation like that of curve *b*) of Fig. 8 occurs. It should be mentioned in this respect that, if (23) does not hold, optical excitons can be generated with a dipole moment which is not perpendicular to their direction of propagation. SEITZ suggested that the relaxation of the selection rule (23) can be responsible for the long tail observed in the low-energy side of the fundamental absorption of silver halides.

On the other hand, crystals of alkali halides that have been plastically deformed show a distinct broadening of the exciton peak which is a function

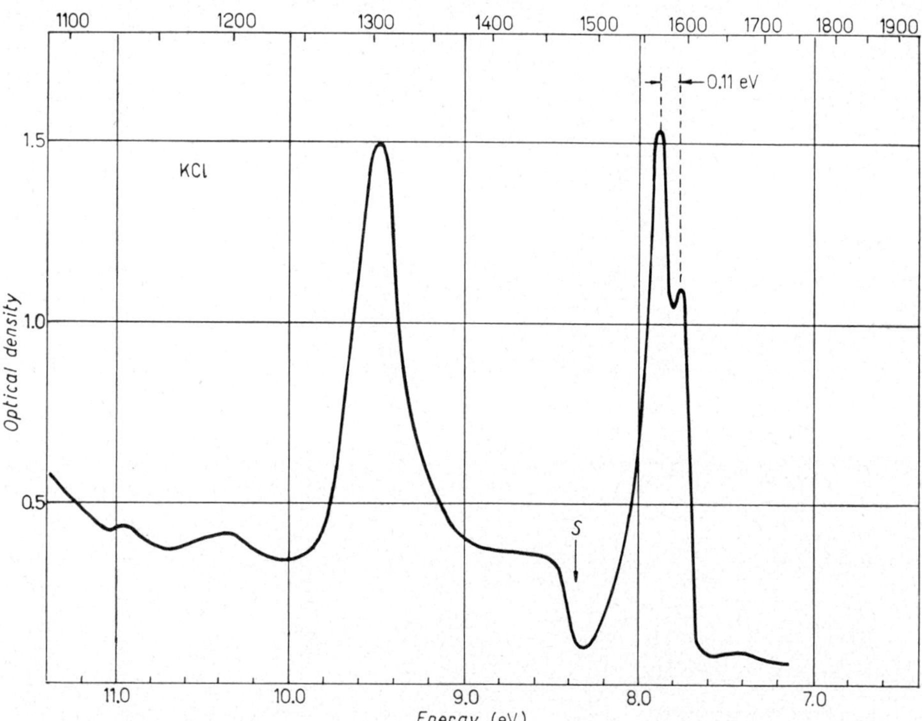

Fig. 9. – The optical absorption spectrum of a thin film of KCl at 80 °K. (After Eby *et al.*, ref. [53]).

of the number of dislocations present in the crystal [72]. Though this effect seems to give experimental support to the ideas outlined in the last paragraph, the interaction of the exciton with the charged jogs at the dislocation lines and with the vacancy clusters created during plastic flow [73], or the change of lattice parameter in the vicinity of a dislocation, might well be an alternative explanation [74].

In case of excitons created in the vicinity of a point defect, an atomistic approach may turn out to be more convenient. Experimentally it is well known that alkali halide crystals containing F-centers show a well defined band, called the β-band, in the low-energy tail of the exciton absorption. When the F-band is partially bleached at low temperatures so that isolated negative-ion vacancies are released into the crystal, a second band, the α band, appears at energies slightly lower [3]. The α and β absorption is generally attributed to excitonic transitions on the ions neighboring a negative vacancy and an F-center, respectively [3]. The two bands were discovered in 1951 by DELBECQ, PRINGSHEIM and YUSTER [75] in KI and their observation has since been extended to the other alkali halides [76-78]. Fig. 10 shows, as an example, the case of KCl.

The α-band can be produced also by X- or γ-ray irradiation at low temperatures and the study of its thermal stability provides a simple and sensitive method to follow the annealing of single vacancies in alkali halides. H. RÜCHARDT [79] has been able to show that, in KBr, the thermal destruction of the α-band occurs in several steps (beginning at $\sim$15 °K and being completed at $\sim$150 °K) which he attributes to the recombination of vacancies of opposite sign which were created within various distances of each other. The activation energies that can be roughly estimated from the slopes of the various steps range from .025 to .09 eV and are much smaller than those reported in Table IX, which refer to migration in the « perfect » crystal. This is most probably due to the attractive interaction between the vacancies, which lowers the barrier opposing their recombination.

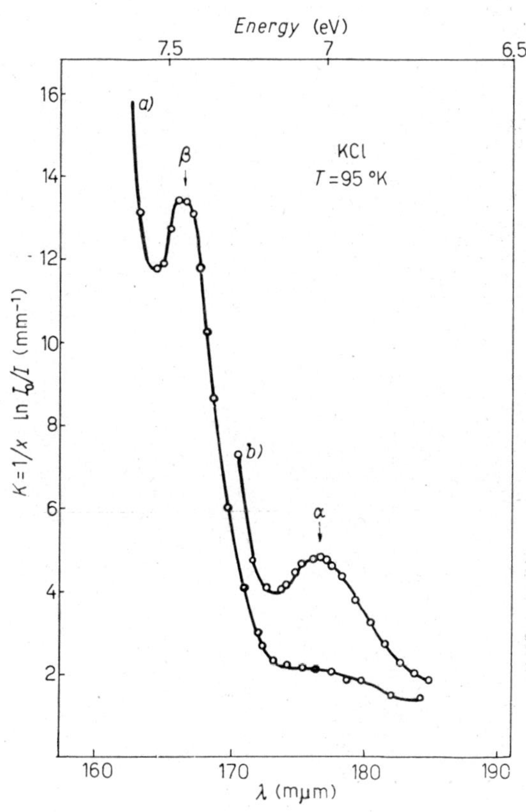

Fig. 10. – The absorption spectrum of a crystal of KCl in the region of the α and β bands. Curve a): crystal X-rayed at 95 °K for 30 min (50 kV, 20 mA); curve b): the α band in a more heavily darkened crystal. (After CHIAROTTI *et al.*, ref. [78]).

The energy of the absorption peak of the α and β bands has been calculated in a number of ways. BASSANI and INCHAUSPÉ [66] extended the semi-classical method of von Hippel [64] to the trapped exciton. According to that procedure, a free exciton is created, transferring an electron from a halogen ion to a neighboring alkali ion, and its energy can be evaluated through the following cycle:

1) extract from the crystal two neighboring ions of opposite sign; the work is $W_- + W_+^{[-]}$;

2) transfer an electron from the halogen ion to the alkali ion; the work is the difference between the electron affinity of the halogen atom (E) and the ionization potential of the alkali atom (I);

3) reintroduce the two neutral atoms into the crystal; we shall call this work Ω.

The energy of the free exciton is then:

$$h\nu_{\text{free}} = W_- + W_+^{[-]} + E - I + \Omega \,. \tag{27}$$

A similar cycle can be easily extended to the case of the α and β exciton. Bassani and Inchauspé assume that the work Ω is the same in the three cases and calculate the energy of the α and β bands relative to the exciton peak. Their results are shown in Table X along with the experimental values

Table X. – *Positions of the α and β bands in alkali halides* (*in* eV).

	$h\nu_{\text{free}} - h\nu_\beta$		$h\nu_{\text{free}} - h\nu_\alpha$		
	Theoretical [66]	Experimental	Theoretical [66]	Theoretical [80]	Experimental
KCl	0.28	0.31	0.53	0.54	0.76
KBr	0.29	0.35	0.49	—	0.63
KI	0.23	0.32	0.44	—	0.59
NaCl	0.19	0.59	0.50	0.58	0.85

Experimental values of $h\nu_{\text{free}}$ from ref. [53].
Experimental values of $h\nu_\alpha$ and $h\nu_\beta$ from ref. [75, 76, 78].

and with similar results obtained by Muto *et al.* using an effective mass approximation [80]. The theory agrees qualitatively with the experiments in predicting that

$$h\nu_{\text{free}} > h\nu_\beta > h\nu_\alpha \,,$$

though quantitative agreement is rather poor.

It may be observed that the calculated energy differences are smaller than the experimental values and that the discrepancies seem worse for the α than for the β band. It has been pointed out in this respect by F. G. Fumi [81] that presumably:

$$\Omega_{\text{free}} > \Omega_\beta > \Omega_\alpha \,,$$

since the neighbors of a vacancy and of an F-center experience a smaller repulsive interaction than the ions in the « perfect » crystal.

The results outlined in the preceding paragraphs show that the optical absorption of the low-energy tail of the exciton band depends very strongly upon the presence of lattice defects. It is the opinion of the writer that an extension of this type of investigation to irradiated materials would increase our understanding of the processes involved in the radiation damage of ionic crystals.

* * *

It is a pleasure to thank Prof. R. FIESCHI (who with Drs. G. BALDINI and R. STERN collected these lectures) for several friendly discussions during the final writing of the manuscript.

REFERENCES

[1] A. B. LIDIARD: *Handb. d. Phys.*, vol. **20** (Berlin, 1957), p. 246.
[2] N. F. MOTT and R. W. GURNEY: *Electronic Processes in Ionic Crystals* (Oxford, 1950), p. 82.
[3] F. SEITZ: *Rev. Mod. Phys.*, **18**, 384 (1946); **26**, 7 (1954).
[4] F. G. FUMI and M. P. TOSI: *The Theory of Ionic Crystals, Solid State Physics* (New York), to be published.
[5] C. TUBANDT: *Handb. d. Exp.*, vol. **12** (Leipzig, 1931), p. 382; C. TUBANDT, H. REINHOLD and G. LIEBOLD: *Zeits. anorg. allg. Chem.*, **197**, 225 (1931).
[6] See for example: J. FRIEDEL: this volume, p. 4.
[7] H. PICK and H. WEBER: *Zeits. f. Phys.*, **128**, 409 (1950).
[8] F. KERKHOFF: *Zeits. f. Phys.*, **130**, 449 (1951).
[9] W. D. COMPTON: *Phys. Rev.*, **101**, 1209 (1956); *Journ. Phys. Chem. Solids*, **1**, 191 (1956).
[10] C. W. MCCOMBIE and A. B. LIDIARD: *Phys. Rev.*, **101**, 1210 (1956).
[11] See for example: R. O. SIMMONS: this volume, p. 568.
[12] C. R. BERRY: *Phys. Rev.*, **82**, 422 (1951).
[13] N. F. MOTT and M. J. LITTLETON: *Trans. Farad. Soc.*, **34**, 485 (1938).
[14] W. JOST: *Diffusion in Solids, Liquids, Gases* (New York, 1955), p. 109.
[15] F. BASSANI and F. G. FUMI: *Suppl. Nuovo Cimento*, **1**, 114 (1955).
[16] M. P. TOSI and F. G. FUMI: *Nuovo Cimento*, **7**, 95 (1958).
[17] M. P. TOSI and G. AIROLDI: *Nuovo Cimento*, **8**, 584 (1958).
[18] O. THEIMER: *Phys. Rev.*, **109**, 1095 (1958).
[19] D. MAPOTHER, H. N. CROOKS and R. J. MAURER: *Journ. Chem. Phys.*, **18**, 1231 (1950).
[20] H. W. SCHAMP jr. and E. KATZ: *Phys. Rev.*, **94**, 828 (1954).
[21] A. B. LIDIARD: *Journ. Phys. Chem. Solids*, **6**, 298 (1958).

[22] L. G. HARRISON, J. A. MORRISON and R. RUDHAM: *Trans. Farad. Soc.*, **54**, 106 (1958).
[23] G. J. DIENES: *Journ. Chem. Phys.*, **16**, 620 (1948).
[24] N. LAURANCE: *Phys. Rev.*, **120**, 57 (1960).
[25] F. BASSANI and F. G. FUMI: *Nuovo Cimento*, **11**, 274 (1954).
[26] G. D. WATKINS: *Phys. Rev.*, **113**, 79 (1959).
[27] G. CHIAROTTI, F. FUMI and L. GIULOTTO: *Defects in Crystalline Solids* (London, 1955), p. 317; E. J. WEST and W. D. COMPTON: *Phys. Rev.*, **108**, 576 (1957); G. REMAUT and W. DEKEYSER: *Physica*, **24**, 20 (1958); M. ISHIGURO, E. SUGIOKA and N. TAKEUCHI: *Journ. Phys. Soc. Japan*, **15**, 1302 (1960).
[28] F. SEITZ: *Phys. Rev.*, **83**, 134 (1951).
[29] P. CAMAGNI, S. CERESARA and G. CHIAROTTI: *Phys. Rev.*, **118**, 1226 (1960).
[30] For a Table of the Madelung constants see for example: F. SEITZ: *The Modern Theory of Solids* (New York, 1940), p. 78.
[31] M. BORN and M. GÖPPERT-MAYER: *Handb. d. Phys.*, vol. **24**/2 (Berlin, 1933), p. 623.
[32] M. BORN and J. E. MAYER: *Zeits. Phys.*, **75**, 1 (1932).
[33] E. J. W. VERWEY: *Rec. Trav. Chim. Pays-Bas*, **65**, 521 (1946).
[34] An expression like (11) with a different choice of r_1 and r_2 is often called the Huggins and Mayer potential: M. L. HUGGINS and J. E. MAYER: *Journ. Chem. Phys.*, **1**, 643 (1933).
[35] L. PAULING: *Zeits. Kristallogr.*, **67**, 377 (1928).
[36] From N. F. MOTT and R. W. GURNEY: op. cit., p. 7.
[37] W. JOST: *Journ. Chem. Phys.*, **1**, 466 (1933).
[38] P. BRAUER: *Zeits. Naturfor.*, **7**, 372 (1952).
[39] F. G. FUMI and M. P. TOSI: *Farad. Soc. Disc.*, **23**, 92 (1957).
[40] T. KUROSAWA: *Journ. Phys. Soc. Japan*, **13**, 153 (1958).
[41] H. W. ETZEL and R. J. MAURER: *Journ. Chem. Phys.*, **18**, 1003 (1950).
[42] H. KELTING and H. WITT: *Zeits. Phys.*, **126**, 697 (1949).
[43] C. WAGNER and P. HANTELMANN: *Journ. Chem. Phys.*, **18**, 72 (1950).
[44] R. GUCCIONE, M. P. TOSI and M. ASDENTE: *Journ. Phys. Chem. Solids*, **10**, 162 (1959).
[45] J. F. ASCHNER: *Thesis* (University of Illinois, 1954).
[46] H. GRUNDIG: *Zeits. Phys.*, **158**, 577 (1960).
[47] J. F. LAURENT and J. BÉNARD: *Journ. Phys. Chem. Solids*, **3**, 7 (1957).
[48] J. A. MORRISON: quoted in ref. [44].
[49] S. AMELINCKX: this volume, p. 422.
[50] See for example: N. F. MOTT and R. W. GURNEY: op. cit., p. 86 ff.
[51] J. FRENKEL: *Phys. Rev.*, **37**, 17 (1931); see also: F. SEITZ, ref. [30], p. 414 ff.
[52] R. HILSCH and R. W. POHL: *Zeits. Phys.*, **59**, 812 (1930); E. G. SCHNEIDER and H. M. O'BRYAN: *Phys. Rev.*, **51**, 293 (1937); P. L. HARTMAN, J. R. NELSON and J. G. SIEGFRIED: *Phys. Rev.*, **105**, 123 (1957).
[53] J. E. EBY, K. J. TEEGARDEN and D. B. DUTTON: *Phys. Rev.*, **116**, 1099 (1959).
[54] E. F. GROSS: *Journ. Phys. Chem. Solids*, **8**, 172 (1959); E. F. GROSS, B. ZAHARCHENIA and N. REINOV: *Dokl. Akad. Nauk USSR*, **99**, 231 (1954).
[55] S. NIKITINE, G. PERNY and M. SIESKIND: *Compt. Rend.*, **238**, 67 (1954); S. NIKITINE: *Journ. Phys. Chem. Solids*, **8**, 190 (1959); M. HAYASHI and K. KATSUKI: *Journ. Phys. Soc. Japan*, **5**, 381 (1950); **7**, 599 (1952).
[56] G. G. MACFARLANE, T. P. MCLEAN, J. E. QUARRINGTON and V. ROBERTS: *Journ. Phys. Chem. Solids*, **8**, 388 (1959).
[57] G. WANNIER: *Phys. Rev.*, **52**, 191 (1937).
[58] G. DRESSELHAUS: *Journ. Phys. Chem. Solids*, **1**, 14 (1956).

[59] R. S. KNOX and N. INCHAUSPÉ: *Phys. Rev.*, **116**, 1093 (1959).
[60] For a more detailed treatment of this problem see for example: D. L. DEXTER: *Suppl. Nuovo Cimento*, **7**, 245 (1958).
[61] W. R. HELLER and A. MARCUS: *Phys. Rev.*, **84**, 809 (1951).
[62] D. L. DEXTER: *Phys. Rev.*, **83**, 435 (1951).
[63] T. MUTO and H. OKUNO: *Journ. Phys. Soc. Japan*, **11**, 633 (1956); **12**, 108 (1957).
[64] A. VON HIPPEL: *Zeits. Phys.*, **101**, 680 (1936).
[65] A. W. OVERHAUSER: *Phys. Rev.*, **101**, 1702 (1956).
[66] F. BASSANI and N. INCHAUSPÉ: *Phys. Rev.*, **105**, 819 (1957).
[67] The separations are: 0.1 eV in the chlorides, 0.44 eV in the bromides and 0.94 eV in the iodides.
[68] E. A. TAFT and H. R. PHILIPP: *Journ. Phys. Chem. Solids*, **3**, 1 (1957).
[69] K. TEEGARDEN: *Photoconductivity in* KI *and* RbI, ASTIA Document no. AD-213087 (1959).
[70] Several attempts to detect fundamental photoconductivity in alkali halides were in fact unsuccessful probably (?) because the photoconductivity was masked by the much stronger photoemission. See for example: J. W. TAYLOR and P. L. HARTMAN: *Phys. Rev.*, **113**, 1421 (1959).
[71] F. SEITZ: *Rev. Mod. Phys.*, **23**, 328 (1951); see also: R. M. BLAKNEY and D. L. DEXTER: *Defects in Crystalline Solids* (London, 1955), p. 108.
[72] G. CHIAROTTI: *Phys. Rev.*, **107**, 381 (1957).
[73] F. SEITZ: *Adv. in Phys.*, **1**, 43 (1952).
[74] D. L. DEXTER: *Solid State Physics*, vol. **6** (New York, 1958), p. 353.
[75] C. J. DELBECQ, P. PRINGSHEIM and P. YUSTER: *Journ. Chem. Phys.*, **19**, 574 (1951).
[76] W. MARTIENSSEN: *Zeits. Phys.*, **131**, 488 (1952); *Nachr. Akad. Wiss. Göttingen*, 111 (1952).
[77] R. ONAKA and I. FUJITA: *Phys. Rev.*, **119**, 1597 (1960).
[78] G. CHIAROTTI, G. GIULIANI and D. W. LYNCH: *Nuovo Cimento*, **17**, 989 (1960).
[79] H. RÜCHARDT: *Zeits. Phys.*, **140**, 574 (1955); *Phys. Rev.*, **103**, 873 (1956).
[80] T. MUTO, S. OYAMA and H. OKUNO: *Progr. Theor. Phys.*, **20**, 804 (1958).
[81] Private communication.

Radiation Effects in Ionic Crystals.

S. AMELINCKX

Centre d'Etude de l'Energie Nucléaire - Mol.

Introduction.

The specific aspects of radiation effects in ionic crystals result from the fact that lattice defects can be created in these materials by ionization only, without the necessity for collisions. In metals, on the contrary, ionizing radiation has very little influence as such, since due to the presence of the free electrons each local charge is very rapidly compensated.

These materials have, further, the particular property that they usually have a large window in the visible part of the spectrum allowing the observation of centers giving rise to optical absorption. Paramagnetic resonance techniques can further be applied with relative ease to these materials and yield specific, detailed models for several of the defects. As a typical example for the irradiation effects in an ionic crystal we may mention the decrease in density and the accompanying coloration of sodium chloride under X-irradiation. Mechanisms for the creation of defects in these crystals have been advanced by SEITZ and VARLEY. These will be discussed further in the light of the experimental evidence.

We intend to review in the following chapters the results of studies of different physical properties as they are influenced by radiation. It will become evident that the study of any given property usually does not yield the information necessary for a complete interpretation. We will further limit ourselves to the alkali halides since most of the available information refers to these salts. It should also be pointed out that some of the studied properties are so structure-sensitive that a comparison of different properties on the same material is necessary to obtain meaningful correlations.

I. – Optical Properties.

One of the most striking effects of irradiation on ionic crystals is the fact that they acquire a pronounced color. NaCl, *e.g.*, turns yellow, whereas KCl becomes blue. This is due to the creation of point defects involving also electrons and holes, so called color centers. The possibility of observing them is obviously due to the presence of absorption bands in the visible part of the spectrum, together with the fact that these crystals, when clear, due to the large band gap, have a large « window » in and around the visible. The « window » depends on the purity, but it usually extends from the U.V. to far into the infrared.

Any center bringing about absorption in this range can therefore be observed by means of its optical absorption. Optical absorption has historically been used to characterize the color centers and to give them a name.

We will summarize here information on the absorption spectra of the main species of color centers as they occur in irradiated crystals. Several centers can be created as well by ionizing radiation as by chemical means. Since in the latter way one can sometimes make better guesses as to what happens to the crystal, chemical coloration has been of great help in establishing models for the color centers.

We do not intend to give here a complete review of all the information that can be obtained from optical spectra on the nature of color centers. We refer for this to the classical papers by SEITZ [1].

We will however give a summary of the main properties of a number of relatively well-known color centers.

A) *F*-Type Centers.

1. – The *F*-center.

1·1. *Model*. – The model for the *F*-center first proposed by DE BOER [2] seems to be established beyond any reasonable doubt. It consists of a halogen vacancy with an electron trapped in it, the electron being shared by the six neighboring alkali ions. The *F*-absorption corresponds to an electron transition from the ground state to a p^2 excited state, close to the bottom of the conduction band. Paramagnetic resonance has confirmed this model. A very simple model, due to STÖCKMANN [3], considers the *F*-center as an electron trapped in a potential box. The energy levels are then given by

$$E_K = \tfrac{1}{8}\, h^2k^2/m^*\, d^2\,, \tag{1}$$

where: k = quantum number
d = lattice constant
m^* = effective mass of the electron.

The frequency of the optical transition between the ground state and the first excited state, which is responsible for the F-band, is then given by

$$\nu = \tfrac{3}{8}\, h/m^*\, d^2\,. \tag{2}$$

This leads to the following simple relation

$$\nu d^2 = \text{constant}\,. \tag{3}$$

This relation is well verified as we will see further (*). This simple model gives of course rise to a sharp line instead of the observed bell-shaped absorption band. A more detailed model has been given, *e.g.*, by PEKAR [4].

1.2. *Methods for producing F-centers.*

a) *Irradiation* with any type of ionizing radiation including ultraviolet light will produce F-centers together with a number of other centers. A typical spectrum of an X-rayed KBr crystal is shown in Fig. 1. The coloration is not

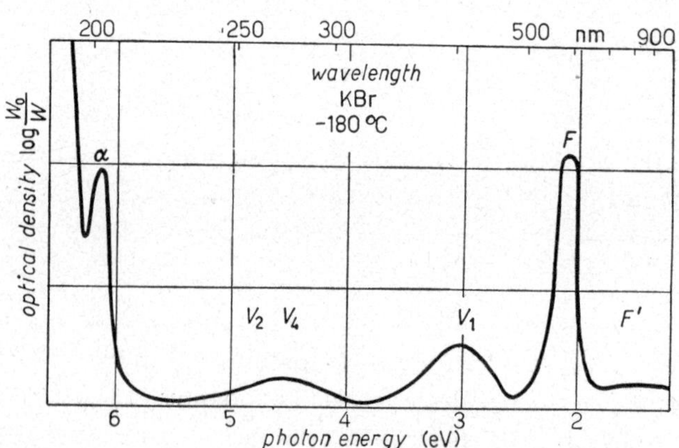

Fig. 1. – X-rayed crystal with absorption bands due to the presence of different types of centers (After: H. PICK: *Suppl. Nuovo Cimento*, **7**, 498 (1958)).

(*) A better value for the exponent is actually 1.84 [3bis].

stable; when exposed to visible light or to heat the absorption bands disappear.

The coloration may be stabilized by adding potassium hydride to potassium bromide. The hydrogen ion occupies a halide position. It gives rise ot an absorption band at 5.51 eV ($\pm$ 2 300 Å), *i.e.*, in the ultra-violet. On X-irradiation such a crystal will develop a strong *F*-band. The energy required to form an *F*-center will now be substantially lower (40 eV) than in the pure crystal (100 eV). The mechanism of this sensitization is simply that the H-ion serves as a hole trap, forming H^0.

b) *Additive coloration* with excess metal.

When an alkali halide crystal is heated in alkali metal vapor and then rapidly cooled to room temperature the crystal acquires a visible coloration depending on the particular alkali halide. The same coloration can also be achieved by applying a potential to a pointed electrode placed on a heated crystal. The coloration then migrates inward from the pointed cathode toward the flat anode, where halogen gas is produced.

The chemical formation of *F*-centers in alkali metal vapor can be described as a migration into the crystal of negative ion vacancies and free electrons. At the surface a metal atom is ionized by giving off an electron, which migrates into the crystal. The metal ion then combines with a Cl-ion at the surface and a new NaCl molecule is attached to the crystal, while a Cl-vacancy migrates inward. In this way both the vacancies and the electrons are produced at the surface. On cooling, the electron is attracted towards the positively charged negative ion vacancy and forms an *F*-center. In practice this vacancy may be a pre-existing vacancy; or a vacancy formed by the additive coloration, or even a negative ion vacancy which was part of a neutral pair. In the latter case the pair dissociates on capturing an electron, the positive ion vacancy wanders away.

1·3. *Equilibrium concentration in additively colored crystals.* – From this picture it is clear that the equilibrium concentration of *F*-centers should be determined by the vapor pressure of the alkali metal at the coloration temperature. The chemical reaction can be written as

$$\text{Na (vapor)} \rightleftarrows F\text{-centers}$$

and it is of the monomolecular form. The concentration of *F*-centers is indeed found to be directly proportional to the vapor pressure of the alkali metal. This was, *e.g.*, shown by RÖGENER [5] in the case of KBr colored with potassium vapor.

The picture given above implies that by additive coloration the density would decrease, proportionally to the number of *F*-centers formed. WITT [6] has studied the density changes caused by electrolytic coloration and found the proportionality to be satisfied. Unfortunately no measurements of lattice parameter were made on the same specimens.

The presence of F-centers implies further the presence of excess alkali metal. It has been shown by KLEINSCHROD [7] that there is in fact proportionality between the stoichiometric excess of alkali metal as measured chemically by dissolving the crystal, and the F-absorption coefficient in KCl.

1'4. *The optical absorption.* – The maxima of the absorption bands of F-centers in the different alkali halides are listed here, together with the half-widths of the absorption peaks and the oscillator strength, where known:

Alkali halide	Position of max. in Å	Half-width in eV at 20 °C	Oscillator strength
NaF	3 400	0.62	—
NaCl	4 650	0.47	0.81
NaBr	5 400	—	—
NaI	5 880	—	—
KF	4 550	0.41	—
KCl	5 630	0.36	0.90
KBr	6 300	0.36	0.80
KI	6 850	0.35	—
RbF	—	—	—
RbCl	6 240	0.31	—
RbBr	7 200	0.28	—
RbI	7 750	—	—

The half-width of the F-absorption is temperature-dependent; it is smallest at low temperatures. The maximum shifts toward shorter wavelengths with decreasing temperature.

Fig. 2 shows a plot of the position of the maximum in the different halides *vs.* the lattice parameter d. It

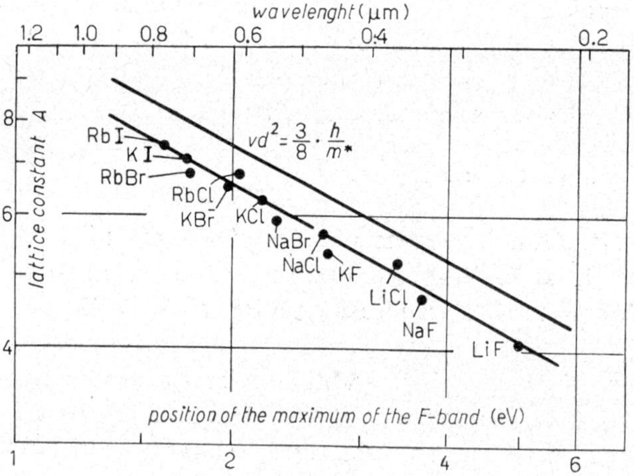

Fig. 2. – The dependence of the F-maximum on the lattice constant of the crystal. (After: H. PICK: *Suppl. Nuovo Cimento*, **7**, 498 (1958)).

is found that the simple relation (3) is well verified. The link between the F-center concentration and the optical absorption is provided by Smakula's formula, (*) which can be written as

$$Nf = \frac{9mc}{2e^2h}\frac{n}{(n^2+2)^2}\mu_{max}W\,, \tag{4}$$

where: N = concentration of F-centers
f = oscillator strength
n = index of refraction of the alkali halide
μ_{max} = the absorption coefficient at the absorption peak in cm^{-1}
W = half-width of the absorption peak at half-maximum (in eV).

For KCl, *e.g.*, this becomes

$$Nf = 1.09\cdot 10^{16}\mu_{max}W\,,$$

where μ_{max} is expressed in cm^{-1} and W in eV; N in number/cm^3.

From the absolute measurements of KLEINSCHROD for KCl the oscillator strength for the F-center was estimated $f = 0.81$; for NaCl the value of f is less accurately known: $f \simeq 0.7$.

More recently DOYLE [8] has redetermined the oscillator strength of the F-center in a number of alkali halides; the best values now appear to be the ones given in the foregoing table.

1·5. *F-centers in mixed crystals.* – The half-width and peak position of the F-band, both produced by additive coloration and by X-irradiation, in mixed crystals were studied by GNAEDINGER [9]. He investigated in greatest detail the system KCl-RbCl where complete miscibility occurs. The peak of the F-band shifts continuously with composition, both at liquid nitrogen and at room temperature, as to be expected on the basis of the relation $\nu d^2 =$ constant. The half-width increases towards the 50:50 composition.

1·6. *The effect of pressure on the F-band.* – If hydrostatic pressure is applied to the crystal, the absorption peak shifts to higher energies in agreement with the relation between the peak frequency and the lattice spacing [10].

The high pressure work has been extended recently by MAISCH and DRICKAMER [11], who find that a new band appears at the high-frequency side of

(*) Smakula's formula has sometimes been misquoted in the literature. R. STRUMANE has recalculated the formula from the original assumptions and found that (4) is the correct version.

the F-band (at 5 700 Å in KBr), under a pressure of 8 300 atm, in both X-irradiated and additively colored crystals. This band is tentatively attributed to an F-center in the vicinity of some imperfection, possibly a dislocation.

1·7. *The F'-center.* – Another example of an electron center of which the model is fairly well established is the F'-center. It consists of an F-center which has captured a second electron [12].

We have seen that the F-absorption corresponds to a transition from the s-type ground state to an excited p-type state near the bottom of the conduction band. At room temperature, and above, the lattice vibrations will transfer enough energy to an electron in this excited state so as to liberate it into the conduction band, *i.e.*, bleaching takes place and photoconductivity is observed. The thermal activation energy is of the order of 0.02 eV. At low temperature, at —100 °C for example, this electron may be recaptured by a vacancy with reformation of an F-center. This process is accompanied by luminescence. It may, however, also be captured by an F-center with the formation of a new center: the F'-center, which is stable only up to —80 °C in KCl. The change in absorption spectrum that results from irradiation in the F-band of KCl at —100 °C, is shown in Fig. 3. It is clear that the F-band decreases and that a new, very broad band is formed with a peak between 6 000 and 8 000 Å, *i.e.*, at the long wavelength side of the F-band: this is the F'-band.

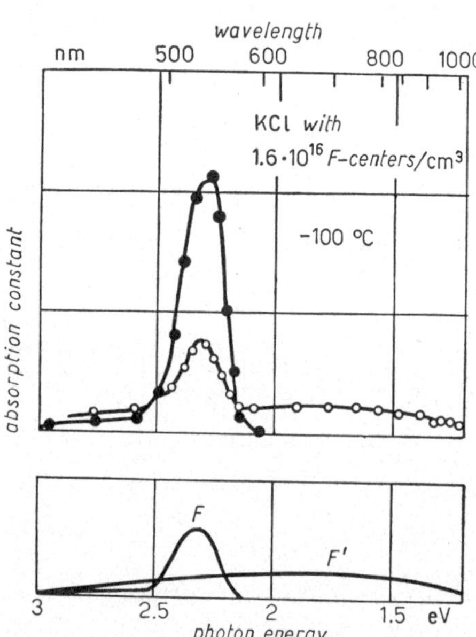

Fig. 3. – The $F \rightarrow F'$ transition in KCl. (After: H. Pick: *Suppl. Nuovo Cimento*, **7**, 498 (1958)).

The conversion of F-center into F'-center is most effective at about —80 °C. At very low temperatures, the lattice does not give enough energy to the electron in the excited state to liberate it, and therefore the conversion is very slow. It speeds up at slightly higher temperatures: at —130 °C all optically excited electrons will be liberated thermally. At these temperatures the initial conversion rate is high, but this slows down rapidly as time goes on, because of the increasingly greater probability of recapture by an empty vacancy. Since, further, the F-band overlaps the F'-band, the F-light will also bleach F'-centers and therefore decrease the number of converted centers. The result is that at any given temperature only a given fraction can be converted; this is 80% at the optimum temperature: -80 °C.

The reverse process, *i.e.*, $F' + h\nu \rightarrow F + e$, is completely effective even at the lowest temperatures ($h\nu$ means now F'-light).

1'8. *Fluorescence of F-centers.* – We have seen that at sufficiently low temperatures thermal activation is insufficient to bring the electron of the F-center into the conduction band. Instead, the electron returns to the ground state under emission of fluorescent light with a maximum somewhere in the infrared at about 1 μm in KCl. No luminescence is observed above -50 °C. The quantum efficiency, which is about 1 at -200 °C, drops rapidly at about -140 °C and becomes zero at -50 °C, according to BECKER and PICK [13]. The quantum efficiency also decreases with increasing F-center concentration ($\sim A/r$) (r is mean distance between F-centers).

The measurements of BOTDEN *et al.* [14] on the other hand, lead to a quantum efficiency of only 1% at 87 °K, and to no dependence on F-center concentration.

The rapid decrease in quantum efficiency at about -140 °C is due to the formation of F'-centers, on irradiation in the F-band.

Recently VAN DOORN [15] has remeasured the quantum efficiency

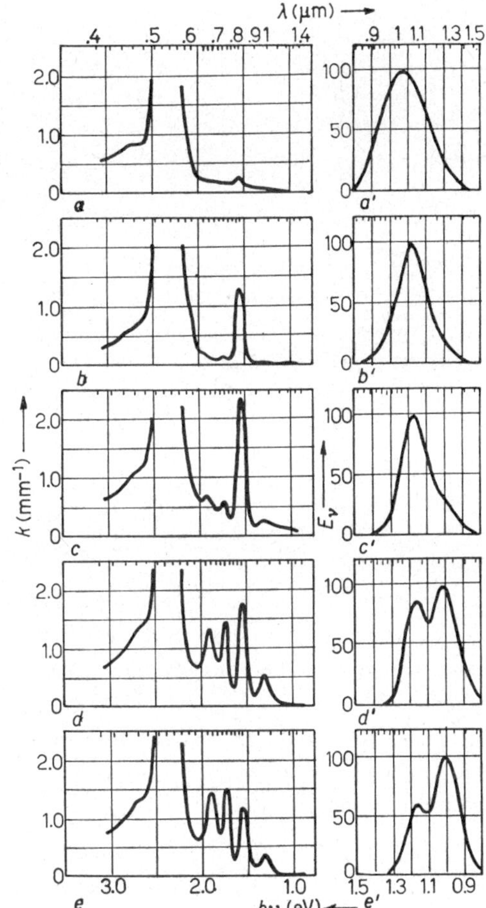

Fig. 4. – Absorption and emission spectra at 77 °K (excitation with *SP* lamp + $CuSO_4$ filter) of a single specimen of additively colored KCl for increasing period of ageing. Times given are total times of ageing at room temperature. *a*, *a'*: immediately after quenching from 610 °C to -196 °C; *b*, *b'*: after 10 min of ageing; *c*, *c'*: after 25 min of ageing; *d*, *d'*: after 165 min of ageing; *e*, *e'*: after 18 h of ageing. (After: C. Z. VAN DOORN and Y. HAVEN: *Philips Res. Rep.*, **11**, 479 (1956)).

and found that for not too high concentration of F-centers ($\sim 5 \cdot 10^{16}$) and for crystals not containing an appreciable M-band the quantum efficiency approaches unity, confirming Becker and Pick's result. During this study VAN DOORN and HAVEN [16] found that the emission spectrum becomes more complicated when the crystal has been kept some time at room temperature. Two peaks now appear in the infrared (Fig. 4). It was found that this was connected with the development of an M-band. If ageing was such as to develop also R-bands, irradiation in this band, or in the F-band, gives rise to a third emission. Since these observations are important for giving information on possible models for the M-center we will discuss them further in some detail.

1·9. *Field ionization.* – Since the excited state ($2p$) of the F-center is so near to the bottom of the conduction band one may expect appreciable field ionization to take place. This was verified by LÜTY [17].

An electrical field was applied to a crystal at -180 °C while it was simultaneously irradiated with F-light. It was found that the rate of reduction of the F-center concentration, which was initially $1.8 \cdot 10^{17}/\text{cm}^3$, is strongly field-dependent and increases with the number of light quanta absorbed.

1·10. *Conversion of F-centers into colloid.* – DOYLE [18] has recently studied the thermal conversion of F-centers in additively colored NaCl into colloid by means of the optical absorption. He finds that in this transformation the total integrated absorption is conserved. The shape of the colloid band is dependent on the temperature of formation; at low temperature (175 °C) a broad and low band is formed, while at high temperature a narrow high band is formed. A theory is given which allows to deduce the particle size from the colloid band width.

Ionizing radiation also produces colloids in NaCl. This was, *e.g.*, found to be the case after electron bombardment, at room temperature and above [19]. The position of the peak and the shape of the band depends on the temperature of irradiation and on the energy of the incident electron.

COMPTON [20] investigated the influence of impurities on the formation of colloids by ionizing radiation in NaCl. He concluded that natural crystals do not form colloids as easily as do synthetic ones. After a long anneal in air the natural crystals, however, behave like the synthetic ones. It is thought that the presence of an OH-ion is responsible for the sensitization of synthetic crystals.

The colloid band overlaps some other bands so that it is not always possible to establish its identity. This can be ascertained by using the following criteria for the colloid band.

a) There is wavelength-dependence of light scattered at right angles to the incident beam; the wavelength of maximum scattering depends upon particle size.

b) Absorption peak is not temperature-sensitive in the range $(77 \div 300)$ °K; the half-width does not change either.

c) Heating may cause the growth of the colloid particles resulting in a shift of the peak towards longer wavelengths.

The formation of colloid by ionizing radiation was previously found by WESTERVELT [21].

2. – *M*-type centers.

2·1. *Formation.* – After irradiation at room temperature a rather broad band at the long-wavelength side of the *F*-band is often developed simultaneously. Also, when additively coloring a crystal it is difficult to obtain a pure *F*-band. Usually some *M*-band absorption is present too, especially in NaCl. In KCl a pure *F*-band can more easily be obtained. The band has been called *M*-band after MOLNAR [22], who made the first systematic study of it. It can be introduced easily by bleaching the *F*-centers at room temperature. Usually other absorption bands, situated between the *F*-band and the *M*-band, the so-called *R*-bands are formed simultaneously . In NaCl the *M*-band is at 7200 Å, whereas it is at 8200 Å in KCl.

2·2. *Models.* – The *M*-center is considered as one of the first coagulation products of *F*-centers and probably involves the migration of lattice defects since it is only formed at temperatures where vacancies become mobile. With this idea in mind, SEITZ [23] proposed that the *M*-center should result from the combination of an *F*-center and a vacancy pair, giving rise to the angular model of Fig. 5. The vacancy pair was considered to be the mobile unit that migrates towards the *F*-center.

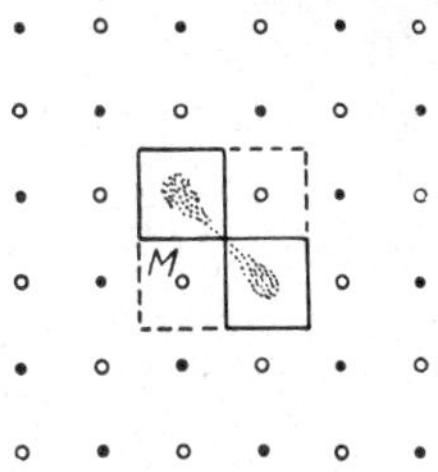

Fig. 5. – Model of the *M*-center: ○ alkali; ● halogen.

VAN DOORN and HAVEN [24], on the other hand, have proposed a model consisting of two adjacent *F*-centers. Recently KNOX [25] proposed a slight modification of the Seitz model. The positive ion, *e.g.* *M* (Fig. 5), would spend half its time in the symmetrical position by jumping back and forth at a relatively high frequency, since the potential barrier between the two positions is rather small. The electrostatic potential has a saddle point at the midway position. In view of the effective positive charges associated with the negative ion vacancies that occupy the corners, the electron will spend most of its time there. A schematic view of this center is given in Fig. 5. This model clearly has an inversion center. The main axis is along [110]. The preferential bleaching experiments using polarized light [26] do not contradict this model.

Paramagnetic resonance [27] lines due to this center have been identified, but no detailed spectra have been obtained and hence no check of this model has been possible.

2'3. *Properties of M-centers.* – We will now review briefly the significant experimental facts and then discuss the merits of the models.

Irradiation with M-light [28] results in a photocurrent, with a quantum efficiency of about 0.10 at room temperature. Also R- and N-centers are formed (as well as by irradiation with F-light).

2'3.1. *Dichroism.* – When polarized bleaching M-light is used (at room temperature) the absorption exhibits dichroism [26], the decrease in absorption being largest for light polarized in the same direction as the bleaching light. The irradiation time is long: several hours. The dichroism is due to preferential bleaching; heating to 60 °C removes it. This experiment shows that the center has no cubic symmetry and hence contradicts neither the Seitz model, nor the Van Doorn and Haven model.

Dichroism of a somewhat different nature has been studied in detail by Van Doorn and Haven [29, 30] and by Kanzaki [31].

We first summarize the results of the former workers. An additively colored KCl crystal containing an M-band is cooled to 77 °K and then irradiated for a few minutes in the F-band with light polarized along the [011] direction.

The results are (Fig. 6):

a) The M-absorption for light polarized in $[01\bar{1}]$ is increased.
b) The M-absorption for light polarized in [011] is decreased.
c) The F-band shows the opposite behavior of the M-band.
d) The dichroism is permanent at the low temperature.
e) The dichroism disappears at 200 °K.

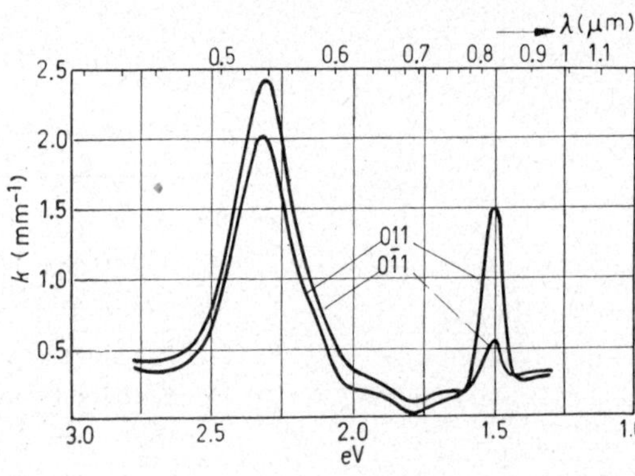

Fig. 6. – Absorption at 77 °K of a colored KCl crystal in the [100] direction, measured with light polarized in the [011] and $[0\bar{1}1]$ directions. The crystal is irradiated beforehand with light ($\lambda = 5461$ Å) polarized in the [011] direction. The absorption curve before irradiation is intermediate between the two shown. (After: C. Z. Van Doorn: *Philips Res. Rep.*, **12**, 309 (1957)).

Irradiation with light polarized along [001] has a similar effect although weaker than in the former case. Irradiation in the M-band does not produce dichroism, contrary to what is observed by UETA at room temperature. In the latter case there is preferential bleaching rather than reorientation of the centers, as is the case here.

The conclusions that can be drawn from these experiments are:

1) The M-center is anisotropic; the dichroism results from an anisotropic distribution of the axis of the centers.

2) From the observed dichroism for [110] and [100] polarized light can be concluded that the axis of the centers are *not* along threefold or fourfold axes of symmetry.

3) The center giving rise to the dichroism of the F-band cannot be the F-center, since it is well established that this center has cubic symmetry.

4) Since irradiation in the F-band causes dichroism in F- and M-bands the centers causing the dichroism in these absorption bands are identical. Additional evidence, from a study of the emitted light, will be discussed below.

An alternative proposal was made by LAMBE and COMPTON [32]. They suggest that energy transfer occurs from the F- to the M-centers, during irradiation in the F-band. This would also explain the large decrease in quantum efficiency of the F-center luminescence if some M-centers are present.

5) The persistence of the dichroism at low temperature suggests that it results from ionic movement, rather than from preferential bleaching. The fact that irradiation in the short wavelength band (the F-band) is necessary to produce the dichroism is also an indication in this sense.

2·3.2. *Properties of the luminescent light.*

1) M-center emission.

a) M-center emission can be excited by irradiation in either the F- or the M-band. If the exciting light is polarized, the emitted light is also polarized. With M-excitation $p=(I_{\parallel}-I_{\perp})/(I_{\parallel}+I_{\perp})$ is positive.

b) Exciting with polarized light in the F-band apparently causes reorientation of the M-center. This can be inferred from the fact that it takes about 30 s before the luminescent light reaches its equilibrium intensity, after the polarizer has been turned to a new orientation. This relaxation effect is absent after M-excitation.

c) If a crystal is first made dichroic by irradiation with polarized light in the F-band and then excited with unpolarized M-light, the M-center luminescence is polarized in the same plane as the bleaching F-light.

d) Analysis of the polarization of the emitted light indicates that the center should be oriented along a [110] direction.

2) *R*-center emission. – *R*-center emission (at 1.24 μm) can be stimulated by irradiating in *F*- or *R*- band. The polarization is, however, different in the two cases.

a) With *F*-excitation the polarization of the luminescent light is negative.

b) With R_1- or R_2-excitation *p* is positive. The luminescent emission is the same in both cases: the angular dependence and the degree of polarization are the same.

2·4. *Discussion of models.*

2·4.1. *M*-center model. – As a model for the *M*-center VAN DOORN and HAVEN propose two adjacent *F*-centers. This model has the required orientation and symmetry. The level scheme consists of a ground state and two excited states of which the highest one is twofold degenerate. Emission and absorption in the *M*-band correspond to transitions between the ground state and the lowest excited state. These transitions have a nonzero moment in the direction of the axis only. The *M*-emission due to absorption in the *F*-band results from excitation to the highest excited state, followed by a radiationless transition to the lowest excited state, before the transition giving rise to the *M*-emission occurs. The energy freed in the radiationless transition can be used to reorient the center. The *F*-excitation transition has a nonzero moment only in the direction perpendicular to the center.

2·4.2. *R-center model.* – VAN DOORN assumes that the R_1- and R_2-bands are due to a single center, because,

1) the ratio of the absorption in R_1 and R_2 is constant in different specimens;

2) the same emission is found for excitation in either one of the bands;

3) the luminescent light has the same characteristics whether excitation in R_1 or in R_2 is used.

An analysis of the polarization of the emitted light seems to indicate that the center is oriented along [111]. More recently COMPTON and KLICK [33] have found that it might be [110]. VAN DOORN proposed a level scheme consisting of a single ground-state and three excited states. The R_2-emission corresponds to a transition from the lowest excited state to the ground state. The inverse transition corresponds to absorption in R_2; R_1-absorption excites the electron to the second excited state, a radiationless transition then brings the electron in the lowest excited state from where it can again given rise to R_2-emission by going to the ground state. All transitions considered so far have a nonzero moment for the direction parallel to the axis of the center. F-excitation corresponds to a transition from the ground-state to the highest excited state, with a nonzero transition moment in a direction perpendicular to the axis of the center. From the highest excited state there is again a radiationless transition to the lowest excited state.

No really satisfactory geometric model is given; two proposals are, however, made: either the system consists of an equilateral triangular arrangement of three F-centers in the (111) plane, or it consists of three F-centers in the configuration of a scalene triangle, also in the (111) plane.

2·5. *Equilibrium between F- and M-centers.* – VAN DOORN [34] recently re-examined the thermal equilibrium at a given temperature between F- and M-center in KCl for different F-center concentrations. He quenched crystals of very pure KCl all of the same dimensions to have the same quenching rates, colored under different potassium pressures and measured both the F- and M-center absorption. A plot of his results is shown in Fig. 7. It is clear

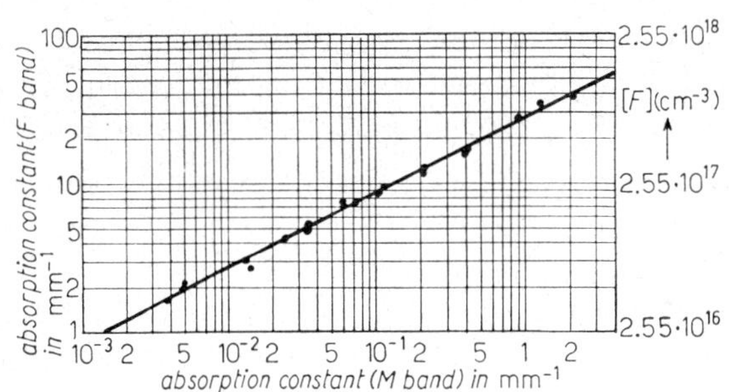

Fig. 7. – Double-logarithmic plot of the concentration of F- and M-centers in equilibrium at 697 °C, expressed as absorption constants at 77 °K of the F- and M-bands, respectively. The number of F-centers per cm³ is calculated from the Smakula formula with $f=0.81$ and a half-value width 0.195 MeV. (After: C. Z. VAN DOORN: *Phys. Rev. Lett.*, **4**, 236 (1960)).

that the M-center concentration varies quadratically with the F-center concentration. This is consistent with the model of Van Doorn and Haven for the M-center but not with the Seitz-Knox model. In the former case the formation reaction is

$$F + \text{vacancy pair} \rightleftarrows M$$

and the equilibrium condition

$$[F]\cdot[\text{vacancy pair}]/[M] = 1/K\,.$$

For the Van Doorn-Haven model, on the other hand, the formation reaction is

$$F + F \rightarrow M$$

and hence the equilibrium condition

$$[F]^2/[M] = 1/K' .$$

It is clear that the second condition is found to be satisfied, giving a strong indication that the Seitz-Knox model for the M-center may be wrong.

Other evidence difficult to reconcile with the Seitz model was found by JACOBS [35]. He explored a wide range of temperatures and frequencies in an attempt to find a dielectric-loss peak due to M-centers, but was unable to find it. The Knox modification of the Seitz model would eventually eliminate this difficulty.

The model of Van Doorn and Haven would also be consistent with the measurements of THEISSEN and SCOTT [36], who found that the formation reaction of the M-center from the F-center obeyed second order kinetics.

On the other hand, if it is confirmed that the M-center is paramagnetic, the model of Van Doorn would be in difficulty.

3. – The R- and N-centers.

3·1. *Production of the centers.* – Room temperature irradiation with F-light of a crystal containing dispersed F-centers results in the formation of several bands situated between the F- and the M-band resulting from the coagulation of F-centers. Irradiation in the M-band also produced R- and N-bands. Particularly effective is a combination of bleaching light and slightly heating the crystal.

Ageing at some 100 °C of additively colored crystals also results in the formation of R-, M- and N-bands. Nor R- or N-bands are produced by irradiation at liquid hydrogen temperature [37, 38].

3·2. *Models.* – Considering that R- and N-centers are produced by the coagulation of F-centers, SEITZ postulated models for these defects. The R_1-center consists of two adjacent negative ion vacancies, which have trapped one electron. The R_2-center is composed of two neighboring F-centers, while the model for the N-center is not specified, but is considered as being more complicated, in view of the fact that it is formed in a later stage of the coagulation process.

3·3. *Some low-temperature properties.* – We have already discussed a number of such properties in the paragraph on the M-center. COMPTON and KLICK [39] made a study of the temporary changes in absorption spectrum at 77 °K and 4 °K, in NaCl and KCl, caused by auxiliary illumination with light absorbed in the different bands. It turns out that R_1-, R_2-, M-, N-, and N_2-bands are all affected by irradiation into the R_1-, R_2-, M- or N_2-bands. The striking fact is that irradiation in the long wavelength bands influences the short-wavelength bands. This seems to suggest that these centers are not isolated but interact with one another.

From the fact that with auxiliary R_1-light the R_1-band bleaches while the R_2-band does not, LAMBE and COMPTON [40] concluded that the same center could *not* be responsible for both bands. This argument is invalidated by the measurements described.

4. – The α- and β-bands.

These bands were found by DELBECQ, PRINGSHEIM and YUSTER [41] when studying crystals of KI either additively colored, or colored by X-rays.

4·1. *Production of the centers.* – The procedures giving rise to an F-band also introduce at the same time the β-band, which is very near to the edge of the fundamental absorption band.

The α-band is generated by optical bleaching of the F-band.

4·2. *Main properties of the absorption bands.*

1) The β-absorption is strictly proportional to the F-absorption. This was investigated in detail by MARTIENSSEN in KBr [42].

2) Bleaching with F-light results in a parallel decrease of the β-band and the F-band, and a parallel increase of the α-band and the F'-band.

3) Heating to decompose the F'-centers causes the α-band to disappear and results in an increase of the β-band and the F-band, which are restored to their original value.

4) Crystals irradiated at very low temperatures show an α-band but no F'-band, excluding in this way that the α- and F'-bands should be due to the same center.

5) The ratio of α-absorption to the F-absorption increases as the irradiation temperature decreases. The sum of the extinction coefficients is larger, however, at the lower temperatures.

6) The α-band is bleached at $-183\ ^\circ\mathrm{C}$ by light absorbed in the α-band but the quantum efficiency is low. Emission of luminescent light accompanies the absorption. This observation implies that migration of halogen ion vacancies takes place as a consequence of the absorption of light, if the model is correct.

7) The decrease in the α-band absorption during bleaching is not accompanied by a decrease in the F-absorption.

The conclusions that can be drawn from these results are:

1) The β-band and the F-band are intimately connected, *i.e.*, due to the same center but to a different electronic excitation process.

2) The α-band and the F'-band are due to a different defect.

4·3. *Models for α- and β-centers.*

1) *α-center.* The center responsible for the α-band is a halogen ion vacancy. The growth of the α-band on bleaching the F-centers is then simply due to the vacancies left by bleached F-centers, the electrons being captured by other F-centers which are transformed into an F'-center. This explains the parallel growth of F'- and α-bands.

The absorption is due to the excitation of an electron of a halogen ion into a bound state associated with the vacancy; or expressed otherwise it consists of an exciton trapped at a negative ion vacancy.

2) *β-center.* The β-absorption is closely connected with the F-center. It is due to the excitation of an electron of a halogen ion into a bound state associated with the F-centers, or described alternatively it is an exciton trapped at an F-center.

4·4. *Characteristics of α- and β-bands.* – The energies corresponding to the peaks of α- and β-bands are given in the following Table.

	α	β
NaBr	6.23 eV	—
KBr	6.15 eV	6.44 eV
KI	5.21 eV	5.48 eV
RbBr	6.04 eV	6.31 eV
RbI	5.16 eV	5.40 eV

The positions of the α- and β-bands have been derived by BASSANI and INCHAUSPÉ [43] using the models just described. They calculated the energy required to create the exciton in the neighborhood of a vacancy and of an F-center, using the transfer model. The obtained values are in reasonable agreement with the observed ones.

B) V-Type centers.

1. – The classical V-bands.

1'1. *Production of V-centers.*

1'1.1. *Chemical method.* – Annealing KBr or KI in the corresponding halogen vapor at high temperature and high vapor pressure, followed by quenching results in the formation of a new set of absorption bands at the short-wavelength side of the F-band [44, 45].

In view of their formation it is reasonable to assume that they are associated with excess halogen, or with positive ion vacancies and holes. The formation can be considered as a reaction at the surface of halogen with metal ions, resulting in the deposition of layers of material at the surface and migration inwards of positive ion vacancies and holes.

The concentration of V-centers is proportional to the concentration of halogen molecules in the vapor. This points toward a diatomic model for the centers introduced in this way (V_2- and V_3-centers).

It was not possible to incorporate excess chlorine into the chlorides even at the highest pressures and temperatures. Similar to the case of excess metal, it is also possible to introduce excess halogen electrolytically. The crystal is electrolysed at high temperature using a pointed anode.

The bands found in chemically colored crystals are shown in Fig. 8, observed at room temperature. There are three peaks, of which the two more pronounced ones are termed V_2 and V_3. The third peak is not found in X-rayed material (see further).

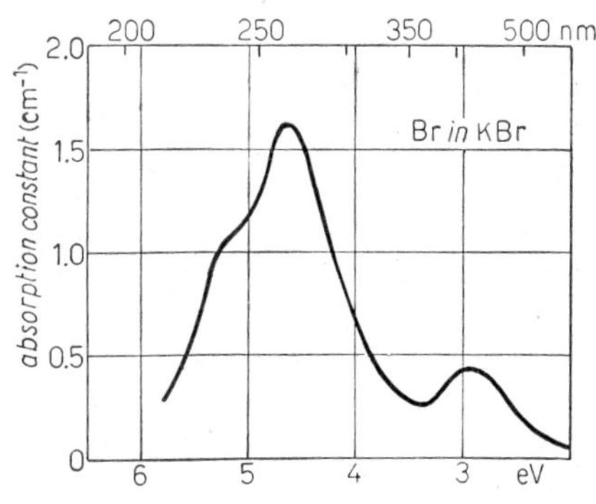

Fig. 8. – The V-bands observed by Mollwo in KBr containing excess Br. The two unresolved peaks on the left are commonly designated V_3 and V_2 in the order given from left to right. The peak near 3 eV is not generally observed at room temperature in X-rayed crystals, although it lies near the V_1-band. (After: F. Seitz: *Rev. Mod. Phys.*, **26**, 7 (1954)).

1·1.2. *Irradiation-induced bands.* – The temperature of irradiation determines the type of V-bands that are formed by ionizing radiation. This is illustrated in a striking way by Fig. 9, due to DORENDORF [46, 47].

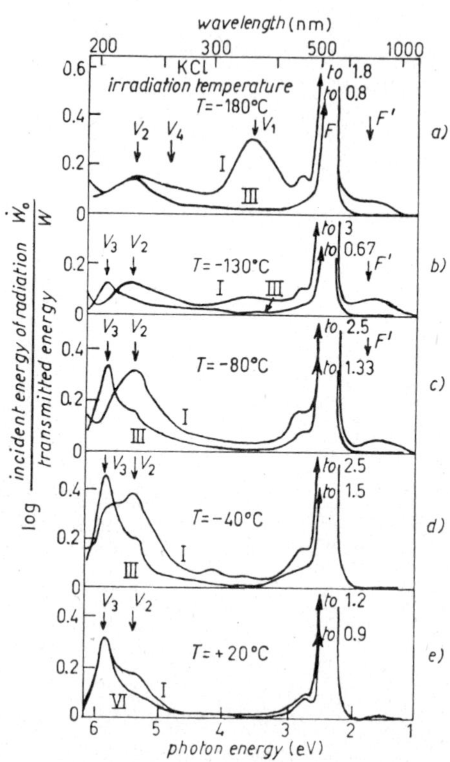

Fig. 9. – The V-bands produced in KCl when irradiated with X-rays at various temperatures. The curve I in each panel shows the absorption spectrum immediately after irradiation, whereas curve III shows the spectrum after the specimen was raised to room temperature. All measurements were made at liquid-nitrogen temperature to achieve maximum resolution. In this material the V_3-band grows on warming, whereas the other bands decrease (after DORENDORF). (After: F. SEITZ: *Rev. Mod. Phys.*, **26**, 7 (1954.))

1) Irradiation at room temperature. Irradiation at room temperature produces the V_3- and V_2-bands, the V_3-band being dominant. The F-band is, of course, also produced. ALEXANDER and SCHNEIDER [48] have described a method for eliminating the F-band in such specimens. They apply an electric field of about 2 000 V/cm, while irradiating with F-light. The V-bands are not changed in this process; it probably consists in field ionization of the F-center (see chapter on F-centers).

2) Irradiation at liquid-nitrogen temperature. Irradiation at liquid-nitrogen temperature produces a prominent V_1-band and smaller V_2- and V_3-bands together with the F- and F'-bands. The V_1-band becomes thermally unstable at -158 °C; V_4 vanishes at -27 °C (in KBr). This process is accompanied by an increase in V_2- and V_3-absorption. A more detailed survey of the properties of these centers is given below.

3) Irradiation at liquid-helium and liquid-hydrogen temperature. A number of V-type centers, involving interstitial halogens, are introduced by irradiation with X-rays at these low temperatures. They have been studied by KÄNZIG and co-workers; the results will be discussed further in detail.

1'2. *Characteristics of the V-bands.* – We summarize here a number of the main characteristics of the V-bands (peak, wavelength and half-width).

	KBr			KCl		
	Wavelength in energy units	Peak	Half-width in energy units	Wavelength in energy units	Peak	Half-width in energy units
V_1	4 100 Å	3.02 eV	0.7 eV	3 560 Å	3.48 eV	0.73 eV
V_2	2 650 Å	4.67 eV	0.6 eV	2 300 Å	5.37 eV	0.5 eV
V_3	2 310 Å	5.35 eV	0.45 eV	2 120 Å	5.83 eV	0.35 eV
V_4	2 750 Å	4.50 eV	0.4 eV	2 540 Å	4.87 eV	?

1'3. *Properties of V-centers* [49].

1) Optical bleaching of the F-band at room temperature results in a large decrease in V_2-centers, but affects very little the V_3-centers. The initial bleaching rate is large and results mainly in the formation of R- and M-centers; the V-centers are not affected. In the later stage the V-centers bleach at the same rate as the F-centers.

2) Warming after irradiation at liquid-nitrogen temperature results in growth of the V_3-band and decrease of the V_2-band. This phenomenon probably results in the thermal release of electrons from F'-centers or other electron centers.

3) The ratio of V_2- to V_3-absorption depends on the history of the specimen.

4) In KBr the V_3-band diminishes and the V_2-band grows when the V_1-center becomes thermally unstable (Fig. 10).

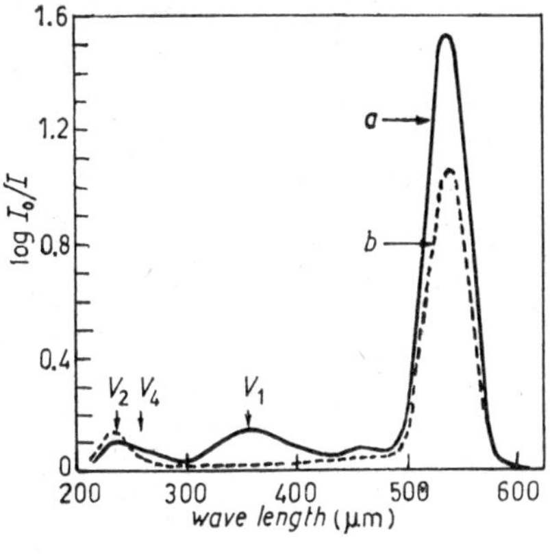

Fig. 10. – The V_1-band produced by Castler, Pringsheim and Yuster by irradiating KCl with X-rays at liquid-nitrogen temperature (full curve). This vanishes when the specimen is warmed to room temperature (dashed curve). The intensity of the F-band diminishes at the same time. There is also a shift at the ultra-violet end of the spectrum, indicating that the V_4-band diminishes and the V_2-band grows. *a*) KCl (184) X-rays 20 min liquid-N_2 temperature; *b*) KCl (184) warmed up to dry ice temperature, cooled down to liquid-N_2 temperature and measured. After: F. SEITZ: *Rev. Mod. Phys.*, **26**, 7 (1954)).

5) In KCl the V_2-band bleaches before the V_3-band on increasing the temperature.

6) Room temperature irradiation with V_2-V_3-light results in a decrease in F-absorption. The V-absorption, however, recovers slowly after the end of the irradiation, suggesting that the V_2 and V_3 have metastable excited states.

7) Irradiation in F- and V-bands simultaneously accelerates the bleaching rate.

1·4. *Low-temperature properties of V-centers in* KBr (*and* KCl). The following table summarizes the results of a detailed study of the annealing processes going on at low temperatures in the region of the V-bands [50, 51].

Simultaneous measurements of the absorption spectrum, the charge release and the luminescent light emission were made.

If the KBr is darkened at —156 °C peak (1) is not observed since no V_1-centers are formed; the V_2- and V_4-bands, on the other hand, are relatively stronger. The peak (2) at —130 °C on the contrary is about 20 × larger, while a new current peak appears at — 90 °C.

Temperature of peak in charge release	Sign of released carrier	Changes in absorption spectrum	Calculated thermal trap depth	Luminescent light
KBr: irradiation temperature —183 °C				
1) —158 °C (—145 °C in KCl)	+	V_1 vanishes F diminishes	0.23 eV	$\lambda > 5\,500$ Å
2) —130 °C (— 68 °C in KCl)	—	V_3, V_2, V_4 grow F' bleaches	0.29	$\lambda < 3\,800$ Å
3) — 90 °C (— 36 °C in KCl)	No current peak	?	0.38 0.38	$\lambda > 5\,500$ Å
4) — 48 °C	+ ?	F-band drops, no other changes	0.46	yes
5) — 27 °C	+ largest pulse	V_4 bleaches F decreases V_2, V_3 stationary	0.50	$\lambda < 5\,500$ Å

1'5. *Models for V-centers.* – The situation concerning the models for V-centers is somewhat strange. Models have been proposed for the four V-centers mentioned before by SEITZ [1]. They are shown in Fig. 11. So far, however, no unambiguous experimental evidence is known for these models, although on the whole they explain reasonably well the observed features in a consistent way. On the other hand, a number of V-centers have been found at low temperatures, but which have entirely different structures. The model for the V_1-center, however, seems to be seriously in doubt as a consequence of the recent work of KÄNZIG and WOODRUFF [52].

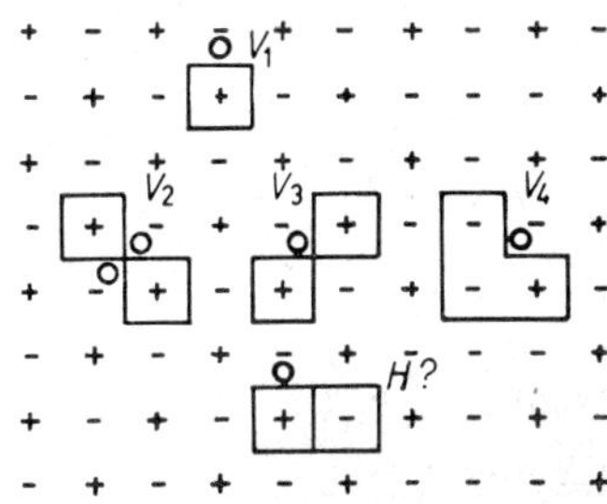

Fig. 11. – Proposed models of the V-centers. V_1 is assumed to be the antimorph of the F-center, consisting of a hole plus a positive-ion vacancy, whereas V_2 and V_3 are the antimorphs of the R-centers. It is suggested that V_3 is the negatively charged unit consisting of one hole and two positive-ion vacancies, which should repel electrons that do not overlap the hole distribution. V_4 is the antimorph of the M-center. (After: F. SEITZ: *Rev. Mod. Phys.*, **26**, 7 (1954)).

We mention here a few of the most striking features that can readily be explained on the basis of Seit'z models.

1) If bleaching of the V_1-band releases a hole (in KBr), the decrease of the V_3-band and the increase in V_1-band can readily be understood. The hole is captured by the negatively charged V_3-center and converted into a V_2-center.

2) The bimolecular nature of the V_2- and V_3-center as required by Mollwo's measurements.

3) The electrons released from F-centers are repelled by the negatively charged V_3-centers and hence they do not bleach, while the V_2-centers are bleached efficiently and converted into V_3-centers.

1'6. *V-bands in mixed crystals.* - The position of the V-bands in mixed crystals has been investigated by MIESSNER and PICK [53]. They considered the series of mixed crystals KCl-RbCl, in which the ratio of the two cations is varied continuously, and also the series KCl-KBr where now the anion is varied. After irradiation at room temperature, which develops V_2- and V_3-bands, they find a chlorine band at about 2100 Å in pure KCl, which shifts continuously to about 2250 Å in pure RbCl. In the KCl-KBr series they find for pure KCl the chlorine band at 2100 Å. As more bromide is added a bromine band at 2650 Å appears, but no continuous shift occurs.

At liquid-nitrogen temperature a prominent V_1-band appears at the short wavelength side of the F-band, *i.e.*, at 3900 Å in KBr-KCl (3:2). In the series KCl-RbCl the position of the V_1-band, *i.e.* at 3600 Å, does not depend on composition, which shows that it is exclusively determined by the anion. On the other hand, in the KCl-KBr series the position shifts from 3600 Å in pure KCl to 4100 Å in pure KBr.

Whereas the position of the F-band does not seem to depend on the chemical composition, but mainly on the lattice parameter, this no longer applies to the V_1-band, where the kind of halogen determines the position.

2. – The H-center.

During an investigation of the V-bands introduced by irradiation with X-rays at 5 °K, DUERIG and MARKHAM [47] discovered a new absorption band, practically coinciding in wavelength with the V_1-band, the so-called H-band. In view of its importance for the formation mechanism of color centers in general, we will discuss its characteristics in some detail.

The peak positions of V_1- and H-bands are given in the table.

alkali halide	V_1	H
NaCl	3 450	3 300
KCl	3 560	3 450
KBr	4 100	3 800

TEEGARDEN and MAURER [55] have further investigated the relation between H- and V_1-band and have made a remarkable discovery. The H-band

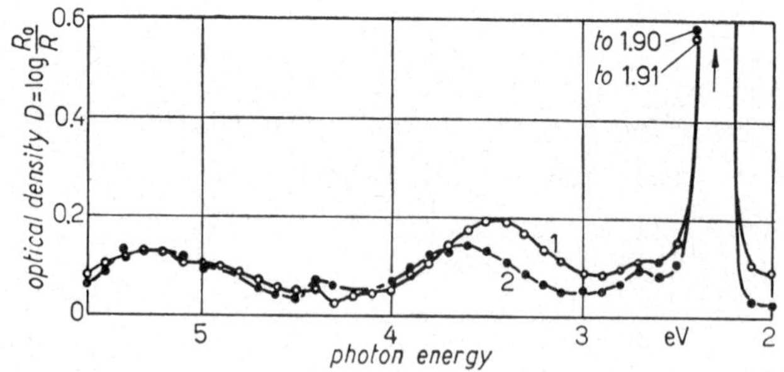

Fig. 12. – Optical absorption of KCl at 35 °K. Curve 1 was taken after irradiating the crystal with X-rays for 1 h at 83 °K. Curve 2 was taken after bleaching the V_1-band at 35 °K with radiation of 3.5 eV photon energy. Approximately $3\cdot10^{16}$ quanta were absorbed by the crystal. (After: K. TEEGARDEN and R. MAURER: *Zeits. Phys.*, **138**, 284 (1954)).

is easily formed at 35 °K; it bleaches almost completely at 78 °K and is then replaced by the V_1-band and by some component of the V_2- or V_4-band. If the crystal is then recooled to 35 °K and the V_1-band optically bleached, the H-band is reformed and the F-band is decreased (Fig. 12).

The heating is accompanied by a charge release in three peaks: at 42 °K, 57° K and at 68 °K, but only if the V_1-band had been exposed to bleaching light at 35 °K. The H-band can be bleached optically at 35 °K; this bleaching is accompanied by bleaching of the F-band but no charge release is observed.

The V_1-band itself can be bleached thermally by heating above 83 °K; the initial bleaching is accompanied by a rapid decrease of F'-band, with little or no change in F-band. No charge release, or very little, accompanies the optical bleaching of the V_1- band.

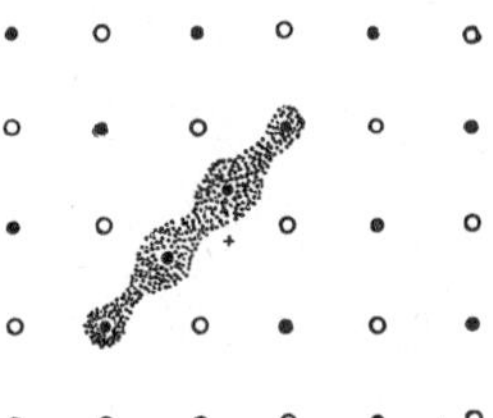

Fig. 13. – Model of the H-center: ○ alkali; ● halogen.

The structure of the H-centers in KCl, KBr and LiF has recently been determined by KÄNZIG and WOODRUFF [52] by means of electron paramagnetic resonance. The center can be visualized as in Fig. 13, *i.e.*, a hole trapped at an interstitial halide ion. Chemically it is a neutral chlorine atom in an interstitial site. The hole spends most of its time with two chlorine ions but is also somewhat more loosely bound to two more ions in a [110] row. The four ions are in a « crowdion » configuration. An alternative description is to say that it is a molecule ion in a halogen vacancy. The whole configuration is axially symmetric and it has no net charge. It is clear that the F-center and the H-center complement each other, *i.e.*

$$F + H \rightleftarrows 0 .$$

KÄNZIG and WOODRUFF [52] found that the ratio of F-band to H-band is independent of temperature (provided it is low enough), suggesting that F- and H-centers are created in pairs.

The bleaching characteristics and the relation to the V_1-center, as optically found by TEEGARDEN and MAURER [55], were confirmed by the resonance technique, showing that the centers under investigation were the same H-centers. In particular the recycling between V_1- and H-centers was studied in some detail.

We summarize here the main facts in the case of KCl. The other halides behave similarly.

a) The growth curves at 20.3 °K for the e.p.r. signal of F-, V- (Cl_2^-) and H-centers are different (Fig. 14). Whereas the first two grow rapidly at first, and then saturate gradually, the second shows no sign of saturation, suggesting that its growth is not connected with imperfections present in the virgin crystal, but rather with imperfections that are created continuously by the irradiation. This picture is in agreement with the two-stage process of F-center formation. It is also in agreement with the observation of DELBECQ, SMALLER and YUSTER [56] that electron traps enhance the formation of halogen molecule ions.

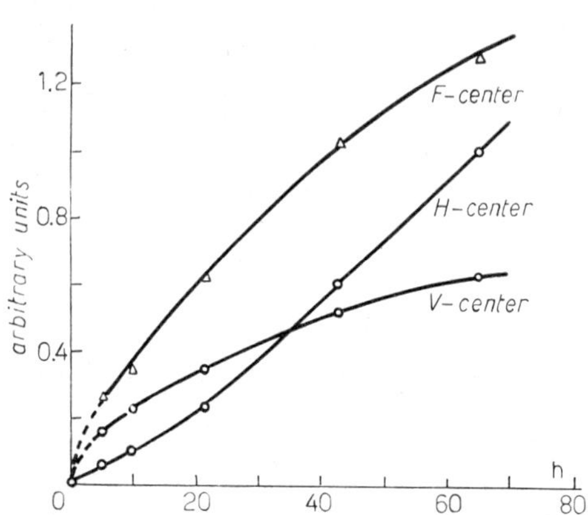

Fig. 14. – Growth of the paramagnetic resonance dispersion of the F-centers, V-centers, and H-centers upon X irradiation of a virgin KCl-crystal at liquid hydrogen temperature. Arbitrary units. The scale factor is about the same for the H-centers and for the V-centers whereas the scale for the F-centers is compressed. Data for the X-ray source: W-target 10 cm from the crystal, filtering equivalent of 4 mm Al, 70 kV, 8 mA. (After: W. KÄNZIG and O. WOODRUFF: *Journ. Phys. Chem. Solids*, **9**, 70 (1959)).

b) Irradiation at 20.3 °K followed by heating at 42 °K for a few minutes, and remeasuring at 20.3 °K, results in:

1) disappearance of the Cl_2^- resonance,

2) F-center concentration decreases by 15 %,

3) H-center resonance grows by 40 %,

4) charge release was observed in this process by TEEGARDEN and MAURER [55].

Since the Cl_2^--centers are thermally stable up to 205 °K the charge release probably consists of electrons which annihilate the Cl_2^--centers. The increase in H-center concentration suggests that the origin of the electron is a trap that becomes an H-center on release of an electron. Such a trap could, *e.g.* be an interstitial Cl^--ion.

c) Warming to 60 °K for a few minutes and remeasuring at 20.3 °K results in:

1) H-center resonance disappears,

2) the F-center concentration diminishes by about 15 %,

3) a small fraction of the Cl_2^--resonances reappears,

4) TEEGARDEN and MAURER observed a charge release at 58 °K,

5) the V_1-band appears,

6) no new resonance is found.

d) X-irradiation at 78 °K results in the formation of a V_1-band (an F-band and Cl_2^--band). Cooling down to 20.3 °K and irradiating with V_1-light causes (Fig. 15):

1) H-center resonance appears and grows to saturation,

2) Cl_2^--resonance disappears before H-center concentration saturates, showing that the H-centers grow at the expense of some other center than Cl_2^-: namely the V_1-center, which can however not be observed by resonance,

3) the F-center concentration is not affected.

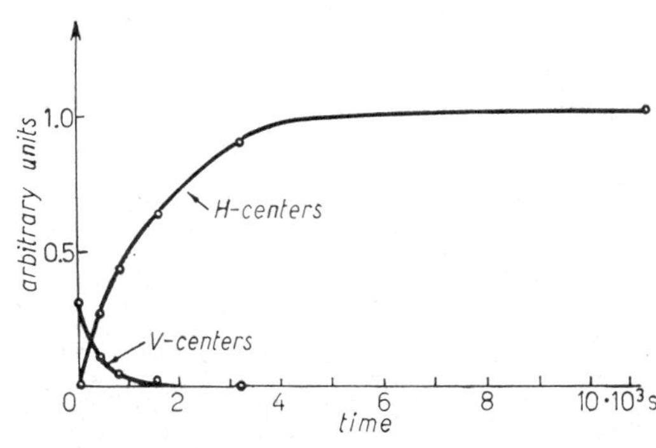

Fig. 15. – Influence of 3 650 Å light at liquid-hydrogen temperature on a KCl-crystal that has been X-rayed at liquid-nitrogen temperature and then cooled to liquid-hydrogen temperature; measured by means of paramagnetic resonance. The H-center and V-center concentrations are plotted on roughly the same scale. (After: W. KÄNZIG and T. WOODRUFF: *Journ. Phys. Chem. Solids*, **9**, 70 (1958)).

e) X-irradiation at 20.3 °K produces H, F, and Cl_2^--centers. Bleaching with V_1-light (3 650 Å) results in Fig. 16)):

1) the H-center resonance decreases. This is due to the fact that no V-centers from which H-centers are formed are present in these circumstances,

2) the Cl_2^--centers bleach (because their absorption peak is at 3 700 Å).

f) The convertibility of V_1-centers into H-centers can be used as a means to study their thermal stability, easier than by optical means. It turns out

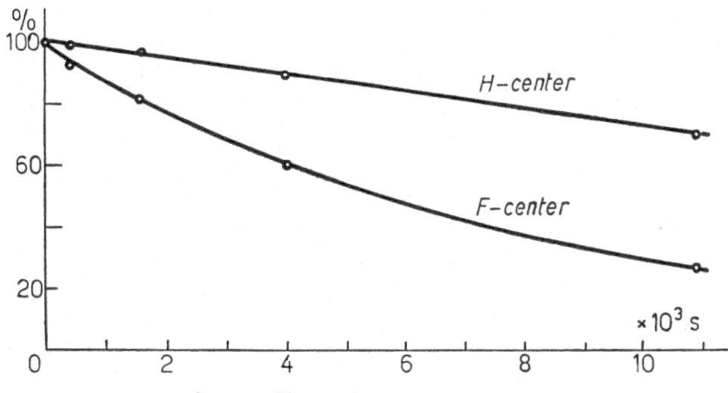

Fig. 16. – Influence of 3 650 Å light at liquid-hydrogen temperature on a KCl-crystal that has been X-rayed and kept at liquid-hydrogen temperature; measured by means of paramagnetic resonance. (After: W. KÄNZIG and T. WOODRUFF: *Journ. Phys. Chem. Solids*, **9**, 70 (1958)).

that at 128 °K in about 30 minutes $(80 \div 90)\%$ of the V_1-centers are bleached. Some, however, survive after heating to 240 °K. This shows that thermal bleaching of the V_1-center at low temperatures involves other centers.

g) Irradiation with *F*-light of crystals which were X-rayed at 20.3 °K resulted in bleaching of *H*, *F* and Cl_2^--band. Such bleaching did not take place when the crystal was X-rayed at 5 °K and then warmed to 20.3 °K. This observation suggests that tunneling is not important, since one would expect this to become more important after irradiation at low temperature, where the separation between *F*- and *V*-centers would presumably be smaller.

A consistent story concerning the production mechanism of color centers at low temperature can now be constructed, which accounts for most of the observed facts, using the model for the *H*-center given by Känzig and Woodruff [52]. This story is based on Varley's mechanism. Although the models proposed by this author do not seem to hold, the essential idea, *i.e.*, the production of interstitials, seems to be an unavoidable assumption.

The production of a pair consisting of an *F*-center and a *H*-center can now take place as follows. The halogen ion becomes positively ionized, and as a consequence decreases in size. It can now migrate fairly easily; it will, however, very soon become neutralized, after having made a small number of jumps. This gives rise to a *H*-center. The vacancy that was left behind will trap an electron and form the *F*-center. On this picture the irradiation at low temperature gives essentially close pairs of *H*- and *F*-centers.

To explain the occurrence of a charge release in KCl at 42 °K Känzig proposes the occurrence of interstitial Cl-ions which could become neutralized by the release of an electron. This could then produce an *H*-center and the electron would destroy a self-trapped hole (Cl_2^-). This process accounts for the growth of the *H*-band and the disappearance of the Cl_2^--band during thermal bleaching at 40 °K. Since this mechanism does not imply the presence of defects before irradiation, it accounts for the shape of the growth curve of *H*-centers.

In order to explain the bleaching and regeneration process, a model of the V_1-center is required. Models have been proposed by Seitz and by Varley, but they do not seem to account for the behavior observed in Känzig's work. In the light of the recent evidence a plausible model seems to be a Cl_2^0-molecule trapped in a halogen vacancy.

When warming up, the *H*-center (Cl_2^- in vacancy) would lose the electron and transform into a neutral Cl_2^0 molecule trapped in a vacancy which we identify with the V_1-center. On irradiation with V_1-light the Cl_2^0 would be ionized and transformed into Cl_2^-, regenerating in this way the *H*-band. The electron which is released from the *H*-center on bleaching would be trapped at a nearby *F*-center to form an *F'*-center. This would agree with the observation that the F-band decreases on thermal bleaching of the H-center. The absence of a paramagnetic resonance spectrum that replaces that of the H-center would agree with the fact that the model for V_1 is not paramagnetic. This model of the V_1-center also agrees with the observed absence of dichroism in the V_1-band at 77 °K [50]. At that temperature the small Cl_2^0 molecule would rotate freely in the halogen vacancy.

Optical bleaching of the V_1-band is probably a complicated process since a number of centers, present at this low temperature, absorb at this wavelength F', V_1 and Cl_2^-. It is, however, wery well conceivable that an electron released by either F' or Cl_2^- is captured by V_1, which transforms this into an H-center. Since the F-band is not increased, however, as it should be if F'-centers are transformed into F-centers, the electron has to originate in some other center.

3. – The halogen molecule ion.

KÄNZIG and co-workers [58-60] analysed in great detail the paramagnetic resonance spectrum of a V-center, which was obtained by irradiating pure alkali-halides KCl, NaCl, LiF and KBr at 80 °K and also at lower temperatures (*e.g.*, 20 °K). They could deduce the model directly from the resonance spectrum: a schematic representation is shown in Fig. 17. The center consists of a hole trapped at, and shared by, two halogen ions, which together form what could be termed a halogen molecule ion: *e.g.*, Cl_2^-. Due to the trapped hole the distance between the two ions has been decreased somewhat. The distance Cl^--Cl^- is 4.4. Å, whille the distance between Cl nuclei in Cl_2^- is 2.16 Å. Intuitively this can be understood since the Coulomb repulsion between the two halogen ions is diminished. The center has roughly axial symmetry, the axis being along one of the six equivalent [110] directions, with equal probability *a priori*.

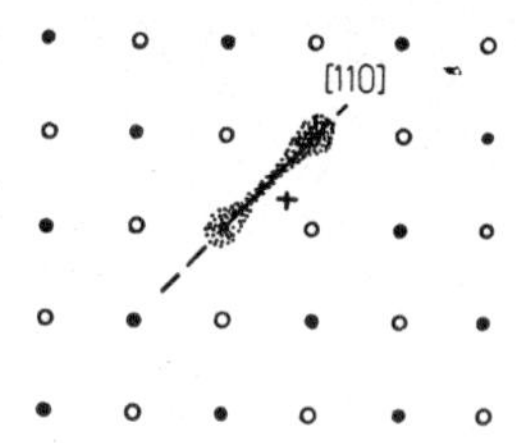

Fig. 17. – Model of the molecule ion: ○ alkali; ● halogen.

Shortly after the study of KÄNZIG and co-workers, DELBECQ, SMALLER and YUSTER [56] were able to correlate the paramagnetic resonance spectra of the halogen molecule ion with the optical absorption due to this center. It is found that the optical absorption is different from the V_1 optical absorption, proving that the Känzig center was new. DELBECQ, SMALLER and YUSTER found also that the production rate of molecule ions can be increased by a factor between 100 and 1000 by adding a small quantity of an electron trap, *e.g.* Ag, Tl or Pb. In such crystals it was possible to obtain the absorption band in a reasonably pure state and study its properties in detail. We summarize here the results of this study.

1) The main band has a peak around 3650 Å in KCl; its exact position depends somewhat on the impurity used. A second peak is found at 7500 Å.

2) The thermal stability of the molecule ion band and the V_1-band are different. Keeping the crystal at —155 °C for some time will bleach the V_1-band completely, but will cause no change in the Cl_2^--resonance or absorption.

3) When light polarized with its electric vector along [011] is sent through the crystal, reorientation of the molecule ions is found, resulting in

a) an increase of the [011] oriented center,

b) a decrease of the [0$\bar{1}$1] oriented centers,

c) a slight decrease of the total absorption.

From this it is concluded that mainly reorientation takes place rather than genuine bleaching.

The dichroism causes changes in the paramagnetic resonance spectrum, which also indicates that the different [011] directions are now unequally populated.

4) The band at 7500 Å does not give rise to dichroism after bleaching with [011] light, but a crystal which was made dichroic by irradiation in the main band (3650 Å) loses this dichroism after irradiation in the long wavelength band.

5) The dichroism disappears at about —100 °C, but no appreciable decrease in Cl_2^--concentration is found until —70 °C. At that temperature recombination of electrons and Cl_2^--centers takes place, accompanied by a glow peak [61].

4. – The antimorph of the *F*-center.

The simplest conceivable *V*-type center would be what Seitz calls the antimorph of the *F*-center, *i.e.*, a hole trapped at a positive ion vacancy. Such a center has actually been observed in LiF, using paramagnetic resonance, by Känzig [62]. The center, however, appears to be much less symmetrical than the *F*-center. Genetically it results from the F_2^- molecule ion. The latter center is known to start migrating at about 125 °K. During this process about 10% of them are trapped at a Li-vacancy and form a new center which is now the antimorph of the *F*-center. A schematic view of the geometry of the center, as deduced from the paramagnetic resonance data, is shown in

Fig. 18. It is seen that the center consists of two F-ions which are pulled together along a [110] axis; the plane of the center is (001). The center has a greater stability than the halogen molecule ion; it anneals out at 230 °K. The center does not cause the optical V_1-band and *no* corresponding defect is found in NaCl, KCl and KBr. The optical absorption is to be expected in the neighborhood of 3 400 Å.

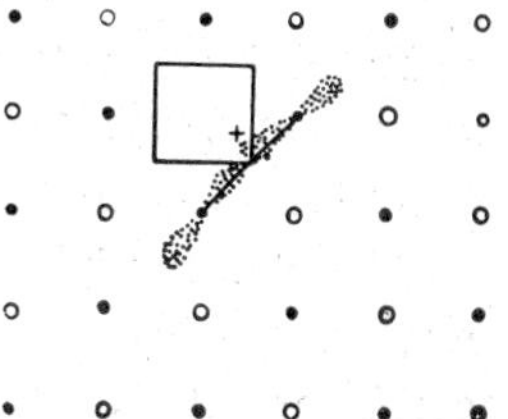

Fig. 18. – Model of the antimorph of the F-center: ○ Li; ● F.

5. – The triangular V-center: V_t.

The structure of a still more complicated V-center in LiF (called V_t) was recently analysed by COHEN *et al.* [63]. The center consists of a hole localized on three fluorine ions, which form an isosceles triangle in the (001) plane with the height along a [110] direction. The hole is associated with three vacancies, which makes it a neutral center. A schematic view is shown in Fig. 19.

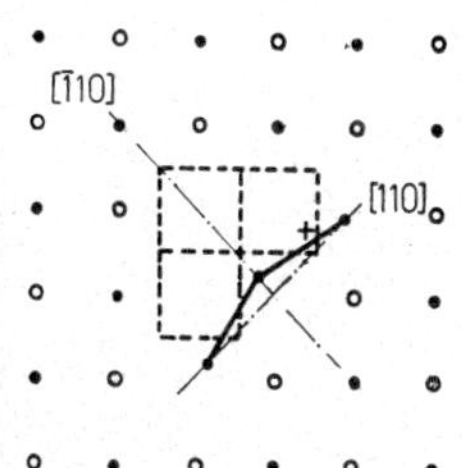

Fig. 19. – Model of the V_t-center: ○ Li; ● F.

This new center is obtained by X-irradiation at liquid-nitrogen temperature. At 130 °K annealing processes go on, resulting in the removal of the V-centers described earlier. This change is accompanied by an increase in the concentration of V_t-centers by a factor of two or three. The V_t-center is relatively stable; it disappears irreversibly between 150 °K and 205 °K.

6. – Recent work on low-temperature annealing.

The work of TEEGARDEN and MAURER and of DUTTON and MAURER was recently confirmed and extended by CAPE and JACOBS [64]. They studied the annealing of KBr and KCl irradiated by X-rays at 10 °K, measuring charge release on heating and the corresponding changes in optical absorption. In KBr the current peaks at 110 °K and 135 °K found by DUTTON and MAURER (after irradiation at 78 °K) were confirmed; additional peaks were found at 30 °K and 155 °K. The peak at 30 °K was attributed to the thermal bleaching of H-centers, by comparison with the e.p.r. work of KÄNZIG and WOODRUFF. The H-absorption (at 3 810 Å) is found to decrease by 25 % at 30 °K. They find that these peaks are accompanied by luminescent light. Further stepwise decreases in 3 810 Å absorption occur at 46 °K (10 %) and at 56 °K (5 %), but no charge release or thermoluminescence takes place.

In KCl current peaks accompanied by thermoluminescence are found at 43 °K and 54 °K in accord with TEEGARDEN and MAURER. The absorption at 3 450 Å (*H*-band) decreases by 15% at 43 °K and by 10% at 56 °K.

The changes in the absorption spectrum of KCl irradiated at 10 °K, during pulse annealing were also followed. The interesting conclusion from these measurements is that presumably three different absorption peaks are located in the region of the *H*-band at 3 450 Å: the *H*-band at 3 350 Å, the self-trapped hole band at 3 650 Å and possibly the V_1-band at 3 500 Å. These different absorptions can be separated by the differences in thermal stability. The self-trapped holes bleach at 43 °K, the *H*-centers at 56 °K, the self-trapped holes reappear between 50 and 60 °K. It could not be established whether V_1-absorption is present after irradiation at 10 °K or whether the V_1-centers are created after annealing to 76 °K. During the complete thermal cycle (10 to 136 °K) the *F*-absorption diminishes gradually, but the F'-absorption never becomes appreciable.

From the described experiment emerges a picture for the low temperature annealing which is somewhat different from the one proposed by KÄNZIG. In order to explain the 43 °K annealing stage, the authors suggest that the Cl_2^0-centers (Cl_2^0 in negative ion vacancy) which are, according to KÄNZIG [62], responsible for the V_1-band, are formed at 10 °K. They are transformed into *H*-centers at 43 °K through the capture of electrons, coming from some non-specified kind of shallow trap, which may be the interstitial negative ion. The observed decrease of self-trapped holes at this same temperature is then due to trapping of electrons also. The annealing stage at 56 °K can then be explained in two ways:

a) The *H*-centers become mobile and annihilate *F*-centers. The recombination energy is used to ionize a Cl ion and leave a self-trapped hole, the electron causing the charge burst. This could explain the observed increase in self-trapped holes.

b) *H*-centers migrate towards negative ion vacancies and form self-trapped holes.

By none of these processes does the F'-band appear in accord with observation.

C) **Impurity centers.**

As in metals and semiconductors the type of centers created during irradiation and especially the annealing behavior depend on the presence of impurities. Without going into all details we wish to describe here some color centers which are known to be connected with the presence of impurities.

We have already mentioned the effect of the presence of impurities, that may function as electron traps, on the production of halogen molecule ions, and we also mentioned the sensitizing effect of some divalent impurities on the growth of the F-band. We will now discuss some centers of which the impurity is an essential part.

1. – The U-center.

When potassium hydride (KH) is added to KBr, the X-ray produced coloration is more stable. This is explained by assuming that the protons take halogen ion positions, which give rise to an absorption band, the U-band at about 5.5 eV. During X-raying the U-absorption decreases and the F-absorption increases. The role of the hydrogen ion then consists in trapping the holes giving rise to neutral hydrogen atoms, which may diffuse into the crystal leaving behind vacancies, which on capturing an electron are transformed into F-centers. By preventing recombination of electrons and holes the F-band growth is sensitized; only 40 eV are required per F-center in such a crystal [65, 66].

Earlier measurements by Thomas [67] concerning the U-band will now be summarized. Irradiation in the U-band produces different results at different temperatures. At high enough temperature, *i.e.*, above -100 °C in KBr, the quantum efficiency for transformation of a U-center into an F-center is 5%. At 600 °C, on the other hand, it is 100% [68]. It is clear that during this process a hydrogen atom must escape from the center.

At lower temperatures, *i.e.* below -100 °C, a different process takes place, the U-band bleaches, but no F-centers are formed; instead the α-band, which is known to be due to halogen vacancies, appears [69, 70]. It is clear that this implies that the hydrogen ion, when excited, has an appreciable probability to leave the halogen site and leave a vacancy. Seitz [71] suggests that it goes into interstitial position; the work of Delbecq, Smaller and Yuster, to be discussed further, has confirmed this.

Irradiation in the α-band restores part of the U-band, while heating to 20 °C restores it completely. This suggests that during bleaching of the U-band the hydrogen ions do not move far away from the vacancy.

On continued irradiation in the α-band at -190 °C a new band appears, the U''-band (at 2 650 Å in KBr) (now called U_1). Irradiation in the U''-band produces F-centers.

1'1. *E.p.r. results.* – In order to see how the hydrogen atom, resulting from bleaching the U-band, is present in the lattice, Delbecq, Smaller and Yuster [72, 73] supplemented these experiments with electron paramagnetic resonance studies and with further optical studies. Their results are now summarized here:

1) Irradiation of KCl-KH crystals at room temperature and measurement at 80 °K does not reveal a resonance due to the hydrogen atoms.

2) Irradiation at liquid-nitrogen temperature in order to reduce the diffusion rate, results in the observation of two absorption peaks on either side of the *F*-center resonance. The detailed structure of the doublet is in agreement with the assumption of a hydrogen atom.

3) To make sure that the doublet originated from H^0 an experiment was performed on deuterium-doped KCl. In this case, due to the different nuclear spins, a triplet instead of a doublet is to be expected. It was found indeed.

4) Pulse annealing experiments showed that the maximum rate of disappearance of the resonance it at about 108 °K, in the hydrogen as well as in the deuterium-containing KCl.

1·2. *Optical measurements.* – The optical measurements, on the other hand, gave the following results:

1) Bleaching of the *U*-band (2120 Å) with ultra-violet light at liquid-nitrogen temperature is accompanied by the appearance of a broad band (the U_1-band) at about 2800 Å (which is Thomas's U''-band).

2) Prolonged irradiation results in the growth of the *F*-band (5400 Å) and the U_2-band at 2360 Å. They grow at about the same relative rate.

3) Irradiation in the U_1-band results in a decrease of that band and in a very rapid proportional increase of the *F*- and U_2-bands.

4) Continued bleaching in U_1 does not change very much *F* and U_2 but causes a slow increase of the *U*-band.

5) Subsequent bleaching with *F*-light causes the *F*- and U_2-band to decrease rapidly by 50%, but on continued irradiation no further changes take place.

6) The same experiment performed at liquid-helium temperature yields essentially the same results.

7) The maximum rate of thermal bleaching of the U_2-band takes place at 108 °K, *i.e.*, at the same temperature where the H^0-resonance disappears. The U_1-absorption disappears gradually in the range (120÷220) °K with a maximum at 160 °K.

1·3. *Interpretation of the U-bands.* – The following models for the centers responsible for the different *U*-bands were proposed and shown to be in agreement with the experimental facts.

1) The U-center is a substitutional hydrogen ion on a halogen site, as was assumed originally.

2) The U_1-center is an interstitial hydrogen ion.

3) The U_2-center is a hydrogen atom in an interstitial site.

On the basis of these models the experimental results can be understood as follows: irradiation in the U-band at 80 °K causes the hydrogen ion to leave the halogen site and produce a vacancy on the one hand and a U_1-center on the other hand. This leaves a crystal with an α-band, a U_1-band, and *no* paramagnetic resonance signal. Irradiation in the U_2-band produces F-centers and U_2-centers. From the simultaneous annealing of the U_2-band and the e.p.r. signal, it can be concluded that the U_2-center is responsible for this resonance, and hence that U_2 is H^0.

That the hydrogen atom and hydrogen ion are located in the same environment (*i.e.*, both interstitials) is strongly suggested by the observation that irradiation in the F-band causes a decrease in F- and U_2-absorption and an increase in U_1-band as well as a relatively small increase in U-band. This shows that the electron liberated from the F-center can be captured by an interstitial atom (U_2) which is then transformed into an interstitial ion (U_1). The inverse process also takes place, *i.e.*, irradiation in the U_1-band causes a decrease in the U_1-band but an increase in F- and U_2-band, because the electron from the ion is captured in the vacancy and forms an F-center.

At temperatures higher than 100 °K the e.p.r. signal disappears, the F-band diminishes only slightly, the U-band rises only slightly, and the U_2-centers disappear. From these remarks it can be concluded that the disappearance of the hydrogen atom is mainly due to pairing into molecules and very little to return into substitutional sites. The latter phenomenon causes the small decrease of the F-band and the small increase of the U-band.

It is now clear why irradiation with U-light does not give rise to an e.p.r. signal at room temperature: migration takes place so rapidly that U_2-centers rapidly transform into H_2-molecules.

1·4. *Infrared spectrum of the U-center* [74]. – The infrared vibration-frequency of a diatomic lattice is given by [75],

$$\omega = \sqrt{\beta_0/\mu_0}\,,$$

where β_0 is the force constant of the lattice, and μ_0 is the reduced mass of a lattice cell. If some of the lattice ions are replaced by light ions, *e.g.*, H-ions, new vibration frequencies ω_s arise. Approximately one has

$$\omega_s/\omega_0 = \sqrt{\mu_0\beta_s}/\sqrt{\mu_s\beta_0}\,,$$

β_s is the force constant in the neighborhood of the foreign ion; μ_s is the effective mass of the perturbed unit cell. Taking as an approximation $\beta_s = \beta_0$, we get

$$\omega_s/\omega_0 = \sqrt{\mu_0/\mu_s} \; .$$

For example, in KCl one expects a band at $\lambda_s = 16.5\ \mu\text{m}$; the band is actually found at about 20 μm. Similar to what is found for F-centers there is a relation between the lattice constant and the frequency of the absorption peak. This relation is of the form

$$h\nu d^x = \text{constant} = C \, ,$$

where d is the lattice spacing and x and C have a different value for different cations:

	x	C (in eV Å^x)
Na – salts	2.22	3.2
K – salts	2.28	4.0
Rb – salts	2.53	6.8

This relation is valid at all temperatures; this evidently follows from the fact that the lattice constant changes in the same proportion as the frequency. The shift in the position of the peak is given approximately by

$$\frac{\Delta(h\nu)}{\Delta T} = 3.4 \cdot 10^{-6}\ \text{eV/°C} \; .$$

The half-width is very temperature-dependent, and only at low temperatures does one obtain a well-resolved peak.

Assuming a modified Smakula formula as a link between the absorption band and the number of centers, an oscillator strength of about 0.5 is found.

Small additions (2%) of RbCl to KCl, *e.g.*, produce additional absorption bands at both sides of the normal band. From their relative intensity Schaeffer deduced that they are probably due to U-centers next to one, two or more Rb-ions.

2. – The Z-bands.

In additively colored crystals containing divalent metal impurities a new set of absorption bands arises, as shown by PICK [76], HEILAND and KELTING [77]: the Z-bands.

2·1. *Production of the Z-bands.* – A KCl crystal is additively colored and quenched in the usual way, so as to contain an F-band (5400 Å). The crystal is then irradiated with F-light, and a band appears at the long wavelength side (5900 Å at —215 °C); this is the Z_1-band.

Heating of such a crystal to 110 °C reconverts some of the Z_1-centers into F-centers, but the majority is converted into the Z_2-band which is at 6100 Å (at —215 °C).

Heating the crystal above 200 °C re-establishes the F-band and bleaches Z_2. Cooling to —90 °C and irradiating in either the F- or the Z_2-band gives rise to the F'-band and to a new broad band at the short wavelength side of Z_2, called the Z_3-band.

2·2. *Models.* – Pick has proposed models for the Z_1- and the Z_2-band; Seitz has postulated another set of models. They are represented schematically in Fig. 20. According to Pick [76], Z_2 consists of an electron captured by a divalent ion, while his model for Z_1 consists of an F-center next to a divalent ion. The model of Seitz [1] for Z_1 is identical to Pick's model for Z_2 and Seitz's model for Z_2 consists of his Z_1-center plus a vacancy pair. The Z_3-center is a Z_2-center which has captured a second electron, according to Seitz.

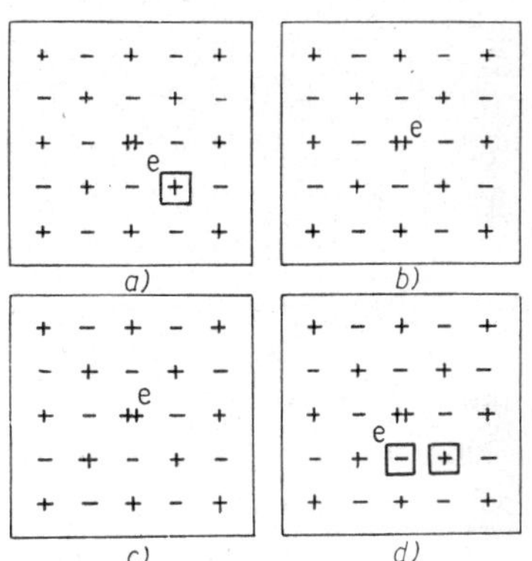

Fig. 20. – *a)* Z_1-center following Pick; *b)* Z_2-center following Pick; *c)* Z_1-center following Seitz; *d)* Z_2-center following Seitz. (After: G. Chiarotti, F. Fumi and L. Giulotto: *Report on the Conf. on Defects in Crystalline Solids* (Bristol, 1954)).

2·3. *Generation mechanism.* – According to Seitz [1], the Z_1-band results from the capture by the divalent impurity of the electron liberated from the F-center. The positive ion vacancy, which is normally associated with the divalent impurity, migrates away and forms a pair with the negative ion vacancy left behind by the F-center. The Z_2-center would then simply result from the migration of a neutral pair towards the Z_1-center.

The Z_3-center further results from a Z_2-center by capturing the photoelectron liberated from an F-center or another Z_2-center.

2·4. *Properties of Z-centers.*

1) The Z_1-center cannot be converted into F-centers by Z_1-light at room temperature.

2) In NaCl the Z_2-center is formed directly on additive coloration. It is suggested that this results directly as a consequence of the coalescence of an F-center and a divalent ion-positive ion vacancy complex, which presumably migrates during the quench toward the F-center.

3) The Z_2-band in NaCl can be bleached by Z_2-light resulting in F- and Z_1-center formation. The Z_2-center probably breaks up, on losing its electron, into the divalent ion and a migrating vacancy pair. The electron can now be captured either by the divalent ion to form a Z_1-center, or by the negative ion vacancy to form an F-center.

4) Z_3-centers are not stable at room temperature.

5) X-irradiation of NaCl containing divalent metal ions, followed by bleaching the F-band at room temperature, also results in the formation of a Z_1-band [78, 79]. The fact that a prominent F-band is formed rather than a V-band seems to suggest that most of the positive ion vacancies are associated with their divalent impurity.

6) The quantum efficiency for generating of Z_1 from F is $\eta = 0.15$.

7) The oscillator strength of the Z_1-band $= 0.84$.

8) The production of Z_1-centers from the F-centers by F-light leads to a limiting ratio of the F- to Z_1-band absorption. The F-band initially bleaches rapidly but this slows down and a limiting ratio is finally obtained.

9) Complete conversion from F- to Z_1-centers can be achieved if the density of F-centers, in additively colored crystals, is much smaller than the divalent ion contents. This can be understood on the basis of Seitz's model, if one assumes that in these cases the concentration of free divalent ions exceeds the number of F-centers. The electrons from F-centers are distilled to divalent impurities.

10) The initial quantum efficiency for conversion of F-centers to Z_1-centers is low, however (~ 0.1). This is explained by the authors by suggesting that the crystals contain an excess of halogen ion vacancies.

The limiting concentration of Z_1-centers is, according to the Italian workers, determined by the concentration of unassociated divalent impurities. With this assumption and a knowledge of the concentration of divalent impurities it is possible to deduce the fraction of unassociated vacancies. Knowing this fraction at different temperatures allows a determination of the association energy: 0.3 eV is found for Sr^{++} in KCl. The value calculated by BASSANI and FUMI [80] is 0.2 eV.

In an attempt to distinguish between the two sets of models for Z-centers, CAMAGNI, CERESARA and CHIAROTTI [81] investigated the equilibrium between the F- and the Z_2-band in KCl doped with $2 \cdot 10^{-4}$ molar fraction of Sr.

Assuming that during the conversion $F \rightarrow Z_2$ the number of color centers remains constant, these authors determine the oscillator strength of the Z_2-center, they find $f_{Z_2} = 0.45 \pm 0.05$. They then determine the equilibrium ratio of both kinds of centers at different temperatures. They find that the ratio of the molar fractions can be expressed as

$$(1) \qquad \frac{x_F}{x_{Z_2}} = A \exp(H/kT) \qquad \begin{array}{l} A = 0.8 \cdot 10^4 \\ H = -0.28 \text{ eV} . \end{array}$$

This relation is now compared with the equilibrium condition as derived from the law-of-mass action when applied to the two different models.

For the Seitz model, the formation reaction can be written as

$$F + C \rightleftarrows Z_2 ,$$

where C means a divalent ion-vacancy complex. The corresponding equilibrium condition is:

$$(2) \qquad \frac{x_F}{x_{Z_2}} = \frac{1}{2} K_0 x_C^{-1} \exp[-\Delta W/kT] ,$$

where ΔW is the energy of association of the F-center with a Sr^{++} positive ion vacancy complex. K_0 is an entropy factor which takes care of the changes in vibrational entropy during the formation reaction. The factor $\frac{1}{2}$ is the ratio between the configurational weights of the complex and the Z_2-center in their ground state.

It turns out that for a reasonable value of the association energy, x_C is practically constant in the temperature range of interest. The empirical relation (1) can therefore be compared directly with the theoretical relation (2). This yields reasonable values for ΔW ($= 0.28$ eV) and for $K_0 = 2Ax_C \simeq 4$. The same type of reasoning using Pick's model does not lead to reasonable values.

This evidence, together with the dichroism observed after bleaching [82] and the presence of a dielectric loss peak [83], seems to suggest that Seitz's model is better than Pick's. The absence of polarized luminescence light is a remaining difficulty. One possibility is that actually different configurations of the same entities exist, *i.e.*, F-center + complex, which would randomize the emitted light.

3. – *V*-type divalent impurity centers.

3·1. *Generation of the centers.* – X-irradiation at liquid-nitrogen temperature of KCl and KBr containing divalent impurities gives rise to self-trapped holes associated with the divalent impurity-vacancy complexes [84].

The self-trapped hole (Cl_2^- or Br_2^-) is aligned approximately along a [100] direction (2° off) in contrast with the normal self-trapped hole center which is aligned accurately along a [110] direction. The resonance spectrum indicates that the two Cl-nuclei are not divalent.

3·2. *Optical properties of the center.* – The corresponding optical absorption spectrum could be deduced by studying the thermal stability of the centers using a pulse annealing technique and observing both the e.p.r. signal and the optical absorption.

It is found that the new absorption peaks depend on the nature of the divalent impurity; they are situated in the ultra-violet (see Table I).

TABLE I.

KCl: Ca	3230 Å	KBr: Ca	3450 Å,
KCl: Sr	3210 Å	KBr: Sr	3450 Å
KCl: Ba	3350 Å, 3900 Å	KBr: Ba	3600 Å, 4100 Å

The doped KCl crystals, irradiated at 195 °K, show the following characteristics:

a) There is a band in the V_2-region with a peak at 2200 Å, *i.e.* shifted with respect to the V_2-peak in pure crystals.

b) The F-absorption is enhanced in agreement with the results of ETZEL.

c) The ratio F/V_2-absorption is larger in the doped samples, indicating that the new centers suppress the V-band and hence are hole traps.

3·3. *Annealing behavior.* – By pulse annealing the following decay temperatures for both the e.p.r. signal and the optical absorption are found:

TABLE II.

KCl: Ca	236 °K	KBr: Ca	243 °K
KCl: Sr	233 °K	KBr: Sr	253 °K
KCl: Ba	231 °K	KBr: Ba	263 °K

The decay temperature is defined as corresponding to the inflexion point in the annealing curve.

3.4. *Dichroism.*

1) Bleaching with light polarized along [001] results in preferential bleaching of the centers aligned along this direction and in a slight enhancement of the number aligned perpendicular to it. The ratio of the numbers

in both orientations is maximum 1:3, against 1:20 for the self-trapped holes in pure crystals.

2) The same dichroism can be inferred from the e.p.r. spectrum.

3) Very little dichroism occurs after bleaching with [110] light, in contrast to the normal self-trapped hole centers.

4) The following reorientation temperatures were established:

KCl:	Ca, Sr or Ba	193 °K
KBr:	Ca	223 °K

These temperatures are higher than the corresponding ones for the self-trapped hole, proving their larger stability.

3·5. *Models.* – Since the centers are not found in undoped crystals they must be associated somehow with the divalent impurity-vacancy complex. The fact that the position of the absorption peak depends on the kind of impurity points in the same direc tion. The presence of the vacancy causes the molecule ion to leave its normal direction and take up a [100] direction. A possible model is therefore shown in Fig. 21. The difference between this new center and the molecule ion is also demonstrated by its different thermal stability.

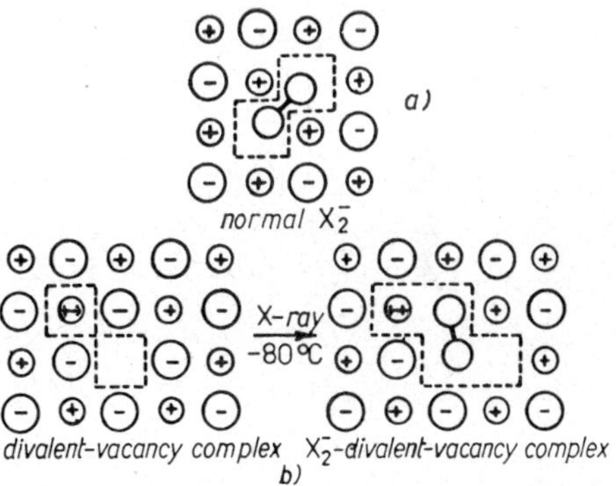

Fig. 21. – Models for X_2^--centers (X is a halogen). The upper model *a*), has been suggested by CASTNER and KÄNZIG, ref. [58], for the [110] oriented centers. It is proposed that irradiation of crystals containing divalent-vacancy complexes, *b*), produces [100] oriented centers. (After: W. HAYES and G. M. NICHOLS: *Phys. Rev.*, **117**, 993 (1960)).

II. – Production of Color Centers by Irradiation.

1. – Formation mechanism of *F*-centers.

One central problem which is still not completely solved in spite of the large amount of thought that has been given to it, is the mechanism of color center production by irradiation in general, of *F*-centers in particular. We will first consider the different basic proposals that have been made; we will afterwards discuss the experimental evidence in the light of these proposals.

1·1. *The Seitz mechanism.* – According to SEITZ [1] color centers are formed at dislocation jogs as a consequence of thermal spikes. The ionizing radiation produces excitons, which on travelling through the crystal meet dislocations, become trapped there and lose their energy in a concentrated burst of lattice vibrations. The thermal spike would be sufficient to put an ion adjacent to a jog, at this jog, and further, to allow the vacancy created in this way to migrate a few atomic jumps away from the source. Further excitons would be responsible for the migration of the vacancies at low temperatures. It is clear that the process is accompanied by climb of the dislocations. SEITZ estimates that dislocations have to climb about 1000 atomic distances to account for the production of 10^{18} vacancies per cm^3. The color centers would then be produced either directly by the capturing of electrons by the negative ion vacancies and holes by the positive ion vacancies, or by the dissociation of an exciton into an electron, attached to an F-center, and a free hole which in turn would produce V-type centers.

We will further comment on the arguments in favor of this hypothesis.

1·2. *The Varley mechanism.* – More recently VARLEY [2] has proposed a rather different mechanism for the production of F-centers. According to this author radiation would directly ionize a halide ion, *e.g.* a Cl^--ion, transforming this into a Cl^+-ion. The cross-section for double ionization is about 1/10 of the value for single ionization. This positive chlorine ion would now be in a very unstable situation. The electrostatic repulsion by the neighboring positive ions would force it into an interstitial position, creating in this way a vacancy. Population of the vacancy by an electron would then transform it into an F-center. Making the assumption that practically all doubly ionized ions will produce an F-center leads to the right order of magnitude for F-center production.

1·3. *The Seitz-Varley mechanism.* – MITCHELL, WIEGAND and SMOLUCHOWSKI [3] have recently proposed a combination of the two previous mechanisms in order to account for the observed F-center growth curves. They propose that the Varley mechanism would take place near dislocations, the interstitials joining the dislocation core and causing the latter to climb as in the Seitz mechanism. It would result in the formation of vacancies only, preferentially located along dislocations. We will further discuss the evidence for this mechanism.

1·4. *Comments on the Varley mechanism.* – An argument of SEITZ and KOEHLER [4] against the Varley proposal is that the interstitial ion would very soon capture one or more electrons and would be sucked back into the vacancy, even without need for an activation energy. HOWARD and SMO-

LUCHOWSKI [5] have considered the Varley mechanism in somewhat more detail using a very simple model. They argue that the interstitial ion may reach a second nearest interstitial site, from where return to the vacancy is sufficiently difficult in a time which is short compared to the lifetime of the positive halogen ion. The lifetime of the positive halogen ion is put equal to the average time that an electron needs to reach it, while the time needed to reach the interstitial site is taken as 10^{-12} s, *i.e.*, the period of vibration of the lattice. They conclude that the mechanism is not improbable.

Very recently DEXTER [6] has questioned the validity of the arguments used by HOWARD and SMOLUCHOWSKI. He points out that these authors have in fact neglected all overlap of wavefunctions of neighboring halogens. If one takes into account this overlap, the possibility arises that an electron will be attracted from a neighboring halogen towards the doubly ionized halogen ion and produced two adjacent halogen atoms, making the Varley mechanism inoperative. The holes can then jump further and increase the distance between halogen atoms. The initial jump time would, of course, depend on the degree of overlap of the wave function, *i.e.*, on the width of the corresponding energy band and on the effective mass of the holes.

In the band scheme one can say that the double ionization corresponds to the production of two holes localized around halogens. The Coulomb repulsion between the two holes would make them separate very rapidly. The initially very large electric field (10^8 V/cm) will make the holes move apart one lattice distance in less than 10^{-15} s even if their mobility is only 1 cm²/V s. Once the holes have separated, the Varley mechanism can no longer operate. In fact the mobility approximation can no longer be used, but considering the holes as particles with an electron mass leads to the same result. Even if one of the holes is « heavy », being located in an inner shell, the separation time is still very small. DEXTER shows that only if both holes are produced in an inner shell does the possibility exist that the lifetime of the doubly ionized halogen is long as compared to 10^{-12} s. A comparison with experimental determined coloration efficiency, however, seems to make this possibility also doubtful.

1) The coloration efficiencies at He temperature of KBr, KCl and NaF, are all the same, suggesting that phenomena in inner shells are not important.

2) In LiF the required energy per F-center is less than the K-ionization energy.

3) The value of 150 eV per F-center found in LiF for coloration at liquid-nitrogen temperature is also not consistent with inner shell phenomena.

The recent results from paramagnetic resonance studies have shown that interstitial halogen, *i.e.* H-centers, are formed at low temperatures.

This seems to be rather strong evidence that the Varley mechanism operates at least at these low temperatures. The low temperature recovery of radiation-induced expansion, as studied by WYEGAND and SMOLUCHOWSKI [7], seems to point also in this direction. The recent work of RABIN and KLICK [8], which will be discussed later, gives still further support to this viewpoint.

2. – *F*-center growth curves for pure crystals.

The early measurements of *F*-center production rates present a wide scattering, because the importance of the state of perfection and purity of crystals was not sufficiently well realized. This resulted in large discrepancies concerning the energies required for the formation of an *F*-center. SCHNEIDER [9] and co-workers, *e.g.*, found that the initial X-ray darkening only requires 18 eV per *F*-center, while the process slows down to a constant rate requiring 53 eV per *F*-center. Other measurements also using X-rays lead to values over 100 eV. In NaCl LEITNER [10] found, using natural NaCl, widely different values depending on whether he used X-rays or γ-rays; for X-rays about 40 eV was required, while using γ-rays 2 000 eV was required. We will now discuss in somewhat more detail the most recent measurements of *F*-center growth curves as well as the resulting conclusions concerning the formation mechanism. As a consequence of the work of GORDON and NOWICK [11], LEVY [12], and MITCHELL, WIEGAND and SMOLUCHOWSKI [3]; it seems now fairly well establishment that *F*-center coloration proceeds in two stages, at least at not too low temperatures.

i) The first rapid stage consists of filling existing vacancies with electrons, and eventually creating a small number of new vacancies and *F*-centers.

ii) The second, slow process consists of creating new vacancies and transforming them into *F*-centers.

The work of CUNELL and SCHNEIDER [13] could in fact already be taken as evidence for such a process. They found that specimens of NaCl and KCl when quenched from 750 °C darkened more rapidly than unquenched ones. According to SEITZ [1], this would be due to plastic deformation and the resulting higher dislocation density. In the light of the new ideas it may, however, be taken as evidence that quenched-in vacancies contributed to the rapid coloration process. An alternative explanation might be that the quench brought some divalent impurities into solution, which as we will see may also enhance the rate of darkenability.

More evidence comes from the older work of M. HACSKAYLO and co-workers [14, 15]. These workers showed that those parts of crystals which were first darkened electrolytically with a pointed cathode and then uncolored by reversing the current had a greater sensitivity to subsequent X-ray coloration. It is clear that the electrolytic coloration left vacancies after bleaching which on subsequent X-irradiation were rapidly transformed into F-centers. The formation of vacancies in the electrolysed crystals was demonstrated by measuring the decrease in density.

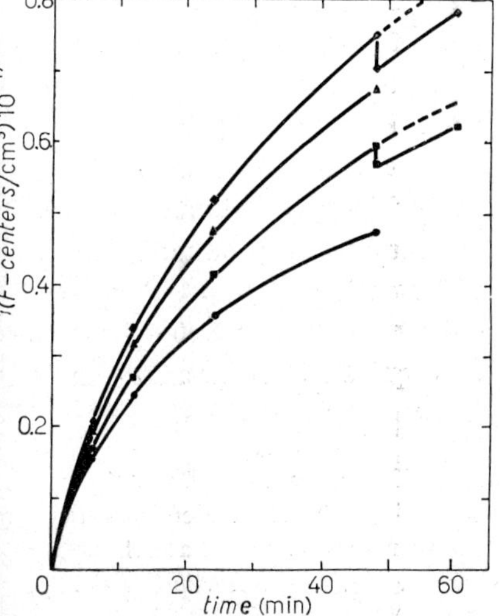

'ig. 22. – The F-band growth curves in he early stage as a function of crystal rigin and heat treatment: ◆ NRL-I; ▲ HAR-I, annealed; ■ HAR-I, as receved; ● HAR-II, annealed. (After: A. . Nowick: *Phys. Rev.*, **111**, 16 (1958)).

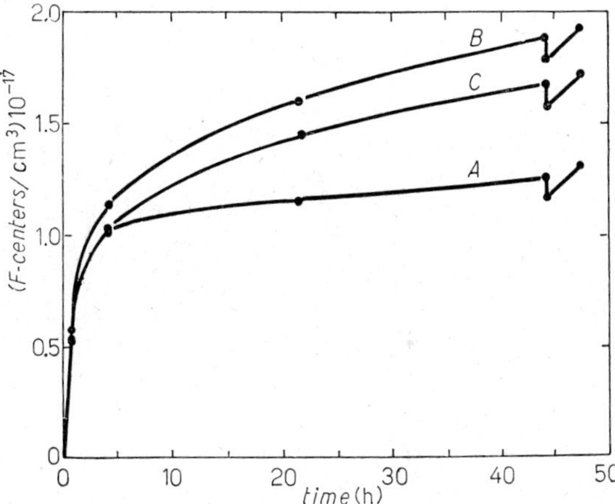

Fig. 23. – The same F-band growth curves as in Fig. 22 carried out to a much larger irradiation time: *a*) annealed (no. 1); *b*) deformation 3.7% (no. 2); *c*) deformation+annealing (no. 3). (After: A. S. Nowick: *Phys. Rev.*, **111**, 16 (1958)).

We now review the more recent evidence, contained in the previously mentioned papers, which describes experiments designed to reveal the two-stage process. In Fig. 22-25 we reproduce some results of the work of Gordon and Nowick [11] on the γ-rradiation (^{60}Co) of NaCl. The two stages can clearly be recognized in the curves corresponding to long irradiations. It is also clear that the initial rate depends on the thermal treatment and not very much on the degree

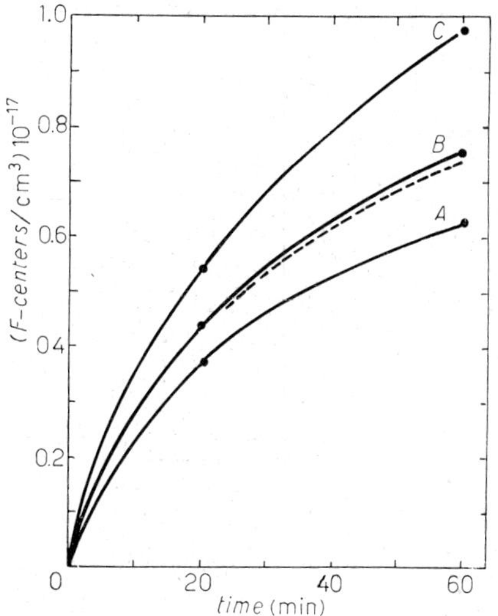

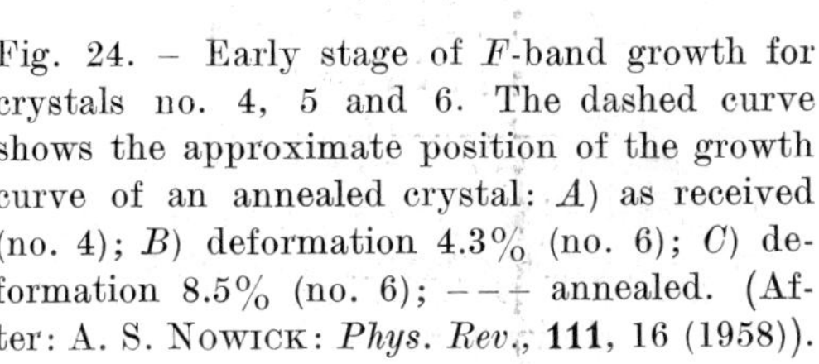

Fig. 24. – Early stage of F-band growth for crystals no. 4, 5 and 6. The dashed curve shows the approximate position of the growth curve of an annealed crystal: *A*) as received (no. 4); *B*) deformation 4.3% (no. 6); *C*) deformation 8.5% (no. 6); – – – annealed. (After: A. S. Nowick: *Phys. Rev.*, **111**, 16 (1958)).

of deformation, *i.e.*, on the dislocation contents (Fig. 22). On the other hand, the production rate in the second, slow stage is strongly dependent on the degree of deformation (Fig. 23). The transition from slow to rapid process is further found to occur at a higher F-center concentration in the more deformed specimens (Fig. 24, 25). The latter remark suggests that vacancies which contribute to the fast process were produced during the deformation.

NOWICK [16] finds 300 eV as the energy required to form an F-center

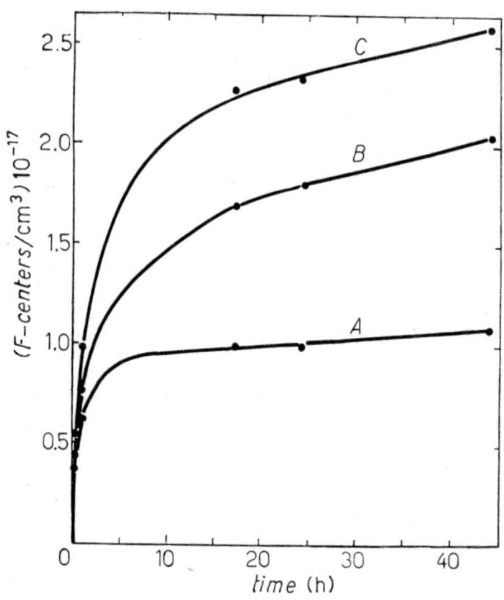

Fig. 25. – The same F-band growth curves as previous figure carried out to a much longer irradiation time: ***A***) as received (no. 4); *B*) deformation 4.3% (no. 5); *C*) deformation 8.5% (no. 6). (After: A. S. NOWICK: *Phys. Rev.*, **111**, 16 (1958)).

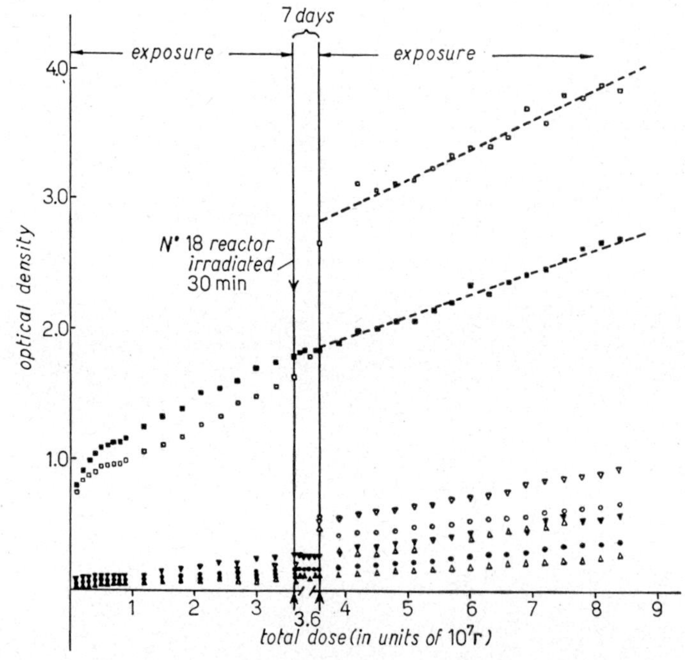

Fig. 26. – NaCl: no. 17: ▼ 5.84 eV, ■ 2.66 eV, ▲ 2.10 eV, ● 1.70 eV; no. 18: ▽ 5.84 eV, □ 2.66 eV « F », △ 2.10 eV, ○ 1.70 eV. (After: P. LEVY (private communications)).

in the first stage; this becomes 500 times larger in the second stage. When the irradiation in the second stage is interrupted for a while so as to allow some bleaching, the same coloration level is rapidly reached on re-irradiation (Fig. 23). The coloration rate in this rapid period is practically the same as in stage one. This observation suggests that bleaching does not remove vacancies but only depopulates them, as mentioned before.

As pointed out by LEVY [17], this phenomenon can be used to detect vacancies introduced by other means, *e.g.* neutron irradiation. When a crystal irradiated up to stage two is further irradiated with neutrons, and subsequently again irradiated with ionizing radiation, one finds a new, short period of high coloration rate, followed by a new slow part, displaced, however, towards higher F-center densities. From the displacement of the curve we can deduce the number of defects introduced by the neutron irradiation.

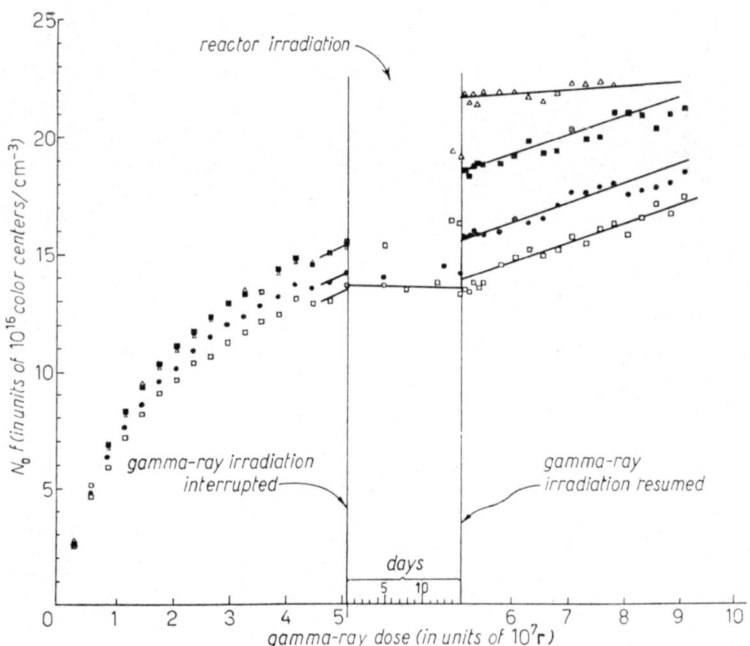

Fig. 27. – □ reactor-irradiated 0 min; ● reactor-irradiated 30 min; ■ reactor-irradiated 60 min; △ reactor-irradiated 120 min. (After: P. LEVY (private communications)).

In Fig. 26, 27 a few of Levy's results (private communications) are reproduced.

The first figure, 26, shows the influence of a short reactor irradiation on the growth of different absorption bands in NaCl.

One crystal was not subject to reactor irradiation, but the γ-irradiation was interrupted during the same interval of time as for the reactor-irradiated crystal. For the crystal not subject to reactor irradiation the growth curves smoothly continued after the interruption, but for the crystal that was irradiated for 30 minutes, a vertical jump occurs. This jump is largest for the *F*-center growth curve. This is fortunate in view of the large temperature stability of the *F*-center. (It may be worth-while to point out that LEVY first verified that the decay of *F*-absorption at high irradiation doses is negligible in the dark.)

Fig. 27 shows that the observed jump in the *F*-center concentration is proportional to the integrated neutron flux. The number of displacements as calculated according to KINCHIN and PEASE fits well, within the experimental uncertainty, with the number of defects observed using the described method. The displacement threshold was taken as 25 eV.

In this relation it is worth-while to point out that ETZEL [18] had already found earlier that the coloration rate of NaCl for ultra-violet radiation can be enhanced by two orders of magnitude when first irradiating with soft X-rays. A recent, more detailed study of this effect by the same author [19] showed that the X-ray-created vacancies are ultimately destroyed by the ultra-violet light. The effect was studied in synthetic and natural crystals irradiated with 2 MeV electrons and ^{60}Co γ-rays. Striking differences were found between synthetic and natural crystals. All crystals were first irradiated by means of 40 kV X-rays during 15 minutes and then optically bleached. The growth curves due to U.V.-irradiation all lie above the virgin growth curve (Fig. 28). While the natural crystals show a monotonic increase in *F*-center concentration, this is not the case with the synthetic crystals which show a maximum followed by a decrease. The final *F*-center approaches, however, the same limit as

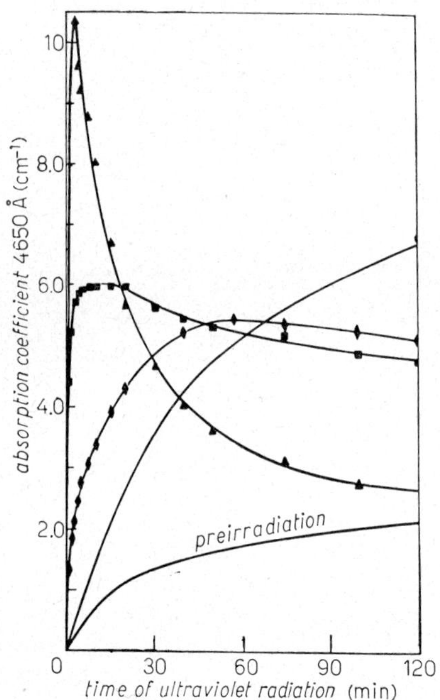

Fig. 28. – Optical absorption measured at the peak of the *F*-band in NaCl as a function of ultra-violet irradiation. All crystals have, prior to exposure to ultra-violet light, been irradiated for 15 min per side with 40 kV X-rays and the resulting color optically bleached. The optical absorption at 1850 Å prior to irradiation was: ● natural (BADEN): ~0 cm^{-1}; ◆ HARSHAW « B »: 4 cm^{-1}; ■ HARSHAW « C »: 15 cm^{-1}; ▲ NRL lot « C »: 31 cm^{-1}. (After: H. W. ETZEL and J. G. ALLARD: *Phys. Rev.*, **116**, 885 (1959)).

in the virgin crystal. The loss of F-centers is attributed to the agglomeration into aggregates which are less effective electron traps. This can be shown by recycling the crystal. The crystal is then irradiated with ultra-violet up to the point where all the « excess » F-centers are practically removed. After that, the crystal is bleached and re-irradiated either with ultra-violet or with X-rays. The maximum F-center absorption will be larger in the second cycle than in the first. The conclusion is that vacancies are not really lost; they only agglomerate into complexes that give no absorption in the visible. The « loss » of vacancies, which occurs only in the synthetic crystals, seems to be related to the presence of OH-ions. We have seen earlier that colloid formation also seems to be influenced by the presence of OH-ions.

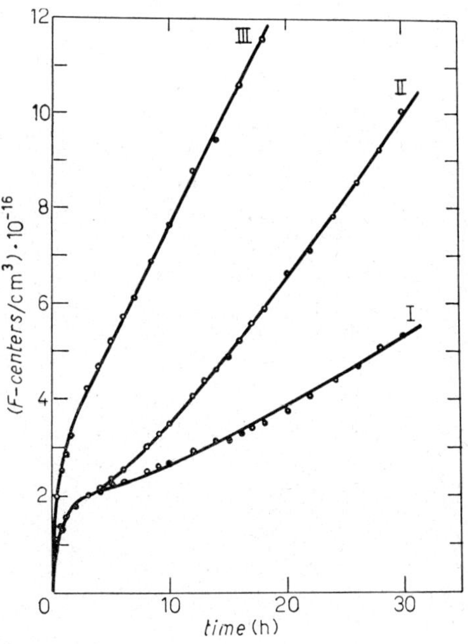

Fig. 29. – **F**-center growth curves in KCl. The lines indicate the best fit of eq. (2) to the data: I) 14000 r/h; II) 24300 r/h; III) 30000 r/h. (After: P. V. MITCHELL *et al.*: NYO-2512).

We now discuss the observations of MITCHELL, WIEGAND and SMOLUCHOWSKI [3]. Fig. 29 shows the growth curves obtained in KCl irradiated with 140 kV X-rays filtered with an Al-filter. The three curves correspond to different fluxes; only the initial parts of the curves are given. For higher doses they showed a tendency to saturate (cfr. NOWICK's work on NaCl). Similar curves were observed by MOZER and LEVY [20] and by ETZEL and ALLARD [21].

A particular feature of these curves is that the linear range does not extrapolate to the origin at $t=0$, but may even have a negative intercept in some cases.

The detailed shape of the curves can be explained according to MITCHELL *et al.* by the two stage process. The equations describing the process are

$$(1)\quad \frac{\mathrm{d}f_i}{\mathrm{d}t}=b(n-f_i)\,,\qquad (2)\quad \frac{\mathrm{d}f_g}{\mathrm{d}t}=c(at-f_g)\,,\qquad f_i=f_g=0\quad \text{at}\quad t=0\,,$$

where f_i and f_g are the concentrations of F-centers respectively generated from initially present and from freshly generated vacancies. The constants a, b, and c are rate parameters, b and c for the capture of electrons, a for the generation of new vacancies; n is the initially present concentration of vacancies. These equations integrate to

$$(3) \qquad f = f_i + f_g = n(1 - \exp[-bt]) + at - \frac{a}{c}(1 - \exp[-ct]) .$$

The observed curves can be fitted by an equation of this type to within 2% as shown in Fig. 29. The value of n is found to be independent of the flux and equal to 10^{16} which is a reasonable value.

The parameter a depends in a quadratic way on the flux, which seems to suggest a two-step process for the creation of a vacancy. The value of b is some 10 to 20 times larger than c, and increases with flux.

The difference in value between b and c is taken as evidence for the different physical environment of the two kinds of F-centers, thus supporting the combined Seitz-Varley mechanism which they proposed.

F-center growth curves have been measured for electron irradiated (5 kV) LiF, NaF, and NaCl at 90 °K, by FISCHER [22]. Single crystals as well as evaporated films were investigated. The films were deposited at different (low) temperatures. The crystals and films were irradiated up to saturation, *i.e.*, up to $0.8 \cdot 10^{20}$ F-centers per cm³ in the films, and up to half this value in the single crystals. Optical density as a function of dose can be represented in all cases by the sum of maximum three exponentials:

$$(1) \qquad S = S_0 - A_1 \exp[-\lambda_1 W] - A_2 \exp[-\lambda_2 W] - A_3 \exp[-\lambda_3 W] .$$

S_0 is the saturation absorption; $S = \ln(I_0/I)$; W is the irradiation dose, λ_1, λ_2, λ_3, A_1, A_2 and A_3 are adjustable constants. The procedure followed in determining the constants is the same as the one used in the analysis of radioactive decay curves. It is found that in single crystals two terms describe the curve accurately, while three are necessary in evaporated layers. There is no obvious relation between the λ_i or A_i and the temperature of condensation of the films. The shape of the curve can be interpreted on the basis of a model, whereby it is assumed that the anion vacancies can result from two or three different sources.

We first consider one group of sources and call their concentration N_s; the concentration of vacancies is N_v and the concentration of F-centers is N_F. The following reactions can take place:

$$\text{source} \underset{b}{\overset{a}{\rightleftarrows}} \text{vacancy} \underset{d}{\overset{c}{\rightleftarrows}} F\text{-center} ,$$

with the indicated probabilities a, b, c, and d. We can then write down the following set of differential equations for the rate of change of the different concentrations with dose φ:

$$\frac{dN_s}{d\varphi} = -aN_s = bN_v\,, \tag{2}$$

$$\frac{dN_v}{d\varphi} = aN_s - (b+d)N_v + dN_F\,, \tag{3}$$

$$\frac{dN_F}{d\varphi} = cN_v - dN_F\,. \tag{4}$$

If we now make the additional assumption that the equilibrium between vacancies and F-centers is established much more rapidly than between sources and vacancies, we can write further

$$a + b \ll c + d$$

and hence

$$N_F = \frac{c}{d} N_v\,. \tag{5}$$

Making use of this relation reduces the system of three equations to a system of two:

$$\frac{dN_s}{d\varphi} = -aN_s + bN_v\,, \tag{6}$$

$$\frac{dN_v}{d\varphi} = aN_s - bN_v\,, \tag{7}$$

with the following initial conditions, at $\varphi = 0$, $N_s = 0$ and $N_s = Q$. The solution of this system is

$$N_F = B(1 - \exp[-\mu\varphi])\,; \qquad \mu = a + b\,; \qquad B = \frac{caQ}{d(a+b)}\,. \tag{8}$$

If interference between different sources of vacancies is excluded, *i.e.* if a vacancy does not migrate far, before becoming and F-center, we can write

$$N_F = N_F^{\max} - B_1 \exp[-\mu\varphi] - B_2 \exp[-\mu\varphi] - B_3 \exp[-\mu\varphi]\,, \tag{9}$$

where the last three terms result from the different types of sources. This relation is of the type (1), experimentally found. It is therefore inferred that the shape of the growth curves is determined by the presence of two or three types of vacancy sources.

Quite interesting results giving further insight into the formation mechanism of F-centers at low temperature are presented in some recent work of RABIN and KLICK [8]. They first established that the coloration rate at liquid helium temperature does not depend on impurity or dislocation contents, in contrast to the room temperature behavior (Fig. 30). In particular, there is no sensitizing effect of divalent impurities or hydrides as is the case at higher temperatures. The growth curve therefore presents only one stage corresponding to the slow stage at room temperature. The reason is probably that the vacancies that are certainly present in the crystal are in the form of aggregates that cannot be broken up by irradiation at low temperature. An indication in this sense is given by the following experiment. A crystal which was X-irradiated, and subsequently bleached with F-light, colored much more rapidly up to the point where it was colored previously (cfr. ETZEL [22]), even at liquid-helium temperature. This experiment proves that *isolated* vacancies can easily be converted to F-centers. The energy required to make an F-center in KCl in this case is only 28 eV per F-center. It is concluded that the production of F-centers at liquid helium temperature is a bulk process characteristic of the alkali-halide and not of the particular crystal.

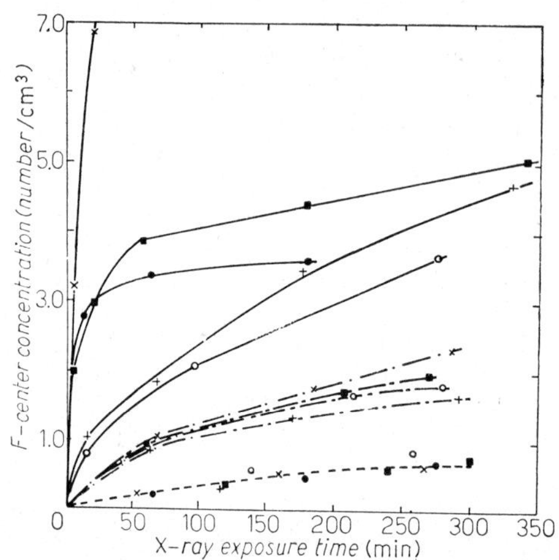

Fig. 30. – Growth of the F-band in various NaCl crystals exposed to X-ray radiation at room, liquid nitrogen, and liquid helium temperatures: ■ Optovac NaCl; × NRL NaCl, 0.5 M% $CaCl_2$; + HARSHAW NaCl; ○ natural NaCl; ● natural NaCl, heated and quenched; – – – liquid-He temperature; –·–·– liquid-N_2 temperature; —— room temperature. (After: H. RABIN and C. C. KLICK: *Phys. Rev.*, **117**, 1005 (1960)).

Once this is established it is possible to compare the energy required to form of an F-center in the different alkali halides at the same low temperature. A list of the values that were obtained is given in the following table:

NaCl	$1.4\cdot10^4$ eV	LiF	$6.2\cdot10^2$ eV
KCl	$1.3\cdot10^3$ eV	KI	$5.2\cdot10^4$ eV
KBr	$1.4\cdot10^3$ eV	NaBr	$8.3\cdot10^4$ eV
NaF	$1.3\cdot10^3$ eV		

These values were obtained over the first 30 minutes of irradiation. In view of a verification of the Varley proposal, it is now of interest to plot these values as a function of the quantity S/D, which is a measure for the space available for an interstitial ion (Fig. 31). (S = space between adjacent halide ions in the [110] direction; D = diameter of halogen atom.) It turns out that, as this space becomes smaller, the energy required per F-center increases very rapidly. Once this value exceeds a certain limit, which is about 0.50, the energy required becomes, however, constant. These experiments lend further support to the proposal of WOODRUFF and KÄNZIG [23] that F- and H-centers are created in pairs by some Varley-type mechanism (at least at low enough temperature).

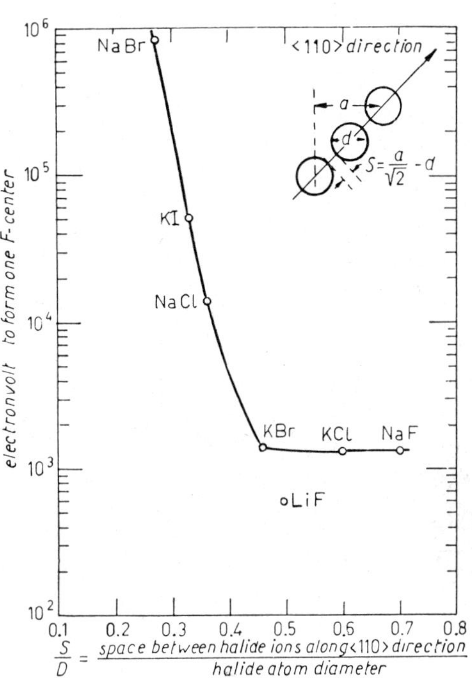

Fig. 31. – Total X-ray energy required to form one F-center at liquid helium temperature for various alkali halides as a function of the ratio S/D, where S is the space between adjacent halides in a [110] direction of the normal lattice and D is the diameter of the halogen atom. S is given by $[(a/\sqrt{2}) - d]$, where a is the lattice constant and d is the halide ion diameter. (After: H. RABIN and C. C. KLICK: *Phys. Rev.*, **117**, 1005 (1960)).

3. – Plastic deformation, point defects and color centers.

It seems now fairly well established that deformation results, among other things, in the formation of point defects. The first evidence for this came from the ionic conductivity measurements of GYULAI and HARTLY [24], which were subsequently confirmed by others [25]. SEITZ [26] has interpreted the effect as being due to the intersection of dislocations resulting in the formation of vacancies; a strain of about 10% would produce about 10^{18} vacancies per cm^3. It is therefore to be expected that the absorption spectrum, especially after irradiation, will be influenced markedly by plastic deformation.

On the other hand, SEITZ [1] has suggested that the sources of the color centers produced during irradiation are the dislocations. The growth of the color center absorption should, as a consequence, be influenced also by the presence of dislocations. We will now review the evidence relative to these two aspects.

3'1. *The influence of plastic deformation on ionic conductivity.* – GYULAI and HARTLY first demonstrated that the room temperature ionic conductivity of NaCl was increased by two orders of magnitude immediately after plastic strain of about 10%. The increase in conductivity decays at room temperature in about twenty minutes. Further increase can be obtained by a new application of strain. The SEITZ interpretation of this phenomenon, which is widely accepted, is that the intersection of dislocations is at the origin of the production of the vacancies which are responsible for the enhanced conductivity. The decay would then be due to the clustering of single vacancies into neutral pairs which no longer contribute to the conductivity.

The creation of point defects by the intersection of dislocations can best be visualized by means of Fig. 32. The moving screw dislocation AB intersects the stationary dislocation CD. Geometrically one can say that the dislocation AB adopts the shape of Fig. 32-*a*). The segments XY and UV have

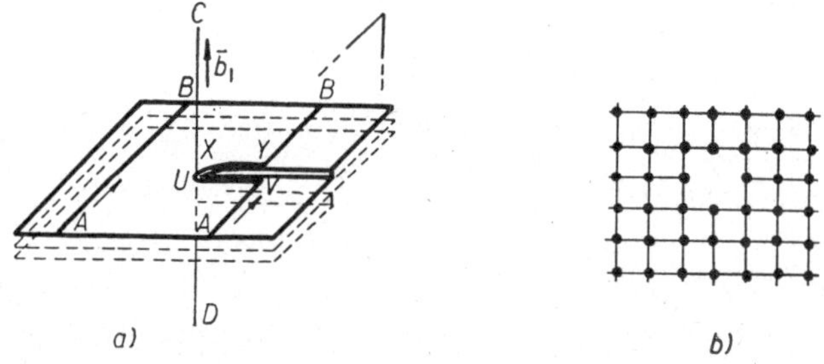

Fig. 32. – Production of vacancies by intersecting screw dislocations.

acquired edge character and they are of opposite sign. The supplementary half-planes end, however, in lattice planes that differ by one atomic distance in level. A cross-section perpendicular to XY is shown in Fig. 32-*b*). It is now clear that a row of vacancies has been formed.

Depending on the relative sign of the two intersecting dislocations one can form either vacancies or interstitials.

The experiments of GYULAI and HARTLY [24] have been confirmed by STEPANOW [25] and by others [26]. More recently FISCHBACH and NOWICK [27] have taken up the subject again and demonstrated that earlier measurements had been obscured by the simultaneous occurence of two phenomena: the just described increase in conductivity and the occurence of a charge flow even in the absence of an applied field. This charge flow had been observed before by STEPANOW, who interpreted it as a piezoelectric effect. According to FISCHBACH and NOWICK, the charge flow is due to inhomogeneous deformation and it results from the movement of charged dislocations in a preferential direction. The charges on the dislocations would result from charged jogs.

A dislocation would acquire a predominance of jogs of one sign because of the difference in formation energy of the two kinds of vacancies.

More recently PRATT [28] and co-workers have measured on the same specimens, deformed by various amounts, the ionic conductivity increase, the change in density and the F-center concentration after irradiation. In principle these three measurements should give all information on the concentration of point defects. The density changes measure the contribution of both kinds of vacancies, the ionic conductivity measures only the positive ion vacancy concentrations; and finally, the F-center concentration informs about the negative ion vacancy concentration. They find that the sum of the latter two figures is within the experimental error equal to the first.

PRATT [28] was also able to demonstrate that the intersection of dislocations is a necessary condition for the production of the conductivity burst. In this way he could explain the apparently contradictory results obtained by previous workers. He finds that the specimen has to be a flat prism to make sure that on compression intersection occurs.

3'2. *The influence of plastic absorption on density.* – VAUGHAN, LEIVO and SMOLUCHOWSKI [29] also studied the density changes due to deformation. They found that density changes only occur after a deformation exceeding about 11% for the type of specimens they used. They also found that the density changes are intimately connected with the occurence of multiple slip. When comparing their results with the results obtained by UETA and KÄNZIG [30], which will be discussed further, they find that about four times more vacancies are formed than electron traps. This result suggests that large clusters of vacancies are formed which are electron traps. The decrease of ionic conductivity after plastic deformation also pointed to cluster formation.

3'3. *The influence of plastic deformation on the absorption.* – UETA AND KÄNZIG [30] deformed crystals containing F-centers, introduced by electrolytic or additive coloration, while exposing the crystals to optical bleaching in the F-band. They find that the initial rate of bleaching of the F-band is sensitive to the degree of deformation. This is interpreted as due to the presence of electron traps which result from vacancies created during deformation (Fig. 33). The optical bleaching releases electrons from F-centers which are subsequently either recaptured by vacancies or by other electron traps such as divacancies, triplets, and quartets (Fig. 34). Assuming the capture cross-sections of the different defects to be roughly equal, it is possible to deduce the number of additional traps, introduced by the deformation, from the difference in initial bleaching rate between an undeformed colored crystal and a deformed crystal.

Chiarotti [31], on the other hand, failed to detect an increase in the α-band (which is known to be due to vacancies), after plastic deformation,

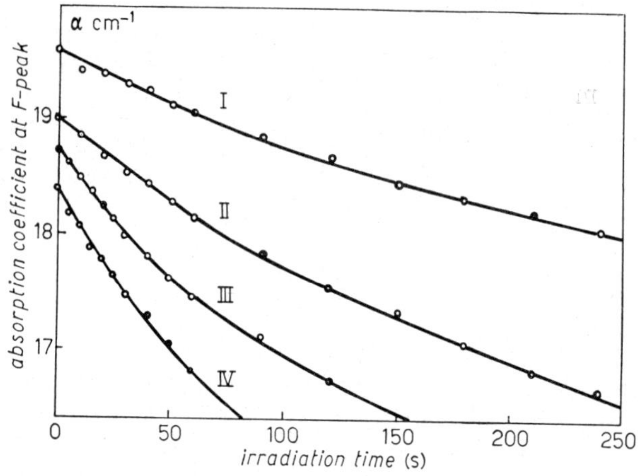

Fig. 33. – Initial optical bleaching rates of the *F*-band in additively colored KCl crystals, measured at room temperature. Bleaching light 546 nm, approximately $5\cdot10^{13}$ quanta s^{-1} cm^{-2}: I) underformed crystal; II) 2.60% plastic strain; III) 4.38% plastic strain; IV) 13.5% plastic strain. (After: K. Ueta and W. Känzig: *Phys. Rev.*, **97**, 1591 (1955)).

which may indicate that mostly complexes rather than single vacancies are formed during deformation.

Colloids may be dispersed by extensive plastic deformation; blue crystals, may, *e.g.*, turn yellow. The production of *M*- and *R*-centers by bleaching with *F*-light is enhanced after deformation.

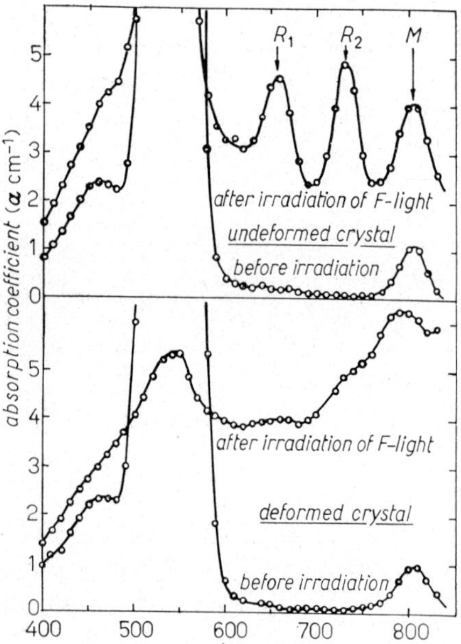

Fig. 34. – *a*) Formation of the *M*- and *R*-bands in additively colored KCl crystal by irradiation with *F*-light at room temperature. *b*) Formation of a broad absorption band by *F*-irradiation at room temperature 48 h after plastic deformation. The crystals were cut from the same colored piece and subjected to the same conditions of irradiation. The spectra were measured at liquid-N_2 temperature. (After: M. Ueta and W. Känzig: *Phys. Rev.*, **97**, 1591 (1955)).

4. – Factors influencing the production rate of F-centers.

It was realized fairly early that the state of perfection and purity of the crystals may have a large effect on the rate of production of color centers. These effects may, moreover, shed some light on the formation mechanism; it is therefore of interest to discuss some of these factors.

It has been established that the following factors are of importance in determining the rate of darkening, at least at room temperature

1) plastic deformation of the crystal,
2) previous heat treatment of the crystal,
3) impurity contents,
4) previous coloration followed by bleaching,
5) presence of dislocations.

4·1. *Influence of plastic deformation.* – We will first discuss the influence of deformation on the point defect contents of such specimens. If the two stage coloration mechanism is correct, the initial coloration rate and the saturation level of the rapid process should depend on the degree of deformation. The mere presence of dislocations will also influence the coloration rate if the Seitz mechanism is correct.

Some evidence can also be found in the F-center growth curves published by Nowick [17]. Fig. 25 taken from his paper shows that the saturation level for the rapid coloration process increases with the degree of deformation. Although Nowick himself does not think so, it is quite probably that this is due to point defect clusters introduced during the deformation and which now act as « easy » sources of F-centers. The initial production rate, on the other hand, is not much enhanced by deformation, which would indicate that dislocations do not play a significant role at this stage.

4·2. *Influence of frozen-in defects on darkenability.* – Although the effect does not seem to have been investigated in detail, there is some indication, from the already mentioned work of Cunell and Schneider, that quenched-in point defects enhance the colorability. We also mentioned already that crystals colored either by electrolytic means or by irradiation, and then bleached, also show enhanced colorability.

Hersh [32] finds, however, that the F-center colorability of crystals irradiated at 5 °K by means of X-rays is not enhanced after the crystals have been irradiated at room temperatures and subsequently optically bleached. The production rate was, however, increased when the X-irradiation was performed at room temperature. This last experiment seems to suggest that vacancy complexes left by the room temperature irradiation cannot be broken up by X-radiation at 5 °K, in agreement with the work of RABIN and KLICK.

4·3. *Influence of impurities.* – Mainly the influence of divalent impurities has been investigated, since these are known to introduce positive ion vacancies. HUMMEL [33] has shown that the addition of Ca^{++} to KCl enhances the room temperature colorability, while ETZEL [34] has found that the F- as well as the V-band grows more rapidly in NaCl containing Ca^{++}-ions. ETZEL finds, on the other hand, that Cd^{++} is not active in NaCl. The difference in behavior is explained as being due to differences in the degree of association between Cd^{++} and Ca^{++}, and vacancies. In the associated complex the vacancy would be much less effective as a hole trap, since the complex is neutral, than in the separated form. The conductivity measurements have shown that the cadmium ions in NaCl are associated with the vacancies at room temperature, but not the calcium ions.

According to SEITZ, the action of the divalent impurities consists in facilitating the negative ion vacancies to wander away from the dislocations after their creation, by forming a neutral pair with a positive ion vacancy. The latter are more abundant in crystals containing divalent positive ions. This explanation would obviously not apply at low temperatures where the positive ion vacancies are associated with the divalent impurities. Nevertheless, MARKHAM [35] finds that even at liquid-helium temperature the pure crystals color less rapidly than the impure ones; this is not confirmed by the more recent work by RABIN and KLICK, discussed before.

An alternative explanation for the action of divalent impurities follows from recent measurements of RABIN. These will be discussed further.

More recently, another striking example of the influence of impurities on colorability has been found by DELBECQ, SMALLER and YUSTER [36]. A small addition of heavy metal ions, *e.g.* Ag-ions, Tl-ions or Pb-ions, enhances the rate of formation of Cl_2^--molecule ions in KCl by a factor of 10^2 to 10^3, during irradiation at liquid-nitrogen temperature. In this case the situation is clear; the ions act as electron traps and prevent recombination with the hole trapped at the Cl_2^--ion.

4·4. *Influence of the presence of dislocations.* – In view of the role played by dislocations in the Seitz formation mechanism, we review in some detail the observations relative to this point.

A rather detailed study of the effect of dislocation density on the F-center growth curve under γ-radiation was made by NOWICK [37]. He finds that the presence of dislocations does not influence appreciably the production rate (at room temperature) in the first stage, but an unambiguous effect is found in the second stage (see Figs. 23 and 25). This is precisely what one would expect if the Seitz mechanisms were operating during the second stage coloration. NOWICK proposed also an explanation for the increased first stage on deformation. He thinks that during plastic deformation precipitates are finely dispersed, taking them in solution. Fhe effect would hence be due to chemical sensitization. HERSH and MARKHAM [38] studied the colorability of compressed KCl. They find that plastic deformation enhances the room temperature colorability by about 430 %, but affects the colorability at low temperature (5 °K and 78 °K) only by about 10 %. They find, however, that the absorption bands due to the Cl_2^--center are enhanced substantially. Since it has been shown previously by DELBECQ and YUSTER that electron traps enhance the production rate of this center (*e.g.*, Ag or Tl addition) the conclusion is clearly that plastic deformation introduces electron traps. This is in accord with UETA and KÄNZIG's results [30].

III. – Geometrical Properties: the Expansion of Irradiated Crystals.

1. – Experimental techniques.

The expansion of alkali halides under irradiation can be detected in several ways:

i) by direct changes in physical dimensions,

ii) by changes in density,

iii) by changes in the X-ray parameter,

iv) by the occurence of a birefringence in the contact zone between irradiated and non-irradiated parts of the crystal.

The lattice parameter can best be determined on single crystal specimens, using a diffractometer. Temperature stabilization is necessary. At integrated fluxes larger than 10^{18}, however, the line profiles become broad and diffuse and accurate determinations become difficult and ambiguous.

Density measurements are usually made by the floatation method. The crystal is immersed in a liquid which has the same density as the crystal (at about room temperature) but a larger thermal expansion coefficient. Considerable care has to be taken that no gases are adsorbed by the crystals. By measuring the temperature of exact floatation the density can be determined. The floatation temperature can most conveniently be determined by an interpolation procedure. The speeds of rise and fall of the specimens are determined at a few temperatures above and below the exact floatation temperature, which is then deduced by interpolation. An accuracy of 1 part in 10^5 and even 10^6 can be obtained with reasonable precautions.

The difficulty with this method is the existence of small temperature gradients and hence density gradients in the liquid. One can exploit this difficulty and use another variation of the floatation method whereby a known density gradient is intentionally introduced in a column of liquid. The floatation level of the crystal is then a measure of its density. The second method is more elegant for comparative measurements, since a number of specimens can be measured simultaneously; the first is more accurate for absolute measurements.

Changes in physical dimensions can be determined by mounting the crystal as one plate of a capacitor and measuring the change in capacitance (see refs. [19-21]).

Length changes can also be measured by the use of strain gauges. For a discussion concerning the measurements of birefringence we refer to PRIMAK *et al.* [1] and to WIEGAND and SMOLUCHOWSKI [2].

2. – Interpretation.

Length changes of a solid are due to two causes:

1) Changes in the average distance between atoms, *i.e.*, the lattice dilatation.

2) Changes in the number of lattice sites as a consequence of the creation of point defects.

It should be pointed out here that the creation of a vacancy increases the number of lattice sites by one, while creating an interstitial has the opposite effect. A lattice parameter measurement only reveals the average distance between atoms. It is therefore possible by combining both measurements to make deductions concerning the change in the number of lattice sites.

An important theorem in this connection has been formulated by ESHELBY [3]. A random distribution of centers of dilatation will produce a uniform dilatational strain over the entire body. When the lattice is dilated as a consequence of point defects the change in physical dimensions $\Delta l/l$ should be equal to $\Delta a/a$, the change in lattice parameter, if no changes in the number of lattice sites occur. If we call f_v and f_i respectively the volume changes due to one vacancy and one interstitial, expressed as a fraction of one atomic volume we have

$$\frac{\Delta a}{a} = \frac{\Delta l}{l} = \frac{1}{3}\,(C_v f_v + C_i f_i)\,, \tag{1}$$

C_i and C_v are the molar fractions of vacancies and interstitials. The values of f_v and f_i have been calculated in a few cases. TEWORDT [4] finds, *e.g.*, $f_i = 1.7$ and $f_v = -0.5$ in the case of copper.

Neglecting the volume effects due to the geometrical changes of the climbing dislocations acting as sources or sinks for point defects, we can give an expression for $\Delta l/l$, for the case where point defects were created:

$$\frac{\Delta l}{l} = \frac{1}{3}(C_v f_v + C_i f_i) + \frac{1}{3}(C_v - C_i) . \tag{2}$$

The last term is due to the creation of lattice sites as a consequence of vacancy and interstitial formation.

It is now easy to see that, in the case of Frenkel disorder, *e.g.*, since $C_v = C_i$, we will have $\Delta l/l = \Delta a/a$.

In the case of Schottky disorder, on the other hand, $C_i = 0$ and we have a direct measure for the concentration of vacancies:

$$C_v = 3(\Delta l/l - \Delta a/a) \tag{3}$$

whereas anti-Schottky disorder, *i.e.* $C_v = 0$, leads to:

$$C_i = 3(\Delta a/a - \Delta l/l) . \tag{4}$$

3. – Parameter and density changes.

3·1. *Work on* LiF. – Most of the work on this subject has been done on LiF. The advantage of using this material is obvious. One makes use of the $^6Li(n, \alpha)^3H$ reaction for thermal neutrons to increase the damage rate and to increase the effects which are small in the other alkali halides. The α-particle acquires an energy of 2.1 MeV and the tritium 2.7 MeV.

Representative results were described by BINDER and STURM [5]. They are summarized in Fig. 35. The significant feature is the proportional increase in the

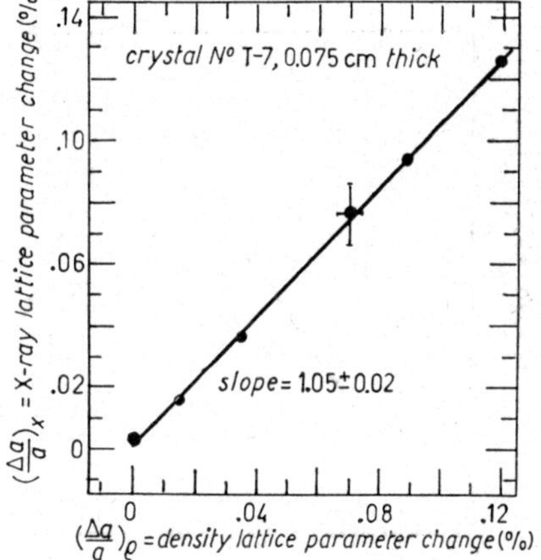

Fig. 35. – The linear relation found between the lattice parameter of irradiated LiF determined by X-ray diffraction and by determination of density. The specimen employed was 0.075 cm thick. (After: F. SEITZ and J. KOEHLER: *Solid State Phys.*, vol. **2** (New York, **1956**), p. 305).

X-ray $\Delta a/a$ and the density $\Delta l/l$, the coefficient of proportionality being very close to 1. The implication of this result is that the disorder created by the radiation is predominantly of the Frenkel type.

BINDER and STURM also studied the annealing kinetics of the damage in neutron-irradiated LiF by measuring the recovery of $\Delta a/a$. They found that the process obeys second-order kinetics, the activation energy being $E=1.5$ eV. They conclude that random recombination of non-neighboring vacancies and interstitials is the process responsible for the recovery. Complete recovery occurs at about 560 °C.

Different authors have investigated the lattice expansion of LiF. Their results do not always agree, due to differences in irradiation temperature and also to difference in flux.

Since the number of Frenkel pairs should be proportional to the integrated flux, at least at the start, we can write

$$3\,\frac{\Delta a}{a} = k\varphi t\,,$$

where k is a proportionality constant. It varies, however, for the different investigations:

BINDER and STURM [5]	$k = 24\cdot 10^{-20}$
SMALLMAN and WILLIS [7]	$k = 3\cdot 10^{-20}$
PERIO, TOURNARIE and GANCE [6]	$k = 4\cdot 10^{-20}$

BINDER and STURM measured crystals which had a dose of $6\cdot 10^{16}$ n/cm² at most. KEATING [8] made measurements at higher integrated fluxes: $(10^{17}\div 10^{18})$ n/cm². He finds considerable line broadening but no lattice expansion. He concludes that these results could be explained by assuming that material was deposited in platelets on cube planes separated by about 500 Å.

PERIO *et al.* have pursued their measurements to

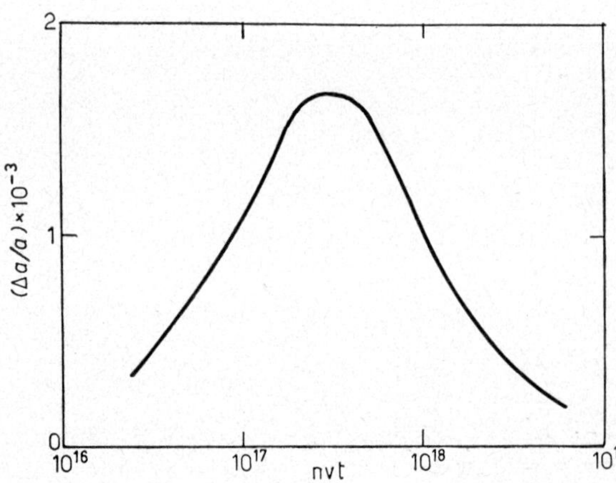

Fig. 36. – Change of lattice constant of LiF as a function of total neutron flux. (After: R. SMOLUCHOWSKI: *Rad. Res., Suppl.*, **1**, 26 (1959)).

very high doses and they find that $\Delta a/a$ goes through a maximum at about $2\cdot10^{17}$ n/cm², then decreases and finally becomes again about zero at an integrated flux of about 10^{19} n/cm² (Fig. 36). The density on the other hand continues to decrease and at 10^{19} n/cm² $\Delta d/d$ is about 2%. This could be explained by the formation of cavities and platelets of lithium metal. At still higher doses the crystal deteriorates completely.

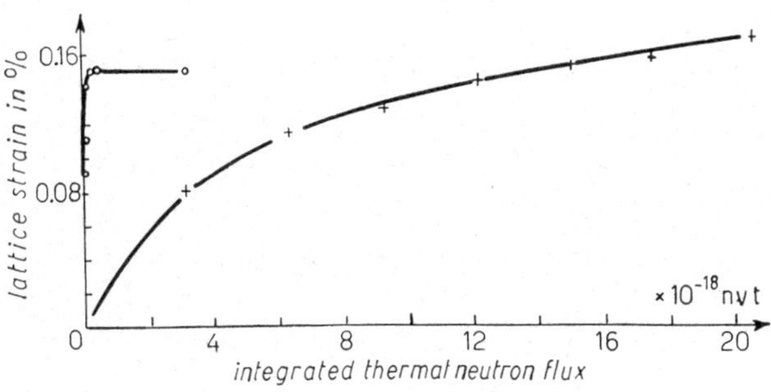

Fig. 37. – Lattice parameter change in LiF: ○ powder at 30 °C; + compact at 185 °C. (After: P. SENIO and C. TUCKER: KAPL-1727).

SENIO and TUCKER [9] also measured parameter changes of LiF powder and compact, at 30 °C and at 185 °C. They find a much more rapid increase at 30 °C than at 185 °C (Fig. 37).

In both cases the curve tend to a saturation values of about $\Delta a/a \simeq 0.16\%$. Although they used exposures up to $23\cdot10^{18}$ n/cm², there is no trace of the maximum found by PERIO *et al.* in single crystals.

The recovery of the lattice parameter takes place in a single stage at about 175 °C, for the powder irradiated at 30 °C, and at about 350 °C for the powder irradiated at 185 °C (Fig. 38).

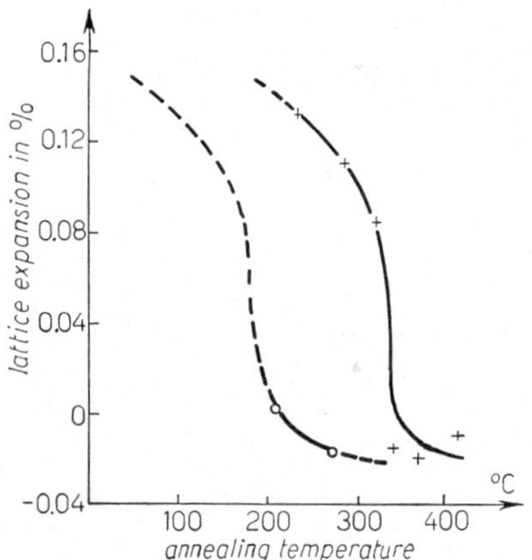

Fig. 38. - Lattice parameter recovery of irradiated LiF: +, irradiation temperature 185 °C, reflection (422) K_α; ○ irradiation temperature 30 °C, reflection (333) K_β. (After: P. SENIO and C. W. TUCKER: KAPL-1727).

The dimensional changes are also quite different at the two irradiation temperatures; at 30 °C about 6% increase in length is found after $20\cdot10^{18}$ n/cm², while at 185 °C only 2% increase occurs, for the same dose. The increase is roughly linear with dose and the same for powder and single crystals (Fig. 39).

SENIO and TUCKER observed by optical microscopy small cavities in their crystals, which accounts for the large decreases in density. These cavities have been studied in detail by GILMAN and JOHNSTON [10].

SPAEPEN [11] measured density changes of crystals irradiated at 80 °C in the region beyond the maximum in lattice parameter and found that the density decrease saturates at a value of about 20% for doses in excess of $1.2 \cdot 10^{18}$ n/cm². It is clear that such large changes correspond to almost macroscopic defects, and it is almost certain that cavities of the kind described by GILMAN and JOHNSTON [10] are responsible for this behavior, especially because of the relatively high temperature of irradiation. Annealing gives a non-recoverable density decrease which is larger in the most heavily irradiated specimens. This again points to cavities or macroscopic defect formation.

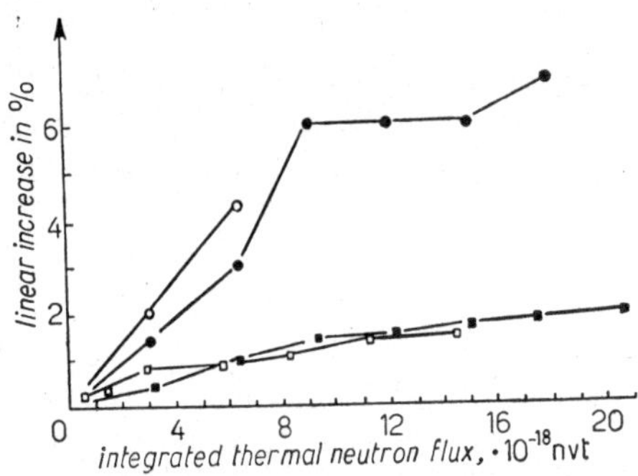

Fig. 39. – Dimensional change in LiF: ○ single crystal at 30 °C; ● hot-pressed compact at 30 °C; □ single crystal at 185 °C; ■ hot-pressed compact 185 °C. (After: P. SENIO and C. W. TUCKER: KAPL-1727).

In view of the many contradictory experimental results it is difficult to attempt a coherent explanation. It should however be pointed out that there is not necessarily a contradiction between the occurrence of a maximum in the lattice parameter and the monotonic decrease in density. This may well be due to an agglomeration of the vacancies into cavities and the interstitials into platelets, with a resulting annealing of the lattice. Cavities were observed after annealing above 700 °C by SENIO and TUCKER as mentioned before, while LAMBERT and GUINIER [12] have found X-ray evidence for the lithium platelets. Recently the occurrence of lithium in neutron-irradiated LiF has been confirmed by resonance techniques.

The smaller and slower effects at higher irradiation temperature are, of course, a consequence of the annealing going on during irradiation. Part of the discrepancy disappears if it is taken into account that the different authors made their irradiations at different temperatures.

3·2. *Work on the other alkali halides.* – ESTERMANN *et al.* [13] have been the first to demonstrate the decrease in density of irradiated alkali halides, using a floatation method.

BERRY [14] measured the lattice parameter increase of X-irradiated KCl and NaCl and found that it was too small to be due to Frenkel disorder, but consistent with Schottky disorder. However, his measurements were made on powders and no simultaneous measurements of optical absorption were made, so that it was not possible to decide in which coloration stage his material was.

KOBAYASHI [15] has examined density changes and subsequent thermal annealing in proton-irradiated sodium chloride, and he has correlated these with the changes in color center concentrations and with stored energy. He has calculated that between 0.8 and $1.2 \cdot 10^{19}$ negative ion vacancies are present in the crystal just after irradiation. His results are summarized in Fig. 40.

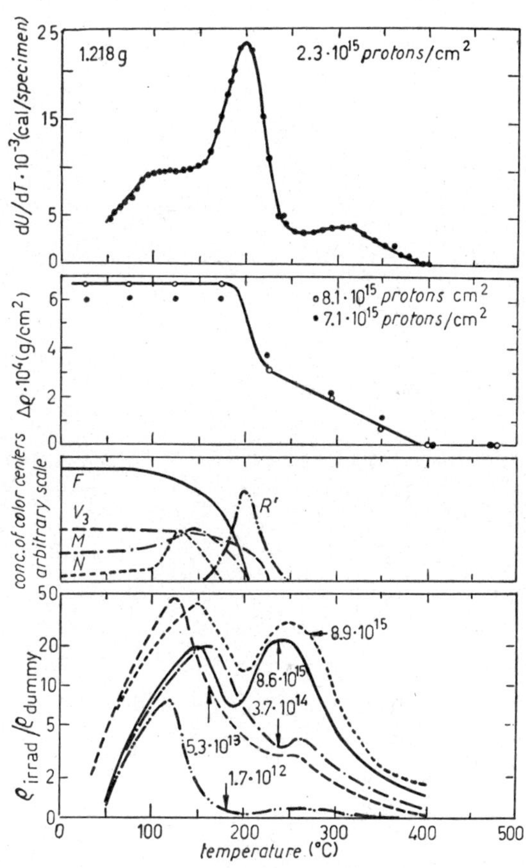

Fig. 40. – Annealing out of stored energy, of density change, of color centers, and of resistivity changes introduced in NaCl by proton irradiation. (After: R. SMOLUCHOWSKI: *Rad. Res. Suppl.*, **1**, 26 (1959)).

At about 200 °C there is a rather abrupt rise in density coinciding with the disappearance of the various color-center absorptions, F, M, V_3 and N (8 400 Å) and the appearance of a new band: the R'-band (5 780 Å). The latter band disappears quickly, and the density then increases very gradually to the normal density which is restored at 400 °C. Already at 250 °C the crystal has become clear, but half the expansion is still present, presumably as higher aggregates of vacancies, quadruplets, etc.

In the temperature range between 100 and 200 °C no density change is observed, but the color center concentration changes gradually, the F-center absorption decreases at the expense of the M- and N-center concentrations, which show a peak just prior to the final drop. The interpretation is straightforward: in this temperature range the concentration of defects does not change appreciably, but a redistribution in the sense of higher complexes takes place. The recovery of the parameter is accompanied by a release of stored energy.

4. – Birefringence studies.

PRIMAK *et al.* [16] have studied the photoeleastic effects associated with the expansion of 21 MeV deuteron irradiated LiF. The sign of the birefringence that results at the boundary between the irradiated and the nonirradiated parts is in accordance with the hypothesis that the strain results from the fact that the irradiated part is held in compression by the nonirradiated part. From the birefringence and a knowledge of the photoelastic constants the volume expansion may be computed. Fig. 41 shows the expansion due to defects together with the vacancy concentration as calculated from the color center concentration as a function of the distance behind the irradiated face. It is seen that the expansion is almost completely due to the volume increase associated with color centers.

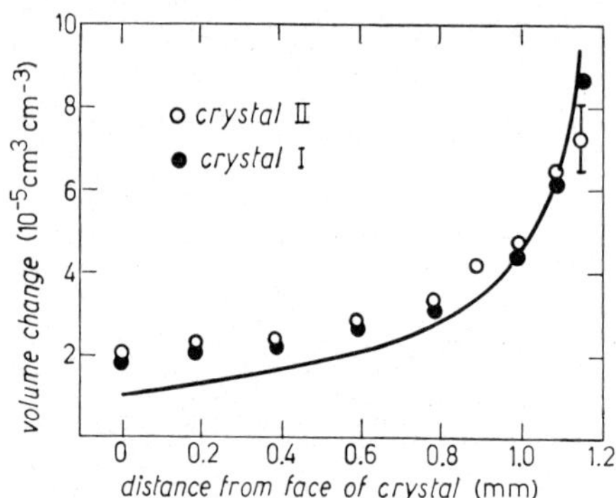

Fig. 41. – A comparison of the dilatation (circles) computed from the birefringence with the volume of vacancies associated with the color centers per unit volume of crystal (solid curve) in a LiF crystal which had been irradiated with deuterons. (After: W. PRIMAK *et al.*: *Phys. Rev.*, **98**, 1708 (1955)).

It was further found that on complete bleaching with ultra-violet light the birefringence diminished to about 10% of its original value. Since vacancies and interstitials, not color centers, are the cause of the birefringence, this seems to indicate that the bleaching causes the vacancies to return to their sources.

The method of Primak *et al.* to measure the expansion has the considerable advantage that it is not very temperature-dependent, and also that it can be used for crystals irra-

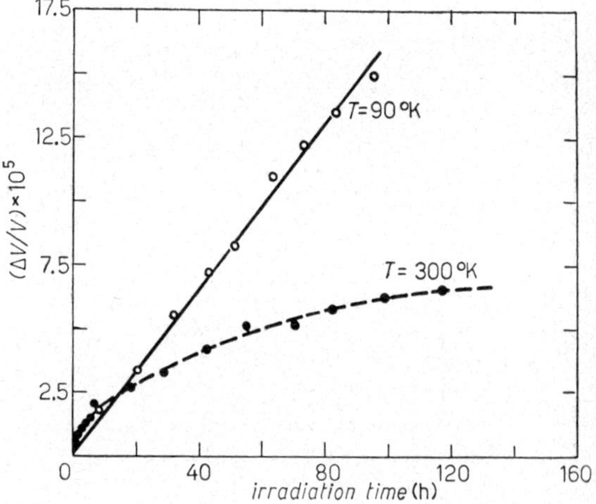

Fig. 42. – Fractional volume expansion of LiF *vs.* irradiation time. (After: D. A. WIEGAND and R. SMOLUCHOWSKI: Internal Report, Carnegie Institute of Technology (1959)).

diated at low temperatures. This possibility has been used by WIEGAND and SMOLUCHOWSKI [17]. These authors have X-irradiated LiF crystals at low temperatures (90 °K) and studied the building up of the expansion at this temperature and the subsequent annealing.

The following significant facts were observed:

1) At low temperature (90 °K) the volume increases linearly with irradiation dose while at room temperature saturation is observed (Fig. 42).

2) The F-center concentration behaves in a way similar to the volume increase, *i.e.* it increases linearly with dose at the lower temperature while it saturates for room temperature irradiation (Fig. 43).

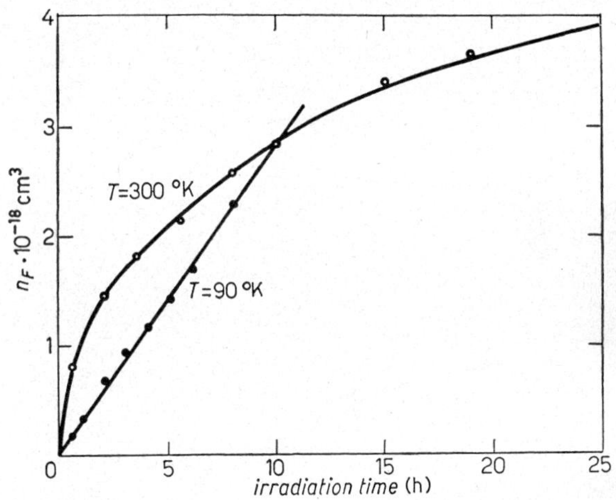

Fig. 43. – Density of F-centers in LiF *vs.* irradiation time. (After: D. A. WIEGAND and R. SMOLUCHOWSKI: Internal Report, Carnegie Institute of Technology).

3) The band at 3 400 Å quickly saturates at the low temperature, in contrast to the F-band which grows linearly (Fig. 44).

4) Between 110 °K and 150 °K, about 75 % of the irradiation-induced expansion anneals out (Fig. 45).

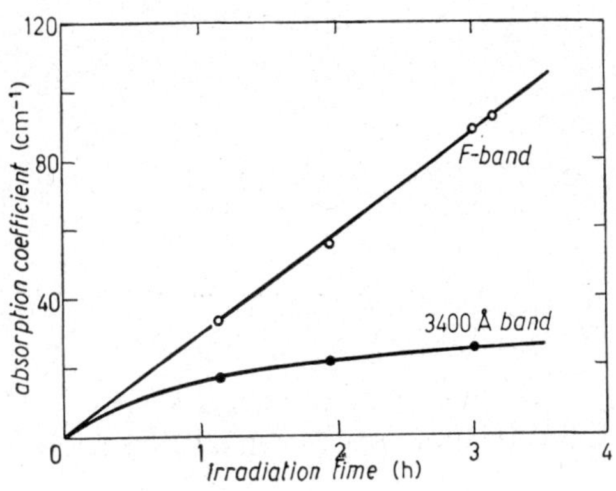

Fig. 44. – Optical absorption constant for LiF at the maximum of the F-band and at 3 400 Å *vs.* irradiation time at 90 °K. (After: D. A. WIEGAND and R. SMOLUCHOWSKI: Internal Report, Carnegie Institute of Technology (1955)).

5) The 3400 Å band anneals out completely at 140 °K (Fig. 45).

6) If irradiation is interrupted for a short time followed by thermal

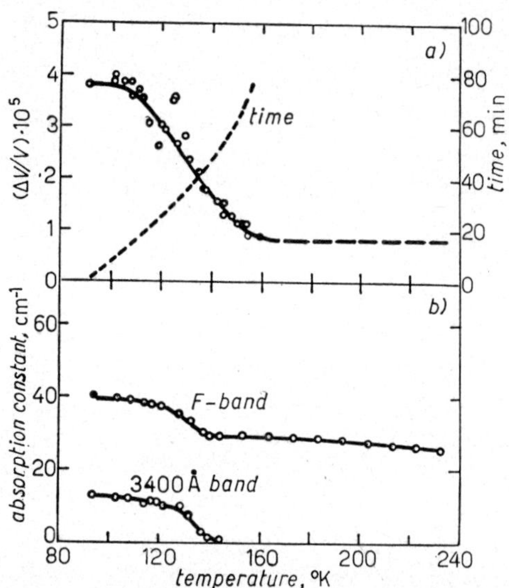

Fig. 45. – *a*) Annealing of the fractional volume change in LiF after irradiation at 90 °K for 44 h. *b*) Annealing of the optical absorption band of LiF at the maximum of the *F*-band and at 3400 Å after irradiation at 90 °K for 3 h. (After: D. A. WIEGAND and R. SMOLUCHOWSKI: Internal Report, Carnegie Institute of Technology 1955)).

bleaching at 160 °K, the volume decreases but grows again at the same rate as before on continued irradiations (Fig. 46).

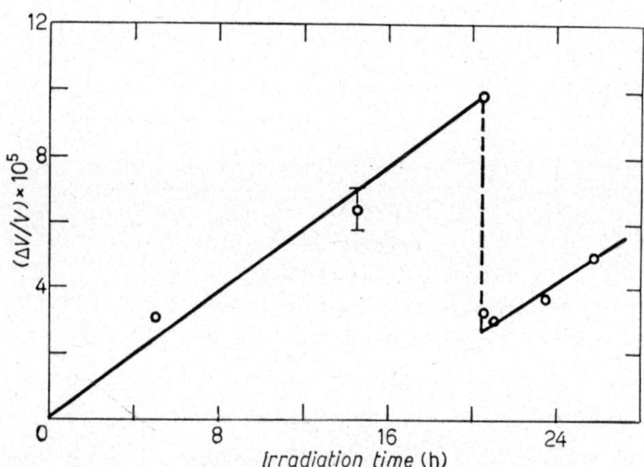

Fig. 46. – Fractional volume change of LiF *vs.* irradiation time at 90 °K. (After: D. A. WIEGAND and R. SMOLUCHOWSKI: Internal Report, Carnegie Institute of Technology (1955)).

The F-center concentration, on the other hand, increases much more rapidly after the partial bleaching and rapidly joins the original linear growth curve (Fig. 47).

From these elements the following picture is constructed.

From the facts (1) and (2) and the corresponding growth rates one could conclude that volume expansion is proportional to the number of F-centers, each F-center contributing roughly the volume of a negative ion vacancy. The correlation of the expansion rate with the growth rate of the 3400 Å band is poor and on this basis it is excluded that the color centers associated with this band cause the expansion.

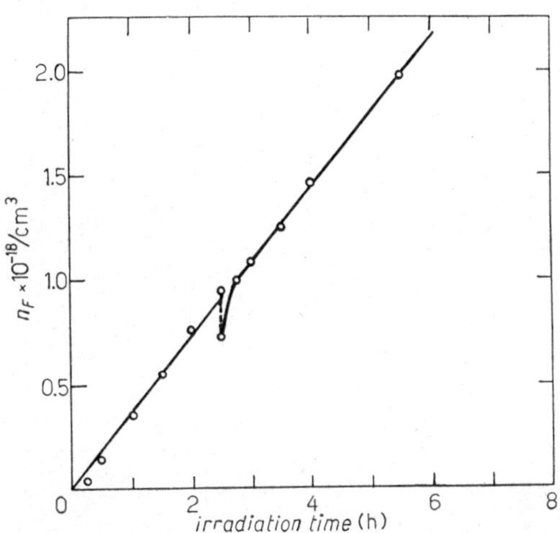

Fig. 47. – Density of F-centers in LiF *vs.* irradiation time at 90 °K. (After: D. A. WIEGAND and R. SMOLUCHOWSKI: Internal Report, Carnegie Institute of Technology (1955)).

According to WIEGAND and SMOLUCHOWSKI, two processes could possibly account for the annealing behavior:

1) Migration of vacancy pairs.

2) Annealing with change of the configuration around a halogen interstitial: a so-called H-center.

We comment on these two possibilities:

1) The activation energy for migration of isolated vacancies is much too large to account for the observed mobility at low temperature. The activation energy for pair migration might, however, be small enough. Annealing would then consist in the formation of small dislocation loops or in climb of the dislocations. The production mechanism would then be the Seitz mechanism. Arguments against this possibility are, however: *a*) that at these low temperatures the production of F-centers seems to be independent of the dislocation density; *b*) no M-center formation is observed during the anneal. This last argument may not be conclusive, since it depends on the model accepted for the M-center.

2) When assuming that at low temperatures the Varley mechanism operates, the possibility arises that the expansion is due to halogen interstitial formation. The interstitials being produced at the same rate as the vacancies, the correlation between F-center growth curves and expansion would

be maintained. The annealing at 130 °K, would be due to a change in configuration of the interstitial and, *e.g.*, not to a recombination of interstitials and vacancies, since the latter mechanism would reduce the number of vacancies, which is not observed.

In their paramagnetic resonance work KÄNZIG and WOODRUFF [18] observed the annealing of the H-center in LiF at 130 °K, *i.e.* at the same temperature where the volume expansion anneals. This suggests that the same annealing process may occur here. KÄNZIG and WOODRUFF [18] suggest that halogen molecules are formed fitting in a negative ion vacancy. The accompanying lattice relaxation may be the cause of the volume decrease.

On the other hand, the annealing behavior suggests that the removal of negative ion vacancies cannot account for the decrease in volume, since the F-center bleaching does not result in a disappearance of the negative ion vacancies. The annealing process at 160 °K rather consists in a release of trapped holes from the 3 400 Å centers which recombine with F-center electrons, without destroying the vacancy. The conclusion from 6) is that not all of the expansion can be attributed to negative ion vacancies.

If the volume expansion can be recovered 75 % by bleaching of the H-center this means that the interstitials would contribute at least this fraction to the expansion. Since, on the other hand, it is found that the expansion is also equal to the volume of the created F-centers, the implication is that the volume increase due to a halogen Frenkel pair is equal to the volume increase due to a negative ion vacancy. This is a rather unexpected result. It should be noted that WIEGAND and SMOLUCHOWSKI do not explicitly identify the 3 400 Å band with the H-center.

From the foregoing discussion it will be evident that the situation is far from clear.

5. – Changes in physical dimensions.

Direct changes in dimensions on X-irradiation of KCl, RbBr and NaCl have been studied at room temperature by SAKAGUCHI and SUITA [19]. The changes in length were detected by measuring the change in capacitance of a capacitor formed by two electrodes, one of which is attached to the end face of the crystal. The increase in length saturates at about 3 to $4\cdot10^{-5}$ cm, corresponding to the creation of about 10^{18} vacancy pairs per cm³. The F-center concentration would correspond with this value within 30 %. One firm conclusion from these experiments is that vacancies are created during the process of the F-center formation.

LIN [20] in similar experiments and using similar equipment found that the expansion starts with a certain delay and goes on for a while after switching off the X-ray beam. This has not, however, been confirmed by recent careful work, which we will now discuss in some detail.

Very careful measurements of expansion and color center concentration in NaCl as a function of X-ray dose have recently been made by RABIN [21].

He also used an apparatus that transforms dimension changes into changes in capacitance. An important characteristic of this apparatus is that it is fully temperature-compensated, resulting in an effective temperature stabilization of $5 \cdot 10^{-3}$ °C. A schematic view is shown in Fig. 48. Crystals are ir-

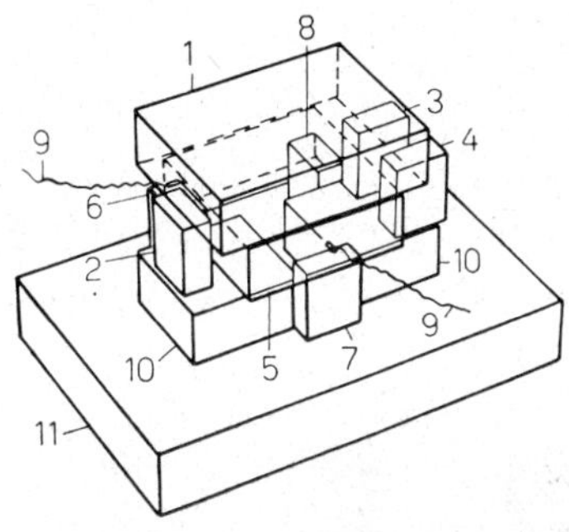

Fig. 48. – Temperature-« insensitive » crystal capacitor for measuring X-ray expansion. Both the upper capacity plate (1) and the lower capacity plate (5) are mounted on sets of three NaCl crystals, (2, 3, 4) and (6, 7, 8). The expansion of the irradiated crystal (7) causes the gap between the plates to close and the capacity change is measured with the aid of fine copper wires (9). The capacity plates, the support blocks (10) and the base block (11) are precision ground tool steel. (After: H. RABIN: *Phys. Rev.*, **116**, 1381 (1959)).

radiated parallel to their smallest dimensions and the expansion is measured continuously. RABIN studied pure NaCl as well as crystals intentionally doped with varying amounts of divalent impurities and with potassium ions.

His results of the expansion measurements can be summarized as follows (see Fig. 49).

1) There is a linear relation between the F-center concentration and the relative expansion $\Delta l/l$.

2) The expansion is most rapid at the start and then gradually slows

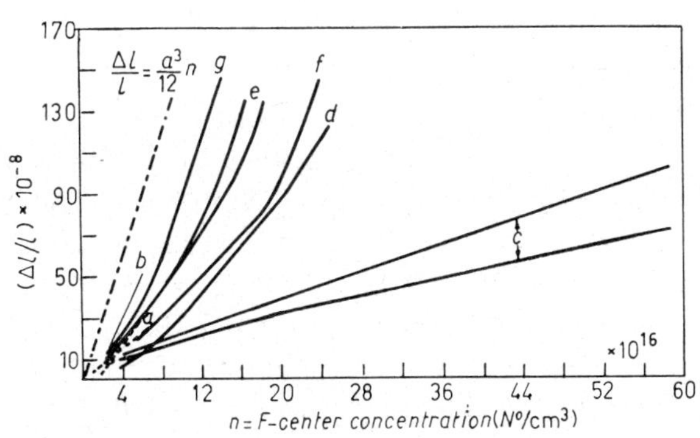

Fig. 49. – Relative linear expansion as a function of F-center concentration. The long dashed line gives the locus of points for which there is a one to one relationship between vacancy pairs and F-centers. This line has slope $a^3/12$ where a is the lattice constant: *a*) natural NaCl; *b*) HARSHAW NaCl; *c*) natural NaCl, 0.5 M% $CaCl_2$; *d*) OPTOVAC NaCl; *e*) natural NaCl, 1.0 M% KCl; *f*) natural NaCl; *g*) natural NaCl, 0.1 M% $CdCl_2$. (After: H. RABIN: *Phys. Rev.*, **116**, 1381 (1959)).

down, giving an indication of saturation in agreement with the work of SAGAGUCHI and SUITA.

3) The expansion starts immediately on X-irradiation, at variance with the findings of LIN (who found an incubation time).

4) The expansion is stable after the end of the irradiation period and it stops immediately after the irradiation is stopped, again at variance with Lin's results.

5) There does not seem to be any correlation between the expansion of the various crystals and their dislocation density.

6) No obvious relation between the relative expansion and the impurity contents was found.

The growth curves for the F-center concentration of the same crystals were also measured. In accord with previous work [22] the Ca doped crystal showed the greatest sensitivity but this did not correspond to the largest expansion. The relation between these two quantities, *i.e.* expansion and F-center concentration, is shown in Fig. 49, the dotted line showing the relationship that would be obtained if one F-center would result from every vacancy pair created, as one would expect in the ideal case.

The crystals showed very little M-band after the irradiation at room temperature, so in the discussion the F-centers only need to be considered.

From Fig. 49 it is evident that most of the curves show two different stages, one with a smaller expansion rate than foreseen by the idealized model, and one for which the slope corresponds very approximately to this model. It is clear that these two stages correspond with the two stages found earlier in growth curves of F-centers. The first stage, which corresponds with populating existing vacancies as well as creating new ones, produces evidently a smaller dilatation than deduced on the simple model. Once the second stage sets in, the dilatation rate should of course increase.

Extrapolating the second stage portion of the curve of Fig. 49 to the x-axis gives a simple means of estimating the number of negative ion vacancies initially present in the crystal. One of the astonishing results of the investigation is that the calcium-doped crystals seem to contain a minimum of about $6 \cdot 10^{17}/\text{cm}^3$ negative ion vacancies, which is considerably more than any of the other crystals. Accepting this fact at its face value, it provides an obvious explanation for the sensitization of Ca-doped crystals, *i.e.* for the higher initial production rate. This explanation is at variance with the one offered previously by ETZEL and SEITZ [23]. Furthermore, it is difficult to understand on the basis of the simple charge compensation model; the number of positive ion vacancies introduced by the calcium should indeed suppress the negative ion vacancy concentration.

Very recently KUCZINKI and co-workers (private communication) measured the expansion on X-irradiation of clear and additively colored crystals. They used strain gauges. They find that the expansion saturates, in agreement with previous work. The saturation value, however, decreases with increasing initial F-center concentration.

IV. – The Effect of Radiation on the Mechanical Properties.

1. – Yield stress and hardness.

Much of the experimental work in this connection has been done with X-rays rather than with particle irradiation. The reason is, of course, that it is much easier to use the first. The results are probably comparable, since the largest fraction of the damage is the result of ionization anyway.

Ionizing radiation introduces a very marked hardening, as first shown by PODACHEWSKI [1] and subsequently studied by a number of authors [2-8]. The observed phenomenon can be summarized as follows: after irradiation with 180 kV X-rays and also with U.V. light:

i) The yield stress increases by a factor of about two.

ii) Optical bleaching of the F-centers does not remove the hardening effect.

iii) In partially irradiated crystals, slip started in the unirradiated parts propagates only with difficulty in the irradiated part and it is generally stopped at the boundary.

The last observation suggests that the observed effect is a bulk effect.

Similar observations were made by YIN-YUAN LI [3] on AgCl irradiated with 50 kV X-rays and U.V. light (several minutes). He finds that surface coloration does not harden the crystal, while bulk coloration does. Also the fracture strength is larger for bulk-colored crystals. Grain boundaries appear to darken preferentially, and in irradiated crystals fracture takes place along grain boundaries. LI also measured the indentation hardness of sodium chloride and found that it could be doubled on X-irradiation.

Even larger increases in microhardness were observed by VAUGHAN, LEIVO and SMOLUCHOWSKI [4] on proton irradiation and by WESTERVELT [8] on electron irradiation. The phenomena described here are partly bulk effects and partly surface effects. Fig. 50 taken from reference [6] shows the microhardness profiles of NaCl crystals irradiated with unfiltered 50 keV X-rays for different intervals of time. It is clearly visible that the hardness decreases rapidly behind the irradiated surface even for long exposures. At a depth of about 0.1 mm the hardening is reduced by half its value, while at a 0.5 mm depth the hardness again has its normal value.

The recovery of microhardness in NaCl and KCl was investigated by

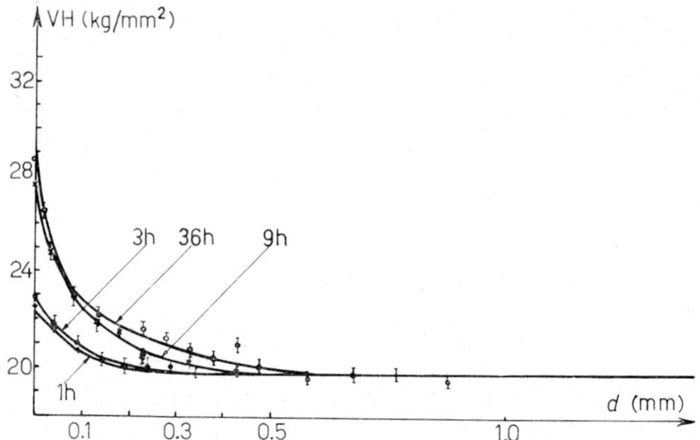

Fig. 50. – Vickers hardness as a function of depth for various irradiation times. (After: E. AERTS, S. AMELINCKX and W. DEKEYSER: *Acta Met.*, **7**, 29 (1959)).

WESTERVELT [8] and by AERTS, AMELINCKX and DEKEYSER [6] who used 50 kV X-rays. Typical isochronal recovery curves are shown in Fig. 51 (from ref. [8].) It is clear that there are three broad annealing stages. At about 150 °C in KCl and at 200 °C in NaCl the first stage removes 50% of the hardening in 20 minutes. In KCl the rest is removed in two steps, one at 200 °C (5 min) and the last one at about 350 °C in about two minutes.

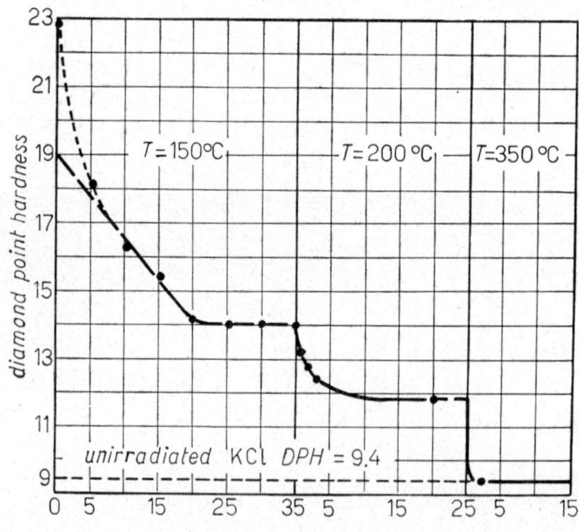

Fig. 51. – Recovery of radiation-induced hardness in electron-irradiated KCl (1 MeV, 2 h at 20 °C). (After: D. WESTERVELT: *Acta Met.*, **1**, 755 (1953)).

Isothermal annealing data were taken in the case of NaCl by CUYPERS and AMELINCKX [9] at temperatures between 100 and 200 °C. The process can, within the experimental accuracy, be described by means of first order kinetics. The activation energy would then be very small, about 0.2 eV. It is very probable that the process is in fact much more complicated and distributed in activation energies, simulating approximately first order kinetics.

On the same crystals used for the hardness profiles, the color center profiles were measured also (Fig. 52, 53). It is obvious that there is no correlation between the F-center concentration, nor the M-center concentration, and the hardness. We know, moreover, that bleaching the F-centers does not influence the hardening. The correlation becomes better for the more complicated N-center (Fig. 53). These observations suggest that complexes of color centers,

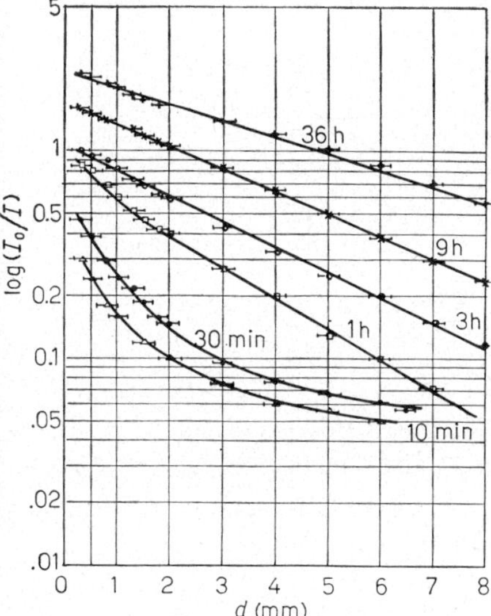

Fig. 52. – Absorption in the F-band *vs.* depth as a function of irradiation time. Measurements performed on different specimens but all values reduced to a thickness of 1 mm. (After: E. Aerts, S. Amelinckx and W. Dekeyser: *Acta Met.*, **7**, 29 (1959)).

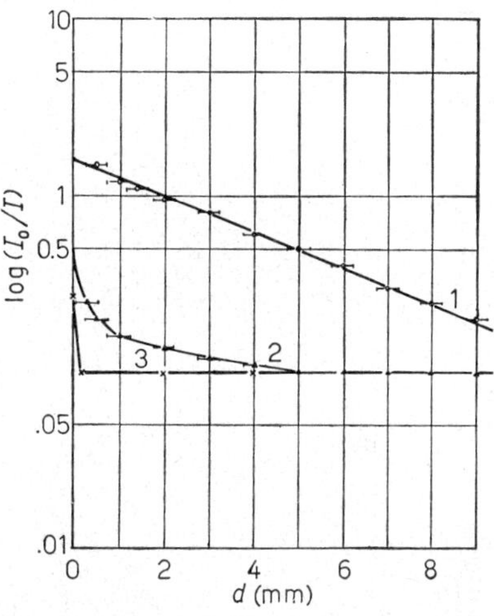

Fig. 53. – Absorption in various bands *vs.* depth for the same crystal (irradiation time 9 h, thickness 0.84 mm; results not reduced to a thickness of 1 mm). 1) absorption curve for $\lambda = 464$ nm; 2) absorption curve for $\lambda = 725$ nm; 3) absorption curve for $\lambda = 820$ nm. Note the increasingly better correlation with increasing complexity of the center. (After: E. Aerts, S. Amelinckx and W. Dekeyser: *Acta Met.*, **7**, 29 (1959)).

i.e. small colloids, are responsible. Large colloids as revealed by the colloid band do not seem to influence the hardness.

An elegant and sensitive method for evaluating the hardening consists of measuring the diameter of the etch pattern associated with an indentation [6, 7]. This diameter gives the maximum distance travelled by the dislocation under the influence of the applied shear stress. It is found that in hardened crystals the distance is very much reduced. Since the dislocations set into movement by an indentation pyramid are certainly fresh dislocations, the hardening is evindently mainly friction hardening and much less source hardening.

2. – Effect of electron irradiation on yield stress.

WHAPHAM and MAKIN [10] investigated in a quantitative way the consequences of lattice hardening on the stress-strain behavior of electron irradiated LiF. They assume that the obstacles to slip are defect clusters. The assumption is, however, not necessary for the theory, since the nature of the obstacles is unessential. If we call N the number of dislocations per unit volume held up against N_z obstacles per unit area of glide plane, and $\dot{\varepsilon}$ the strain rate at temperature T and stress σ we have

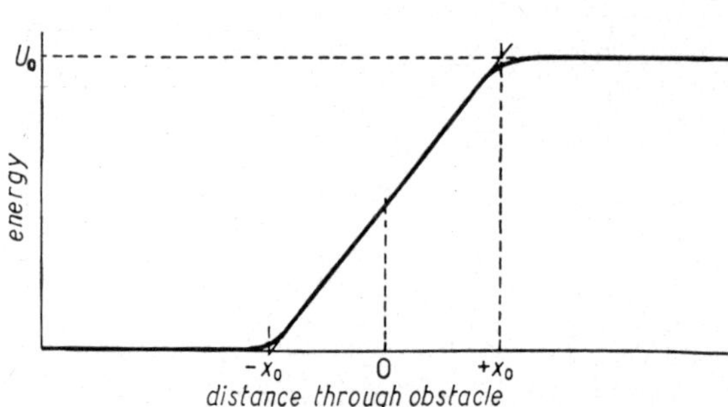

Fig. 54. – Energy profile of a dislocation cutting through an obstacle at zero externally applied stress. (After: A. D. WHAPHAM and A. G. MAKIN: *Phil. Mag.*, 5, 237 (1960)).

$$\dot{\varepsilon} = \frac{Nbv_0}{N_z} \exp\left[-U(\sigma)/kT\right]. \tag{1}$$

From this equation σ can be calculated as a function of N_z if we know $U(\sigma)$.

The energy profile for a dislocation cutting through an obstacle may be pictured as in Fig. 54, in the absence of an applied stress, and as in Fig. 55, in the presence of a stress σ. The mean distance between obstacles in the slip plane is l_0'.

According to MOTT [11] and SEEGER [12], one can write to a good approximation

$$U = U_0 \left(1 - \frac{\sigma}{\sigma_0}\right)^{\frac{3}{2}}, \tag{2}$$

where U_0 is the activation energy at zero stress and σ_0 the stress required to overcome the barrier with-

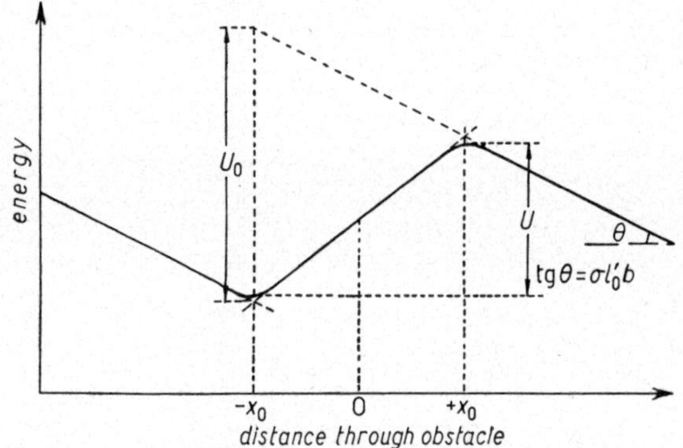

Fig. 55. – Energy profile of a dislocation cutting through an obstacle when an external stress σ is applied. (After: A. D. WHAPHAM and A. G. MAKIN: *Phil. Mag.*, 5, 237 (1960)).

out thermal activation. The latter can be found by expressing that the work done by the applied stress over the distance between obstacles, *i.e.* $b\sigma l_0'$, is equal to the work necessary to overcome the barrier, *i.e.* $U/2x_0$. We then have

$$U = U_0\left(1 - \frac{2x_0 b l_0' \sigma}{U_0}\right). \tag{3}$$

Assuming the obstacles distributed uniformly over the glide plane

$$l_0' \simeq N_z^{-\frac{1}{2}}.$$

From eq. (1) we then deduce

$$\sigma = \frac{N_z^{\frac{1}{2}} U_0^{\frac{3}{2}}}{(2x_0 b)^{\frac{3}{2}}}\left[1 - \left\{\frac{kT}{U_0}\ln\frac{Nb\nu_0}{N_z\dot{\varepsilon}}\right\}^{\frac{2}{3}}\right]^{\frac{3}{2}}. \tag{4}$$

According to FRIEDEL [13] the value of l_0' is stress-dependent and given by

$$l_0' = (\mu b/\sigma N_z)^{\frac{1}{3}}. \tag{5}$$

This can be used to modify slightly the previous expression [4]. In any case the stress depends on the square root of the density of obstacles.

We still have to link N_z to the irradiation dose. Initially the number of obstacles will be directly proportional to the dose, but as more defects are created the probability that they cluster with existing defects increases. The rate of formation of obstacles can therefore be obtained from a differential equation of the kind:

$$\frac{\mathrm{d}N_z}{\mathrm{d}t} = a\varphi - b\varphi N_z. \tag{6}$$

When a is the number of obstacles produced per electron, φ is the flux. This

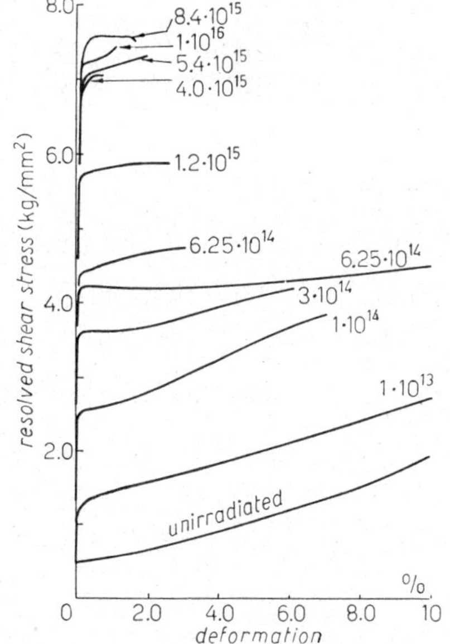

Fig. 56. – Stress-strain curves of irradiated lithium fluoride specimens tested in compression. (After: A. D. WHAPHAM and A. J. MAKIN: *Phil. Mag.*, **5**, 237 (1960)).

equation integrates to

$$N_z = \frac{a}{b}[1 - \exp[-b\varphi t]]. \tag{7}$$

Calling Φ the integrated flux, we find finally

$$\sigma_i = A(1 - \exp[-B\Phi])^{\frac{1}{2}}. \tag{8}$$

This relation can be compared with the empirical formula found for copper by BLEWITT [14]:

$$\sigma_i \simeq \Phi^{\frac{1}{3}}.$$

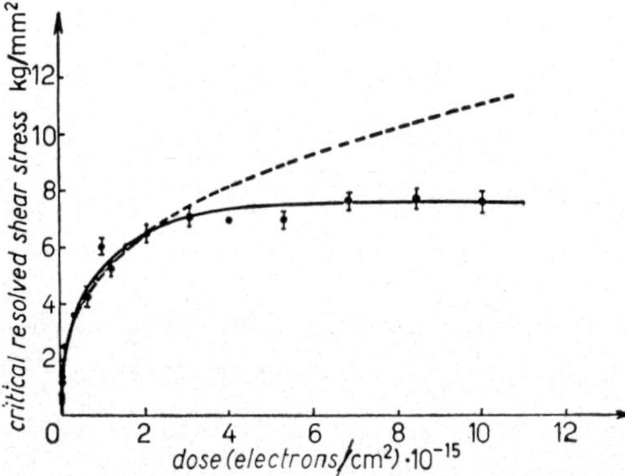

Fig. 57. – Plot of the critical resolved shear stress *v.s.* irradiation dose. The relation $\sigma = (0.5+7.13)(1-\exp[-6.18\cdot 10^{-16}\varphi])^{\frac{1}{2}}$ is shown as a solid line; the broken line is $\sigma = 5.18\cdot 10^{-5}\varphi^{\frac{1}{3}}$. (After: A. D. WHAPHAM and A. J. MAKIN: *Phil. Mag.*, **5**, 237 (1960)).

The measured critical shear stress is then $\sigma = \sigma_u + \sigma_i$, where σ_u is the initial shear stress corresponding to unirradiated material.

The experimental results for LiF are shown in Fig. 56. Irradiation was performed with 1 MeV electrons from a Van de Graaff generator. Excellent fit of the experimental results with the proposed relation (8) is found, while the data could not be fitted with a $\Phi^{\frac{1}{3}}$ law (Fig. 57).

3. – Creep.

The effect of X-irradiation on the creep behavior in compression of NaCl single crystals has been investigated by LAD and METZ [15]. The crystals were irradiated with 50 kV X-rays while rotating with respect to the X-ray beam. In this way all surfaces were equally exposed. It was found, by comparison with an unirradiated specimen, that the constant b in the creep equation (*i.e.*, the initial deformation)

$$\gamma = a \log(1 + \nu t) + b \qquad \begin{pmatrix} \gamma = \text{creep strain} \\ t = \text{time} \\ \nu = \text{frequency} \end{pmatrix},$$

is larger for short irradiations, but gradually decreases to below its original value on continued irradiation. The constant a increases with irradiation but at a smaller rate than b, and attains its maximum after much longer irradiations than necessary to make b maximum. It thus turns out that the initial effect (for short irradiations) is a softening, followed by a hardening after long irradiation periods (Fig. 58).

LAD and METZ [15] think that the initial softening is connected with the formation of F-centers from existing complexes, breaking these up into smaller clusters, which would be less effective in impeding dislocation motion. On continued irradiation new vacancies would be formed at dislocation jogs and this would result in hardening.

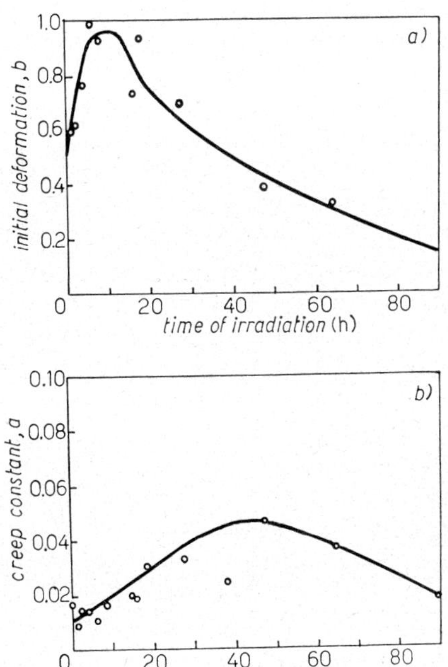

Fig. 58. – *a*) Variation of the initial deformation, b, with irradiation time for an annealed crystal. *b*) Variation of the creep constant, a, with irradiation time for an annealed crystal. (After: R. A. LAD and F. METZ: *Journ. Mech. Phys. Solids*, **4**, 28 (1955)).

4. – Internal friction.

FRANKL and READ [16] have investigated the internal friction and Young's modulus of NaCl single crystals irradiated with 40 kV X-rays. Even after removal of the surface layers it is found that the internal friction is much reduced for strain amplitudes not exceeding $5\cdot10^{-5}$, while Young's modulus is increased by 0.1%.

The decrement is almost amplitude-independent in this range (see Fig. 59).

To give an idea of the sensitivity of this effect: after 2 min irradiation the decrease in increment is observable and the decrease saturates after 20 min. On subsequent bleaching the internal friction still further decreases. Annealing for 30 min at 200 °C followed by slow cooling, on the other hand, increases the internal friction again to about its original value.

When crystals were irradiated at liquid nitrogen temperature and bleached at that temperature without being warmed up, they did not show a significant decrease in decrement when measured at room temperature. On the other hand, it does not make much difference whether crystals are irradiated at low temperature or at room temperature provided they are bleached at room temperature. The latter observations demonstrate that diffusion must play a role in the phenomenon, while the bleaching experiment shows that the *F*-centers

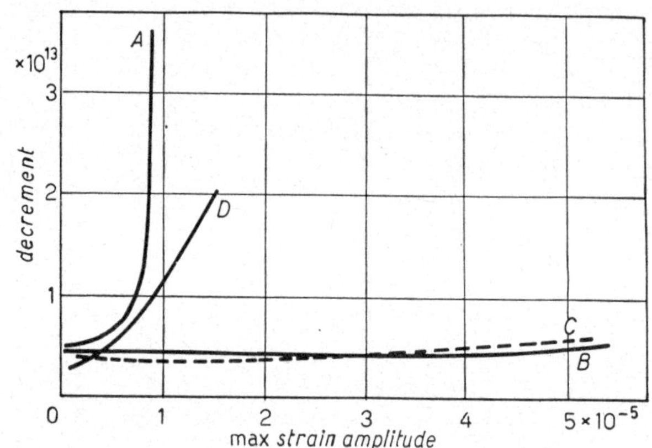

Fig. 59. – Effect of room temperature X-ray irradiation on the internal friction of NaCl single crystals. *A*) before irradiation; *B*) irradiated; *C*) bleached; *D*) annealed. (After: D. R. FRANKL and W. T. READ: *Phys. Rev.*, **89**, 663 (1953)).

themselves are not responsible for the effect. According to SEITZ [17], the clusters of vacancies of both signs are the pinning agents in this process rather than the isolated positive ion vacancies proposed by FRANKL [18].

GORDON and NOWICK [19] have complemented the experiments of FRANKL and READ. They showed that the decrease in internal friction is largest in crystals which were originally deformed so as to introduce a number of free dislocations. If the crystals are handled carefully and annealed prior to irradiation, the irradiation effects are much reduced and the amplitude-dependence of the internal friction is suppressed. The change in Young's modulus is shown to be entirely due to the elimination of the dislocation contribution.

They also found that very few pinning points are introduced in crystals when irradiated at 78 °K and slowly warmed up under strong bleaching illumination. From their experiments, using a simple dislocation pinning model, they conclude that a crystal which was deformed 4% contained of the order of $(10^8 \div 10^9)$ dislocations per cm^2, the free loop length being of the order of 100 atomic distances.

Recently BAUER and GORDON [20] have remeasured the dislocation damping in irradiated sodium chloride crystals, as well as the changes in the elastic modulus. They use the method of the composite piezoelectric resonator operating at 89.7 kHz. They determine simultaneously the *F*-center concentration by means of optical absorption and estimate directly the dislocation density by means of etch pits, only taking into account dislocations *not* in sub-boundaries. The data are interpreted on the basis of the Granato-Lücke theory [21] on the one hand, the theory of Gordon and Nowick [19] on the other hand.

They also measured the strain-amplitude-dependent and strain-amplitude-independent parts of the decrement, as well as changes in elastic modulus, for different dislocation densities. They find that the number of pinning points per unit length increases by deformation. The exact nature of the pinning points cannot, of course, be determined by these methods, but one can conclude that about $4\cdot10^5$ F-centers are required per pinning point. It is quite probable that this figure is too large, because in the initial stage of coloration F-centers are formed from existing vacancies and these probably do not contribute to hardening.

The mean loop length deduced from the Granato-Lücke model is $5\cdot10^{-4}$ cm, in agreement with values found by direct means, *e.g.* by decoration. The displacement of the dislocations at a strain amplitude of $5\cdot10^7$ is found to be 36 Å.

5. – Interpretation of the hardening.

Although the mechanical effects are not completely understood at present it is nevertheless worth-while to review the different explanations offered and to compare their merits. Hardening is evidently the result of either a decreased mobility of dislocations or a decreased multiplication rate, *i.e.* friction hardening or source hardening. Both ideas have been used the explain the radiation effects.

According to PRATT [2], radiation hardening originates in the climb of edge dislocations out of the glide plane as a result of the production of vacancies following the Seitz mechanism. The climb of the edge dislocation would cause them to be severely jogged and hence much less mobile, since jogs inhibit the motion.

Interaction between positive ion vacancies and divalent impurities and dislocations has been recognized as a source of hardening by BASSANI and THOMSON [22]. They calculated that the association energy with the core of the dislocations is about 0.4 eV. With this association energy and taking into account the concentration of vacancies it is found that this effect is sufficient to pin dislocations at room temperature.

The experiments on internal friction seem to be satisfactorily accounted for by assuming the introduction of pinning points. The nature of the pinning points, either jogs or single vacancies, or clusters of vacancies is, however, undecided. The experiments on hardening of the surface layer as measured with indentations point, however, to another interpretation. It is quite conceivable that we have in fact two phenomena going on: in a thin surface layer on the one hand, where we measure the indentation hardening, and in the bulk on the other hand, where we measure the mobility of freshly introduced dislocations, while the internal friction measures the mobility of dislocations present during the irradiation. In the first case friction hardening is probably more important, while in the second case pinning is more important.

The hardness measurements as a function of depth behind the irradiated face show that qualitative agreement with color centers density becomes best for the more complicated centers (*e.g.*, *N*-centers), suggesting that the obstacles are defect clusters rather than isolated point defects.

The initial softening on irradiation, found by LADD and METZ [15], as well as by PRATT [2], has been explained as due to the dispersal of existing vacancy clusters on irradiation, resulting in the formation of *F*-centers and the wandering away of positive ion vacancies in the way suggested by SEITZ. Since isolated defects would be less effective in pinning, this results in a softening. The hardening resulting after long irradiation times is then in agreement with the two-stage production mechanism for *F*-centers.

V. – The Effect of Radiation on Transport Properties.

1. – Ionic conductivity.

Naively one would expect, since irradiation introduces defects, that the conductivity would increase on irradiation. On the other hand one might also say: since irradiation populates the vacancies with electrons or holes, *i.e.* makes them neutral, and therefore destroys them as carriers, we would expect the conductivity to decrease. The real situation is far more complicated, as shown by CUNELL and SCHNEIDER [1], NELSON, SPROULL and CASWELL [2], PEARLSTEIN [3], PEARSLTEIN and INGHAM [4], KOBAYASHI [5], CHRISTY and HARTE [6] and recently by INGHAM and SMOLUCHOWSKI [7].

The KOBAYASHI [5] data on NaCl are shown in Fig. 40. He irradiated his crystals with 350 MeV protons, the integrated fluxes being between $1.7\cdot10^{12}$ and $9\cdot10^{15}$ protons per cm². This caused a small increase in resistance at room temperature but a much larger increase results after heat treatment. The conductivity measurement was made while the temperature was rising at a rate of 2 °C/min.

Two maxima were observed for the ratio $\varrho_{\text{irrad}}/\varrho_{\text{initial}}$. The first, between 120 and 160 °C, is not very dose-dependent, while the second, which occurs at about 250 °C, depends very much on the total flux. These curves are « irreversible », *i.e.*, once the crystal is brought up to higher temperatures its conductivity at a given temperature will be different, the defect configuration having changed. The defects we are studying are also the ones responsible for the effect we are measuring; this makes its study more complicated than, *e.g.*, electrical conductivity of metals or semiconductors, where the carriers are electrons or holes.

CHRISTY and HARTE [6] have investigated the isothermal annealing of the resistivity increase of NaCl caused by irradiation with X-rays so as to produce $6 \cdot 10^{16}$ F-centers. They limited themselves to temperatures in the range $(150 \div 200)$ °C, *i.e.*, the temperature range where KOBAYASHI found the first resistivity maximum in his isochronal anneal, more specifically the descending part of the maximum. We know from Kobayashi's work that at these small F-center concentrations the second maximum would be small anyway.

The results of CHRISTY and HARTE [6] can be summarized as follows:

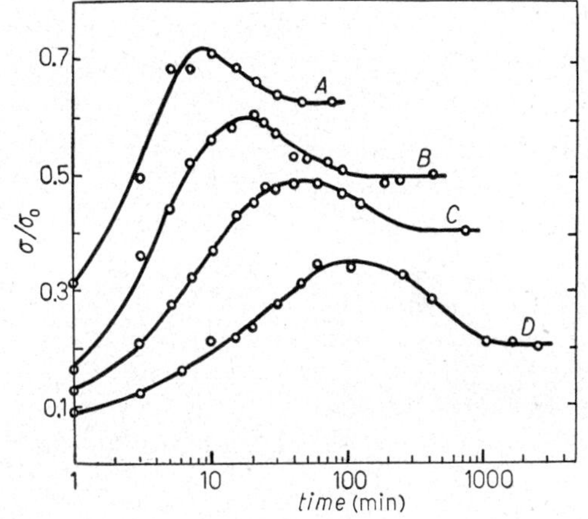

Fig. 60. – Effect of temperature on relative conductivity of rapidly cooled NaCl irradiated 10 min: *A*) 203° C; *B*) 188 °C; *C*) 173 °C; *D*) 151 °C. (After: R. W. CHRISTY and W. E. HARTE: *Phys. Rev.*, **109**, 710 (1958)).

1) On isothermal anneal they find a maximum for σ/σ_0, which is in general smaller than 1 (Fig. 60).

2) The height of the maximum depends strongly on the state of annealing of the crystal. The best crystals give a maximum which is larger than 1.

3) The position of the maximum (*i.e.*, the time after which it occurs) shifts to smaller times with increasing temperature, and to longer times with increasing dose.

4) The conductivity does not return to normal, even after 10^3 minutes, at temperatures as high as 253 °C.

5) Optical bleaching of the crystal, prior to the conductivity measurement, leads to a larger initial resistance, and to a much slower recovery of the conductivity (Fig. 61).

The authors interpret their results in terms of the immobilization of positive ion vacancies as a consequence of the formation of V-centers. The initial rise of the conductivity is attributed to thermal bleaching of V-centers which could in this way become carriers. An activation energy of 0.75 eV is found for this initial rise. The decrease in conductivity after the maximum is then attributed to the disappearance of the extra positive ion vacancies introduced by irradiation. The activation energy for this process would be the migration energy of positive ion vacancies. The observed activation energy is 26 kcal/mole, as compared to 20 kcal/mole found from ionic conductivity measurement by ETZEL and MAURER [8]. As a possible explanation for this deviation the authors propose that neutral pairs may diffuse away with this activation energy. It is, however, not clear how the disappearance of a neutral pair may change the number of carriers, since once the pair is formed the positive ion vacancy has already ceased to exist as a carrier. The influence of bleaching also remains obscure.

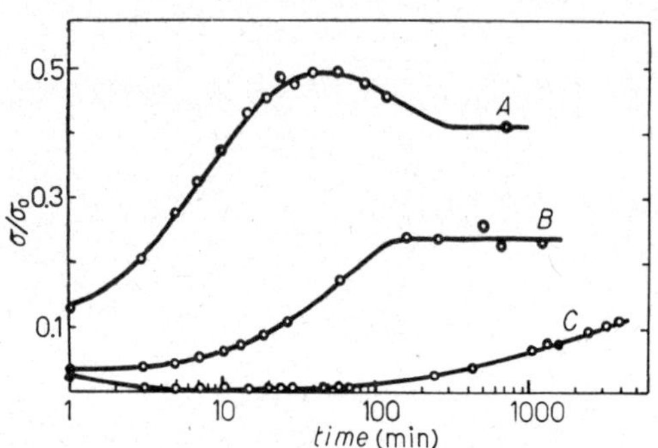

Fig. 61. – Effect of optical bleaching on relative conductivity at 173 °C of NaCl X-irradiated 10 min. *A*) rapidly cooled, colored. *B*) rapidly cooled, bleached with white light. *C*) slowly cooled, bleached with white light. (After: R. W. CHRISTY and W. E. HARTE: *Phys. Rev.*, **109**, 710 (1958)).

We will now discuss the more detailed work of INGHAM and SMOLUCHOWSKI [7] on γ-irradiated (^{60}Co-source) sodium chloride. The results are qualitatively the same as those found by KOBAYASHI for proton irradiation. The conductivity is invariably decreased after irradiation. The ratio still decreases on further anneal, and exhibits two minima at about (100÷180) °C and a second at about 250 °C. At about (300÷400) °C the conductivity returns to its pre-irradiation value.

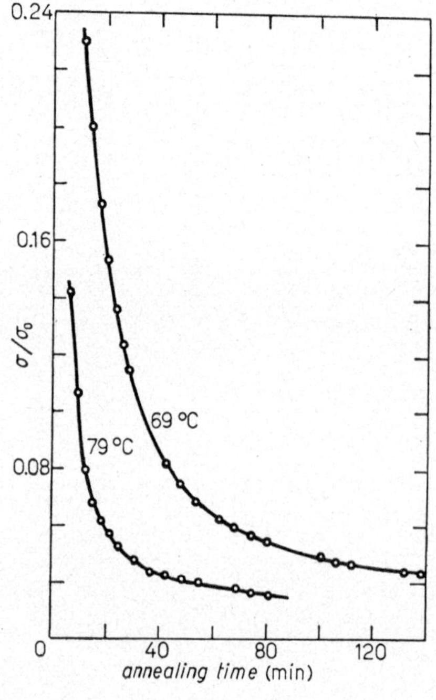

Fig. 62. – σ/σ_0 for irradiated crystal *vs.* *t*. Isothermal anneals are shown for two different temperatures. (After: H. S. INGHAM and R. SMOLUCHOWSKI: Internal Report, Carnegie Institute of Technology).

From the complex behavior it is clear that several processes are operating. The isothermal measurements of INGHAM and SMOLUCHOWSKI are mainly concerned with the processes going on during the first *decrease* in conductivity on anneal, *i.e.*, in the rising part of the first peak observed by KOBAYASHI, while those of CHRISTY and HARTE were mainly concerned with the first *increase* in conductivity.

Their isothermal annealing curves at 79 °C and 69 °C are shown in Fig. 62. They can be interpreted on two different assumptions:

a) According to SEITZ, the positive ion vacancies trap holes and become immobile; this is the same hypothesis as used by CHRISTY and HARTE.

b) According to SMOLUCHOWSKI, clustering of the defects occurs, resulting in the elimination of carriers. If the vacancy approaches a trap closer than some critical distance, it is captured.

In view of the observation of KOBAYASHI that the density does not change in the temperature range considered here, but that extensive rearrangement in the sense of clustering does occur, the second assumption seems reasonable.

INGHAM and SMOLUCHOWSKI interpret their results on this model. They assume that a bimolecular trapping process is going on, the positive ion vacancies A diffusing towards the traps B and forming a complex AB with them and hence becoming immobile.

Schematically: $A + B \rightarrow AB$.

In this model the number of carriers n_A changes according to

$$\frac{dn_A}{dt} = -Kn_A[n_{B_i} - (n_{A_i} - n_A)]\,, \tag{1}$$

where the index i refers to initial concentrations of vacancies n_{A_i} and traps n_{B_i}. The rate constant

$$K = K_0 \exp[-E_m/kT] \tag{2}$$

where E_m is the migration activation energy for A. Integration of the differential equation leads to the well-known solution

$$n_A = \frac{n_{A_i} - n_{B_i}}{1 - (n_{B_i}/n_{A_i}) \exp[-K(n_{A_i} - n_{B_i})(t - t_0)]} \tag{3}$$

This can brought into the form

$$1 - \frac{n_\infty}{n_A} = C_0 \exp[-K_e t]\,, \tag{4}$$

where

$$n_\infty = n_{A_i} - n_{B_i}; \quad K_e = K n_\infty \quad \text{and} \quad C_0 = \frac{n_{B_i}}{n_{A_i}} \exp [K_e t_0].$$

The significance of n_∞ is either the number of traps remaining after all free positive ion vacancies have been captured, or the number of free vacancies remaining after all traps have been saturated.

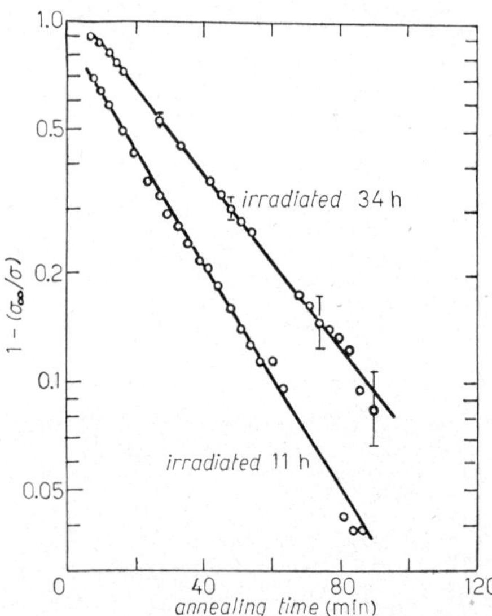

Fig. 63. – log $(1 - \sigma_\infty/\sigma)$ *vs.* t. Both anneals were at about 75 °C. (After: H. S. INGHAM and R. SMOLUCHOWSKI: Internal Report Carnegie Institute of Technology).

Expressing relation (4) in terms of the conductivity one finds

$$(5) \qquad 1 - \frac{\sigma_\infty}{\sigma} = C_0 \exp [-K_e t] ,$$

when accepting that the mobility is not affected by the irradiation.

The curves of Fig. 62 can be plotted to allow verification of this equation, and to determine at the same time the different parameters occurring in it. The agreement is reasonable as can be judged from Fig. 63, although the model is certainly oversimplified. As to the nature of the traps, INGHAM and SMOLUCHOWSKI assume that these are negatively charged vacancy clusters.

The slower rise in conductivity of *optically* bleached samples in the experiment of CHRISTY and HARTE may be due to the presence of negative ion vacancies resulting from bleached F-centers, which may act as traps.

The following three formation processes for traps are considered:

1) A neutral cluster is made positive by ionization.

2) Vacancy pairs may be created at dislocation jogs and migrate together or to other smaller traps already existing.

3) The ionizing radiation may break up some of the existing large clusters. The F- and M-absorption decreases during the decrease in conductivity; this is considered as an indication that these centers operate as traps.

The authors also investigated the isothermal increase in conductivity which occurs at higher temperatures, *i.e.*, in the range 113 °C to 135 °C. The increase saturates only after about three hours at the lower temperatures; this is shown in Fig. 64. They interpret the increase as a release of vacancies from the traps. After very long anneals at the highest temperature, *i.e.*, at 135 °C, they find a decrease in conductivity, in agreement with the result of CHRISTY

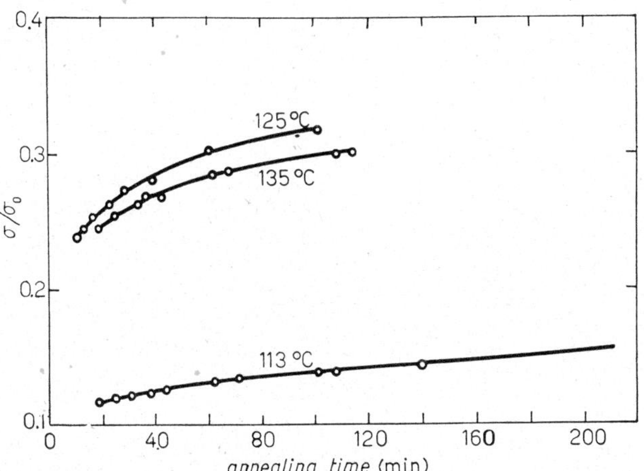

Fig. 64. – σ/σ_0 for irradiated crystals *vs.* time for three different annealing temperatures. (After: H. S. INGHAM and R. SMOLUCHOWSKI: Internal Report, Carnegie Institute of Technology).

and HARTE at somewhat higher temperatures. This is considered as being due to the increase of the number of traps, consisting of small clusters, which results from the breaking-up of large clusters during anneal.

CHRISTY and FUKUSHIMA [9, 10] further investigated the isothermal anneal, at (150 ÷ 200) °C, of irradiation-induced changes of ionic conductivity in KCl

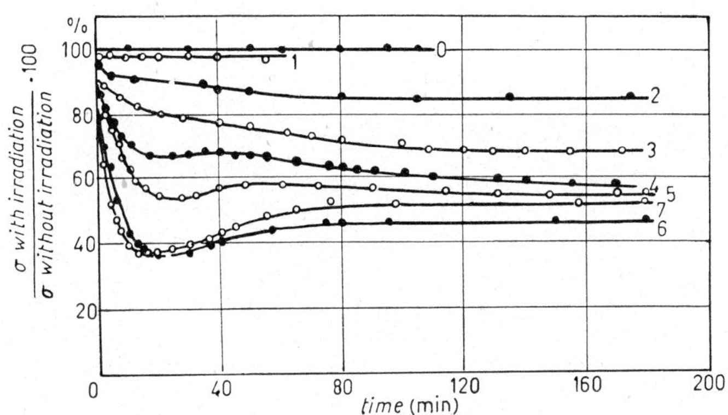

Fig. 65. – Relative conductivity changes of a crystal of NaCl during irradiation, in function of time for different temperatures. 0) control measurement; 1) 366 °C; 2) 330 °C; 3) 306 °C; 4) 284 °C; 5) 268 °C; 6) 239 °C; 7) 216 °C. (After: J. HACKE: *Zeits. Phys.*, **155**, 628 (1959)).

containing about 10^{16} F-centers per cm^3. They find that, if both F- and V-bands (presumably the V_3-band) are present, the conductivity increases monotonously towards the pre-irradiation value. If, on the other hand, the F-band is bleached optically and the V-band remains, the conductivity first increases very rapidly, attains a maximum and then decreases again to a fraction of the initial value in the clear crystal. The peak in the conductivity may be of electronic nature; it may, *e.g.*, be due to electrons released from F-centers on thermal bleaching.

In contrast with previous work. HACKE [11] has measured the effect of X-irradiation on the ionic conductivity of NaCl, the measurement being made during irradiation. The conductivity first decreases rapidly, reaches a minimum for temperatures below 284 °C, increases again and stabilizes at some value which is smaller than the initial value. The results are shown in Fig. 65.

Under irradiation the ionic conductivity seems to be influenced only in the impurity range and it is systematically smaller. At the lowest temperatures the activation energy is, however, the same as in the unirradiated condition; it differs at the higher temperatures of the impurity range (see Fig. 66).

It is clear that a complete picture has not yet been obtained; in particular, no information is available concerning Kobayashi's second maximum, and the first maximum is not completely understood. This is evidently due to the lack of parallel measurements of other quantities on the same crystals. The situation is complicated by the fact that insufficient attention has been devoted to the electronic contributions.

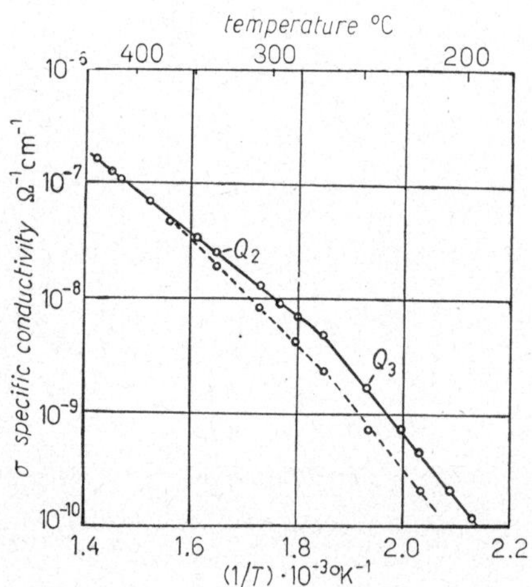

Fig. 66. – Behavior of the specific conductivity of a crystal in function of temperature with or without irradiation; —— without irradiation; – – – with irradiation. (After: J. HACKE: *Zeits. Phys.*, **155**, 628 (1959)).

2. – Self-diffusion.

In relation with the work on ionic conductivity it is of interest to note here that MAPOTHER [12] has found that the self-diffusion coefficient of Na^+ in NaCl is decreased by a factor of about three in crystals subject to X-irradiation during diffusion. The remarkable feature is that the effect is only noticed in the impurity range and disappears in the intrinsic range, in agreement with Hacke's results on ionic conductivity. Although this may simply be a temperature effect, it is also possible that the divalent impurities play an important role in decreasing the mobility of the positive ion vacancies under irradiation. The experiment should be made at the same temperature for two different specimens, one which is intrinsic at a given temperature and another which is still in the impurity range at this temperature. The implications of the experiment are in any case that positive ion vacancies become temporarily trapped in complexes involving divalent impurities, and probably electrons and holes.

3. – Thermal conductivity.

The thermal conductivity at low temperature is mainly determined by phonon-phonon scattering. Since the probability of such a process diminishes exponentially with temperature, at sufficiently low temperatures the thermal conductivity rises steeply. However, due to the increase in mean free path of the phonons, scattering at the boundaries becomes important. This in turn limits the thermal conductivity at very low temperatures, and therefore a maximum occurs in a plot of thermal conductivity *vs.* temperature.

Also, lattice defects—boundaries, dislocations and point defects—are effective scatterers for phonons, and low-temperature thermal conductivity is therefore a promising tool for studying such defects.

Not very much experimental work has been done on the specific subject of thermal resistivity due to point defects in ionic crystals. For a complete review we refer to BERMAN [13].

The thermal resistance due to F-centers, introduced by additive coloration, has been investigated in KCl at 98 °K, 200 °K and 298 °K by DEVYATHOVA and STILBANS [14]. They measured crystals with concentrations of F-centers ranging from 0.3 to $3\cdot10^{-4}$ F-centers per potassium ion.

The thermal conductivity is found to decrease linearly with increasing F-center concentration up to a concentration of $1\cdot10^{-4}$. They showed that plastic deformation had no influence in the temperature range used.

The resistivity increase for a concentration of 10^{-4} was found to be constant at the three temperatures and equal to $\Delta W = 1.4$ cm deg/W.

The thermal resistivity introduced by point defects associated with divalent impurities in KCl has been investigated by SLACK [15], who finds resistivity increase of the same magnitude as the previous authors. His experimental results are in agreement with Klemens' theory [16] if the scattering centers are point defects.

COHEN [17] examined the thermal conductivity of lithium fluoride (Fig. 67), in the temperature range $(4 \div 50)\,^\circ$K, irradiated with thermal-neutron doses up to a few times $10^{17}\,$n/cm^2 and also with ^{60}Co γ-rays, up to $20 \cdot 10^8\,$R.

An increase in the thermal resistance is found for neutron doses up to $1 \cdot 10^{17}\,$n/cm^2; for higher doses the thermal resistance decreases again. The γ-irradiated crystals behave rather similarly. The temperature-dependence of the radiation-induced thermal resistance is $T^{-1.7}$ to $T^{-2.0}$.

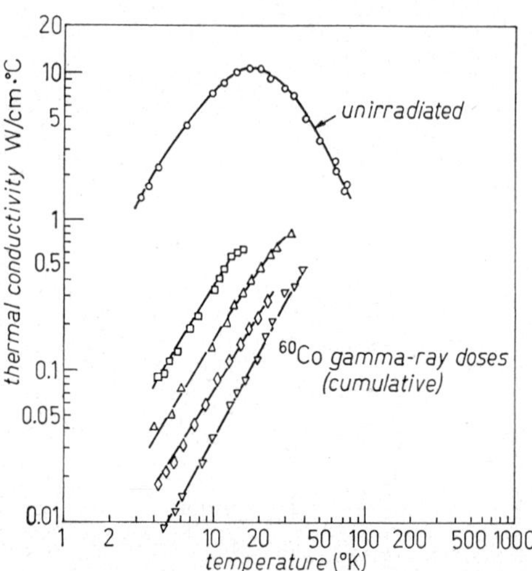

Fig. 67. – Thermal conductivity of lithium fluoride crystal before and after irradiation with ^{60}Co γ-rays. (After: A. F. COHEN: *Bull. de l'Institut Intern. du Froid, Suppl.* (1958)).

The neutron dose at which the thermal conductivity starts to increase again corresponds approximately to the dose that makes the lattice parameter maximum (see Part III). It is therefore thought that this increase is related to strain release that occurs at this dose level.

The thermal resistance appears to be greater than expected on the basis of isolated point defects, and it is therefore probably due to clusters, even at doses as low as $4.5 \cdot 10^{15}$. The temperature-dependence also points in this direction.

VI. – Various Properties.

1. – Paramagnetic susceptibility.

Many color centers, *e.g.* the F-center, contain unpaired electrons and are therefore paramagnetic as a consequence of the magnetic moment of the electron. The paramagnetic susceptibility due to F-centers is given by an expression of the form [1]:

$$\chi = [Ng^2\beta^2/4\,kT][1 - \tfrac{1}{3}(g\beta H/2\,kT)^2 - \delta(T)]\,,$$

where: $g = g$-factor; $\beta =$ Bohr magneton; $k =$ Boltzmann constant; $H =$ external magnetic field; $N =$ number of centers/cm^3 and $\delta(T)$ is a correction due to overlap of the centers.

Writing this as a Curie law, applicable for temperatures above $2\,^\circ$K, one obtains

$$\chi = C/T + \chi_{\text{dia}} ,$$

where the diamagnetic susceptibility is temperature-independent. This leads to the simple relation valid for LiF:

$$N = 1.62 \cdot 10^{24} \cdot C .$$

One can, on the other hand, deduce the number of centers from the optical absorption curve

$$Nf = 8.21 \cdot 10^{16} \frac{n}{(n^2+2)^2} \cdot A ,$$

where: A is the area under the absorption peak in $\text{cm}^{-1} \times \text{eV}$; n = refractive index; f = the oscillator strength.

A comparison of both measurements in the same specimens gives a value for f. Such measurements have been made by RAUCH and HEER [2] on additively colored alkali halides and by BATE and HEER [3] on neutron-irradiated LiF.

The results of these measurements are summarized in Table I, where the oscillator strength is given for two different assumptions concerning the line shape: Lorentzian (L) or Gaussian (G). In the case of LiF the actually observed line shape leads to $f = 0.54$. It should be mentioned that the value given for KCl is much inferior to that found by Kleinschrod by chemical methods: $f = 0.81$.

TABLE I.

	f_L	f_G
KCl	0.66	0.45
KBr	0.71	0.48
KI	0.46	0.31
CsBr	0.38	0.26
LiF	0.82	0.56

We discuss in some more detail the work on LiF. Plots of the magnetic susceptibilities *vs.* the inverse temperature are perfectly linear up to the lowest temperatures, showing that $\delta(T)$ is vanishingly small and hence suggesting that there is no interaction between neighboring F-centers even at the highest neutron doses used (*i.e.*, $3 \cdot 10^{16}$ n/cm²).

The number of magnetic centers is found to increase rapidly at small doses (10^{11} n/cm²) and saturates at the higher doses ($3 \cdot 10^{16}$) to a value of $8 \cdot 10^{19}$

magnetic centers per cm³. In the intermediate range about 5000 defects are formed per incident neutron. It is interesting to note that the density and the lattice parameter were found to increase linearly up to doses that are ten times larger than the saturation dose found here.

The rapid initial increase corresponds to the first stage in *F*-center formation, *i.e.*, conversion of existing vacancies into *F*-centers.

From a comparison of optical and magnetic data it was not possible to decide whether the *M*-center is paramagnetic or not. The *F*-center paramagnetism is reduced on transforming *F*-centers into *F'*-centers in agreement with the models for these centers.

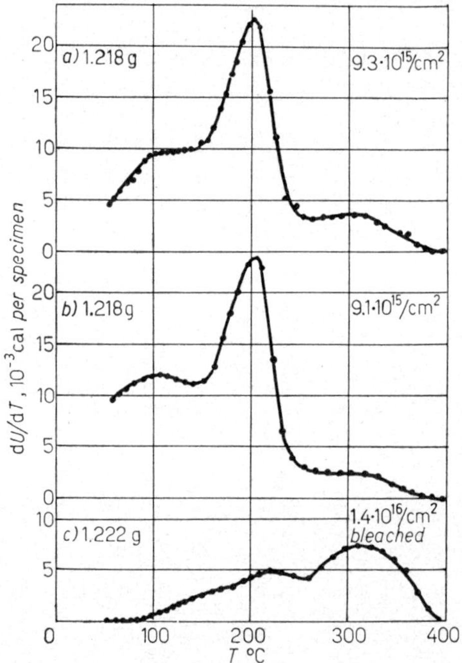

Fig. 68. – Stored energy released from NaCl crystal irradiated with protons during annealing at a rate of 2 °C per min; *a*) total flux of $9.3\cdot10^{15}$ protons per cm²; *b*) total flux of $9.1\cdot10^{15}$ protons per cm²; *c*) crystal bleached at 90 °C for six days after irradiation with $1.4\cdot10^{16}$ protons per cm². (After: K. KOBAYASHI: *Phys. Rev.*, **102**, 348 (1956)).

2. – Stored energy.

Stored energy measurements were made by KOBAYASHI [4] on proton-irradiated sodium chloride. The integrated fluxes were of the order of $10^{16}\cdot350$ MeV protons per cm². The main release of energy takes place between 150 and 250 °C with the maximum at about 200 °C. A second, much smaller maximum appears at about 310 °C (Fig. 68).

In a crystal, optically bleached at 90 °C, only the high-temperature peak remained. The main release in energy corresponds to the disappearance of *F*-, *M*-, and *V*-centers in accordance with the result in bleached crystals. The total energy release after $9\cdot10^{15}$ protons is about 1.43 cal/g.

Taking a few eV for the energy released by the recombination of a vacancy-interstitial pair, one obtains about 5000 defects per incident proton.

* * *

I would like to thank Mr. R. STRUMANE for help in collecting these lecture notes.

REFERENCES

PART I

[1] F. SEITZ: *Rev. Mod. Phys.*, **18**, 384 (1946); **26**, 7 (1954).
[2] J. H. DE BOER: *Rec. Trav. Chim. Pays-Bas*, **56**, 301 (1937).
[3] F. STÖCKMANN: *Naturwiss.*, **39**, 230 (1952).
[3bis] H. E. IVEY: *Phys. Rev.*, **47**, 341 (1947).
[4] S. I. PEKAR: *Journ. Phys. USSR*, **10**, 341, 347 (1946).
[5] H. RÖGENER: *Ann. Phys.*, **29**, 386 (1937).
[6] H. WITT: *Nachr. Akad. Wiss. Göttingen*, 17 (1952).
[7] F. KLEINSCHROD: *Ann. Phys.*, **27**, 97 (1936).
[8] W. T. DOYLE: *Phys. Rev.*, **111**, 1072 (1958).
[9] R. J. GNAEDINGER: *Journ. Chem. Phys.*, **21**, 323 (1953).
[10] D. S. JACOBS: *Phys. Rev.*, **93**, 993 (1954).
[11] W. G. MAISCH and H. G. DRICKAMER: *Journ. Phys. Chem. Solids*, **5**, 328 (1958).
[12] R. HILSCH and R. W. POHL: *Zeits. f. Phys.*, **68**, 721 (1931); H. PICK: *Ann. d. Phys.*, **31**, 365 (1938).
[13] K. H. BECKER and H. PICK: *Nachr. Akad. Wiss. Göttingen*, 167 (1956).
[14] P. J. BOTDEN, C. Z. VAN DOORN and Y. HAVEN: *Philips Res. Rep.*, **9**, 469 (1954).
[15] C. Z. VAN DOORN: *Philips Res. Rep.*, **13**, 296 (1958).
[16] C. Z. VAN DOORN and Y. HAVEN: *Philips Res. Rep.*, **11**, 479 (1956).
[17] F. LÜTY: *Color Center Symposium at Argonne Nat. Lab.* (Nov. 1, 1956).
[18] W. T. DOYLE: *Phys. Rev.*, **111**, 1067 (1958).
[19] S. Q. YOSHIDA and T. IKEDA: *Journ. Phys. Soc. Japan*, **12**, 1422 (1957).
[20] W. D. COMPTON: *Phys. Rev.*, **107**, 1271 (1957).
[21] D. R. WESTERVELT: *Phys. Rev.*, **92**, 531 (1953).
[22] J. P. MOLNAR: cited after SEITZ [1].
[23] F. SEITZ: see ref. [1].
[24] C. Z. VAN DOORN and Y. HAVEN: *Philips Res. Rep.*, **11**, 479 (1956).
[25] K. S. KNOX: *Phys. Rev. Lett.*, **2**, 87 (1959).
[26] M. UETA: *Journ. Phys. Soc. Japan*, **7**, 107 (1952).
[27] N. W. LORD: *Phys. Rev.*, **106**, 1100 (1957).
[28] C. BARTH: *Zeits. f. Phys.* (see SEITZ [1]).
[29] C. Z. VAN DOORN and Y. HAVEN: *Phys. Rev.*, **100**, 753 (1955).
[30] C. Z. VAN DOORN: *Philips Res. Rep.*, **12**, 309 (1957).
[31] A. KANZAKI: *Phys. Rev.*, **110**, 1063 (1958).
[32] J. LAMBE and W. D. COMPTON: *Phys. Rev.*, **106**, 684 (1957).
[33] W. D. COMPTON and C. C. KLICK: *Phys. Rev.*, **112**, 1622 (1958).
[34] C. Z. VAN DOORN: *Phys. Rev. Lett.*, **3**, 236 (1960).
[35] G. JACOBS: *Journ. Chem. Phys.*, **27**, 218 (1957).
[36] F. E. THEISSEN and A. B. SCOTT: *Journ. Chem. Phys.*, **20**, 529 (1952).
[37] E. BIRSTEIN and J. J. OBERLY: *Phys. Rev.*, **76**, 1254 (1949); **79**, 903 (1950).
[38] S. PETROFF: *Zeits. Phys.*, **127**, 443 (1950).
[39] W. D. COMPTON and C. C. KLICK: *Phys. Rev.*, **112**, 1622 (1958).
[40] J. LAMBE and W. D. COMPTON: *Phys. Rev.*, **106**, 684 (1957).

[41] C. J. Delbecq, P. Pringsheim and P. H. Yuster: *Journ. Chem. Phys. Solids*, **19**, 574 (1951); **20**, 746 (1952).
[42] W. Martienssen: *Zeits. Phys.*, **131**, 488 (1952); W. Martienssen and R. W. Pohl: *Zeits. Phys.*, **133**, 153 (1952); W. Martienssen: *Nachr. Akad. Wiss. Göttingen*, 111 (1952).
[43] F. Bassani and N. Inchauspe: *Phys. Rev.*, **105**, 819 (1957).
[44] E. Mollwo: *Nachr. Akad. Wiss. Göttingen*, 215 (1935).
[45] E. Mollwo: *Ann. Phys.*, **29**, 394 (1937).
[46] H. Z. Dorendorf: *Zeits. Phys.*, **129**, 317 (1951).
[47] H. Z. Dorendorf and H. Pick: *Zeits. Phys.*, **128**, 166 (1950).
[48] J. Alexander and E. E. Schneider: *Nature*, **164**, 653 (1949).
[49] R. Casler, P. Pringsheim and P. H. Yuster: *Journ. Chem. Phys.*, **18**, 887, 1564 (1950).
[50] D. Dutton and R. J. Maurer: *Phys. Rev.*, **90**, 126 (1953).
[51] D. Dutton, W. R. Heller and R. J. Maurer: *Phys. Rev.*, **84**, 363 (1951).
[52] W. Känzig and T. O. Woodruff: *Journ. Phys. Chem. Solids*, **9**, 70 (1958).
[53] G. Miessner and H. Pick: *Zeits. f. Phys.*, **134**, 604 (1953).
[54] W. Duerig and J. J. Markham: *Phys. Rev.*, **88**, 1043 (1952).
[55] K. Teegarden and R. Maurer: *Zeits. f. Phys.*, **138**, 284 (1954).
[56] C. J. Delbecq, B. Smaller and P. H. Yuster: *Phys. Rev.*, **111**, 1235 (1958).
[57] J. Lambe and E. J. West: *Phys. Rev.*, **108**, 634 (1957).
[58] T. G. Castner and W. Känzig: *Journ. Phys. Chem. Solids*, **3**, 178 (1957).
[59] W. Känzig: *Phys. Rev.*, **99**, 1890 (1955).
[60] T. G. Castner, W. Känzig and T. O. Woodruff: *Suppl. Nuovo Cimento*, **7**, 612 (1958).
[61] C. J. Delbecq, B. Smaller and P. H. Yuster: *Phys. Rev.*, **111**, 1235 (1958).
[62] W. Känzig: *Phys. Rev. Lett.*, **4**, 117 (1960).
[63] M. H. Cohen, W. Känzig and T. O. Woodruff: *Phys. and Chem. of Solids*, **11**, 120 (1959).
[64] J. Cape and G. Jacobs: *Phys. Rev.*, **118**, 946 (1960).
[65] W. Martienssen and H. Pick: *Nachr. Akad. Wiss. Göttingen*, 17 (1952); *Zeits. f. Phys.*, **135**, 309 (1953).
[66] W. Martienssen and H. Mette: *Naturwiss.*, **41**, 331 (1954).
[67] H. Thomas: *Am. Phys.*, **38**, 601 (1940).
[68] R. Hilsch and R. W. Pohl: *Trans. Farad. Soc.*, **34**, 883 (1938).
[69] W. Martienssen: *Zeits. Phys.*, **131**, 488 (1952).
[70] W. Martienssen and R. W. Pohl: *Zeits. Phys.*, **133**, 153 (1952).
[71] F. Seitz: II, p. 90 (see ref. [1]).
[72] C. J. Delbecq, B. Smaller and P. H. Yuster: *Phys. Rev.*, **104**, 599 (1956).
[73] C. J. Delbecq and P. H. Yuster: *Phys. Rev.*, **104**, 605 (1956).
[74] G. Schaeffer: *Phys. and Chem. of Solids*, **12**, 233 (1960).
[75] M. Born: *Dynamik der Kristalgitter*, *Fortschritte Mathem. Wiss.*, **4** (1915).
[76] H. Pick: *Ann. Phys.*, **35**, 73 (1939); *Zeits. Phys.*, **114**, 127 (1939).
[77] G. Heiland and H. Kelting: *Zeits. Phys.*, **126**, 689 (1949).
[78] P. Camagni, G. Chiarotti, F. G. Fumi and L. Giulotto: *Phil. Mag.*, **45**, 225 (1954).
[79] C. Chiarotti, F. G. Fumi and L. Giulotto: *Rept. Conf. on Defects in Crystalline Solids* (London, 1955), p. 316.
[80] F. Bassani and F. G. Fumi: *Nuovo Cimento*, **11**, 274 (1954).
[81] P. Camagni, S. Ceresara and C. Chiarotti: *Phys. Rev.*, **118**, 1226 (1960).

[82] G. REMAUT and W. DEKEYSER: *Physica*, **24**, 20 (1958).
[83] G. JACOBS: *Journ. Chem. Phys.*, **27**, 217 (1957).
[84] W. HAYES and C. M. NICHOLS: *Phys. Rev.*, **147**, 993 (1960).

PART II

[1] F. SEITZ: *Rev. Mod. Phys.*, **26**, 81 (1954).
[2] J. H. O. VARLEY: *Journ. of Nuclear Energy*, **1**, 130 (1954); *Progr. Nucl. Energy*, **1**, 672 (1956).
[3] P. V. MITCHELL, D. A. WIEGAND and R. SMOLUCHOWSKI: *Phys. Rev.*, **117**, 442 (1960).
[4] F. SEITZ and J. S. KOEHLER: *Solid State Physics*, vol. **2** (New York, 1956), p. 307.
[5] R. E. HOWARD and R. SMOLUCHOWSKI: *Phys. Rev.*, **116**, 314 (1959).
[6] D. L. DEXTER: *Phys. Rev.*, **118**, 934 (1960).
[7] D. A. WIEGAND and R. SMOLUCHOWSKI: *Phys. Rev.*, **116**, 1069 (1959).
[8] H. RABIN and C. C. KLICK: *Phys. Rev.*, **117**, 1005 (1960).
[9] E. E. SCHNEIDER: *Photographic Sensitivity* (London, 1951), p. 13.
[10] I. LEITNER: *Sitz. der Akad. Wiss. Wien*, **145**, 407 (1936).
[11] R. B. GORDON and A. S. NOWICK: *Phys. Rev.*, **101**, 977 (1956).
[12] P. W. LEVY: *Symposium on « Color Centers in Alkali Halides »* (Oregon, 1959).
[13] O. CUNELL and E. E. SCHNEIDER: unpublished, cited after SEITZ [1].
[14] M. HACSKAYLO and G. GROETZINGER: *Phys. Rev.*, **87**, 790 (1952).
[15] M. HACSKAYLO and D. OTTERSON: *Journ. Chem. Phys.*, **21**, 552 (1953).
[16] A. S. NOWICK: *Phys. Rev.*, **111**, 16 (1958).
[17] P. LEVY: private communication.
[18] H. W. ETZEL: *Phys. Rev.*, **100**, 1643 (1955).
[19] H. W. ETZEL and J. B. ALLARD: *Phys. Rev.*, **116**, 885 (1959).
[20] B. MOZER and P. LEVY: private communication.
[21] H. W. ETZEL and J. C. ALLARD: *Phys. Rev. Lett.*, **2**, 452 (1959).
[22] F. FISCHER: *Zeits. Phys.*, **154**, 534 (1959).
[23] W. KÄNZIG and T. O. WOODRUFF: *Journ. Phys. Chem. Solids*, **9**, 70 (1958).
[24] Z. GYULAI and D. HARTLY: *Zeits. Phys.*, **51**, 378 (1928).
[25] A. W. STEPANOV: *Zeits. Phys.*, **81**, 560 (1933).
[26] F. SEITZ: *Adv. in Phys.*, **1**, 1 (1952).
[27] D. B. FISHBACH and A. S. NOWICK: *Journ. Phys. Chem. Solids*, **5**, 302 (1958).
[28] P. PRATT: private communication.
[29] W. H. VAUGHAN, W. J. LEIVO and R. SMOLUCHOWSKI: *Phys. Rev.*, **110**, 652 (1958).
[30] M. UETA and W. KÄNZIG: *Phys. Rev.*, **97**, 1591 (1955).
[31] G. CHIAROTTI: *Phys. Rev.*, **107**, 381 (1957).
[32] H. N. HERSH: *Journ. Chem. Phys.*, **30**, 790 (1959).
[33] H. HUMMEL: *Thesis* (Göttingen University, 1950).
[34] H. W. ETZEL: *Phys. Rev.*, **87**, 906 (1952).
[35] J. J. MARKHAM: *Phys. Rev.*, **88**, 500 (1952); *Journ. Phys. Chem.*, **57**, 26 (1953).
[36] C. J. DELBECQ, B. SMALLER and P. H. YUSTER: *Phys. Rev.*, **111**, 1235 (1958).
[37] A. S. NOWICK: *Phys. Rev.*, **111**, 16 (1958).
[38] H. N. HERSH and J. J. MARKHAM: *Journ. Phys. Chem. Solids*, **12**, 207 (1960).

PART III

[1] W. Primak C. J. Delbecq and P. H. Yuster: *Phys. Rev.*, **98**, 1708 (1955).
[2] D. A. Wiegand and R. Smoluchowski: *Phys. Rev.*, **116**, 1069 (1959).
[3] J. J. Eshelby: *Solid State Physics*, vol. **3** (New York, 1956), p. 79; *Journ. Appl. Phys.*, **25**, 255 (1954); **24**, 1249 (1953).
[4] L. Tewordt: *Phys. Rev.*, **109**, 61 (1958).
[5] D. Binder and W. J. Sturm: *Phys. Rev.*, **96**, 1519 (1954); **99**, 603 (1955).
[6] P. Perio, M. Tournarie and M. Gance: *Action des rayonnements de grande énergie sur les solides* (Paris, 1956), p. 109.
[7] R. Smallman and R. Willis: *Phil. Mag.*, **2**, 1018 (1957).
[8] D. T. Keating: *Phys. Rev.*, **97**, 832 (1955).
[9] P. Senio and C. W. Tucker: KAPL-1727 (1957).
[10] J. J. Gilman and W. G. Johnston: General Electric Research Report, 58-RL-1923.
[11] J. Spaepen: *Phys. Rev.*, **109**, 663 (1958).
[12] M. Lambert and A. Guinier: *Compt. Rend.*, **244**, 2791 (1957); M. Lambert: Rapport CEA-1080 (1959).
[13] I. Esterman, W. J. Leivo and O. Stern: *Phys. Rev.*, **75**, 627 (1949).
[14] C. R. Berry: *Phys. Rev.*, **98**, 934 (1955).
[15] K. Kobayashi: *Phys. Rev.*, **107**, 41 (1957); **102**, 348 (1956).
[16] W. Primak, D. J. Delbecq and P. H. Yuster: *Phys. Rev.*, **98**, 1708 (1955).
[17] D. A. Wiegand and R. Smoluchowski: *Phys. Rev.*, **116**, 1069 (1959).
[18] W. Känzig and T. O. Woodruff: *Journ. Phys. Chem. Solids*, **9**, 70 (1959).
[19] K. Sakaguchi and T. Suita: *Techn. Rept. Osaka Univ.*, **2**, 177 (1952)
[20] L. Y. Lin: *Phys. Rev.*, **102**, 968 (1956).
[21] H. Rabin: *Phys. Rev.*, **116**, 1381 (1959).
[22] H. W. Etzel: *Phys. Rev.*, **87**, 906 (1952).
[23] F. Seitz: *Rev. Mod. Phys.*, **26**, 63 (1959).

PART IV

[1] M. N. Podachewski: *Phys. Zeits. Sowjetunion*, **8**, 81 (1935).
[2] P. L. Pratt: *Rep. Conf. of Defects in Crystalline Solids* (*Phys. Soc.*), 402 (1955).
[3] Yin-Yuan Li: *Acta Met.*, **1**, 155 (1953).
[4] W. H. Vaughan, W. J. Leivo and R. Smoluchowski: *Phys. Rev.*, **91**, 245 (1953).
[5] R. B. Gordon and A. Nowick: *Phys. Rev.*, **101**, 977 (1956).
[6] E. Aerts, S. Amelinckx and W. Dekeyser: *Acta Met.*, **7**, 29 (1959).
[7] A. D. Whapham: *Phil. Mag.*, **3**, 103 (1958).
[8] D. R. Westervelt: *Acta Met.*, **1**, 755 (1953).
[9] R. Cuypers and S. Amelinckx: *Acta Met.*, **8**, 551 (1960)).
[10] A. D. Whapman and M. J. Makin: *Phil. Mag.*, **5**, 237 (1960).
[11] N. F. Mott and F. Nabarro: *Rept. Conf. on the Strength of Solids* (London, 1948), p. 1.
[12] A. Seeger: *Second United Nations Int. Conf. on the Peaceful Uses of Atomic Energy*, A/Conf. 15/P/998 (1958).
[13] J. Friedel: *Les dislocations* (Paris, 1956).

[14] T. H. Blewitt: *Dislocations and Mechanical Properties of Crystals* (New York, 1957), p. 573.
[15] R. A. Lad and F. I. Metz: *Journ. Mechanics Physics Solids*, **4**, 28 (1955).
[16] D. R. Frankl and W. T. Read: *Phys. Rev.*, **89**, 663 (1953).
[17] F. Seitz: *Rev. Mod. Phys.*, **26**, 7 (1954).
[18] D. R. Frankl: *Phys. Rev.*, **92**, 573 (1953).
[19] R. B. Gordon and A. S. Nowick: *Acta Met.*, **4**, 514 (1956).
[20] C. L. Bauer and R. B. Gordon: *Journ. Appl. Phys.*, **31**, 945 (1960).
[21] A. Granato and K. Lücke: *Journ. Appl. Phys.*, **27**, 583 (1956).
[22] F. Bassani and R. Thomson: *Phys. Rev.*, **102**, 5 (1956).

PART V

[1] E. Cunell and E. E. Schneider: unpublished.
[2] C. M. Nelson, R. L. Sproull and R. S. Cashwell: *Phys. Rev.*, **90**, 364 (1953).
[3] E. A. Pearlstein: *Phys. Rev.*, **92**, 881 (1953).
[4] E. A. Pearlstein and H. S. Ingham: *Phys. Rev.*, **94**, 1409 (1954).
[5] K. Kobayashi: *Phys. Rev.*, **102**, 348 (1956).
[6] R. W. Christy and W. E. Harte: *Phys. Rev.*, **109**, 710 (1958).
[7] H. S. Ingham and R. Smoluchowski: *Phys. Rev.*, **117**, 1207 (1960).
[8] H. W. Etzel and R. J. Maurer: *Journ. Chem. Phys.*, **18**, 1003 (1950).
[9] R. W. Christy and E. Fukushima: *Phys. Rev. Lett.*, **4**, 386 (1960).
[10] R. W. Christy and E. Fukushima: *Phys. Rev.*, **118**, 1222 (1960).
[11] J. Hacke: *Zeits. f. Phys.*, **155**, 628 (1959).
[12] D. E. Mapother: *Phys. Rev.*, **89**, 1231 (1953).
[13] R. Berman: *Adv. in Phys.*, **2**, 103 (1953).
[14] E. D. Devyathova and L. S. Stilbans: *Journ. Techn. Phys. USSR*, **22**, 968 (1952).
[15] R. Slack: *Thesis* (Cornell University, 1956); *Phys. Rev.*, **105**, 832 (1957).
[16] P. G. Klemens: *Proc. Roy. Soc.*, A **208**, 108 (1951).
[17] A. F. Cohen: *Bull. Inst. Intern. Froid, Suppl.*, **1**, 173 (1958).

PART VI

[1] J. Korringa and J. G. Daunt: *Phys. Rev.*, **102**, 92 (1956).
[2] C. J. Rauch and C. V. Heer: *Phys. Rev.*, **105**. 914 (1957).
[3] R. T. Bate and C. V. Heer: *Journ. Phys. Chem. Solids*, **7**, 14 (1958).
[4] M. Kobayashi: *Phys. Rev.*, **102**, 348 (1956).

Radiation Damage in Covalent Crystals.

E. W. J. MITCHELL

University of Reading, J. J. Thomson Physical Laboratory - Reading

1. – Introduction.

These lectures will deal mainly with the use of optical properties for studying defects, but in the case of diamond will also include a brief discussion of electrical measurements.

I shall begin with a few remarks about covalent binding, followed by some general remarks about the absorption spectra of crystals, together with a brief discussion of the absorption coefficient and its relation to the number of centres. Following this I shall try to summarize the optical effects which have been observed in diamond, silicon and quartz. It will be convenient to distinguish 5 classes:

a) Vibrational effects.
b) Interaction of damage (displacement) and impurity.
c) Point defects and small aggregates.
d) Changes arising from major structural disorder.
e) Interaction of damage (ionization) and impurity.

Each optical centre which is discovered has to be the subject of a major study. Consequently I will illustrate each of these categories with an example chosen to demonstrate various aspects of colour centre work.

The great advantage of optical studies is that they are spectroscopic—different defects absorb and emit in different parts of the spectrum. Consequently one fairly readily sees effects which are hidden, and perhaps only revealed during annealing, when using integrating methods. For example, electron energy levels are sensitive to the neighbouring atomic configuration and thus it might prove possible to detect effects arising from the various stages of separation of pairs of defects. I think that the great disadvantage is that one frequently has so much experimental detail that the essential features are difficult to extract.

2. – Characteristics of covalent solids.

Diamond is the prototype covalent solid. Each carbon atom is surrounded tetrahedrally by 4 atoms, each pair of atoms being joined by a directed orbital to which each atom of a pair contributes one electron. The unit cell is a cube containing 8 atoms. The structure comprises two interpenetrating f.c.c. lattices, one based on 0, 0, 0, and the other on $\frac{1}{4}$, $\frac{1}{4}$, $\frac{1}{4}$.

The highest lattice vibration frequency corresponds to a vibration of one of these lattices with respect to the other. This vibration does not produce a dipole moment so that there is normally no infrared absorption at the fundamental frequency. The main difference between the covalent series C, Si, Ge and grey-Sn on the one hand and the III-V compounds (*e.g.* GaAs, InSb, etc.) on the other, is that in the III-V compounds electron sharing is only complete after an electron has been transferred from a group V atom to a group III atom. Thus the group III atom is, on the average, negatively charged so that the infrared absorption corresponding to the fundamental lattice frequency is allowed. Apart from this difference the III-V compounds have many properties—particularly the semiconducting ones—similar to the true covalent materials.

Another characteristic of the diamond structure and substituted diamond structure (zinc blende) materials is that there are very open and natural interstitial sites (8 per unit cell). Thus, one might expect that most of the work needed to displace an atom comes from breaking the four two-electron bonds rather than from the process of making room for the interstitial. This is discussed in the seminar given by Dr. BÄUERLEIN.

In studying the optical properties of defects in crystals, one is limited to the transparent window between the intrinsic band-to-band absorption and the onset of infrared vibrational absorption. Although there is no absorption at the fundamental lattice frequency (ν_L) in C, Si and Ge, there is absorption at somewhat higher energies corresponding to 2-phonon processes. It is this 2-phonon absorption which limits the window on the low-energy side. Some values are given in Table I.

TABLE I.

	Band to band	Vibrational effects	$(h\nu_L)$
C	5.4 eV	0.33 eV (3.75 μm)	0.165 eV
Si	1.2 eV	0.075 eV (16.5 μm)	0.063 eV
Ge	0.7 eV	~0.03 eV (33 μm)	0.037 eV

3. – General points about optical properties.

Much of what I shall have to say about covalent solids will be concerned with optical properties so I will start by discussing some of the basic parameters.

In general, there are three properties which one might investigate in order to study defects:

1) Absorption of light.
2) Fluorescence emission.
3) Scattering of light.

Most of what I shall say will be concerned with absorption, although I shall discuss one fluorescent centre. Very little work has been done on light scattering by defects—one might hope to get some information, from the wavelength dependence, of the size of larger disordered regions. WHITEHOUSE at Reading is carrying out measurements on quartz, but the experiment is difficult to interpret because of the presence of absorbing and fluorescent centres in the irradiated crystal.

Absorption coefficient. – An important quantity is the absorption coefficient which is defined by

$$\frac{\mathrm{d}I_x}{\mathrm{d}x} = -\mu I_x\,, \tag{1}$$

where I_x is the light intensity at a depth x in the material; $\mathrm{d}I_x$ is the amount of energy absorbed per cm^2 per s in an element of thickness $\mathrm{d}x$, and μ is the absorption coefficient. Thus

$$I_t = I_0 \exp[-\mu t]\,,$$

where I_t is the intensity transmitted by a specimen of thickness t when the incident intensity is I_0. In practical cases, reflection losses have to be taken into account. Taking multiple reflections into account the transmission for near-normal incidence is given by

$$\frac{I_t}{I_0} = \frac{(1-R)^2 \exp[-\mu t]}{1-R^2 \exp[-2\mu t]}\,, \tag{2}$$

where R is the reflection coefficient. Provided that R and μ are not too large this reduces to the well-known relation which includes the effect of only two reflections:

$$\frac{I_t}{I_0} = (1-R)^2 \exp[-\mu t]\,. \tag{3}$$

For high refractive index materials (*e.g.* C, Si, Ge, etc.) eq. (2) must be used to calculate the absorption coefficient, but eq. (3) is adequate for quartz, sapphire and alkali halides.

R can either be measured at the same time as I_t/I_0, or calculated from the known refractive indices. In the case of absorption spectra arising from defects, the latter is usually adopted since the effect of the defects on the refractive index, and hence R, is usually negligible.

The relation of the absorption coefficient to the concentration of absorbing centres. – The strength of an absorption band is determined by the concentration of absorbing centres and the probability that absorption occurs. The Einstein absorption probability (B_{12}) is defined as the probability per unit time per unit energy density of radiation that the transition $1 \rightarrow 2$ takes place. Thus, for N_1 centres per cm³ in state 1 the energy absorbed per cm² per s in an element $\mathrm{d}x$ is

$$\mathrm{d}I_x = -N_1\,\mathrm{d}x\,\varrho(\nu)\,\mathrm{d}\nu\,B_{12}h\nu\,.$$

The energy density $\varrho(\nu)\,\mathrm{d}\nu = I\nu\,\mathrm{d}\nu/c$, where $I(\nu)\,\mathrm{d}\nu$ is the intensity of light in the frequency range $\mathrm{d}\nu$.

If the absorption coefficient is approximately constant over a region $\Delta\nu$ near ν and zero elsewhere, and if we write ΔE as the energy corresponding to $\Delta\nu$ then

$$\mu\Delta E = \frac{h^2\nu}{c}\,N_1\boldsymbol{B}_{12}\,. \tag{4}$$

Quantum-mechanically, the transition probability is related to the overlap of the wavefunctions of an electron in the initial and final states. For allowed transitions the probability is determined by the electric dipole moment matrix defined by

$$M_{12} = e\int\psi_2^*\cdot\boldsymbol{r}\cdot\psi_1\,\mathrm{d}V\,,$$

and

$$B_{12} = \frac{2\pi}{3\hbar^2}\,|M_{12}|^2\,,$$

so that

$$\mu\Delta E = \frac{8\pi^3}{3c}\,\nu\,|M_{12}|^2N_1\,. \tag{5}$$

It will be clear from this that optical absorption can only be used to determine relative numbers of absorbing centres, *e.g.* during irradiation or during annealing. Wavefunctions of electrons in defects have not been calculated with anything like the accuracy required to compute $|M|$.

The oscillator strength or f-value. – It is customary to specify the transition probability by a dimensionless number called the f-value. This came about in the following way. The classical expression for the polarizability arising from electron oscillators of resonant frequency ν_0 is

$$\alpha = \frac{l^2}{4\pi^2 m} \cdot \frac{1}{(\nu_0^2 - \nu^2)} \, .$$

The quantum mechanical expression is similar except that we now have a series of stationary states i of dipole moment $M_{0i}|$ and

$$\alpha = \sum_i \frac{2\,|M_{0i}|^2}{h} \, \frac{\nu_{0i}}{(\nu_{0i}^2 - \nu^2)} \, .$$

Thus the system behaves like series of classical oscillators of strength f given by

(6) $$f_i = \frac{8\pi^2 m \nu_{0i}\,|M_{0i}|^2}{e^2 h} \, .$$

We use this quantity to give the appropriate dipole moment in eq. (5) and then

(7) $$\mu \Delta E = \left(\frac{\pi^2 e h}{3mc}\right) Nf \, .$$

If μ is in cm^{-1}, ΔE in eV, and N in cm^{-3}, this gives

$$\mu\,\Delta E \approx 10^{-16}\, Nf \, .$$

(For a more exact formula see the article by DEXTER in [1].)

For an f-value of unity, which would correspond to all the absorption being concentrated in one excited state of a one electron system, and for a half-width of 0.5 eV, an absorption coefficient of 2 cm^{-1} would correspond to 10^{16} centres per cm^3. However, in covalent solids, the orbitals will generally be mixtures of pure s, p, etc., functions and the transition may be considered as being allowed, for example, because of the s-part of a ground state and the p character of the excited state. Consequently f may be considerably less than 1, for example 0.1 and conceivably 0.01. Thus the sensitivity of optical absorption as a means of detecting defects is completely determined by the detailed, but unknown, form of the wave function in the neighbourhood of the defect.

If we take $f = 0.1$ as a better guide than $f = 1$ we have

$$\mu = 2\ \text{cm}^{-1} \equiv 10^{17}\ \text{cm}^{-3}\ .$$

There is a further point to bear in mind when comparing absorption strengths with defect concentrations. For example, a particular defect may only become observable when it traps an electron, or a hole. Whether the defect is observable can depend on the position of the Fermi level in the crystal at the beginning of the irradiation, or whether lower energy traps are also produced during the irradiation. This is illustrated by the work of FAN and RAMDAS [2] on silicon. They found that the radiation induced 3.3 μ band was not formed in p-type material with the Fermi level low in the energy gap.

A similar effect, referred to as the « radiation bleaching » of an impurity trapping centre in quartz, will be described later.

In general, then, if N is the concentration of particular defects

$$\mu \Delta E \approx 10^{-16} x f N\ , \tag{8}$$

where x is the fraction of defects in a state to be observed optically.

Finally, we note that when one has a distribution of absorbing centres through a crystal whose thickness is greater than the extent of the distribution, the index of the exponential in eq. (3), $\int \mu(t)\,\mathrm{d}t$, is related to the total number of centres in the crystal.

Résumé of optical properties of unirradiated diamonds.

i) Observed in all diamonds. Absorption is found in the $(3\div 6)$ μm region of peak strength ca. 10 cm^{-1}. There is a sharp drop at 3.75 μm (equal to twice the energy of the highest optical vibration), the absorption on the higher energy side being attributed to 3-phonon processes. (See LAX and BURSTEIN [3], STEPHEN [4], HARDY [5].)

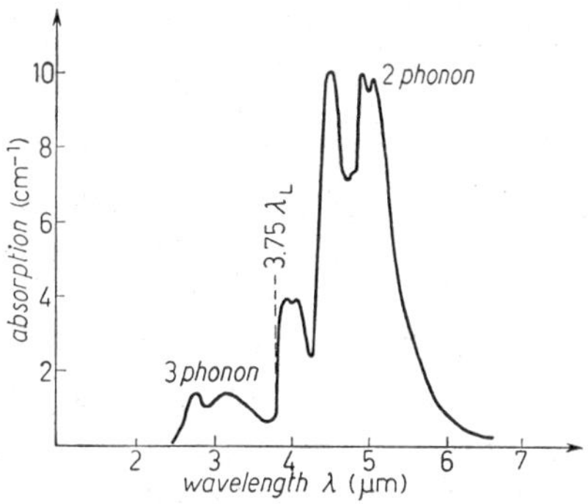

Fig. 1. – Infra-red absorption common to all diamonds.

TABLE IIa. – *Diamond.*

Position of band	Conditions of formation	Remarks
Main line at 1.673 eV (7410 Å) with absorption and structure on high-energy side.	e^-, γ or n^0 all crystals	Form of structure depends on condition of irradiation (see Figs. 4 and 16).
2.6 eV (convenient measure of background absorption).	e^- ($E > 1.0$ MeV), n^0	CLARK and MITCHELL [15] have shown that there is absorption at 2.6 eV which is not due to overlap from lower- or higher-energy bands, and which is not produced significantly for $E < 1.0$ but is for higher e^- energies.
U.V. absorption about 4.5 eV.	e^-, γ, n^0	Probably produced in all diamonds but can be detected in type II crystals only.
(2.54 to 2.62) eV.	Found in II a crystals heat-treated after e^- irradiation.	Formed at $\sim$600 °C as the 1.673 eV and U.V. bands decrease. Subsequently removed by heat treatment at 800 °C.
Main line at 2.464 eV (5032 Å) with absorption on high-energy side.	Found in type I crystals which have been heat-treated after e^-, γ, or n^0 irradiation.	Formed at $\sim$ 600 °C. Stable at higher temperatures. Strongly fluorescent centre.
Continuous tail to absorption edge extending into visible.	By heat treatment after e^-, γ, n^0 irradiation.	Cf. 2.6 eV above. This is the only permanent optical effect which remains in type II crystals after heating at $\sim$ 900 °C. Similar to tail in unirradiated II*a* crystals.
6.5 μm and 7.5 μm.	n^0	Type II*a*. Absorption in one-phonon vibrational region for $\lambda > 7.5$ μm. Separate peak at 6.5 μm.

TALLE II*b*. – *Silicon* (FAN and RAMDAS [2]).

Position of band	Conditions of formation	Remarks
0.69 eV (1.8 μm) (Fig. 5).	n^0, d^+, e^-. Strongest in crucible-grown material; not observed in e^--irradiated floating zone crystals but has been seen when these are n^0-irradiated.	Observed in near intrinsic or *p*-type. Requires a level about 0.2 eV below the conduction band to be unoccupied.
Absorption extending to to the absorption edge.	n^0, d^+	
0.37 eV (3.3 μm) shows structure similar to diamond; see Fig. 6.	n^0, e^-	Observed in *n*-type, not in *p*-type or higher resistivity *n*-type. Requires a level about 0.2 eV below the conduction band to be occupied.
0.22 eV (5.5 μm).	n^0	Observed in lower resistivity *n*-type but absent in material of higher resistivity. Requires a level about 0.16 eV from conduction band to be occupied. Also exhibits photoconductivity.
0.32 eV (3.9 μm).	n^0	Observed in *p*-type if resistivity not too high. Requires level about 0.25 eV above valence band to be occupied. Also exhibits photoconductivity.
0.21 eV (6.0 μm).	Heat treatment (170 °C) after n^0 irradiation.	Is not observed in a specimen which had the Fermi level in a position corresponding to $T=170$ °C, and which is only irradiated.
0.06 eV (20.5 μm).	n^0	All specimens independently of the Fermi level.

TABLE IIc. – *Quartz*.

Position of band	Conditions of formation	Remarks
2.8 eV and 2.0 eV.	Any ionizing radiation.	Effect related to Al impurity content.
Absorption (4—7) eV.	Any ionizing radiation.	Related to above.
5.8 eV (*C*).	n^0	—
7.4 eV (*E*).	n^0	—
2.79 μm (χ) (0.444 eV).	n^0	Tends to saturate Damage + H impurity (see text).
(8.1 to 8.5) eV.	n^0	Strong absorption in n^0-irradiated quartz at 8.1 eV instead of absorption edge originally at 8.5 eV.

ii) Electronic absorption edge. This edge occurs at 5.4 eV and is particularly sharp in the semiconducting (II*b*) crystals. On such specimens CLARK [6] has studied the temperature-dependence of the indirect band to band absorption. Type II*a* specimens (*e.g.* CLARK *et al* [7]) show an absorption edge at 5.4 eV but with a specimen-dependent tail extending to lower energies (see also Table II*a*).

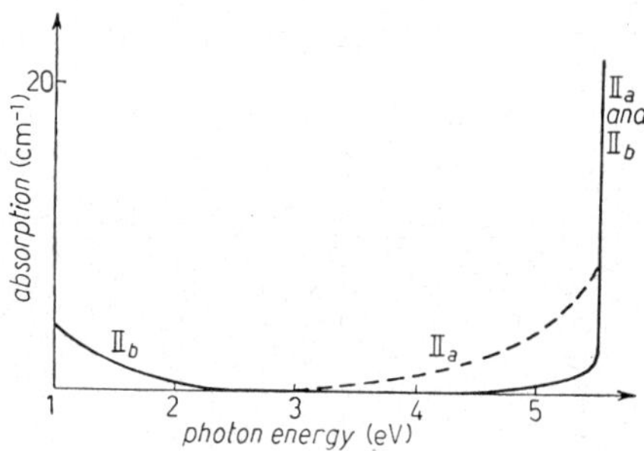

Fig. 2. – Absorption spectra for type II diamonds.

iii) Extrinsic features.

a) In semiconducting diamonds.

Extra infra-red lines are observed which are mostly superposed on the vibrational absorption. These lines lead to a continuum which extends into the visible. The strength of the lines and the continuum correlates at room temperature with the concentration of vacant acceptor levels as measured electrically. They appear to be due to the excited states of the acceptor centre (WEDEPOHL [8], MITCHELL [9]).

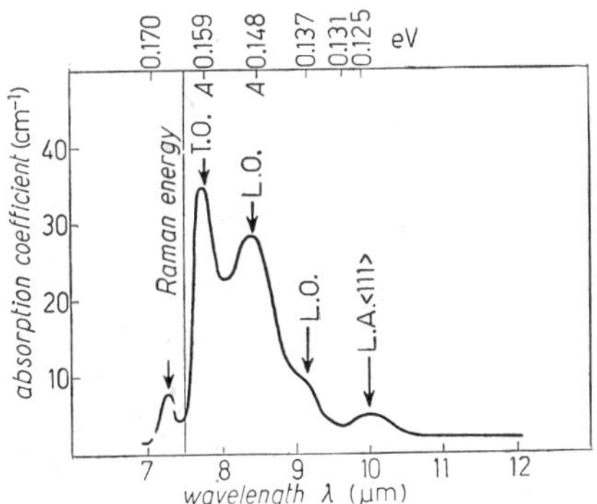

Fig. 3. – Infra-red absorption in the neighbourhood of Raman frequency in type I diamonds, after SMITH and HARDY [13], and showing their phonon assignments.

b) Various features in so called type I diamonds.

These include:

α) Strong absorption at 4 000 Å, thereby obscuring the fundamental absorption edge.

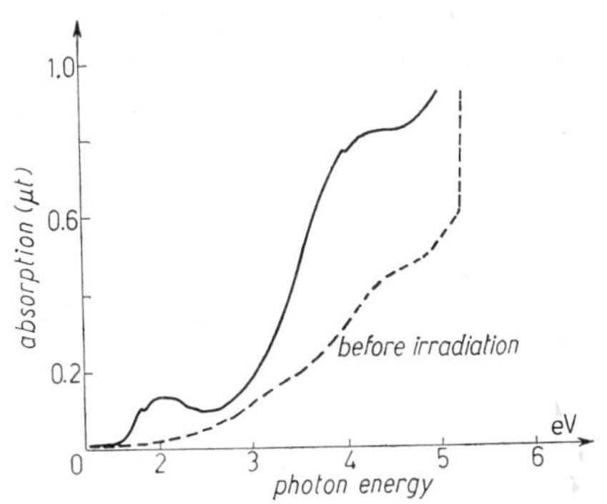

Fig. 4. – Typical absorption spectrum produced by electron irradiation of type II*a* diamond (CLARK *et al.* [7]).

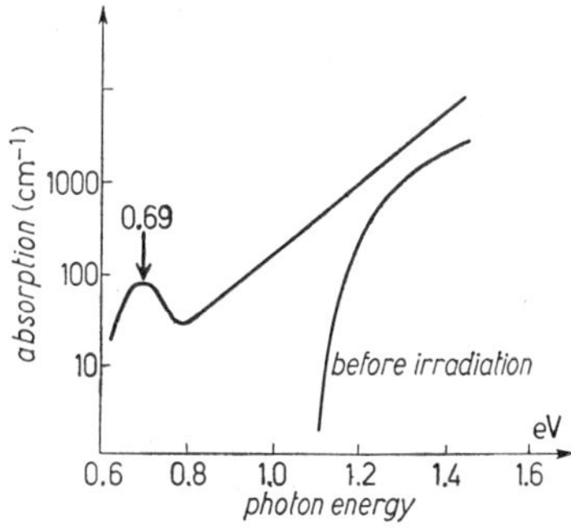

Fig. 5. – Absorption produced in Si by d⁺ irradiation (after FAN and RAMDAS [2]).

β) Absorption in the region of 7.5 μm and higher wavelengths, corresponding to 1-phonon vibrational effects. KAISER and BOND [10] have found that the main peak at 7.8 μm is related to the nitrogen content, although it is not yet clear in what form the nitrogen provides the coupling to the lattice vibrations (see ELLIOTT [11] and KEMMEY and MITCHELL [12]).

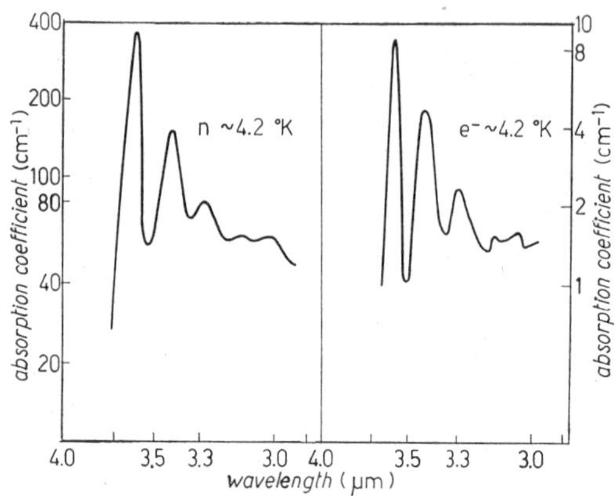

Fig. 6. – The 3.3 μm band in silicon.

γ) Various absorption centres such as the 4150 Å centre. This absorbs on the high energy side of 4150 and emits in the blue (see DYER and MATTHEWS [14]).

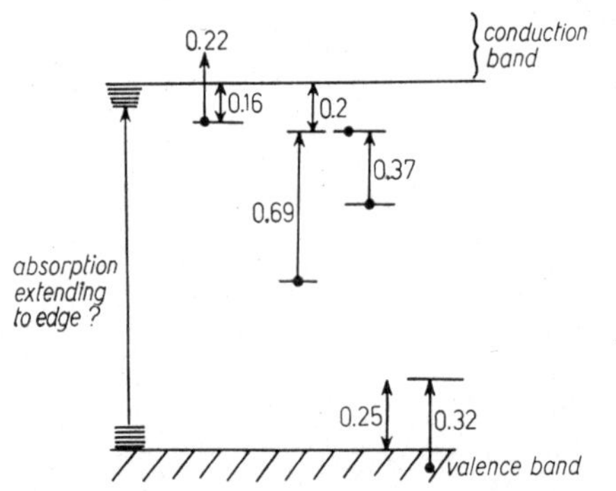

Fig. 7. – Possible energy level arrangement for optical absorption effects in irradiated silicon.

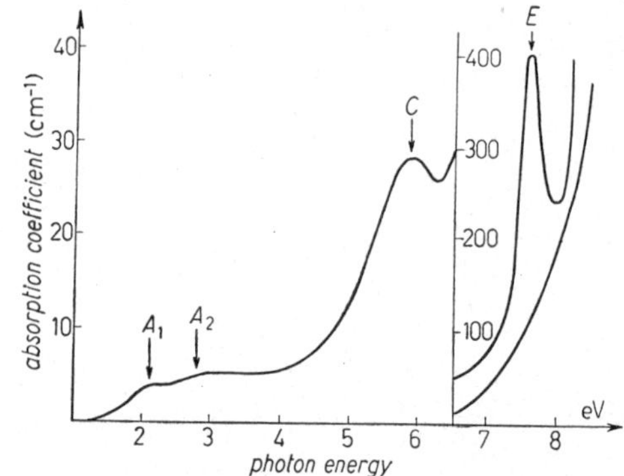

Fig. 8. – Radiation-induced spectrum in quartz (reactor irradiation).

4. – Optical absorption centres induced by irradiation in diamond, silicon and quartz.

The centres which have been observed in these materials are summarized in Table II.

Of the various absorption bands referred to in these tables we can distinguish the following general types:

1) Vibrational effects associated with damage.
2) Displacement effects interacting with impurities.
3) Point defects, and small aggregates.
4) Changes in absorption arising from major structural changes in the lattice.
5) Ionization effects associated with impurity centres.

4·1. *Vibrational effects.* – I shall refer to these briefly, not because they are not important, but because very little work has yet been done. There are two possibilities:

i) Changes in the infrared vibrational spectrum of the crystal.

ii) Infrared absorption associated with localized vibrations.

The former is of particular interest in single element diamond structure materials since infrared absorption is normally forbidden in the neighbourhood of the highest vibrational frequency. The interaction of two such atomic vibrations however causes a local deformation of the electronic charge cloud and allows weak absorption to occur. The highest energy at which this can occur is $2(\nu_L)$, where ν_L is the Raman frequency. Absorption will extend to lower energies corresponding to two phonon processes involving lower-energy phonons. The local symmetry will also be changed by static defects and this, in principle, should lead to a means of coupling to the lattice vibrations. The extent of the coupling and strength of absorption will be dependent on the amount of charge deformation which occurs.

Various people have shown that the spectrum of vibrations should contain the continuous region of the perfect crystal, together with a localized vibration on the high-energy side.

The two observations which have been made of vibrational effects (diamond and silicon) have both resulted from reactor irradiation.

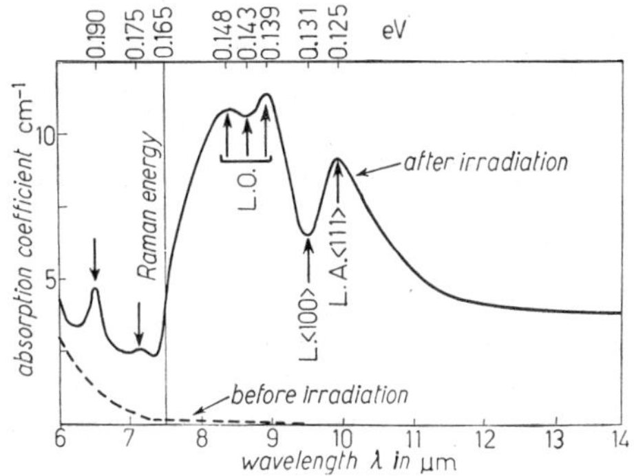

Fig. 9. – Infra-red absorption (near Raman frequency), induced in a II*a* diamond by fast neutron irradiation after SMITH and HARDY [13], and showing their phonon assignments.

In silicon a band was produced at 20.5 μm which was not sensitive to the position of the Fermi level. Clearly one would expect a vibrational coupling effect to be less sensitive to the presence or absence of an electron than an effect which was associated with a transition involving that particular electron. On the other hand, there is some evidence in silicon that the effect may be associated with regions of damage larger than point defects. Thus, FAN and RAMDAS [2] have found that although the 20.5 μm band decreased in the heat treatment at 140 °C, the rate of decrease depended on the position of the Fermi level. In fact, a small increase was obtained when the Fermi level was close to the valence band. They suggest that the coupling to the lattice vibrations may be via an aggregate, the dispersal of which depends on the charge carried by defects.

Potentially, this is a method of studying defects which is less dependent on electron occupancy than many optical defects. However, the sensitivity is poor, *e.g.* absorption coefficient induced in diamond ca. 10 cm^{-1} for a fast dose of $3\cdot10^{17}$ n^0 cm^{-2}. It will be of great interest to see if the effect can be produced by electron irradiation.

Concerning localized vibrations associated with defects all that can be said at present is that the peak observed at 6.5 μm by HARDY and SMITH [13] at Reading on the high-energy side of the one-phonon absorption appears to be of this type.

4·2. *Damage+impurity.* – It now appears that the 1.8 μm Si centre is a product of damage associated with oxygen impurity. FAN reported the at Prague Semiconductor Conference that this band was not produced in electron-irradiated floating zone material. The 1.8 μm absorption therefore appears to be associated with the same centre which gives the paramagnetic resonance observed by BEMSKI [16] and WATKINS *et al.* [17]. However, the situation in confused by the observation of the 1.8 μm band in some neutron-irradiated floating zone material.

Another centre in silicon appears to be of this category, namely, the paramagnetic centre observed by WATKINS *et al.* [17] which consists of a vacancy associated with a phosphorus atom.

The band observed in neutron-irradiated quartz at 2.79 μm seems also to be of this type. This band was not found by MITCHELL and RIDGEN [18] in electron or X-irradiated quartz, but only in neutron-irradiated crystals. The strength tended to saturate at relatively low neutron doses (ca. 10^{18}) indicating some interaction of damage and impurity. The position of the band is very close to that at which isolated O—H vibrational absorption occurs in many crystals. Furthermore, unirradiated synthetic quartz shows an absorption band at 2.81 μm which MITCHELL and RIDGEN [18] suggested was associated with O—H incorporated during the hydrothermal growth. This is supported by the recent observation of KING *et al.* [19] that the band was not observed in crystals (unirradiated) grown using heavy water.

From the known strength of O—H vibrational absorption MITCHELL and RIDGEN estimated that the number of oxygen displacements which were produced was in an order-of-magnitude agreement with the Kinchin and Pease model as applied to quartz by MITCHELL and PAIGE [23].

Also one of the centres in diamond is of this kind, the 5 032 Å centre. This sometimes occurs naturally but otherwise may be induced in type I diamonds by high energy irradiation followed by heat treatment, as found by CLARK *et al.* [7]. Once introduced it is quite stable. It has to be distinguished from the other effects in diamond for this reason.

The 5 032 Å centre absorbs at 5 032 Å and on the high-energy side, while it emits on the low-energy side giving the characteristic green emission. Both absorption and emission show fine structure, and the occurence of the main lines at the same frequency means that there is not much relaxation of atoms around the centre when it is in the excited state. I should like to discuss some of the optical work on this centre as an example of a method which is now being applied to many materials—the study of the polarization of luminescence.

The application of this technique to centres in cubic crystals was first made by FEOFILOV [21, 22] and by ourselves [9, 22].

The object is to try to determine the symmetry axis of the centre. In principle, there are several techniques which can be used for determining the symmetry axis of a centre. We may study:

I) Magnetic field effects. (As used in paramagnetic resonance and the optical studies of low temperature impurity and exciton absorption in germanium).

II) Stark effects.

III) Elasto-optical effect. (Recently used by FAN and RAMDAS [24], who showed that the 1.8 μm band in Si had axis [110].)

IV) Preferential bleaching (bleach with polarized light, measure absorption and find anisotropy because of unequal populations).

V) Polarization of luminescence.

Polarization of luminescence. – It is not at once obvious that this will give an anisotropic effect. But suppose we represent the centre by a dipole oscillator whose axis is the symmetry axis of the centre. We suppose that there are equal populations in the crystallographically equivalent centres—*e.g.* equal numbers along [100], [010] and [001]. If we assume that, when excited, a centre cannot relax into an equivalent direction, then the degree of polarization (p), as a function of the angle β of the incident light makes with the [100], is as shown in Fig. 10 for the straight through and perpendicular experiments.

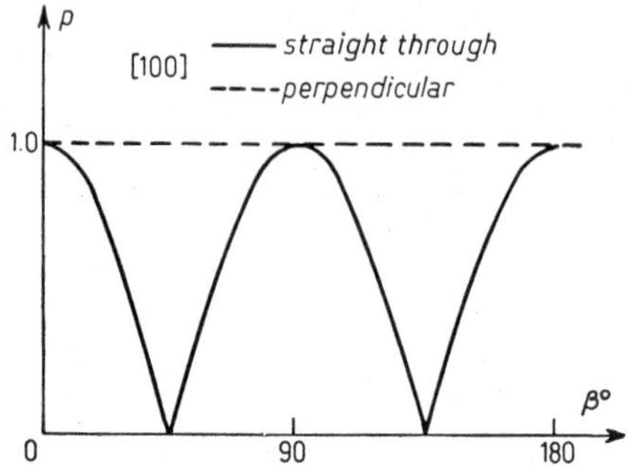

Fig. 10. – Degree of polarization (p) as a function of the angle of polarizer (β) for [100] centres.

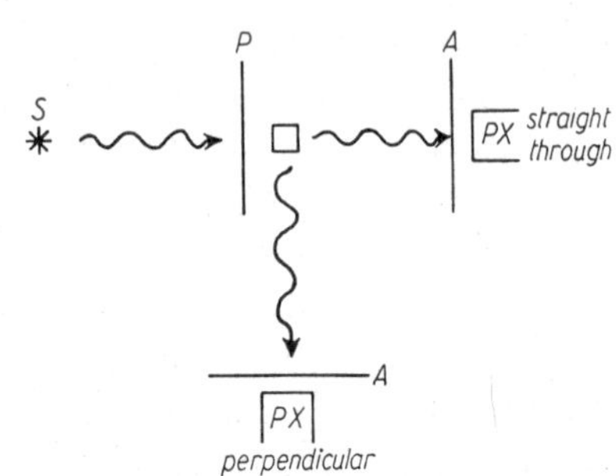

Fig. 11. – Diagram of apparatus for studying polarization of luminescence.

The experiment is carried out as shown schematically in the diagram Fig. 11, for the « straight-through » and « perpendicular » conditions. The analyser is rotated continuously and the recorder trace then appears as in Fig. 12 if the light is partially polarized.

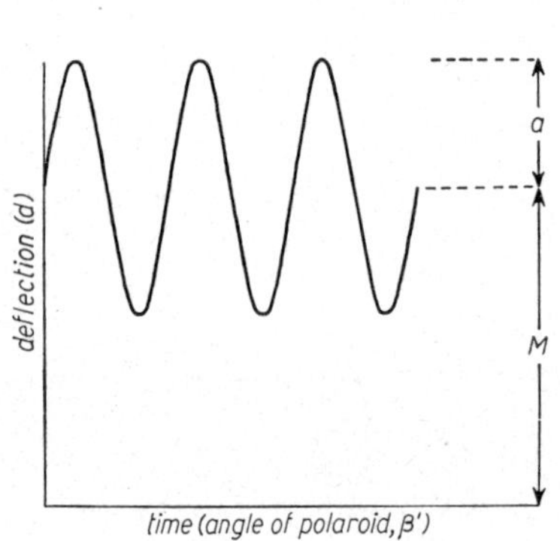

Fig. 12. – Intensity passing analyser as a function of time (analyser continuously rotating).

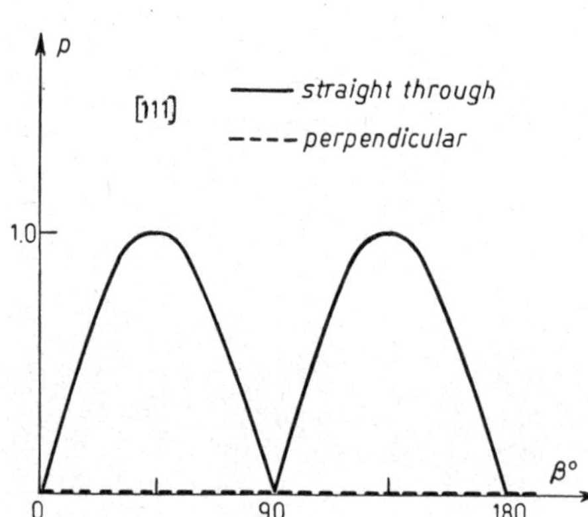

Fig. 13. – Degree of polarization (p) as a function of the angle of the polarizer (β) for [111] centres.

The degree of polarization (p) is defined as $p = a/M$ and will in general be a function of the angle (β) the incident $\boldsymbol{E}$ makes with the crystallographic axis of the crystal, or more conveniently in practice, one of the surface normals of the crystal.

The emitted intensity can be shown to be:

$$I = \frac{I_0}{3}\{\sum_{lmn} l^2 l'^2 + [\sum_{\lambda\mu\nu} \lambda^2\mu^2][1 + 2\sum_{lmn}(ll')^2 - 5\sum_{lmn} l^2 l'^2]\}, \tag{9}$$

where I is the intensity emitted having $\boldsymbol{E}$ of direction cosines $l'm'n'$, where (l, m, n) are the direction cosines of the incident light and (λ, μ, ν) are the direction cosines of the axis of the centre. In a specimen bounded by (100), the variation of p with β can be shown to be as in Fig. 13 and 14.

The experimental results for 3650 and 4358 Å excitation are as shown in Fig. 15(a) and (b) for the simple orientation.

The general form is similar to that expected for [110] centres but there are systematic differences:

a) There is considerable depolarization

b) The experimental curve does not go to zero at 90° in the perpendicular condition.

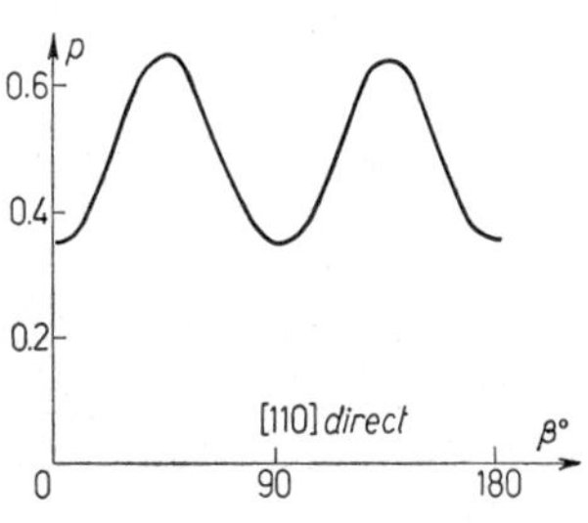

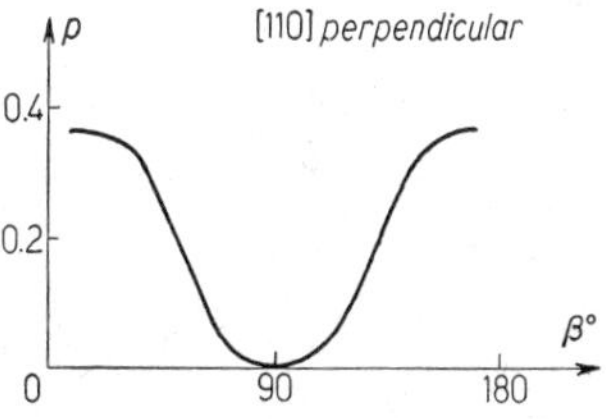

Fig. 14. – Degree of polarization (p) as a function of the angle of the polarizer (β) for [110] centres.

Several factors may contribute to this depolarization:

i) The transition may be associated with p_x and p_y oscillators perpendicular to the axes $[\lambda\mu\nu]$ considered.

ii) The fact that, with 3650 Å and 4358 Å light, one is providing a large excess energy in the excited electronic state. This energy has to be

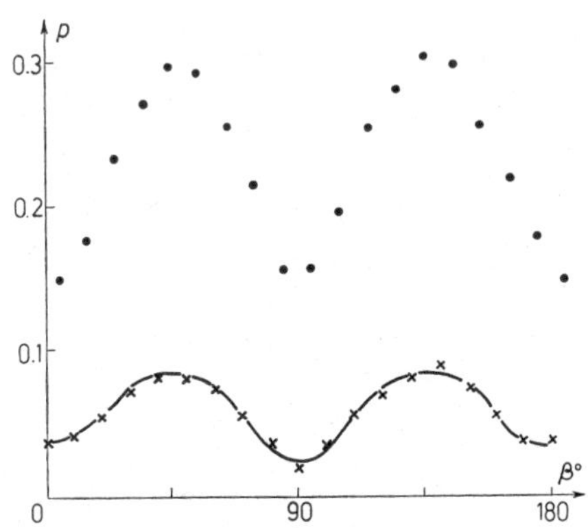

Fig. 15a. – Experimental results for the polarization of luminescence of the 5 32 centres (straight through experiment: ● ● ● 4358Å excitation; ××× 3650Å excitation).

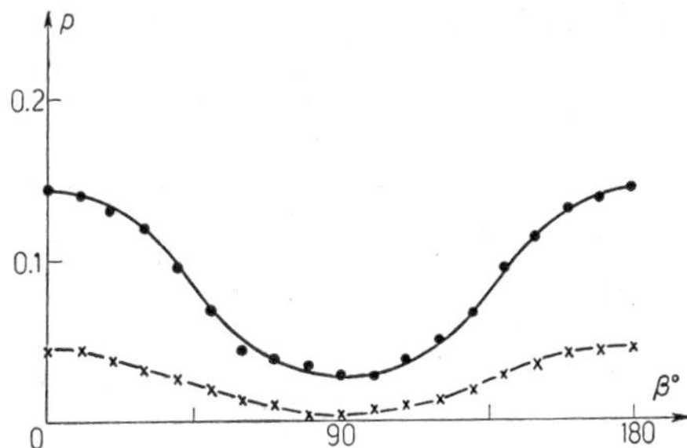

Fig. 15b. – Experimental results for the polarization of luminescence of the 5032 centres (perpendicular experiment: ● ● ● 4358Å excitation; ××× 3650Å excitation).

dissipated thermally during which process some changes in orientation might be produced. The fact that a larger p is found using 4 358 Å is some support for this suggestion.

iii) The normal lattice vibrations could lead to a small depolarization.

iv) Departure from the perfect crystal symmetry arising from atomic relaxations around the defect.

Nevertheless, the results appear to be best explained by [110] centres being perturbed by these various effects, rather than by centres lying in completely different directions. At the present time CLARK and MAYCRAFT at Reading are examining in great detail the deviations from the simple interpretation.

The simplest case of a (damage+impurity) centre which would give [110] axes is an interstitial atom anchored to an interstitial impurity.

4·3. *Point defects and small aggregates.* – As an example in this category I shall discuss the work which has been done at Reading on the 1.673 eV (7 410 Å) centre in diamond (CLARK, DITCHBURN and DYER [7]; CLARK, KEMMEY and MITCHELL [15]).

A detailed discussion of the recent work on this band is shortly to be published by CLARK and MITCHELL [25]. In this section a summary of the work will be presented.

The band is produced in all diamonds by high energy radiation. The rate of production has been studied extensively for electron irradiations and is found to be almost linear. In the cases in which rate curves have been obtained on several II*a* specimens (1.5 and 2.0 MeV), the rate of increase is independent of specimen, within the experimental error. These observations indicate that the band is probably associated with a primary product of damage.

Form of spectrum. – The absorption spectrum under various conditions of irradiations is shown in Fig. 16, the spectra all being measured at liquid N_2 temperature.

The most clearly resolved spectrum is that obtained after a room-temperature electron irradiation. It will be seen that this spectrum is verys imilar to the radiation-induced band in Si at 3.3 μm and also to the 5 032 Å (2.64 eV) band in diamond, both of which have been referred to earlier.

We have not observed luminescence from the 7 410 Å centre, although attempts have been made to observe emission out to 1 μm at liquid N_2 temperature. It is not clear yet whether the failure to observe luminescence is because of a low quantum efficiency, or of a large Frank-Condon shift. If the latter were the case it would be evidence in favour of the vacancy model since one expects larger relaxation effects around the vacancy than around interstitial atoms (cf. of 5 032 Å centre).

In diamond, the sharp lines observed in the low-temperature spectrum are separated by about 0.04 eV compared with 0.02 in the 3.3 μm band in silicon. This may arise from strong coupling to a particular lattice vibration, or pos-

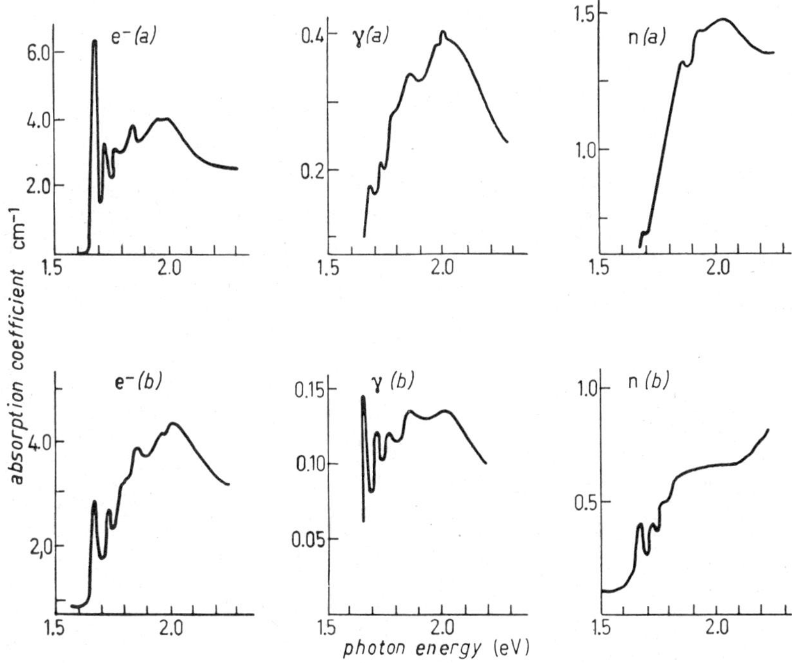

Fig. 16. – The absorption coefficient as a function of photon energy for the 7410 Å band under various conditions: e⁻: (*a*) produced by electron-irradiation at room temperature; (*b*) produced by electron-irradiation at 195 °K; γ: (*a*) produced by γ-irradiation; (*b*) after heating at 723 °K; n: (*a*) produced by pile-irradiation at about 313 °K; (*b*) after heating at 723 °K.

sibly from excited electronic states of the system. In diamond the constancy of the spacing throughout the region of absorption would be better accounted for by the former explanation.

It will be seen that the spectrum induced by γ-irradiation or neutron-irradiation is much less well resolved, although the measurements were all carried out at liquid N_2 temperature. The main difference between the two conditions of irradiation is in the flux of ionizing radiation which is absorbed—high in the case of the electron irradiation, low in the γ and neutron-irradiations. During low temperature heat treatment (< 500 °C) of the γ and neutron-irradiated crystals, the absorption strength decreases, but the lines sharpen considerably and the characteristic structure is obtained. It is suggested that this corresponds to the annealing of close pairs which were annealed during the irradiation when electrons were used. The broadening could arise from the perturbation of the energy levels of, say, the vacancy by a nearby interstitial. When electron-irradiations were carried out at $-80\ ^\circ\mathrm{C}$, a reduction of the height of the main peak relative to the rest of the absorption system was observed.

Threshold. – The rates of production of the 7410 Å band have been studied for a range of electron energies up to 2.0 MeV. The results up to 1 MeV are shown in Fig. 17 by the open circles.

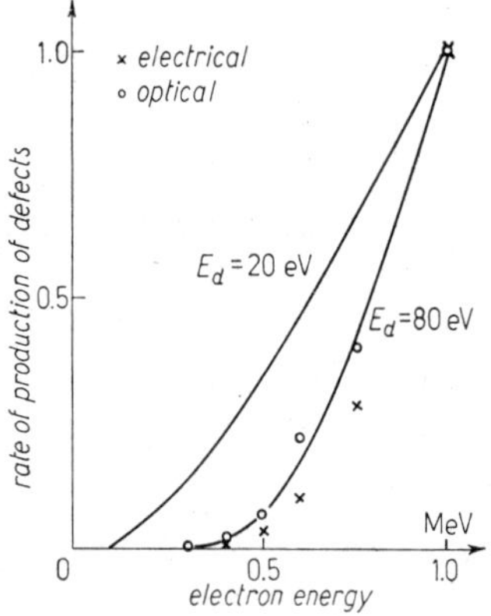

Fig. 17. – Threshold curves for radiation damage effects in diamond.

The shape of this curve has been compared with the shapes of curves for producing displacements. We have used the full form of the cross-section determined from the McKinley and Feshbach [26] differential scattering cross-section. Thus the total cross-section, as a function of the incident electron energy E_i, is as given in eq. (11). In this equation E_i is contained in the parameter E_m (the maximum recoil energy obtained for E_i) given by

$$E_m = \frac{4E_i}{Mc^2}\left(\frac{E_i}{2} + m_0c^2\right), \tag{10}$$

where M is the mass of the struck nucleus. Then

$$\sigma_p(E) = 4\pi A\left\{\left(\frac{E_m}{E_d} - 1\right) - \beta^2 \ln\left(\frac{E_m}{E_d}\right) + \pi\alpha\beta\left[2\left\{\left(\frac{E_m}{E_d}\right)^{\frac{1}{2}} - 1\right\} - \ln\frac{E_m}{E_d}\right]\right\}, \tag{11}$$

where $A = (Z^2e^4(1-\beta^2))/4m_0^2c^4\beta^4)$, $\alpha = Z/137$ and the remaining symbols have their usual meanings.

Because the measurements were made on specimens whose thickness was greater than the range of the electrons we have to integrate over all electron energies down to E_t (the electron energy for which $E_M = E_d$).

We represent the energy loss by electron interaction by

$$\frac{\mathrm{d}E}{\mathrm{d}x} = -f^n(E)\,.$$

We then note that the range is given by

$$R = \int_{E_i}^{0} \mathrm{d}x = \int_{0}^{E_i} \frac{\mathrm{d}E}{f^n(E)},$$

and the depth of penetration of damage effects by

$$R_d = \int_{E_i}^{E_t} \mathrm{d}x = \int_{E_t}^{E_i} \frac{\mathrm{d}E}{f^n(E)} .$$

The range-energy relationship has not been measured for carbon but in our calculation of the shape of the threshold curve we only have to use the energy-dependence of the range. We take this to be similar to that in aluminium and note that scaling the aluminium data according to the density ratio produces absolute range values which are approximately correct. Thus for diamond we take

$$R = 0.116\, E_i^{1.38} \qquad \text{up to } 1\ \text{MeV}\ (E_i \text{ in MeV}, R \text{ in cm}),$$

so that

$$\frac{\mathrm{d}R}{\mathrm{d}E} = \frac{1}{f^n(E_i)} = 0.16 E^{0.38} .$$

The total number of displacements (N_d) produced at a depth x, where the energy of the electrons is assumed to be E in an element dx is

$$N_d = N_i N_A \int_{E_i}^{E_t} \sigma_p(E)\, \mathrm{d}x,$$

$$= (N_i N_A) \int_{E_t}^{E_i} \sigma_p(E) \frac{\mathrm{d}E}{f^n(E)} ,$$

where N_i is the incident flux ($\text{cm}^{-2}\,\text{s}^{-1}$) and N_A is the atomic concentration (cm^{-3}). We then plot $y = \sigma_p(E)/f^n(E)$ as a function of $\boldsymbol{E}$ and evaluate the integral graphically. Results for $E_d = 80$ eV and 20 eV are shown by the full lines of Fig. 17. The calculated curves are normalized at 1 MeV. Curves have been calculated for a range of values of E_d and the best fit is obtained using $E_d = 80$ eV.

Determination of threshold curve from measurements on semiconducting diamond. – It will be convenient to discuss the electrical measurements in this section. As shown principally by WEDEPOHL [8], semiconducting diamond is a partially compensated p-type conductor, the energy levels of which are indicated in Fig. 18.

The carrier concentration is given by

$$p = \frac{(N_A - N_D - p)}{N_D + p} \left(\frac{2\pi m^* kT}{h^2}\right)^{\frac{3}{2}} \exp\left[-\frac{\varepsilon}{kT}\right] .$$

After electron irradiation it was found by WEDEPOHL that p decreased but that the slope of $\ln p$ *vs.* $1/T$ in the low temperature region was not changed. This led WEDEPOHL to suggest that only radiation-induced donors were important in determining the effect of irradiation on the carrier concentration, the acceptors being too far from the valence band to have any measurable effect.

On the basis of these models for unirradiated and irradiated semiconducting diamond, it is easy to show that the carrier concentration after irradiation (p_R) as a function of electron dose (D) is given by

$$\left(\frac{p_R}{p_0}\right)^{-1} = 1 + \frac{KD}{N_D/N_A(1-N_D/N_A)-(N_D/N_A)KD}, \tag{12}$$

where the concentration of induced donor levels is assumed to increase linearly with dose so that

$$\frac{N_R}{N_A} = KD\,.$$

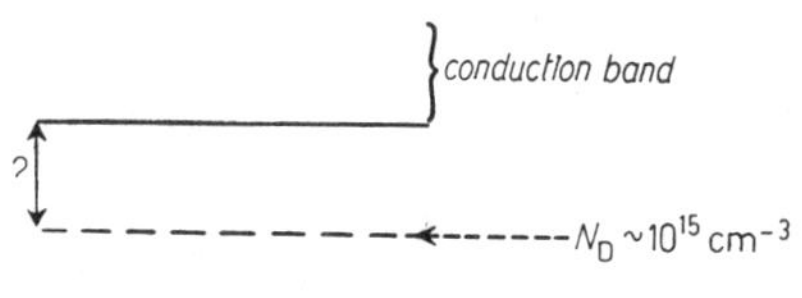

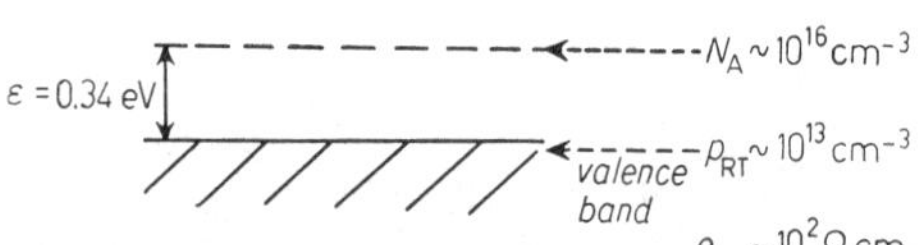

Fig. 18. – Energy levels in semiconducting diamond.

Experimental results for successive irradiations at 1.5 MeV are shown in Fig. 19. In this figure we have plotted the experimental points for the resistivity ratio, ϱ_R/ϱ_0. Although changes in Hall mobility have been measured, they are small compared with the changes of carrier concentration.

Therefore to a good approximation we can write

$$\frac{\varrho_R}{\varrho_0} \approx \left(\frac{p_R}{p_0}\right)^{-1}. \tag{13}$$

The irradiation was at 120 °K, but, owing to the large probe resistances at low temperatures, it was not possible to measure resistivity changes until the temperature had risen to 190 °K. Immediately after irradiation the resistivity increase was small. On warming to room temperature for

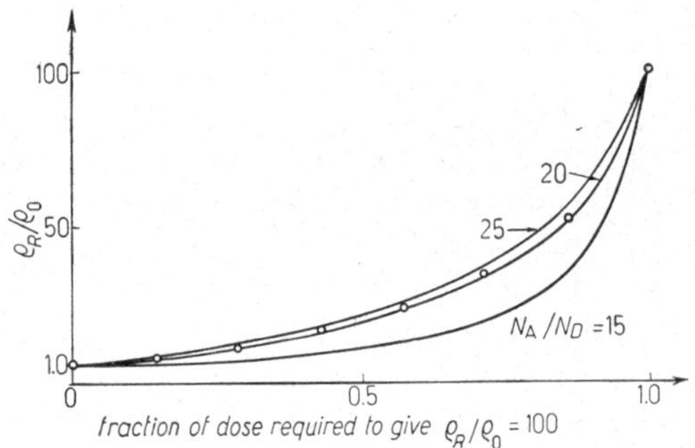

Fig. 19. – The variation of the resistivity of semiconducting diamonds as a function of electron irradiation at 1.5 MeV: —— calculated curves for different amounts of compensation; ○ ○ experimental points for 1.5 MeV irradiation.

the first time after each irradiation and recooling to 190 °K, a much larger increase was found, which was not affected by subsequent warming to room temperature. This increase in resistivity on warming (cf. decrease expected to result from annealing) is attributed to the existence of a nonequilibrium distribution of electrons at low temperatures after irradiation.

It will be seen that the results are in good agreement with the calculated shapes if $N_A/N_D \approx 20 \div 22$. This quantity can be measured before irradiation from the shape of the Hall constant *vs.* $1/T$ curves. The value which had previously been found for this specimen was $N_A/N_D = 24$. We consider this to be in good agreement with the model. A fuller account of this work is being published by KEMMEY and MITCHELL [27] and the experiment is also referred to in the paper by the same authors at the Prague Semiconductor Conference.

It can also be seen from eq. (12) and (13) that, at low doses, the variation of ϱ_R/ϱ_0 is linear whith dose. Subsequently we have verified this for electron energies in the range $0.4 \div 2.0$ MeV. These results are shown by the crosses on the threshold curve of Fig. 17. The shape of the threshold for the changes in electrical properties is close to the optical results up to 1 MeV and the calculated curve for $E_d = 80$ eV, but deviates significantly, indicating a higher displacement energy. On the other hand, the number of donors introduced per electron (see Table III) compares favourably with the calculation of the number of displacements for energies up to 1 MeV. Clearly, the shape is very sensitive to the precise value of E_d.

TABLE III.

Beam energy (MeV)	Displacement calculation N/N_i	Experimental yields: donors/N_i
0.4	0.0023	0.0023
0.5	0.0105	0.0083
0.6	0.028	0.024
0.75	0.06	0.071
1.0	0.15	0.25
1.25	0.26	1.02
1.5	0.40	2.55
2.0	0.90	11.5

The rapid increase in rate of introduction beyond 1 MeV is also shown in Fig. 20. Although at 2 MeV the maximum recoil energy of a carbon atom is 1000 eV, it is not possible to account for the shape of the curve in this region by the production of secondaries. This point will be discussed more fully by KEMMEY and MITCHELL [27].

In contrast to the electrical results the optical results show that above 1.5 MeV the rate of introduction of the 7410 Å absorption system is approximately constant. This effect is not understood. It cannot arise from the saturation value of the cross-section because the specimen thicknesses have all been greater than the range, so that according to eq. (11) N_d should increase with E_i.

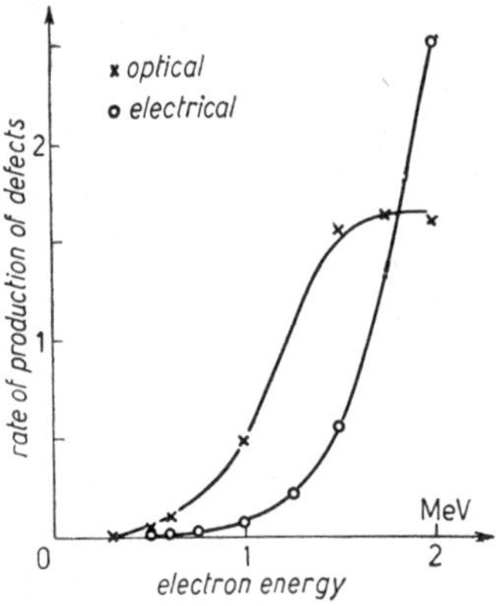

Fig. 20. – Threshold curves for irradiation effects in diamond.

The major difference between the experimental conditions for the two sets of experiments was that for the electrical measurements the crystals were irradiated at 120 °K whereas for the optical measurements the irradiation temperature was about 300 °K. A low-temperature optical experiment is in progress.

Annealing. – The kinetics of the decrease of 7 410 Å absorption induced by 2 MeV electron irradiation is being studied in detail by CLARK and PALMER at Reading [28]. Their results may be summarized as follows:

i) There is a recovery stage around 300 °C. The amount of recovery in this stage depends on the temperature of irradiation. The ratios are 6% for 20 °C, 18% for −80 °C and 40% for −140 °C.

ii) This is followed by a second order process at about 500 °C. Both the 7 410 Å and the U.V. absorption decrease at approximately the same rate.

iii) There is a third recovery stage in the region (600÷700) °C. This process has an activation energy of (1.8 ± 0.2) eV. During the recovery of 7 410 Å and U.V. absorption in this stage the new band system (2.54÷2.62) eV appears.

iv) At higher temperatures, all bands are annealed, leaving at 950 °C only the enhanced continuous tail to the absorption edge.

The 7 410 Å band is not regenerated by irradiation with X-rays at the end of i). Therefore, we do not think that this is a bleaching (electronic) effect. As discussed above, we have considered that it arises from the recombination of close pairs. The second stage corresponds with the stage of annealing found by PRIMAK [29] when studying lattice expansion.

4·4. *Effects associated with major structural disorder.* – The following effects have been observed:

i) In neutron-irradiated crystalline quartz the absorption edge is broadened on the low energy side so that it resembles that of fused quartz (*viz.* increasing at 8.1 eV rather than 8.5 eV) (MITCHELL and PAIGE [23]).

ii) In diamonds irradiated with electrons of $E_i > 1.0$ MeV and with neutrons, there is evidence for a background absorption in two parts of the spectrum. After heat treatment, a well marked region of continuous absorption can be seen on the low-energy side of the absorption edge. That the latter is an absorption effect and is not due to light scattering was shown by the integrating sphere measurement of BASTIN *et al.* [30].

iii) The extra absorption found between the 1.8 μm band and the edge (1.2 μm) in neutron and deuteron irradiated silicon by FAN and RAMDAS [2].

When interpreting such results one has to be careful to show that the effect does not arise from a thermally broadened (width $(0.5 \div 1.0)$ eV) strong band occurring in a region of the absorption edge where the absorption is increasing rapidly. It does not appear that such a band could account for the results in the three cases referred to.

It is more probable that, owing to variations of lattice distances around point defects, but more significantly around groups of defects, a continuum of levels is introduced below the conduction band and above the valence band. These groups of defects are most likely to occur in the displacement spike.

At the present time the observations and the interpretation of effects of this type are only qualitative.

4·5. *Effects associated with the interaction of damage (ionization) with impurity.* – I shall illustrate this category of effects by a detailed discussion of the origin of the visible colour centres (A band) induced in quartz by ionizing radiation.

Condition of formation and rate curves. – Crystalline quartz irradiated in a reactor becomes smoky due to the formation of a broad band having a peak at about 2.70 eV and having a small shoulder on the low-energy side. The effect can also be produced by X-rays. After a sufficient X-ray dose, the absorption saturates, whereas with reactor-irradiation the absorption increases rapidly at first and then decreases slowly from a flat maximum. The amount of absorption induced in a crystal is specimen-dependent and does not commonly exceed 20 cm^{-1}, usually being about 5 cm^{-1}.

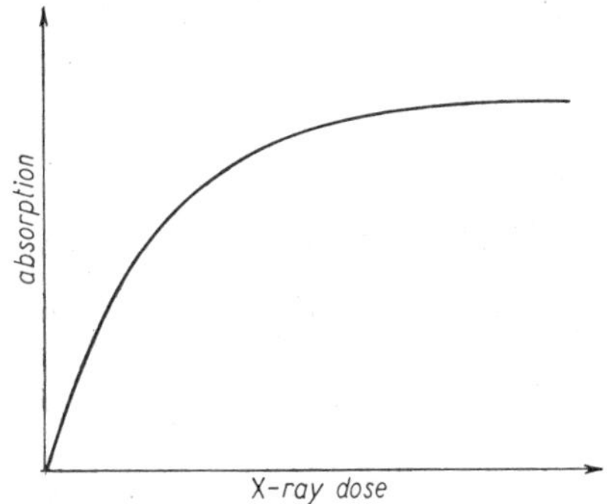

Fig. 21. – Rate curve for formation of A-bands in quartz.

There seems to be no doubt that the absorption band arises from the trapping of electrons and holes—released by the ionizing radiation—at impurity trapping sites. The saturation value of the absorption is then a complicated function of the capture and loss cross-sections for holes in the hole trap, for electrons in the electron trap and of the concentration of hole and electron traps. It is important to remember when discussing band strengths in such cases that the value of x (eq. (8)) for a particular centre may be considerably less than 1, depending on the concentration of the complementary traps.

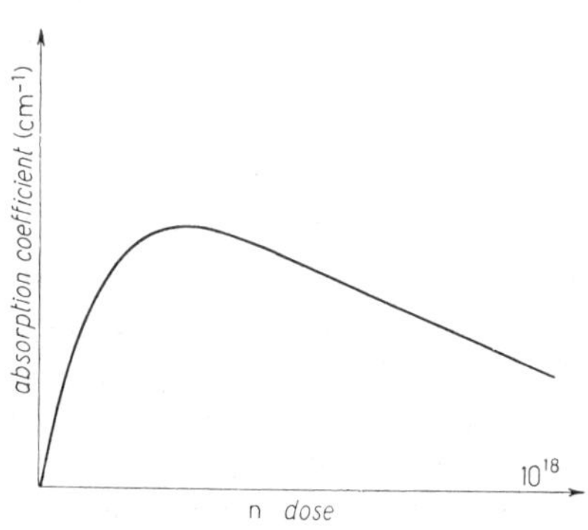

Fig. 22. – Rate curve for formation of A-bands in quartz by reactor-irradiation.

The slow decrease with reactor-irradiation can be explained on the basis of the gradual introduction of displacement traps having lower energy levels than the impurity traps. The displacement traps are required to have a large enough capture cross-section for the originally filled impurity traps to be emptied under the influence of ionizing radiation simultaneously with the formation of the displacement traps by the fast neutrons. The kinetics of the process is clearly complicated, but PAIGE [31] has obtained very good agreement with the form of the experimental curves.

The impurity. – The next question is what is the impurity responsible for the effects. The absorption in the visible is always accompanied by absorption in the U.V., the ratio of the amounts of absorption being roughly constant for X-ray and low-dose neutron irradiation. At higher neutron doses specifically damage effects occur in the U.V. and the impurity trapping effects can only be seen in the slowly decreasing visible bands. Both the visible and U.V. impurity trapping effects are related to the Al content of the crystals. The variation is roughly linear, the uncertainties arising from the inaccuracy of spectroscopic analysis and from the fact that the ratio of impurity in appropriate positions to form traps, to the total content, can presumably vary from crystal to crystal.

There are crystals in which the distribution of the colour is nonuniform; frequently such crystals are coloured in layers. If banded (or « layered ») crystals are heated to 700 °C and irradiated it is found that the layers are in the same positions as they were previously, indicating that the Al responsible for the effect has not diffused out of the layer at 700 °C. On the other hand, Al will readily diffuse into quartz as may be seen by immersing a crystal in molten Al at 700 °C. The reasonable conclusion from these results is that Al can migrate easily via interstitial positions through the quartz lattice, and that the trapping site moves much less readily and is therefore probably associated with substitutional Al (DICTHBURN *et al.* [32]; MITCHELL and PAIGE [20]).

It is difficult to be certain, however, that Al is necessarily responsible for one of the trapping centres. In growth conditions in which Al was more easily incorporated, other impurities might have been incorporated in greater concentration also, and there might be impurities not readily detected by standard spectroscopic analysis. In the absence of control over growth in which a specific impurity can be varied—which does not yet seem to be the case with synthetic quartz—it is not possible to decide further about the chemical nature of the centre from optical experiments alone.

Paramagnetic resonance. – Additional information comes from the paramagnetic resonance measurements of GRIFFITHS, OWEN and WARD [33] who first established uniquely that the centre produced by X-irradiation was associated with Al.

The paramagnetic resonance is found in specimens irradiated with X-rays or in a reactor. As with the optical effects, the paramagnetic effects can be removed by heating at about 300 °C, by illuminating with U.V. light and as described above, by prolonged reactor irradiation. There is no doubt that the effects are associated with the same centres, although it is difficult to decide which part of the optical absorption (visible or U.V.) is associated with the paramagnetic centre now to be described. GRIFFITHS *et al.* [33] found that there were 6 paramagnetic units having the same principal g values ($g_{\parallel} = 2.06$, $g_{\perp} = 2.00$) and oriented at equal intervals around the c-axis. All units had $g_{\parallel}$ directions at about 58° to the c-axis. Each line showed hyperfine structure consistent with the electron moving in orbits near nuclei having nuclear spin of $I = \frac{5}{2}$. Of the few possibilities, ^{27}Al is the most likely and it was the only impurity having $I = \frac{5}{2}$ which was found by spectroscopic analysis to be present. Further details of the hyperfine structures showed that, first, the direct effect of the magnetic field on the nuclear levels was also consistent with the gyromagnetic ratio for ^{27}Al; and second, lines were also present arising from quadrupole interaction. The axis of symmetry of the various hyperfine effects did not correspond with the axes of the g-tensor.

The O'Brien model. – The intensity of the hyperfine effects was small and this indicated that, although the electron energy levels were influenced by the ^{27}Al, the electrons taking part in the resonance did not spend very much time near the ^{27}Al nuclei. O'BRIEN [34] has put forward a model which satisfactorily accounts for the features of the magnetic resonance spectrum. It is assumed that initially in the crystal ($Al + e^-$) replaced Si, the extra electron having been derived from the Na or Li which are also found to be present. Thus, in the unirradiated state, the binding around the substitutional Al is complete, the electrons being primarily localized on the oxygen. When irradiated with ionizing radiation, an electron is removed from the oxygen adjacent to the Al and becomes trapped at the monovalent impurity. It is the levels of the group Al—O—Si which give the observed magnetic resonance. There are six such units symmetrically arranged around the c-axis, the perpendiculars to the triangle making 51°3′ (p_x) to the c-axis, the Al—Si direction (p_y) 54° and the direction perpendicular of Al—Si (p_z) 58°40′ to the c-axis.

The angle quoted by GRIFFITHS *et al.* [33] corresponds to the perpendicular to Al—Si direction, rather than the Al—Si direction itself which they stated in their paper. However, in O'Brien's molecular orbital model the most loosely bound electron corresponds to a p_x orbital (Fig. 23).

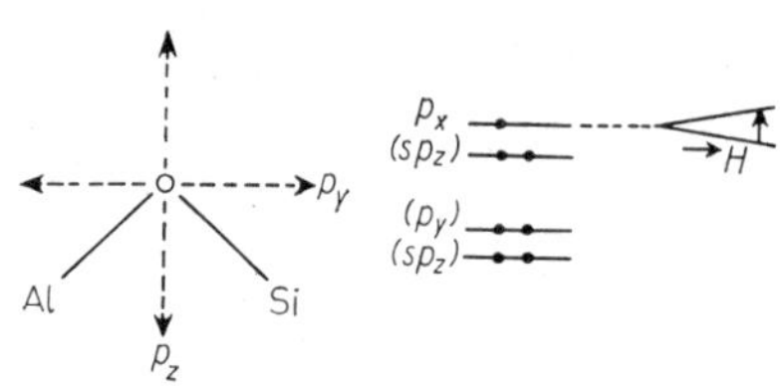

Fig. 23. – The orbital directions and relative energies in the O'Brien model for the aluminium center in quartz.

The relation of the optical results to the model. – We are now in a position to discuss whether the visible absorption is associated with the trapped hole ($Al^{3+}\,O^-\,Si^{4+}$) or the trapped electron (Li, Na or ?). The discussion is based on two experimental results:

a) That the visible absorption is very broad (2 eV at half-absorption).

b) That whereas both bands, U.V. and visible, are bleached when the crystals are illuminated with U.V. light, neither is bleached when illuminated with visible light.

In order to account for the observed width of the visible bands it has been suggested that the transitions are to or from one of the energy bands of the crystal. In this case it is much more likely to be the valence band, for in partially ionic crystals like quartz, one expects that the hole will have a very much higher mass than the electron for motion through the crystal. We should then be able to excite the centre and allow it to return to the ground state before the hole moves away under thermal influences. Thus optical bleaching would not occur, which is in agreement with experiment.

The anisotropy of the absorption. – Another experimental observation which may be discussed in relation to the model is the anisotropy of the optical absorption. It was found by MITCHELL and PAIGE [20] that the anisotropic ratio $\mathscr{A}=\mu_{E\parallel c}/\mu_{E\perp c}$ was 1.5, although the value associated with the main peak at 2.70 eV is probably a little less when the effect of the unexplained shoulder is subtracted. They showed that this was in reasonable agreement with a level scheme in which the p_x energy level was uppermost ($s-p_x$, $\mathscr{A}=$ $=1.3$ cf. 1.06 for p_y and 0.78 for p_z). The U.V. absorption induced by X-rays is practically isotropic and is thus not consistent with the Al centre orbitals as discussed by O'BRIEN.

We have assumed, in discussing the band width, that the energy levels of the bonding orbitals are in the valence band and that only the antibonding orbitals have levels in the energy gap of the crystal. This does not affect the anisotropy since the transition is allowed by virtue of the *s*-character of the lower levels. In the valence band one expects to have the levels of the normal O^{--} (as opposed to an O^{--} adjacent to Al); therefore, throughout the valence band there will be levels having some *s*-character in the atomic part of their Bloch functions.

The electron trap. – Regarding the electron trap, there is very little information. It is possible that it is Li or Na but this requires that the amounts of substituted Al be exactly compensated by the Li or Na concentration. If this were not so one would expect to see either the visible or the U.V. absorption in unirradiated crystals. This is not observed. Another possibility for exact compensation would be to have an oxygen ion vacancy for each two substituted Al, with the $|O^{--}|$ acting as the electron trap.

The enhancement of the visible coloring. – Finally, it is interesting to note that the amount of visible coloring (substituted Al) may be increased by successive cycles of reactor irradiation—heat treatment—reactor irradiation. This can be readily explained if excess interstitial Al migrated during heat treatment, in competition with displaced Si, to the Si vacancies created by the neutron irradiations.

5. – Final comments.

Probably the most important contribution which optical work can make to the study of radiation damage is to the knowledge of the electronic structure of the various defects. This can be done using one of the several « anisotropic effects » referred to. The study of these « anisotropic effects » and paramagnetic resonance are complementary means of providing information about the electrons of the defect.

Optical effects may be used to study the relative increases and decreases of defect concentrations but care must be taken to ensure that the electronic occupancy does not change during the treatment.

REFERENCES

[1] D. L. Dexter: *Solid State Physics*, **6**, 353 (1958).
[2] H. Y. Fan and A. K. Ramdas: *Journ. Appl. Phys.*, **30**, 1127 (1959).
[3] M. Lax and E. Burstein: *Phys. Rev.*, **97**, 39 (1955).
[4] M. J. Stephen: *Proc. Phys. Soc.*, **74**, 485 (1958).

[5] J. R. Hardy: to be published (1961).
[6] C. D. Clark: *Journ. Phys. Chem. Sol.*, **8**, 481 (1959).
[7] C. D. Clark, R. W. Ditchburn and H. B. Dyer: *Proc. Roy. Soc.*, *F* **234**, 363 (1956); A **237**, 75 (1956).
[8] P. Wedepohl: *Proc. Phys. Soc.*, B **70**, 177 (1957); *Ph. D. Thesis* (University of Bristol, 1957).
[9] E. W. J. Mitchell: *Journ. Phys. Chem. Solids*, **8**, 444 (1959).
[10] W. Kaiser and W. L. Bond: *Phys. Reev.*, **115**, 857 (1959).
[11] R. J. Elliott: to be published (1960);
[12] P. Kemmey and E. W. J. Mitchell: *Proc. Prague Semiconductor Conference*, in print (1960).
[13] J. R. Hardy and S. D. Smith: *Phil. Mag.*, in print (1960).
[14] H. B. Dyer and I. G. Matthews: *Proc. Roy. Soc.*, A **243**, 320 (1957).
[15] C. D. Clark, P. Kemmey and E. W. J. Mitchell: *Proc. of Prague Semiconductor Conf.*, in print (1960).
[16] G. Bemski: *Journ. Appl. Phys.*, **30**, 1195 (1959).
[17] G. D. Watkins, J. W. Corbett and R. M. Walker: *Journ. Appl. Phys.*, **30**, 1198 (1959).
[18] E. W. J. Mitchell and J. D. Rigden: *Phil. Mag.*, **2**, 941 (1957).
[19] J. C. King, D. L. Wood and D. M. Dodd: *Phys. Rev. Lett.*, **4**, 518 (1960).
[20] E. W. J. Mitchell and E. G. S. Paige: *Phil. Mag.*, **46**, 1353 (1955).
[21] P. Feofilov: *Dokl. Akad. Nauk SSSR*, **92**, 545 (1953); *Proc. of Paris Luminescence Conf., Journ. de Phys. et Rad.*, **17**, 656 (1956).
[22] R. J. Elliott, I. G. Matthews and E. W. J. Mitchell: *Phil. Mag.*, **3**, 360 (1958). [Also brief report in Discussion of Paris Luminescence Conference: *Journ. de Phys. et Rad.*, **17**, **661** (1956)].
[23] E. W. J. Mitchell and E. G. S. Paige: *Phil. Mag.*, **1**, 1085 (1956).
[24] H. Y. Fan and A. K. Ramdas: *Proc. Prague Semiconductor Conf.*, in print (1960).
[25] C. D. Clark and E. W. J. Mitchell: to be published (1961).
[26] W. A. McKinley and H. Feshbach: *Phys. Rev.*, **74**, 1759 (1948).
[27] P. Kemmey and E. W. J. Mitchell: to be published (1961).
[28] C. D. Clark and D. W. Palmer: *Physica*, in print (1960); *Proc. Amsterdam Conf. on « Reactivity of Solids »*.
[29] W. Primak: *Phys. Rev.*, **100**, 1677 (1955).
[30] J. Bastin, E. W. J. Mitchell and J. Whitehouse: *Brit. Journ. Appl. Phys.*, **10**, 412 (1959).
[31] E. G. S. Paige: *Phil. Mag.*, **2**, 864 (1957).
[32] R. W. Ditchburn, E. W. J. Mitchell, E. G. S. Paige, J. F. H. Custers, H. B. Dyer and C. D. Clark: *Defects in Crystalline Solids, Report of Bristol Conference* (1954) (Phys. Soc., London 1955).
[33] J. H. E. Griffiths, J. Owen and J. M. Ward: *Defects in Crystalline Solids; Report of Bristol Conference* (1954) (Phys. Soc., London, 1955).
[34] M. C. M. O'Brien: *Proc. Roy. Soc.*, A **231**, 404 (1955).

Radiation Damage in Metals.

On the Behavior of Vacancies in Pure Metals.

E. GERMAGNOLI

Laboratori C.I.S.E. - Milano
Istituto di Fisica del Politecnico - Milano

Radiation damage in metals is very important from a technological standpoint because many structural elements and fuel elements in nuclear reactors are metallic. A satisfactory understanding of the nature of changes in size, shape, mechanical properties, and so on, of irradiated metals involves a very careful investigation of defects introduced mainly by heavy charged particles, like fission products and recoil nuclei. These defects are usually described in terms of spikes.

If basic facts concerning the nature and the behavior of lattice imperfections are considered with the double purpose of achieving new information in the field of solid state physics and of finding a satisfactory approach to the answer of pratical questions put by nuclear engineers, it is necessary to investigate the simplest defects first and convenient metals have to be selected for experiments. It is desirable that simple point defects are introduced into metals at a controllable rate and that their mutual interactions are unlikely, so that they do not change their nature during the experiments.

Three methods have been extensively used in order to produce defects in metals; namely

a) thermal excitation
b) irradiation
c) cold work.

Noble metals have been preferred for both theoretical and experimental investigations because of the intrinsic simplicity of both crystal lattice and electronic structure and because they are available in a rather pure form.

Concerning again the production of defects, theoretical calculations by HUNTINGTON and SEITZ [1] for copper leave very little doubt that thermal excitation produces only single unassociated lattice vacancies in a wide range of temperature; this happens because the formation energy of interstitials is about three times as large as the formation energy E_F of vacancies (~ 1 eV). It may be consequently assumed that no interstitials are present even near the melting point.

Moreover vacancies are expected to be almost totally dissociated in equilibrium conditions, provided the binding energy of divacancies (B) is rather small and the concentration of vacancies (C_v) is small.

In fact, for typical values of B and E_F, one finds

$$\frac{C_D}{C_v} \simeq 6C_v \exp\left[\frac{B}{kT}\right] = 6 \exp\left[-\frac{E_F - B}{kT}\right] \ll 1 \,,$$

in a wide range of equilibrium temperatures, C_D being the concentration of divacancies.

It is therefore apparent that very simple defects (single vacancies) are produced by thermal excitation in noble metals.

Irradiation results also in simple defects whenever the bombarding particles are light and of low energy (electron of a few MeV, for instance), the produced defects being mainly widely spaced Frenkel pairs.

The damage introduced by cold work is somewhat more complicated in nature, motion of dislocations resulting probably in the generation of interstitials and rows of vacancies, which probably do not migrate as single defects through the lattice.

2. A very good picture of the behavior of simple defects in a convenient metal (Cu, Au and perhaps Pt, and Ag) could be obtained if vacancies and interstitials were produced in it with the help of all three listed methods separately, and changes in several properties were investigated. In fact each defect affects differently each property, and annealing studies in a wide range of temperature are likely to be the most convenient way of separating the effect of each kind of defect. It would be highly desirable if a similar investigation were carried out with specimens from the same origin, and equally handled, because small differences in the impurity content or in the preliminary annealing could be responsible for different behaviors.

A good effort in this direction was made by PIERCY [2], who investigated the recovery of platinum after 10 % extension at liquid-nitrogen temperature, quenching from above 1600 °C and irradiation with fast neutrons at 50 °C. The measured properties were electrical resistivity, lattice parameter and density.

Interstitials and vacancies are probably nearly equivalent in affecting the electrical resistivity: in fact about $4 \cdot 10^{-6}\ \Omega$ cm is a reasonable figure for the contribution of 1% Frenkel pairs to extra resistivity, and theoretical calculations [3] show that a 1% concentration of lattice vacancies contributes $(1 \div 2) \cdot 10^{-6}\ \Omega$ cm to extra resistivity. The lattice parameter is much more sensitive to interstitials than to vacancies, according to calculations by TUCKER and SAMPSON [4]; moreover, it is expected that volume and lattice parameter behave in the same way when Frenkel defects are present, while volume should have a larger change than lattice parameter if vacancies are introduced into the specimen.

Isochronal recovery of resistivity in Piercy's experiments showed a single annealing stage after irradiation and quenching, the migration energies involved being 1.43 eV and 1.13 eV respectively. Density decreased after irradiation, while the lattice parameter did not show any significant change. These results indicate that interstitials are absent in both cases because they are not produced by thermal excitation and, probably, because the temperature at which irradiation was performed was too high to freeze-in interstitials. The different migration energies resulting from these experiments need some further discussion: we will consider this fact later and assume at the moment that either single vacancies or simple aggregates of them are left within the specimens after quenching and irradiation.

Recovery after cold work at liquid temperature showed two annealing stages, the involved activation energies being 0.73 and 1.43 eV. The high-temperature annealing stage is attributed to vacancies in view of the previoulsy discussed results; the low-temperature annealing stage should consequently be ascribed to interstitials. Actually, interstitials are generally expected to be mobile at much lower temperature, the migration energy being presumably a few tenths of an eV; according to Piercy 0.73 eV is the energy which is needed to release interstitials from trapping sites.

3. It is convenient to compare these results with the ones which were obtained by Germagnoli *et al.* [5, 6] from quenched platinum specimens. Three different diameters (0.1, 0.07, and 0.04 mm) and different cooling rates were used: this was achieved by letting the wires cool down after switching off the heating current or by immersing the hot wires in water. Cooling times ranging between 35 ms and 800 ms were obtained, the initial rate of cooling being about $6\cdot10^4$ °C/s for water-quenched specimens. Fig. 1 shows how the extra resistivity due to quenching depends on temperature. E_F is equal to $(1.20\pm\pm0.04)$ eV and the linear relation-

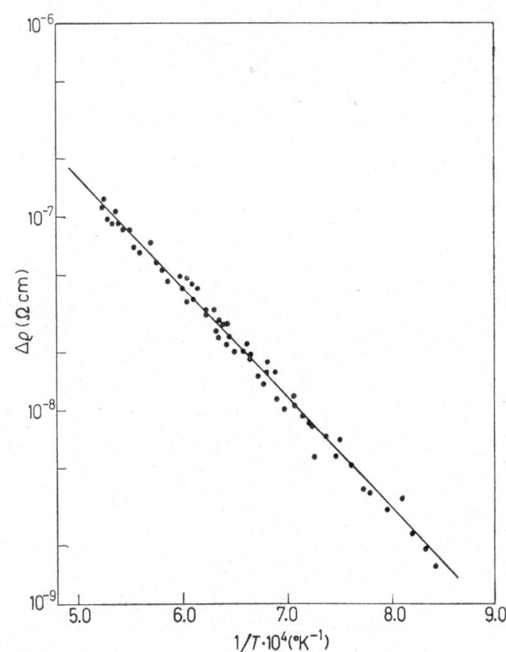

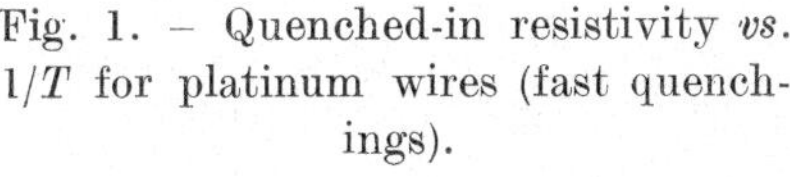
Fig. 1. – Quenched-in resistivity *vs.* $1/T$ for platinum wires (fast quenchings).

ship between $\log \Delta\varrho$ and $1/T$ demonstrates that vacancies are not annihilated during quenching even at high temperature.

Recovery was investigated at temperatures ranging from 320 to 540 °C, the temperature being so chosen that the total annealing times ranged from a few minutes to about twenty hours. Specimens quenched at different rates were used at all temperatures and the quenching temperatures were four: 1050, 1140, 1380 and 1630 °C. The percentage of annihilated defects was almost 100% the only exception being in the specimens quenched at highest temperature, in which case about 5% of the resistivity remained.

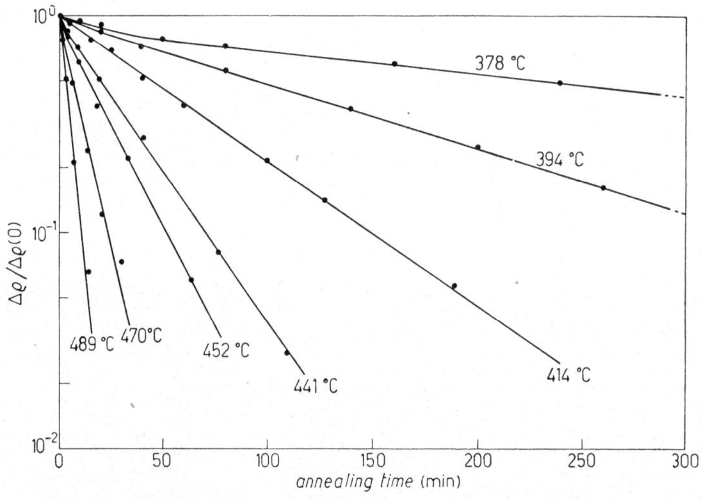

Fig. 2. – Typical annealing curves for platinum (fast quenching from low temperature).

Fig. 2 shows typical annealing curves after low-temperature quenchings. Assuming that only single vacancies are frozen within the specimen, that they migrate either to the surface [7] or to dislocations, and that no clustering takes place, we expect that

$$\frac{\mathrm{d}C_v}{\mathrm{d}t} = -\,12\exp\left[-\frac{E_M}{kT}\right]\frac{\nu}{\omega}\,C_v\,,$$

which gives for the relaxation time

$$\tau = \frac{0.693\omega}{12\nu}\exp\left[\frac{E_M}{kT}\right].$$

Here the pre-exponential factor is taken equal to 1, ω is the number of jumps a vacancy makes before disappearing at sinks ($\simeq 10^6$), ν is the jump frequency, and E_M is the migration energy of vacancies.

Fig. 2 shows that the simple hypotheses leading to an exponential annealing law are probably fulfilled whenever the initial concentration of vacancies is as low as 10^{-5} or less. A different behavior seems to result at low annealing temperatures and for a short initial period, during which some defects probably disappear into neighboring dislocations. Also the exponential dependence of τ on $1/T$ is quite evident from Fig. 3 which gives $E_M = (1.48 \pm 0.08)$ eV.

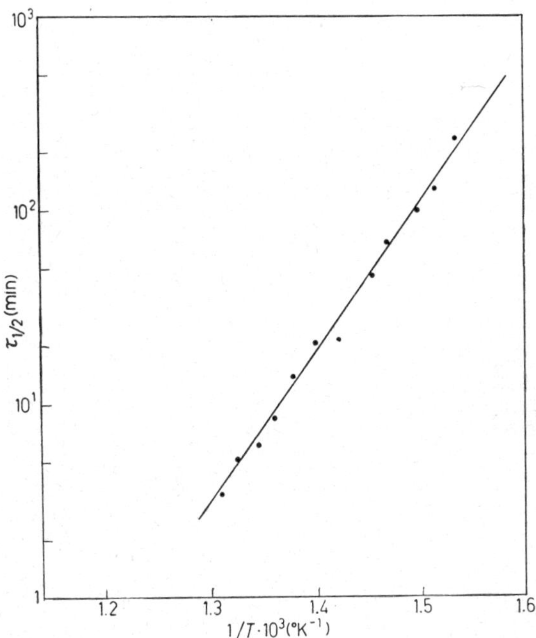

Fig. 3. – Lifetime of vacancies *vs.* $1/T$ for platinum (fast quenching from low temperature).

At high quenching temperatures, or if the cooling rate is slow, the annealing kinetics are more complicated. From Fig. 4 and 5 it is apparent that either the quenched-in defects are not of a unique kind when the specimen has reached room temperature or that single vacancies congregate during the annealing itself. The space and time-dependence of the concentration of defects within a quenched specimen was studied by KOEHLER, SEITZ and BAUERLE [8], who suggested that annealing data which are derived with higher initial concentration of vacancies should reflect the behavior of divacancies and of more complex vacancy clusters. Divacancies have larger mobilities than single vacancies and anneal out more rapidly. This is true according to results shown in Fig. 4 and 5.

Moreover, complicated kinetics are found also in the annealing of slowly quenched specimens, and in this case the amount of frozen-in vacancies has little influence upon the shape of annealing curves which only at high temperature become nearly exponential. This behavior probably cannot be explained in terms of divacancies, which must be very few in low-temperature-quenched

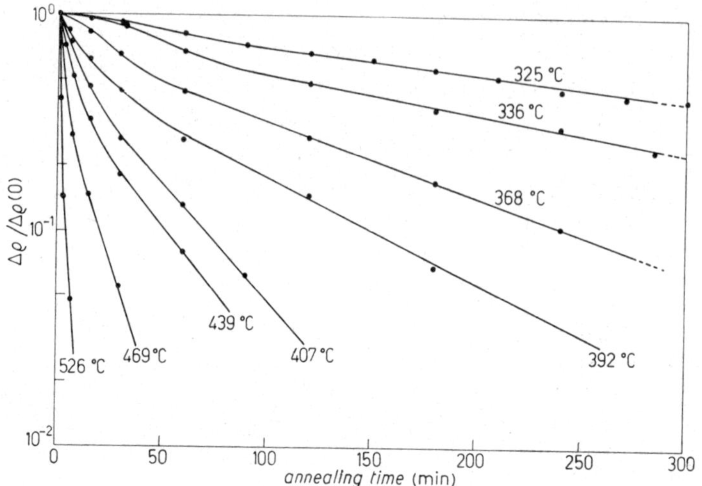

Fig. 4. – Typical annealing curves for platinum (fast quenching from high temperature).

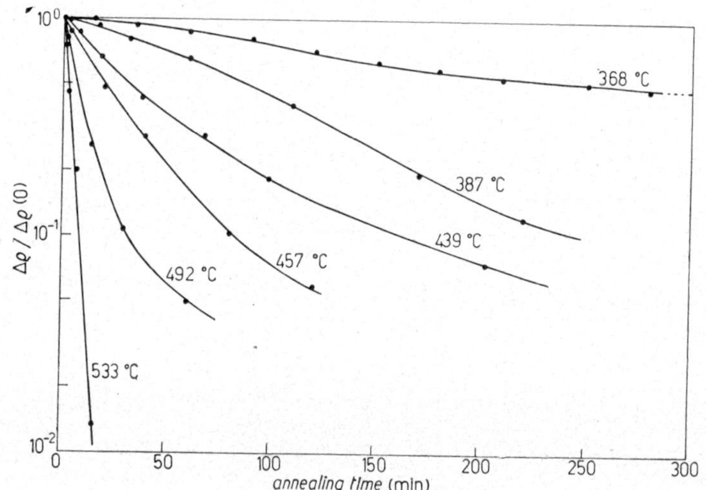

Fig. 5. – Typical annealing curves for platinum (slow quenching).

specimens, and is likely to be related to interactions between vacancies and impurity atoms.

4. If the results discussed in the previous section are taken into account, it is not difficult to understand Piercy's results with quenched specimens and why they suggest a lower migration energy. A migration energy of about 1 eV resulted from the measurements by GERMAGNOLI *et al.* if the quenching temperature was above 1600 °C and this was attribued to divacancies produced by clustering of vacancies during quenching.

It may consequently be assumed that in platinum $E_F \simeq 1.3$ eV (from the quoted results and from others by LAZAREV and OVCHARENKO [9], BRADSHAW and PEARSON [10]), and $E_M(1.4 \div 1.5)$ eV. These values add up to $(2.7 \div 2.8)$ eV, which is near 2.96 eV, the self-diffusion energy measured by KIDSON and ROSS [11]. This substantiates the idea that single vacancies are indeed the responsible defects in the observed changes of properties.

Even closer agreement has been found between the results of self-diffusion and quenching and annealing experiments in gold, copper and aluminum: similar pictures seem to hold in the cases of gold and aluminum, the metals which have been more estensively studied.

The situation is, however, far from being completely clear. Two main topics need futher consideration: the influence of impurities in controlling the annealing kinetics of defects and the connection between the discussed results and the electron microscope observations of quenched specimens by HIRSCH and coworkers [12]. This new technique is exceedingly useful in showing what the ultimate fate of least part of the quenched-in defects is. No discussion of these arguments will be attempted here because they both are covered in detail in other lectures.

5. It is apparent from the above considerations that the quenching method is very useful but not completly satisfactory because its basic hypothesis is that the defects which are present within the specimen in equilibrium condition at high temperature may partly disappear and partly aggregate during quenching. An equilibrium method would be more satisfactory, even if more difficult from an experimental point of view.

FEDER and NOWICK [13] and very recently SIMMONS and BALLUFFI [14] carried out equilibrium measurements by comparing at the same temperature the changes in lattice parameters with the expansion coefficient. It is known that vacancies contribute to macroscopic changes of volume becouse if vacancies are created within the specimen the atoms removed from their lattice sites are brought to the surface, thus adding new lattice planes. Lattice parameter is not affected to a large extent by vacancies. If both volume and lattice parameter are plotted as a function of temperature, the curve giving volume changes stays above the lattice parameter curve in the range of temperatures where the lattice vacancies are produced thermally to a noticeable extent, while the two curves coincide at low temperatures. The formation energy of vacancies in aluminum was obtained with a sufficient degree of accuracy using this method. The value which was found agrees well with the one obtained with the quenching method.

Unfortunately, measurements of both microscopic and macroscopic expansion are probably not accurate enough at very high temperature to allow this method to be used for platinum, while other interesting metals, like copper and gold, can possibly be studied.

Some other experimental methods are available to detect point defects, the most extensively used being the measurements of mechanical properties and of stored energy. The amount of energy which is stored within the specimen after quenching-in the form of lattice defect is rather small and experimental determinations of it may be very difficult; stored energy measurements are much more useful with irradiated specimens particularly when combined with resistivity measurements, because from the ratio of these two quantities it is possible to derive definite conclusions concerning the type of defects being responsible for the observed effects.

REFERENCES

[1] H. B. Huntington and F. Seitz: *Phys. Rev.*, **61**, 315 (1942).
[2] G. R. Piercy: *Phil. Mag.*, **5**, 201 (1960).
[3] F. Abeles: *Journ. Phys. et Rad.*, **16**, 345 (1955); P. Jongenburger: *Appl. Sci, Res.*, B **3**, 237 (1953).
[4] C. W. Tucker and J. B. Sampson: *Acta Met.*, **2**, 433 (1954).
[5] A. Ascoli, M. Asdente, E. Germagnoli and A. Manara: *Journ. Phys. Chem. Solids*, **6**, 59 (1958).
[6] G. L. Bacchella, E. Germagnoli and S. Granata: *Journ. Appl. Phys.*, **30**, 748 (1959).
[7] A. Blandin and J. Friedel: *Acta Met.*, **8**, 384 (1960).
[8] J. S. Koehler, F. Seitz and J. E. Bauerle: *Phys. Rev.*, **107**, 1499 (1957).
[9] B. G. Lazarev and O. N. Ovcharenko: *Dokl. Akad. Nauk SSSR*, **100**, 875 (1955).
[10] F. J. Bradshaw and S. Pearson: *Phil. Mag.*, **1**, 812 (1956).
[11] G. V. Kidson and R. Ross: *Proc. Intern. Conf. on Radioisotopes in Scientific Research* (Paris, 1957), p. 185.
[12] See for instance: P. B. Hirsch, J. Silcox, R. S. Smallman and K. W. Westmacott: *Phil. Mag.*, **3**, 897 (1958).
[13] R. Feder and A. S. Nowick: *Phys. Rev.*, **109**, 1959 (1958).
[14] R. O. Simmons and R. W. Balluffi: *Phys. Rev.*, **117**, 52 (1960).

Recent Progress in a Theory of Vacancy-Annealing in Metals (*).

A. C. DAMASK (**)

Pitman-Dunn Laboratories, Frankford Arsenal - Philadelphia, Penn.

1. – Introduction.

The annealing of vacancies in quenched, cold-worked, and irradiated metals is now a rather standard method for the measurement of the activation energy for their mobility. It is well established that vacancies can become bound to some impurity atoms, but no theoretical analysis has been made of the effect of this binding on the annealing kinetics. For instance the purity of the metal required to yield accurate data is not known, but in general investigators feel that the metal should be quite pure. Several annealing curves have shown deviations from exponential, and it is not known if this can be caused by impurity binding.

Modern theories of impurity diffusion in metals require that vacancies be bound to the impurities to form a « Johnson molecule ». Calculations have been made of this binding energy [1-4] and the results have been checked against measured diffusion coefficients. Agreement has been rather poor in many cases casting some doubt on the calculations. However, there are other factors, in addition to vacancy-impurity binding, which can affect the diffusion of impurities [2,5] and the existence of these possibilities implies that diffusion measurements are not a fair test of the validity of binding energy calculations. One of the natural results of a theory of vacancy annealing in the presence of impurities will be the suggestion of a more direct type of experiment by which the binding energy of impurities to vacancies can be determined.

The problem of vacancy-impurity interaction is treated in the most simple form by solving the corresponding differential equations on the analog computer (Electronic Associates, Inc., Type 31 R) at Brookhaven National Laboratory. It is realized that divacancies [6] can form which can alter the kinetics and that

---

(*) This work is being done in collaboration with Dr. G. J. DIENES and is supported in part by the U. S. Atomic Energy Commission.

(**) Guest Scientist at Brookhaven National Laboratory, Upton, N. Y.

the formation of trivacancies [7] and larger clusters probably supply an increased number of sinks for the removal of the vacancies. This general problem, which is obviously much more complex, is currently being studied, and the results will be published in a later paper. However, it is believed that as long as the vacancy concentration is low, clusters of vacancies can be ignored. This is indicated by experiments which show that significant deviations from exponential decay usually occur for high-temperature quenches where the initial concentration of vacancies is high.

It will be shown that, regardless of the impurity concentration, an exponential decay almost always occurs. However the rate constant of this decay is only partly related to the activation energy of vacancy mobility. Even metals of 10^{-5} impurity content can yield false values for vacancy migration energy, and only zone-refined metals of purity of at least 10^{-7} can guarantee a true value. This requirement of extremely high purity has been anticipated in the experiments on aluminum by DeSorbo and Turnbull [8].

2. – Theory.

The two reactions in the annealing of vacancies to sinks in the presence of impurities to which they can be bound are:

$$v + I \underset{K_2}{\overset{K_1}{\rightleftharpoons}} C\,, \tag{1}$$

$$v \overset{K_3}{\rightarrow} \text{sinks}\,, \tag{2}$$

where v, I and C are the concentration (atomic fraction) of vacancies, unbound impurities and vacancy-impurity complexes respectively, and the K's are the corresponding rate constants. The physical meaning of equation (2) is that vacancies disappear by migration to a fixed number of sinks (for example, dislocations). The differential equations for these reactions can be written as (after substitution $I = I_0 - C$)

$$\frac{\mathrm{d}C}{\mathrm{d}t} = K_1 I_0 v - K_1 C v - K_2 C\,, \tag{3}$$

$$\frac{\mathrm{d}v}{\mathrm{d}t} = - K_1 I_0 v + K_1 C v + K_2 C - K_3 v\,, \tag{4}$$

where I_0 is the total impurity concentration, which is a constant for any given experiment. Experimentally, for example by resistivity methods, the total vacancy concentration, *i.e.*, the sum of C plus v, is the measured quantity. Thus the pertinent quantity to be calculated is $N = C + v$, which from equations (3) and

(4) is described by the differential equation

$$\frac{dN}{dt} = \frac{d(C+v)}{dt} = -K_3 v \,. \tag{5}$$

Equations (3) and (4) form a set of non-linear coupled differential equations which when solved will describe the complete annealing behavior of the system. The equilibrium concentration of vacancies at the annealing temperature is negligibly small, and v and C approach zero as time approaches infinity. (The equilibrium concentration is easily included, if desired, by a simple change in variables.)

These equations were solved on the analog computer for a wide variety of parameters (initial vacancy concentration, impurity concentration, and binding energy) and the details of these calculations will be discussed in the next section. The first general result of interest from the machine calculation was the finding that the number of complexes, C, increased very rapidly during the early stage of the annealing. During this same transient period the concentration of free vacancies decreased rapidly. After these fast transients, C and v decayed steadily. The physical basis for this behavior is as follows: the equilibrium concentration of complexes at the annealing temperature is much larger than that at the quench temperature. The fast transient is therefore the establishment of the new equilibrium and is largely governed by the jump rate of the vacancies (see Appendix I). The rapid elimination of these transient conditions suggested that an analytic approximation could be used for the bulk of the decay curve. Equilibrium for the first reaction, equation (1), implies that

$$\frac{C}{v(I_0 - C)} = \frac{K_1}{K_2} = K \,, \tag{6}$$

or

$$C = \frac{KI_0 v}{1 + Kv} \,. \tag{7}$$

Substitution into equation (5) gives

$$\left[\frac{1}{v} + \frac{KI_0}{v(1+Kv)^2}\right] \cdot dv = -K_3\, dt \,. \tag{8}$$

Integration gives

$$\ln v + \frac{KI_0}{1+Kv} - KI_0 \ln\left(\frac{1+Kv}{v}\right) + A = -K_3 t \,, \tag{9}$$

where A is the constant of integration. Equation (9) gives v as a function of time. The value of C corresponding to any value of v can be calculated from equation (7) and thereby $C + v$ can be determined as a function of time.

Equations (7) and (9) were found to fit all of the curves obtained in the machine calculations. Somewhat surprisingly, however, many of the decay curves (the change of N with time) were to be found simply exponential in time which implies that the ratio of C to v remained constant This constancy of C/v arises from a further approximation in equation (6), namely $C \ll I_0$. This latter approximation is valid over a wide range of the physically interesting parameters. Substitution of

$$\frac{C}{v} = \frac{K_1}{K_2} I_0 , \tag{10}$$

into equation (5) and integration gives

$$C + v = N = B\left(1 + \frac{K_1}{K_2} I_0\right) \exp\left[- K t\right] , \tag{11}$$

where

$$K_e = \frac{K_3}{1 + (K_1/K_2)I_0} . \tag{12}$$

Equations (11) and (12) can also be derived from equation (9) with the approximation that $Kv < 1$ and $v < 10^{-3}$. (This latter approximation allows one to neglect KI_0 with respect to $|KI_0 \ln v|$.)

Two things are immediately evident from equation (12). First, K_e is a composite of all the rate constants and the impurity concentration and will therefore, in general, not obey a simple Arrhenius equation even though the decay curves are purely exponential. Secondly, the pre-exponential term contains two of the rate constants and is therefore temperature-dependent. It is therefore obvious that the determination of activation energy by change of annealing temperature and calculation of the slope ratio is an unsatisfactory method.

It is also clear from eq. (12) that the effective rate constant decreases with increasing impurity concentration. The physical basis for this behavior may be described as follows. The vacancies, in their random migration toward sinks, encounter impurity atoms at which they become trapped temporarily, *i.e.* the complexes must dissociate to furnish free vacancies for further annealing. Thus, the whole annealing process is slowed down.

3. – Details of calculations and results.

A wide range of physically interesting parameters was selected for the machine solution of the general coupled nonlinear eq. (3) and (4). The pertinent parameters, which determine the rate constants and the initial conditions, are the annealing temperature, the vacancy migration energy, the effective sink concentration, α, the vacancy formation energy, the quench temperature, the impurity concentration and the vacancy-impurity binding energy. The following parameters were held constant throughout the calculation: the annealing temperature, 100 °C; the vacancy migration energy, E_M, 0.8 eV; the vacancy sink concentration α, 10^{+10}, (see ref. [10], p. 143, and ref. [11], p. 1716), [12] and the vacancy formation energy, 1.0 eV. The variable parameters were the quench temperature, 600, 800, 1000 °C; the impurity concentration, 10^{-5}, 10^{-4}, 10^{-3}; and the vacancy-impurity binding energy, B, 0.20, 0.25, 0.35 eV.

The initial concentration of free vacancies was assumed to be the equilibrium concentration at the quench temperature and therefore calculated from the relation

$$v_0 = \exp\left[-\frac{E_F}{kT}\right],$$

where E_F is the energy of formation. This assumes that the number of free vacancies is independent of the number of bound vacancies. This assumption is valid up to a concentration of about 10^{-3} impurity atoms; at this concentration the error is about 1% (because 13 I_0 lattice sites are not accessible to the free vacancies). The initial concentration of complexes was calculated from eq. (6) using the above values. for v_0. The K's are written as follows:

$$K_1 = 42\nu \exp\left[-\frac{E_M}{kT}\right],$$

$$K_2 = 7\nu \exp\left[-\frac{(E_M + B)}{kT}\right],$$

$$K_3 = \alpha\nu\lambda^2 \exp\left[-\frac{E_M}{kT}\right],$$

where 42 and 7 are the appropriate combinatory numbers for association and dissociation of complexes respectively, and the values assigned to the other constants are $\nu = 10^{13}$ and $\lambda^2 = 10^{-15}$.

A typical solution for the early stages of the annealing is shown in Fig. 1. The rapid build up of the complexes and the associated decay of the free vacancies are clearly observable. The transients obviously disappear very fast with respect to the decay of N. For comparison the annealing of vacancies in the absence of impurities is also shown.

Fig. 2 shows some selected curves which have been plotted semilogarithmically. For these curves the binding energy is 0.2 eV. The lower four curves represent runs at the same quench temperature but different impurity concentrations. The upper curve has the same parameters except for a different quench temperature. It is seen to be parallel to the curve at equivalent impurity concentration but of lower quench temperature. All of these curves are straight which

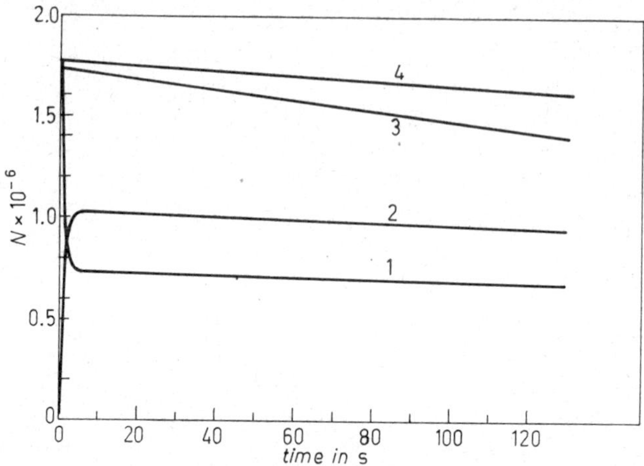

Fig. 1. – Computer-produced curves of eq. (3), (4) and (5) with $B=0.25$ eV, $T_q=600$ °C and $I_0=10^{-4}$. Curve 1: concentration of free vacancies; curve 2: concentration of complexes; curve 4: concentration of $N=C+v$; curve 3: v (and N) *vs.* time for pure metal, *i.e.*, $I_0=0$.

indicates that each has a single decay constant. It is also seen that the decay constant is the K_e of eq. (11) and (12), and K_e calculated by these equations is exactly the same as read from these curves. The important point demonstrated is that a good exponential plot of vacancy annealing data does not mean that the activation energy thereby determined is the activation energy of motion of the vacancy.

The approximation which applies in the above cases is that the number of complexes is small compared to the number of impurities. It is therefore expected

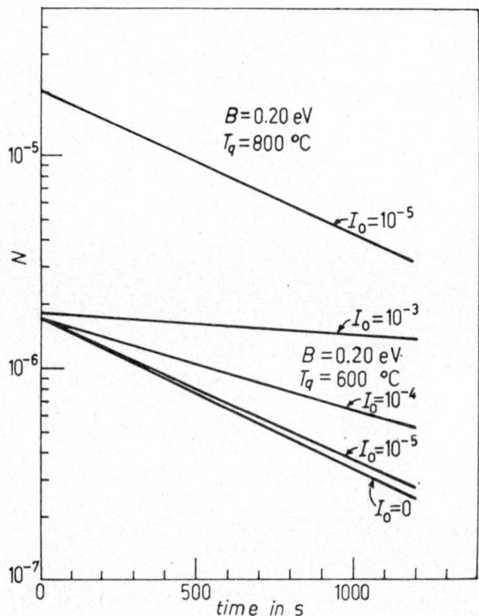

Fig. 2. – Semilogarithmic plots of curves of the type shown in Fig. 1 for the decreases of N with time. All curves in this figure are straight lines.

that this approximation will become invalid at higher vacancy concentration, *i.e.*, higher quench temperatures, high binding energies, and low impurity concentrations. This deviation from linearity is shown by the examples of Fig. 3. These curves show how the deviation from linearity increases with quench temperature. For this high binding energy even the lowest curve $T_q = 600$ °C, is not quite linear. For these curves the more complete solution of eq. (9) must be applied. An example of the validity of this analysis is shown in Fig. 4. This is the original machine-drawn curve from which the upper curve of Fig. 3 was plotted. The constant A of eq. (9) was evaluated

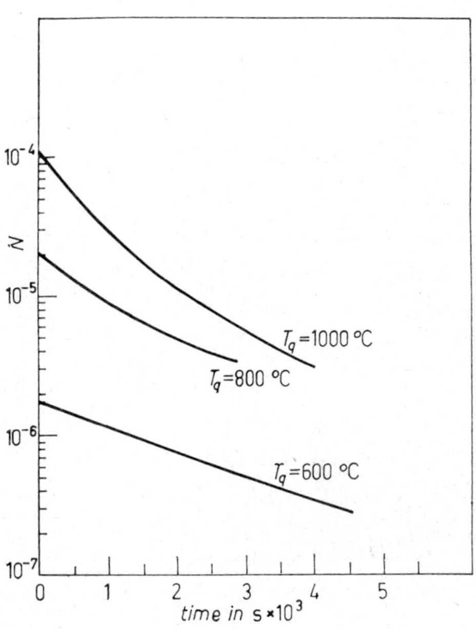

Fig. 3. – Semilogarithmic plots of computer-produced curves of the same type as in Fig. 2 showing decrease of N with time in cases where exponential approximation is invalid.

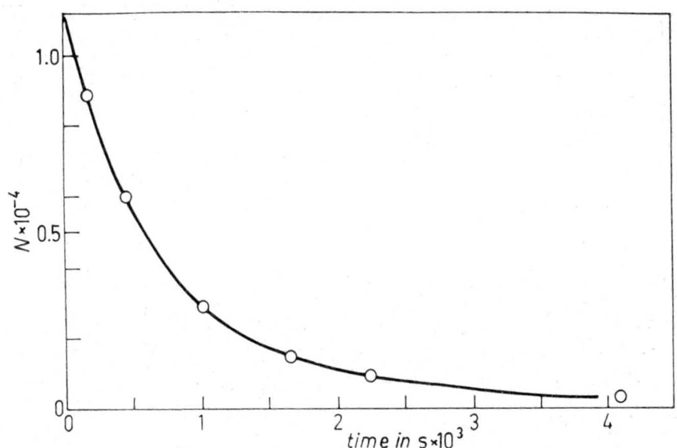

Fig. 4. – Computer-produced curve for the case $B = 0.35$, $I_0 = 10^{-5}$, and $T_q = 1000$ °C. Circles are points calculated from eq. (9).

at the first (early time) point on the curve to avoid transient effects, and the succeeding points were calculated from the same equation. It is seen that the equilibrium solution fits the general solution with excellent accuracy. The curvature of the examples of Fig. 3 diminishes with increasing time since the vacancies are being removed and the condition approaches the approximation of eq. (10). This behavior of a rather fast early decay followed by exponential behavior has been observed experimentally in quenched samples [13-16], although divacancy formation may cause some of the early variation (Appendix II). A similar early fast decay has been observed during the annealing of copper irradiated at low temperature [17]. It is possible that interstitials interact with impurities in this case; the formal theory of this interaction is identical to the vacancy-impurity interaction discussed here. According to the present theory, deviations from pure exponential behavior due to the presence of impurities are expected to be predominant for low impurity concentrations.

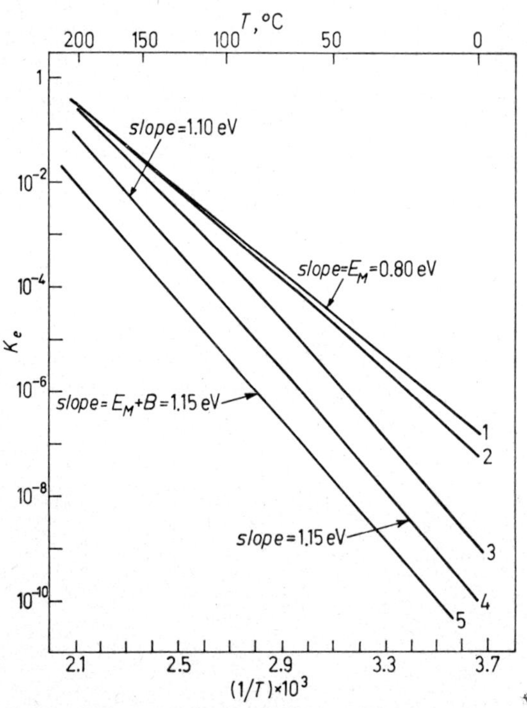

Fig. 5. – Plot of calculated K_e *vs.* $1/T$ for selected parameters.

Even if the early parts of annealing curves are avoided, difficulties in analysis still arise. As was previously stated, eq. (11) will not obey an Arrhenius law. It is of interest to calculate the temperature-dependence of eq. (12) for some selected parameters to show what may be expected experimentally. All variations will, of course, occur within the two limiting slopes of E_M and E_M+B. These two limits are shown in Fig. 5 by curves 1 and 5. The limiting case of E_M+B cannot be attained with a binding energy lower than 0.35 for an impurity concentration as low as 10^{-3}. Conversely, if the binding energy is 0.2 eV, 10^{-6} impurity concentration will begin to cause deviation from the E_M limiting slope in the lower temperature region. This means that if the binding energies of the impurities in a metal are not known, the measurement of vacancy migration energy cannot be guaranteed to be correct even with an impurity concentration of 10^{-7}. Although not shown in this figure, a binding energy of 0.35 will correspond to a slope larger than E_M for an impurity concentration as low as 10^{-7}. This may well be an extreme case, but the general picture given by this figure is that any measurements on metals less pure than zone-refining processes permit will contain a probable error of a considerable fraction of the unknown energy. An example of the nonlinearity of this Arrhenius plot is evident in curves 3 and 4. The change in slope with temperature is visually evident in curve 3 and is calculated and labeled on curve 4. It is evident from this analysis that the influence of impurities is emphasized by low temperature annealing runs.

4. – Discussion.

The requirements for the study of vacancy migration in impure metals can now be examined. In order to obtain the energy for vacancy migration, zone-refined metals must be used and caution must be exercised in the subsequent handling of the material to prevent the introduction of impurities. The guarantee of results can perhaps be establised by performing the same experiment after a second zone-refining to see if a change has occured. Once the vacancy migration energy has been measured, binding energy experiments can be done. This is achieved by making the same measurements on a zone-refined specimen to which a known amount of a single impurity has been added. It was shown in Fig. 5 that in order to attain the E_M+B slope with a low binding energy, impurity concentrations considerably greater than 10^{-3} must be added. This can lead to problems in the association of impurities and also to a breakdown of the present simple theory. However in order to obtain the value of B, the slope E_M+B need not be achieved. The binding energy can be calculated immediately from any exponential decay curve by use of eq. (12) once E_M is accurately known.

For the purposes of computation, the annealing data should be taken in the range where an exponential decay occurs. This is achieved by either low-temperature quenches or analysis of only the long-time portion of the decay curve where eq. (11) is expected to be obeyed.

5. – Further work in progress.

It is easily seen from the geometry of Fig. 6 why a divacancy moves faster in the f.c.c. lattice than the single vacancy. If the atom marked + is to interchange with the vacancy at the end of the arrows it must pass through a barrier of 4 atoms (marked with numbers). Since it must come closer than nearest neighbor position to these four atoms the repulsive contribution to the potential energy accounts for about 50 to 75% of the total migration energy. If the second vacancy is placed at the atom marked 1 then not only

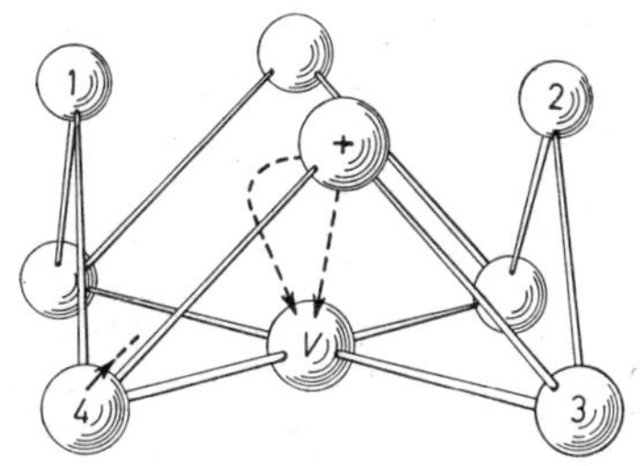

Fig. 6. - Face-centered cubic lattice.

is one of the repulsive terms eliminated but the moving atom can now deviate in its path (curved arrow) so that it does not come closer than nearest neighbor to any of the other three atoms in the barrier. Thus all of the repulsive terms are effectively eliminated, and the divacancy migration energy is much lower than that of the single vacancy.

The trivacancy is quite stable. If the trivacancy is created geometrically in an equilateral triangle (atoms marked +, 1, and V arrowhead) then there is only one atom [4] which is nearest neighbor to all three vacancies. This atom relaxes in the direction of its arrow into the center of the tetrahedron so that three vacancies are shared equally on four atomic sites. In order to migrate this relaxed atom must be pushed back into its original position. This gives a large contribution to the migration energy of the trivacancy and its resultant total migration energy is about twice that of a single vacancy.

Summary of the divacancy calculation. The second calculation is virtually complete. This is the reaction

$$V_1 + V_1 \underset{K_2}{\overset{K_1}{\rightleftharpoons}} V_2$$

$$V_1 \xrightarrow{K_3} \text{sinks}$$

$$V_2 \xrightarrow{K_4} \text{sinks} .$$

Unfortunately the solution cannot be expressed in as simple an analytical form as in the impurity calculation, but the following general features are observed.

1) An inflection point can be produced by combined mono- and divacancy annealing. This comes from the second derivative as given in Appendix II. (Other physical processes can also produce an inflection, of course.)

2) Development of an inflection point, which is associated with a hump in the divacancy concentration *vs.* time curve, is favored by high binding energy and high activation energy for V_2 motion.

3) If the energies given in 2) are low, no hump is produced and the V_2 concentration is a very small steady-state one (almost zero). Under these conditions the system drains by forming V_2's which anneal fast. There is a closed solution but it is neither exponential nor bimolecular (actually the differential equation for V_1 contains a linear and a quadratic term and neither is negligible).

The calculation of the addition of impurities to the single and divacancy case is now being prepared for computation. The final calculation with the inclusion of trivacancies and a variable sink concentration is under study.

APPENDIX I

The analog computer solutions have indicated that the transient is fast compared to the steady decay of the defects. Since the analog computer solutions were obtained only at one annealing temperature, we examine here the importance of the transient under more general conditions.

From eq. (1), (2) and (12), of the text the ratio of the transient rate, R_t, to the steady decay rate, R_s, may be written

$$\frac{R_t}{R_s} = \frac{K_1 v(I_0 - C)}{K_e(C + v)} . \tag{A-I.1}$$

This ratio, which should be large for a fast transient, is small when K_e is maximum, *i.e.* $K_e = K_3$ (a minimum of binding). Thus

$$\frac{R}{R_s} \geqslant \frac{K_1 v(I_0 - C)}{K_3(C + v)} . \tag{A-I.2}$$

At $t = 0$ $C \ll v$ and $C \ll I_0$ and therefore

$$\left(\frac{R}{R_s}\right)_{t=0} \simeq \frac{K_1 I_0}{K_3} . \tag{A-I.3}$$

Using the values for K_1 and K_3 given in the text

$$\left(\frac{R}{R_s}\right)_{t=0} \sim \frac{4 \cdot 10^{16}\, I_0}{\alpha} \sim 40 , \tag{A-I.4}$$

for $\alpha = 10^{10}$ and $I_0 = 10^{-5}$ (which is again the low limit for the R_t/R_s ratio). Thus, the initial rate of approach to equilibrium is much faster than the steady decay for physically reasonable choices of the parameters, and, the equilibrium of the reaction represented by eq. (1) is rapidly established, as already shown by typical analog computer solutions.

APPENDIX II

Experiments reported in the literature to date indicate that annealing of quenched-in defects has the following characteristics:

1) The overall defect concentration decreases monotonically, *i.e.* $\mathrm{d}N/\mathrm{d}t$ is always negative.

2) In most cases the second derivative, $\mathrm{d}^2N/\mathrm{d}t^2$, is positive. For quenches from high temperature, decay curves with an inflection point have also been observed. The latter would imply a second derivative that is negative at $t=0$.

The annealing equations for the vacancy-impurity mechanism are examined for these characteristics in this Appendix.

Eq. (5) of the text,

$$\frac{\mathrm{d}N}{\mathrm{d}t} = -K_3 v\,, \tag{A-II.1}$$

shows immediately than $\mathrm{d}N/\mathrm{d}t$ is always negative as required by condition 1) above.

The second derivative is given by

$$\frac{\mathrm{d}^2N}{\mathrm{d}t^2} = -K_3\frac{\mathrm{d}v}{\mathrm{d}t} = -K_3[-K_1v(I_0-C)+K_2C-K_3v]\,. \tag{A-II.2}$$

At $t=0$, I_0 and C are related by the equilibrium condition at the quench temperature, *i.e.*

$$\frac{C}{v(I_0-C)} = \frac{K_1^1}{K_2^1} = 6\exp\left[\frac{B}{kT_q}\right]. \tag{A-qI.3}$$

At $t=0$, therefore,

$$\frac{\mathrm{d}^2N}{\mathrm{d}t^2} = K_3K_2\left[\frac{K_3}{K_2}v_0+\frac{K_1/K_2}{K_1^1/K_2^1}C_0-C_0\right]. \tag{A-II.4}$$

Since $T_q > T_a$, $\exp[B/kT_q] < \exp[B/kT_a]$ and, therefore, $K_1^1/K_2^1 < K_1/K_2$: Thus, $(K_1/K_2)/(K_1^1/K_2^1) > 1$ and, therefore, $\mathrm{d}^2N/\mathrm{d}t^2$ is always positive.

Thus, the vacancy-impurity mechanism cannot explain those decay curves which show an inflection point. The inflection point very probably arises from the presence of quenched-in divacancies. We plan to examine the kinetics of annealing in the presence of divacancies by the techniques discussed in this paper.

REFERENCES

[1] N. F. Mott and H. Jones: *The Theory of the Properties of Metals and Alloys* (New York, 1958), p. 88.

[2] D. Lazarus: *Phys. Rev.*, **93**, 973 (1954).

[3] F. J. Blatt: *Phys. Rev.*, **99**, 600 (1955).

[4] L. C. R. Alfred and N. H. March: *Phys. Rev.*, **103**, 877 (1956); *Phil. Mag.* **46**, 759 (1955).

[5] A. Ascoli and A. C. Damask: *Bull. Am. Phys. Soc.*, **5**, 182 (1960).

[6] J. S. Koehler, F. Seitz and J. B. Bauerle: *Phys. Rev.*, **107**, 1499 (1957).

[7] A. C. DAMASK, G. J. DIENES and V. G. WEIZER: *Phys. Rev.*, **113**, 781 (1959).

[8] W. DESORBO and D. TURNBULL: *Phys. Rev.*, **115**, 560 (1959).

[9] It is assumed throughout that the electrical resistivity of a bound vacancy is the same as a free one.

[10] G. J. DIENES and G. H. VINEYARD: *Radiation Effects in Solids* (New York, 1957).

[11] G. J. DIENES and A. C. DAMASK: *Journ. Appl. Phys.*, **29**, 1713 (1958).

[12] The quantity frequently measured experimentally is the mean number of jumps a vacancy makes before annihilation which, from a random walk approximation, is roughly the reciprocal of the atomic fraction of sinks. α, from ref. [10] is given as $\alpha = 2\pi N_0/\ln r_1/r_0 \sim N_0$ where N_0 is the number of dislocation lines per cm^2. Therefore the concentration of sinks is $N_0 \times$ number of lattice sites per cm of line, and the atomic fraction of sinks is $N_0 \times$(number of lattice sites/cm^3)$^{-\frac{2}{3}}$ if it is assumed that (sites /cm of line)^3 = (lattice sites)/cm^3.

[13] F. J. BRADSHAW and S. PEARSON: *Phil. Mag.*, **1**, 812 (1956); **2**, 379 (1957).

[14] G. L. BACCHELLA, E. GERMAGNOLI and S. GRANATA: *Journ. Appl. Phys.*, **30**, 748 (1959).

[15] G. AIROLDI, G. L. BACCHELLA and E. GERMAGNOLI: *Phys. Rev. Lett.*, **2**, 145 (1959).

[16] J. E. BAUERLE and J. S. KOEHLER: *Phys. Rev.*, **107**, 1493 (Fig. 7) (1957).

[17] T. H. BLEWITT, R. R. COLTMAN and G. E. KLABUNDE: *Bull. Am. Phys. Soc.*, **4**, 135 (1959).

The Experimental Study of Point Defects in Pure Metals.

R. O. SIMMONS

University of Illinois, Department of Physics - Urbana, Ill.

1. – Introduction.

1'1. – The production of point lattice defects in a crystal changes many of its macroscopic physical properties. Some of these properties are more sensitive to changes in the internal structure of the crystal than others. Examples of sensitive properties are the residual electrical resistivity in metals, the minority carrier lifetime in semiconductors, and the absorption of light in ionic crystals.

In order to formulate unique atomic models for the defects produced under given conditions, we require more than observations of a change in a sensitive property, however. We require an intervening theory, which gives the specific property change per defect, based upon an assumed model for the defect. Further, we would like some assurance that the property change is proportional to the defect concentration or is related in some known way to the concentration. Finally, in the usual case of several types of defects being present simultaneously, we would like some assurance either that only one of the defect types is changing in concentration or that a known interaction between defects of different types is occuring.

In practice, of course, these conditions are seldom satisfied. A circular argument may appear in the analysis of the results of an experiment, the theoretical estimates are qualitative, and the multiplicity of defect structure is not fully known. Further, changes in one type of defect are almost always intimately associated with other lattice defects in the crystal [1].

Therefore, while the general species of possible point, linear, and planar defects have been known for a long time, and much speculation on their possible occurrence and influence in actual crystals has been put forward, relatively few cases have been established in which a unique atomic model for the defect structure is valid. These few cases have usually involved either direct observation on a near atomic scale, as in the decoration and electron transmission techniques for study of the geometry of dislocation networks, or the simultaneous measurement of changes in more than one physical property of the crystal studied, as in the study of the F-center in alkali halide crystals.

Because of their small size, point defects have not yet been observed directly, except possibly in some studies with the field ion microscope [2]. Coordinated measurements of several macroscopic properties have therefore proven to be more useful.

Among those properties which when suitably compared can give important and unique information about point defects are changes in the macroscopic size of a crystal and the X-ray lattice parameter. We consider here the application of such techniques in establishing atomic models for point defects produced in crystals by various means. In particular, we examine the situation when the defect concentrations are so small (10^{-2} or less) that the usual methods of X-ray diffraction structure analysis are inapplicable [3].

First, the well-justified principles underlying this expansion comparison technique are reviewed, with particular emphasis upon the careful delineation of the proper experimental conditions required. Examples are drawn from the literature to illustrate specific points. Second, the properties of some simple point defects in metals which have been established by measurements of this kind are discussed. An assessment is made of the contribution of such work to the present understanding of irradiation effects in solids in terms of atomic models. Third, the complementary relation this type of approach bears to others is analysed.

1'2. – It should be noted throughout this discussion that emphasis is placed on the *changes* taking place as the defect structure of the crystal is altered. To illustrate several reasons for this approach, let us consider a closely related technique for investigating possible defect structures, that of the direct comparison of densities. In principle this is an attractive method of determining defect concentrations.

For a perfect crystal the bulk density is given by $(n_0 M)/\Omega$ where M is the mass of the n_0 atoms in the unit cell of volume Ω. Measurement of Ω in an actual crystal by X-ray diffraction gives by this definition an ideal X-ray density, $\varrho_0 = (n_0 M)/\Omega$, which can be compared with the measured bulk density of the same actual crystal. The actual bulk density is $\varrho = (nM)/\Omega$ where n is now the mean number of atoms per unit cell. Then the added fraction of substitutional atomic sites in the actual crystal, compared to a perfect crystal, is given by

$$(\varrho_0 - \varrho)/\varrho_0 = (n_0 - n)/n_0 = \Delta N/N \, .$$

A number of practical difficulties arise in attempts to apply this relations: 1) Direct high-precision density measurements are restricted in flotation methods to a rather small temperature interval where suitable stable liquids exist. For most irradiated solids these temperatures correspond to a condition in which considerable thermal annealing of the primary damage has already occurred. While we may be interested in atomic models for this condition, we may have difficulty in constructing unique ones without knowledge of the prior conditions the material has passed through. 2) The value of Avogadro's number, N_0, which must be used in converting atomic weight to true atomic mass, is apparently uncertain by about one part in 20 000. 3) Macroscopic inhomogeneities and flaws may be difficult to avoid in actual crystals. When several types of defect are present, it may not be possible to vary the concentration of the one under study independently of the others. 4) The X-ray wavelength standards are not yet determined with the accuracy required, and discussion of the relative merits of different methods of determining the peak positions of X-ray diffraction lines continues in the literature. In practice, therefore, the direct method has been successful only in cases for which the defect concentrations are large, of the order of several atomic percent.

2. – Principles of expansion measurements for point defects.

Consider now the influence of the introduction of point defects upon the dimensions and shape of a solid and upon its X-ray diffraction pattern. The standard state of the crystal can be somewhat imperfect if measurements only of changes are required. Further, X-ray methods are more reliable for measuring changes than for measuring absolute values. The study of defects can then be extended reliably to substantially smaller concentrations than in the direct method, down to about 10^{-5}. We shall see that in many problems of interest the concentrations are of this magnitude.

2·1. *Volume and shape changes.* – Point defects act as centers of dilatation, because they produce strains in their immediate neighborhood. Models for point defects have been considered in detail by Eshelby for a solid treated as an elastic continuum [4]. Here we sketch very briefly only some principal results.

Length and lattice parameter changes may be analysed using a general sphere-in-hole model for the defects. The production of the defects can be thought of in the following way: (*a*) cut out the region to be damaged, (*b*) produce the damage in the region, and (*c*) replace the damaged region in the original cavity, welding the cut edges together again. The volume of the damaged region will in general be different from the original volume, and dilatation of the solid is therefore produced. It can be shown, for cubically symmetric defects in an isotopic continuum, that 1) a uniform random distribution of such defects produces a change in volume of the solid without change of shape. Further, 2) the volume changes measured macroscopically and by X-rays are the same. Finally,

(3) the magnitude of the volume change can be related quantitatively to the size and elastic properties of the misfitting inclusion and of the matrix. This third point is important, for example in estimating volume changes from detailed calculations on discrete models for particular defects.

Macroscopic shape changes will occur in a solid containing a polarized array of point defects which have less than cubic symmetry. The expansion of the solid will be homogeneous, however, for a dense distribution of such defects, and the principal strains as measured macroscopically and by X-rays will be the same. The most precise treatments require, of course, that the anisotropy of the continuum properties of the solid, the symmetry of the defects, and many details of the atomic structure be taken into account.

The first two conclusions, concerning homogeneous volume changes and their correspondence as measured by the two methods, have been shown to follow for an arbitrary solid possessing sufficient crystallographic symmetry, even for point defects for which the usual assumptions of linear elasticity and superposition of effects no longer apply, provided only that a sufficient density of point defects of usual type is present [5]. The minimum density of defects required (about $10^{18}/cm^3$), is quite compatible with the maximum sensitivity available at present in measuring X-ray lattice parameter changes.

The final result is that macroscopic length and X-ray lattice parameter changes are equivalent in a solid in which point defects are produced, provided that the total number of substitutional atomic sites remains constant. A valuable corollary then follows: in a specimen of constant mass, any difference observed between length and lattice parameter expansions is the result of a change in the number of substitutional atomic sites. Because the two expansions due to centers of dilatation are equivalent, the concentration of such added sites due to defect formation or annihilation can be determined without any knowledge of the lattice relaxation about the defects.

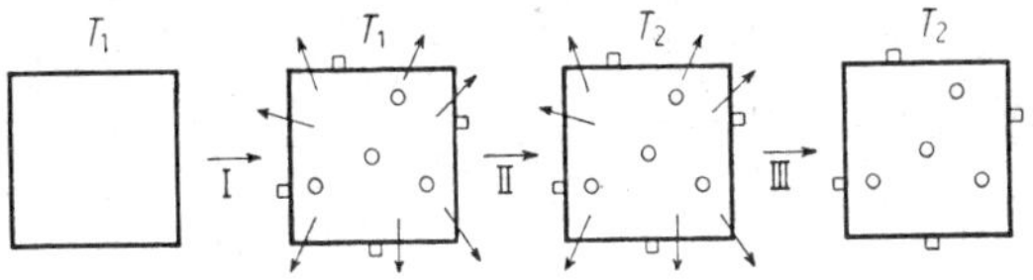

To see most simply how this occurs in a specific case, we imagine the thermal generation of vacancies as a three-step process, as shown in Fig. 1. In step I, vacant lattice sites are produced at temperature T_1 by removing atoms from the interior of the solid and placing them on

T_1 $\xrightarrow{\text{I}}$ T_1 $\xrightarrow{\text{II}}$ T_2 $\xrightarrow{\text{III}}$ T_2

$$\text{I}\qquad \frac{\Delta a}{a}=0\,,\qquad \frac{\Delta L}{L}=\frac{1}{3}c_v\,,$$

$$\text{II}\qquad \frac{\Delta a}{a}=\alpha\,,\qquad \frac{\Delta L}{L}=\alpha\,,$$

$$\text{III}\qquad \frac{\Delta a}{a}=\beta\,,\qquad \frac{\Delta L}{L}=\beta\,,$$

$$\therefore\qquad \frac{\Delta L}{L}-\frac{\Delta a}{a}=\frac{1}{3}c_v\,.$$

Fig. 1. – Schematic diagram of the sequential process of vacancy production described in the text. The added concentration of vacancies, c_v, is given by $3(\Delta L/L-\Delta a/a)$ regardless of the value of the lattice relaxation, β.

the surface, thereby creating new substitutional atomic sites. Meanwhile the solid is rigidly constrained by forces to prevent any lattice relaxation about the defects; $\Delta a/a$, the fractional change in lattice parameter, is zero. For a cubic solid the additional fraction of atomic sites is then $c_v = 3(\Delta L/L)$ where $(\Delta L/L)$ is the fractional change in length. In step II the solid is heated to a new temperature T_2 and thermal expansion $\alpha = (\Delta L/L) = (\Delta a/a)$ occurs. In step III at temperature T_2 the forces are removed and the crystal relaxes about the defects. This relaxation is by an amount $\beta = (\Delta L/L) = (\Delta a/a)$; the effect on length and lattice parameter is the same. The net effect of heating from T_1 to T_2 has therefore been to produce a difference

$$(\Delta L/L) - (\Delta a/a) = \tfrac{1}{3} c_v \, .$$

A similar argument shows that for interstitial formation the difference will be negative.

This simple picture requires several additions, for completeness. Defects of more than one type may be produced; the difference between $(\Delta L/L)$ and $(\Delta a/a)$ measures the net added concentration of substitutional atomic sites, $\Delta N/N$, and does not specify how they are distributed among different possible types of defects. For example, if divacancies, trivacancies, and interstitial atoms, etc., are present, one has for a cubic solid

$$(1) \qquad \Delta N/N = 3(\Delta L/L - \Delta a/a) = (c_{1v} + 2c_{2v} + 3c_{3v} + \dots) - (c_{1i} + \dots) \, .$$

Note that again there is the advantage that the relaxation about any particular defect type need not be known.

The added sites due to vacancy generation appear not only at the surface but also at dislocation sources. The resulting average volume changes are isotropic in a cubic crystal containing a random distribution of dislocations because of the high symmetry. These questions and others are discussed in different forms in several articles [6-8].

2·2. X-*ray diffraction changes.* – In the foregoing we have assumed that suitable measurements of X-ray lattice expansion of a crystal containing point defects can be made. This is justified because the effects of point defects on the X-ray diffraction pattern of a crystal are analogous to the effects of thermal agitation. A standard treatment of temperature effects is given by JAMES [9]. The two types of disorder are similar because the result of both is to produce random displacements of the atoms from the positions assumed in a perfect lattice [10]. In both cases a perfect reference lattice can be defined, from which few atomic displacements occur which are larger than usual interatomic distances; the atoms remain near the nodes of an average periodic lattice. Again, we only list the results of the calculations.

One finds that (1) the sharpness of the Laue-Bragg intensity maxima is unaffected, (2) the intensity of the Laue-Bragg maxima is decreased, (3) characteristic patches of diffuse scattering appear, having in each case a nearly centrosymmetric distribution about the reciprocal lattice points, and, as stated earlier, (4) the positions of the reciprocal lattice points are shifted.

Calculations using specific defect models have confirmed these general predictions [11]. For point defects in a pure metal the peak intensity effect, (2), and the diffuse scattering effect, (3), are very small for usual defect concentrations, although in principle they could be used to infer the defect structure and concentration. Interest therefore centers on the shift of the Laue-Bragg maxima, (4), whose precise measurement depends upon their non broadening. For alloys, while the shift, (4), has been interpreted to give some interesting results when considered as a function of electron-to-atom ratio [12], the diffuse scattering effects, (3), appear to hold the most promise for future investigation. All of the effects have been demonstrated qualitatively in some heavily irradiated covalent solids [13].

Quantitative verification of the nonbroadening effect, (1), has been made both i) in the case of thermal motion of the atoms and (ii) in the case of point

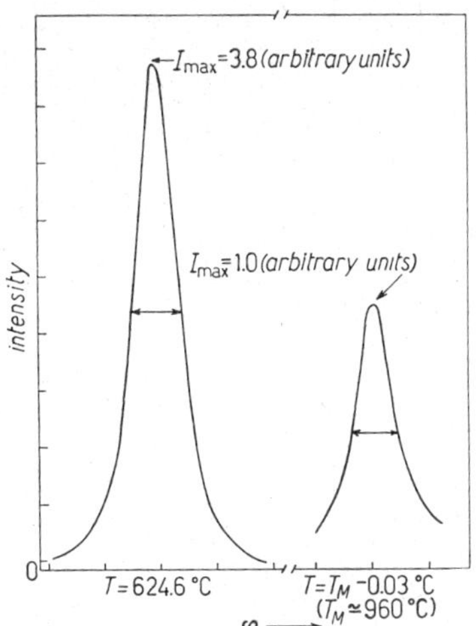

Fig. 2. – The [422] NiKα_1 diffraction maximum from pure Ag at two different temperatures, from counter diffractometer measurements. Increasing the amplitude of thermal vibration of the atoms in the lattice does not change the width of the diffraction maximum.

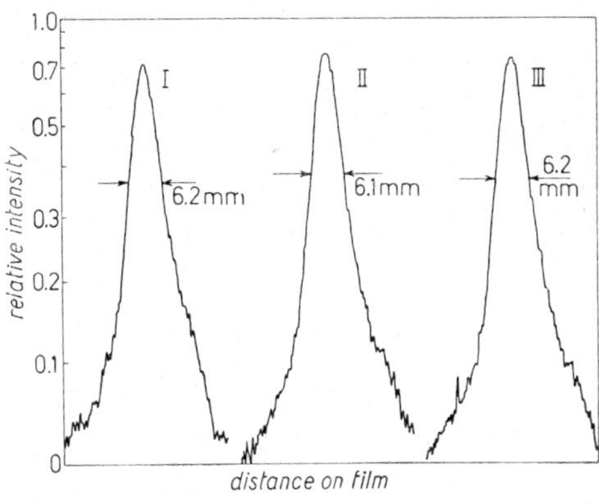

Fig. 3. – The [400] CoKα_1 diffraction maximum from irradiated Cu near liquid helium temperature, from microphotometer tracings of films; profile I before irradiation; profile II after $6.3\cdot10^{16}$ deuterons/cm^2; profile III after irradiation and subsequent recovery at 302 °K. No apparent line broadening is produced by a Frenkel defect concentration of about $5\cdot10^{-4}$.

defect production by radiation damage. (i) The profile of a high-angle back-reflection line (the [422] $NiK\alpha_1$) from pure silver was recorded by a counter diffractometer while the silver was heated to temperatures near the melting point [14]. Fig. 2 shows a comparison between a « low temperature » profile at 624.6 °C and a « high temperature » profile taken less than 0.03 of a degree below the melting point near 960 °C. The latter temperature presumably corresponds to very appreciable amplitudes of atomic vibration, because of its extreme closeness to the melting point (it is within about 2 parts in 10^5 of the absolute melting temperature). The greatly decreased intensity confirms this. Yet the half-width of the diffraction line is unchanged; evidently the displacements of the atoms in the silver lattice are still quite random. ii) The profile of the high-angle back reflection line (the [400] $CoK\alpha_1$) from a crystal of pure copper near liquid-helium temperature was recorded on film at various times during 12 MeV deuteron irradiation [6]. Fig. 3 shows microphotometer records of the results before irradiation, after irradiation, and after subsequent thermal annealing. The production of about $5\cdot10^{-4}$ Frenkel defects does not affect the width of the diffraction maximum.

In both these cases, then, the presence of random defects in no way interferes with precise measurement of changes in lattice parameter.

3. – Methods of expansion measurements.

First we mention briefly some techniques which have been applied successfully in measuring macroscopic and lattice parameter expansions due to lattice defects. Then we consider some of the necessary precautions to be observed, if interpretable results are to be obtained.

3'1. *Experimental techniques.* – Lattice expansions can be easily measured by a rotating-single-crystal high-angle-back-reflection technique employing film. From the Bragg law,

$$\Delta d/d = \Delta\lambda/\lambda - \Delta\theta \operatorname{ctg}\theta\,,$$

where d is the interplanar spacing, λ the wavelength, and θ the Bragg angle. If the diffraction line shape is unchanged, then effectively $\Delta\lambda/\lambda \simeq 0$ and for large θ the shift in angle, $\Delta\theta$, is a sensitive measure of lattice expansion. Fig. 4 shows a device used to measure the very small expansion of deuteron-irradiated copper near liquid helium temperature [6]. The linear dispersion on the film, $\Delta a/a$ per cm, is about 10^{-3}; this great sensitivity allows expansions of 10^{-5} to be easily detected. An advantage of the method is that it is insensitive to small

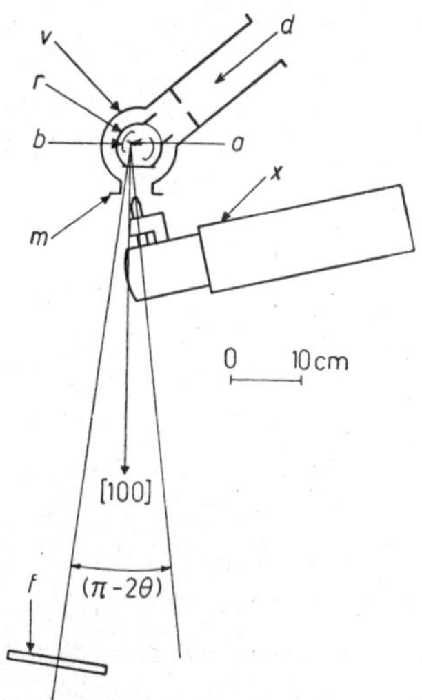

Fig. 4. – Lattice expansion apparatus for deuteron irradiation at liquid-helium temperature, top view (schematic). The X-ray tube and collimator, *x*, and the film, *f*, are rigidly connected and rotate about vertical axis « *a* » passing through the tin specimen crystal. *d* = deuteron path; *v* = vacuum jacket with « Mylar » window, *m*; *b* and *r* are helium and nitrogen tempe-r aturer adiation shields, respectively.

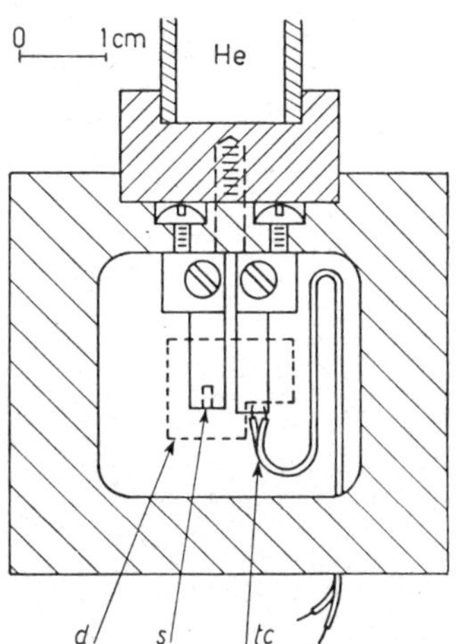

Fig. 5. – Specimen mount for lattice expansion measurement during deuteron irradiation. The X-ray sample, *s*, is essentially stress-free. The cross-section of the deuteron beam, *d*, does not include the thermocouple, *tc*, which is attached to the dummy specimen. The thermal radiation shields are not shown.

uncertainties or changes in position or orientation of the sample; such changes are difficult to avoid if the sample is maintained at high or low temperatures.

For charged-particle irradiation the sample must be a thin foil; it can be cooled near liquid-helium temperature by conduction as shown in Fig. 5. Conduction cooling of such a sample is satisfactory because for nominally pure metals the thermal conductivity maximum occurs in the range 5 to 20 °K, while for semiconductors the thermal conductivity is

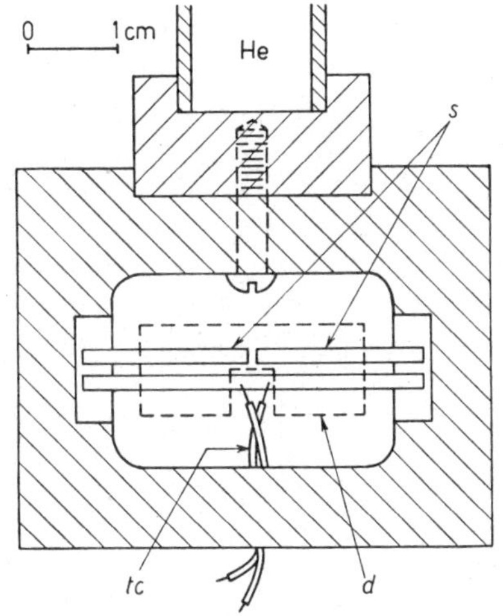

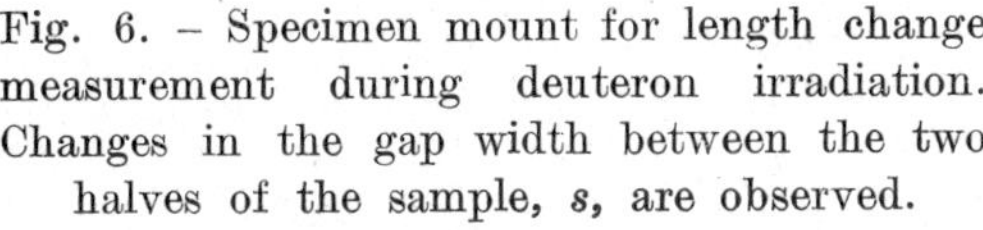
Fig. 6. – Specimen mount for length change measurement during deuteron irradiation. Changes in the gap width between the two halves of the sample, *s*, are observed.

enhanced by the non-equilibrium carrier concentrations present during irradiation. Temperature measurements can be made on an identical dummy using a calibrated thermocouple.

Length changes in irradiated solids can be measured using the principle of the specimen mount shown in Fig. 6 [15]. The expansion of a two-piece sample is measured relative to a rigid yoke of material having closely similar thermal expansion characteristics, for convenience in thermal recovery studies. The gap between the two halves of the specimen foil may be photographed through a microscope equipped with a relay lens. The accuracy of the method is about 10^{-5}, provided sharp fiduciary marks are used.

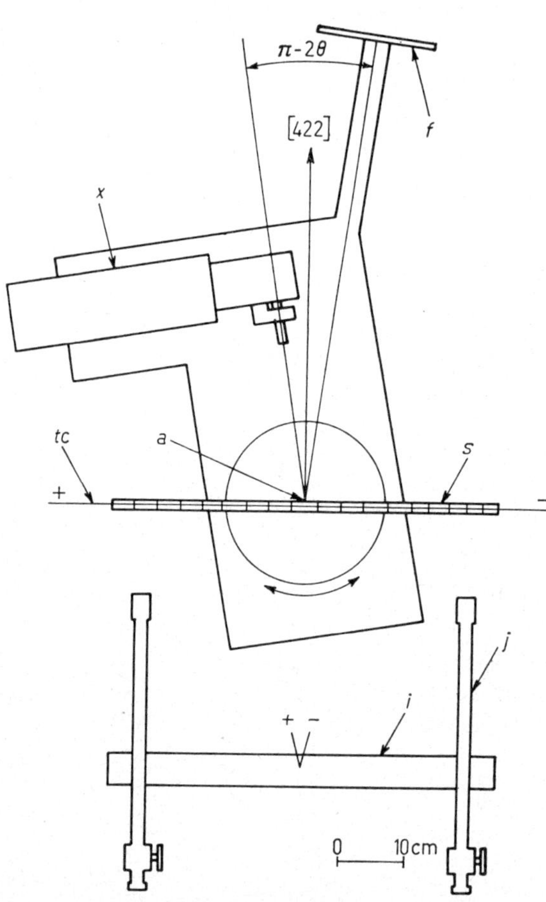

Fig. 7. – Top view of method for simultaneous measurement of length and lattice parameter expansions. The X-ray apparatus rotates about vertical axis, *a*. An invar bar, *i*, rigidly holds the microscopes, *j*, for length change measurements. The temperature distribution along the sample, *s*, is measured using the butt-welded thermocouple, *tc*.

An arrangement which has been used to measure both lattice and length expansions at high temperatures is shown in Fig. 7 [7]. The X-ray technique is the same as before, but the X-ray crystal is now part of a long bar which is supported on a horizontal, essentially frictionless surface. Use of a single crystal method allows short exposure times, usually less than 10 minutes. Changes in length of the bar are measured directly by observing changes in the separation of fiduciary marks near the ends using a parallel pair of filar micrometer microscopes equipped with relay lenses. A cross-section of the associated resistance-heated furnace is shown in Fig. 8. A long graphite cylinder is a suitable support for many metals. Temperatures differences along a 50 cm length of sample can be maintained smaller than 0.2 of a degree in a furnace about 3 m long.

It should be noted that a common characteristic of all the above methods is the absence of any temperature gradient in the measuring apparatus, as well as the absence of appreciable constraint of the sample. This is particularly important in obtaining reliable results. While many very sensitive dilatometric methods have been devised over the years, including capacitors, mutual inductances, optical levers, differential expansion, and so on, experience has shown that serious systematic errors may be present due to temperature gradients or to sample constraint and that these errors may be difficult to localize or to eliminate.

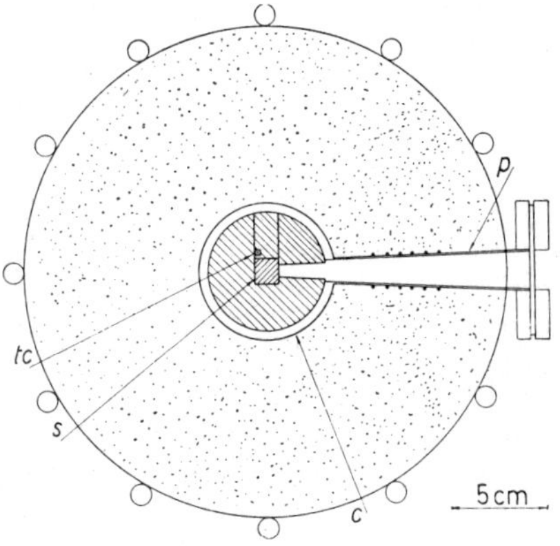

Fig. 8. – Cross-section of furnace used in length and lattice expansion measurements. The sample, *s*, is maintained essentially without constraint in a controlled atmosphere by the metal jacket, *c*; narrow ports, *p*, are used for observation. Temperatures are measured by the thermocouple, *tc*.

3'2. *Stress precautions.* – It is pertinent to remark that the results of the theory outlined in Section **2** hold only for samples which are not stressed (except in the case of pure hydrostatic pressure). Stress can arise from external constraint of the sample, from inhomogeneity of defect content, or from a combination of the two. In radiation damage studies using charged particles, some inhomogeneity of damage is nearly always present because of the relatively short range of the incident particles (with a consequent change in their efficiency in producing displacements) and because of the finite extent of the particle beam and its possible inhomogeneity in cross-section. Nor are reactor-irradiated samples immune from this difficulty, because of the inhomogeneity in composition of their surroundings in many cases.

When stresses are present, the observed results should be treated with great reserve; a unique interpretation may become difficult to make. An example is furnished by work on deuteron-irradiated crystal plates of III-V compounds, in which the irradiated portion was the central portion, the stresses being furnished by an unirradiated border of the same crystal, by inhomogeneity of damage through the plate thickness, and by a flat backing support [16]. Very pronounced tilting of the lattice planes in the irradiated portion was observed; this was related to large internal stresses postulated as due to « displacement spikes », whose relative importance has been debated in radiation damage for many years. Just what change in dimensions these lattices would show at low temperature under unstressed conditions is as yet unknown. The related lattice Ge has been shown to expand very slightly under such circumstances [17, 18], whereas the naive expectation from the «spike» hypothesis would be for contraction to occur, because these materials are more dense in the liquid phase (*). An example of a case of inhomogeneous damage treated with caution is some work on neutron-irradiated boron glass [19]. The complexity of the required analysis in this work shows the advantage of controlling the stress distribution in a sample. Finally, at temperatures near the melting point, any stress on the sample, as from a dilatometer, may lead to creep or other irreversible effects [20].

Photoelastic techniques applied to transparent crystals may have great sensitivity [21]. From our present viewpoint their principal advantage is as a sensitive index of damage or recovery, to be classed with other sensitive methods, not with absolute measurements of expansion.

3·3. *High temperatures.* – We shall see that in pure metals the equilibrium defect concentrations are at most 0.1%, which corresponds to a maximum measured difference between $\Delta L/L$ and $\Delta a/a$ of about $3\cdot10^{-4}$. In order to measure this difference with a few percent accuracy, the precision of the measured difference $(\Delta L/L - \Delta a/a)$ should therefore be of order 10^{-5}. Table I, as an example, demonstrates the difficulty of making quantitative inferences about the properties of thermally-generated defects in metals simply by comparing the results of different thermal expansion investigations. It is readily seen that neither in the macroscopic nor in the X-ray measurements is the desired agreement to the last digit present [22].

TABLE I. – *Aluminum.*

$\Delta L/L$ (20 to 600 °C)$\cdot 10^3$		$\Delta a/a$ (20 to 600 °C)$\cdot 10^3$	
16.73	ESSER and EUSTERBROCK (1941)	16.74	WILSON (1942)
17.96	RICHARDS (1942)	16.80	ELLWOOD and SILCOCK (1948)
16.78	FEDER and NOWICK (1958)	16.68	FEDER and NOWICK (1958)
16.76	SIMMONS and BALLUFFI (1959)	16.60	SIMMONS and BALLUFFI (1959)
		16.55	NENNO and KAUFFMAN (1960)

The desired accuracy in $(\Delta L/L - \Delta a/a)$ is near the limit of present techniques which have the following features: *a*) Measurement of $\Delta L/L$ and $\Delta a/a$ on the same

(*) *Note added in proof.* – Careful mearurements have now been made upon electron-irradiated InSb and GaAs (F. L. VOOK: *Phys. Rev.*, **125**, 855 (1962)). These compounds *expand* upon irradiation below 100 °K. Further, the expansion is large compared to the expansion of Si and Ge under similar circumstances. Thermal annealing of the expansion is complicated.

specimen using an identical temperature scale so that thermal expansion contributes no error; two 0.5 degree uncertainties would themselves amount to $3\cdot10^{-5}$ for a typical metal. *b*) Very smooth and unconstrained support of the sample so that its dimensional stability is better than 10^{-5} for temperature cycling between the reference temperature and the melting point; any irreversible behavior (*e.g.*, creep) is unacceptable in an experiment which purports to study thermal equilibrium conditions. *c*) Lattice expansion measurements of a precision near 10^{-5}.

4. – Irradiation damage expansion.

The simplest result to be expected from displacement collisions in an irradiated material is the prodution of pairs of interstitial atoms and vacant lattice sites (Frenkel pairs). Clearly, the formation of such a pair does not alter the number of substitutional atomic sites in the solid: the vacancy can be imagined as produced by the removal of a lattice atom from the crystal; the interstitial atom can be supposed to be added to the crystal from an external source. If the actual result of irradiation of a cubic crystal under specified conditions is the production of Frenkel pairs, then any measured relative length and lattice parameter changes will be congruent.

This congruence has been demonstrated for deuteron-irradiated copper near 10 °K. [6,15] The results are shown in Fig. 9. Further, the number of substitutional atomic sites is preserved essentially constant in copper throughout the various well-known stages of thermal recovery. The low temperature results (Stage I) are shown in Fig. 10.

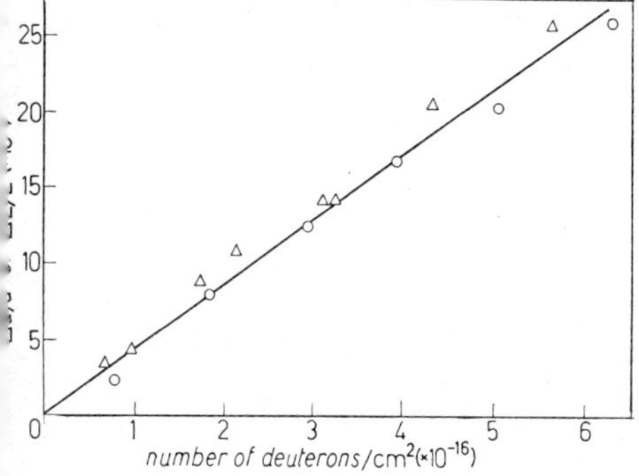

Fig. 9. – The relative changes in length and lattice parameter in deuteron-irradiated copper at low temperature are equal within experimental error. ○ lattice parameter (SIMMONS and BALLUFFI); △ length (VOOK and WERT).

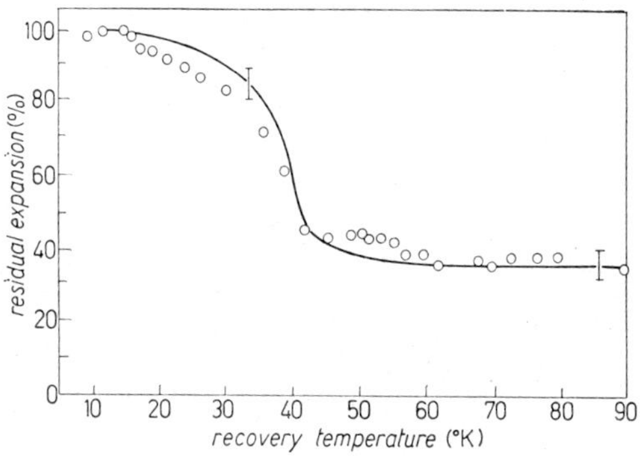

Fig. 10. – Comparison of thermal recovery in Stage I of lattice parameter and length changes in deuteron-irradiated Cu. The number of substitutional atomic sites is unchanged. ○ lattice parameter (SIMMONS and BALLUFFI); I length (VOOK and WERT).

It is conceivable, of course, that the production and annealing of more complex damaged regions could produce the same result (constancy of substitutional atomic sites); they would act as centers of dilatation of variable strength. However, the simpler « each one (interstitial) make one (vacancy) » hypothesis for irradiation and the corresponding « each one take one » for thermal recovery in stage I below 50 °K in copper has now been elaborated and substantiated in detail by more recent annealing experiments of greater sensitivity on electrical resistance [23,24] and on energy release [25]. The picture is not yet complete at higher temperature; it appears probable that trapping phenomena are involved and they have not yet been fully investigated.

An early hope of the expansion measurements on deuteron-irradiated copper [6,15] was to « calibrate » the amount of damage which was produced, in order to compare the observed damage rate with theoretical predictions. Calculations of electrical resistivity increment per Frenkel pair differed by more than an order of magnitude, while calculations of the dilatation expected per pair varied only by a factor of two. A net positive expansion, due primarily to the interstitial atom, is expected for the Frenkel pair in a close-packed metal. The result indicated that for copper the deuteron damage rate was only $\frac{1}{5}$ to $\frac{1}{10}$ the value expected from the simple hard-sphere theory for secondary displacements, and that for the Frenkel pair $\Delta\rho = 2$ to 4 microohm·cm/atomic percent. This range of values corresponds to volume changes per vacancy of 0 to $-\frac{1}{2}$ atomic volume and per interstitial of $\frac{3}{2}$ to 3 atomic volume. Later calculations of volume changes, using both Born-Mayer and Morse potentials [26], have not as yet reduced the uncertainty to any marked degree. There remains some question about the correct interionic potential to be used. For example, potentials derived from shock-wave studies, which correspond to greater departures from the equilibrium atomic positions, appear to be appreciably different from those derived from elastic constants [27].

For molybdenum irradiated near room temperature with neutrons, $\Delta L/L$ is about twice $\Delta a/a$ [28]. This is consistent with the behavior of tungsten, which has been studied in some detail [29], in which a mobile defect, presumably the interstitial, is free to migrate at this temperature and disappear at sinks in the grain boundaries.

Measurements either of $\Delta L/L$ or of $\Delta a/a$ alone may give only limited information. An example is the work by KOBAYASHI [30] on proton-irradiated NaCl. The irradiation-induced volume expansion was shown to be unchanged through annealing until about 170 °C, even though very marked changes in the optical absorption indicated clustering of the defects. Apparently the volume change per atomic site was nearly constant as the number of atomic sites involved in the individual defects increased due to aggregation.

It is to be seen that combined mesurements of $\Delta a/a$ and $\Delta L/L$ during irradiation and thermal recovery can place useful constraint upon the interpretation of irradiation effects as measured by more sensitive methods. Relatively little detailed work of this type has yet been reported, particularly at low irradiation temperatures, and few calculations have been made of the expansion due to specific defect models in the various types of solids.

5. – Vacancy concentration measurements.

5'1. *Relation to radiation damage.* – There is general agreement that one of the important primary defects produced in irradiated solids is the lattice vacancy. Further, pioneering calculations had strongly suggested that vacancies should be the predominant thermally-generated defect in noble metals because their energy of formation appeared to be lower than that of interstitial atoms [31]. These calculations remained the only evidence for many years that the process of self-diffusion in these metals should proceed *via* a vacancy mechanism. Kirkendall-effect and sintering experiments give evidence of mass transport during diffusion but neither an interstitial nor a vacancy mechanism is uniquely specified. Quenching work using electrical resistivity measurements can retain and study some mobile defects near room temperature but cannot identify them.

Fortunately, X-ray and expansion measurements can obtain unambiguous identification of the predominant thermally-generated defects, and in favorable cases, can determine some of their properties.

The actual equilibrium concentrations of defects which occur in a solid at a given temperature of course depend not only upon the energy of formation E^f, but also upon the entropy of formation, S^f, that is, upon the local disorder of the lattice near the defect. One has, for a defect of type j at a temperature T, the concentration

$$c_j = g_j \exp[-G_j^f/kT] = g_j \exp[S_j^f/kT] \exp[-E_j^f/kT]\,, \tag{2}$$

where G_j^f is the free energy of formation, exclusive of configurational entropy, and g_j^f is a constant geometrical factor which gives the number of possible orientations of the defect in the lattice.

Measuring the concentration, c, as a function of temperature therefore in principle determines the formation energy, E^f. If self-diffusion at elevated temperatures takes place *via* a vacancy mechanism, then the self-diffusion energy, Q, is given by

$$Q = E^f + E^m\,, \tag{3}$$

where E^m is the motion energy of the vacancy. This relation can be used to compute an expected motion energy if Q and E^f are known. This motion energy E^m might be expected to appear in the kinetic analysis of thermal annealing of radiation damage or of cold work if the single vacancy (monovacancy) is an important mobile defect in such annealing. The measurement of concentration also in principle yields the formation entropy. A comparison of the observed S^f with theoretical models then yields some information on the lattice disorder around the vacancy. Some properties of one member of the primordial Frenkel pair are then accounted for, and by subtraction therefore one can obtain more information on the properties of the interstitial atom, a more complex defect.

5'2. *Experimental results.* – In this section we collect the results of measurements of thermally-generated equilibrium vacancy concentrations made by Dr. R. W. BALLUFFI and the author on the metals aluminum [7], silver [32], and gold [33]. Fig. 11 shows the complete measurements on aluminum. Three

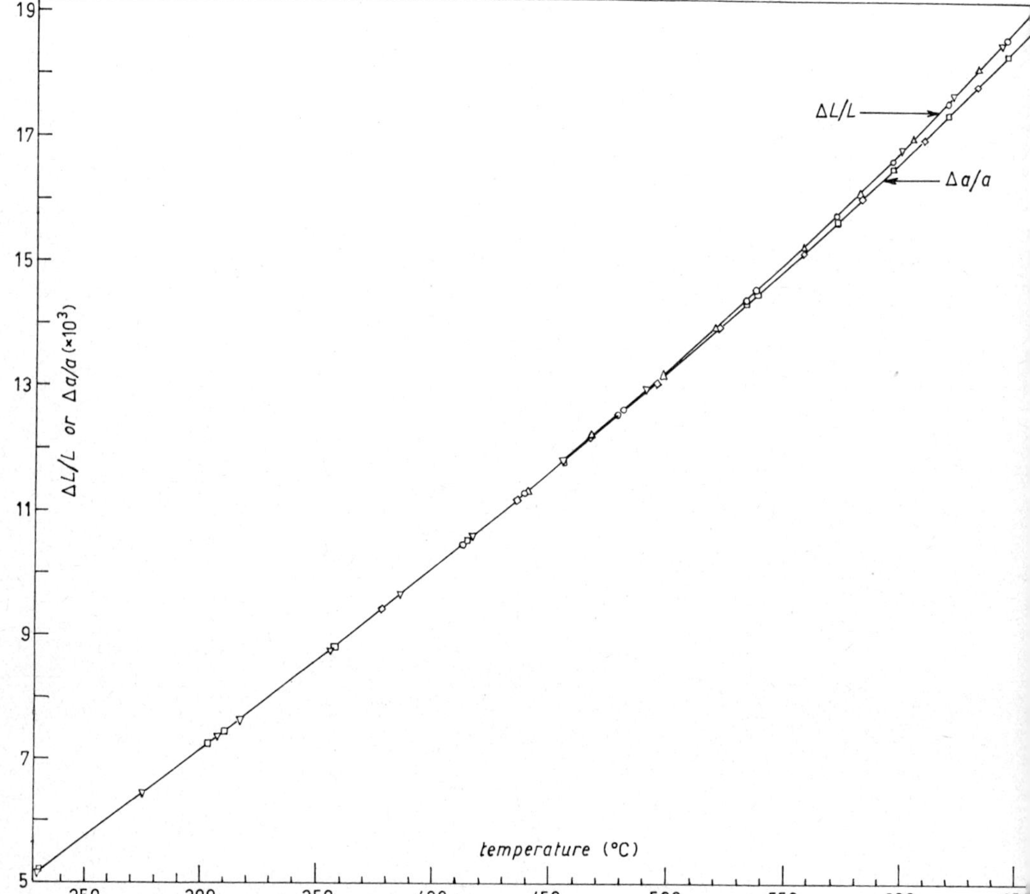

Fig. 11. – The predominant thermally-generated defect in aluminum is identified by the positive sign of the difference ($\Delta L/L - \Delta a/a$), indicating added substitutional atomic sites, lattice vacancies. $\Delta L/L$ curve: ○ cooling run; △ heating run; ▽ cooling run. $\Delta a/a$ curve: □ cooling run; ◊ heating run.

things are apparent: (*a*) both expansion measurements are reproducible as the temperature is cycled, (*b*) the total thermal expansion is very much larger than the difference $(\Delta L/L - \Delta a/a)$, and (*c*) the length expansion is larger than the lattice parameter expansion, providing unequivocal identification of the predominant thermally-generated defects as lattice vacancies.

As noted earlier in eq. (1), the added number of substitutional atomic sites is given as a function of temperature by the difference $(\Delta L/L - \Delta a/a)$, without regard to the relative numbers of various possible defects which may be present. For the three most likely defects, single, double, and triple vacancies we have

$$\text{(4)} \qquad \begin{cases} c_{v1} = \exp[-G^f_{v1}/kT] \\ c_{v2} = g_{v2}\exp[-G^f_{v2}/kT] \\ c_{v3} = g_{v3}\exp[-G^f_{v3}/kT]\,, \end{cases}$$

together with the condition that

$$\text{(1')} \qquad \Delta N/N = c_{v1} + 2c_{v2} + 3c_{v3}\,.$$

The neglect of interstitial concentrations will be considered later. Now the binding energies, G^b, of the divacancy and trivacancy are given by the relations

$$\text{(5)} \qquad \begin{cases} G^b_{v2} = 2G^f_{v1} - G^f_{v2} \\ G^b_{v3} = 3G^f_{v1} - G^f_{v3}\,, \end{cases}$$

so that from eq. (1′), (4), and (5) one obtains three equations

$$\text{(6)} \qquad \begin{cases} g_{v2}\exp[G^b_{v3}/kT]\,c^3_{v1} + g_{v2}g_{v3}\exp[G^b_{v2}/kT]\,c^2_{v1} + c_{v1} = \Delta N/N \\ c_{v2} = g_{v2}\,c^2_{v1}\exp[G^b_{v2}/kT] \\ c_{v3} = g_{v3}\,c^3_{v1}\exp[G^b_{v3}/kT]\,. \end{cases}$$

Given the configurational entropy factors, g, and the binding energies, G^b, for the divacancy and trivacancy one can therefore assign the relative proportions of the defects present at a given temperature.

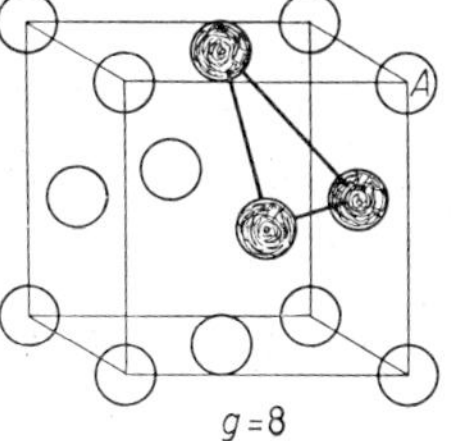

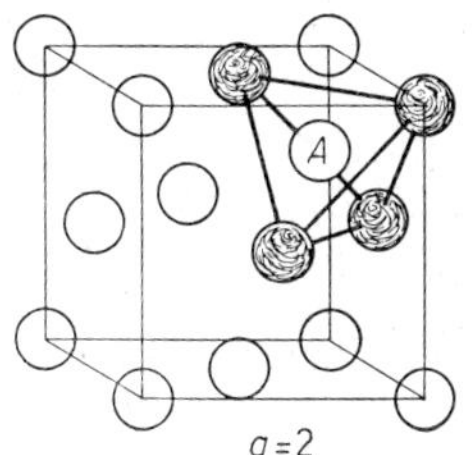

Fig. 12. – Formation of a tetrahedral trivacancy configuration in the face-centered cubic lattice. The orientational entropy factor, g, is different in the two configurations shown.

The factors g are now known with some assurance. The divacancy is almost certainly two adjacent lattice sites, for which $g_{v2} = 6$. It appears probable that the stable trivacancy may have tetrahedral symmetry for which $g_{v3} = 2$ [34]. This configuration results if a neighboring atom, A, relaxes toward the center of a triangle formed by three nearest neighbor vacancies, as shown in Fig. 12.

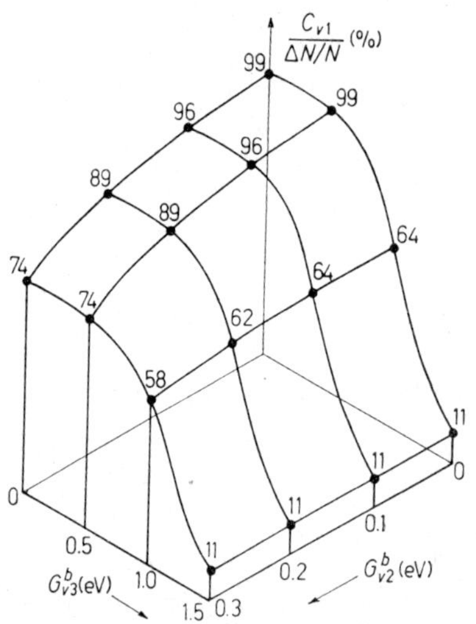

Fig. 13. – The fraction of added substitutional atomic sites present as monovacancies for aluminum near the melting temperature, 660 °C, where $\Delta N/N = 9.4 \cdot 10^{-4}$. G^b_{v2} and G^b_{v3} are divacancy and tetrahedral trivacancy binding energies.

The binding energies, G^b, are not as yet determined in any metal. The difficulties attendant to making theoretical estimates have been discussed by LOMER [35]. For this reason, we have chosen to present the results of eq. (6) as in Fig. 13, where the fraction of substitutional sites present for aluminum at 660 °C (immediately below the melting temperature) is shown as a function of the binding energies. For thermal equilibrium conditions the proportion of single vacancies increases as either the temperature is decreased or as the binding energies are decreased.

Fig. 14 shows the monovacancy concentration in aluminum as a function of temperature for two different values of G^b_{v2} (it is assumed crudely that $G^b_{v3} \simeq 2G^b_{v2}$). A monovacancy concentration is also shown at much lower temperatures, obtained from resistivity measurements after quenching [36] together with an estimate of the resistivity increment per monovacancy of three μΩ cm per atomic percent [37]. There is overall agreement within a factor of two. The formation energies (the slopes of the lines) agree within experimental error. The directly determined formation entropy, S^f_{v1}, is about $2k$, quite close to many theoretical estimates in the literature which assume the vacancy structure to be essentially a simple vacant lattice site.

The results obtained for high-purity silver [30] are shown in Fig. 15 and 16. It is seen here again that vacancies are the predominant defect with a concentration at the melting temperature, 960 °C, only about one-sixth that in aluminum. The value is $\Delta N/N = (1.7 \pm 0.5) \cdot 10^{-4}$. The corresponding equilibrium proportion of vacant lattice sites appearing as monovacancies is probably higher than in aluminum, therefore. When concentrations are so small a direct determination of E^f_{v1} is impossible; only a combined value for the entropy and energy of formation is known, at the highest temperatures. If a value of $S^f_{v1}/k = 1.5 \pm 0.5$

is assumed, then the formation energy in silver is given to within 10 percent, as (1.09 ± 0.10) eV. This agrees closely with a value of (1.10 ± 0.04) eV obtained from electrical resistivity measurements after quenching from lower temper-

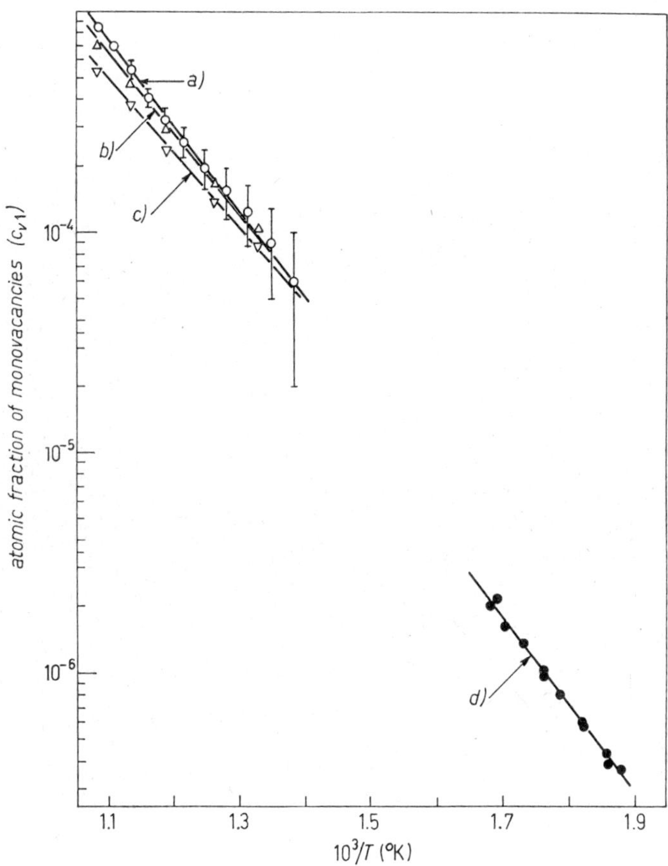

Fig. 14. – Monovacancy concentration *vs.* temperature for Al. Values are shown for two different assumed divacancy and trivacancy binding energies, G^b_{v2} and G^b_{v3}. *a*) ○ SIMMONS and BALLUFFI: $3(\Delta L/L - \Delta a/a) = \Delta N/N = e^{2.44} \exp[-0.76\ \text{eV}/kT]$; *b*) △ if $G^b_{v2} = 0.25$ eV; $c_{v1} = e^{2.04} \exp[-\Delta.74\ \text{eV}/kT]$; $G^b_{v3} = 0.50$ eV; *c*) ▽ if $G^b_{v2} = 0.35$ eV; $G^b_{v3} = 0.70$ eV; *d*) ● DE SORBO and TURNBULL, from quenched-in resitivity using $3\ \mu\Omega$ cm per 1% monovacancies.

atures [38]. If it is assumed that the quenching retains the equilibrium vacancy concentration then the resistivity per atomic percent is $(1.3 \pm 0.7)\ \mu\Omega$ cm; this value at least serves to establish a lower limit.

Recent measurements on gold [33] give the vacancy concentration immediately below the melting point, 1063 °C, as $(7.2 \pm 0.6) \cdot 10^{-4}$, a number intermediate between the silver and aluminum values. The general appearance of the proportion of monovacancies *vs.* binding energies plot for gold at the melting temperature, Fig. 17, is intermediate between that of silver and aluminum. For an assumed $S^f_{v1}/k = 1.5$, one obtains $E^f_{v1} = (1.01 \pm 0.1)$ eV, again a value in close agreement with quenching work [39] which gives 0.98 eV. The actual quenched-in mobile vacancy concentrations, as measured calorimetrically during

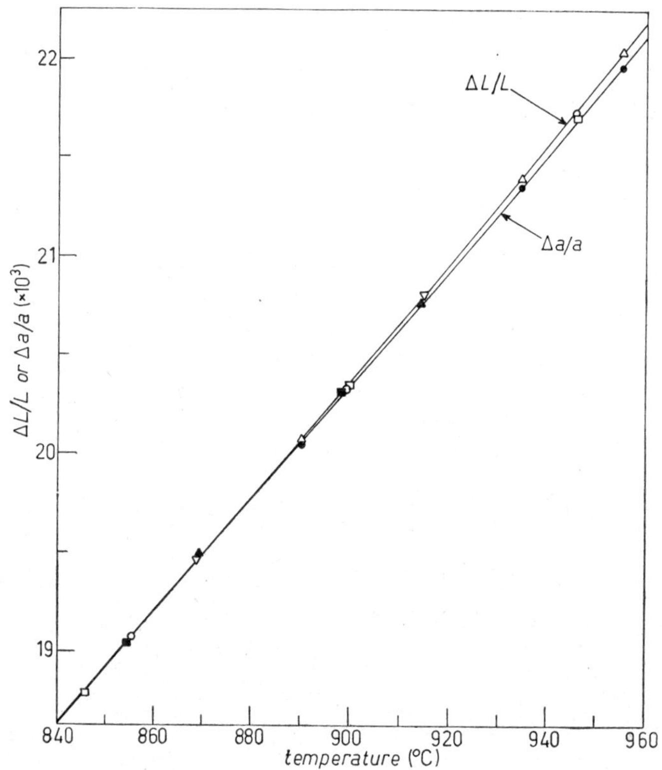

Fig. 15. – Difference between $\Delta L/L$ and $\Delta a/a$ for Ag in the range below the melting temperature (960 °C). $\Delta L/L$ curve: ○ cooling; △ heating; ▽ cooling. $\Delta a/a$ curve: □ heating; ■ cooling; ● heating; ▲ cooling.

annealing near room temperature [40], appear to be lower than the equilibrium values by some 30 to 40%, however. This point discussed further in Section **6**.2.

The neglect of interstitial concentrations in all the preceding considerations can be justified by using the Frenkel pair formation energies found calorimetrically during energy release during stage I recovery in radiation damage. The pair formation energy in Cu and Al is appreciably larger than twice the vacancy formation energy.

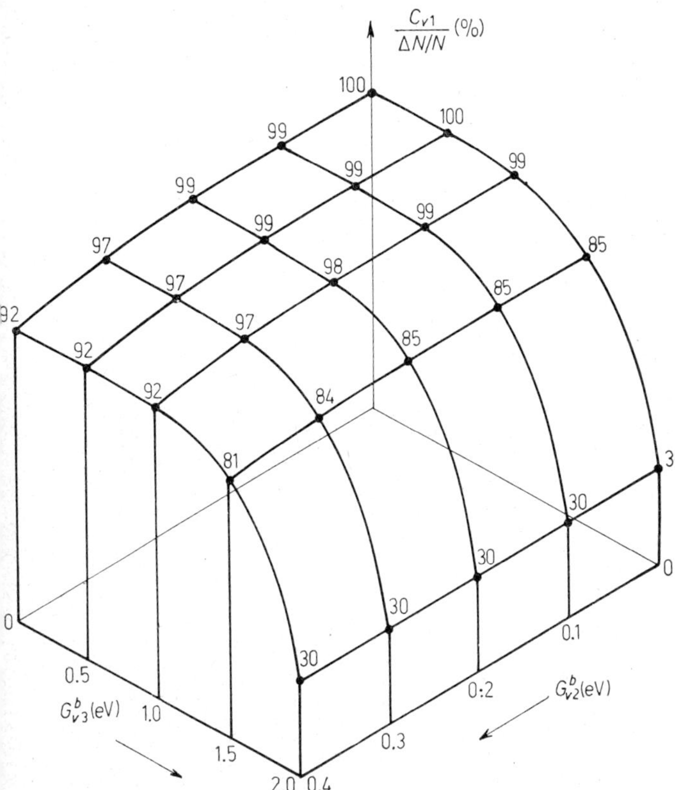

Fig. 16. – Relative monovacancy abundance, $c_{v1}/(\Delta N/N)$, as a function of divacancy and tetrahedral trivacancy binding energies (G^b_{v2} and G^b_{v3}) in Ag near the melting temperature, 960 °C. $\Delta N/N = 1.7\cdot10^{-4}$.

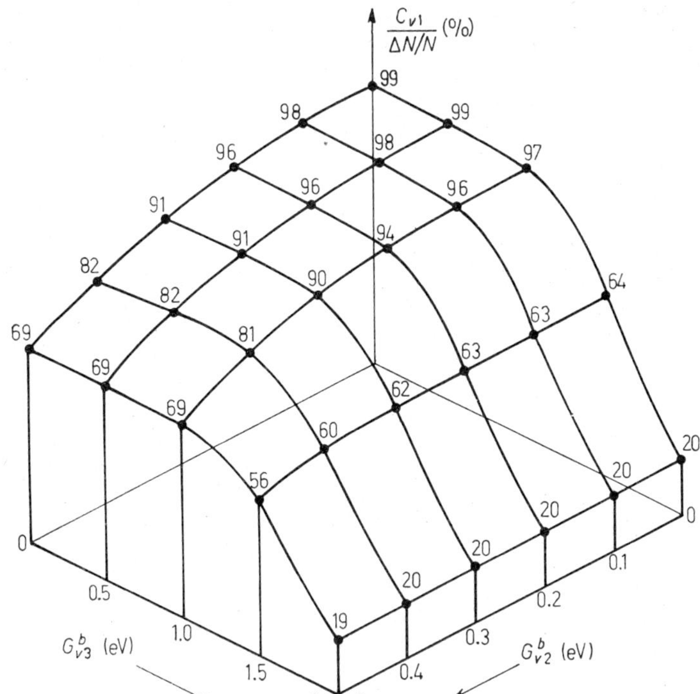

Fig. 17. – Relative monovacancy abundance, $c_{v1}/(\Delta N/N)$, as a function of divacancy and tetrahedral trivacancy binding energies (G^b_{v2} and G^b_{v3}) in gold near the melting temperature, 1063 °C. $\Delta N/N = 7.0\cdot10^{-4}$.

We have seen, then, how combined expansion measurements, without any assumption as to the lattice relaxation about the defects, can provide unequivocal identification of the predominant thermally-generated lattice defects, can measure directly in equilibrium the added fraction of substitutional atomic sites, and can yield valuable information on the formation energy and entropy of the defects, and therefore about their atomic structure.

6. – Discussion.

A number of interesting comparisons can now be made. We consider the results of equilibrium vacancy concentration measurements and the results of experiments using radioactive tracer techniques for the study of self-diffusion and using quenching techniques with electrical resistivity, release of stored energy, and trasmission electron microscopy. These remarks can be roughly categorized as related to the motion and formation energies, respectively.

6·1. *Vacancy motion energies.* – Some attempts have been made to correlate certain point defect properties with the melting temperatures of materials. For example, a recent publication [29] puts forward the empirical rule that the motion energy for vacancies should be equivalent to an approximately constant fraction of the absolute melting temperature, T_m. Such crude relations are useful as working assumptions in investigating new materials, but it can now be seen that such relations are certainly approximate. The melting temperature does not appear to be directly related to the properties of the thermally-generated point defects in those materials (Ag, Au, Al) which have been investigated so far. Consider Table II, which displays the various quantities involved.

The ratio E^f/kT_m is seen to be somewhat variable. There is an indirect relation between E^f and T_m, of course; such a relation arises because the values of the elastic constants determine to a certain extent the properties of point defects (which are centers of dilatation producing elastic strains in the material). And

TABLE II.

Property	Ag	Au	Al
$\Delta N/N$ at the melting point, T_m	$1.7\cdot10^{-4}$	$7.2\cdot10^{-4}$	$9.4\cdot10^{-4}$
Vacancy formation energy, E^f	1.09 eV	1.0 eV	0.76 eV
Self-diffusion energy, Q	1.91 eV	1.81 eV	1.4 eV
Melting temperature, kT_m	0.107 eV	0.115 eV	0.081 eV
Ratio E^f/kT_m	10.2	8.7	9.5
Ratio E^f/Q	0.5_7	0.5_4	0.5_4

the shear elastic constant, G, is related to the melting temperature by the well-known Lindemann rule, $(Gd^2/T_m)=$ (a constant), where d is the nearest neighbor distance.

The ratio of vacancy formation energy to self-diffusion energy is seen to be remarkably constant for the three metals considered. This is not surprising, because self-diffusion must proceed *via* a vacancy mechanism. The ratio E^m/Q would be as constant since the sum $E^m_{v1}+E^f_{v1}$ is equal to Q. Divacancies contribute little to measured Q values.

The other noble metal, copper, which is the most fully investigated metal in fundamental radiation damage studies, has shown after electron or deuteron irradiation, a prominent thermal recovery process having an activation energy near 0.65 eV. From the product $(Q)_{\text{Cu}}(E^m/Q)_{\text{Ag,Au}}$, one gets $E^m=0.9$ eV for the monovacancy in Cu (*). It therefore appears doubtful that this prominent recovery peak (stage III) in irradiated Cu is due to the simple motion of monovacancies. Similar reserve may be expressed about the corresponding process in other materials.

A number of alternative possibilities exist; we mention two of them. The decrease of observed motion energy with increasing quenching temperature in Au [39] has been attributed to the presence of divacancies formed during quenching from the higher temperatures [41]. There is a tendency for the preferential formation of divacancies in the primary irradiation damage process. In addition, measurements [42] and calculations [43] have both demonstrated the influence of minute concentrations of foreign solutes upon measured vacancy motion energies and recovery kinetics.

6·2. *Vacancy formation energies and entropies.* We have seen in Section **5** that in Al and Au, the equilibrium vacancy concentrations may be as much as a factor $\frac{3}{2}$ to 2 larger than the largest reported quenched-in concentrations. How, then, can quenching measurements yield accurate formation energies?

It was recognized from the beginning of quenching investigations that the cooling rates employed might not be sufficient to retain the equilibrium point defect concentrations. In addition to the possible loss of defects at sinks in the crystal, some of the defects being associated with a consequent change in the dislocation structure, the aggregation of defects may occur, clusters of varying sizes being formed [44, 45]. The type and number of clusters formed may be expected to depend not only upon the mobility and upon the binding energy of

(*) *Note added in proof.* – Equilibrium vacancy concentrations have now been measured in high-purity copper (R. O. SIMMONS and R. W. BALLUFFI: *Bull. Am. Phys. Soc.*, **7**, 233 (1962)). Just below the melting temperature, $\Delta N/N=(2.0\pm0.5)\cdot10^{-4}$. Assuming $S^f_{vl}/k=1.5\pm0.5$ one deduces that $E^f_{vl}=(1.17\pm0.11)$ eV. Because for copper $Q=2.05$ eV this implies that E^m_{vl} is about 0.88 eV, which agrees with the estimate in the text.

the intrinsic crystal defects, but also upon the type and concentration of foreign solute atoms present [46].

While these processes are interesting in themselves, it is not obvious that their study may be easily interpreted to give any direct information about such equilibrium properties of the point defects as their formation energies and entropies and their binding energies with each other and with foreign atoms. For example, quenching work on pure metals by different investigators seldom agrees as to the magnitude of residual resistivity increase produced by quenching from a given temperature. The situation is shown for three studies of Al in Fig. 18, where the largest increment was produced by the study having the *intermediate* quenching rate. This type of work is further complicated by the possible existence of quenching strains, either thermal or mechanical, which may inject additional defects into the sample.

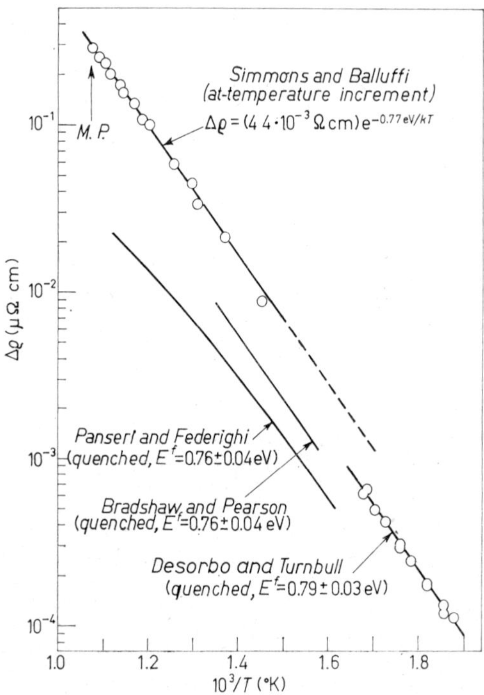

Fig. 18. – Comparison of residual resistivity values attributed to vacancy-type defects in Al, from three quenching investigations. The upper curve was obtained from at-temperature measurements [37].

The results are clearest in Au, for which the calorimetric measurements of DESORBO [40] indicate concentrations in quenched foils which are 30 to 40% lower than the equilibrium values. No doubt, at least part of this discrepancy can be accounted for by the aggregation and collapse of some vacancies into stable dislocation structures [44] which do not anneal at the temperatures considered. The detailed comparisons that DESORBO makes between his concentration measurements on foils and the length and resistivity measurements of BAUERLE and KOEHLER [39] on wires, in order to infer the resistivity increment ((1.8 ± 0.6) μΩ cm/atomic percent) and volume per vacancy ((0.6 ± 0.05) atomic volume) depend not only upon the « correction » made for differences in their respective quenching rates but also upon the relative contribution of the dislocation tetrahedra to electrical resistivity and energy release.

It is a curious but fortunate fact that, in a number of cases, apparently consistent values for the vacancy formation energy can be obtained, at least at the lower pre-quenching temperatures, in spite of these apparent differences in concentration. Certainly there is quite satisfactory agreement about E^f values obtained by the equilibrium measurements completed to date and by the results of careful quenching.

Inspection of Table II reveals another feature. The vacancy concentration in Ag appears to be anomalously low at the melting temperature, although the concentration is just that expected from a consideration of the self-diffusion energy and the constant ratio E^f/Q. This suggests that any connection between the predominant thermally-generated defects in close-packed metals and the atomic mechanism of melting is either indirect or absent.

A number of attempts have been been made to deduce formation energies of defects in solids from high-temperature deviations of physical properties from the «expected» or «ideal» values. We now see that the actual equilibrium concentrations of vacancies in metals are usually considerably less than 0.1% and that therefore defects make a very small relative contribution to the values of the property in the actual solid [37]. Only in very exceptional circumstances can a clear separation of effects be obtained; present knowledge of the high-temperature physical properties of solids is very meagre, and investigations of this type appear of limited usefulness at present.

The formation entropy can, of course, only be obtained from equilibrium measurements. The values obtained in face-centered cubic metals are all in the range 1 to 2 entropy units and indicate an essentially simple structure for the vacant lattice site. A remarkable feature of the theoretical situation here is that a number of very diverse methods have given results of about this magnitude when the monovacancy is considered essentially as an atom missing from the atomic site.

7. – Conclusion.

We considered the advantages of comparison measurements of volume and lattice parameter changes in solids containing point defects. Such a comparison technique has unique features which make it a valuable complement to other investigations using more sensitive physical properties, although it is at present limited to defect densities exceeding $10^{18}/cm^3$. In irradiated solids, an irradiation or a recovery process can be examined to determine whether the number of substitutional atomic sites is preserved in the resulting defect structure. Experimental values of the volume change are useful when combined with experimental values of energy release and electrical resistivity changes, for comparison with theoretical calculations using specific atomic models for the defects in metals. From high temperature measurements, the predominant thermally-generated defect can be identified and some of its properties determined.

REFERENCES

[1] For a comprehensive view of crystal defects, see F. SEITZ, pp. 3-76 in *Imperfections in Nearly Perfect Crystals* (edited by W. SHOCKLEY and others (New York, 1952)). See also F. SEITZ: *Suppl. Nuovo Cimento*, **7**, 414 (1957), and the lectures of J. FRIEDEL, this volume p. 4.

[2] E. W. MÜLLER: *Zeits. Phys.*, **156**, 399 (1959): in *Advances in Electronics and Electron Physics*, edited by L. MARTON, vol. **13** (New York, 1960), p. 83.

[3] We will not consider here other X-ray techniques which can be employed for the study of other crystal defects; those are reviewed in the lectures of A. GUINIER (this volume p. 122).

[4] J. D. ESHELBY: *Journ. Appl. Phys.*, **25**, 255 (1954); *Solid State Physics*, edited by F. SEITZ and D. TURNBULL (New York, 1956), vol. **3**, p. 79.

[5] R. W. BALUFFI and R. O. SIMMONS: *Journ. Appl. Phys.*, **31**, 2284 (1960).

[6] R. O. SIMMONS and R. W. BALLUFFI: *Phys. Rev.*, **109**, 1142 (1958).

[7] R. O. SIMMONS and R. W. BALLUFFI: *Phys. Rev.*, **117**, 52 (1960).

[8] R. O. SIMMONS and R. W. BALLUFFI: *Journ. Appl. Phys.*, **30**, 1240 (1959).

[9] W.R. JAMES: *The Optical Principles of the Diffraction of X-Rays* (London, 1954).

[10] W. H. ZACHARIASEN: *Theory of X-Ray Diffraction in Crystals* (New York, 1945).

[11] See, for example, W. COCHRAN and G. KARTHA: *Acta Cryst.*, **9**, 941 (1958) who consider an interstitial atom in copper.

[12] See the summary in the introduction to W. B. PEARSON: *Lattice Spacings and Structures of Metals and Alloys* (New York, 1958). But see also the evidence of C. B. WALKER and M. MAREZIO: *Acta. Met.*, **7**, 769 (1959).

[13] C. W. TUCKER jr. and P. SENIO: *Acta Cryst.*, **8**, 371 (1955); *Phys. Rev.*, **99**, 1777 (1955).

[14] D. BEAMAN, R. W. BALLUFFI and R. O. SIMMONS (as yet unpublished).

[15] R. VOOK and C. WERT: *Phys. Rev.*, **109**, 1529 (1958).

[16] U. GONSER and B. OKKERSE: *Phys. Rev.*, **109**, 663 (1958).

[17] F. L. VOOK and R. W. BALLUFFI: *Phys. Rev.*, **113**, 62 (1959).

[18] R. O. SIMMONS: *Phys. Rev.*, **113**, 70 (1959).

[19] C. MYLONAS and R. TRUELL: *Journ. Appl. Phys.*, **29**, 1252 (1958).

[20] R. FEDER and A. S. NOWICK: *Phys. Rev.*, **109**, 1959 (1958).

[21] D. A. WIEGAND and R. SMOLUCHOWSKI: *Phys. Rev.*, **116**, 1069 (1959).

[22] It is obviously fallacious to attempt deductions from a supposed disagreement between X-ray data of average accuracy and a 150° extrapolation of length measurements at lower temperatures (S. NENNO and J. W. KAUFFMAN: *Journ. Phys. Soc. Japan*, **15**, 220 (1960)).

[23] G. D. MAGNUSON, W. PALMER and J. S. KOEHLER: *Phys. Rev.*, **109**, 1990 (1958).

[24] J. W. CORBETT, R. B. SMITH and R. M. WALKER: *Phys. Rev.*, **114**, 1452 and 1460 (1959).

[25] A. V. GRANATO and T. G. NELAN: *Phys. Rev. Lett.*, **6**, 171 (1961).

[26] K. H. BENNEMAN and L. TEWORDT: *Zeits. Naturforsch.*, **15a**, 772 (1960). References are given in this paper to earlier work.

[27] J. S. KOEHLER and G. E. DUVALL: *Bull. Am. Phys. Soc.*, **4**, 283 (1959). See also the discussion of atomic interaction potentials in the lectures of G. LEIBFRIED, (this volume p. 227).

[28] J. ADAM and D. G. MARTIN: *Phil. Mag.*, **3**, 1329 (1958).

[29] M. W. THOMPSON: *Phil. Mag.*, **5**, 278 (1960).
[30] K. KOBAYASHI: *Phys. Rev.*, **102**, 348 (1956); **107**, 41 (1957).
[31] H. B. HUNTINGTON and F. SEITZ: *Phys. Rev.*, **61**, 315 (1942); H. B. HUNTINGTON: *Phys. Rev.*, **91**, 1092 (1953).
[32] R. O. SIMMONS and R. W. BALLUFFI: *Phys. Rev.*, **119**, 600 (1960).
[33] R. O. SIMMONS and R. W. BALLUFFI: *Phys. Rev.*, **125**, 862 (1962).
[34] A. C. DAMASK, G. J. DIENES and V. G. WEIZER: *Phys. Rev.*, **113**, 781 (1959).
[35] W. M. LOMER: *Progress in Metal Physics*, vol. **8** (New York, 1959), p. 255. References to specific calculations are given here.
[36] W. DESORBO and D. TURNBULL: *Acta Met.*, **7**, 83 (1959).
[37] R. O. SIMMONS and R. W. BALLUFFI: *Phys. Rev.*, **117**, 62 (1960).
[38] M. DOYAMA and J. S. KOEHLER: *Phys. Rev.*, **119**, 939 (1960).
[39] J. E. BAUERLE and J. S. KOEHLER: *Phys. Rev.*, **107**, 1493 (1957).
[40] W. DESORBO: *Phys. Rev.*, **117**, 444 (1960).
[41] J. S. KOEHLER, F. SEITZ and J. E. BAUERLE: *Phys. Rev.*, **107**, 1499 (1957).
[42] W. DESORBO and D. TURNBULL: *Phys. Rev.*, **115**, 560 (1959).
[43] A. C. DAMASK and G. J. DIENES: *Phys. Rev.*, **120**, 99 (1960).
[44] J. SILCOX and P. B. HIRSCH: *Phil. Mag.*, **4**, 72 (1959).
[45] C. PANSERI and T. FEDERIGHI: *Phil. Mag.*, **3**, 1223 (1958).
[46] G. THOMAS: *Phil. Mag.*, **4**, 1213 (1959).

Electron-Induced Radiation Damage in Pure Metals (*).

R. M. Walker

General Electric Research Laboratory - Schenectady, N. Y.

1. – Introduction.

Electron bombardment of metals at low temperatures provides a particularly simple type of radiation damage. For example, if 1.5 MeV electrons are used to irradiate copper, the average initial kinetic energy, transferred to atoms which are displaced is ~ 40 eV. Under these conditions the damage consists primarily of isolated Frenkel pairs. The basic simplicity of the damage permits a quantitative treatment of both production and recovery processes. It is this quantitative aspect of electron damage experiments which we wish to emphasize in the present paper.

The material to be presented is divided into five main sections. The first section considers some of the general features of electron irradiation of solids. The second section reviews work on the low temperature electron bombardment of high purity copper. It is shown that there is reasonable agreement between theory and experiment for both the production and recovery of damage at low temperatures. The third section discusses some recent work on the influence of lattice imperfections on the damage and recovery processes. New results in Al, Ag, Au, Ni and Fe are presented in the fourth section. In the final section we discuss some current outstanding problems.

Only information available as of mid-1960 is included in this paper.

2. – General remarks on the use of electrons in radiation damage experiments.

Although electron beams are used primarily to produce changes in materials which are sensitive to ionization, we will ignore this aspect and concentrate instead on the use of electrons to study radiation damage caused by direct atom displacement. The outstanding feature of the electron bombardments,

(*) This work was sponsored by a contract from the Air Research and Development Command United States Air Force.

as opposed to fast neutron or typical heavy charged particle irradiations, is the low kinetic energy transmitted to the atoms in the irradiated material. This makes electron irradiations valuable for two types of studies. Firstly they may be used to study the fundamental atom displacement process—particularly if measurements are made as a function of bombarding energy. Secondly the low recoil energies also make it possible to use electrons as a tool for introducing and studying simple lattice defects. Both types of studies are considered briefly in this section.

2·1. *Energy of recoil atoms and the threshold for damage production.* – The problem of calculating the number of displaced atoms produced by a beam of incoming particles is divided conceptually into two parts. The first part of the calculation consists in evaluating the spectrum of recoil energies which the crystal atoms receive as a result of primary interactions with the incoming radiation. This part of the calculation is quite reliable. The second part of the calculation consists of evaluating what happens to the atoms once they possess recoil energy. This part of the calculation is not reliable. The simplest assumption one can make is to assume that all atoms are bound in a simple square-well potential. T_d, the height of the well, is therefore a threshold energy for damage production. For this case the probability of atom displacement as a function of the atom recoil energy has the simple step form shown in Fig. 1(a). In what follows we will first assume this simplest type of threshold function and then discuss the limitations of this approximation. We will also assume that $T_d = 25$ eV. Actual values are expected to vary considerably, and the numerical calculations given below are thus only intended to be illustrative.

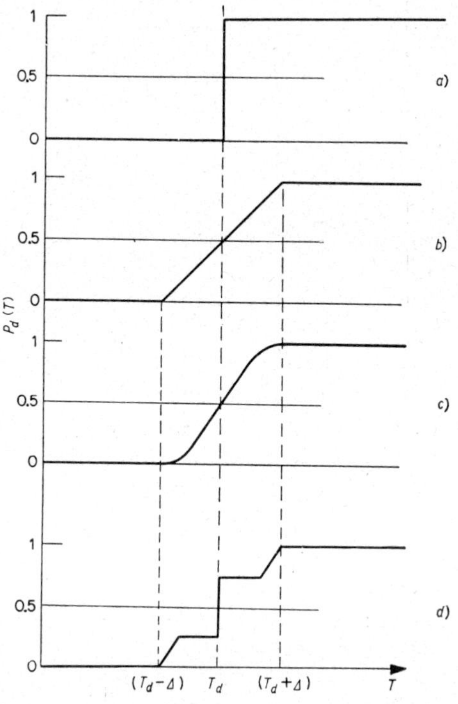

Fig. 1. – Different forms for $P_d(T)$, the probability that a struck atom be displaced, as a function of the kinetic energy, T, transferred to the struck atom: (a), step function; (b) linear function; (c) sin χ function, and (d) multiple step function. These functions, which are all antisymmetrical about the point $P_d(T) = \frac{1}{2}$, were used to calculate the curves of Fig. 4 which show the variation of displacement cross-section with bombarding electron energy.

The maximum nuclear recoil energy, T_m, which can be transmitted in an electron-nucleus collision is given by

$$T_m(\text{in eV}) = \frac{561}{M}\,\frac{E}{m_e c^2}\left(\frac{E}{m_e c^2}+2\right), \tag{1}$$

where M is the mass of the recoiling atom and E is the energy of the bombarding electrons. If we set $T_m = T_d$, the solution of eq. (1) for E, gives the minimum bombarding electron energy necessary to produce displacement. Fig. 2 shows numerical results of such a calculation for several elements (assuming $T_d = 25$ eV). It can be seen that the electron energies lie in the range from 0.1 to 1.5 MeV. The threshold energy for damage production can therefore be measured directly by varying the energy of bombarding electrons in this range.

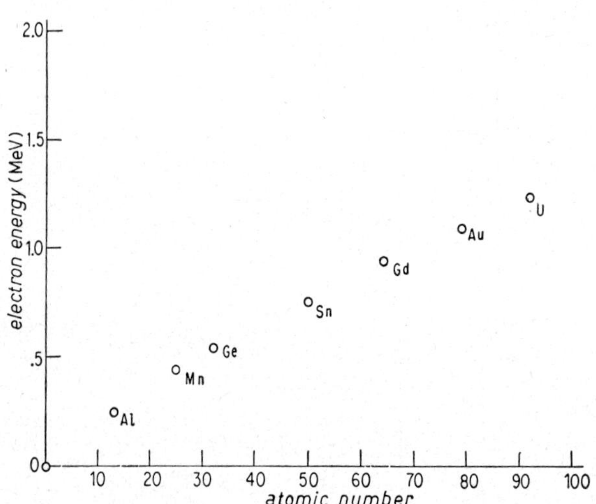

Fig. 2. – Minimum electron energy necessary to impart 25 eV of recoil energy to a target atom plotted for several elements.

The spectrum of recoil energies for a given bombarding electron energy can be calculated to a good approximation [1] for light elements from the following equation which gives the differential cross-section (in cm²) for energy transfer between T and $T+\mathrm{d}T$:

$$\mathrm{d}\sigma = \frac{\pi z^2 e^4(1-\beta^2)}{m_e^2 c^4 \beta^4}\left[1-\beta^2\frac{T}{T_m}+\pi\alpha Z\beta\left\{\left(\frac{T}{T_m}\right)^{\frac{1}{2}}-\frac{T}{T_m}\right\}\right]\frac{\mathrm{d}T}{T^2}, \tag{2}$$

where $\beta = V_e/c$ and the other symbols have their conventional meaning. Because the basic interaction arises from the long-range Coulomb force, there are many more low-energy collisions than high-energy ones. As a consequence, even at bombarding energies well above threshold, the *average* recoil energy of displaced atoms is quite low. Fig. 3 gives some numerical calculations based on an assumed threshold of 25 eV. It can be seen from this curve that at energies considerably above threshold, the recoil atoms possess an average energy less than twice T_d (50 eV). Under these circumstances the damage is particularly simple, consisting primarily of isolated Frenkel pairs.

A complication in the calculation of radiation damage arises when the atoms possess recoil energies much greater than the threshold energies. The recoiling atoms themselves can then displace other atoms, and a single primary collision will produce a cluster of displaced atoms. This is the typical situation for fast neutron bombardments where theory and experiment are not in good agreement. Electrons with energies greater than 1 MeV can also, in principle,

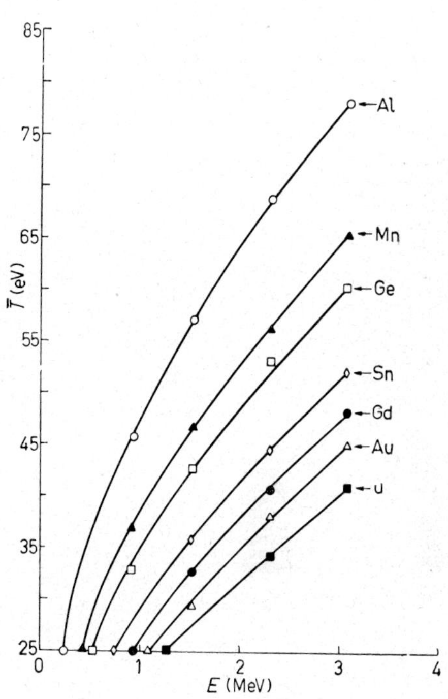

Fig. 3. – Average recoil energy, $\bar{T}_d$, plotted as a function of bombarding electron energy, E, for several different elements. These curves are calculated for a threshold energy of 25 eV. Since the actual values of threshold energy will, in general, be different, these curves are for illustrative purposes only.

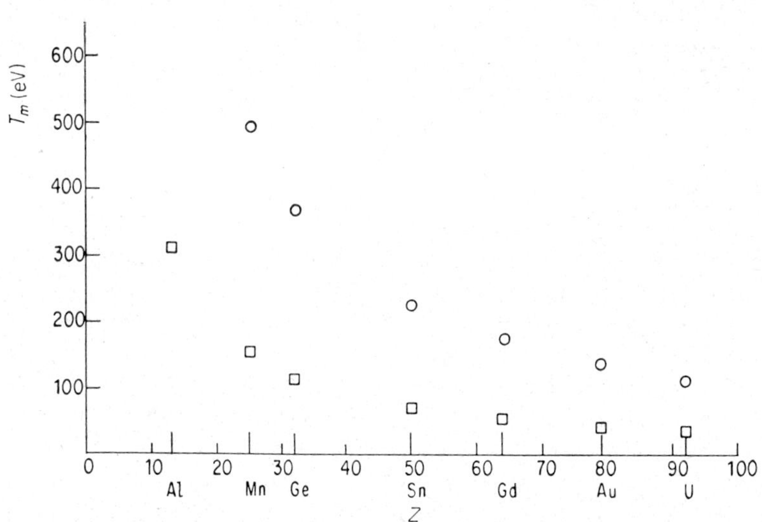

Fig. 4. – Maximum atom recoil energy transmitted in an electron-atom collision plotted for several elements at two different bombarding electron energies. ○ 3.0 MeV, □ 1.5 MeV.

be used to study the onset of these cascade effects. Fig. 4 shows numerical calculations of T_m for typical bombarding energies of 1.5 and 3.0 MeV. It can be seen that, with 1.5 MeV electrons, the most energetic collision in Al could result in as many as 12 displaced atoms. To date, no electron bombardment study of cascade processes has been reported.

2.2. *Onset and average threshold energies.* – We have so far assumed that atoms have a single threshold energy. However, this assumption that atoms are bound in a simple square-well potential cannot be correct in detail. For one thing, we expect that the crystalline direction in which an atom recoils may be important in determining whether or not it is displaced. As a consequence, the displacement probability function shown in Fig. 1(*a*) is appropriate for only a single crystal direction. The total displacement probability averaged over all angles is probably a function which starts from zero at some true threshold—the minimum kinetic energy for the *onset* of damage—but

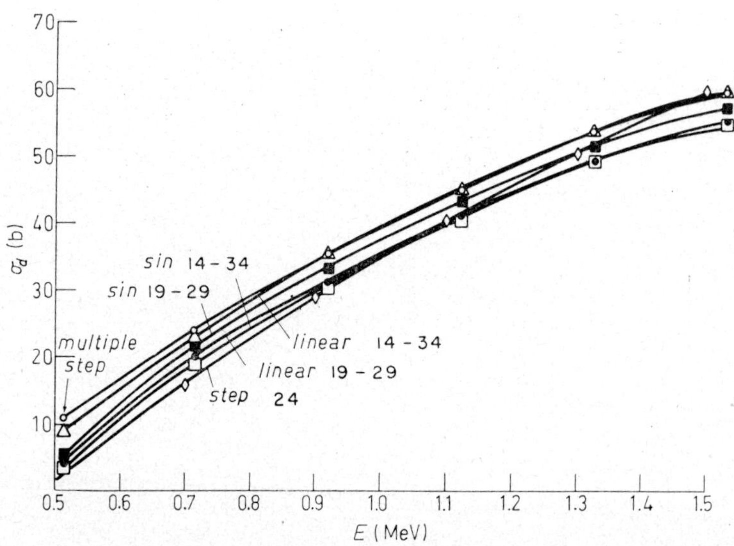

Fig. 5. – Displacement cross-section, σ_d, *vs.* bombarding electron energy for different forms of the displacement probability $P_d(T)$ shown in Fig. 1. All the curves have $P_d(T)=\frac{1}{2}$, at $T=24$ eV for the struck copper atom. The numbers for each curve give the values of T at which $P_d(T)=0$ and 1.

which does not reach unity until some higher energy. A linear approximation to such a displacement function is shown in Fig. 1(*b*). In a paper discussing the threshold energy in copper, Corbett *et al.* [2] showed that—*at values well above the threshold for the onset of damage*—the cross-section for damage production for the linear displacement function of Fig. 1(*b*) is nearly equal to the value calculated for the simple step function of Fig. 1(*a*). This point is illustrated graphically in Fig. 5. This has two important consequences:

a) if the true threshold function can be reasonably approximated by a linear function, it is meaningful to carry through the calculations based on a simple step-function threshold provided the threshold energy is interpreted as an « average » threshold energy, and

b) in order to measure the « average » threshold energy, it is necessary to measure the shape of the damage production curve *vs.* bombarding electron energy at electron energies well above the threshold for the onset of damage.

It should be remarked that it is much more difficult to measure the shape of the damage production curve over a range of energies, in order to determine the average threshold, than it is to measure the onset threshold. In the former experiment it is necessary to do accurate dosimetry and take into account such effects as multiple scattering and energy straggling of the electrons.

Both onset and average threshold energies are important parameters. As we have discussed, the average threshold is a potentially useful quantity for assessing the amount of damage produced. The onset energy is valuable because it can be calculated from theory. Interatomic potentials are not well known at the energies relevant for damage calculations. Comparison of theory and experiment for onset thresholds should be useful in this connection. A recent summary of experimental information on threshold determinations has been given by WALKER [3].

2·3. *Point defect studies.* – We have already noted that at moderate energies, electrons produce predominantly simple Frenkel pairs. The experiments to be described in copper suggest that the concentration of such pairs can be calculated approximately if the average threshold energies are measured. Electron bombardment therefore provides a valuable tool for introducing simple point defects whose properties can then be studied. Since no impurity atoms or extended disordered regions are introduced by the electrons, the fundamental point defect interactions can be observed.

One very useful technique is to study the recovery of damage following annealing at high temperatures. In general, several thermally-activated recovery processes are observed. Measurements of the activation energies and kinetics can be used to obtain information about the defect processes. One complication which is inherent is that the interstitial and vacancy in a Frenkel pair are often produced in close spatial proximity. Any kinetics analysis must take into account this spatial correlation. However, once migration of one of the defects begins, the correlation is effectively destroyed, and there is a transition to a region where it is valid to treat the interstitials and vacancies as separately random populations. This considerably simplifies the analysis of further kinetics data.

2'4. *Some experimental considerations.* – Electrons lose most of their energy in ionization and very little goes into producing displaced atoms. For example, for a 1 MeV electron beam passing through a 0.005 in. copper foil, each electron suffers an average ionization loss of $0.25 \cdot 10^6$ eV. However, only 1/50 of the electrons transmit the requisite 22 eV atom recoil energy for displacement. Since many of the interesting experiments are done at low temperatures, this poses a considerable problem in that there is a large ratio of dissipated heat to damage. Most electron experiments are therefore done with low damage concentrations. However, such low concentrations are generally desirable in studying basic defect processes. It should be remarked that it is possible to produce considerable lattice disruption in reasonable irradiation times, with conventional beam sources, if the temperature of the sample is not critical. Some typical total cross-sections calculated for a 25 eV threshold are given in Fig. 6.

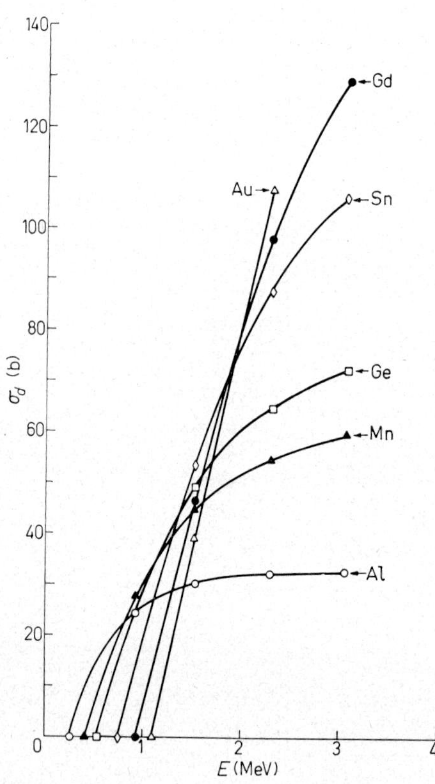

Fig. 6. – Total damage cross-section, σ, plotted as a function of bombarding electron energy, E, for several different elements. These curves are calculated for a threshold energy of 25 eV. Since the actual threshold values will, in general, be different, these curves are for illustrative purposes only.

The total penetration of a 1 MeV electron is only 0.4 gm/cm² and an inherent limitation on electron damage experiments near threshold is the necessity of using thin samples in order that the energy loss be small. Even with a low average energy loss, however, electrons show a wide nonsymmetrical distribution of energies after traversing an absorber. This energy « straggling » may be an important consideration in threshold measurements and complicates the analysis of such measurements. Electrons also undergo multiple scattering which results in a spreading of the beam and a corresponding loss of homogeneity of damage production. The necessity of using thin samples can be overcome by using γ-rays to produce the damage. In this way the basic simplicity of the damage is retained even for moderately large specimens. However, the important feature of being able to vary the energy of the electrons in a series of discrete values is lost.

2·5. *Summary.* – In this section we have pointed out some of the general features of electron bombardments which makes them a valuable tool ford amage research. It was shown that they can be used to study the fundamental aspects of the damage process in the following ways:

a) Measurements of the threshold energy for the onset of damage. These serve to identify the basic mechanism of damage and give information about interatomic forces.

b) Measurements of the average threshold energy. These serve to further explore the damage mechanism and are useful in calculating the number of defects produced.

c) Measurement of production rates at high energies. These can explore the transition from single to multiple defect processes.

d) Measurements of recovery behavior. These give information about the types of defects and their spatial distribution.

It was also pointed out that electron bombardment serves as a useful tool for introducing point defects which can then be studied. Some particular features here are:

a) The point defects consist mostly of isolated Frenkel pairs.

b) The concentration of these defects can be approximately calculated from theory [coupled with measurements of the average threshold energy].

c) The Frenkel pairs separate upon warming to form individual, random populations of interstitials and vacancies. Thus, the kinetics describing the interaction of these point defects with each other and with other imperfections are very simple.

d) No impurity atoms or extended disordered regions are introduced. Thus it is possible to study fundamental point defect processes free from complications inherent in many other experiments.

In the material which follows we describe specific experiments which illustrate some of these features.

3. – Production and recovery of electron-induced damage in pure copper bombarded at very low temperatures.

3·1. *Production of damage*. – In this section we will review low-temperature experiments on both the production and recovery of damage.

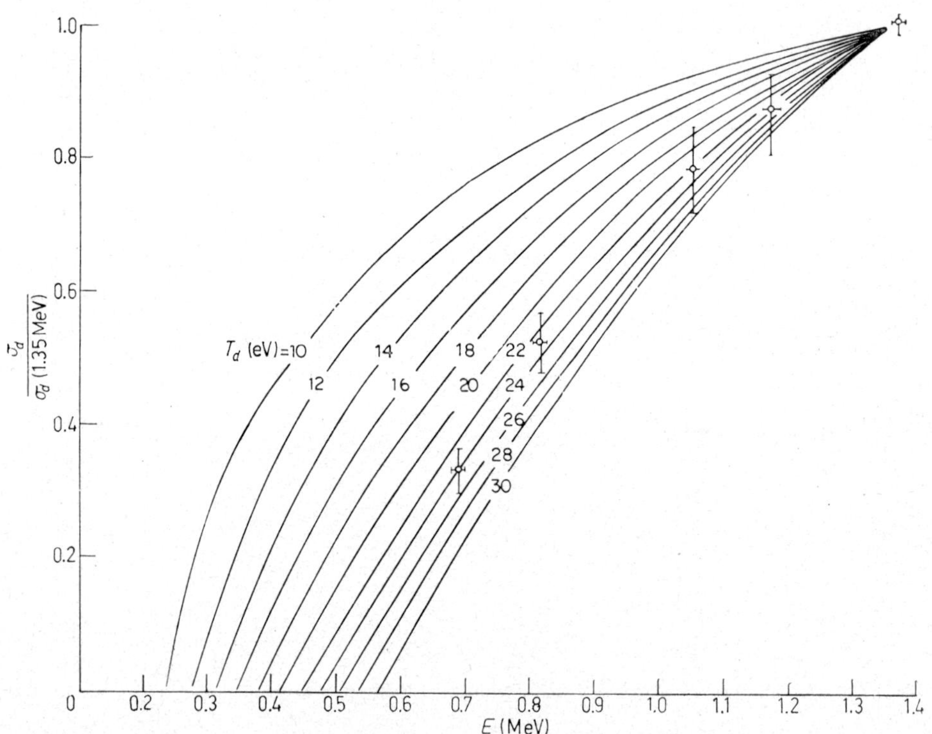

Fig. 7. – Comparison of experimental data with theoretical curves of normalized displacement cross-section *vs.* bombarding electron energy. All the curves were calculated under the assumption that the displacement probability is a step-function and the numbers refer to the assumed value of the threshold energy. Error limits include the uncertainty in normalization.

Fig. 7 shows previously published [2] experimental results for the threshold determination in copper. The best fit to the experimental data gives an average threshold energy of (22 ± 3) eV. Using the simple displacement theory and the measured value of resistivity, we previously inferred from this experiment that the resistivity change for 1 at. % Frenkel pairs, ϱ_f, is equal to 1.5 μΩ cm.

We now inquire about the validity of this number in light of present experiments. During the past few years a number of measurements have been made of various properties in irradiated materials. Table I summarizes the

TABLE I. – *Summary of low-temperature irradiations in copper.*

	Electrons	Deuterons	Neutrons
Resistivity, $\Delta\varrho$	$8.3\cdot10^{-27}\ \Omega$ cm/(e/cm^2) [1.37 MeV] ([a])	$2.3\cdot10^{-24}\ \Omega$ cm/(d/cm^2) [9.5 MeV] ([c])	$1.15\cdot10^{-26}\ \Omega$ cm/(n/cm^2) [fast] ([l])
Stored energy, ΔE	$2.8\cdot10^{-20}$ (cal/g)/(e/cm^2) stage I recovery ([b])	$1.6\cdot10^{-17}$ (cal/g)/(d/cm^2) stage I recovery ([d])	—
Length change, $\Delta L/L$	—	$3.8\cdot10^{-21}$/(d/cm^2) [8.5 MeV] ([e])	—
Lattice parameter	—	$4.1\cdot10^{-21}$/(d/cm)) [7 MeV] ([f])	—
$\Delta E/\Delta\varrho$	4.8 (cal/g)/$\mu\Omega$ cm	7.1 (cal/g)/$\mu\Omega$ cm	2.9 (cal/g)/μ Ωcm ([g])
$\Delta\varrho/(\Delta L/L)$	—	$7.2\cdot10^{-4}\ \Omega$ cm	$7.6\cdot10^{-4}\ \Omega$ cm ([g])
$\Delta E/(\Delta L/L)$	—	$5.1\cdot10^{3}$ (cal/g)	$2.2\cdot10^{3}$ (cal/g) ([g])
« Average » threshold energy	(22 ± 3) eV ([a])	—	—
Discrete activation energies	stage I (.05÷.12) eV ([h]) stage III .62 eV ([i])	stage I (.05÷.12) eV ([k]) stage III .68 eV ([m])	—

(*a*) CORBETT, DENNEY, FISKE and WALKER: *Phys. Rev.*, **108**, 954 (1957).
(*b*) MEECHAN and SOSIN: *Phys. Rev.*, **113**, 424 (1959).
(*c*) COOPER, KOEHLER and MARX: *Phys. Rev.*, **97**, 599 (1955).
(*d*) NILAN: *Bull. Am. Phys. Soc.*, **5**, 175 (1960).
(*e*) VOOK and WERT: *Phys. Rev.*, **109**, 1529 (1958).
(*f*) SIMMONS and BALLUFFI: *Phys. Rev.*, **109**. 1142 (1958).
(*g*) BLEWITT *et al.*: private communication (1960).
(*h*) CORBETT, SMITH and WALKER: *Phys. Rev.*, **114**, 1400 (1959).
(*i*) MEECHAN and BRINKMAN: *Phys. Rev.*, **103**, 1193 (1956).
(*k*) MAGNUSON, PALMER and KOEHLER: *Phys. Rev.*, **109**, 1990 (1958).
(*l*) BLEWITT, COLTMAN, KLABUNDE and NOGGLE: *Journ. Appl. Phys.*, **28**, 639 (1957).
(*m*) OVERHAUSER: *Phys. Rev.*, **94**, 1951 (1954).

different measurements in copper, bombarded at low temperatures. Different theoretical estimates of the stored energy release for the annihilation of Frenkel pairs [4-6] are in moderately close agreement. Assuming 4 eV released per pair the stored energy experiments of Sosin and Meechan [7], and Nilan and Granato [8] lead to values of $\varrho_f = 3.0$ and $2.0\ \mu\Omega\cdot\text{cm/at.}\ \%$, respectively The experiments of Sosin and Meechan were done with electrons of comparable energies to ours and hence should be directly applicable. The Nilan and Granato result is more precise but was obtained using deuterons. The strong similarity of the recovery in electron-irradiated and deuteron-irradiated [9] copper suggests strongly, however, that the same defects are involved. The reasonable agreement between the values of ϱ_f inferred from the simple displacement theory ($\varrho_f = 1.5\ \mu\Omega\cdot\text{cm/at.}\ \%$) and the values obtained from the stored energy experiments ($\varrho_f = 2$ to $3\ \mu\Omega\cdot\text{cm/at.}\ \%$) lend strong support to the basic validity of the displacement theory for low-energy collisions. Additional measurements of threshold energies and Frenkel pair resistivities are presently in progress.

3·2. *Recovery measurements.* – Previous measurements [10, 11] in electron-irradiated copper have shown that $\sim 90\ \%$ of the induced resistivity recovers

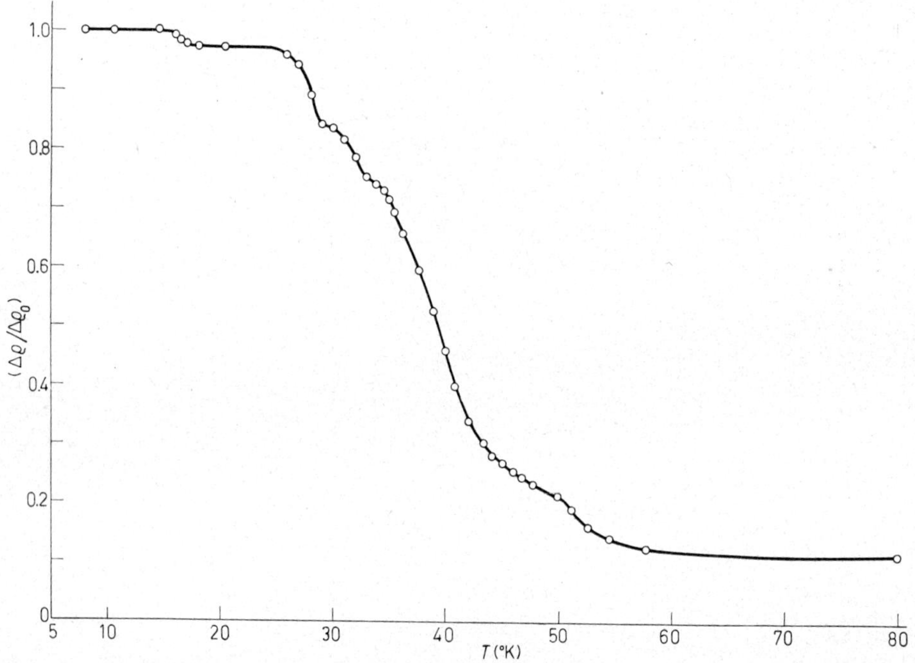

Fig. 8. – Isochronal annealing. The experimental points were obtained by pulse-heating the specimen and holding it for ten-minute periods at successively higher temperatures — each ten-minute annealing being followed by a resistivity measurement at 4.2 °K.

between 4 °K and 65 °K (stage I). It has been further found that this stage I recovery is sub-divided into five sub-stages labeled I_A-I_E in order of increasing temperature. Fig. 8 shows an isochronal recovery curve demonstrating the presence of these recovery sub-stages. The first three sub-stages have been

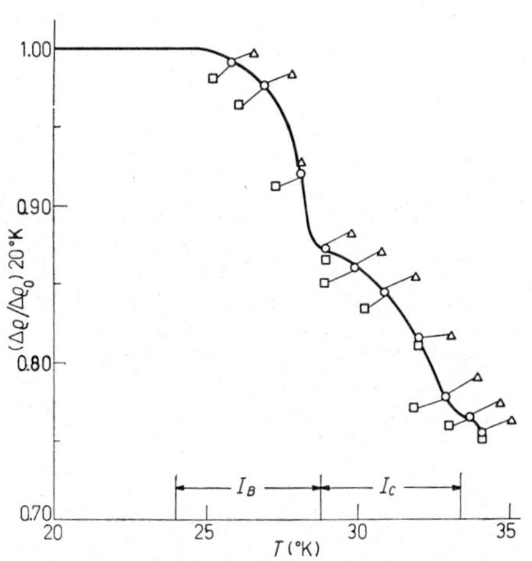

Fig. 9. – Concentration-dependence of the isochronal annealing of I_B and I_C recovery. The recovery is normalized at 20.4 °K. As discussed in the text, the initial defect concentrations corresponding to these curves are $1.0\cdot10^{-6}$, $6.0\cdot10^{-6}$, and $1.8\cdot10^{-5}$, respectively. □ $3.0\cdot10^{-10}$ Ω·cm; ○ $1.8\cdot10^{-9}$ Ω·cm; $5.4\cdot10^{-9}$ Ω·cm.

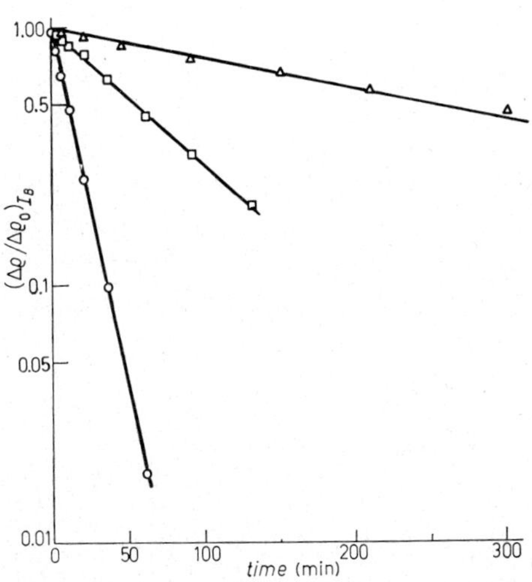

Fig. 10. – Isothermal recovery data in region I_B plotted against $\ln(t)$. The straight lines indicate that the recovery is a monomolecular process. △ 25.8 °K; □ 26.9 °K; ○ 28.1 °K.

identified as close-pairs of interstitials and vacancies which self-recombine due to their mutual interactions. The following pieces of evidence exist:

a) The fractional recovery in I_A, I_B, and I_C is independent of concentration (see Fig. 9) as would be expected for local processes.

b) The recovery does not depend on trace impurities in the specimens.

c) The recovery kinetics in each sub-stage is monomolecular (see Fig. 10).

d) The number of jumps to annihilation calculated from the measured activation energy is of the order of unity.

e) At lower bombarding energies the close-pair sub-stages become more important [12] (see Fig. 11).

Sub-stages I_D and I_E cannot be due to close-pairs as they do not exhibit the above features. These stages are found to have a common activation energy, with I_E possessing features characteristic of the free diffusion of a

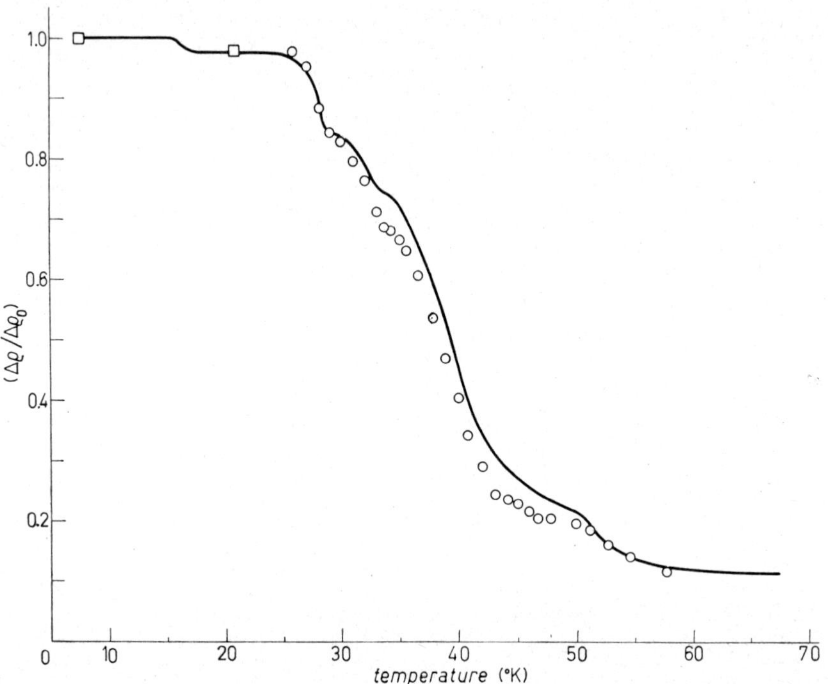

Fig. 11. – Isochronal recovery curves for several different bombarding energies. ○ 0.69 MeV; □ 0.80 MeV; —— 1.40 MeV.

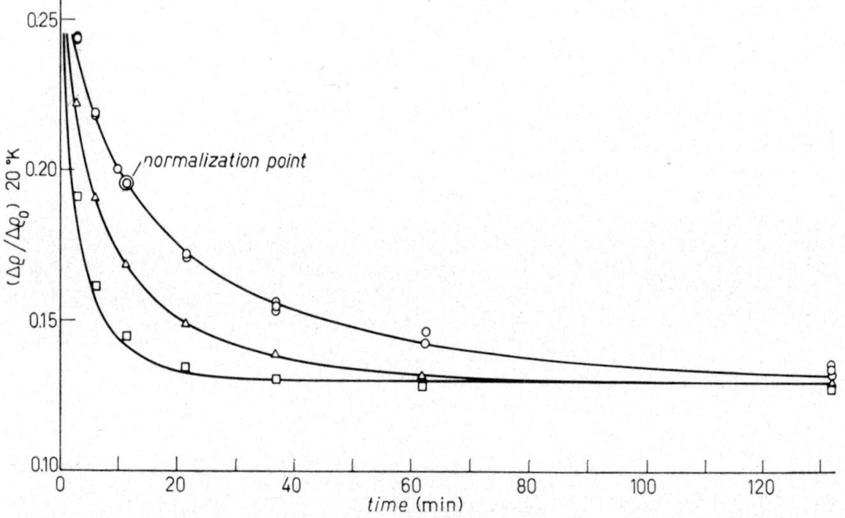

Fig. 12. – Concentration-dependence of the 52.7 °K (I_E) isothermal recovery. The solid lines are calculated for an interstitial clustering model. The subscript 20 °K refers to the irradiation temperature. ○ standard dose: $\Delta\varrho_0 = 2.74 \cdot 10^{-10}\ \Omega \cdot \text{cm}$ (three runs); △ medium dose: $\Delta\varrho_0 = 6.04 \cdot 10^{-10}\ \Omega \cdot \text{cm}$; □ heavy dose: $\Delta\varrho_0 = 16.17 \cdot 10^{-10}\ \Omega \cdot \text{cm}$.

mobile interstitial. Sub-stages I_D and I_E are interpreted as arising respectively from the correlated recovery (a wandering interstitial recombines accidently with its own vacancy) and uncorrelated recovery (a wandering interstitial combines with a distant vacancy) of migrating interstitial atoms. The evidence for free migration in I_E is as follows:

a) The rate of recovery is strongly concentration-dependent as would be expected for a diffusing defect (see Fig. 12).

b) Prior irradiation at 80 °K strongly enhances the final recovery in I_E (radiation doping effect). This shows that the radiation-induced defects are interacting with each other (most probably by diffusion) and not with impurities.

c) The recovery is strongly dependent on the presence of trace impurities in the sample.

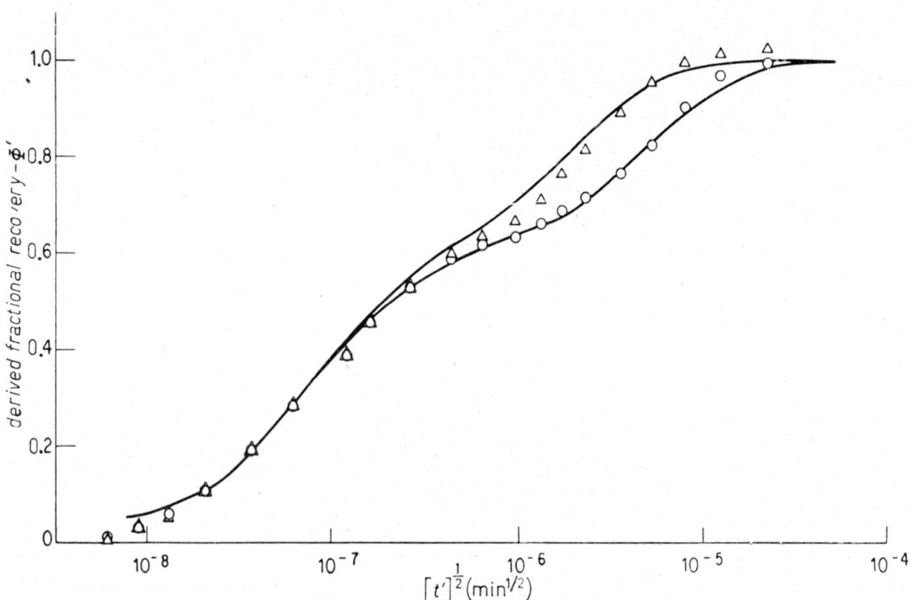

Fig. 13. – The points are taken from a normalized plot of recovery data as a function of equivalent time, t'. This latter quantity is defined as $t' = t_{exp} \exp[-Q/aT]$, where t_{exp} is the measured recovery time, and Q is an activation energy chosen to superpose experimental data. The region at low times corresponds to I_D, and the region at longer times to I_E. The solid lines are calculated from theory. The fit forms the primary evidence for assigning I_D to the correlated recovery and I_E to the uncorrelated recovery of a migrating defect. ○ $\Delta\varrho_0 = 3.00 \cdot 10^{-10}$ Ω·cm; △ $\Delta\varrho_0 = 18.33 \cdot 10^{-10}$ Ω·cm.

Sub-stage I_D is assigned to the correlated recovery of a migrating interstitial because:

a) It has the same activation energy as I_E.

b) The recovery data fit the theory of Waite [13] which treats the problem of correlated and uncorrelated recovery. The fit of the experimental data with the theory is shown in Fig. 13.

The residue which remains after stage I is complete is attributed to clusters of interstitials which form during I_E recovery, and a corresponding number of isolated vacancies. The qualitative arguments which leads to this point of view are sketched below. At low defect concentration it is observed that prior irradiation at 80 °K enhances the stages I_D and I_E of a subsequent low-

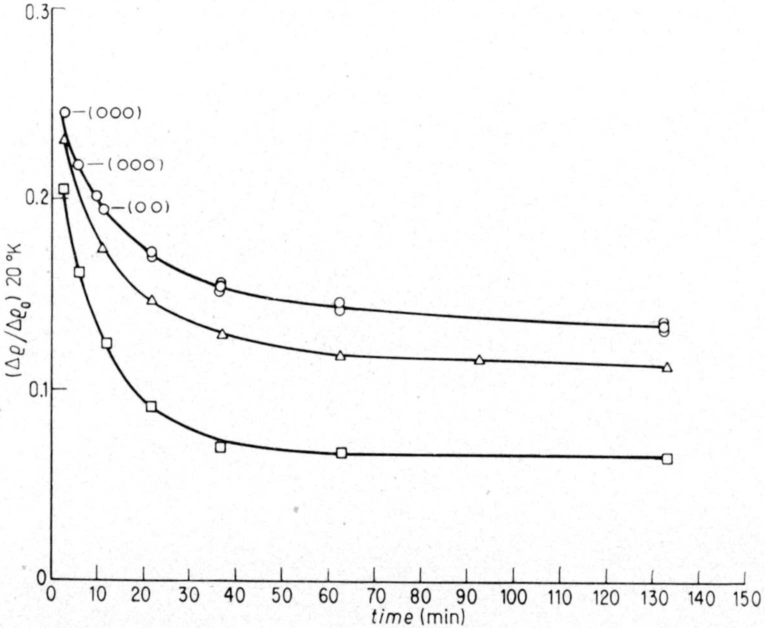

Fig. 14. – The effect of 80 °K radiation doping on the 52.7 °K (—) isothermal recovery. The subscript 20 °K refers to the irradiation temperature for the isothermal experiments. ○ standard irradiation, no doping: $\Delta\varrho = 2.74 \cdot 10^{-10}\ \Omega\cdot$cm, $\Delta\varrho_0 = 0$; △ 80° doping run: $\Delta\varrho_0 = 2.72 \cdot 10^{-10}\ \Omega\cdot$cm, $\Delta\varrho_0 = 0.35 \cdot 10^{-10}\ \Omega\cdot$cm; □ 80° doping run: $\Delta\varrho = 2.73 \cdot 10^{-10}\ \Omega\cdot$cm, $\Delta\varrho = 1.35 \cdot 10^{-10}\ \Omega\cdot$cm.

temperature irradiation of comparable magnitude. This is demonstrated in Fig. 14. The result implies that the radiation-induced defects are interacting primarily with each other and not with impurities. However, the final value of a low-temperature irradiation and recovery experiment, in a sample with no prior irradiation, is independent of concentration (see Fig. 12). This behavior is expected if the interstitials are interacting with each other to form clusters, and a clustering model is found to fit the experimental data quite precisely.

It has recently been proposed that the residue remaining after stage I is complete is due to the existence of a second type of interstitial which is immobile at these temperatures. We previously considered this possibility and rejected it for the following reasons:

a) If all the resistivity remaining after stage I is complete is due to an immobile interstitial, then prior irradiation should not affect this interstitial; *i.e.*, contrary to what is observed, no radiation-doping effect is expected.

b) In an irradiation performed at 80 °K the immobile interstitial should contribute a constant resistivity increment per unit flux. This is contrary to what is observed.

In samples of very pure copper the recovery of the resistivity that remains after stage I is complete takes place primarily in a single stage near room temperature (stage III). Very little stage II is observed. The appearance of a distinct stage III recovery in samples which show a pronounced radiation-doping effect at low temperature shows that stage III is an intrinsic process and not an impurity-dominated phenomenon as proposed recently by HASIGUTI [14].

4. – Influence of imperfections and temperature on the production and recovery of radiation damage in copper.

In the preceding section we described experiments in very high purity copper done at very low temperatures. Under these conditions it is found that experimental results are reproducible for different samples and are due to intrinsic processes. In this section we describe recent experiments done at higher temperature and in samples with different initial concentrations of lattice imperfections. Experimentally it is found in high-temperature irradiations that both the production and recovery of the electron-induced damage are completely dominated by the interaction of the radiation-induced defects with other crystal imperfections. It will be shown that the observed effects can be understood by considering the possible interactions of a mobile defect and, in fact, provides additional confirmation for the existence of such a defect at the end of stage I recovery.

It is important to realize that, in a real crystal containing imperfections, the variety of interactions possible for any migrating defect creates a complicated situation to analyse. Therefore, due to the simplicity of the defects produced, the electron experiments are useful because they provide a system in which it is possible to illustrate the general sorts of things that can happen in more complicated experiments. For example, an important question for the technological aspects of radiation damage is whether or not a low-temperature irradiation followed by a high-temperature anneal is equivalent to a high-temperature irradiation to the same dose. The work described here shows that, in certain cases, the two are not equivalent either in the amount or the nature of the damage which is produced.

4·1. *Production of damage at* 80 °K. – The striking influence of imperfections can be seen in experiments on the production of damage at 80 °K. Three different samples are considered « pure », « impure », and impure cold-worked. The pure (*) sample was prepared from a zone-refined bar formed from copper obtained from the American Smelting and Refining Company. This sample was used for all the low-temperature studies previously discussed. The « impure » sample was formed directly from the above starting material without the zone-refining process. The supplier states that it is 99.999% pure and hence it is only « impure » relative to the zone-refined sample. The impure cold-worked sample was formed by rolling the impure material at room temperature to a 90% area reduction. It was further annealed at ~ 400 °K for 30 minutes before being irradiated.

As can be seen in Fig. 15, the three samples give quite different production curves at 80 °K. We interpret these results in the following way. At 80 °K the free migration of interstitial atoms normally responsible for stage I_E recovery proceeds very rapidly. The instantaneous concentration of interstitials is very small and hence clustering is suppressed. Instead, the interstitials encounter impurities and are trapped. The production curves bend over eventually because of the build-up of vacancy sinks which are left behind by the trapped interstitials. Specifically, we find it is possible to account for the data with the following model:

1) We assume that a constant concentration of interstitials is formed per unit time during bombardment.

2) These interstitials do not interact directly with each other but go to one of four types of sites:

a) vacancies,

(*) As previously described, the existence of a radiation-doping effect can be used to demonstrate that the radiation-induced defects are interacting primarily with each other and not with impurities. Thus a « pure » sample can be defined operationally as one which possesses a radiation-doping effect of the proper magnitude.

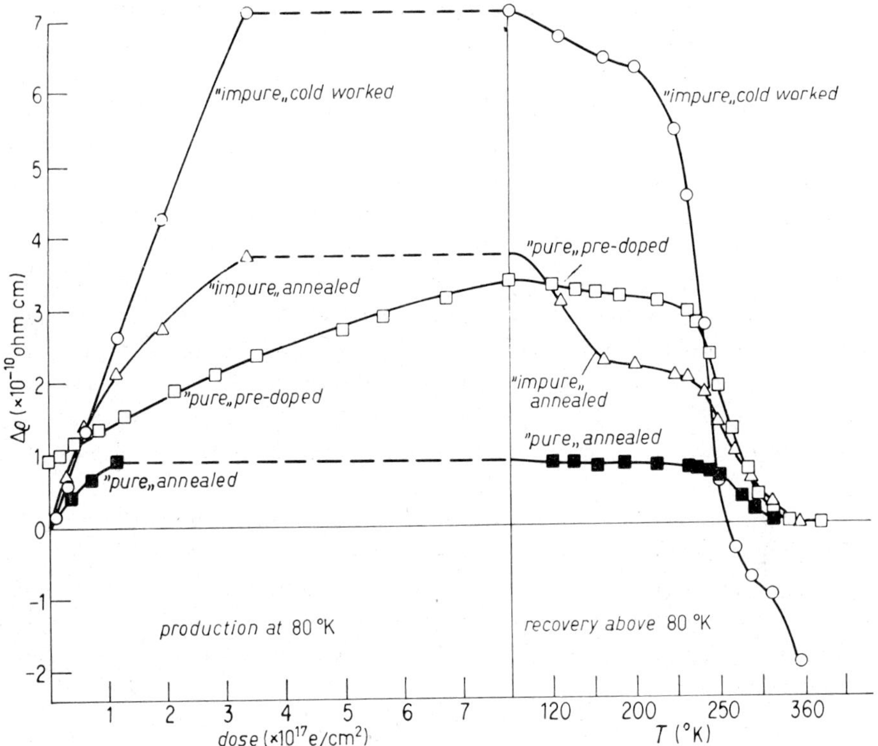

Fig. 15. – Production and recovery of residual electrical resistance in samples of copper with different imperfections initially present. All irradiations were performed at 80 °K with a bombarding electron energy of ~ 1.5 MeV. The different samples are described in the text.

b) unsaturable traps,

c) nucleation traps,

d) saturable traps.

3) The resistivity of a given concentration of interstitials is constant whether or not the interstitials are trapped.

The various trapping sites are defined as follows:

a) A saturable trap is one which can accept only one interstitial, and then is no longer effective in trapping.

b) An unsaturable trap is one which can accept interstitials without limit, without changing its probability for subsequent interstitial capture — a dislocation is an example of such a trap.

c) A nucleation trap is one in which the capture of an interstitial enhances the probability of subsequent interstitial capture. Specifically, we assume that the effective number of such traps at any time is given by $[N_n(0)+\gamma n_n]$ where $N_n(0)$ is the initial number of such traps, n_n is the number of interstitials previously trapped, and γ is an arbitrary parameter $\leqslant 1$ which is determined by fitting to experimental data. Physically this could correspond to the build-up of a platelet of interstitials around a chemical impurity.

Let n_s, n_u, and n_n represent respectively the number of interstitials trapped at saturable sites, unsaturable sites, and nucleation sites at any dose φ. If N_s, N_u, N_n are the number of such traps at any dose, the differential equations corresponding to the above model are:

$$(3)\qquad \begin{cases} (a)\ \dfrac{\mathrm{d}n_s}{\mathrm{d}\varphi} = \dfrac{KN_s(\varphi)}{D} = \dfrac{K[N_s(0)-n_s]}{D}\,, \\[2ex] (b)\ \dfrac{\mathrm{d}n_u}{\mathrm{d}\varphi} = \dfrac{KN_u(\varphi)}{D} = \dfrac{KN_u(0)}{D}\,, \\[2ex] (c)\ \dfrac{\mathrm{d}n_n}{\mathrm{d}\varphi} = \dfrac{K[N_n(0)+\gamma n_n]}{D}\,, \\[2ex] (d)\ \dfrac{\mathrm{d}n_v}{\mathrm{d}\varphi} = K\left[1-\dfrac{n_v}{D}\right], \end{cases}$$

where D is given by the expression,

$$(4)\qquad D = N_s(\varphi) + N_u(0) + n_v(\varphi) + \big(N_n(0) + \gamma n_n(\varphi)\big)\,.$$

In these equations, $n_v(\varphi)$ is the instantaneous concentration of vacancies, K is a constant $= fR$, where R is the constant introduction rate of defects expected at liquid helium temperature and f equals the fraction of such defects corresponding to stage I_E in the recovery spectrum.

With the assumption that the resistivity of a trapped interstitial is equal to that of a free interstitial it follows that $\varrho(\varphi)$, the observable resistivity change, is given by

$$(5)\qquad \varrho(\varphi) = n_v(\varphi)\varrho_f\,.$$

The above equations lead to simple solutions in the following special cases:

A) If traps far outweigh radiation-induced defects, then

$$(6)\qquad \varrho(\varphi) = C_1\varphi\,.$$

B) If only saturable traps are present, then

$$\varrho(\varphi) = \varrho_f N_s(0)(1 - \exp[-K\varphi/N_s(0)]) , \tag{7}$$

hence at high doses,

$$\varrho \simeq C_2 . \tag{8}$$

C) If only unsaturable traps are present, then

$$\varrho(\varphi) = \varrho_f N_u(0) \left[\left(\frac{2K\varphi}{N_u(0)} + 1\right)^{\frac{1}{2}} - 1\right] . \tag{9}$$

Hence at high doses,

$$\varrho(\varphi) \sim C_3 \sqrt{\varphi} . \tag{10}$$

D) If only nucleation traps are present, then

$$K\varphi = (1 + \gamma)/\gamma n_n(\varphi) - \frac{N_n(0)}{\gamma^2} \ln\left[1 + \frac{\gamma n_n(\varphi)}{N_n(0)}\right] , \tag{11}$$

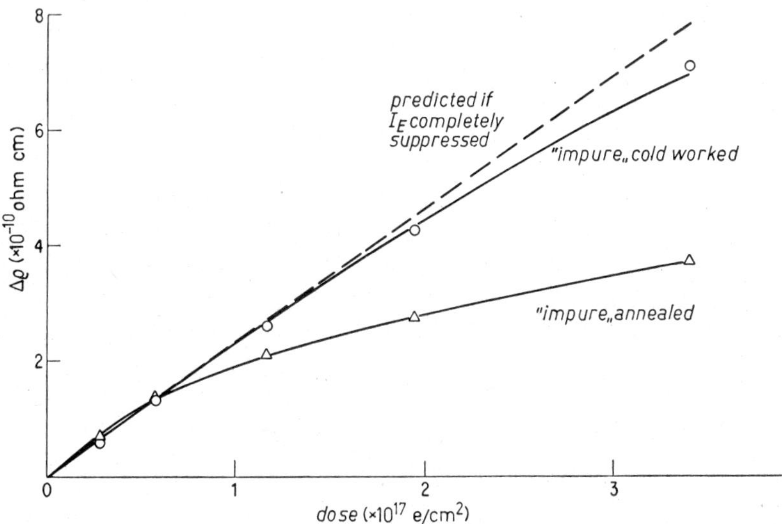

Fig. 16. Production of damage at 80 °K in « impure » samples of Cu. One of the samples was plastically deformed prior to irradiation, while the other was a well-annealed, soft specimen. The dotted line shows the curve predicted if I_E recovery were completely suppressed.

from which it follows that at high doses,

$$\varrho(\varphi) = C_4\varphi \,. \tag{12}$$

We now consider the application of these equations to experiment. The solid lines of Fig. 16 show the data for the cold-worked and impure samples while the dotted line is the prediction corresponding to case A) above where all the interstitials are trapped. The agreement is satisfactory. In Fig. 17 the data for the pure sample are plotted *vs.* the square root of electron flux. The solid curve is calculated from eq. (6) corresponding to the unsaturable trap case and is seen to provide an excellent fit to the data. In Fig. 18 we plot data of BRINKMAN and MEECHAN [15] for an equivalent electron irradiation at 90 °K. These data were chosen because they extend to a much higher total flux than is feasible in our experiments. The solid line is calculated from eq. (8) ($\gamma = 0.3$) corresponding to the case of nucleation traps.

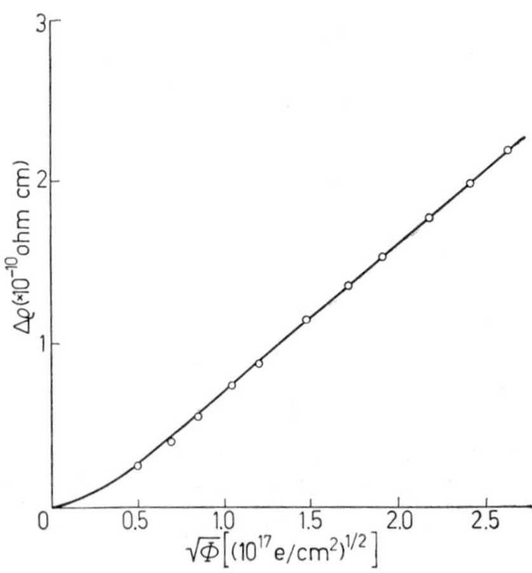

Fig. 17. – Production of damage at 80 °K in a pure, zone-refined sample of Cu plotted against the square root of dose. The solid line is a theoretical curve calculated for the unsaturable trap model described in the text.

The fact that there are a number of different parameters available for fitting the production curves means that the precise fits obtained should perhaps not be taken too seriously. There can be no doubt, however, that the model provides a satisfactory framework for explaining all the observed results.

In the above explanation for the observed effects on production rates at high temperature we have assumed that all the differences arise because of the different trapping reactions of the free interstitials. If this is true then the stage I recovery in these samples should be identical through stages I_A-I_D, with only I_E showing any differences. Experimentally this is found to be essentially true with only stage I_E suppressed in less pure samples. In the case of the cold-worked specimen there appears to be a slight effect on the rate, but not the final value, of recovery in stages I_B and I_C. This effect is illustrated in Fig. 19 and is interpreted as due to a smearing and lowering of the recombination energies due to the strain fields of the dislocations introduced by the cold-working.

There remains the possibility that at least part of the enhanced damage in the impure specimens—particularly the cold-worked specimens—could be

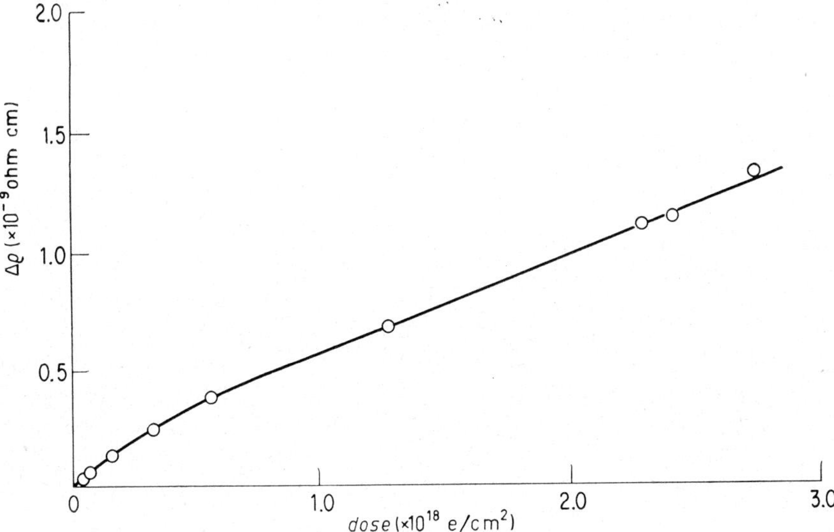

Fig. 18. – Production of damage at 80 °K in a sample similar to those shown in Fig. 16. The data points are due to MEECHAN and BRINKMAN ([15]). The solid line is a theoretical curve calculated for the nucleation trap model described in text.

due to a true enhanced damage production rate of the sort treated by LEIBFRIED [16]. Unfortunately, our experiments do not measure absolute changes in resistivity precisely so we can say little on this point. An indirect argu-

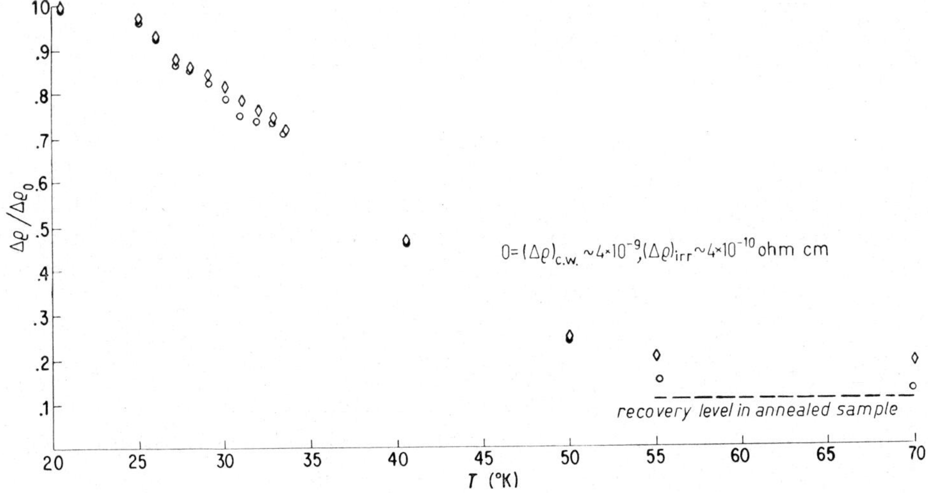

Fig. 19. – Stage I recovery in two cold-worked, pure samples. The rate of recovery is enhanced at low temperatures and suppressed at high temperatures in the sample which is plastically deformed.

ment based on the recovery curves suggests, however, that this is not an important effect.

The analysis of the above experiments has some interesting consequences in connection with two important problems in radiation damage work. The first problem is that of reciprocity—the question of whether a low-temperature irradiation followed by a high-temperature anneal is equivalent to a high-temperature irradiation to the same flux. In Fig. 20 we compare the pro-

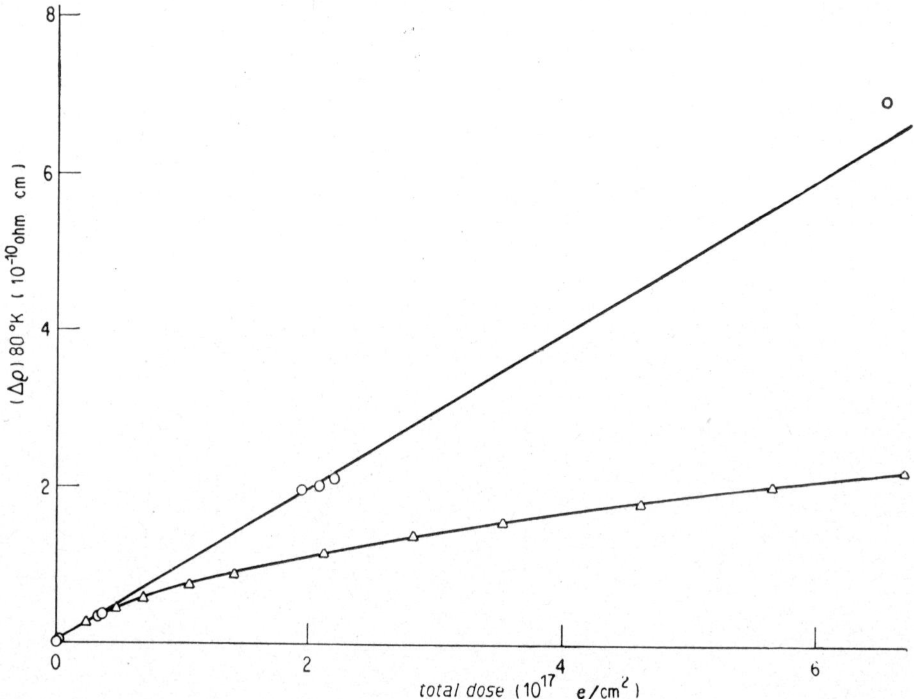

Fig. 20. – Comparison of damage production rates at 80 °K for two different methods of introducing damage. In one experiment the sample is irradiated at 20 °K and then annealed at 80 °K. Each of the points represents a separate experiment starting with a completely recovered sample. In the other experiment the sample is irradiated directly at 80 °K. ○ irradiation at 20 °K with subsequent anneal at 80 °K; △ irradiation at 80 °K.

duction data for the pure sample for two different experiments. In the first experiment the damage is produced by irradiating at 20 °K and then annealing to 80 °K. This is compared to an experiment where the damage is introduced by irradiating directly at 80 °K. Certainly the damage production rates are quite different. The nature of the damage is also different, as can be seen from studies of the radiation-doping effect. For the same resistivity increment, damage introduced in the two different ways has a different effect on a subsequent irradiation. This effect is shown in Fig. 21. In this case, then, reciprocity does not hold. The failure in this case arises from the different instantaneous concentration of defects in the two experiments and the corresponding differing probabilities for clustering and trapping in the two experiments.

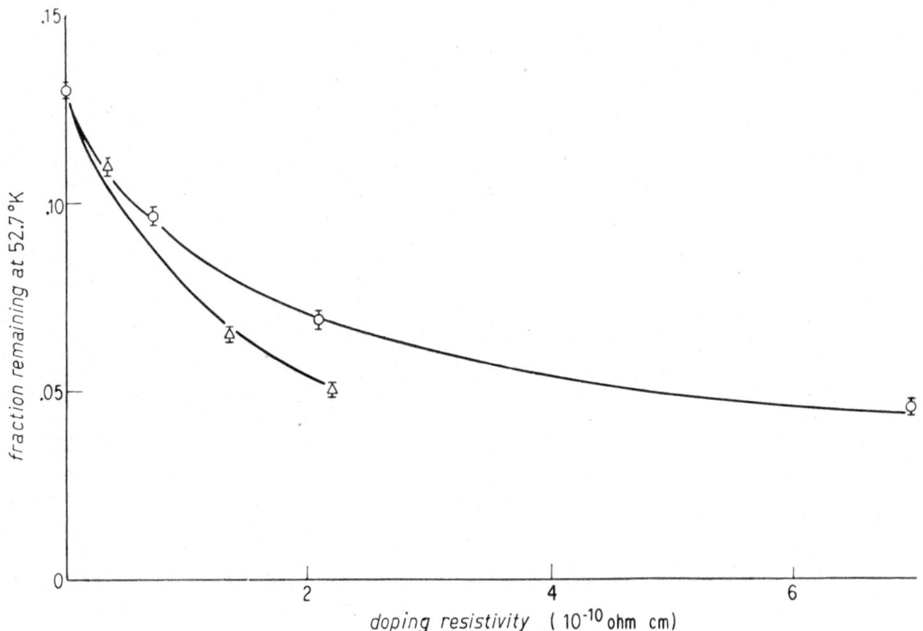

Fig. 21. – Radiation doping. The effect of prior irradiation on the saturation value of I_E recovery. The prior irradiation is done in two different ways. In one experiment the sample is irradiated at 20 °K and then annealed to 80 °K. In the second experiment the doping resistivity is added by bombarding directly at 80 °K. The solid lines are theoretical as described in ref. [11]. ○ 20°—80° doping runs; △ 80° doping runs.

There are at least two other reasons which can lead to a failure of reciprocity in damage experiments. Firstly, if the experiment is performed at very high temperatures, then the concept of a close pair loses meaning. The relative probability that an interstitial will jump toward its vacancy rather than away from it is proportional to $\exp[\Delta Q/kT]$, where ΔQ is the energy difference between the two types of jumps. At low temperatures even a slightly reduced barrier in the direction of the direction of the vacancy heavily weights this type of jump. As the temperature increases, however, the jump probabilities become more nearly equal. Hence, in a high-temperature irradiation, more migrating interstitials are formed. The second effect is the possibility that the threshold energy itself is temperature-dependent.

We have given above examples of reciprocity failure; however, reciprocity is observed in our experiments on the cold-worked sample between 20 °K and 80 °K. Here the concentration of traps is so large that all the interstitials are trapped in either a low- or high-temperature irradiation. The last two effects mentioned above are also not important in these experiments. It is not possible, therefore, to make any general assertions about reciprocity—each damage experiment must be examined individually.

Another problem of interest is the question of whether the rate of irradiation affects the damage which is produced. At high dose rates the trapping equations given above for an 80 °K irradiation would be modified by the advent of clustering effects and would therefore predict a dose-dependence. It may be argued that a 20 °K irradiation followed by an 80 °K anneal is equivalent to a very high dose experiment at 80 °K. The difference in the two curves of Fig. 20 therefore demonstrates that damage can depend on dose rate.

4·2. *Recovery above* 80 °K. – In Fig. 15 we have also plotted the high-temperature recovery of the different samples. As noted previously, the pure sample recovers almost completely in a single stage (stage III) in the vicinity of room temperature. Very little stage II recovery is observed. This behavior is essentially the same whether the defects are added at 20 °K or 80 °K. The impure sample, on the other hand, shows a very large and well-defined stage II recovery. We interpret this sudden appearance of a stage II recovery as being due to the release of the trapped interstitials. In studying the recovery of the damage shown in Fig. 18, Brinkman and Meechan [15] found that a considerable fraction of the damage remained after stage III. It is clear that one can alter the high-temperature recovery almost at will depending on the impurities in the material. Extreme caution must therefore be used in interpreting recovery data.

The cold-worked sample shows an interesting phenomenon whereby the final resistivity of the sample is less than before irradiation. Several explanations for this behavior can be constructed but, in view of the complexities introduced by cold-work, it is difficult to say what is happening with any certainty. If vacancies were migrating in stage III, these could find dislocations and rearrange and modify these in such a way as to lower the net residual resistivity of the sample. An alternative explanation is to suppose that the cold-working serves to disperse impurity atoms in the material. When vacancies migrate, they may be trapped by these impurities and then serve to enhance the diffusion of the impurities to form precipitates.

Meechan *et al.* [17] have reported more extensive experiments on the effects of cold-work which they interpret as evidence for interstitial atom migration in stage III. Discussion of this view is deferred until the final section of this paper.

5. – Production and recovery of radiation damage in metals other than copper.

5·1. *Damage production.* – Recently we have initiated a series of measurements in metals other than copper. To date we have bombarded high-purity samples of Al, Ag, Au, Ni, and Fe with ~1.5 MeV electrons at a temperature of 20.4 °K. Liquid helium irradiations have also been performed for Ag and Au. The production data are shown in Fig. 22. The low damage production

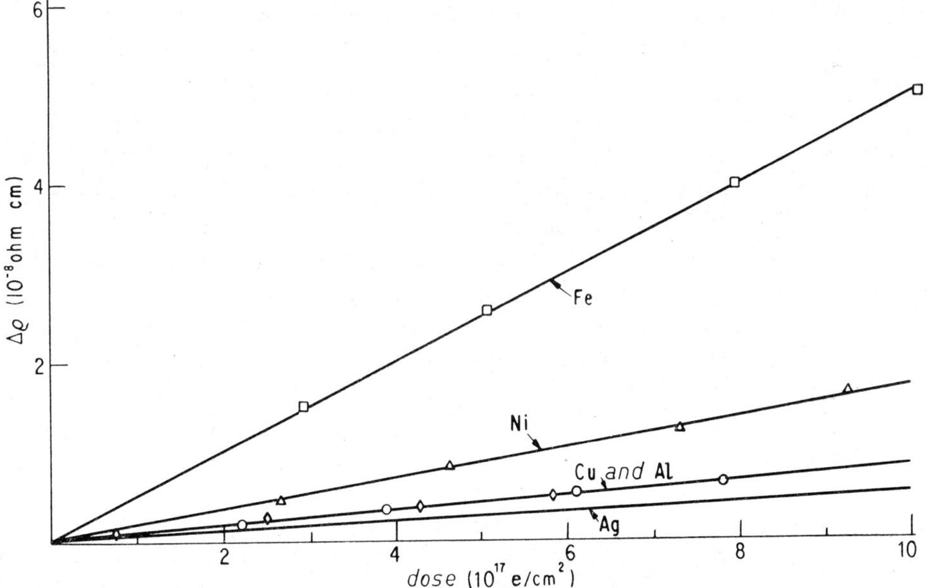

Fig. 22. – Change of residual electrical resistivity in several metals bombarded at 20.4 °K with 1.5 MeV electrons.

rates in Ag and Au (no significant change observed in Au) have previously been discussed by us [18]. The essential conclusions are:

a) The average threshold energies probably increase with increasing Z in the series Cu, Ag, Au, being respectively ~22, 30 and 40 eV.

b) The conclusion by COOPER, KOEHLER and MARX [19] that the observed Z-dependence of damage production in deuteron-irradiated Cu, Ag and Au gives confirmation of the basic displacement theory, is probably not correct.

The production rates in Ni and Fe relative to Cu are respectively ~ 5 and ~ 2. Corresponding ratios of 8 and 3 have previously been observed in neutron experiments by BLEWITT *et al.* [20]. This suggests the following tentative hypotheses:

1) The damage thresholds may be similar in Fe, Cu and Ni.

2) The basic damage mechanisms may also be similar.

3) Point-defect resistivities are probably much higher in Ni and Fe than in Cu.

Threshold experiments now in progress should serve to test these points.

5·2. *Stage I recovery.* – Low temperature recovery data are shown in Fig. 23. A striking feature of this data is the existence of recovery substructure in all metals so far studied. In silver, measurements starting at 4° K (not shown)

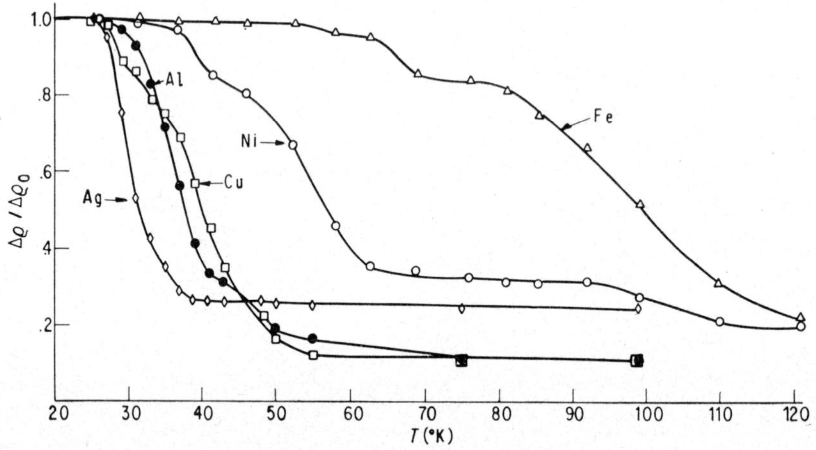

Fig. 23. – Stage I recovery of several metals bombarded at 20.4 °K with 1.5 MeV electrons. The recovery curve is of the isochronal type obtained by pulsing the samples to the specified temperatures and holding them there for 10 min. The samples are then quenched to 20.4 °K for measurement.

indicate the existence of 3 sub-stages, similar to those previously found in an activation energy analysis by MAGNUSON, PALMER, and KOEHLER [9]. Ag is also interesting because the latter part of stage I recovery is sensitive to trace impurities—as is the case in copper. This is shown in Fig. 24 where the recovery is plotted for samples of different purity. The « impure » sample was prepared from a silver obtained from Handy-Harmon, Inc. (99.9+). The pure sample was formed from a single crystal bar grown from silver starting

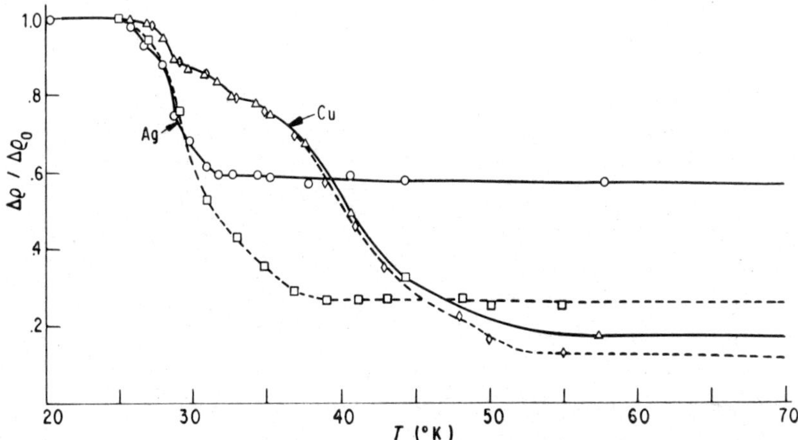

Fig. 24. – Stage I recovery in « pure » and « impure » samples of Ag and Cu. The samples are described in the text. Solid lines are « impure » samples, dashed lines are « pure » samples.

material (stated purity 99,9999%) obtained from the Consolidated Smelting and Refining Company of Canada, Ltd. Silver appears to be quite similar to copper except that the recovery for stage I is depressed to lower temperatures. Also, we have been so far able to resolve only three sub-stages in silver compared to five in copper.

Nickel has previously been studied by Sosin and Brinkman [21] who found behavior generally similar to copper. The present results confirm this and show moreover the existence of the characteristic structure in the stage I region. A word of caution should be interjected here concerning the counting and labeling of various sub-stages. As we showed in the previous section, once the interstitials become mobile, then trapping and re-release processes can give rise to a number of recovery stages. Thus the sub-stage occurring around 100 °K in nickel is probably due to an impurity effect. The lower recovery sub-stages are, however, undoubtedly intrinsic.

Iron is the only non-face-centered cubic metal we have studied so far, and it is interesting to note that this body-centered metal also possesses the recovery sub-structure. In fact, the structure in iron is the most pronounced which has yet been seen. At least four peaks are observed, and it is possible that a more careful experiment will resolve more structure in the region from 80 °K to 110 °K.

Aluminum appears to show only two sub-stages at low temperatures. However, it is quite possible that additional structure will appear when experiments are performed at helium temperatures.

In their work on nickel, SOSIN and BRINMKAN [20] found that the high-temperature recovery curves could be closely superposed on the copper curves, if plotted *vs.* T/T_m—where T_m is the melting point of the material. The same is approximately true for the low temperature Ni data of Fig. 23. However, no such simple relations appears to hold for the other metals. The ratios of the temperatures at which stage I is half complete to the melting temperatures for the elements Al, Ag, Cu, Ni and Fe are, respectively, 0.056, 0.031, 0.036, 0.036, and 0.062.

Since we have not as yet studied the recovery kinetics or looked for radiation-doping effects in these metals, we cannot say with certainty that the recovery procesess in these metals are identical with copper. However, the general similarity of the recovery curves suggests that the behavior previously outlined for copper is valid for these other metals as well. It seems likely that discrete close pairs and interstitial atoms which are mobile at very low temperatures are features common to many metals.

5'3. *Recovery above stage I.* – The higher temperature recovery behavior is shown in Fig. 25. As previously noted, it is difficult to interpret these data without performing additional experiments to assure that higher-temperature recovery stages are not due to the release of interstitial atoms trapped in stage I. With this reservation in mind we will note here only a few points

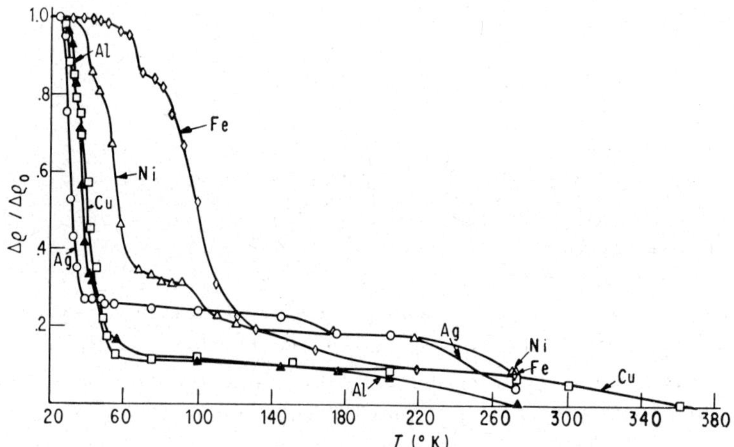

Fig. 25. – Recovery of several metals bombarded at 20.4 K with 1.5 MeV electrons. The recovery curve is of the isochronal type obtained by pulsing the samples to the specified temperatures and holding them there for 10 min. The samples are then quenched to 20.4 °K for measurement.

concerning the high-temperature recovery. The case of aluminum is particularly interesting. This was a high-purity specimen from the same starting material as DeSorbo and Turnbull [22, 23] used in their quenching experiments. The final resistivity recovering after stage I in the irradiated specimen is about the same as the added resistivity in the quenching experiments. Consider the recovery between 190 °K and 270 °K in the irradiated sample. It appears that this recovery occurs at a considerably lower temperature than the dominant recovery stage in aluminum quenched from low temperatures. If we identify the (190 ÷ 270) °K recovery with the analogous stage III recovery in irradiated copper, this suggests that the dominant defect observed in the quench experiments is different from that responsible for stage III recovery in irradiated metals. This same conclusion is reached if we identify the recovery in the silver sample between 200 °K and 270 °K with stage III. However, this is not a firm conclusion. In the first place, the identification of the high-temperature recovery stages in Ag and Al as the equivalent of stage III in copper is still uncertain. Secondly, the irradiation experiments differ fundamentally from quench experiments in that the distribution of sinks for mobile defects is quite different. It is therefore necessary to measure activation energies for each stage rather than just the temperature at which recovery occurs. A third complication in the case of aluminum is that, even in the case of electron bombardment, many multiple defects such as divacancies, should be formed. The results of the present experiments are thus, so far, inconclusive on the important question of the relationship of the quench defects to irradiation defects. In the final section of this paper we shall return to the question of the identification of the defects responsible for the high-temperature recovery.

6. – Current problems.

We have attempted to show in this paper that the low-temperature electron experiments give a consistent picture of both the production and recovery of damage in metals. However, there are a number of outstanding problems on which we would like to comment in this final section.

6·1. *Identification of recovery stages.* – One long standing problem is the identification of the defects responsible for the various recovery stages. No attempt will be made here to summarize the many models which have been proposed. We shall instead concentrate on the point of view developed from the electron experiments. As we have shown, the recovery in pure samples of electron-irradiated copper is particularly simple—consisting of essentially two recovery stages, I and III. Earlier in this paper we showed that the radiation-doping effect demonstrates that both stages I and III are due to intrinsic defects. In the picture we developed, stage I recovery is attributed to the recombination of close pairs and the free diffusion of interstitials. The damage remaining, after stage I recovery is complete, is attributed to vacancies and di-interstitials. Stage III therefore must be ascribed to the direct motions of either of these defects or to the dissociation of the di-interstitials. This last alternative seems to be precluded by the observation of MEECHAN and BRINKMAN [15] that stage III obeys second-order kinetics. The possibility of di-interstitial migration cannot be ruled out but seems difficult to reconcile with the impurity experiments where those samples in which the interstitials were supposedly trapped and not clustered, also showed a large stage III recovery. All the experiments that we have performed can be most easily interpreted by assuming that vacancies migrate in stage III. In particular, this explains the presence of stage III in all the impurity experiments. Since the free vacancy is always present, one should always see stage III. The second-order kinetics of stage III and the undershoot effect observed in cold-worked samples, can also be explained by single vacancy migration. The major argument against single vacancy migration in stage III is the measured activation energy for motion, E_m. MEECHAN and BRINKMAN [15] found 0.62 eV in an electron bombardment while OVERHAUSER [24] found 0.68 eV in a deuteron experiment. From the considerations below, these values seem low for vacancy migration.

In recent years considerable information on the formation and migration energies of defects has been obtained from quenching experiments. It is found in several materials that the measured formation and migration energies add to give the measured energy for self-diffusion, as would be expected if the quenched defects were single vacancies. Recent measurements of the difference in length and lattice parameter [25-27] confirm the formation energies found in the quenching experiments in Al, Ag and Au. These experiments also definitely identify the defects as vacancies. Unfortunately, direct measurements of this type have not been done in copper. If we assume that in copper the ratio of mobility energy to self-diffusion energy is the same as in Au [30] then we expect a value for $E_m \sim 0.9$ eV, which is higher than the values quoted above for the stage III recovery following irradiation. AIROLDI, BACCHELLA and GERMAGNOLI [29] obtained even higher values of 1.3 and 1.6 eV in a quench experiment (these latter values seem too high, however, as they do not check with the self-diffusion energy). We have already pointed out that both Ag and Al show a stage III recovery (tentative identification only) somewhat lower in temperature than would be expected from quench experiments. SOSIN and BRINKMAN [21] have previously reached a similar conclusion concerning the recovery in Ni. These and several other authors have long supported the view that stage III is not due to single vacancies. In summary, there seems to be some evidence that what we call stage III recovery in irradiated metals has a lower activation energy by perhaps 0.1 to 0.3 eV than the dominant recovery attributed to single vacancies in quenching experiments.

However, this is by no means yet established. For example, KIMURA, MADDIN and KUHLMANN-WILSDORFF [28] give a value of 0.72 eV for single vacancy migration in copper as a result of their study of quench hardening. In Al, TUCKER and WEBB [31] found evidence of electron-radiation enhanced diffusion, presumably by a vacancy type defect, in a temperature range corresponding to our observed stage III recovery in this material.

The major reason for the uncertainty in the relationship of irradiation and quench defects is that *complete* experiments of both types have not been performed on the same materials. Ideally, both types of experiments should be done on the same sample. We have already pointed out how trace impurities modify the recovery following irradiation. It should be expected that they will also affect the recovery in quench experiments. Another possibility is that the quenching experiments are not measuring single vacancies.

MEECHAN, SOSIN, and BRINKMAN [17] have interpreted their work dealing with the influence of cold-work on the recovery of irradiated Cu, as evidence for two types of interstitials—a crowdion interstitial responsible for stage I and a normal interstitial responsible for stage III. In their model, the residue after stage I is complete is attributed to the normal interstitial. The suppression of recovery in cold-worked samples is attributed to the conversion of the crowdion to the normal configuration. We do not subscribe to this interpretation for the following reasons. As we noted earlier, both the radiation doping effect and the shape of the 80 °K production curve for the pure samples argue strongly against the view that the fraction left after stage I is due to an immobile interstitial. As we also showed, all the impurity effects can be accounted for by a simple trapping model. Further, the reasonable [10] progression of activation energies from close pairs to the migrating interstitial, and the fit with the Waite analysis, are both consistent with a single interstitial. There appears, therefore. to be no strong experimental evidence for two types of interstitials. It is possible to argue that in the electron case, only the crowdion is produced and that this converts to the normal interstitial during migration. We view this explanation as improbable.

In summary, our view of the recovery stages in copper is as follows. Stage I is due in part to close pairs and in part to a migrating interstitial. In electron experiments, stage II is variable within wide limits and is due primarily to the release of trapped interstitials. Other defects such as di-vacancies or extended clusters may also play a role, particularly in bombardments with heavy particles. We do not find it possible to assign stage III to a particular defect with any certainty. We favor the single vacancy, but more work is apparently needed.

6·2. *Damage prodution rates in heavy particle experiments.* – Another major problem is the large discrepancy of >5 found between simple displacement theory and experiment in irradiations with neutrons and deuterons [32]. We now discuss a crude modification of the displacement theory which tends to resolve this discrepancy and which we feel may be suggestive of the final solution of the problem. Suppose the displacement probability function rises very quickly from the onset threshold to a saturation value of the displacement probability, P_s, less than one (physically, this could correspond to the fact that it may be very difficult to produce damage in certain crystal directions). The shape of the experimentally determined curve of relative cross-section *vs.* bombarding electron energy would be the same as if the displacement probability had reached unity, but our conclusions on absolute damage rates in the electron experiments would be in error by a factor P_s. The predictions for heavy particle experiments are modified more strongly, because the factor P_s enters sequentially into the calculation of the cascade process. In order to check this point, we have calculated the damage production rates for electrons, pile neutrons, and 9 MeV deuterons using a saturated probability function. We used the formalism outlined in SEITZ and KOEHLER [1] and assumed that $P_s=\frac{1}{2}$. We find that the ratio of the damage calculated assuming $P_s=1$ to that calculated for $P_s=\frac{1}{2}$ is 2 for the electron case, 7.3 for the deuteron case, and 34 for the pile irradiation case. The fact that we have grossly overestimated the correction in the last case indicates that the assumption that the threshold function stays saturated to high energies is too extreme.

There are some other interesting consequences of the saturated probability function. It is possible to calculate the fraction of displaced atoms which find themselves in clusters of different sizes—where a cluster is defined as the number of atoms produced by a single primary hit. SEITZ and KOEHLER have shown that the average number of displaced atoms per primary is ~ 6. This does not imply, however, that most of the atoms are in small clusters. The results of the distribution calculation are shown in Table II, and it is clear that for $P=1$ most of the displaced atoms are in large clusters. If this is true it is difficult to understand the fact that MAGNUSON, PALMER and KOEHLER [9] observe well-resolved, close-pair recovery peaks. One would expect that the close proximity of other defects would broaden the peaks considerably. Table II also shows the distribution calculation for $P_s=\frac{1}{2}$. Here most of the defects are produced singly, and the resolution of the substructure would be expected. The distributions given in Table II also qualitatively account for the different stage I recovery values observed in irradiations with different particles. In the electron experiments we find that approximately $\frac{1}{2}$ the resistivity is retained when free migration begins. If we assume that the recovery in a cluster is completely self-contained, then we would

TABLE II. – *Distribution of damage in an* 8.5 MeV *deuteron irradiation, calculated for two saturation values,* P_s, *of the displacement probability function.*

	$P_s=1$	$P_s=\frac{1}{2}$
Fraction of atoms in single clusters	.11	.73
Fraction of atoms in double clusters	.045	.11
Fraction of atoms in triple clusters	.032	.05
Fraction of atoms in quadruple clusters	.024	.03
$\geqslant$ 5	.78	.03
$\geqslant$ 50	.55	—
$\geqslant$ 100	.49	—

expect $\sim\frac{1}{2}$ of the cluster's resitivity to be retained on annealing. On this basis we would predict $\sim 23\%$ and $\sim 50\%$ should be retained after stage I in deuteron and neutron experiments. The measured values are 35% and 63%.

6·3. *Details of the production process.* – In the treatment of the damage production we have so far talked only in terms of displacement probability functions. Such a treatment ignores any of the details of the damage process. Another outstanding current problem is the necessity of obtaining more detailed information about the damage process, including the spatial distribution of defects and the variation of threshold energy with crystal direction. Several of the papers at this course have emphasized the importance of the crystal structure in determining the nature of the damage. BROWN and AUGUSTYNIAK [33] have made the only reported measurement of the dependence of threshold on crystal orientation. In germanium, well above threshold, they found a difference in damage production rates of about 40% for different crystal orientations. However, the onset of damage occurred at about the same electron energy, and the interpretation of the experiments is not clear. In our laboratory we have recently initiated experiments on whiskers of both copper and iron. There appear to be measurable differences in the close pair recovery structure with different bombardment directions, but more work needs to be done to measure the effect accurately.

6·4. *Future use of electron bombardment.* – In the first section of this paper we listed a number of ways in which electron bombardment provides a useful tool for damage research. In succeeding sections we discussed experiments which illustrated specifically some of these general features of the electron bombardment technique. We now consider briefly the extent to which this technique is likely to prove useful in the future.

In many materials it is not even known whether direct displacement is the fundamental mechanism of damage production. Electron bombardment experiments can answer this question, but to date only a few materials have been investigated. For example, the survey by WALKER [3] lists only nine materials whose threshold behavior has been studied. Most of these were studied only for the onset threshold. The investigations described elsewhere in this paper show that in order to realize the maximum potential of electron experiments, it is generally necessary to work at very low temperatures and in very pure materials. These conditions have not been satisfied in most of the reported work. Only one measurement of an orientation effect has been published. No measurements exist which investigate the transition between single and multiple defect production.

In view of the many advantages of the electron bombardment technique and the limited amount of work so far reported, it is our opinion that the technique will show increasing usefulness in the future.

* * *

Most of the work described herein was done in collaboration with Dr. J. CORBETT. We gratefully acknowledge the efforts of E. FONTANELLA, who participated in much of the experimental work. We also wish to thank Dr. P. LUCASSON for valuable discussions.

REFERENCES

[1] For a fuller discussion of the theory, including numerical tables, see: F. SEITZ and J. S. KOEHLER in *Solid State Physics*, vol. **2** (New York, 1956), pp. 307-442.

[2] J. W. CORBETT, J. M. DENNEY, M. D. FISKE and R. M. WALKER: *Phys. Rev.*, **108**, 954 (1957).

[3] R. M. WALKER: *Survey of Radiation Damage Thresholds*, Gov't. Document, AFCRC-TN-59-552.

[4] H. HUNTINGTON and F. SEITZ: *Phys. Rev.*, **61**, 315 (1942).

[5] L. TEWORDT: *Phys. Rev.*, **109**, 61 (1958); also private communication (1960).

[6] E. MANN and A. SEEGER: *Journ. Phys. Chem. Solids*, **12**, 326 (1960).

[7] C. J. MEECHAN and A. SOSIN: *Phys. Rev.*, **113**, 424 (1959).

[8] T. NILAN: *Bull. Am. Phys. Soc.*, **5**, 175 (1960).

[9] G. D. MAGNUSON, W. PALMER and J. S. KOEHLER: *Phys. Rev.*, **109**, 1990 (1958).

[10] J. W. CORBETT, R. B. SMITH and R. M. WALKER: *Phys. Rev.*, **114**, 1452 (1959).

[11] J. W. CORBETT, R. B. SMITH and R. M. WALKER: *Phys. Rev.*, **114**, 1460 (1959).

[12] J. W. CORBETT and R. M. WALKER: *Phys. Rev.*, **115**, 67 (1959).

[13] T. R. WAITE: *Phys. Rev.*, **107**, 463 (1957).

[14] R. R. HASIGUTI: *Proc. of the Japan Academy*, **36**, 336 (1960).

[15] C. J. MEECHAN and J. A. BRINKMAN: *Phys. Rev.*, **103**, 1193 (1956).

[16] G. LEIBFRIED: *Journ. Appl. Phys.*, **31**, 117 (1960).

[17] C. J. MEECHAN, A. SOSIN and J. A. BRINKMAN: *Phys. Rev.* (to be published). We wish to thank these authors for sending us a report of this work prior to publication.

[18] J. W. CORBETT and R. M. WALKER: *Phys. Rev.*, **117**, 970 (1960).

[19] H. G. COOPER, J. S. KOEHLER and J. W. MARX: *Phys. Rev.*, **97**, 599 (1955).

[20] T. H. BLEWITT, R. R. COLTMAN, D. K. HOLMES and T. S. NOGGLE: *Dislocations and the Mechanical Properties of Solids*, J. C. FISHER editor (New York, 1957).

[21] A. SOSIN and J. A. BRINKMAN: *Acta Met.*, **7**, 478 (1959).

[22] W. DESORBO and D. TURNBULL: *Acta Met.*, **7**, 83 (1959).

[23] W. DESORBO and D. TURNBULL: *Phys. Rev.*, **115**, 560 (1959).

[24] A. W. OVERHAUSER: *Phys. Rev.*, **94**, 1551 (1954).

[25] R. O. SIMMONS and R. W. BALLUFFI: *Phys. Rev.*, **117**, 52 (1960).

[26] R. O. SIMMONS and R. W. BALLUFFI: *Phys. Rev.*, **119**, 600 (1960).

[27] S. NENNO and J. W. KAUFFMAN: *Journ. Phys. Soc. Japan*, **15**, 220 (1960).

[28] H. KIMURA, R. MADDIN and D. KUHLMANN-WILSDORF: *Acta Met.*, **7**, 154 (1959).

[29] G. AIROLDI, G. L. BACCHELLA and E. GERMAGNOLI: *Phys. Rev. Lett.*, **2**, 145 (1959).

[30] J. E. BAUERLE and J. S. KOEHLER: *Phys. Rev.*, **107**, 1493 (1957).

[31] C. W. TUCKER and M. B. WEBB: *Acta Met.*, **7**, 187 (1959).

[32] D. K. HOLMES, J. W. CORBETT, R. M. WALKER, J. S. KOEHLER and F. SEITZ: *Proc. of the Second United Nations Conference on Peaceful Uses of Atomic Energy*, paper no. 2385 (Geneva, 1958).

[33] W. L. BROWN and W. M. AUGUSTYNIAK: *Journ. Appl. Phys.*, **30**, 1300 (1959).

Low-Temperature Irradiation Studies.

T. H. BLEWITT (*)

Solid State Division, Oak Ridge National Laboratory - Oak Ridge, Tenn.

1. – Introduction.

It is very difficult to indicate the big discrepancies which exist between experimental results and the theory of radiation damage, especially neutron irradiation effects. However, the Sunday London Times does an excellent job in ponting out a similar situation in the field of outer space, and it may be pertinent to refer to this article. The article points out that the data from the satellites have been proving the old axiom that a good experiment is one that gives an answer that could not reasonably have been foreseen; and a better experiment is one that provides theorists with something to argue about. On this basis, radiation damage has had its share of good experiments. Apparently, the author of this article was an experimentalist, as he goes on to say that when the figures are put in and comparisons are made with evidence of other kinds there is no one explanation that stands up. It is further pointed out that this is by no means an unusual situation in science; but it is one that the experimentalist enjoys greatly, for he feels that the theorist is being held at bay and many more experiments will be needed. It would seem that this is a rather good description of the current status of radiation damage.

In experimental radiation damage the trend in the past ten years has been toward experiments at lower and lower temperatures, and in particular toward lowering bombardment temperatures. At this writing, bombardment temperatures have gone down to liquid-helium temperatures. It doesn't seem as though any individual can take the credit for this trend in research. It started a long time ago; as far back as 1948 [1] at Oak Ridge there was work going on to build a cryostat to go down to liquid-nitrogen temperature in the Graphite Reactor. In about 1950, the people at Atomic International [2] (it was then called North American Aviation) succeeded in bombarding samples at liquid

(*) Now at Argonne National Laboratory.

nitrogen temperature using α-particle bombardment. Perhaps one of the driving forces toward this tendency to bombard at lower temperatures was the fact that the numbers of defects induced from experiments were always considerably smaller than the numbers that the theoreticians predicted. It was natural to assume that some of the defects produced by the bombardment were annealed out, and that better agreement could be obtained by going to lower temperatures. Although the lower bombardment temperatures indicated a bigger change in induced resistivity, and hence more defects, the theorists refused to co-operate, as their improved calculations suggested that the resistance of the defects should be higher than originally estimated. So during the past few years, despite the utilization of low temperatures, the discrepancy between the theoretical and experimental estimates of the number of defects formed still largely remains. Another driving force to the very low-temperature bombardment was the calculation of HUNTINGTON [3], who pointed out that interstitials would be expected to be mobile at a very low temperature, a temperature somewhere in the neighborhood of 30 to 60 °K. These two factors were, then, motivations for low-temperature studies fo radiation damage.

The first low-temperature bombardment of copper was done by COOPER,

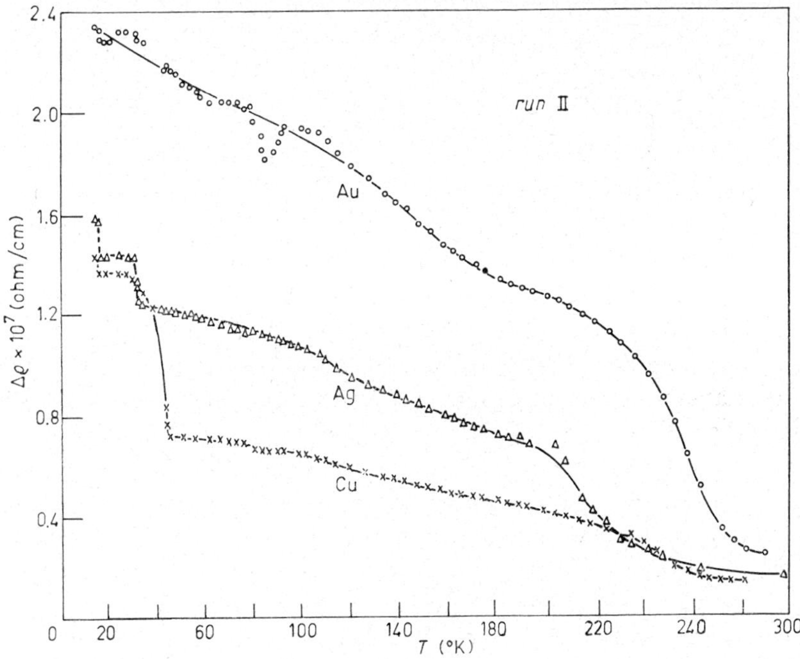

Fig. 1. – The decrease of bombardment-induced resistivity of copper, silver, and gold as the samples are warmed slowly from liquid helium temperatures. After COOPER, KOEHLER and MARX.

KOEHLER and MARX [4] at the University of Illinois, using 12 MeV deuterons. They measured not only the change in resistivity as a function of dose but also the recovery of the resistivity. The latter part of the experiment was especially interesting (see Fig. 1) as the data showed that the recovery occurred by a number of discrete annealing stages. Altogether, three stages can be seen in this experiment. Stage I was labeled as that occurring from 30 to 50 °K, Stage II from 50 °K to 240 °K, and Stage III from 240 °K to 270 °K. Additional annealing stages were subsequently found by other experimenters at higher temperatures. A small annealing stage, which is somewhat controversial, has been found in the region near 375 °K (Stage IV), and the final annealing stage was found between 600 °K and 700 °K (Stage V), at which the radiation hardness recovers. These major peaks have also been observed when bombardments utilized other than 12 MeV deuterons. For example, CORBETT [5] and co-workers at General Electric Research Laboratories using 4 MeV electrons to study radiation damage found similar results. At Oak Ridge [6], studies of the bombardment of metals at low temperatures with reactor neutrons also show the same general annealing scheme. It should be noted, however, that the details of the recovery do depend on the nature and the energy of the bombarding particle, and one of the major considerations of this series of lectures will be the discussion of this point.

The most important feature of this annealing scheme is, however, the very fact that the low-temperature recovery occurs, for it is this which requires utilization of low-temperature bombardments for basic radiation effects research.

Another important facet of radiation damage which will be considered is the interpretation of the various annealing stages. Considerable latitude is offered in building up a model to explain the recovery of radiation damage, as five annealing peaks are available. At the moment most workers in the field agree that Stage I results from the migration of interstitials. There is, however, considerable disagreement as to the defect responsible for Stage III and Stage V.

Finally, another problem of major importance which should be considered is radation-hardening. It turns out that very substantial effects on the mechanical properties of metals can be introduced by neutron bombardment. For example, the critical shear stress, or the stress at which plastic flow occurs, can be raised from a few tenths of a kilogram per mm^2 to as high as 8 kilograms per mm^2 at room temperature, and a much higher value at lower temperatures. Yet, Stage I annealing does not substantially affect radiation hardening, and it appears that the majority of this hardness is recovered in Stage V. One of the major problems in radiation damage is the understanding of radiation-hardening.

2. – Experimental techniques.

The first things which come to mind in the design of a low-temperature irradiation facility are the production of refrigeration, the heat load, and the bombardment temperature. Regardless of the type of irradiation being considered, the easy accessibility of liquid nitrogen and its cheap price make it an obvious source of refrigeration. In the case where the bombarding particles have a long range, as is true in the case of energetic neutrons, it is feasible to consider bombarding the sample in liquid nitrogen. In this case a simple dewar with facilities for filling is all that is required. A word of caution should be interjected at this point, however, as experience at several laboratories shows the necessity of keeping air out of the system. It is apparent that the ionizing radiation converts the oxygen to ozone, which violently reacts with aluminum and possibly other metals, causing the dewar to be destroyed. There are two approaches to the solution of this problem. One of these, used at Oak Ridge[7], is to use helium gas cooled by liquid nitrogen as the refrigerant. The flow diagram of such a scheme is illustrated in Fig. 2. Further reference to this

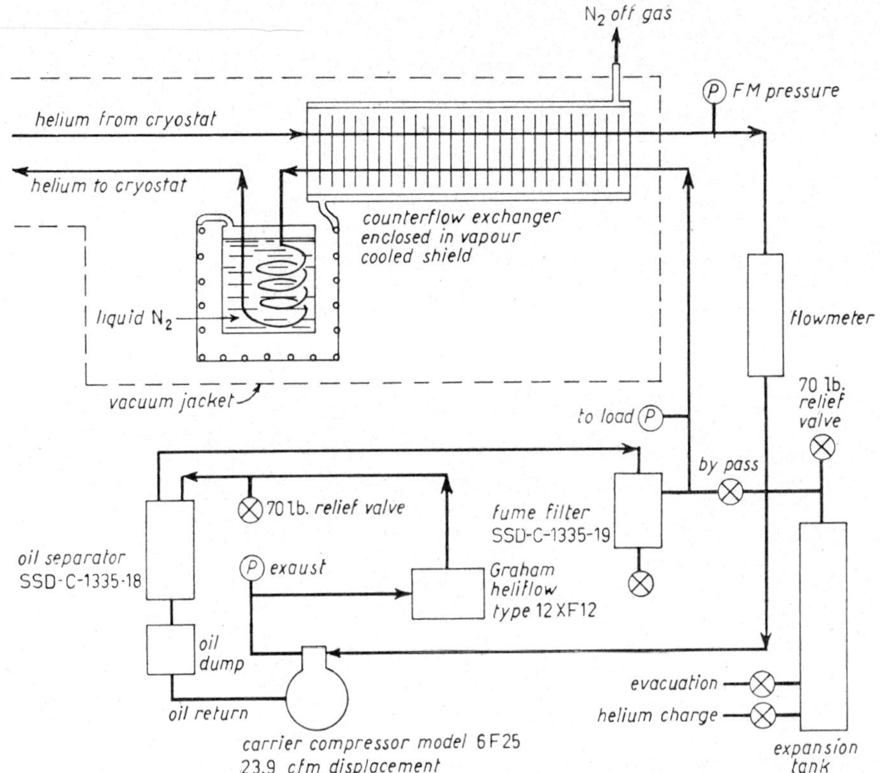

Fig. 2. – Schematic diagram of Hole 50 cryostat. After Howe, Busby and Coltman.

scheme can be found in the literature. The other scheme was developed at Grenoble [8]. The sample is bombarded in liquid nitrogen which has been specially purified. This gas is kept in the system by condensing the boil-off by impure nitrogen which is kept out of the system. It is obvious that in both of these schemes the heat load must be considered when designing the system. For example, in a high flux, water-moderated reactor such as the MTR, extremely high γ heating produces a heavy heat load. In the case of the MTR a γ flux of 20 W/g is observed in the central core. In this case, assuming a cryostat, sample, nitrogen mass of 600 g in the γ flux, the nitrogen consumption would amount to 30 liter/h. This illustrates that major problems can exist from high heat loads.

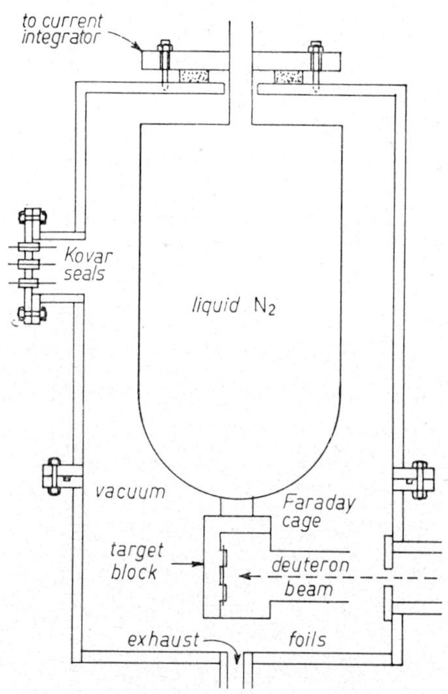

Fig. 3.– Cryostat for deuteron bombardment.

The design of a facility to provide liquid-nitrogen temperature when the bombardment is by charged particles is a somewhat different problem, as these particles (of moderate energy) have short ranges. This generally precludes the direct cooling of the sample in liquid nitrogen, as the attenuation of the beam will be too great. The method developed by the University of Illinois [9] can then be used. The sample is cooled by conduction. A schematic diagram of this apparatus is shown in Fig. 3. This same apparatus can be used for liquid-helium-temperature irradiations by replacing the liquid nitrogen with liquid helium. It should be noted that the method suggested by Oak Ridge [6] for reactor irradiations at liquid-nitrogen temperatures, *viz.*, gas cooled by a liquid, could also be adopted for these studies.

Liquid-helium irradiation in a reactor is a rather major problem. At Oak Ridge, bombardments at liquid-hydrogen temperatures (14 to 20 °K) were utilized as a stepping stone [10]. The method was essentially that used for liquid-nitrogen-temperature bombardments with the refrigeration from liquid nitrogen being replaced by refrigeration from an isentropic expansion of helium. A flow diagram of this apparatus is shown in Fig. 4. The refrigerator used helium as a refrigerant, which is cooled by doing external work in expanding against a piston. It can be seen from Fig. 4 that the gas is compressed (Carrier compressors originally designed for freon service but modified for helium service) to about 250 psi, cooled with water, passed through a counterflow heat exchanger, then allowed to expand doing work on the pistons, passed through the cryostat, and back through the counterflow heat exchanger to the com-

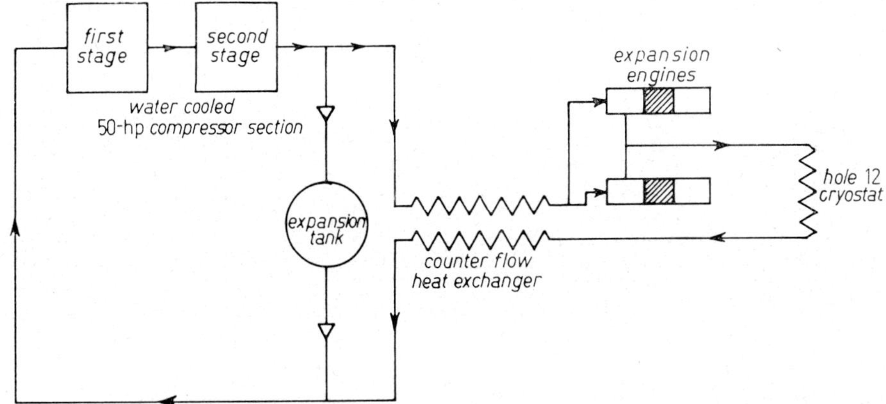

Fig. 4. – Flow diagram of a 10 to 20 °K refrigeration cycle used in reactor irradiation.

pressors. The compressors and engines were of sufficient capacity that the refrigeration capacity of the system was about 40 W/°K from a terminal temperature of 8 °K (*i.e.*, a temperature of 20 °K could be maintained with a heat load of 480 W). In the original operating conditions of the system a total load of about 160 W (about $\frac{2}{3}$ thermal radiation and about $\frac{1}{3}$ γ-ray) was encountered, so that engine discharge temperatures of approximately 12 °K were the rule. Heat was taken from the samples to the cryostat walls by means of helium exchange gas. While the reactor was operating the sample temperature was 4 °K higher than the cryostat wall temperature. This difference in temperatue is a direct consequence of the γ heating. As the heat load increases the ΔT between the sample and the wall must increase, as the heat flow through the static exchange gas (due to convection cooling) can only increase by an increase in the ΔT. While some improvement in this factor can be made by adjusting the sample surface to volume ratio, it is obvious that for high γ heat loads static exchange gas will not be sufficient to do the job and that to obtain low sample temperatures the sample will have to be placed in the gas stream (*).

(*) Increased heat exchange can also be obtained by utilization of a static liquid in place of the static exchange gas. For example, hydrogen could be substituted for the helium exchange gas. At appropriate cryostat temperature (13 to 20 °K) this will be condensed to a liquid which will be much more efficient. In like fashion, in the liquid-nitrogen temperature cryostat previously described (helium gas operated), the utilization of nitrogen exchange gas will result in its condensation and consequent improved heat exchange.

Extending the temperature down to liquid-helium temperatures is a rather major problem owing to the inherent low refrigeration efficiency, and in most cases will be feasible only where low heat loads are involved. This fact, coupled with the low heat of vaporization of liquid helium and the high specific heat of the gas (only 1 % of the refrigeration available in a quantity of liquid helium is present in the heat of vaporization), makes it mandatory to design a closed system. A schematic diagram of such a system is shown in Fig. 5.

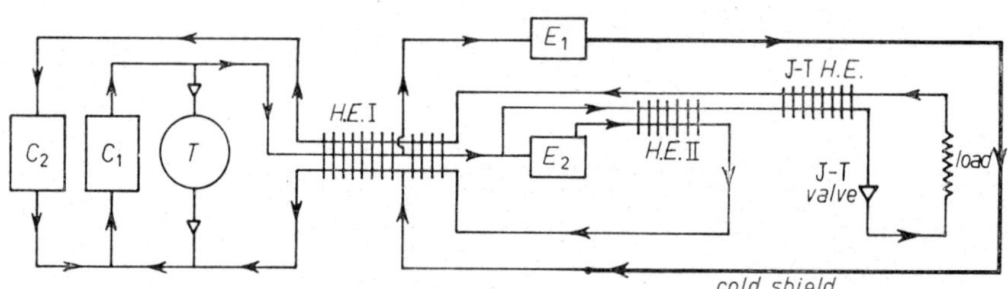

Fig. 5. – Idealized refrigerator cycle for temperatures in the 2 °K to 4 °K temperature interval.

The compressor C_1 has the necessary stages to raise the suction pressure p_1 from a few pounds gauge to about 250 pounds gauge. The high pressure gas p_2 then passes through the main counterflow heat exchanger H.E.I. The expan-

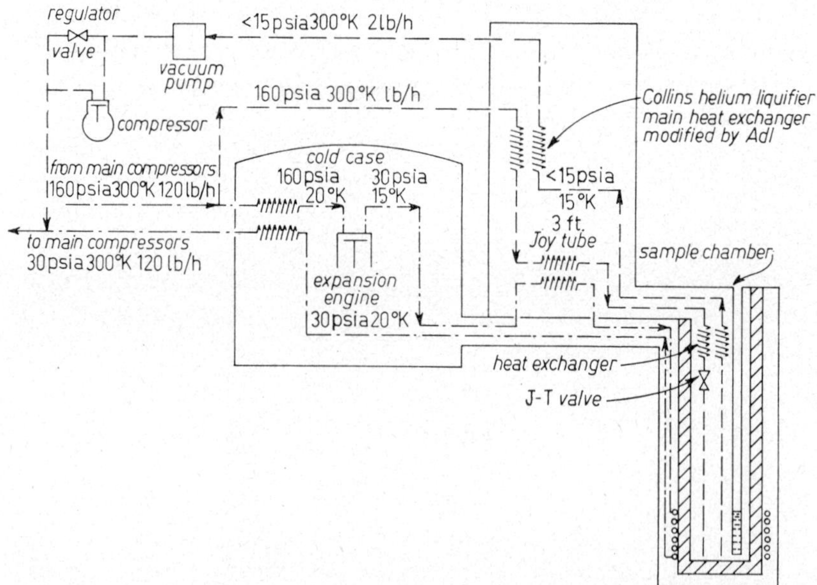

Fig. 6. – Flow cycle of the Oak Ridge hole 12 liquid helium facility: - - - proposed liquifier section; —— vacuum; –·–·– original helium refrigerator.

sion tank T and associated regulating valves serve to regulate the pressures p_1 and p_2. Part of the high-pressure gas is diverted from the heat exchanger H.E.I at a temperature of about 70 °K and is expanded and cooled in expansion engine E_1. This gas serves as a radiation shield for the remainder of the ystem downstream from engine E_2 and is returned to the main heat-exchanger H.E.I. The remainder of the gas flow through H.E.I to expansion engine E_2 where it is expanded and cooled to a temperature of about 10 °K.

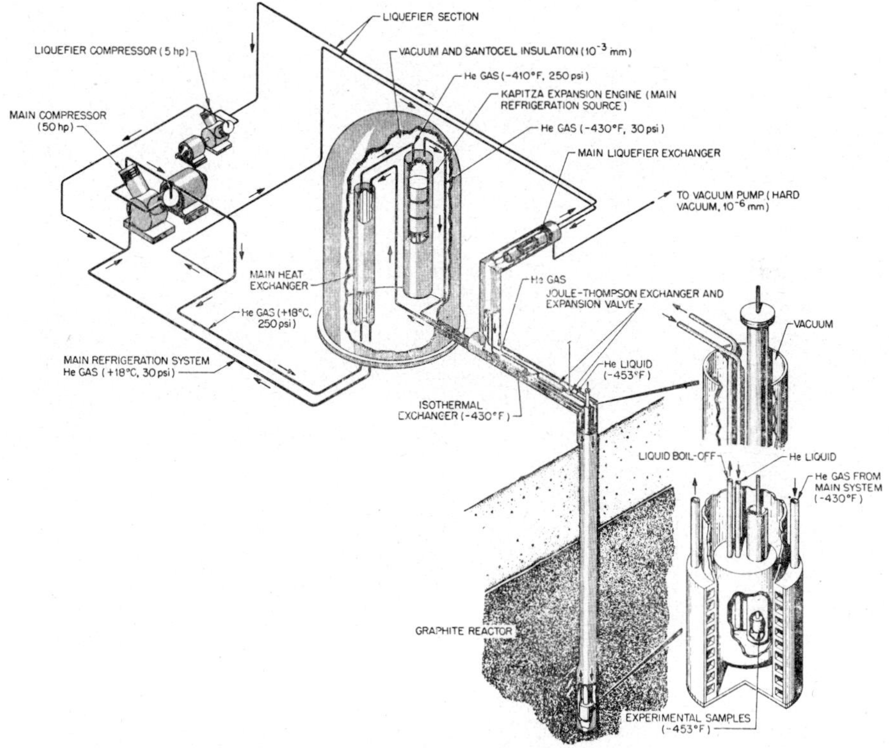

Fig. 7. - Pictorial of the Oak Ridge Hole 12 facility.

This gas then passes through heat exchanger H.E.II where it cools the gas to be liquefied to near 10 °K and passes to the low-pressure side of the main exchanger H.E.I and back to the compressors. The stream diverted just before engine E_2 passed through H.E.II, which is the heat sink for the liquefier circuit, to the Joule-Thompson exchanger, through the Joule-Thompson throttle valve where liquefaction occurs, to the heat load, back through the Joule-Thomson exchanger to the main exchanger H.E.I.

It should be noted that the above circuit is an idealized one and that considerable modification may be desiderable depending on the relative values of the thermal radiation and the γ radiation load. Each reactor will in general present a separate problem so that the mass flows, engine size, temperature of the radiation, etc., must be decided to fit the particular problems involved.

The Oak Ridge design, for example, was determined by the refrigeration plant available and is considerably different from the idealized design shown above. The high impedance of the heat exchanger made it impossible to lower the pressure on the discharge side to a point below the critical pressure of liquid helium; consequently, a separate heat exchanger for the liquefier circuit had to be arranged. This is shown in the schematic diagram of Fig. 6.

A word might be said about the cryostat used at liquid helium temperatures. A pictorial diagram of the whole apparatus is shown in Fig. 7. The details of the apparatus can be seen in the schematic drawing of Fig. 8. The

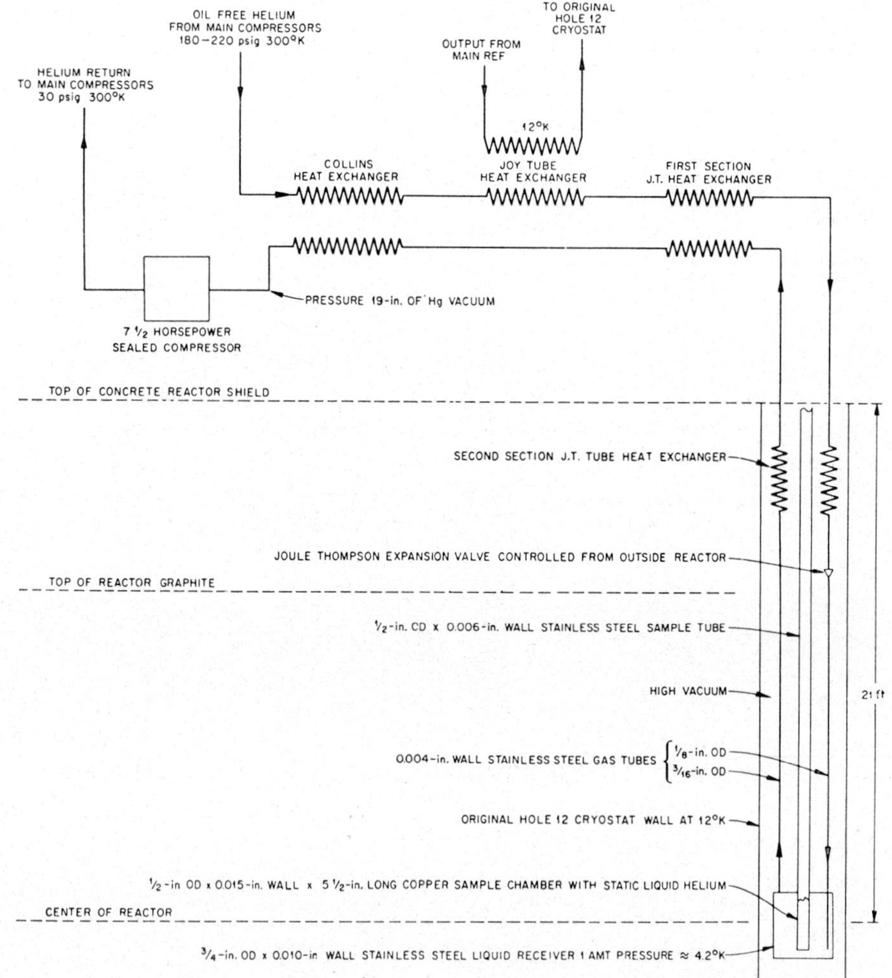

Fig. 8. – The liquid helium cryostat of the Oak Ridge Hole 12 facility.

fluid flow from the Joule-Thomson valve is brought into and out of the reactor in vacuum-jacketed lines (Fig. 8) and is returned to the Joule-Thompson heat exchanger. The sample chamber is a separate tube which runs into the liquid receiver. The portion within the receiver is copper for good heat transfer, whereas the remaining portion is thin-walled stainless steel. The samples are cooled in the sample tube by condensation of helium gas. The amount of liquid in the sample tube is monitored by the liquid level and by the amount of gas admitted to the chamber. This particular feature was designed with two objects in mind. First, it was desirable to keep all objects out of the main gas stream which could cause radioactive contamination. The only possible contamination is from the sample and its associated leads; consequently, isolation of the sample minimizes the possibilities of radioactive contamination of the refrigeration equipment (*).

Perhaps a more important consideration in the utilization of this design arises from the experimental advantages which result. It is possible, for example, to thermally isolate the sample from the refrigeration system. This makes it possible to raise the sample temperature without affecting the operation of the liquefier.

3. – Temperature measurements.

The usual difficulties in measuring temperature in the region below 20 °K are compounded when the measurement is made in a reactor owing to the pressure of an additional variable—the neutron flux. It is quite difficult to ascertain by either theory or experiment the influences of this variable as most standard thermometers will also be affected by the radiation. A gas thermometer, which would otherwise be satisfactory, is difficult to design due to the long distance from the bulb to the gauge (normally about 20 in). With the utilization of bombardments in liquid helium the problem has been somewhat simplified as the temperature of the liquid can be determined by its vapor pressure. Studies of the effect of radiation on the output of a copper-constantan thermocouple and the resistance of an Allan-Bradly carbon resistor were made in the liquid-helium baths [11]. On the basis of these studies it was determined that temperatures could best be measured in the region below 200 °K by carbon resistors with a nominal resistance of 1000 ohm or more and at higher temperatures with a copper-constantan thermocouple. Neutron-irradiation will increase the resistance of radio resistors; however, the temperature-dependence of the grain boundary scattering (which is unaffected by irradiation)

(*) It has recently been shown that adequate protection against contamination in helium systems is afforded by the use of micrometallic filters in the gas stream.

is so large (especially in the resistors of high nominal resistances) that the increase in resistance due to irradiation effects, at least to a dose of 10^{18} neutrons/cm, was of negligible proportion below 200 °K. In the case of copper-constantan thermocouples while radiation (up to 10^{18} neutrons/cm^2) did not affect the output—a change smaller than 10^{-7} V was observed at 4.0 °K [11]—the presence of spurious emf's detracted from the thermocouple's usefulness. These spurious emf's, probably ther esult of inhomogeneities in the thermocouples which generate a Thomson emf as thermal gradients move up the wire, are especially serious at the very low temperatures where the thermoelectric power is small.

It might be mentioned that superconductive transition temperatures which are unaffected (for practical considerations as temperature detectors) by irradiation can effectively serve as temperature check points.

4. – Isochronal annealing.

The study of annealing kinetics has been one of the most useful tools in the study of neutron irradiation. There are in general two different studies which can be made. Isothermal annealing, the measurement of property changes as a function of time at constant temperature; or isochronal annealing, essentially the measurement of property changes as a function of temperature at constant time. It is important to note that when the property change being studied in either of these studies is radiation-induced electrical resistivity all measurements must be made at a reference temperature; that is, pulse annealing must be used. The resistance must be measured at a base temperature T_0, preferably 20 °K or less, pulsed to a temperature T_i for a time t, and then returned to the base temperature T_0 where the resistance is again measured to determine the effect of the pulse. Attempts to measure the property change at a temperature will lead to misleading results because the incremental change in resistance is temperature-dependent. This was first noted at Oak Ridge [12] and at Illinois [13] and was originally attributed to changes in the Debye characteristic temperature. Subsequent measurements at Oak Ridge [14] have established that changes in the resistance due to pulses at 40 °K are considerably different when measured at 35 °K from those measured at 4.2 °K (*).

Pulse measurements are made satisfactorily at Oak Ridge by the following

(*) From measurements of the decrement and the changes in length, it appears that changes in the Debye temperature cannot account for the observed results. It thus appears that the suggestion originally made by A. Seeger that there is an interaction between phonon scattering and defect scattering is valid (that is, Mathieson's rule is not valid). This problem can be circumvented by making the measurements at 3 °K where the phonon scattering can be reduced to negligible proportions.

technique. The sample and a heater are placed in a vacuum-tight copper can which in turn is placed in the sample chamber. During the bombardment this can and the sample chamber are filled with liquid helium. Following the bombardment nuclear heating is decreased by an order of magnitude so that a few hundred micron of exchange gas in the sample can and sample chamber are sufficient to hold the sample temperature at 4°K. To make a pulse the exchange gas in the sample chamber is pumped out and the heater energized. Normally ten to fifteen seconds are sufficient to raise the temperature to T_i. The sample can then be returned to the base temperature T_0 by turning off the heater and injecting exchange gas onto the sample temperature. A few seconds are normally sufficient for this process. Relatively square pulses are thus obtained.

5. – Experimental dose rates.

For neutron doses less than $2 \cdot 10^{18}$ neutrons·cm² the relationship between resistivity and dose is a linear one for a wide variety of metals (*) [15].

The slope is, however, found to vary greatly with the various materials. The damage rates are found to vary from $1 \cdot 10^{-26}$ ohm cm/neutrons·cm² for the noble metals to $1 \cdot 10^{-22}$ ohm cm/neutrons·cm² for the semimetal bismuth. Typical damage rates are summarized in Table I.

TABLE I. – *Rates of damage to various metals by fast neutrons at a flux of* $6 \cdot 10^{11}$ n·cm^{-2}·s^{-1} *in hole* 12 *of the graphite reactor.*

Specimen	Residual resistivity before bombardment (Ω·cm)	Damage rate $d\varrho/dt$ (Ω·cm/h)	Bombardment temperature (°K)	Run
Copper	$6.2 \cdot 10^{-10}$	$2.46 \cdot 10^{-11}$	3.17	HL-2
Copper (cold-worked)	$4.8 \cdot 10^{-8}$	$3.35 \cdot 10^{-11}$	4.17	HL-2
Gold	$3.5 \cdot 10^{-8}$	$3.02 \cdot 10^{-11}$	4.06	HL-4
Tin	$5.4 \cdot 10^{-8}$	$4.4 \cdot 10^{-11}$ (*)	4.06	HL-*
Silver	$2.0 \cdot 10^{-9}$	$5.15 \cdot 10^{-11}$	4.06	HL-4
Platinum	$1.4 \cdot 10^{-7}$	$6.60 \cdot 10^{-11}$	4.17	HL-2
Aluminum	$4.0 \cdot 10^{-9}$	$8.43 \cdot 10^{-11}$	3.9	HL-5
Nickel	$2.2 \cdot 10^{-8}$	$1.33 \cdot 10^{-10}$	4.2	HL-6
Iron	$8.6 \cdot 10^{-7}$	$1.6 \cdot 10^{-10}$	4.3	HL-1
Zinc	$4.5 \cdot 10^{-9}$	$2.13 \cdot 10^{-10}$	4.17	HL-2
Magnesium	$3.9 \cdot 10^{-8}$	$2.55 \cdot 10^{-10}$	4.2	HL-6
Bismuth	$1.7 \cdot 10^{-5}$	$2.28 \cdot 10^{-7}$	4.2	HL-6

(*) Single crystal.

(*) Pyrolytic graphite is the only material found to have a nonlinear relationship.

These experimental facts can best be described by consideration of the factors responsible for the electrical resistivity. Since it would be expected that irradiation would only affect n, the number of current carriers or N, the number of radiation-induced scattering centers, the resistivity may be written as

$$\varrho = \frac{C}{n} N + \frac{C}{n} N_0 , \tag{5.1}$$

so that where N_0 are the non-radiation-induced scattering centers

$$\frac{d\varrho}{d\varphi} = \frac{C}{n^2} (N + N_0) \frac{dn}{d\varphi} + \frac{C}{n} \frac{dN}{d\varphi} . \tag{5.2}$$

However, at 4.2 °K it is reasonable to expect that the number of radiation defects N will be composed of equal numbers of vacancies and interstitials. It is further reasonable to expect that if n, the number of carriers, changes it will be the result of the vacancies and interstitials acting respectively as acceptors or donors of unequal strength. We can express these two assumptions mathematically by

$$n = n_0 + kN \tag{5.3}$$

and substituting in (5.2) we get

$$\frac{\Delta\varrho}{d\varphi} = \frac{C}{n_0 + kN} \left(1 - \frac{k(N + N_0)}{n_0 + kN}\right) \frac{dN}{d\varphi} . \tag{5.4}$$

Consider now the noble metals. It is observed that $\Delta\varrho/\Delta\varphi$ is constant and since it would be expected that $n_0 \gg kN$ for the doses considered, it can be concluded that $dN/d\varphi =$ constant (*i.e.*, radiation-annealing is of no consequence). Since the energy of the primary displacement will vary inversely as the atomic mass A it is certainly safe to conclude that $dN/d\varphi$ is a constant for all metals of higher atomic mass than copper, and it is reasonable to extend this conclusion for somewhat smaller doses to include all the metals of mass higher than 18. Under this condition $d\varrho/d\varphi$ can only be a constant if $k = 0$, and it may therefore be concluded that with the exception of graphite all materials in Table I do not change their carrier concentrations with bombardment, and eq. (5.4) becomes

$$\frac{\Delta\varrho}{d\varphi} = \frac{C}{n_0} \frac{dN}{d\varphi} . \tag{5.5}$$

It can thus be concluded that certainly the major portion of the widely divergent damage rates arises from the n_0 term. On the other hand, the constant C will include the cross-section of the scattering factor which will vary with the material. $\mathrm{d}N/\mathrm{d}\varphi$ will also vary with the material, although it would be surprising if there were such differences between materials with nearly the same mass. It is therefore difficult to determine any of these individual factors from the damage rate (*).

An interesting experimental exercise was conducted to determine the effect of the number of carriers on the damage rate. Single crystals of bismuth and antimony were prepared with the basal plane perpendicular to the longitudinal direction and others with the basal plane parallel to the longitudinal direction. Measurements of the electrical resistivity were made as a function of temperature and as a function of the neutron dose for both metals in both crystallographic orientations [16]. Provided there is no change in the carrier concentration as a result of temperature or of neutron flux, eqs. (5.6) and (5.7) below hold for both metals,

$$\frac{\mathrm{d}\varrho_\perp}{\mathrm{d}T} = \frac{c'}{n_\perp}\,\frac{\mathrm{d}(1/L)}{\mathrm{d}t}\,, \tag{5.6}$$

$$\frac{\mathrm{d}\varrho_\parallel}{\mathrm{d}T} = \frac{c'}{n_\parallel}\,\frac{\mathrm{d}(1/L)}{\mathrm{d}t}\,, \tag{5.7}$$

$$\frac{\mathrm{d}\varrho_\perp}{\mathrm{d}\varphi} = \frac{c}{n_\perp}\,\frac{\mathrm{d}N}{\mathrm{d}\varphi}\,, \tag{5.8}$$

$$\frac{\mathrm{d}\varrho_\parallel}{\mathrm{d}\varphi} = \frac{c}{n_\parallel}\,\frac{\mathrm{d}N}{\mathrm{d}\varphi}\,. \tag{5.9}$$

Combining eqs. (5.6) and (5.7) and eqs. (5.8) and (5.9) results in

$$\frac{\mathrm{d}\varrho_\perp/\mathrm{d}T}{\mathrm{d}\varrho_\parallel/\mathrm{d}T} = \frac{n_\parallel}{n_\perp} = \frac{\mathrm{d}\varrho_\perp/\mathrm{d}\varphi}{\mathrm{d}\varrho_\parallel/\mathrm{d}\varphi}\,. \tag{5.10}$$

Good experimental agreement of eq. (5.10) is found to exist for both bismuth and antimony. Fig. 9 shows the damage rates for both $\parallel$ and $\perp$ bismuth crystals. The temperature coefficients of resistivity for each of these crystals were also measured between $(15 \div 85)$ °K and the ratio of the coefficients was found to agree very well with the ratio of the slopes of the damage rates. Similar results also exist for antimony. These experiments thus demonstrate

---

(*) Thanks are due to D. K. HOLMES for suggesting this treatment and for frequent discussions.

that the magnitude of the radiation-induced resistivity is strongly dependent on the density of current carriers.

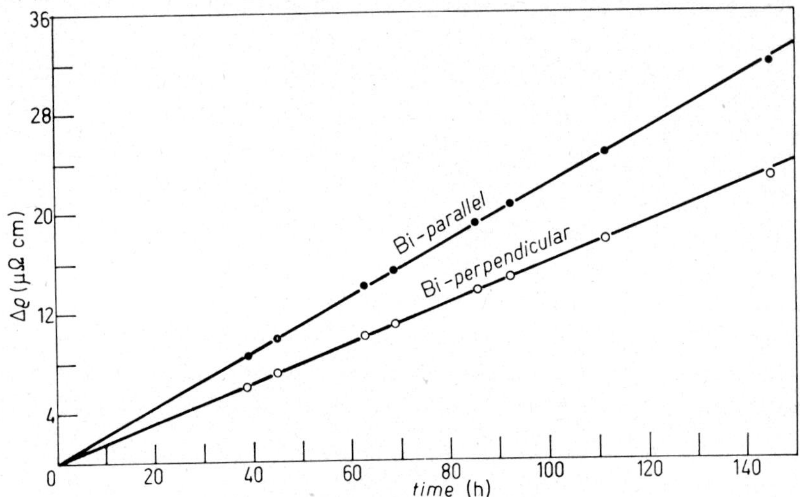

Fig. 9. – Damage rate of bismuth; bombardment temperature 16 °K, fast flux $6\cdot10^{11}$ neutrons/cm$^2\cdot$s.

6. – Isochronal annealing studies.

The isochronal annealing studies have proven to be a valuable tool in the study of radiation damage. Measurements of this type have been made in the temperature range from 10 °K or lower, following neutron bombardment [13], and electron bombardment [5, 18]. In these experiments the energy of these particles has been widely divergent so that the energy of the primary displacements has also been widely divergent. In the case of electron irradiation the energy of the bombarding electrons (about 1 MeV) is so low that even under the most favorable circumstances the energy of the primary displaced atoms will not be sufficient to displace an additional atom (atoms of mass 60). As a result, electron irradiation with energies of about 1 MeV will result in a relatively homogeneous distribution of individual vacancies and interstitials. On the other hand, neutron irradiation is usually done in a reactor where the neutrons have an energy distribution which can be approximated in most cases by $N(E)=C/E$. When it is considered, however, that the damage is proportional to the energy of the displacement (and hence of the neutrons), the total number of displacements will be given by

$$N_{\mathrm{D}} = C'\int\limits_0^{2\,\mathrm{MeV}} N(E)\,E\,\mathrm{d}E = C\int\limits_0^{2\,\mathrm{MeV}}\mathrm{d}E\,.$$

Thus, most of the displacements are the result of the high-energy neutrons (the 10% above $\frac{1}{2}$ MeV doing 75% of the damage.) The primary displacements will then in general have sufficient energy to displace several hundred additional atoms.

It should, therefore, be expected that a reactor-bombarded metal would in general have an inhomogeneous distribution of defects and, in fact, they would be present as islands in an undisturbed matrix. As the dose increased, however, the islands would overlap (radiation annealing), and at very high doses the defects would become homogeneous and the defect concentration would be constant. The defect distribution following energetic deuteron (or proton) bombardment (10 MeV or so) should be characteristic of both the neutron case and the electron case. Both individual defects relatively homogeneously distributed and islands of high defect-density should exist.

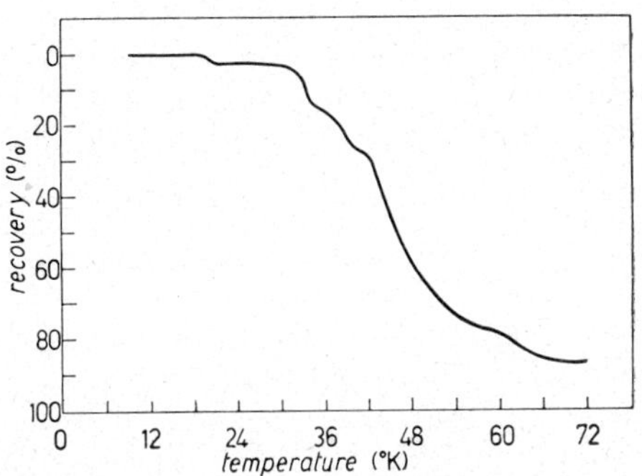

Fig. 10. – Isochronal annealing curves of 1.25 MeV electron-irradiated copper. After CORBETT.

These differences become apparent when the isochronal annealing curves are studied. Consider the results obtained by CORBETT, WALKER *et al.* [5], on the bombardment of copper foils at 10 °K by 1.25 MeV electrons. The isochronal annealing results are shown in Fig. 10. These results are significant from two standpoints. First, the large fraction of resistivity ((80 ÷ 90) %) that recovers in the so-called Stage I region and, second, the structure which appears in Stage I. It can clearly be seen that five discrete annealing stages are observed. It is now generally accepted that these annealing peaks of Stage I are due to some form of interstitial migration and their subsequent annihilation (the vast majority at vacant lattice sites). CORBETT, WALKER *et al.*, believe, and some indirect evidence supports their hypothesis, that the three sub-peaks at the lowest temperatures (17, 27, and 32 °K) are the result of the recombination of three distinct vacancy-interstitial pairs. The major peak at 37 °K is attributed to freely migrating interstitials recombining with their own vacancies (correlated annihilation), whereas the highest sub-peak near 45 °K is attributed to freely migrating interstitials falling into random vacancies (uncorrelated annihilation). This last peak was found to be dose-dependent (the higher the dose the lower the temperature of this recovery), whereas the temperature at which all other peaks were found was independent of the dose.

In the case of neutron irradiation of copper samples at 4 °K [19], no evidence of structure was found in the isochronal annealing curves.

The results of a very detailed isochronal annealing curve of a sample of copper bombarded at 4 °K to a dose of $8 \cdot 10^{17}$ neutrons/cm² (*) is shown in Fig. 11 [19]. No structure is observed and the differences between neutron and electron irradiation are rather obvious (**).

In addition, it is interesting to note

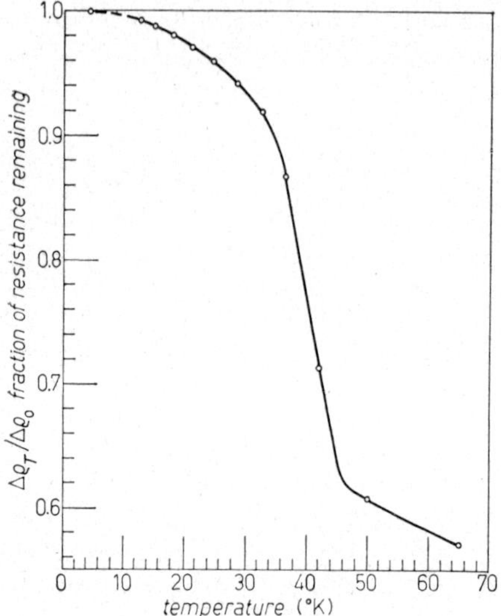

Fig. 11. – Isochronal annealing curve of reactor-irradiated copper. Bombardment temperature 4.16 °K; dose $4.6 \cdot 10^{17}$ n/cm²; 3 min pulses; $\varrho_0 = 6.14 \cdot 10^{-9}\ \Omega$ cm; $\Delta\varrho = 4.69 \cdot 10^{-9}\ \Omega$ cm. After BLEWITT, COLTMAN and KLABUNDE.

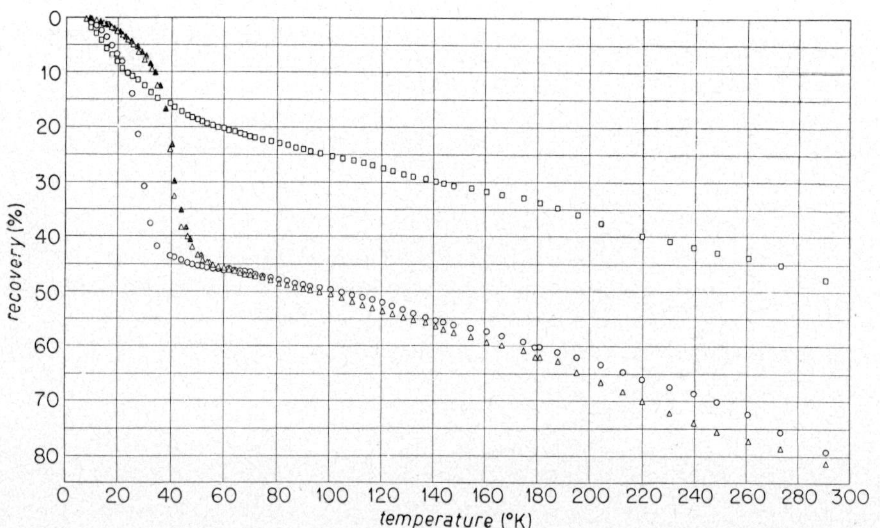

Fig. 12. – Isochronal annealing curves of reactor-irradiated Cu, Ag and Au. Dose $1 \cdot 10^{18}$ n/cm². Bombardment temperature 4.2 °K. After BLEWITT, COLTMAN and KLABUNDE.

(*) This dose is a relatively small one. The resistance-dose curve was a linear one indicative of the fact that appreciable overlap of the damaged regions did not occur.

(**) It should be noted, however, that the absence of structure might be interpreted by critics as evidence that sloppy techniques were used, and a more careful experiment might show up sub-annealing peaks. One possible source of difficulty in this connection could be the presence of a large thermal gradient in the sample; however, no appreciable gradient could be detected during the isochronal anneal.

that detectable recovery is observed as low as 7 °K, whereas in electron-irradiation no recovery is observed below 17 °K.

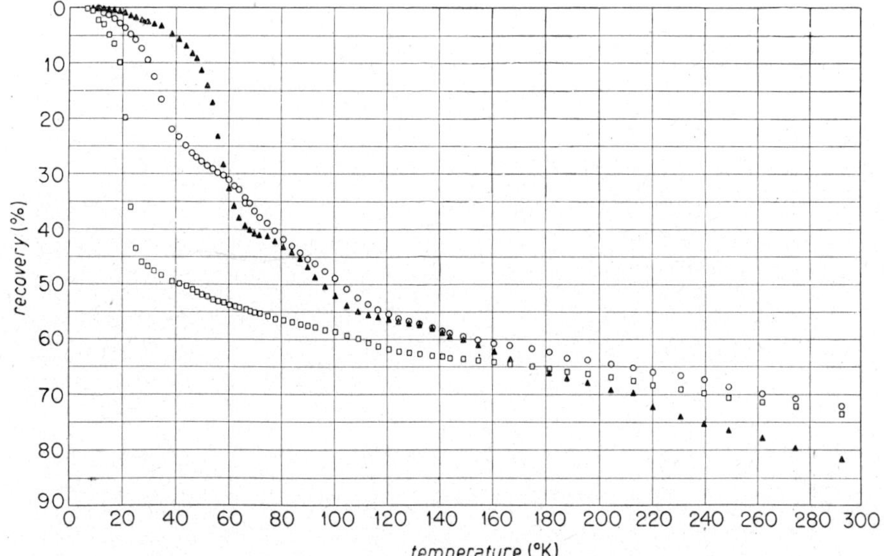

Fig. 13. – Isochronal annealing curves of reactor-irradiated Ni, Pd, and Pt. Bombardment temperature 4.2°K. Dose $1 \cdot 10^{18} n/cm^2$. After BLEWITT, COLTMAN and KLABUNDE.

Reproducibility of these measurements can be judged by comparing the results of Fig. 11 (Run I) as plotted again in Fig. 12 along with an independent Run II on copper.

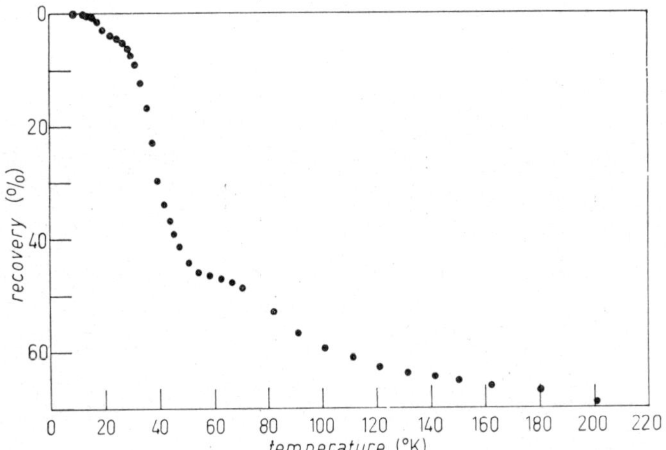

Fig. 14. – Isochronal annealing curves of reactor-irradiated aluminum. Dose $1 \cdot 10^{18} n/cm^2$. Bombardment temperature 4.2°K. After BLEWITT, COLTMAN and KLABUNDE.

Detailed isochronal annealing curves of Au, Ag, Pt, Pd, and Ni were made at the same time as the original copper measurements [19]. Consequently, all these measurements can be compared with each other with considerable confidence. The dose was $8 \cdot 10^{17}$ neutrons and as in the case of the copper a linear dose-resistance curve was noted for all these metals.

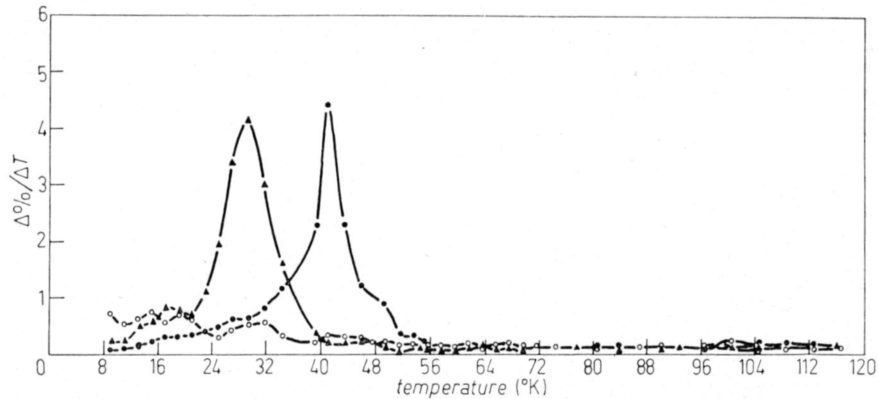

Fig. 15. – The differential of the isochronal annealing curves of Fig. 12: ▲ Ag; ● Cu; ○ Au.

The isochronal annealing curves for Ag and Au together with copper are shown in Fig. 12, for Ni, Pd, and Pt in Fig. 13, and data for Al obtained in a separate run are shown in Fig. 14. The differentials for these isochronal an-

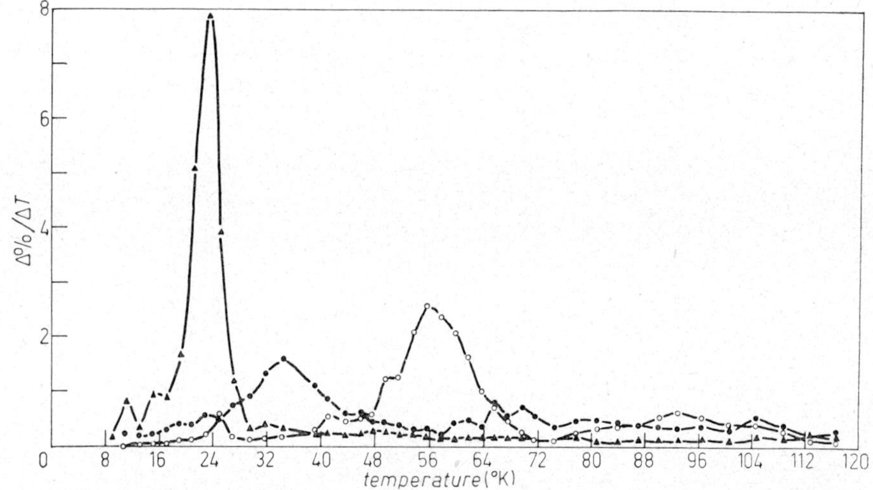

Fig. 16. – The differential of the isochronal annealing curves of Fig. 13: ▲ Pt; ● Pd; ○ Ni.

nealing curves are plotted respectively in Figs. 15, 16, and 17. The most important features evident from Figs. 12 and 15 are the absence of structure in the main annealing peak of Ag and Cu, the absence of a discrete annealing peak in Au, and the absence of a discrete annealing peak in the region just below room temperature in all three metals. In the Ni, Pd, and Pt series shown in Figs. 13 and 16, the outstanding features are the complicated annealing spectrum of Ni and Pd and the relative simplicity of the Pt annealing spectrum, which shows a major peak with two satellites.

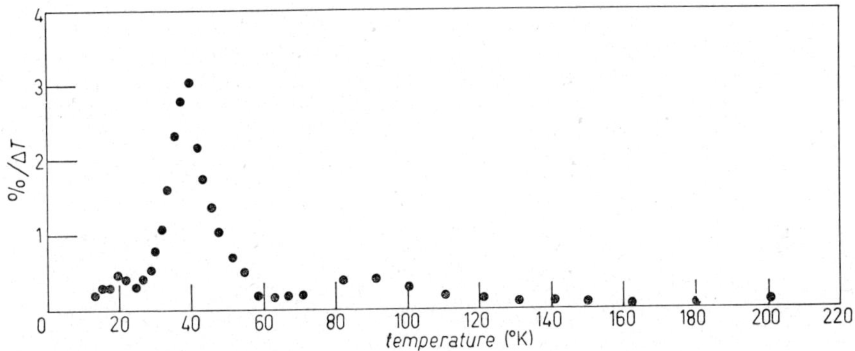

Fig. 17. – The differential of the isochronal annealing curves of Fig. 14.

It is also interesting to note that in both the Cu and Ag series and the Ni, Pd, and Pt series the temperature of the major annealing peak shifts to lower values as the mass increases (or as the Debye temperature θ_D decreases).

7. – Effect of dose on the annealing kinetics.

Experiments in the case of neutron-irradiation have also shown that the Stage I annealing is independent of dose in both copper and in aluminum [20]. Isothermal annealing curves were obtained at 46 °K for both these metals following a bombardment of $1 \cdot 10^{16}$ neutrons/cm^2 and following a bombardment of $4 \cdot 10^{17}$ neutrons/cm^2. The similarity of the annealing curves for each dose can be seen in Fig. 18 for copper and in Fig. 19 for aluminum. This absence of a dose-dependence must mean either that the mobile defects do not escape from the region of the primary hit, or that they are annihilated at existing traps such as their density is independent of dose.

Subsequent experiments will show rather conclusively that the vast majority of the recovery in Stage I is vacancy interstitial annihilation. It can thus be concluded that there is little interaction between damaged regions.

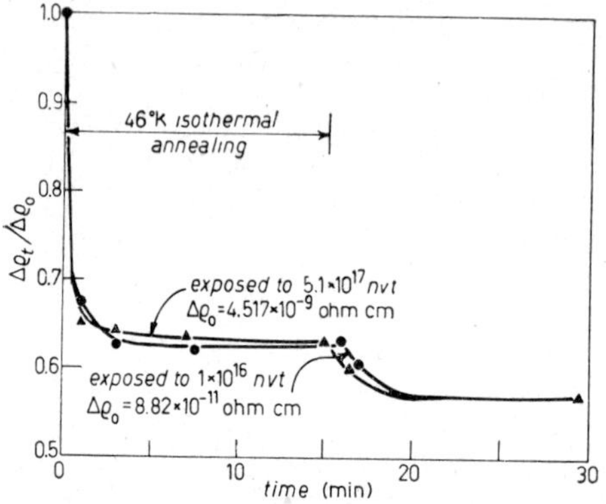

Fig. 18. – Isothermal annealing curves of reactor-irradiated copper after two doses. Note the similarity of the two annealing curves indicating a 1st order process. Bombardment temperature 15 °K; $\varrho_0 = 5.126\cdot10^{-9}\ \Omega$ cm.

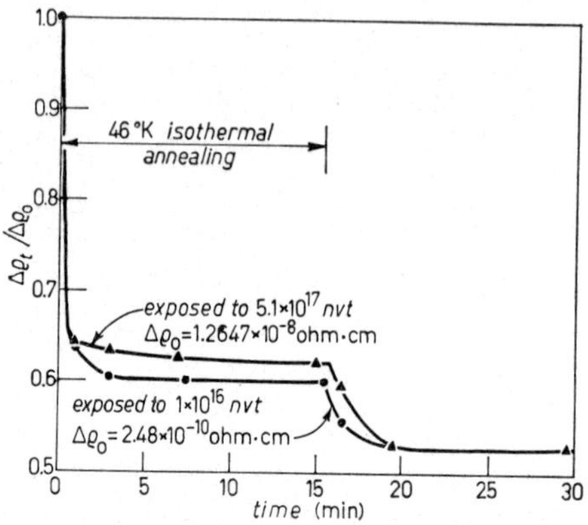

Fig. 19. – Isothermal annealing curves of reactor-irradiated aluminum after two doses. Note the similarity of the two curves indicating a 1st order process. Bombardment temperature 15 °K; $\varrho_0 = 11.507\cdot10^{-9}\ \Omega$ cm.

8. – Nonfissile doping experiments.

It was originally pointed out by LOMER and COTTRELL [21] that impurity atoms would interact with point defects and affect the annealing kinetics. Experimental verification of this suggestion was first made at Oak Ridge National Laboratory [20]. Dilute copper alloys of one tenth and of one atomic percent Be, Si, Ni, Au and Zn were prepared. Of these alloying elements Be and Si were undersized atoms (causing a decrease in the lattice parameter) while Au and Zn were oversized atoms (causing an increase in the lattice parameter). Ni is very nearly equivalent in atomic size (lattice parameter shifts are negligible). These samples were bombarded at 15 °K in the hole 12 facility. It was found that the electrical resistivity increased with neutron dose at the same rate in all of these alloys as in the case of pure copper, implying that the impurity atoms had little effect on the defect production. On the other hand the annealing kinetics were found to be drastically changed by the presence of the over and undersized impurity atoms. The isochronal annealing curves are shown in Figs. 20 through 24. It can be seen in these figures that the undersized atoms Be and Si completely trap the mobile defects and present the appearance of the Stage I annealing in the normal temperature range. A large annealing peak is observed, however, at approximately 150 °K and this may well be attributed to Stage I annealing. If this is indeed the case the difference in temperature may represent the binding energy of the interstitial atom and the undersized impurity atom.

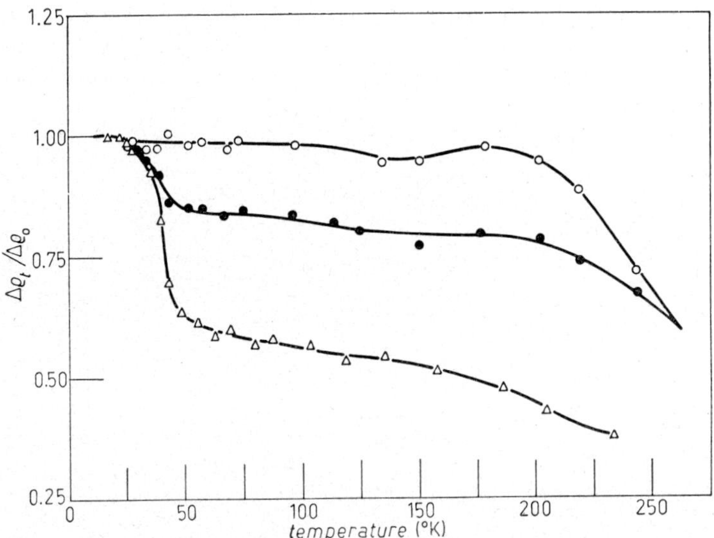

Fig. 20. – The isochronal annealing of beryllium-doped copper following a reactor irradiation at 14.5 °K: ○ 1% Be, $\varrho_0 = 5.352 \cdot 10^{-7}\ \Omega$ cm; ● 0.1% Be, $\varrho_0 = 4.98 \cdot 10^{-8}\ \Omega$ cm; △ 99.999+% Cu, $\varrho_0 = 7.6 \cdot 10^{-10}\ \Omega$ cm.

The oversized atoms Zn and Au on the other hand also affect the Stage I annealing—in a different way, however, from that observed with the undersized atoms. In this case the Stage I annealing becomes pretty well smeared out over a big temperature range appearing to be similar to that of Stage II.

Attention should be called to the differences of the 0.1% doping and the 1% doping. It is significant that the smaller impurity concentration does not affect the Stage I annealing at its lowest temperature but does suppress the higher-temperature recovery.

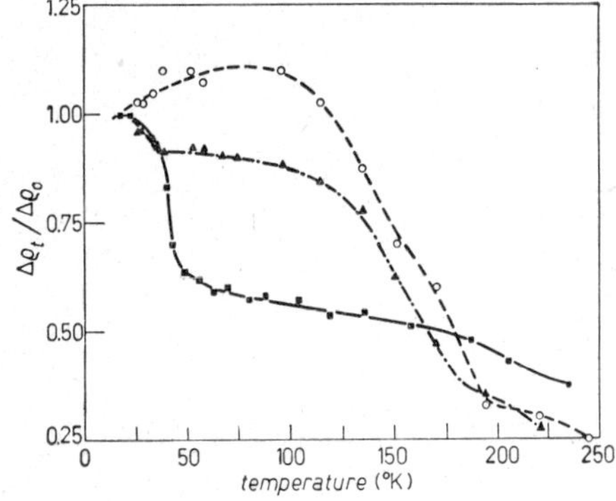

Fig. 21. – The isochronal annealing curve of silicon-doped copper following a reactor irradiation at 14.5 °K: ○ 1% Si, $\varrho_0 = 3.6895 \cdot 10^{-6}\ \Omega$ cm; ▲ 0.1% Si, $\varrho_0 = 3.342 \cdot 10^{-7}\ \Omega$ cm; ■ 99.999+% Cu, $\varrho_0 = 7.6 \cdot 10^{-10}\ \Omega$ cm.

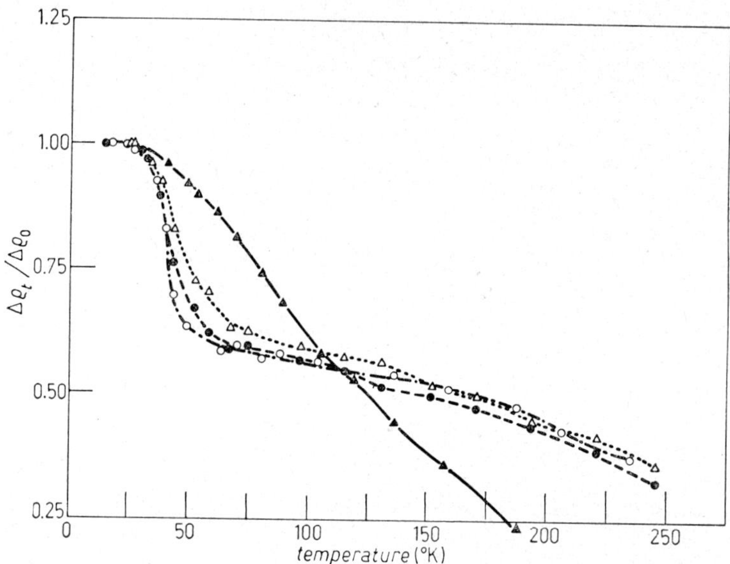

Fig. 22. – The isochronal annealing curve of zinc-doped copper following a reactor irradiation at 14.5 °K: △ ∼0.1% Zn, $\varrho_0 = 5.46 \cdot 10^{-8}\ \Omega$ cm; ● ∼0.01% Zn, $\varrho_0 = 7.65 \cdot 10^{-9}\ \Omega$ cm; ○ 99.999+% Cu, $\varrho_0 = 7.6 \cdot 10^{-10}\ \Omega$ cm; ▲ 13% Zn, $\varrho_0 = 2.36 \cdot 10^{-6}\ \Omega$ cm.

Perhaps these results can be explained in terms of the number of jumps the defect makes before annihilation. A long migration distance would increase

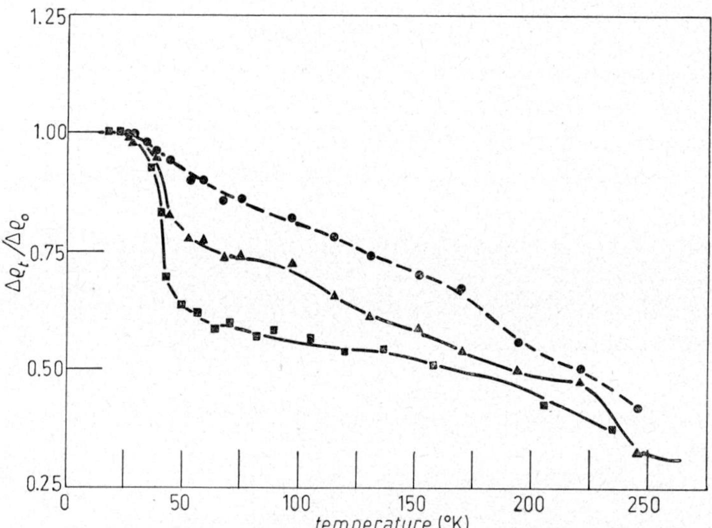

Fig. 23. – The isochronal annealing curve of gold-doped copper following a reactor irradiation at 14.5 °K: ● 1% Au, $\varrho_0 = 5.882 \cdot 10^{-7}\ \Omega$ cm; ▲ 0.1% Au, $\varrho_0 = 6.354\ \Omega$ cm; ■ 99.999+% Cu, $\varrho_0 = 7.5 \cdot 10^{-10}\ \Omega$ cm.

the probability of the mobile defect finding an impurity atom and being locked by it. If the Stage I peak were uniquely activated, the impurity-doping would thus tend to be more effective at the higher temperatures. Unfortunately, it was shown earlier that Stage I does not seem to be uniquely activated. The interpretation of this phenomenon will be deferred to a later time.

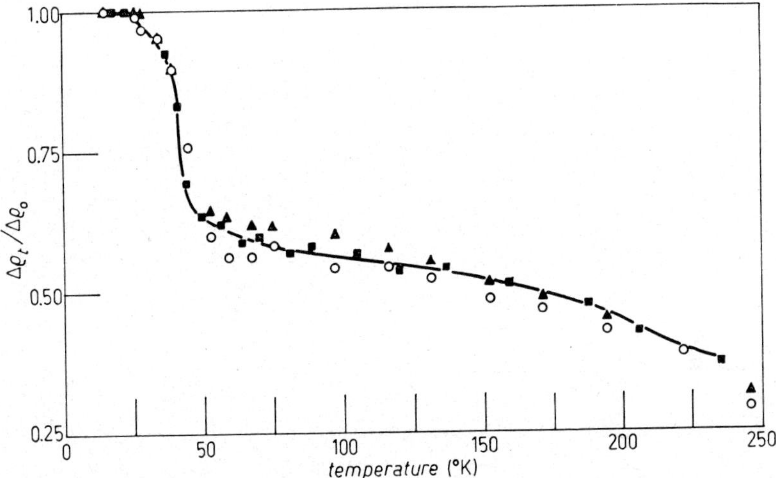

Fig. 24. – The isochronal annealing curve of nickel-doped copper following a reactor bombardment at 14.5 °K: ○ 1% Ni, $\varrho_0 = 1.326^{-6}$ Ω cm; ▲ 0.1% Ni, $\varrho_0 = 1.317 \cdot 10^{-8}$ Ω cm; ■ 99.999+% Cu, $\varrho_0 = 7.6 \cdot 10^{-10}$ Ω cm.

The measurement of the activation energy associated with Stage I annealing has not yielded completely satisfactory results in the case of neutron-irradiated copper and aluminum [22]. Both isothermal and isochronal annealing techniques have been utilized. In the region between 10° and 20° the activation energy of both aluminum and copper determined from the change in slope method (first used by OVERHAUSER) showed a continual increase in activation energy from .02 eV to .10 eV. The activation energies are much too high for the temperatures considered to be attributed to a simple process. This is apparent when the number of jumps before annihilation is computed using rate theory and the experimentally determined activation energies. For temperatures above 14 °K the number of jumps is much smaller than one. This result leads to the conclusion that something is wrong with the theoretical treatment. It may well lie in the fact that the determination of the energies is based on an assumption for unique activation energies. The fact that the activation energy is not unique, may account for the anomalous results. It would thus appear that the activation energies determined in this way are incorrect.

9. – Radiation effects in copper and aluminum arising from fissile impurities.

It has been seen that the isochronal annealing curve obtained from resistivity measurements on copper bombarded at temperatures below 10 °K by reactor neutrons differs in some important aspects from that observed when the bombardment is performed by electrons whose energy is slightly in excess of the displacement threshold. Since the majority of the neutron damage arises from primary displacements whose energy is several orders of magnitude greater than the displacement threshold, these differences in recovery can be attributed to the energy of the primary displacement. Experimental evidence to support this concept cannot be obtained from neutron elastic interactions as it is difficult to change the neutron spectrum; however, by the utilization of fission reactions introduced by inelastic neutron interactions, particles of widely different energy can be introduced into a metal. In the experiment performed at Oak Ridge [23] approximately 0.1 at. % of ^{235}U, ^{238}U, ^{10}B, and ^{11}B were added to aluminum and copper. In the cases of ^{235}U and ^{10}B it is well known that slow-neutron capture results in fission, with the ^{235}U yielding two fragments (masses about 90 and 140) and about 150 MeV of energy. The ^{10}B yields ^{7}Li and an α-particle with a combined energy of about 2.7 MeV. The isotopes ^{238}U and ^{11}B are nonfissile and were added for control purposes.

The results obtained are as follows:

1) The initial rate of increase of resistivity with dose in ^{235}U-doped copper and aluminum is 150 times the rate for the pure metals. When the cross-sections of the processes are considered, it can be concluded that initially each fission of ^{235}U produces 900 times as many defects as a primary displacement arising from a reactor neutron.

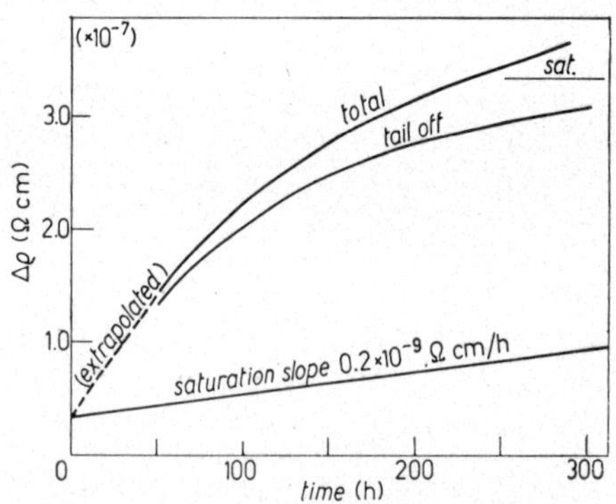

Fig. 25. – Damage rate of 0.1% ^{235}U-doped copper. Bombardment temperature 4.5 °K, flux $6\cdot10^{11}$ n/cm^2.

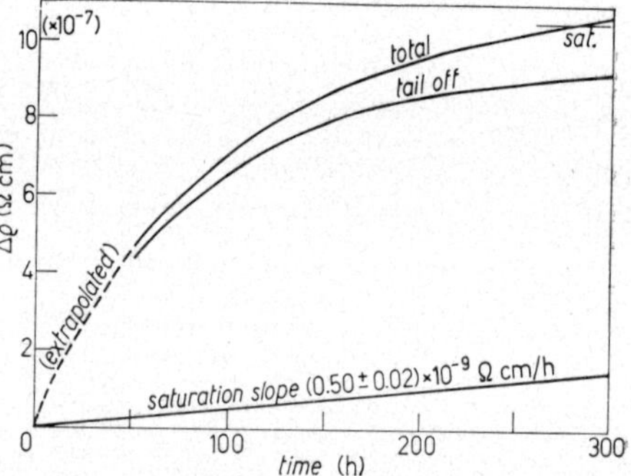

Fig. 26. – Damage rate of 0.1% ^{235}U-doped aluminum.

2) In ^{235}U-doped copper and aluminum the resistivity increases in accordance with the following equation: $\varrho = A(1-\exp[-\alpha\varphi]) + B\varphi$. The saturation value, A, of the exponential term is in good agreement with that found by COOPER, KOEHLER and MARX [4]. The experimental data can be seen in Figs. 25 and 26.

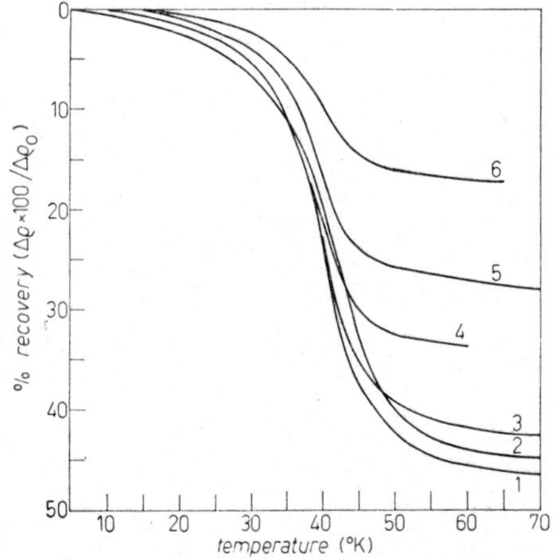

Fig. 27. – Isochronal annealing of pure copper and 0.1% ^{235}U-doped copper after various doses: 1) pure copper, $\Delta\varrho = 4.00\cdot10^{-9}$; 2) pure copper, $\Delta\varrho = 8.38\cdot10^{-9}$; 3) ^{288}U, $\Delta\varrho = 4.97\cdot10^{-9}$; 4) ^{235}U, $\Delta\varrho = 3.41\cdot10^{-9}$; 5) ^{235}U, $\Delta\varrho = 140\cdot10^{-9}$; 6) ^{235}U, $\Delta\varrho = 306\cdot10^{-9}$.

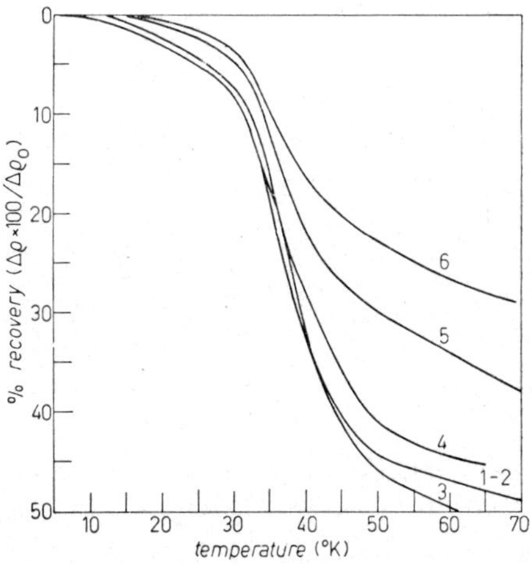

Fig. 28. – Isochronal annealing of pure aluminum and 0.1% ^{235}U-doped aluminum after various doses: 1) pure aluminum, $\Delta\varrho = 1.21\cdot10^{-8}$; 2) ^{238}U, $\Delta\varrho = 1.42\cdot10^{-8}$;, 3) ^{235}U, $\varrho = 1.29\cdot10^{-8}$; 4) pure aluminum $\Delta\varrho = 2.40\cdot10^{-8}$; 5) ^{235}U, $\Delta\varrho = 63.1\cdot10^{-8}$; 6) ^{235}U, $\Delta\varrho = 82.5\cdot10^{-8}$.

3) The isochronal annealing curves of ^{235}U-doped copper (*) and aluminum are similar to those of the pure metals when small fission doses are considered ($\Delta\varrho < 5\cdot10^{-8}$ ohm cm). At higher doses the annealing peak in the region from 35 to 45 °K is diminished from that observed in the pure metals. This can be seen in Figs. 27 and 28.

4) In the case of ^{10}B-doped copper (**) the resistivity increases at ten times the rate of pure copper. When scattering and absorption cross-sections are considered, it can be concluded that each fission produces eight times as many defects as are produced from a primary displacement by a reactor neutron.

(*) A difficulty in dissolving uranium in copper results in local segregation which is dependent upon the thermal history. This segregation results in an apparent decrease of the 35 to 45 °K annealing peak.

(**) Boron is immiscible with aluminum.

5) The resistivity-dose curve of ^{10}B-doped copper is linear (to a first approximation). This is shown in Fig. 29.

6) The isochronal annealing curve of copper irradiated by ^{10}B fragments differs in some aspects from that observed from fast-neutron-irradiated copper. A higher percentage of the induced resistivity is observed to anneal in the temperature region below 60 °K than is observed in the case of fast-neutron irradiation. This is illustrated in Fig. 30. Furthermore, when the details of the annealing curve are examined in the range from 7 to 35 °K, three distinct annealing peaks are found superimposed on the continuum found in neutron-irradiated copper. This is illustrated in the isochronal annealing curves shown in Fig. 31 and in the differential of the isochronal curve shown in Fig. 32.

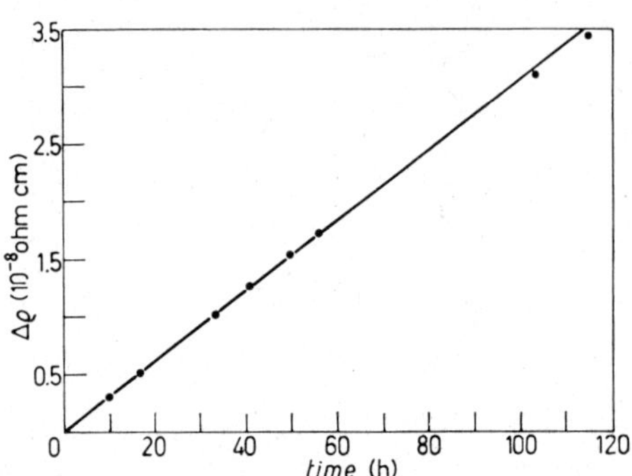

Fig. 29. – Damage rate of 0.1% ^{10}B-doped copper. Bombardment temperature 4.5 °K, flux $6 \cdot 10^{11}$ n/cm^2.

The appearance of discrete peaks in the low-temperature isochronal annealing of the boron-doped copper is highly significant as it establishes the differences

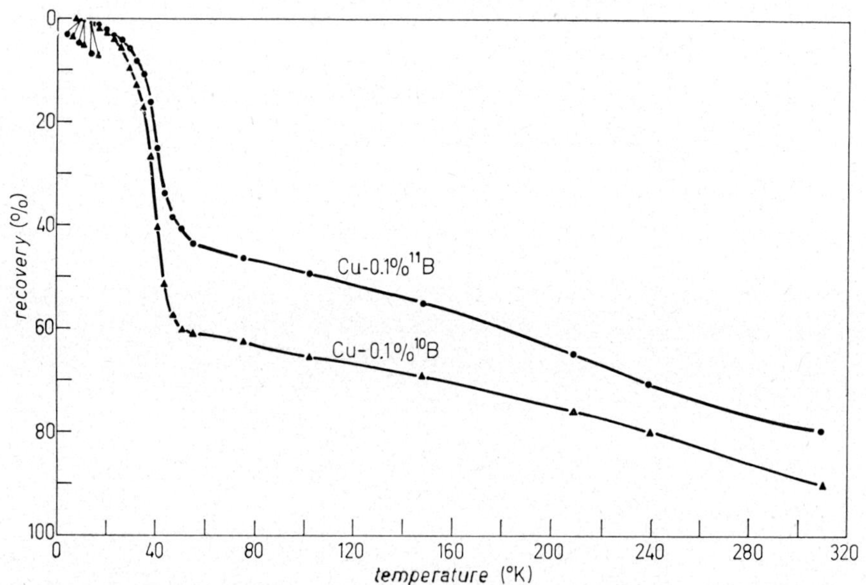

Fig. 30. – Isochronal annealing curves of 0.1% ^{10}B-doped copper and 0.1% ^{11}B-doped copper following neutron irradiation of $6 \cdot 10^{11}$ n/cm^2. The ^{10}B is fissile and the ^{11}B is nonfissile.

and similarities of neutron- and electron-irradiated copper. It can be readily seen from Fig. 32 where the differential isochronal annealing curves of electron, neutron, and ^{10}B fission fragment (α-particle) irradiated copper are shown, that the damage can be separated into a portion similar to neutron irradiation and a portion similar to electron irradiation. It can also be concluded that the main annealing peak in neutron-irradiated copper ((35÷45) °K) and its satellite ((50÷60) °K) coincide with those ob-

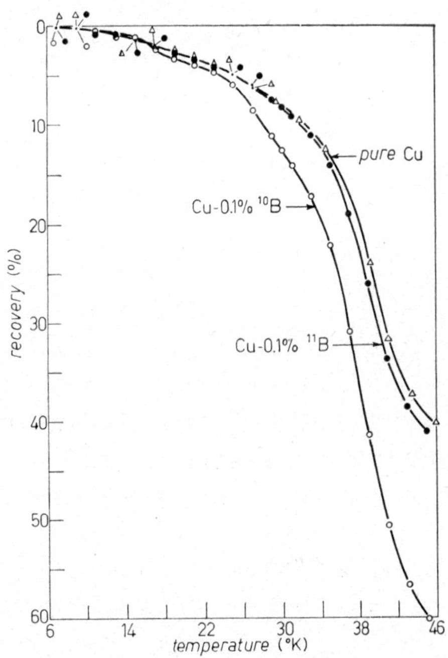

Fig. 31. – Details of the isochronal annealing curves of reactor-irradiated ^{10}B and ^{11}B-doped copper in the temperature region from 6 °K to 46 °K. After BLEWITT, COLTMAN and KLABUNDE.

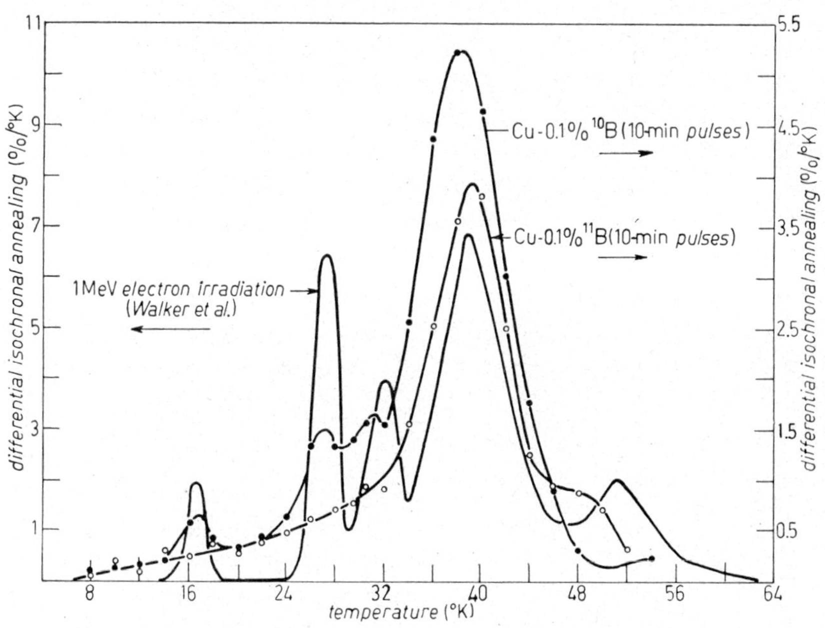

Fig. 32. – The differential isochronal annealing curves of reactor-irradiated ^{10}B and ^{11}B-doped copper and of electron-irradiated copper in the temperature region from 6 °K to 65 °K. After BLEWITT, COLTMAN and KLABUNDE.

served in electron irradiation. The main difference between the two types of damage, then, appears to be in the fact that the discrete peaks below 35 °K are smeared into a continuum for neutron damage. On the other hand, it does appear that the main peaks in both electron and neutron damage ((35 ÷ 45) °K) are probably the result of the same defect. These experiments, then, offer substantial evidence that the thermal spike does not play a serious role in neutron-irradiated copper.

The observed result that the resistivity-dose curve of ^{235}U-doped copper can be separated into two components, a linear term plus an exponential term, implies that two different kinds of lattice damage are occurring. Additional evidence to support this conclusion can be obtained by annealing a sample to room temperature after a high dose (*e.g.*, $\Delta\varrho \sim 3 \cdot 10^{-7}$ ohm·cm). A large fraction of the resistivity will remain, presumably associated with the linear terms; however, on rebombarding at 4 °K the initial rate of resistivity increase is observed to be in agreement with that of a previously unbombarded sample. The deduction that at least two kinds of damage result from neutron bombardment is in agreement with that deduced from experiments on radiation hardening.

10. – The gold paradox.

One of the most perplexing facts in the complex problem of radiation damage is the absence of a discrete annealing peak in the low-temperature region of gold. This is illustrated in Figs. 12 and 15 which show the isochronal annealing spectrum in neutron irradiated gold. This is particularly interesting as it is difficult to understand why the basic recovery process (of Stage I) attributed to interstitial migration and subsequent annihilation at vacancies should be absent, especially when it is so pronounced in copper and silver. Any interpretation of this paradox based purely on the heavy mass of the gold atom would seem to be difficult based on the fact that platinum shows a very pronounced annealing peak (Figs. 13 and 16).

Possibility that a bombardment by higher-energy particles might result in the appearance of the Stage I annealing led to the study of fission fragment damage in gold [23]. For this experiment .1% atomic percent of ^{235}U was added to the high-purity gold. Since the sample was prepared in an electric arc furnace, the dilute alloy was in the solution quenched state. It was then rolled and drawn into wire specimens. Two of these wire specimens were used following heat treatment. One of these was annealed at 150 °C and the other at 950 °C. They were then bombarded at 4.6 °K along with a sample of pure gold in the hole 12 cryostat. The initial change in resistivity in both of the uranium doped gold samples was 500 times the rate in the pure gold.

Therefore, the vast majority of the damage was caused by fission fragments. On the other hand in the pure gold a small but appreciable part of the damage arises from recoil interactions due to neutron capture and decay. The recoil energy from the reaction is considerably smaller than that from the fast neutron elastic scattering interactions, and consequently, the defect concentration and arrangement may be considerably different in these two cases. On comparing the isochronal annealing curves of the doped and undoped crystals of Fig. 33,

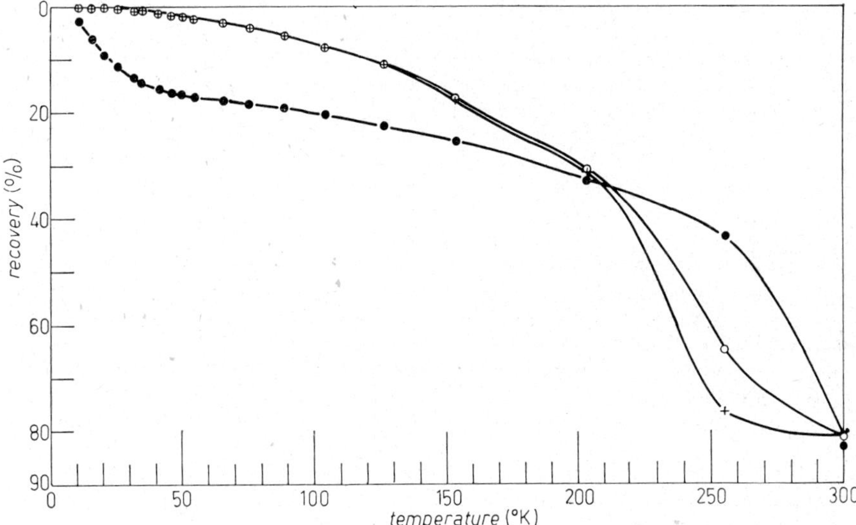

Fig. 33. – The isochronal annealing of reactor-irradiated 0.1% ^{235}U-doped gold and pure gold. Two samples of ^{235}U-doped gold are shown. One is in the as-drawn condition (heavily worked) and the other in the annealed condition. ● pure Au, $\varrho_0 = 1.85 \cdot 10^{-8}\ \Omega$ cm, $\Delta\varrho = 5.45 \cdot 10^{-9}\ \Omega$ cm; + Au — 0.1% ^{235}U, 970 °C anneal, $\varrho_0 = 0.71 \cdot 10^{-6}\ \Omega$ cm, $\Delta\varrho = 6.53 \cdot 10^{-9}\ \Omega$ cm; ○ Au — 0.1% ^{235}U, 150 °C anneal, $\varrho_0 = 0.52 \cdot 10^{-6}\ \Omega$ cm, $\Delta\varrho = 6.63 \cdot 10^{-9}\ \Omega$ cm.

it can be seen that there is a considerable difference in their recovery. The pure gold shows a relatively large recovery at (10÷30) °K which is absent in the doped gold. On the other hand there is a more rapid recovery in the ^{235}U-doped gold in the region from 30 °K to 200 °K. It may very well be that these differences appear as the result of the low-energy recoils as discussed above.

Of particular interest is the large annealing peak which occurs in all these samples from 200 to 300 °K. It is rather obvious that this annealing peak is a second-order (or higher) process from the fact that recovery temperature is dose-dependent.

11. – Stored energy measurements.

Measurements of the stored energy associated with radiation damage are very informative because the energy of formation of a vacancy-interstitial pair is known to within much narrower limits than any other property of these defects. It is unfortunate, however, that it is in general very difficult to measure this property. Most of the experiments have been performed at low temperatures and have attempted to measure the energy release associated with Stage I recovery, although some experiments have been performed at higher temperatures. The lower-temperature experiments are easier to perform than the higher-temperature experiments because the specific heat at the low temperatures is small making it possible to observe relatively large temperature changes during the energy release. Measurements of the energy release associated with the Stage I recovery of copper have been made following low-temperature neutron- and deuteron-irradiation. Each of these will be discussed in turn.

A very intensive program of energy release measurements associated with Stage I recovery of reactor-irradiated copper has been undertaken during the past five years at Oak Ridge [10, 24, 25]. During this period some modifications of experimental technique have occurred, but in general the experiment has been performed in the following way. The sample, usually of the order of 30 g, has been suspended by a copper-constantan thermocouple. During the bombardment, varying from one week to three weeks, a heat switch has been closed keeping the sample in thermal contact with the cryostat wall so that its temperature was maintained below 22 °K. Following the bombardment the heat switch was opened isolating the sample from the cryostat wall. Heat was applied to the sample by means of nuclear heating from the reactor. This heat (mostly γ-rays) is homogeneously absorbed in the sample so that equilibrium conditions are always present. This means that it is possible to determine specific heats by the measurement of a time-temperature curve; the specific heat being proportional to the slope of the time-temperature curve. Mathematically the following equation exists:

$$C_p \Delta T = \gamma \Delta t \,, \tag{11.1}$$

where T is the temperature, t is the time, C_p is the specific heat, and γ is the heat input, and

$$C_p = \gamma \frac{\Delta t}{\Delta T} \to \gamma \frac{\mathrm{d}t}{\mathrm{d}T} \,. \tag{11.2}$$

Thus, in the limit the exact specific heat can be determined by this method, whereas in the classical scheme of specific heat determination only the average specific heat in a temperature interval could be determined.

The heat switch and the thermocouple are the key items in this technique.

The most recent experiments [25] in pure copper used a heat switch illustrated in Fig. 34. The samples were bombarded at 15 °K for three weeks with the switch closed. The switch was then opened by pumping out the helium ($\frac{3}{4}$ of an atmosphere was left in the sample chamber to maintain the bellow-wall at 14 °K). The time-temperature curve was then determined. The heat switch was then closed, the sample cooled, and another run was made. The results of these two runs are shown in Fig. 35 where the slope of the time-temperature curve is plotted as a function of absolute temperature. The depression in the data of run 1 between 35 and 45 °K is the result of the energy release which makes the specific heat seem too small. It should be noted, however, than run 2 does not fall on run 1. This is probably the result of spurious emf's in the thermocouple arising from inhomogeneities in the thermocouple wire and a change in the temperature gradient from run 1 to run 2. In order then to evaluate the energy release a smooth curve was drawn in run 1, and the arc between it and the measured specific heat was taken as the energy release. This is shown in Fig. 35 as the cross-hatched area. This area was normalized to energy by utilizing known values of the specific heat of copper to evaluate γ. It was assumed that the heat leak was negligible in the temperature interval from 20 °K to 50 °K. The validity of this assumption can be judged by noting GIAUQUE and MEADS' data [26] in Fig. 35. (It should be noted that a heat leak will make the results too large.) Under these considerations the cross-hatched area indicates the energy release associated with Stage I following a three-week bombardment. The change in resistivity occurring in the region from 35 to 45 °K, *i.e.*, a temperature region corresponding to that associated with the energy re-

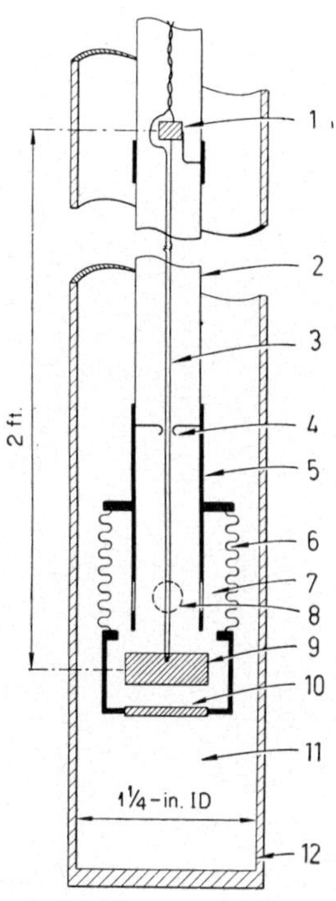

Fig. 34. – The heat switch utilized in stored energy measurements of pure copper: 1) insulated sample suspension clamp on constantan thermocouple lead; 2) $\frac{1}{2}$ in. stainless steel, 0.01 in. wall; 3) copper constantan thermocouple, fiberglass sleeve insulated; 4) thin stainless guide; 5) OFHC copper tube; 6) brass bellows; 7) high vacuum (0,02 μm); 8) vacuum by-pass holes; 9) sample; 10) high purity copper disk; 11) helium exchange gas: 100 μm for sample insulation, 20 psig for sample cooling; 12) cryostat sample chamber wall at 15 °K.

lease, following a one-week bombardment has previously been found to be $1.2 \cdot 10^{-9}\ \Omega$cm. Thus, the ratio of stored energy to resistivity in the Stage I annealing is .56 cal mol/$3.6 \cdot 10^{-9}\ \Omega$cm $= 1.55 \cdot 10^{2}$ cal mol/$\mu\Omega$ cm or 2.5 cal/g$\cdot\mu\Omega$ cm. It

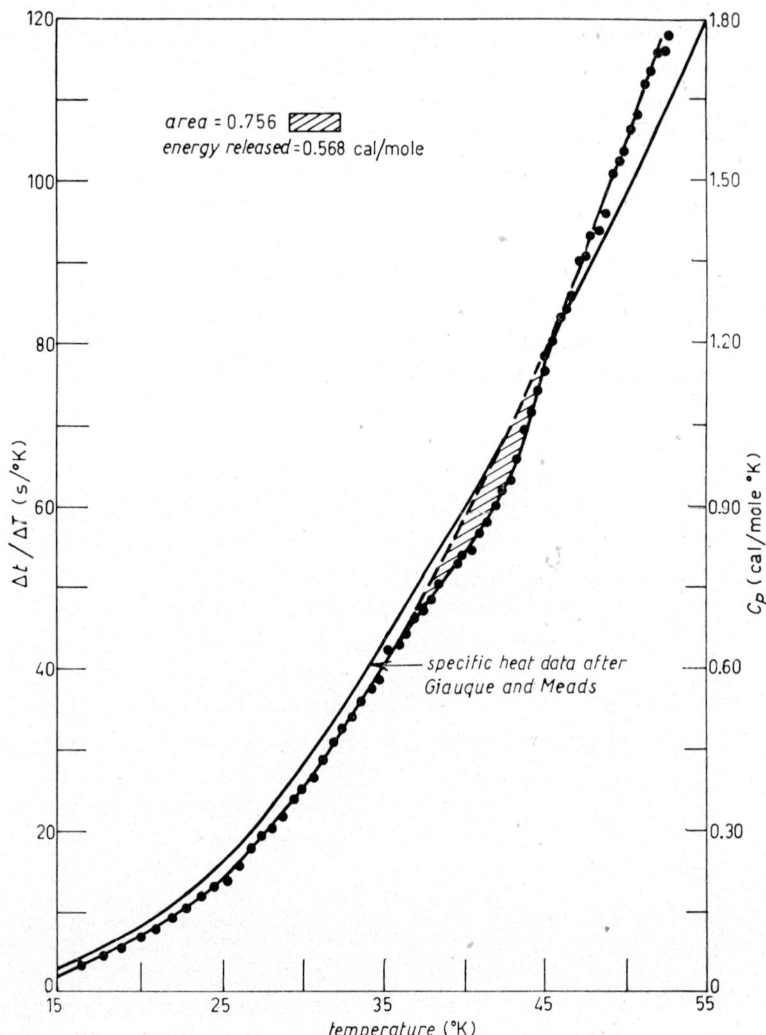

Fig. 35. – The differential time-temperature curves of irradiated copper heated by nuclear heating. The differentials $\Delta t/\Delta T$ are adjusted experimental values and are proportional to the specific heat.

should be noted that the method of determining the area of the stored energy is in all probability to loow. This can be seen from the differential of the isochronal annealing curve (Fig. 15) and the schematic drawing of Fig. 36. The drawing, of a smooth curve between 35 and 45 °K in the energy release curve of

Fig. 35, is equivalent to considering only the energy represented by the single cross-hatched area of Fig. 36. On the other hand, the resistivity of $3.6 \cdot 10^{-9}\ \Omega$ cm is representative of the total area (single and double cross-hatched area) under the curve of Fig. 36. Since the double cross-hatched area is 50% of the single cross-hatched area, the energy associated with the 35 to 45 °K release and the ratio of this energy to the resistivity should be increased by 50%. Thus, the revised ratio should amount to 3.8 cal g/$\mu\Omega$ cm.

Similar measurements have also been made for aluminum [17]. A somewhat different heat switch was used. A thin walled stainless steel tube transmitted a load to apply pressure to the sample and dissipate the nuclear heating through a mechanical contact. This is illustrated in Fig. 37. It was found necessary to add helium exchange gas (25 μm) to hold the temperature below 25 °K when the reactor was on. This was not serious, as the mechanical contact was sufficient to hold the temperature under reactor off and low power conditions. It was then possible following the bombardment to remove this gas by pumping (a pumping period of 10 hours being used) without warming the sample. Following the removal of the gas and stabilization of reactor power at .3 of full power, the heat switch was opened by raising the weight, thus suspending the sample by the thermocouple. As before, a time-temperature curve was determined. The derivative of this curve ($\Delta t/\Delta T$) is plotted as a function of temperature in Fig. 37. The specific heat of aluminum (GIAUQUE and MEADS [26]) was utilized to normalize $\Delta t/\Delta T$. This bump in the curve indicated an energy release of .48 cal mol for the bombardment of $4 \cdot 10^{17}$ neutrons. This was associated with a recovery of $4.8 \cdot 10^{-9}\ \Omega$ cm. The energy-to-resistivity ratio

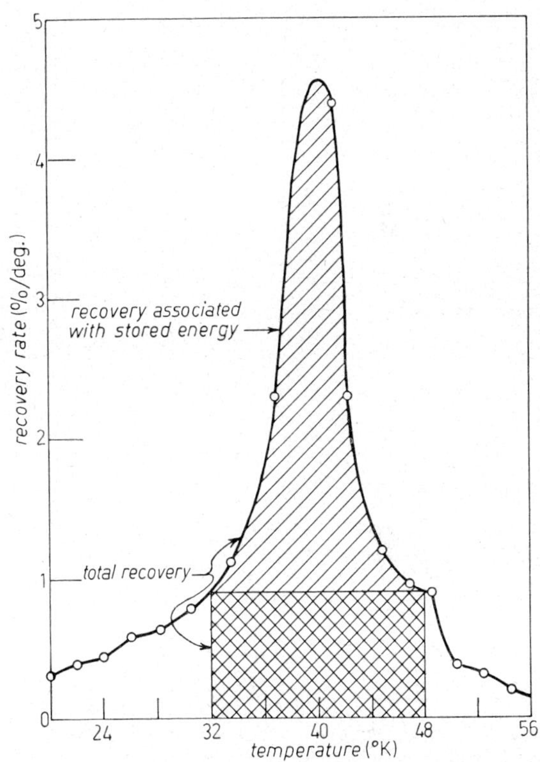

Fig. 36. – Schematic drawing illustrating the correction applied to the stored energy results. The single cross-hatched area represents the resistivity associated with the measured release. The double crossed-hatched area represents the total resistivity change measured.

is then 3.6 cal/g·μΩ cm for aluminum. This value as in the case of copper errs in being too low because some of the energy is not being accounted for when just the bump in the one warm-up curve is concerned. The error is smaller

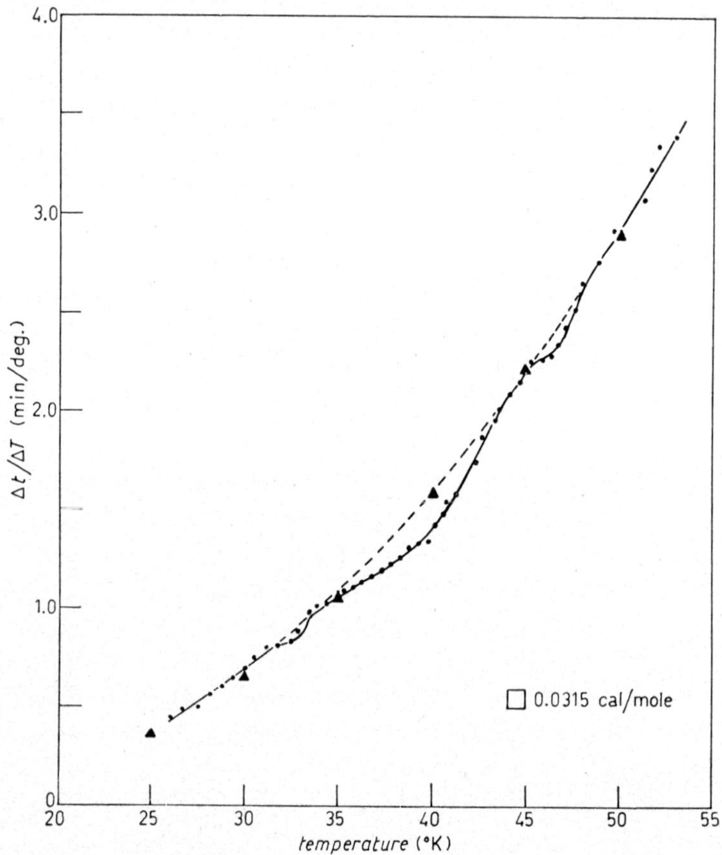

Fig. 37. – Differential heating curves of neutron-irradiated aluminum normalized to the specific heat of aluminum. The bump in the curve at the highest temperature is an instrumental error. After BLEWITT, COLTMAN and KLABUNDE. Integrated flux $\sim 4\cdot 10^{17}$ nvt; time ~ 150 h; exchange gas ~ 25 μm; ▲ GIAUQUE and MEADS, $\gamma=0.315$.

than in the case of copper amounting to about 20%. The corrected value is thus 4.4 cal/g·μΩ cm. When comparing the energy release in Stage I of aluminum with that of Stage II in copper, it must be remembered that the electronic structure (number of current carriers) plays a big role in the magnitude of resistivity change. It is thus more convenient to compare the energy release per unit bombardment time for the two metals. Since in both metals Stage I is about the same fraction of the total recovery, and these metals have about the same neutron elastic cross-section, the stored energy measurements

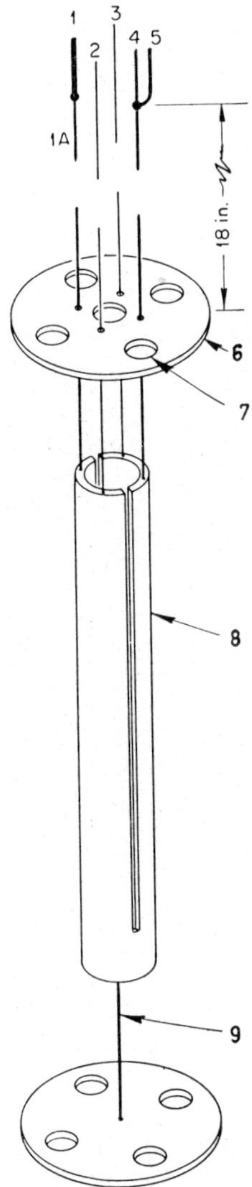

Fig. 38. – Specimen design used so that stored energy measurements and resistivity measurements could be measured on the same specimen. After Blewitt, Coltman and Klabunde: 1) and 5) no. 40 copper (current); 1A) no. 30 constantan (thermal stand-off); 2) and 3) no. 40 copper (potential); 3) and 4) copper constantan thermocouple; insulation: copper-Formvar, constantan-ceramic tubing; 6) Lavite spacer disk; 7) lighting and circulation holes; 8) copper-^{10}B sample (slotted tube shape: 2 in. $\times \frac{1}{4}$ in. $\varnothing \times 0.040$ in. wall); 9) nichrome support for lower disk.

of these metals can be compared and considered representative of the total defect production. Thus, the value of 8.5 cal/mol·week for aluminum should be compared with 2.7 cal/mol·week. Apparently then, in aluminum 2.1 times as many defects are formed than are formed in copper for the same neutron dose. On the billiard ball model the primary knock-on on an aluminum atom should from mass considerations be 2.3 times more energetic than the copper knock-on. Since the observed damage rate is so close to that expected from simple displacement theory without ionization considerations, it is suggestive that ionization losses are small even for a metal as light as aluminum.

More recently stored energy measurements have been made on ^{10}B-doped copper [27]. A considerably greater amount of damage was introduced by the fissions of the ^{10}B making for a relatively easy measurement. In addition, it was possible to measure the

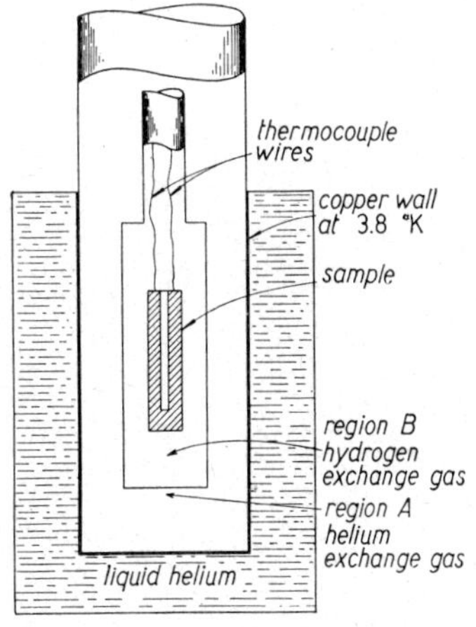

Fig. 39. – The heat switch used in stored energy measurements of ^{10}B-doped copper.

resistivity associated with the release of the stored energy. The sample design is as shown in Fig. 38.

The hollow cylinder was selected as it was easiest to cool by convection while the slit was added to increase the L/A ratio important to the resistivity measurements. The thermocouple and potential probes are also shown. The heat switch was also a novel idea. It is illustrated in Fig. 39.

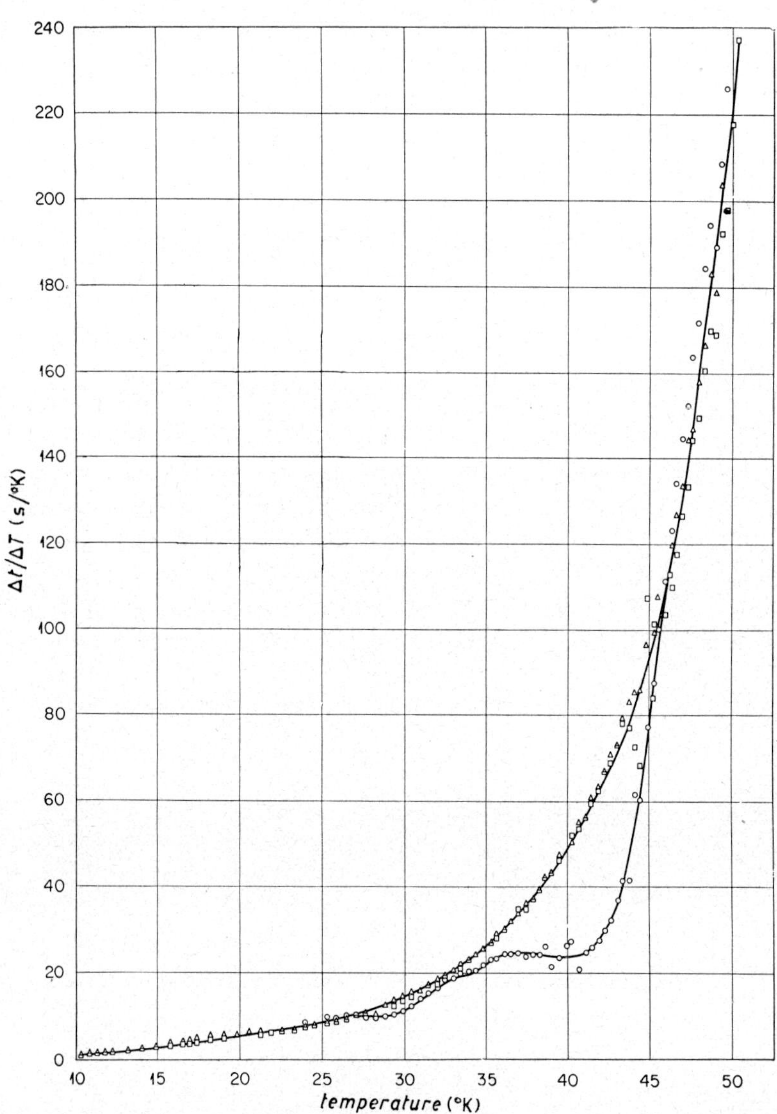

Fig. 40. – The differential heating curves of ^{10}B-doped copper. Run 1 (○) obtained immediately after a dose of $4\cdot10^{17}$ thermal neutrons/cm^2. Runs 2 (□) and 3 (△) were obtained in order following run 1.

The sample chamber wall is maintained at 3.8 °K throughout the experiment. Helium exchange gas is added to region A. The vapor pressure was adjusted so that wall temperature of region B was at 10 °K when the switch was closed. At this temperature hydrogen has a vapor pressure of about 100 μm and a sample temperature of about 20 °K resulted. The switch was opened by pumping sufficient helium into region A to condense liquid at 3.8 °K. At this temperature the vapor pressure of hydrogen is of the order of 10^{-2} μm, and the sample was insulated. In practice, some α-particles were produced and escaped during the bombardment so that a small amount of helium was generated in region B. This was not too serious, however, as the resulting heat leak was relatively small in the interesting temperature region and was reproducible. The reproducibility arose from the fact that region B was a static system throughout the experiment. This particular heat switch had the advantage of relative simplicity along with an additional advantage that the entire region B contained exchange gas (hydrogen) during the cool-down so that the thermocouple quickly attained steady-state conditions, so that the Thomson emf was not of serious consequence.

As in the other stored energy experiments, a time-temperature curve was measured following the bombardment. The slope of this curve is plotted as a function of absolute temperature in Fig. 40. There such measurements were made following the bombardment. Only one of these, run A, contains stored energy. It can, however, be noted that there is excellent reproducibility in run 2 and run 3. The difference between run 1 and runs 2 and 3 represents the energy release. To evaluate this difference, it is necessary to know the effective heat input. It has been pointed out that the formation of α-particles results in a heat leak. The effective gamma heating, γ', can be evaluated from equation

(11.3) $$\gamma' = \gamma - \delta = C_p \frac{\mathrm{d}T}{\mathrm{d}t} ,$$

since C_p, the specific heat is well known with the value given by GIAUQUE and MEADS [26] being used here. Since the other variable $\mathrm{d}T/\mathrm{d}t$ has been determined experimentally, the value of γ' can be readily determined. These values are shown as a function of temperature in Fig. 41.

The stored energy released in run A can be included in the specific heat term if it is treated as a specific energy release ε where the stored energy E is given by

(11.4) $$E = \int \varepsilon \, \mathrm{d}T .$$

Thus, run A can be represented mathematically as

(11.5) $$(C_p - \varepsilon) \, \mathrm{d}T_A = \gamma' \, \mathrm{d}t_A ,$$

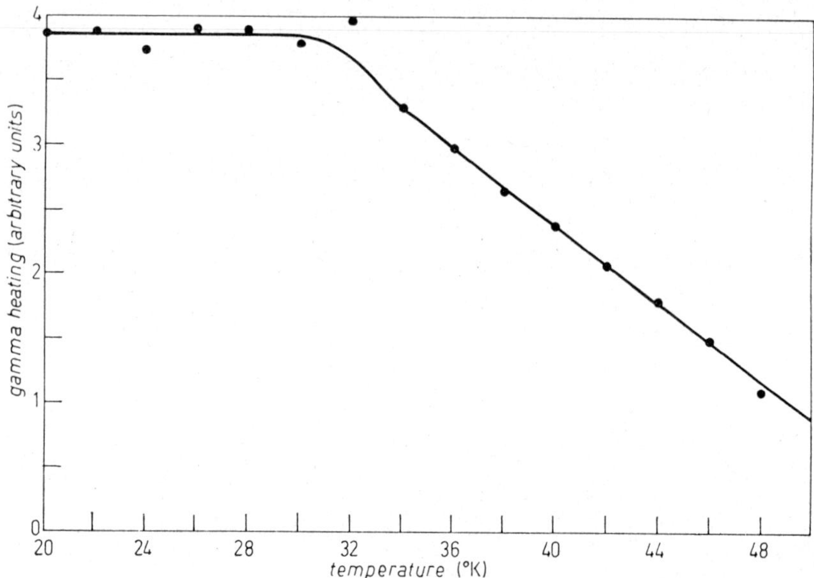

Fig. 41. – The effective heat input, k', determined from the experimental values of dt/dT and Giauque and Meads' determination of the specific heat of copper.

or

$$\varepsilon = C_p - \gamma' \left(\frac{dt}{dT}\right)_A = \gamma' \left\{\left(\frac{dt}{dT}\right)_B - \left(\frac{dt}{dT}\right)_A\right\}. \tag{11.6}$$

Thus, the specific energy release ε is just equal to the effective heat input multiplied by the difference in the slope of the heating curve for run 1 and run 2 (or run 3). In Fig. 42 the lower curve is $\gamma'(dt/dT)_A$ and the upper curve is the specific heat. The shaded area is then the energy released, E or $\int\gamma'\{(dT/dt)_B - (dt/dT)_A\}\,dT$. This experimental value is found to be 4.54 cal/mol for the one-week bombardment ($4\cdot10^{17}$ thermal neutrons). Now following this determination, the sample was recooled and rebombarded and an exact repetition of the stored energy run was made. This time, however, the resistance was read before and after the warm-up. It was found that the resistivity decreased by $1.77\cdot10^{-8}$ ohm cm.

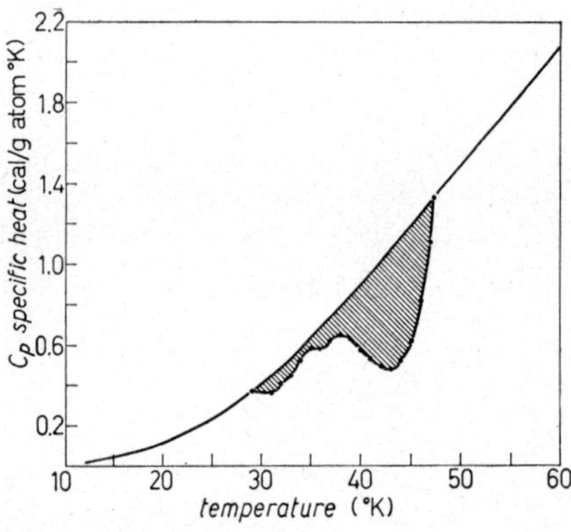

Fig. 42. – The energy release in reactor-irradiated 0.1% ^{10}B-doped copper following a dose of $4\cdot10^{17}$ thermal neutrons/cm^2.

This decrease in resistivity can be

used as a criterion for the amount of damage introduced into the sample. Thus, this experiment has shown that an energy release of 4.54 cal/mol will be associated with a recovery of $1.77 \cdot 10^{-2}$ μΩ cm. Thus,

$$\frac{E}{\Delta\varrho} = \frac{4.54}{1.77 \cdot 10^{-2}} = \frac{256 \text{ cal/mol}}{\mu\Omega \text{ cm}} = \frac{4.01 \text{ cal/g}}{\mu\Omega \text{ cm}} . \tag{11.7}$$

In evaluating the accuracy of this figure it should be noted that a very simple technique is used along with a very simple analysis. Only one assumption is used in the analysis—the reproducibility of the time-temperature curve in the region where the heat is evolved. The reproducibility of runs 2 and 3 substantiates the validity of this assumption. The fact that energy release spectrum is in rather close agreement to differential isochronal annealing curves (resistivity recovery see Fig. 31) is also satisfying.

12. – Stored energy results on deuteron bombardment.

NILAN and GRANATO [28] at the University of Illinois have also performed stored energy measurements on irradiated copper. They studied foils of copper which were bombarded near 15 °K with 11 MeV deuterons. The stored energy was measured by a differential technique. Two foils, one of which was irradiated, were heated electrically. The temperature difference between these two samples was recorded. A very careful calibration of the heat losses was made. The stored energy was determined from this loss measurement and the observed difference in temperatures of the two foils. In this temperature range from 25 to 56 °K they found that for $8.25 \cdot 10^{15}$ deuterons/cm² a release of $92.8 \cdot 10^{-3}$ cal/g was observed; a smaller dose, $2.89 \cdot 10^{15}$ deuterons/cm², yielded a release of $35.3 \cdot 10^{-3}$ cal/g. These two results are in excellent agreement with each other and show structure similar to that seen in Fig. 31. This experiment was very carefully done ad the agreement between the two runs emphasizes this care. In evaluating this result with electrical resistance measurements some difficulties occur. NILAN and GRANATO utilized the data of COOPER, KOEHLER and MARX [4] which were obtained a considerable period earlier. Using these values of resistivity per deuteron, they obtained a value of

$$\frac{E}{\Delta\varrho} = \frac{7.1 \text{ cal/g}}{\mu\Omega \text{ cm}} . \tag{12.1}$$

This is almost a factor of two greater than that obtained at Oak Ridge. The difference between these two may very well lie in the determination of the electrical resistivity associated with the energy of release.

13. – High-temperature energy release.

The measurement of the stored energy associated with the recovery of radiation damage in the 600 to 700 °K region represents a rather difficult problem as a comparatively small amount of energy is released over a relatively large temperature interval. Furthermore, in most cases the specific heat is relatively high and the thermal radiation losses are quite substantial, compared to the energy release even when thermal radiation shields of relatively low emissivity are used. Classically this basic problem is solved by measuring the difference in specific heat between a standard or « dummy » sample ad the sample containing the stored energy. In the SYKES [29] method both samples are placed in the same temperature environment (to reduce radiation effects), and the temperature of the environment and of each of the samples is raised at the same rate by electrical heat. The energy release is determined from the difference in heat input of the two samples.

The method used at Oak Ridge [25] for the high-temperature energy release is a unique one insofar as the temperature range is concerned. Heating by γ-rays supplied by the Oak Ridge National Laboratory Research Reactor is substituted for the electrical heating used in the Sykes method. This has several advantages. First, it permits a high heat input which is absorbed homogeneously in the sample so that equilibrium conditions always exist. In this experiment the γ-ray heating amounted to 0.7 W/g and in the case of copper a heating rate of about 100 °C/min. Secondly, the construction of radiation shields is relatively simple as the γ-rays are also absorbed uniformly in the radiation shield, heating them at the same rate as the sample (providing they are made of the same material). It is thus possible to keep the samples in a temperature environment which has the same characteristics as the sample. These two advantages make it possible to determine the stored energy by measuring the difference in temperature between a sample and a dummy sample.

It should be noted that considerable experimental difficulty was experienced in the construction of a suitable differential thermocouple. The major difficulty arose from spurious emf's apparently arising from inhomogeneities in the thermocouples as the temperature gradient changed during the heating (Thomson emf). Careful selection of standard thermocouple wire did not correct this difficulty. Good results were obtained when statistical wire (*) was used as both legs of the differential thermocouple.

The details of the experimental facility are shown in Fig. 43. The sample

(*) Statistical wire is a multistranded copper wire developed by Leeds and Northrup Company for lead wires in applications where a spurious emf must be reduced to a minimum.

assembly, consisting of an irradiated sample ($3.5 \cdot 10^{19}$ fast neutrons/cm²) (*) and a dummy sample in a polished copper radiation shield, was thermally insulated from the reactor pool in an evacuated aluminum tube. This sample assembly was suspended in this tube by the thermocouple wires. Two thermo-

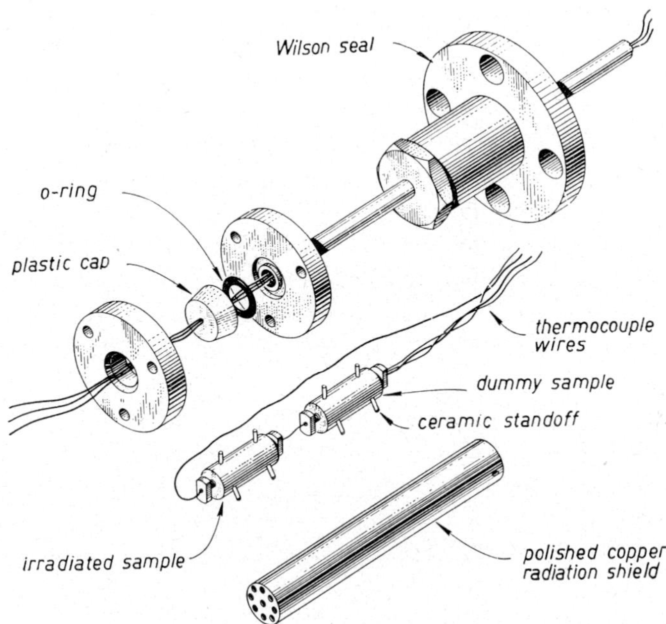

Fig. 43. – Experimental details of the specimen assembly used in high-temperature stored energy experiments.

couples were used. A copper-constantan thermocouple was held in a well on the top of the upper sample (the dummy or unirradiated sample) along with an additional copper lead which formed one leg of a differential thermocouple. The lower sample was suspended from the upper sample by a constantan wire of about one-half inch in length. The junction of these wires formed the hot and cold junction of the differential thermocouple. A copper lead was held in a well at the bottom of the lower specimen. The thermocouple wires were brought out of the evacuated chamber by moulding them into a plastic cap which was clamped to a flange (an « O » ring seal being used) on the end of a $\frac{1}{4}$ in. OD stainless steel tube four feet long. This tube in turn passed through a Wilson seal so that the sample assembly could be moved four feet from the

(*) This sample was bombarded in the same ORR facility described above for six weeks, being cooled by helium gas to the ambient temperature of the water (60 °C). The dose is equivalent to $1.7 \cdot 10^{20}$ n/cm² whose energy is distributed between 1 eV and 2 MeV in a $1/E$ distribution.

center of the flux field by withdrawing the rod. This distance proved sufficient to reduce the γ field (and the neutron field) to negligible proportions.

The experimental procedure was then as follows. The sample assembly was held in the upper position by withdrawing the stainless steel rod, and the aluminum tube was then evacuated to $2 \cdot 10^{-4}$ mm Hg (two hours being required for the evacuation). The stainless steel tube was then pushed in causing the sample assembly to be on the center line of the reactor flux field. A time-temperature curve for the upper sample was then determined by recording the output of the copper-constantan thermocouple. The output of the differential thermocouple was also recorded.

The time-temperature curve obtained from the copper-constantan thermocouple can be used to estimate the heat losses during the warm-up as well as to monitor the absolute temperature.

To a good first approximation the specific heat of copper, C_p, is given as

$$C_p = 5.39 + 1.5 \cdot 10^{-3} T \text{ cal/mol} \tag{13.1}$$

in the temperature range from 0 to 600 °C [30]. During the heat input we have

$$\int_{336\,°\text{K}}^{T} C_p \,\mathrm{d}T = \int_{0}^{t} \gamma \,\mathrm{d}t \,, \tag{13.2}$$

where: γ = the γ-ray heating (cal/mol·s),

t = time in seconds

and T = the absolute temperature,

then

$$\int_{336\,°\text{K}}^{T} (5.39 + 1.5 \cdot 10^{-3}\, T)\,\mathrm{d}T = \gamma t \,, \tag{13.3}$$

or

$$\gamma = \frac{5.39\,T - 1.895 \cdot 10^{3} + 7.5 \cdot 10^{-4}\, T^{2}}{t} \,. \tag{13.4}$$

During the experiment which lasts about six minutes, it is safe to assume that γ is a constant and any deviation in γ is a result of heat losses. Fig. 43*a* shows the plot of γ as a function of temperature as determined from the experimental time-temperature curve and the above equation. It can be seen that only about six percent of the heat input is lost, even at 600 °C. The addition of a second radiation shield would reduce this loss still further.

In Fig. 43*b* the output of the differential thermocouple is plotted as a function of temperature. This graph represents the difference in temperature between the dummy sample and the irradiated sample as a function of tem-

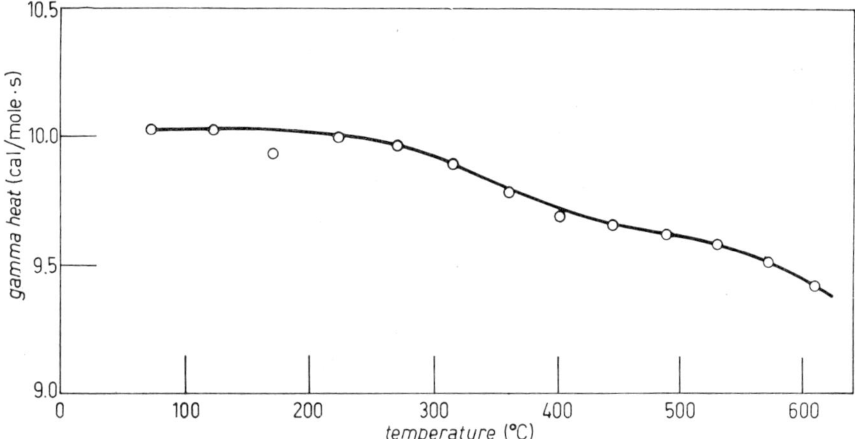

Fig. 43*a*. – γ-heating during high-temperature stored energy experiment.

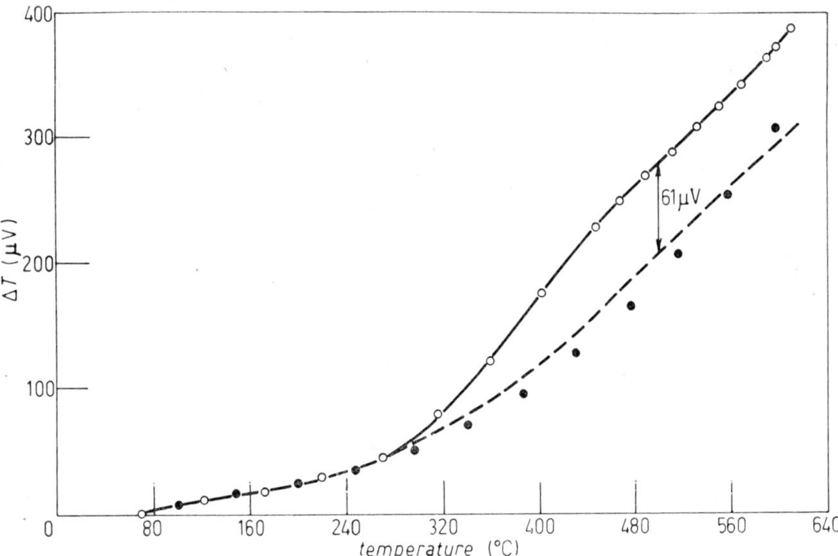

Fig. 43*b*. – Energy release in neutron-irradiated copper. The output of the differential thermocouple is plotted as a function of temperature. The difference between run 1 and run 2 is the energy release. ○ Run 1; ● Run 2; – – – extrapolated curve.

perature. The bump in the curve of the first run between 290 and 420 °C arises from the release of the energy associated with the removal of defects introduced by the bombardment, whereas the second run shows a smooth curve between 70 and 600 °C. The differences between the two curves presumably arise as a result of the energy release. This corresponds to 91 μV or 1.50 °C at 460 °C. It would appear, however, that some difficulty arises from spurious Thomson emf's, as in the region from 460 to 600 °C curve 2 is not parallel to curve 1. It would seem then that an extrapolation of curve 1 in the region from 280 to 600 °C, making the portion in the region from 460 to 600 °C parallel to the experimentally determined curve, might more accurately fit the picture (*). In doing this it can be seen that the 73 μV difference appears which corresponds to a 1.2 °C rise in temperature in the irradiated sample. If we use this latter figure the stored energy in the sample amounts to 7.7 cal/mol after a bombardment of $1.7 \cdot 10^{20}$ fast neutrons/cm^2 ($1/E$ distribution).

Samples suitable for resistivity and tensile measurements were simultaneously bombarded with the stored energy sample. It was found that the resolved critical shear stress for plastic flow was increased from 0.2 kg/mm^2 to 12.8 kg/mm^2 at 4.2 °K (5.2 kg/mm^2 at 300 °K). The electrical resistivity had increased $3.35 \cdot 10^{-2}$ μΩ cm following the bombardment. These samples were annealed for ten minutes at 250 °C. This anneal did little to the critical shear stress but reduced the resistivity to $4.5 \cdot 10^{-3}$ μΩ cm. This anneal was followed by an anneal similar to that in the stored energy anneal by the use of γ-ray heating. This latter anneal reduced the resistivity to $2.9 \cdot 10 \cdot 10^{-2}$ μΩ cm and the critical shear stress to 0.7 kg/mm^2 at 4.2 °K and to 0.5 kg/mm^2 at 300 °K. It can thus be concluded that a release of 7.7 cal/mol is accompanied by a recovery of $2.9 \cdot 10^{-2}$ μΩ cm and 11.8 kg/mm^2 critical shear stress at 4.2 °K (4.7 kg/mm^2 at 300 °K). Thus, the ratio $E/\Delta\varrho$ is 264 cal/mol μΩ cm or 4.12 cal/g μΩ cm which is in excellent agreement with the low temperature results.

14. – Summary of stored energy results.

Excellent measurements of the energy release associated with Stage I recovery have been made following low temperature neutron, deuteron and boron fission fragment bombardment. Consideration of the annealing spectrum following neutron, boron fission fragment (very nearly the same as deuteron bombardment) and electron bombardment (Fig. 32) show that the main annealing peak (Stage ID) in the Stage I annealing occurs at thes ame temperature for all three cases. It is highly probable that the same defect (interstitial-vacancy annihilation) is involved regardless of the method of bombardment. The energy release per unit damage in resistivity, which is assumed to be proportional to the number of defects, should then be the same for all types of bombardment. It has been shown that that is the case for neutron and boron fission damage where the energy release is about 4.0 cal/g μΩ cm,

(*) It is assumed that the small increase in C_p with temperature will be just about compensated by the increase in thermoelectric power of the thermocouple. In any event, the correction will be small.

whereas for deuteron bombardment a value of 7.1 cal/g μΩ cm was observed. In view of the fact that the resistivity change associated with the energy release for the case of the neutron and boron fission fragment bombardment is much more reliable than that associated with the energy release for the case of deuteron bombardment, 4.0 cal/g·μΩ cm is believed to be more reliable.

In the case of the high-temperature stored energy a similar value was found. It should be expected even if interstitials alone were being removed during this peak that a value in the vicinity of that associated with the Stage I recovery would be observed. The closeness of the experimental results thus supports to some extent the value of 4.0 cal/g·μΩ cm for Stage I annealing.

15. – Length change measurements.

It has been emphasized that stored energy measurements are important because the measurement of this property makes it possible to determine the number of defects within narrow limits. A similar argument can also be used in the case of the measurement of volume changes resulting from neutron bombardment. Several calculations have been made of the volume associated with an interstitial and a vacancy, and these yield volume increase ranging from 1 to 3 atomic volumes per interstitial-vacancy pair. Thus, the measurement of this property will determine the number of defects to within a factor of three. A still more important reason for the measurement of this property lies in the fact that the net volume change involves a mass transport of material as well as a relaxation phenomenon. In the case of the vacancy, the mass transport is the more important of the two factors, whereas in the interstitial the reverse is true. This is illustrated below:

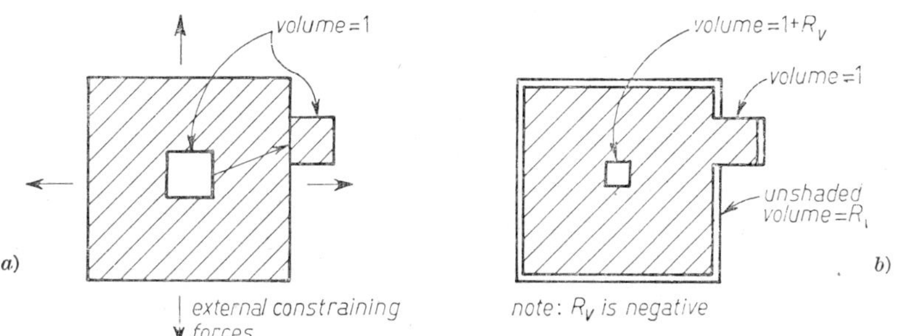

Fig. 44. – Schematic diagram of the change in volume associated with a vacancy. In *a*) a unit volume has been moved to the surface but constraining forces prevent a collapse around the vacancy. In *b*) the forces have been removed and a collapse of R_v atomic volumes results.

Consider that a unit volume is removed from square *a*) of Fig. 44 and placed on the surface, and assume that the square is constrained preventing relaxation around the hole. Then the volume will increase by a unit volume due to the transport of mass to the surface. Now, remove the constraining forces so that the crystal can relax by an amount R_v. Under these conditions the net change in volume for the creation of a vacancy will be given by eq. (5.1)

$$\Delta V_v = 1 + R_v \,, \tag{15.1}$$

where R_v, the relaxation of a vacancy, is negative. A similar equation can be written for the interstitial if a mass from the surface is brought into an interstitial position. Thus,

$$\Delta V_i = R_i - 1 \,. \tag{15.2}$$

R_i the relaxation around an interstitial is positive. In both cases ΔV will be positive for metal crystals. The term R_v will always be negative but less than unity while the term R_i will be positive and greater than unity. For the noble metals the computations suggest that R_v is of the order $-.5$ while R_i may be as large as 3.5. Since the mass term is an important one in the length change but does not influence the resistivity, it is rather unlikely that the resistivity of the vacancy would bear the same relationship to its volume change as the resistivity of interstitial atoms does to its volume change.

Hence, a simultaneous determination of the length change and the resistivity change during recovery will provide valuable information pertaining to the type of defect which is mobile.

16. – Experimental volume changes.

The volume change associated with low-temperature reactor and deuteron bombardments have been studied. In each of these cases the volume change-dose relationship was determined as well as isochronal annealing curves.

The first measurements of these types were made on copper at the University of Illinois with the bombardments being made at 10 °K with 7 MeV deuterons. SIMMONS and BALLUFFI [31] measured the volume changes by the change in the X-ray lattice parameter. On the other hand, VOOK and WERT [32] subsequently measured changes in length as a function of 8.5 MeV deuteron bombardment. The results from the isochronal annealing curves from both of these experiments are shown in Fig. 45. It should be noted that X-ray measurements measure only the relaxation term while the length change measurement includes the mass transport term as well. Thus, an agreement between the two annealing curves implies that the number of vacancies and interstitials must remain equal. The data of Fig. 45 show that this is approximately the case for Stage I annealing. However, consideration of the density of sinks for interstitials, assuming these are the mobile defects, clearly shows that vacancies are orders of magnitude more dense than any other defects for the doses used. Thus, the vast majority of the recovery should be the result of vacancy-inter-

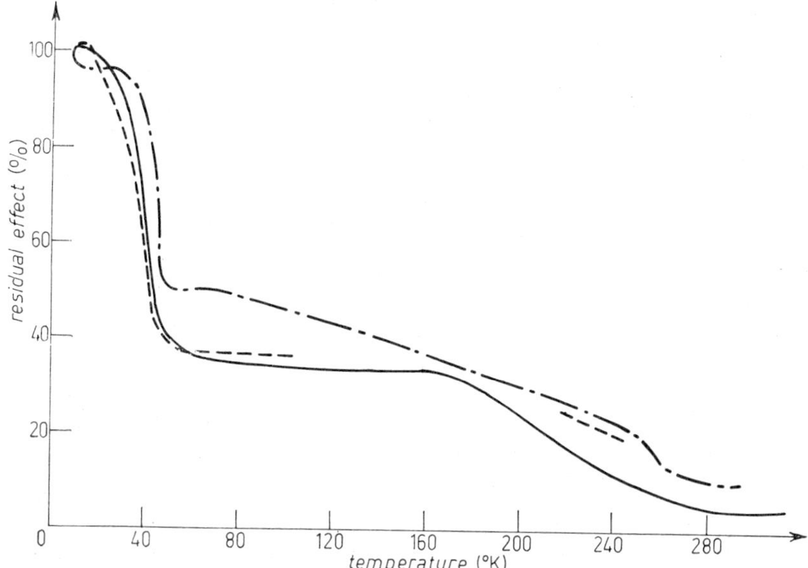

Fig. 45. – Comparison of low temperature recovery effects: resistivity, lattice parameter and length change. After VOOK and WERT. —— length, R. VOOK, Run II; – – – lattice parameter, R. O. SIMMONS and R. W. BALLUFFI; –·–·– resistivity: COOPER, KOEHLER and MARX.

stitial annihilation. This is approximately verified by these two experiments. A critical unanswered question does, however, lie in the fraction of defects which escape this type of annihilation. While the above results are of high precision, it does not seem valid to consider a more detailed analysis as the annealing treatments and the bombardments varied in the two measurements.

The ratio of the length change to the resistivity change determined from the initial slope of the length change-dose curve and the initial slope of the resistivity-dose curve is $1.5 \cdot 10^3\ \Omega\ \text{cm}^{-1}$ for the Vook-Wert measurements and $1.32 \cdot 10^3\ \Omega\ \text{cm}^{-1}$ for the Simmons-Balluffi measurements.

The reactor irradiations were made at Oak Ridge by BLEWITT, COLTMAN and KLABUNDE [33]. The measurements were made in aluminum and in copper. Both of these measurements were made utilizing a bimetallic strip. The bimetal consisted of a pure metal, either copper or aluminum, with the other half being the same pure metal with a small amount (0.1 atomic percent) of fissile material. During the bombardment, the neutrons present in hole 12 facility cause defects to be produced with the same density in both parts of the bimetal so that no bending is produced from these neutrons. On the other hand, the thermal neutrons produce fission and these energetic fragments as we have seen produce copious damage. The doped sample will thus expand at a greater rate than the pure sample, and the bimetal strip will bend in accordance with the laws of elementary physics. The deflection of the bimetal strip will only be a function of the fission damage. In the case of aluminum the fissile impurity was ^{235}U, and in the case of copper it was ^{10}B. The selection of these doping materials was determined by their solubility.

Consider now the results of the copper study. The bimetal strip was fabricated from pieces of .010 in. thick by .250 in. wide and 4 in. long. The two pieces were sweated together with soft solder. The top end of the strip was clamped and the bottom free to move with an iron core attached to this lower end. This core entered a coil and the deflection of the strip thus changed the magnetic induction of the coil. The deflection was then measured by the changes in magnetic induction. This method was selected as a relatively small deflection was expected, and there is no mechanical coupling between the strip and the detector. This assembly was then mounted in a can with a heater similar to that described previously in Section **2**, so that isochronal annealing studies could be made. Also included in the sample can was a strip of doped material cut adjacent to that used in the bimetal strip. Potential probes and current leads were attached to this so that resistivity measurements could be made simultaneously with the length change.

During the bombardment the can was was filled with helium and the change in resistivity and the change in length were measured as a function of dose. Three different runs were made. The results are shown in Fig. 46.

The specific change in length (strain) $(\Delta l/l)$ was found to be $6\cdot10^{-5}$ cm/cm corresponding to a change in resistivity of $5.2\cdot10^{-8}\ \Omega$ cm (*). These values were determined from the initial slope of dose curves. Since the length change is only that due to the fission fragments while that of the resistivity is due to fast neutrons as well as the fission fragments, the resistivity due to the fast neutron events, $4\cdot10^{-9}\ \Omega$ cm, must be subtracted from $5.2\cdot10^{-8}$. Thus, a ratio of $1.25\cdot10^{3}\ (\Omega\,\text{cm})^{-1}$ is found. This compares very well with the work of SIMMONS and BALLUFFI [31] but is somewhat smaller than the value of VOOK

(*) It should be noted that there is a slight concave curvature in the length-dose curve while a slight curvature in the opposite sense is observed in the resistivity measurements. This is not a real effect. The curvature in the length change is the result of glass wool which was placed in the can as a vibration dampening medium. It slightly deflected the bimetal strip and on bombardment lost its elasticity causing a small shift in the zero point. These effects decrease with bombardment, and by the time run 3 was made the dampening was negligible. On the other hand, the curvature in the resistivity is the result of inhomogeneity in the doping material which resulted from its heat treatment. This resulted in an early appearance of radiation annealing. These effects are of little consequence in the interpretation.

and WERT [32]. As in the case of the stored energy measurements, it is felt that the above ratio is more representative as resistivity measurements were made simultaneously with the length change measurements.

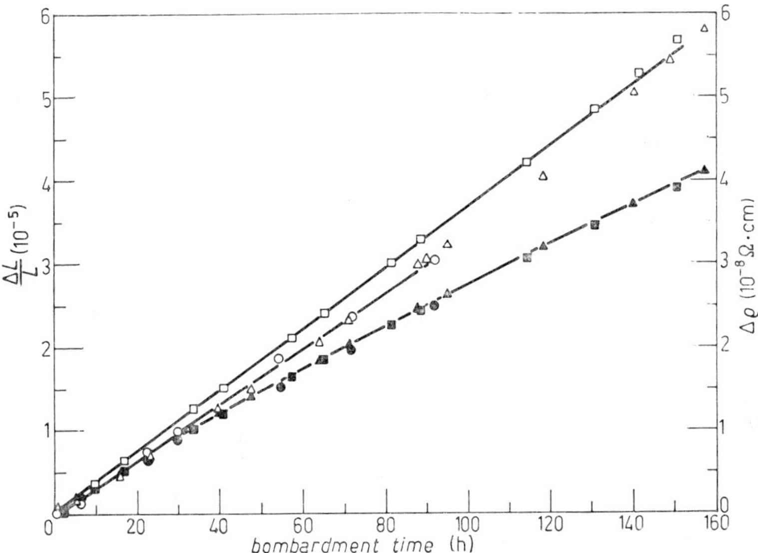

Fig. 46. – Change in length as a function of dose in 0.1% ¹⁰B-doped copper. After BLEWITT, COLTMAN and KLADUNDE. Run 1: △ $\Delta L/L$, ▲ $\Delta\varrho$; Run 2: □ $\Delta L/L$, ■ $\Delta\varrho$; Run 3: ○ $\Delta L/L$, ● $\Delta\varrho$.

Isochronal annealing studies were also made. The usual technique was followed. The fact that both the resistance and length samples received the same thermal cycle made these results particularly interesting. The results of the three runs are shown in Fig. 47. Three minute pulses were used throughout. These data are also plotted in Fig. 48. Here the resistivity is plotted as a function of the expansion. Plotting the data this way clearly shows the variation in the resistivity-length change ratio. A linear relationship between these two variables can only exist if the ratio of the length change to the resistivity is the same for a vacancy as it is for an interstitial, or if the number of vacancies is always equal to the number of interstitials (interstitial-vacancy annihilation). It can be seen in Fig. 48 that a linear relationship does not exist throughout the entire annealing spectrum. A linear relationship does appear in Stage I, however, in Stage II the ratio of resistivity recovery to length change recovery decreases. In Stage III the ratio reverses and returns to the original line found in Stage I. This is true for all three runs. The importance of this nonlinearity is apparent as it verifies the nonequality of the resistivity-length ratios of the vacancy and the interstitial. Further, the fact that these ratios decrease and then increase offers good evidence that a different defect is moving in Stage II

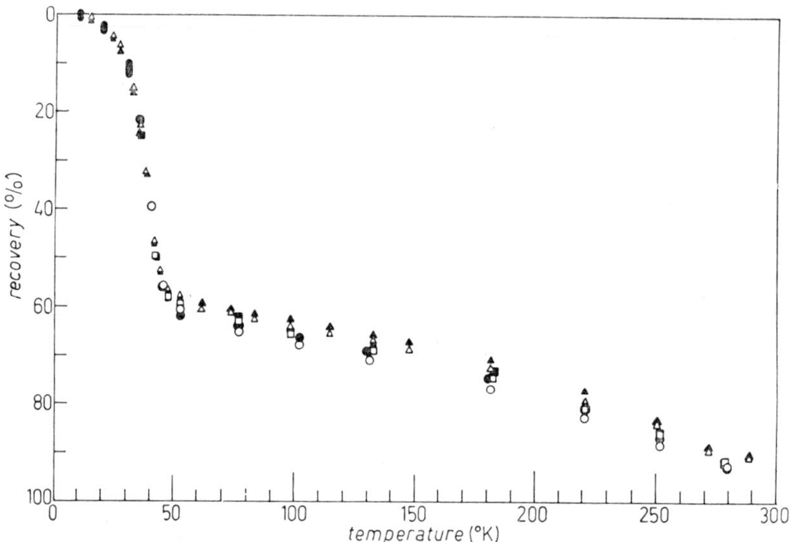

Fig. 47. – Isochronal annealing in 0.1% ^{10}B-doped copper. The recovery is plotted from length change and resistivity data. After BLEWITT, COLTMAN and KLABUNDE. Run 1: △ $\Delta L/L$, ▲ $\Delta\varrho$; Run 2: □ ΔL, ■ $\Delta\varrho$; Run 3: ○ ΔL, ● $\Delta\varrho$.

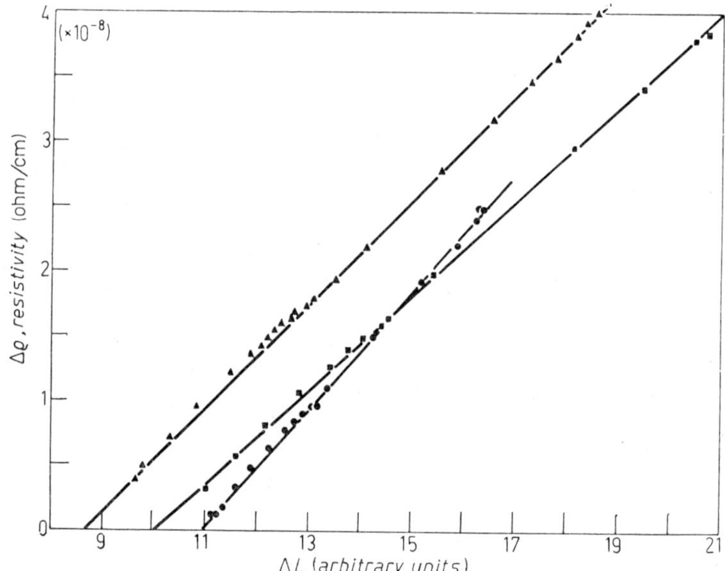

Fig. 48. – Recovery of resistivity and length change in neutron irradiated 0.1% ^{10}B-doped copper. Stage I (60% of the total recovery, 20 °K to 40 °K) is the linear portion of the curve; stage II (60% to 74% of the recovery) is the portion with the lowest slope; stage III (75% to 88% recovery) has the highest slope. ▲ Run 1, $4\cdot10^{17}$ nvt; ■ Run 2, $4\cdot10^{17}$ nvt; ● Run 3, $2\cdot10^{17}$ nvt.

than in Stage III. Thus, this important result, particularly, in regard to the viewpoint of SEEGER [34], implies that if interstitials are moving during Stage II (*) then vacancies must be moving in Stage III. During Stage II then there will be an excess of vacancies since some of the interstitials arrive at sinks other than vacancies. Since the value of $\Delta\varrho/\Delta V$ is greater in Stage II than it is in Stage I, it can thus be concluded that $\Delta\varrho/\Delta V)_v > \Delta\varrho/\Delta V)_i$.

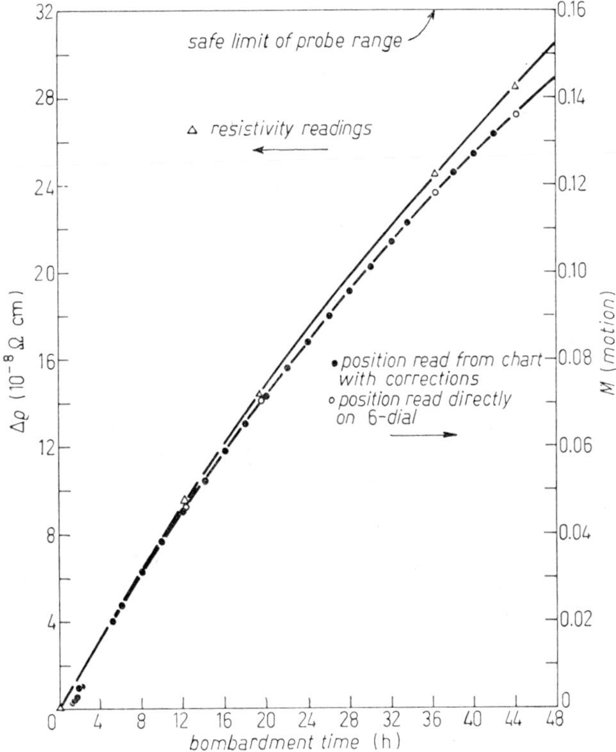

Fig. 49. – Changes in resistivity and of length of 0.1% ^{235}U-doped aluminum with bombardment at 4°K in the Oak Ridge hole 12 cryostat: $\Delta L/l = 2.4\cdot 10^{-3}\,M$.

Consider now the results in aluminum. The same general technique was used instead of the same amount of boron and the motion detector was changed from coil-core arrangement to a resistance slide wide, otherwise the method was unchanged. Since the damage rate is two orders of magnitude greater from the fissions of the ^{135}U than for the fast neutrons, only the fission damage need be considered. The results of this measurement are shown in Figs. 49, 50 and 51. In Fig. 49 the dose-length and dose-resistivity curves are shown.

(*) It is generally agreed that interstitials are more mobile than vacancies.

It is interesting to note that both of these curves are of an exponential form (radiation annealing) and can be normalized relative to each other. The ratio of length change to resistivity change is given by $1.23\cdot10^{3}$ $(\Omega\ \text{cm})^{-1}$. It should also be noted that the motion of the bimetal strip is quite large being of the order of 3.5 mm at the end of the one week bombardment. The corresponding strain is $3.5\cdot10^{-4}$.

The isochronal annealing curves are shown in Figs. 50 and 51. These were obtained in an identical way to that used in the copper experiment. It should be noted that in Fig. 50 the isochronal recovery curves for the uranium-

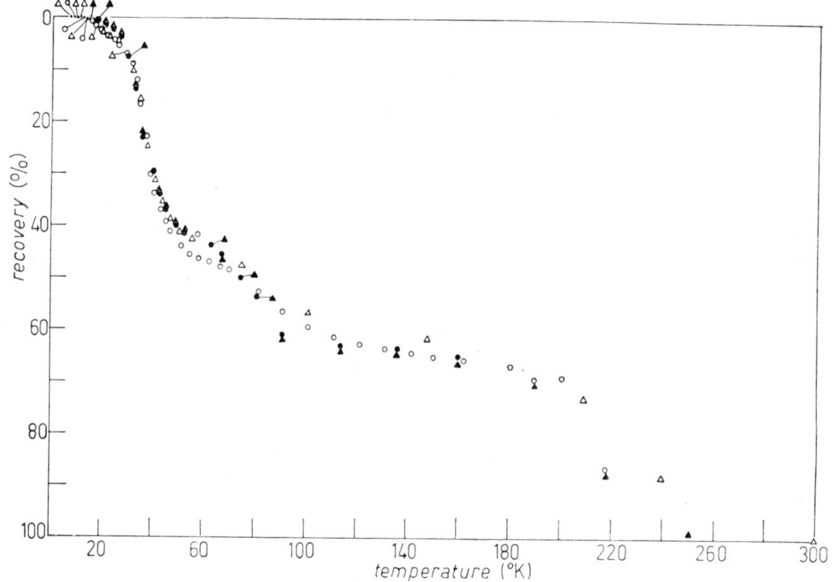

Fig. 50. – Isochronal annealing of pure aluminum, 0.1% ^{235}U-doped aluminum and 0.1% ^{11}B-doped aluminum. ● Δl, Al — 0.1% ^{235}U; ▲ ΔR, Al — 0.1% ^{235}U; ○ ΔR, Al; △ ΔR, Al — 0.1% ^{11}B.

doped sample are identical to those of pure aluminum. It is also interesting that the recovery of the length change shows a one to one correspondence to that of the resistivity. This is more dramatically shown in Fig. 51 where the resistivity is plotted as a function of the length change. It can readily be seen that unlike in copper a linear relationship exists throughout the annealing spectrum. If the unlikely condition that the ratio of the resistivity to length change is the same for a vacancy as for an interstitial is ignored, then it must be concluded that equal numbers of vacancies and interstitials (I-V pair annihilation) are present throughout the annealing spectrum.

On the other hand electron microscope studies also show that aluminum and copper behave differently from each other. In the case of copper neutron radiation introduces copious numbers of dislocations loops [35]; whereas, in the case of aluminum few if any loops are found [36]. It is tempting to attribute the non-linearity of the resistivity-length curve in the case of copper to

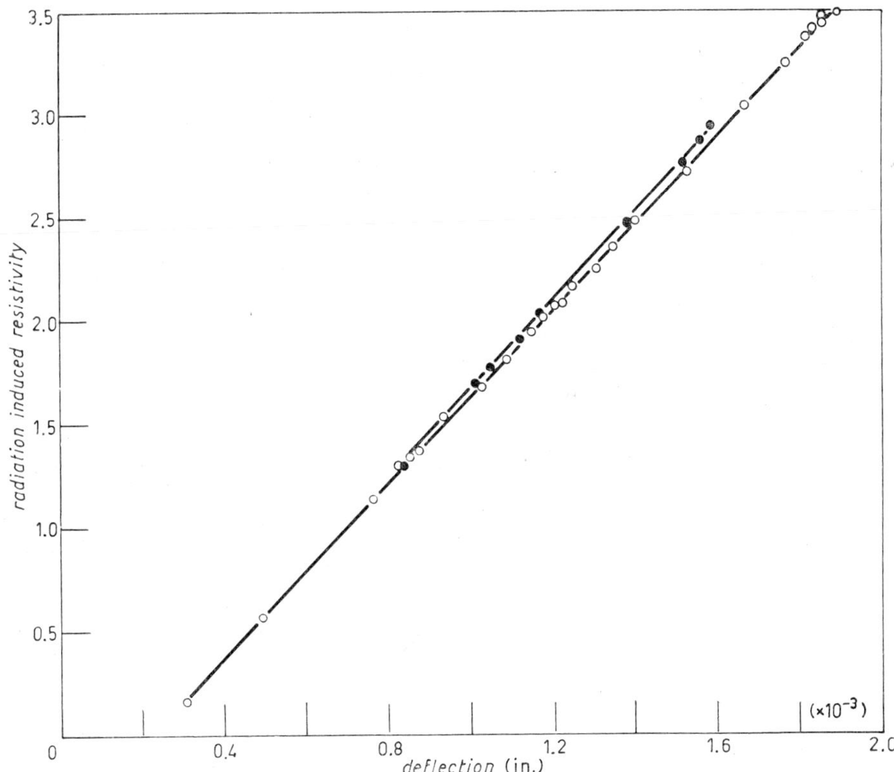

Fig. 51. – Isochronal recovery in 0.1% ^{235}U-doped aluminum. Length and resistivity changes were observed and these are plotted as a function of each other. Two runs are shown. The open circles are the data of Fig. 50.

the formation of the loops, especially since there is some evidence for them to be formed from coagulated interstitials [37]. Thus, it is possible that in the case of copper some fraction of the interstitials in Stage II coagulate and ultimately become loops. In this way interstitials could be moved to the surface without removing vacancies, explaining the non-linearity of the resistivity-length curve. In the case of aluminum, however, apparently interstitials will not agglomerate in large sizes and will not collapse into loops. Hence, interstitials would not be able to escape to the surface by the same method as in copper. Hence, no loops are observed, and a linear resistivity-length change curve results.

17. – Estimation of interstitial extension and formation energy.

The expansion data, the resistivity, and the stored energy data associated with recovery studies in radiation damage make it possible to estimate formation energies of interstitials if the corresponding values are known for vacancies. The resistivity is used primarily as a measure of the dose so that stored energy can be related to the expansion. Thus,

$$\varrho_{\text{I+V}} = \frac{\Delta\varrho_E}{n_{E/N_0}} = \frac{\Delta\varrho_L}{n_{L/N_0}}, \tag{17.1}$$

where $\varrho_{\text{I+V}}$ is the resistivity of an interstitial vacancy pair, $\Delta\varrho_E$ is the resistivity change measured in the energy determination; n_E is the number of interstitial-vacancy pairs associated with the energy change; $\Delta\varrho_L$ is the resistivity associated with the length change; n_L is the number of I-V pairs associated with the length change; and N_0 is the total number of atoms in the sample, since

$$\frac{n_E}{N_0} = \frac{\Delta E}{\alpha N_a}\cdot 2.6\cdot 10^{19} = \frac{\Delta E}{\alpha}\, 4.34\cdot 10^{-5}, \tag{17.2}$$

where ΔE is the energy release in cal/mol; α is the formation energy of an I-V pair in electronvolt and N_a is Avogadro's number, and

$$\frac{n_L}{N_0} = \frac{3(\Delta l/l)}{\beta}, \tag{17.3}$$

where β is the expansion per pair in atomic volumes, and $\Delta l/l$ is the measured strain. Combining (17.1), (17.2) and (17.3) gives

$$\frac{\Delta\varrho_E\cdot\alpha}{\Delta E\cdot 4.34\cdot 10^{-5}} = \frac{\Delta\varrho_L\cdot\beta}{3(\Delta l/l)}, \tag{17.4}$$

or

$$\beta = \left(\frac{\Delta l/l}{\Delta\varrho_L}\right)\left(\frac{l/\Delta E}{\Delta\varrho_E}\right)\left(\frac{3\cdot 10^5}{4.34}\right)\alpha, \tag{17.5}$$

which, using the experimental values obtained at Oak Ridge, gives

$$\beta = R_i + R_v = 0.338\alpha = 0.338(\alpha_i + \alpha_v). \tag{17.6}$$

Now, the formation energy of a vacancy in copper lies between 1.0 and 1.2 eV. For these considerations it will be taken as 1.1 eV. On the other hand, the value of R_i has never been measured for copper. It has been computed to lie between -0.5 volumes [38] and -0.6 volumes [39].

In the case of gold, there is good experimental evidence that .5 atomic volumes are associated with a vacancy [40]; and the expansion of quenched material yields a value of .53. It is thus reasonable to assume .5 for this calculation. Equation (17.6) thus becomes

$$(17.7)\qquad \begin{cases} \beta = R_i - 0.5 = 0.338(\alpha_i + 1.1) \\ \text{and} \\ R_i = 0.338\alpha_i + 0.872\,. \end{cases}$$

TEWORDT [38] has computed the formation energy of an interstitial as 2.6 eV and a relaxation term R_i which ranges from 1.5 to 1.8 atomic volumes per interstitial. Using Tewordt's formation energy the value of R_i turns out to be 1.7 which is, of course, in excellent agreement with his estimate of the dilatation associated with a pair.

An estimate of the resistivity of a pair can, of course, be made from (17.1) using either (17.2) or (17.3). Using then the value of 3.7 eV or 1.2 atomic volumes per pair ($R_i + R_v$), the resistivity per percent of I-V pair turns out to be 3.2 μΩ cm. This analysis can be carried one step further by utilizing the deduction that $\Delta\varrho/\Delta V)_v > \Delta\varrho/\Delta V)_i$ (see Section **16**) to estimate the lower limit and upper limit of the resistivity of vacancies and the upper limit of interstitials. Using then the value of 3.2 μΩ cm as the sum of the two and the volume change associated with each defect results in the deduction that 1.4 μΩ cm $< \Delta\varrho_v <$ 3.2 μΩ cm and that $\Delta\varrho_i <$ 1.8 μΩ cm. On consideration of the fact that $\Delta\varrho/\Delta V$ changes by about 5% in Stage II and that the excess of vacancies in this stage is of the order of a few percent it is quite likely that the resistivity of a vacant lattice site exceeds that of an interstitial. An educated guess would suggest a value of 2 μΩ cm for 1% of vacancies and 1.2 μΩ cm to 1% of interstitials.

18. – Radiation hardening.

The research described here has been centered about the study of the mechanical properties of copper single crystals with measurements of the stress-strain curve and the yield stress being made at temperatures ranging from room temperature to liquid-helium temperature. The observation of strain markings associated with radiation hardness and the annealing of radiation hardness has also been studied. For the most part these measurements have been made following a room temperature bombardment after sufficient time (about one week) for radioactive decay to occur so that the usual techniques followed for the study of the mechanical properties of unirradiated crystals could be used. These techniques have been previously described [41, 42]. In those cases where modifications were necessary, a description of the modification will be made.

Samples were bombarded in the Oak Ridge Graphite Reactor when moderate doses were desired ($6\cdot10^{18}$ nvt or less). This reactor with a thermal neutron flux of $1\cdot10^{12}$ neutron/cm^2 is air-cooled, graphite-moderated, and fueled with natural uranium. With the exception of a few samples bombarded near liquid hydrogen temperature, all samples were bombarded in a natural uranium cylinder located near the geometrical center of the reactor. The ambient temperature in this facility is about 30 °C. The spectrum of the neutron energies in this reactor is given by $N(E)\propto 1/E$, where $N(E)$ is the number of neutrons of energy E, but, of course, in the center of the uranium cylinder the spectum is greatly enhanced at the fission energy at the expense of the thermal neutrons. These thermal neutrons converted to fission energy increase the damage rate, measured by the changes of the electrical conductivity and the yield stress in copper, by a factor of 4 to 5 relative to the normal $1/E$ spectrum. In the case of bombardment in hole 12, the flux has been accurately measured, and the distribution of the flux can be determined from these measurements. The doses for samples bombarded in the graphite reactor will be specified in this paper by the thermal neutron dose.

Heavy neutron doses were obtained by bombardment in the Oak Ridge Low Intensity Test Reactor. This reactor, an MTR type with a thermal neutron flux of $2\cdot10^{13}$ neutrons/cm^2, is water-cooled, water-moderated, and fueled with enriched uranium. The samples were bombarded in a specially prepared fuel element (MTR type) with the central 9 plates removed to provide a rectangular opening approximately 1 in. $\times$ 4 in. Since there was only about $\frac{1}{8}$ in. water between the nearest enriched fuel plate and the sample, the neutron spectrum was probably somewhat similar to that in the uranium cylinder of the graphite reactor. The flux of the fuel element facility in the LITR was calibrated in relation to the flux in the uranium cylinder of the graphite reactor by determining the change in yield stress of copper single crystals. Thus, the thermal neutron dose ascribed to samples bombarded in the LITR reactor is that which would produce an equivalent amount of radiation hardness in a copper crystal bombarded inside a uranium cylinder with a $1/E$ neutron spectrum.

19. – Stress strain curves.

The room temperature stress-strain curves of a series of copper single crystals bombarded in the Oak Ridge Graphite Reactor are shown in Fig. 51.

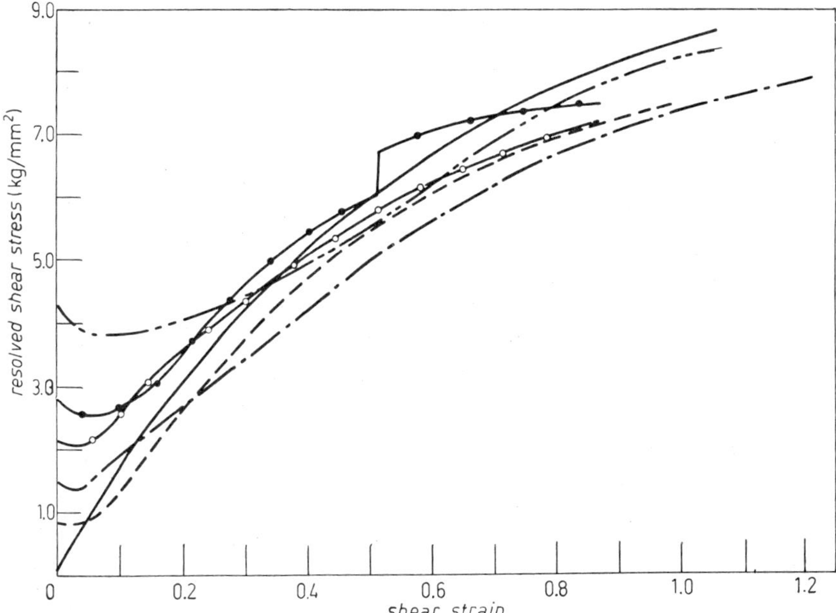

Fig. 52. – The stress-strain curves of copper crystals after various neutron doses. The crystals had not the same orientation. —— no irradiation; – – – $1.4 \cdot 10^{17}$ nvt; –·–·– $6 \cdot 10^{17}$ nvt; –o–o– $1.1 \cdot 10^{18}$ nvt; –●–●– $5 \cdot 10^{18}$ nvt; –··–·· $2 \cdot 10^{19}$ nvt.

These results were obtained before it was realized that the stress-strain curve had an orientation dependence, and since each sample of Fig. 52 [43] had a different orientation, quantitative results cannot be deduced from these curves. They do, however, illustrate quite well in a qualitative way the four signif-

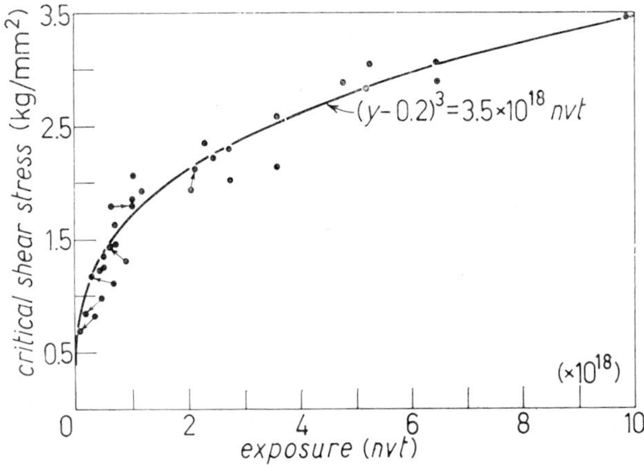

Fig. 53. – The effect of neutron dose on the room-temperature yield stress of copper single crystals. The solid curve satisfies the equation $(y - 0.2)^3 = 3.5 \cdot 10^{18}$ n/cm².

icant changes induced by neutron irradiation. First, it is noted that the yield stress increases with the neutron dose. These effects are quite considerable; for example, the yield stress for $2\cdot10^{19}$ neutron/cm² being increased by a factor of 22. Second, it is noted that some evidence for an upper yield point is apparent in that the flow stress falls following the yield stress. Third, there is a region of slight work hardening near the origin suggestive of a Lüders band. Fourth, following the region of slight work-hardening (deformation by a Lüders band), the sample appears to work-harden in the normal fashion of the unirradiated crystal. The results of experiments designed to examine each of these points in detail will now be discussed.

20. – The yield stress.

The yield stress has been measured as a function of temperature and of dose [44]. In Fig. 53 the variation of yield stress is shown as a function of the neutron dose up to 10^{19} nvt. The samples were bombarded in the graphite reactor and in the LITR reactor at essentially room temperature, and the yield stress was also measured at room temperature (300 °K). It can be seen that the increase in the yield stress fits a curve given by

$$(20.1)\qquad (\sigma - 0.2) = \sigma' = 1.48\cdot10^{-6}\varphi^{\frac{1}{3}}\,,$$

where $(\sigma - 0.2) = \sigma'$ is the increase in yield stress in kg/mm², and φ is the neutron dose [45] in neutrons/cm². In Fig. 54 the logarithm of the yield stress is plotted against the logarithm of the flux. The fact that a straight line of slope $\frac{1}{3}$ can be drawn through the data clearly shows that σ' are proportional to the cube root of the flux from $5\cdot10^{16}$ nvt through $1\cdot10^{20}$ nvt (*).

The yield stress has also been determined as a function of temperature following bombardment at reactor ambient temperatures [46, 47]. This property shows a strong dependence on the temperature, increasing significantly as the temperature decreases. These data are plotted in Fig. 54 along with the room temperature data. The yield stress at 78 °K is given by

$$(2.0)2\qquad (\sigma - 0.2) = \sigma' = 2.80\cdot10^{-6}\varphi^{\frac{1}{3}}$$

and at 4.2 °K by

$$(20.3)\qquad (\sigma - 0.2) = \sigma' = 3.80\cdot10^{-6}\varphi^{\frac{1}{3}}\,.$$

(*) It should be noted that these are essentially fission spectrum neutrons. In so far as the hardness is concerned, these neutrons have five times the effect of pile neutrons, *i.e.*, neutrons of a $1/E$ spectrum.

While the yield stress varies as the cube root of the flux over the entire range of flux investigated for data obtained at both 300 °K and at 78 °K, it is clear that some form of saturation in the yield stress is observed when measured at 4.2 °K following heavy neutron doses. The yield stress is observed to be

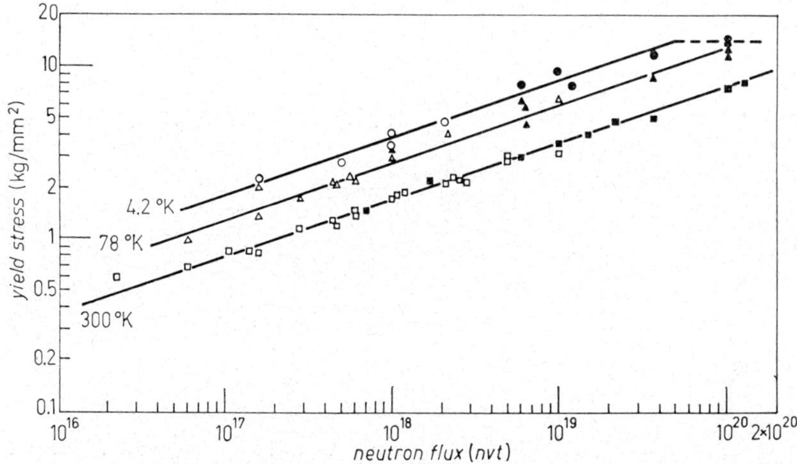

Fig. 54. – Effect of neutron irradiation on the yield stress of copper at various temperatures. The log of the yield stress is plotted as a function of the log of the dose. A straight line of slope $\frac{1}{3}$ is drawn through each set of points. Open symbols: bombarded in graphite reactor; closed symbols: bombarded in LITR.

of the order of 14 kg/mm². It is believed that this shear stress is the limiting value which can be introduced owing to a change in the mechanism of deformation.

The details of the temperature-dependence of the critical shear stress are shown in Figs. 55, 56, 57. In Fig. 55 the critical shear stress is plotted as a function of temperature for samples bombarded at fluxes from $5\cdot10^{17}$ to $1\cdot20^{20}$. In Fig. 56 the critical shear stress is plotted as a function of $T^{\frac{1}{2}}$. A straight line can be drawn through the data as long as the temperature is greater than 40 °K, indicating that the relationship between temperature and shear stress will fit a formula of this type

$$(\sigma_0 - \sigma) = B - AT^{\frac{1}{2}} \qquad \text{when } T \geqslant 40\,^\circ\text{K}. \tag{20.4}$$

The details of the temperature-dependence in the low-temperature region are shown in Fig. 57. These data were obtained on a sample bombarded for one month in the graphite reactor ($2\cdot10^{18}$ neutrons/cm²) and deformed to the yield point at each indicated temperature.

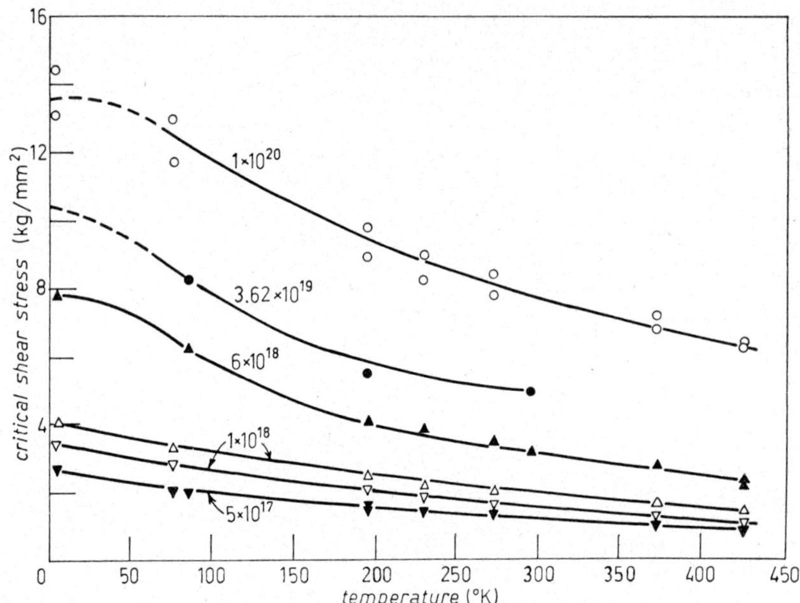

Fig. 55. – The temperature-dependence of the yield stress of reactor-irradiated copper single crystals at various neutron doses. The yield stress is plotted as a function of temperature.

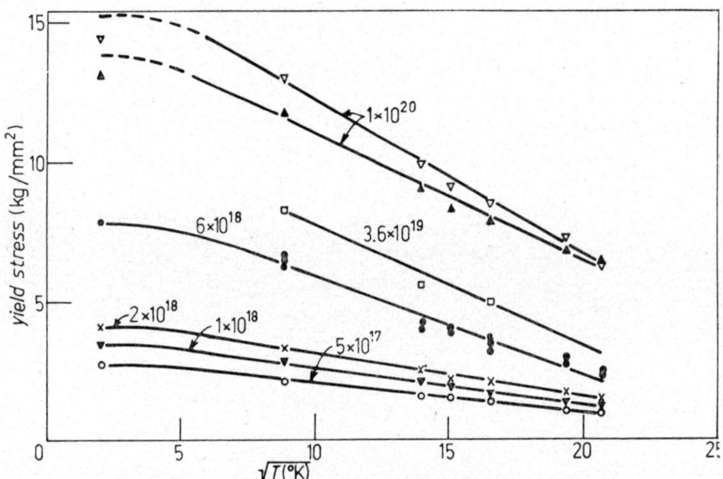

Fig. 56. – The temperature-dependence of the yield stress of reactor-irradiated copper single crystals at various neutron doses. The yield stress is plotted as a function of $T^{\frac{1}{2}}$ The curvature at $T < 40$ °K is deduced from Fig. 6. For $T > 78$ °K, a linear relationship can be noted between yield stress and $T^{\frac{1}{2}}$.

It is worth emphasizing that the above data, particularly those illustrated in Fig. 57, conclusively show that the critical shear stress can be written as

$$\sigma = g(\varphi)\, f(T)\,, \tag{20.5}$$

where g is independent of (T) and f is independent of (φ).

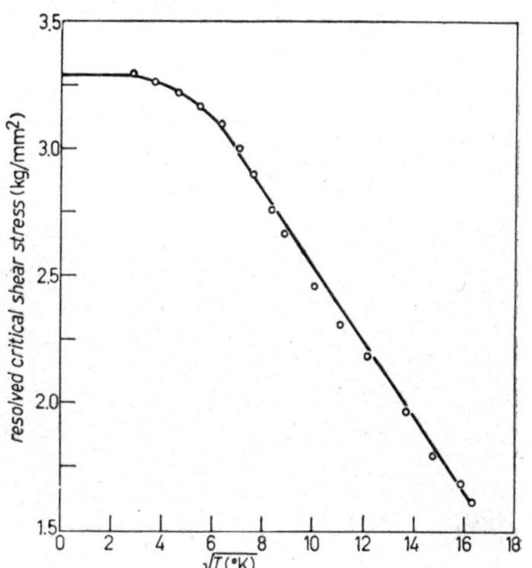

Fig. 57. – The temperature-dependence of a reactor-irradiated copper crystal. The dose was $1 \cdot 10^{18}$ n/cm². The yield stress is plotted as a function of $T^{\frac{1}{2}}$.

21. – The upper yield point and the Lüders band formation.

A yield point followed by a region of small work-hardening has been observed on all samples regardless of the temperature of deformation. This yield point and region of small work-hardening is intimately connected with the fact that the plastic flow is inhomogeneous. This is rather dramatically illustrated in Fig. 58 where the localized deformation can be macroscopically seen. Slip commences at one end of the crystal, and as the deformation continues the deformation front advances toward the other end of the crystal. This mode of deformation, called a Lüders band, has been studied in irradiated crystals utilizing the density of slip lines. An experiment was performed whereby the slip lines were removed by electropolishing so that the progress of the deformation front could be followed. Fig. 59 schematically shows the results of this study. It can be seen from this figure that the greatest density of slip lines lies at the front of the Lüders band. No slip lines were observed in advance of the Lüders band, but slip continues behind the advancing front, although of diminished intensity. A photomicrograph illustrating this can be seen in Fig. 60.

The fact that the load decreases following the yield stress can probably be explained by the local stress magnification introduced at the advancing front of the Lüders band. The upper yield stress can thus be directly attributed to the inhomogeneous nature of the Lüders band. Nothing can be deduced about the nature of the work-hardening in the Lüders band. This is

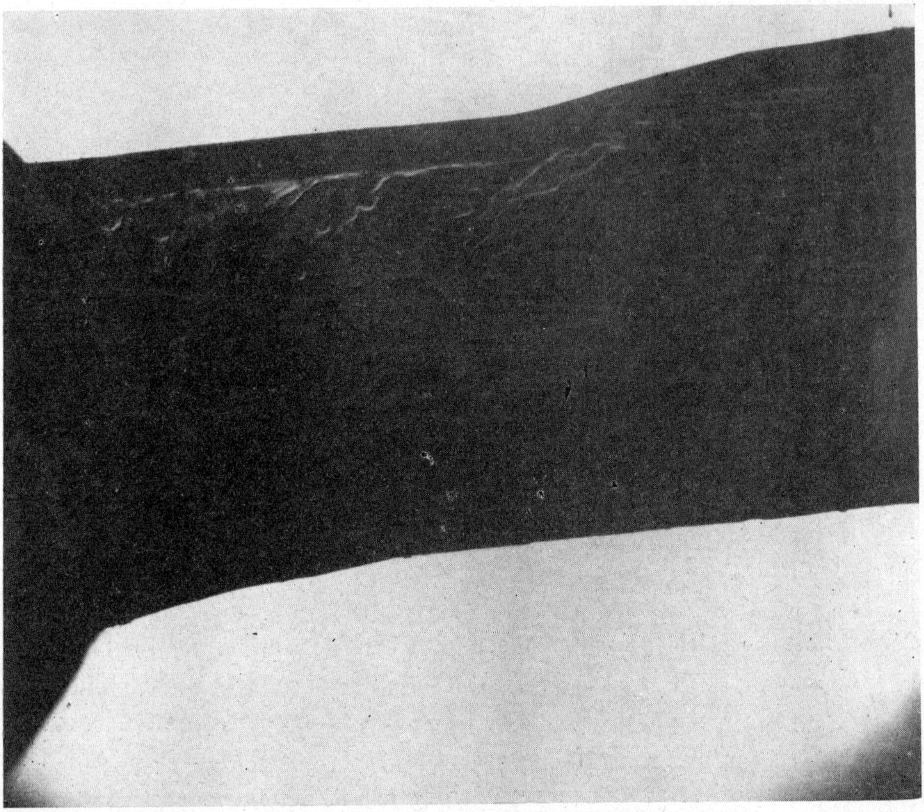

Fig. 58. – The silhouette of a heavily irradiated copper crystal after a small deformation. The deformation can be seen to be localized by the offset in the edge of the crystal. Magnification 20×.

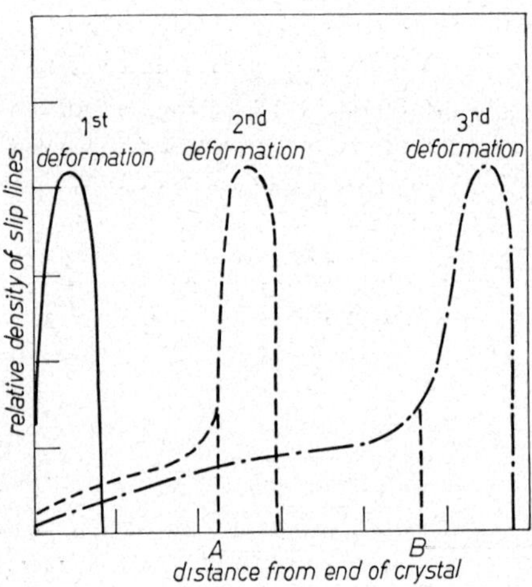

Fig. 59. – Schematic diagram illustrating the method of Lüders-band formation. The density of slip lines is plotted as a function of strain. After the first deformation, the sample was deformed until the Lüder band had propagated to point *A*. After all strain markings were polished from the surface and the second deformation was made, the slip lines associated with the deformation were studied. As the schematic diagram shows, no slip lines were observed in the region in advance of the Lüders band, but a small number of lines were observed in the region through which the band had passed.

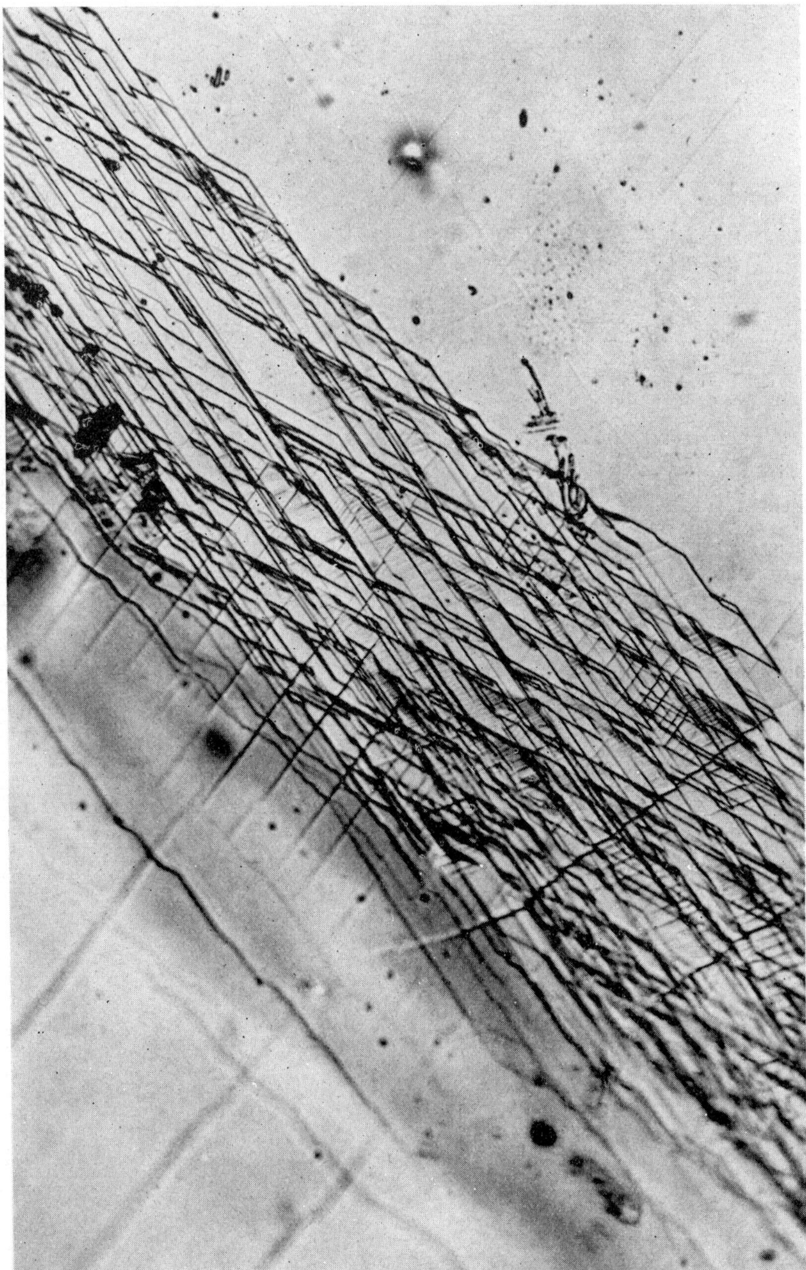

Fig. 60. – The Lüders band in a heavily irradiated copper crystal. The orientation of this crystal lay on the dodecahedral plane so that simultaneous slip occurred on two systems. The copious amounts of cross-slip apparently are the result of the interaction of the slip systems. This sample had been previously deformed, and the slip lines removed by electropolishing. The sharp delineation of the Lüders band can be observed. Magnification 200×.

of course, a result of the fact that the hardening occurs on a microscale, whereas the load-elongation curve is determined on a macroscale. All that can be deduced is the shear stress necessary to activate the Lüders band and to keep it propagating. There is, of course, some work-hardening as there is a reduction of area and a rotation of the crystal which will increase the stress despite the fact that the load remains nearly constant during the Lüders band propagation (aside from the upper yield stress effect). Thus, at the point where the crystal is filled with the Lüders band and homogeneous strain occurs, a representative yield stress can again be computed; however, between these two points nothing can be deduced about the stress-strain curve. In the stress-strain curves of Figs. 61, 62, and 63, the stress was computed without taking into consideration a change in area and thus depicts the stress necessary to propagate the Lüders band. The discontinuity at the end of the Lüders band arises from the change in area. This discontinuity does not necessarily represent the amount of work-hardening occurring in the Lüders band and, in point of fact, probably arises from a slip process more nearly similar to that in homogeneous flow due to the reduction in area increasing the stress. Undoubtedly, these in combination with the constra'nts at the grips account for the slip lines occurring behind the front of the Lüders band.

It is worth commenting on the obviously high step height of the slip lines in the Lüders band. The slip lines are clearly visible with the naked eye. A photomicrograph of the front end of the Lüders band is shown in Figs. 60 and 64. It is readily observed that these lines are much coarser than

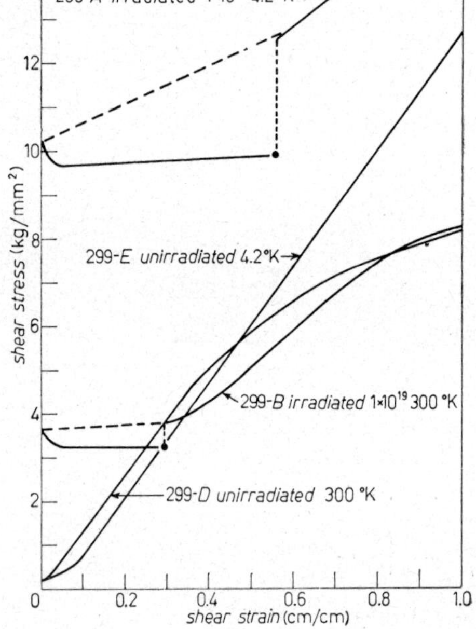

Fig. 61. – The shear stress-shear strain of copper crystals obtained at 4.2°K and at 300 °K for unirradiated crystals and crystals bombarded for $1 \cdot 10^{19}$ n/cm². The solid line associated with the region of slight work-hardening was determined from the load-elongation curve and the original orientation. This method of computation which differs from that normally used was based on the observation of the Lüders band propagation. The discontinuity at the end of the Lüders band arises as a result of the work-hardening which occurs during the Lüders band deformation, and the upper stress at this point is determined by assuming a homogeneous rotation of the crystal. The height of the discontinuity represents the minimum work-hardening which occurs in the Lüders band.

those in unirradiated copper and superficially, at least, are similar to those observed in α-brass. In addition, copious amounts of cross slip are observed [46]. This is readily observed in Fig. 60. Cross-slip is slip which is in the same slip

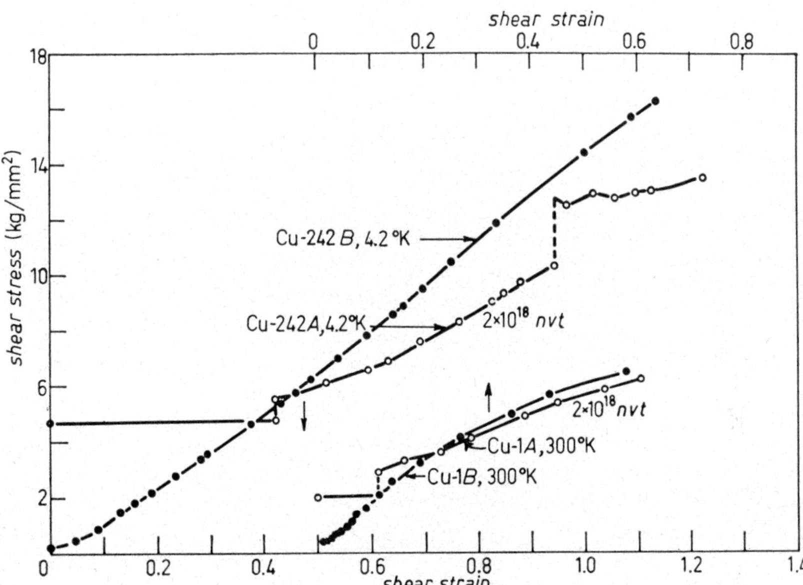

Fig. 62. – Shear stress-shear strain curves of two pairs of copper crystals of same orientation. One pair was deformed at 78 °K and the other at 300 °K. One sample of each pair was irradiated to $2\cdot10^{18}$ n/cm² and the other unirradiated. The solid line associated with the region of slight work-hardening was determined from the load-elongation curve and the original orientation. This method of computation which differs from that normally used was based on the observation of the Lüders-band propagation. The discontinuity at the end of the Lüders-band arises as a result of the work-hardening which occurs during the Lüders-band deformations, and the upper stress at this point is determined by assuming a homogeneous rotation of the crystal. The height of the discontinuity represents the minimum work-hardening which occurs in the Lüders band. The second discontinuity in sample 242-A arises from the onset of duplex slip. ○ irradiated, • unirradiated.

direction as primary slip but in a different slip plane. If, for example, one labels the primary slip plane as the (111) plane, then the cross-slip plane is the $(1\bar{1}\bar{1})$ plane. It has been verified that the strain markings do indeed occur on the primary system and on the cross-slip system from geometrical considerations utilizing the method outlined by BARRETT. Cross slip has never been found in pure annealed copper deformed at helium temperatures and at higher temperatures only after extensive strain in the nonlinear portion of the stress strain curve. On the other hand, copious amounts of cross-slip have been observed in the Lüders band of α-brass. It might also be noted that the cross-slip may be associated with slip on the latent system. It has been noted that relatively small amounts of cross-slip are observed in samples whose tensile

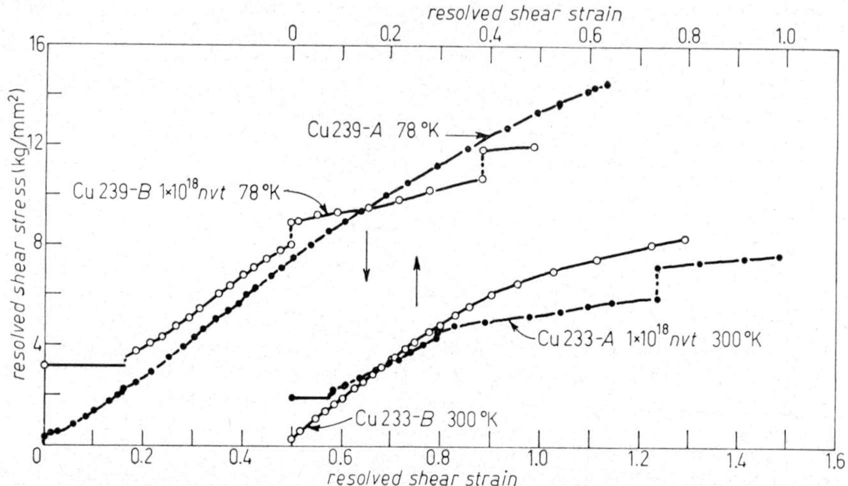

Fig. 63. – Shear stress-shear strain curves of two pairs of copper crystals of same orientation. One pair was deformed at 78 °K and the other at 300 °K. One sample of each pair was irradiated to $1 \cdot 10^{18}$ n/cm² and the other unirradiated. The solid line associated with the region of slight work-hardening was determined from the load-elongation curve and the original orientation. This method of computation which differs from that normally used was based on the observation of the Lüders-band propagation. The discontinuity at the end of the Lüders band arises as a result of the work-hardening which occurs during the Lüders band deformation, and the upper stress at this point is determined by assuming a homogeneous rotation of the crystal. The height of the discontinuity represents the minimum work-hardening which occurs in the Lüders band. The discontinuity in the irradiated samples beyond the first is the result of duplex slip.

axis is near the center of the stereographic net, whereas those samples whose tensile axis is on the dodecahedral plane have extremely large amounts of cross-slip.

The large step height of slip lines observed in the optical microscope has been verified by examination at magnifications up to 10 000 × on the electron microscope (*). Fig. 65 shows a photomicrogaph obtained on the electron microscope. The sample and field of view are the same as those of Fig. 60

(*) The photomicrographs of Figs. 65 and 66 were the work of T. S. Noggle and J. O. Stiegler.

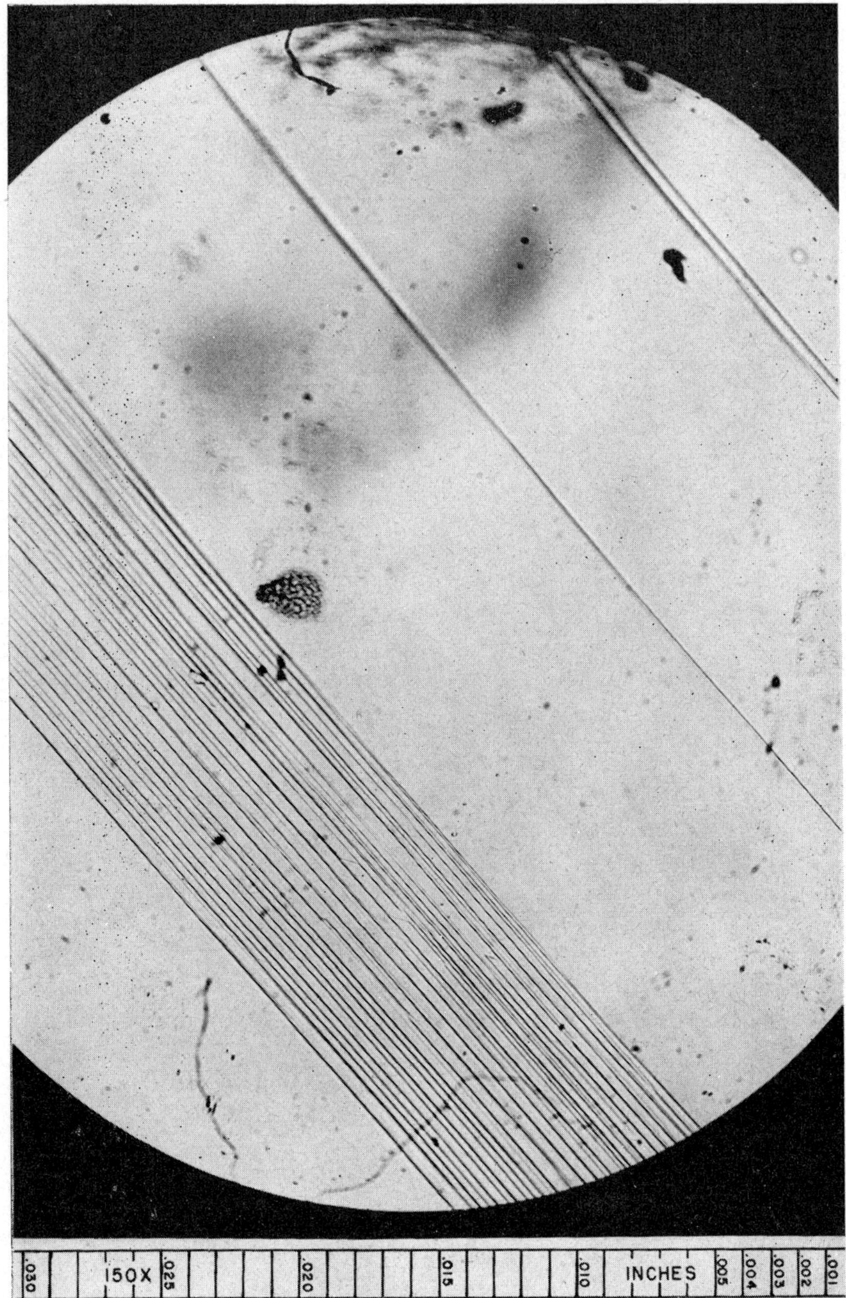

Fig. 64. – A Lüders band in irradiated copper. The tensile axis of the crystal is near the center of the stereographic triangle. Small amounts of cross-slip can be seen. The dose was $1 \cdot 10^{18}$ n/cm^2.

Fig. 65. – Micrographs of the slip lines in the Lüders band of an irradiated copper crystal shown in Fig. 60 obtained with an electron microscope. Magnification 6 000×. Obtained through the co-operation of T. S. NOGGLE.

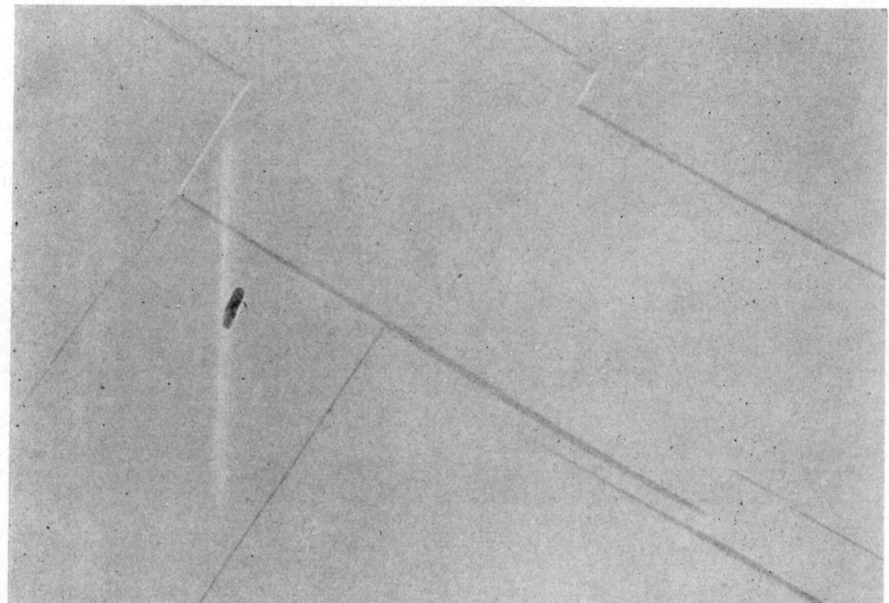

Fig. 66. – Micrographs of slip lines in an irradiated copper crystal. Bombardment dose $1 \cdot 10^{18}$ n/cm^2. Tensile axis near the center of the net. Field of view has an unusually large density of cross-slip.

which were obtained with the light microscope. It is clear that these lines are considerably different from those of unirradiated copper and that they bear a resemblance to slip lines in α-brass. The step height seems to be about 1 μm. Fig. 66 is a photomicrograph of a slip line in a sample whose tensile axis is near the center of the net. In this sample cross-slip can be seen infrequently.

22. – Stress-strain curve following the Lüders band.

In the previous sections we have seen that irradiation dramatically changes the yield stress and associated phenomena. Following the completion of deformation by the Lüders band the effects of neutron irradiation are less pronounced. Fig. 67 shows that the transition from the Lüders band to a more

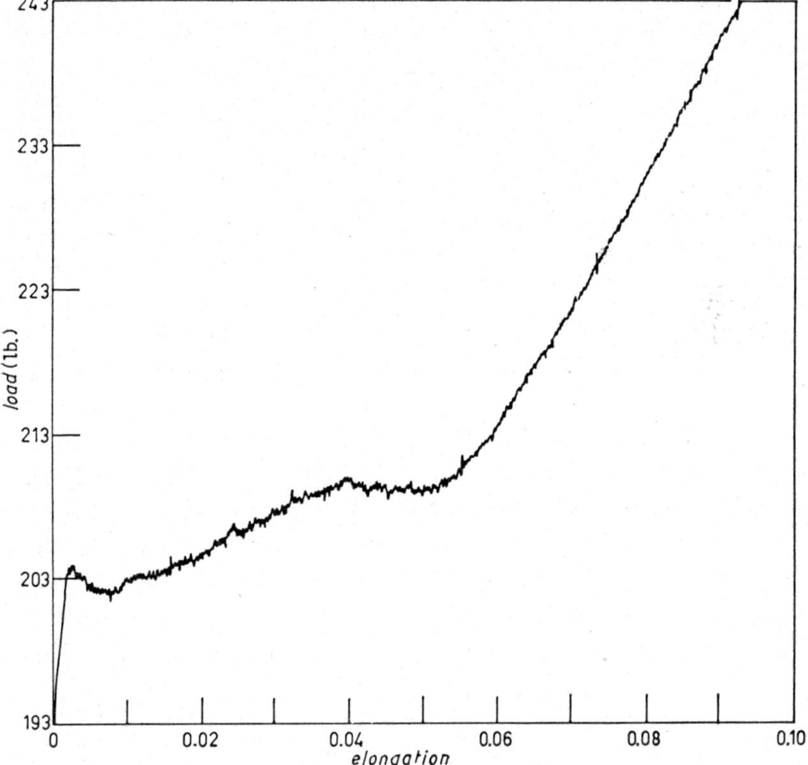

Fig. 67. – Load-elongation curve of a copper crystal deformed at room temperature following the exposure to $2.5 \cdot 10^{18}$ n/cm^2. The sharp transition from Lüders band deformation to homogeneous deformation is typical and readily observable.

normal rate of work-hardening seems to be a sharp one. The rate of work-hardening after this transition point does not seem to be greatly affected by neutron bombardment at least for moderate doses [47]. This can be seen from Figs. 62, 63, and 68. For high doses the rate of work-hardening seems to be somewhat smaller, as illustrated by Fig. 61. It would thus seem that the neutron irradiation does not greatly affect the mechanism of work-hardening.

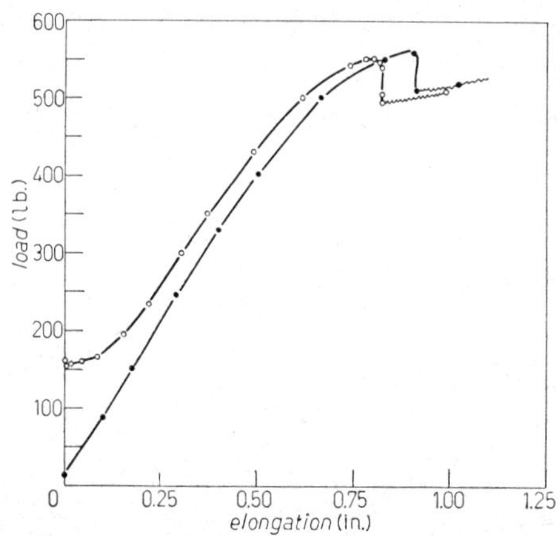

Fig. 68. – Load-elongation curve of copper crystals of identical orientation obtained at 78 °K. One crystal was irradiated for a dose of $1 \cdot 10^{18}$ nvt, and the other was retained in its initial condition. ● Cu 419 *C*, nonirradiated, initial gage length 3.835 cm, initial area 11.55 mm²; ○ Cu 419 *B*, irradiated $1 \cdot 10^{18}$ nvt, initial gage length 3.845 cm, initial area 12.568 mm². Tested in liquid N_2.

Neutron irradiation does, however, strongly affect the stress-strain curve at the point where slip commences on the second slip system. In the case of the tensile deformation of face centered cubic metals, deformation proceeds on the (111) plane in a [110] direction.

Since there are four such planes, each of which has three [110] directions, slip will proceed only on that system which has the highest resolved shear stress. This system is called the primary slip system. As deformation proceeds, however, the constraints of the grips cause the tensile axis to rotate relative to the crystallographic axis. This effect eventually will cause the tensile axis to lie in the dodecahedral plane (the great circle in the stereographic net connecting poles of the (100) and (111) planes). At this point the resolved stress on a second slip system, called the latent system, becomes equal to the primary system. In the case of high-purity crystals slip then occurs simultaneously on both slip systems and the tensile axis of the crystals remains on the dodecahedral plane. This new mode of deformation, duplex slip, does not affect the rate of work-hardening and in point of fact cannot be detected in the load-elongation or stress-strain curves. In the case of alloy crystals, however, the onset of duplex slip occurs in a different manner [48]. For reasons which are not understood, the latent system does not become active when the resolved shear stress is equal to that on the primary system but, rather, slip continues on the first system. The tensile axis thus continues to rotate and crosses over the dodecahedral plane (the phenomenon is generally referred to as overshoot). The latent plane then has a higher resolved shear stress than the primary plane. The extent of this overshoot and, thus, the degree to which the latent plane has hardened increases with the content of the alloying elements. In contrast to the case for high-purity metals, a change in slope is observed in the load-elongation curve upon the onset of duplex slip. This is a direct consequence of the fact that the latent plane is harder than the active plane. In the stress-strain curve there will, of course, be a discontinuity in stress at the strain where duplex slip occurs.

The stress-strain curves of neutron-irradiated crystals clearly show a discontinuity which arises at the point where the latent slip system is operative [49]. From this standpoint the effect of neutron irradiation behaves in the same manner as the addition of an alloying element [50]. The investigation of this point was done in some detail. The load-elongation curve of sample 88 is shown in Fig. 69. The strain markings were examined at various points of the load-elongation curve. Photomicrographs were taken at points 6, 8, 9, 10 and 11 of Fig. 69. Following examination of the strain markings, the samples were electrolytically polished to remove strain markings at points 7 and 8. Up to point 8 only one set of lines, the primary set, could be observed despite the fact that at point 6 the shear stress in the latent slip system exceeded that of the primary system. The strain markings at points 8, 9, 10 and 11 are shown in Figs. 70, 71, 72 and 73, respectively. The photomicrograph taken at point 8 shows the high density of slip lines from the primary system plus a few slip lines from the latent system. As has been noted earlier, the sample was polished at this point to remove all slip lines. As slip progresses beyond this point and in coincidence with the change in slope, Figs. 71, 72 and 73 show that the strain marking are predominatingly in the latent slip system. It is worth noting that the photomicrographs show the clustering of slip bands characteristics of Lüders band formations upon the onset of slip on the latent system. A Lüders band has been observed on several samples with the onset of duplex slip. These photomicrographs thus demonstrate that the discontinuity in the load-elongation curve is associated with slip commencing on the latent system. The discontinuity associated with slip changing back to the

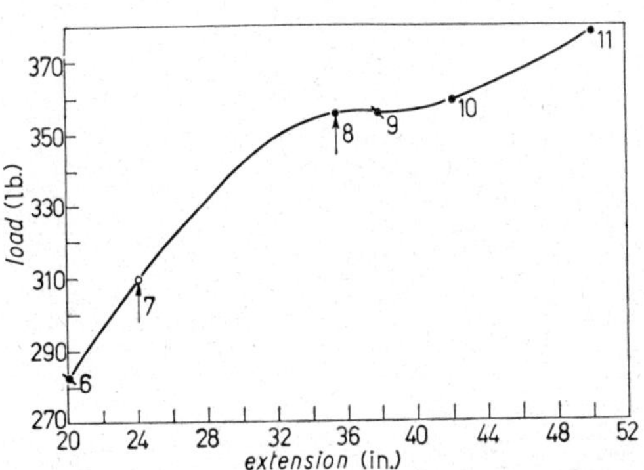

Fig. 69. – The load-elongation curve of copper crystal no. 88 irradiated for $1 \cdot 10^{18}$ n/cm^2 and deformed at room temperature. At all numbered points the sample was metallographically examined, at points 6, 8, 9, 10 and 11 photomicrographs were obtained, at points 7 and 8 the sample was electrolytically polished to remove all slip lines following examination, and at points 6 and 9 Laue back reflection X-ray photograms were obtained.

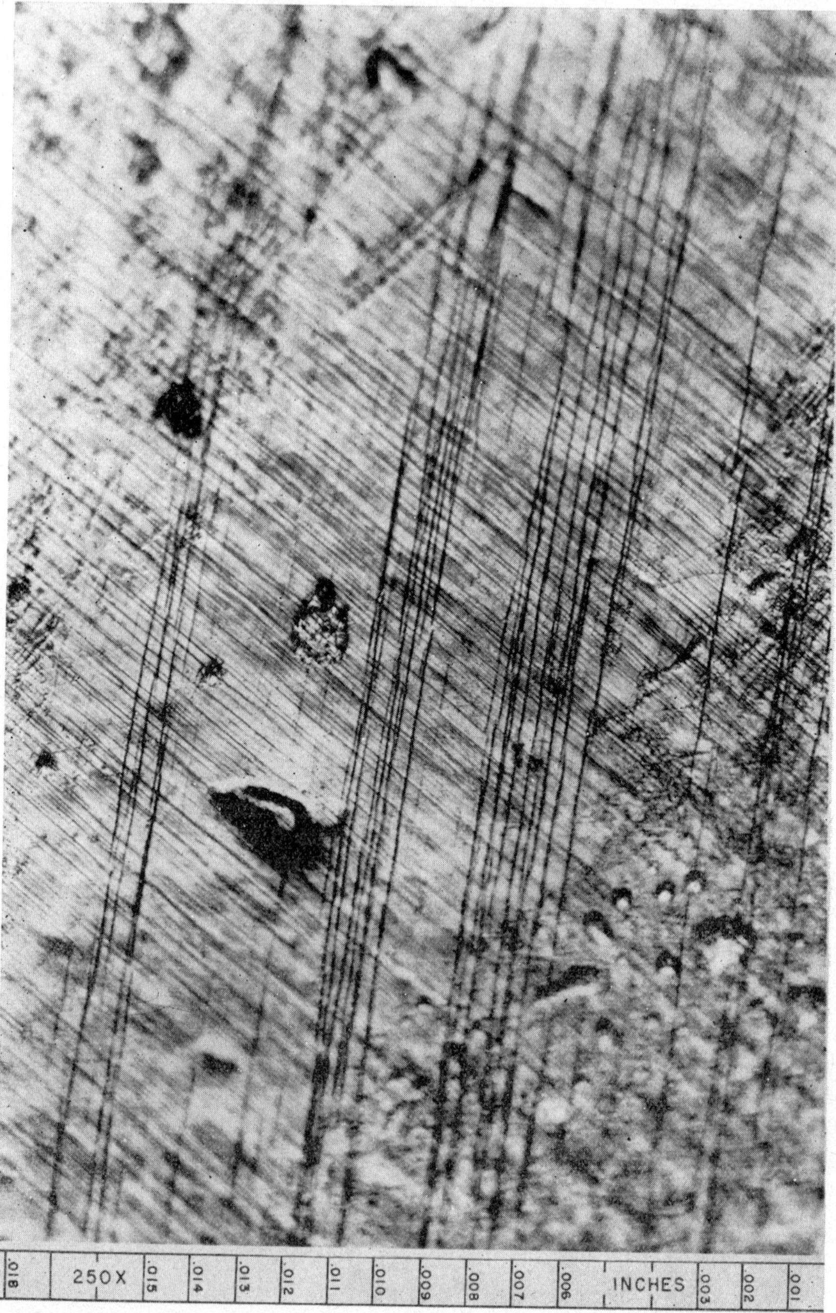

Fig. 70. – Photomicrograph taken at point 8 of Fig. 69. Bands of clustered slip lines of large step height from the latent system can be seen superimposed on the background of slip lines from the primary system. Magnification 250×.

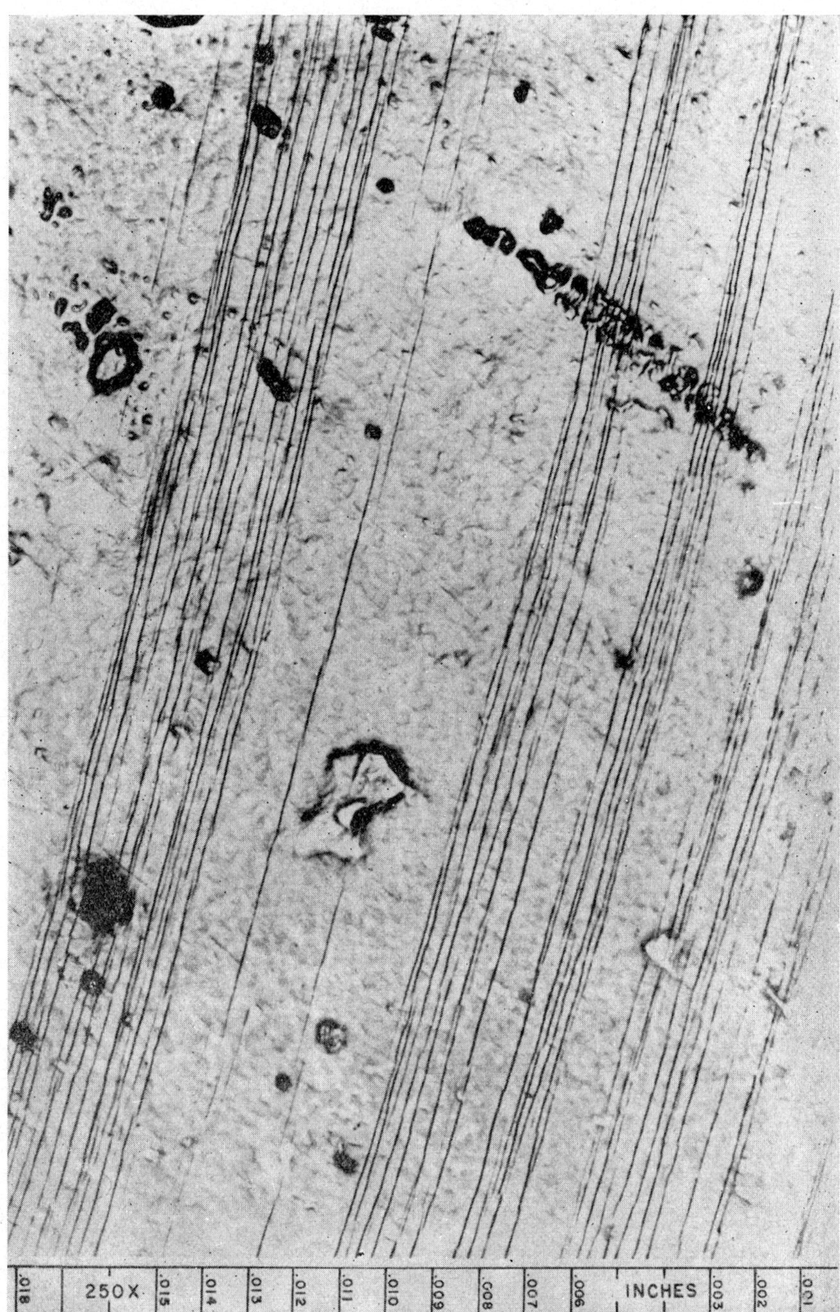

Fig. 71. – Photomicrograph taken at point 9 of Fig. 69. The slip lines seen in Fig. 70 taken at point 8 have been removed by electrolytic polishing. Slip lines from the latent system predominate almost to the point of exclusion of slip lines from the primary system. Magnification 250×.

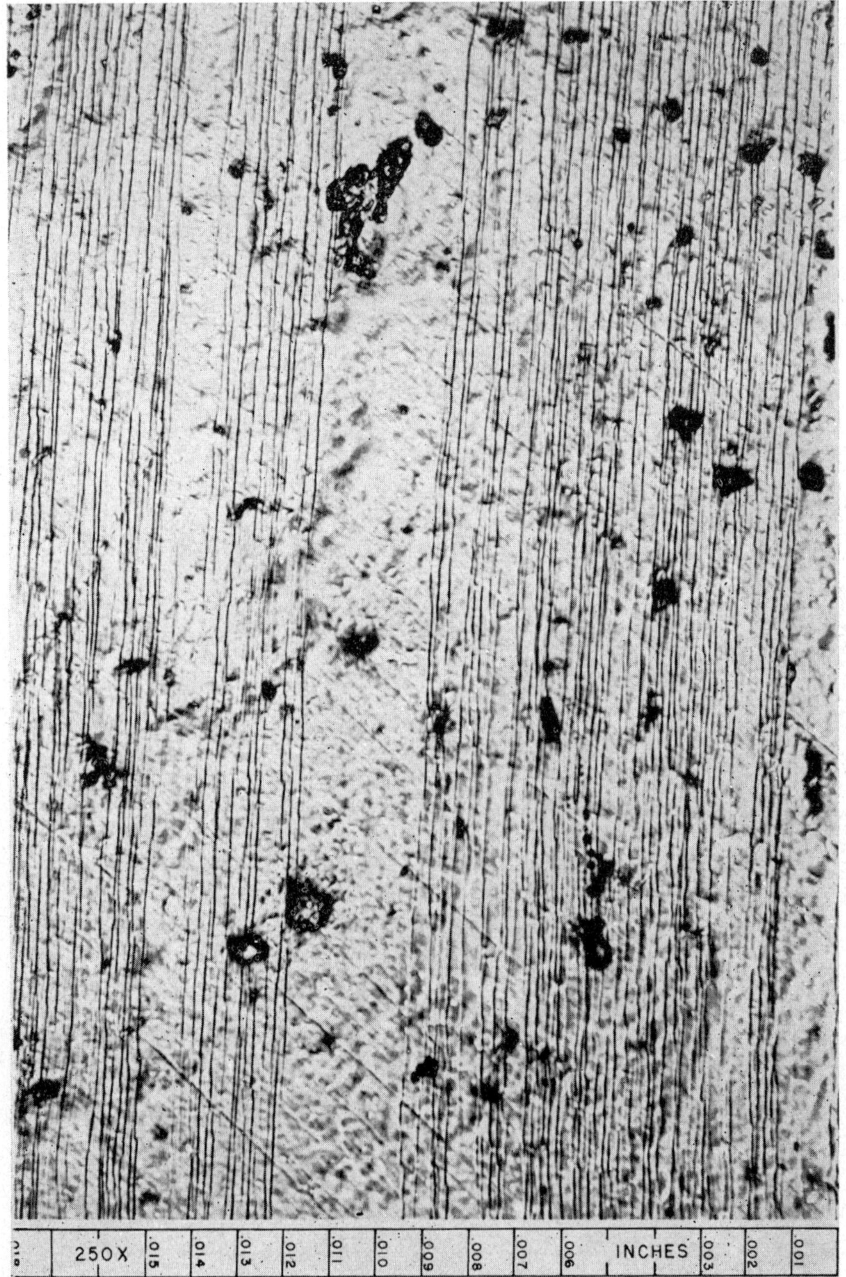

Fig. 72. – Photomicrographs taken at point 10 of Fig. 69. Slip lines from the latent system predominate almost to the point of exclusion of slip lines from the primary system. Magnification 250×.

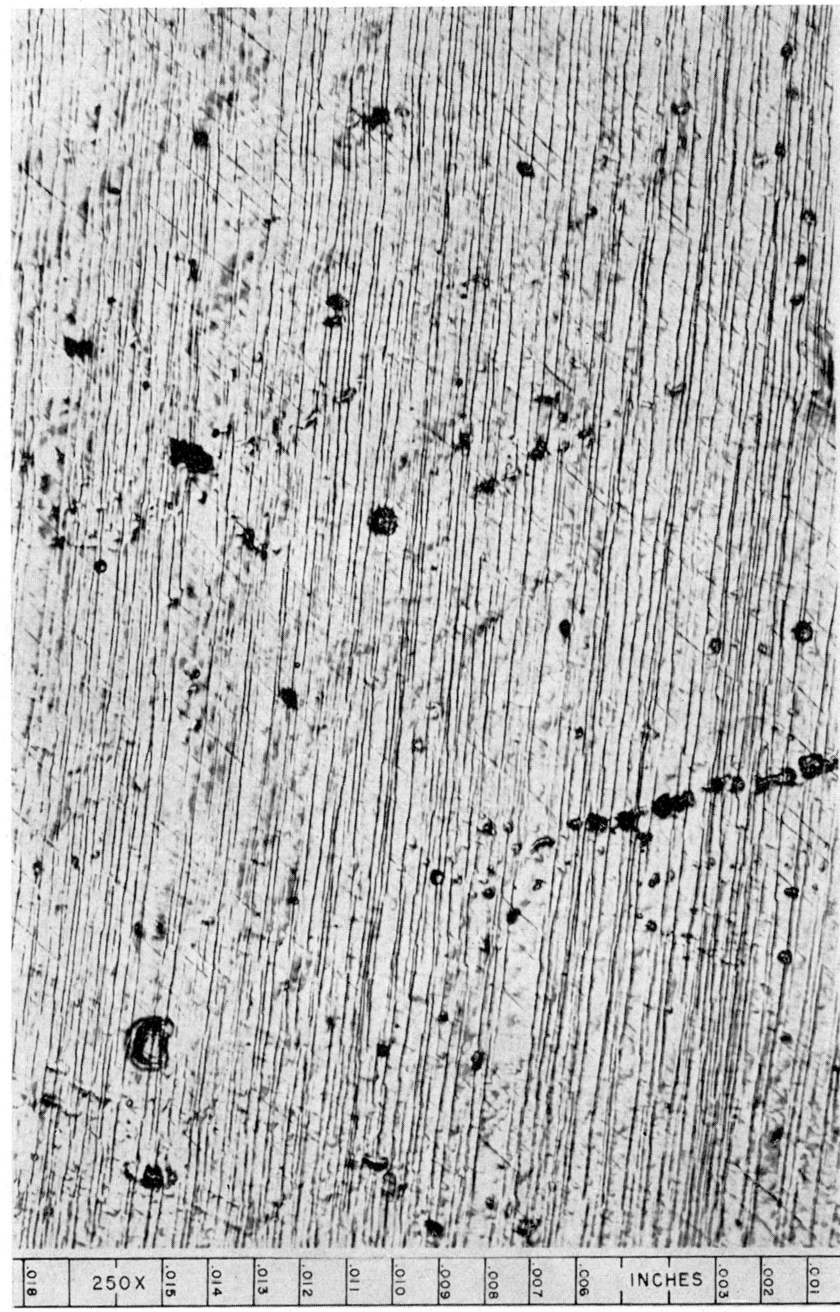

Fig. 73. – Photomicrographs taken at point 11 of Fig. 69. At this point the Lüders band associated with the latent slip system has filled up the crystal and a uniform density of slip lines, predominatingly those of the latent slip system, is visible.

primary system has also been observed. This is shown in Fig. 74, where the discontinuities are plainly evident.

This phenomenon of overshooting has important consequences to the yield stress when the tensile axis lies very near to the dodecahedral plane. In this case both the primary and conjugate slip systems have resolved shear stresses which are nearly the same. Both systems can become operative independently, and the interaction of the two with each other causes the yield stress to be greatly enhanced. For example, six samples of a crystal with an orientation on the dodecahedral plane were bombarded for a dose of $1.5 \cdot 10^{19}$ nvt. Three of these initially deformed on one slip system and the yield stress was 4.1 kg/mm². The remaining three deformed initially by slip on the conjugate and primary systems with an average yield stress of 7.1 kg/mm². (The photomicrograph of Fig. 60 is one of the three with the abnormally high yield stress.) These data thus show that the interaction of two slip systems will raise the yield stress significantly.

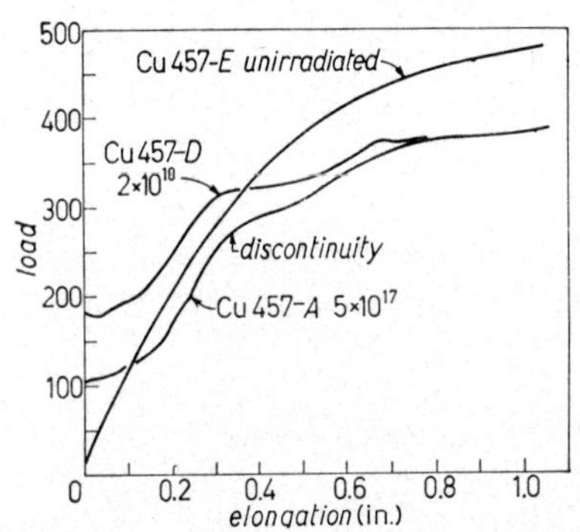

Fig. 74. – Load-elongation curves of copper crystals deformed at 78 °K following neutron bombardment. These curves show the discontinuities which arise from the onset of a second slip system. The first discontinuity near 0.30 in elongation is the result of slip changing from the primary system to the latent system. The second discontinuity near 0.7 in elongation is the result of slip changing from the latent system back to the primary system. It can be noted that an increase in dose results in a sharpening up of the discontinuity due to an increase in the Lüders band formation.

23. – Annealing studies of radiation-hardening.

In the earlier sections the five annealing peaks in irradiated copper and their interpretation in terms of fundamental imperfections were discussed in some detail. An understanding of the role of each of the annealing peaks on the radiation-hardening would be of great value. Studies of this type, while not complete, have been performed at Oak Ridge National Laboratory. Perhaps the most significant experiments in this regard were those performed in the hole 12 cryostat of the Oak Ridge Graphite Reactor. In these experiments samples were tested in a tensile machine specially designed to permit the determination of the yield stress at very low temperatures in the confined space of the hole 12 cryostat [51]. The load was applied hydraulically using helium as the fluid. The piston was constructed of graphite and the cylinder of 24 ST aluminum. Lubrication was provided by adjusting the clearance between these two components so that the helium gas acted as the lubricant after the principle of the Kapitza expansion engine. The extension was measured by means of a differential transformer. An exploded diagram of the tensile machine is shown in Fig. 75.

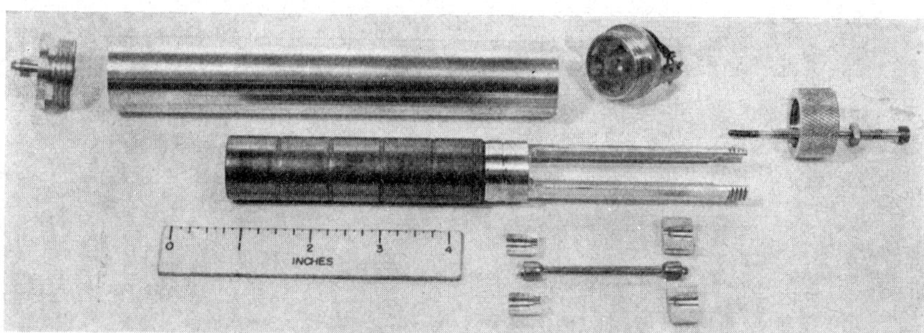

Fig. 75. – The in-pile tensile machile. The load is applied with helium gas pressure on the graphite piston. The extension is measured with a diffierential transformer, the core being mounted on the piston assembly and the coils being mounted on the cylinder assembly.

The experiment was performed by determining the yield stress at 25 °K of a copper crystal utilizing the tensile machine described above in the hole 12 cryostat. The samples were then bombarded for three days at a temperature of 15 °K (a total dose of $1.6 \cdot 10^{17}$ n/cm^2) and the critical shear stress was again determined *in situ*. Following this determination of the flow stress the cryostat was warmed to 78 °K *in situ* so that the crystal was heated above the temperature at which a large fraction of the resistivity recovers. The yield stress was then redetermined after the sample had been cooled to 20 °K. The results of these experiments are shown in Table II.

TABLE II. – *Effect of low-temperature annealing on the flow stress of high-purity copper.*

Sample no.		
Cu 316	Cu 425-A	
yield stress		
0.59	0.5926	Yield point at 25 °K before bombardment
2.48	2.168	Yield point at 25 °K after bombardment
2.39	2.085	Yield point at 25 °K after anneal at 80 °K
1.80	—	Yield point at 25 °K after anneal at 300 °K

Bombardment temperature — 20 °K
Dose = $1.6 \cdot 10^{17}$ nvt

A similar experiment was performed utilizing a beryllium-doped copper sample. It has been shown earlier that the presence of this small amount of beryllium prevents the electrical resistivity from annealing until temperatures of 130 °K are reached. Samples of 1% beryllium in copper were then bombarded at 15 °K and withdrawn in a bath of liquid nitrogen. The yield stress of these samples was then determined in a bath of liquid nitrogen utilizing an Instron tensile machine without allowing the sample to warm up. The samples were then annealed at various temperatures and then reimmersed in liquid nitrogen, and the flow stress was again measured. The results of these experiments are shown in Table III.

TABLE III. – *Effect of annealing on the flow stress of high-purity copper.*

Sample no.			
Cu 190	135	1% Be (*)	
113	14	14	Bombardment temperature (°K)
$5\cdot10^{17}$	$8\cdot10^{17}$	$8\cdot10^{17}$	Dose
0.2	0.22	0.83	Yield stress at 78 °K before bombardment (kg/mm²)
2.12	2.69	2.45	Yield stress at 78 °K after bombardment (kg/mm²)
—	—	2.37	Yield stress at 78 °K after anneal at 180 °K (kg/mm²)
—	—	2.30	Yield stress at 78 °K after anneal at 233 °K (kg/mm²)
1.8	2.28	2.18	Yield stress at 78 °K after anneal at 300 °K (kg/mm²)

(*) Due to uncertainty in orientation the absolute magnitude may be in error by ± 10 %.

The data of both Table II and Table III clearly show that the annealing associated with the annealing peak at (30 ÷ 50) °K had a negligible influence on the hardening. In the case of high-purity copper, however, the evidence suggests that a low-temperature bombardment will increase the shear stress by greater than an equivalent neutron dose at higher temperatures. This was shown by bombarding two sets of samples to the same dose in hole 12, one set being kept at 14 °K during the bombardment and the other at 320 °K. The yield stress samples were measured in both cases at room temperature in the Instron tensile machine. The results are shown in Table IV.

Measurements on the effect of annealing temperatures in the range from 80 °K to 300 °K on the yield stress have also been measured. Samples were bombarded in the graphite reactor at 14 °K in hole 12 and removed in a bath of liquid nitrogen. Measurements of the yield stress were then made without warm-up and after warming to room temperature. The results, which are shown in Table II, indicate that about 20 % of the flow stress is recovered by the room-temperature anneal. A definitive experiment has not been performed so that this annealing may be attributable to either the garbage annealing (50 °K to 230 °K) or to that usually attributed to vacancy migration (230 °K to 270 °K). It should also be noted that annealing in (80÷300) °K

TABLE IV. – *Effect of bombardment temperature on the yield stress of high-purity copper.*

Sample no.	C.S.S. (kg/mm²)	
	300 °K	78 °K
Samples bombarded at 14 °K, annealed at room temperature		
Cu 377-D	1.31	1.89
Cu 377-E	1.28	1.97
Cu 377-F	1.08	1.55
Cu 378-D	0.93	1.44
Cu 378-E	1.19	1.88
Cu 378-F	1.16	1.84
Samples bombarded at 300 °K, annealed at room temperature		
Cu 377-A	1.09	1.37
Cu 377-B	0.92	1.19
Cu 377-C	0.971	1.21
Cu 378-B	0.88	1.11
Cu 378-C	0.78	1.01

does not apparently effect the temperature-dependence of the flow stress. A sample was bombarded at 14 °K and the yield stress measured at 4.2 °K

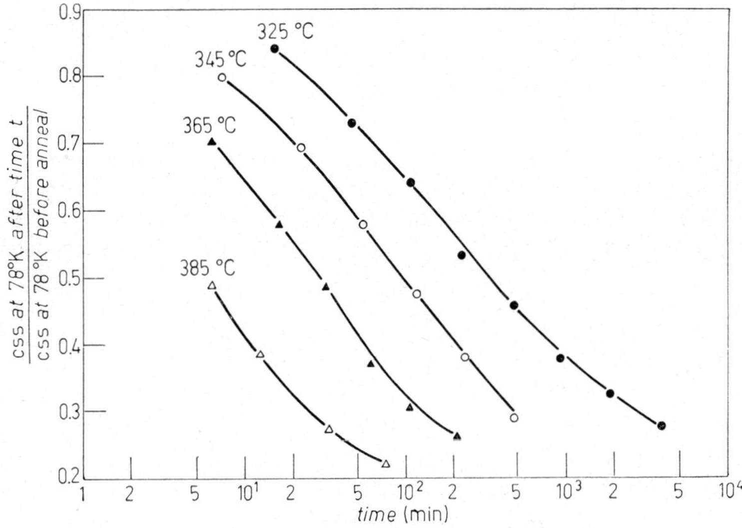

Fig. 76. – Isothermal annealing of the yield stress of copper crystals irradiated to a dose of $1 \cdot 10^{19}$ n/cm². Deformation temperature 78 °K.

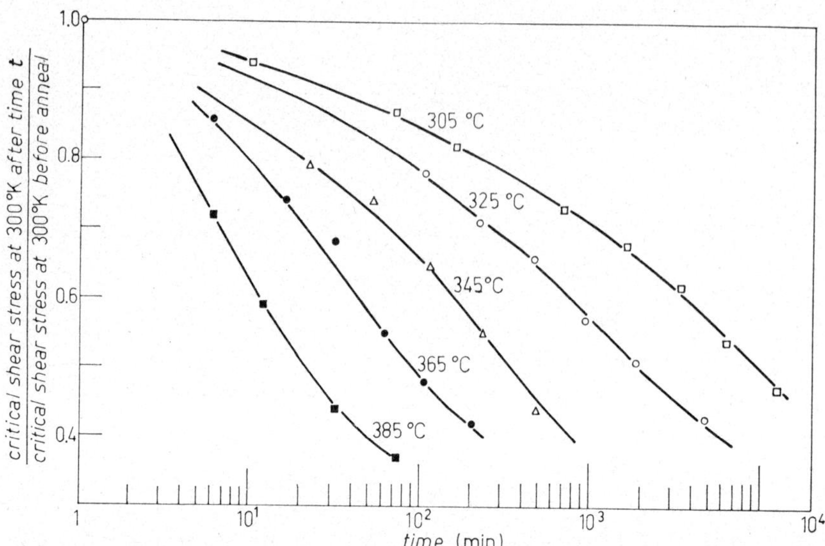

Fig. 77. – Isothermal annealing of the yield stress of copper crystals irradiated to a dose of $1 \cdot 10^{19}$ n/cm². ○ $\varepsilon/k = 2.31 \cdot 10^4$ °K, $\varepsilon = 2.00$ eV; △ $\varepsilon/k = 2.59 \cdot 10^4$ °K, $\varepsilon = 2.24$ eV; □ $\varepsilon/k = 2.79 \cdot 10^4$ °K $\varepsilon = 2.41$ eV; ● $\varepsilon/k = 2.94 \cdot 10^4$ °K, $\varepsilon = 2.54$ eV; ■ $\varepsilon/k = 2.92 \cdot 10^4$ °K, $\varepsilon = 2.52$ eV, $\tau = A \exp[\varepsilon/kT]$.

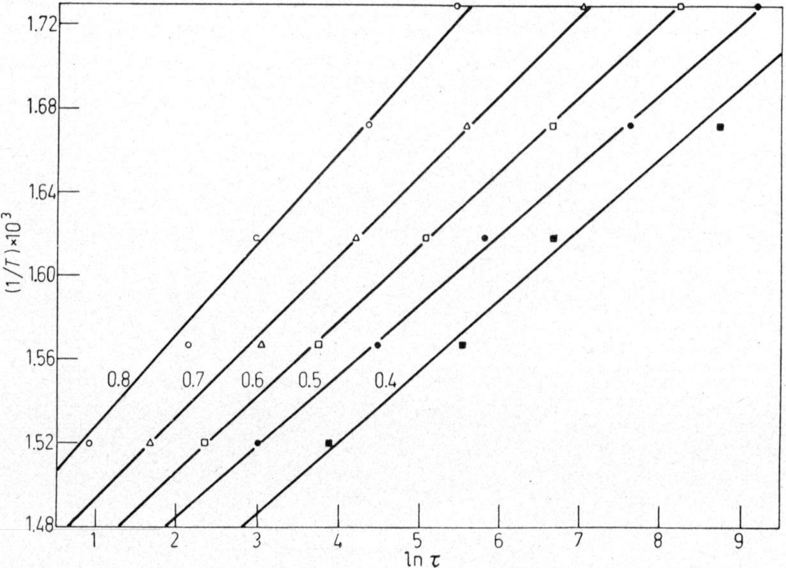

Fig. 78. – Phenomenological determination of the activation energy for the recovery of radiation hardness in copper. The ln of the relaxation time T or the time required for the recovery of 0.8, 0.7, 0.6, 0.5 and 0.4 of the yield stress (measured at room temperature) is plotted as a function of the reciprocal of the absolute temperature. The apparent activation energy is proportional to the shape of the line. $\tau = A \exp[\varepsilon/kT]$, $\ln \tau = \ln A + (\varepsilon/k) \cdot (1/T)$; ○ $\varepsilon/k = 2.31 \cdot 10^4$°K, $\varepsilon = 2.00$eV; △ $\varepsilon/k = 2.59 \cdot 10^4$°K, $\varepsilon = 2.24$ eV; □ $\varepsilon/k = 2.79 \cdot 10^4$ °K, $\varepsilon = 2.41$ eV; ● $\varepsilon/k = 2.94 \cdot 10^4$ eV, $\varepsilon = 2.54$ eV; ■ $\varepsilon/k = 2.92 \cdot 10^4$ °K, $\varepsilon = 2.52$ eV.

and at 78 °K following a long anneal at 78 °K. The yield stresses of 3.6 and 2.7 kg/mm² are in good agreement with samples bombarded at 300 °K.

Annealing experiments conducted in the region above room temperature [52] show that the remaining radiation hardness is annealed in the region from 300 °C to 400 °C. Samples bombarded in the LITR reactor to a flux of 10^{19} n/cm² were utilized to make these measurements. Isothermal annealing was done in a salt bath at 325, 345, 365 and 385 °C. The critical shear stress was measured at both 78 °K and 300 °K (Figs. 76, 77). The apparent activation energy was determined in the usual way, and a value ranging from 2.1 to 2.3 eV was found (Fig. 78). The results of this section are summarized in Fig. 79.

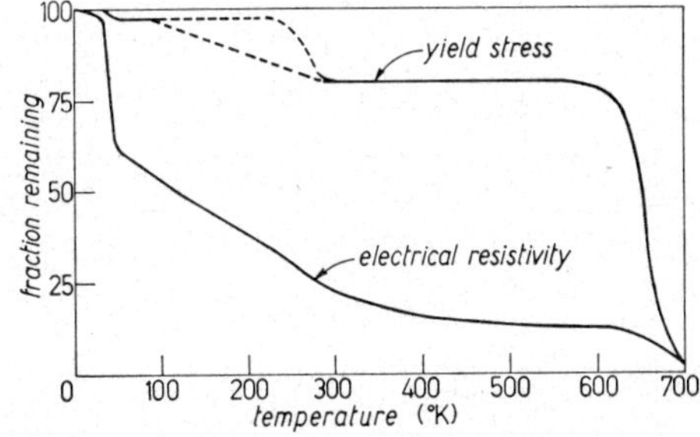

Fig. 79. – Schematic diagram of the effect of temperature on the critical shear stress and on the electrical resistivity. In both curves the data are taken at a reference temperature (yield stress 25 °K, resistivity 4 °K) so that these curves represent an annealing phenomenon with any temperature-dependence eliminated. The shape of the yield stress curve in the region between 80 °K and 290 °K has not been determined. It would be expected, however, that curve would fall between the two dotted lines.

24. – Discussion of radiation hardening.

The previous sections have clearly shown that substantial changes in the mechanical properties of copper crystals occur as the result of neutron bombardment. It is quite clear that the the defects produced by the bombardment must interact with the dislocations to produce these changes. Two types of interaction may occur. Some of the radiation-induced defects may lie in the vicinity of the Frank-Read generators (dislocation sources) acting as barriers to their operations (source-hardening). The defects may form a Cottrell atmosphere, they may lie in the region of the stacking faults, or they may form clusters on the dislocation line. Instead of this type of interaction, however, the radiation-induced defects may impede the motion of the dislocations after they have been formed (friction-hardening). The barriers to the motion of the dislocations after they have formed may be clusters of vacancies or interstitials, the debris from a thermal spike, or a small recrystallized region. In order to understand the basic mechanism of radiation-hardening, it is imperative to decide which of these two types of interaction results in the hardening.

Unfortunately, our present state of knowledge in the field of plastic deformation does not permit a definitive experiment to be performed in order to distinguish between these two alternatives. For example, the temperature-dependence of the yield stress, the hardening of the slip system, the formation of an upper yield stress and Lüders band propagation, and the mechanism of cross-slip are not sufficiently understood so that these phenomenon can be utilized to distinguish between source- and friction-hardening. There are, however, a few clues available in the data presented in this paper, and these will now be discussed.

First of all, the results of the flow stress measurements which show that $\sigma(\varphi, T) = g(\varphi) f(T)$, make it improbable that radiation-hardening is a mixture of friction- and source-hardening. The fact that the above equations exist means that $g(\varphi)$ and $f(T)$ must be the same for both types of hardening or that the contribution of each of these mechanisms must remain independent of the flux if the flow stress σ is assumed to be the result of a joint contribution of source- and friction-hardening. Since it is rather unlikely that either of these conditions exist, it is perhaps safe to draw the conclusion that either source- or friction-hardening, but not both, is responsible for radiation-hardening for doses ranging from 10^{17} to 10^{20} n/cm^2.

Now the problem remains as to which of these mechanisms is responsible for radiation-hardening. The substantial temperature-dependence which for temperatures greater than 30 °K can be written as $f(T) = h(T^{\frac{1}{2}})$ does not help in resolving the dilemma since either mechanism can account for this temperature-dependence. It does, however, make the specific mechanism of source-hardening arising from vacancy clusters in the dislocation line, suggested by FRIEDEL [53], most unlikely as this model predicts a much smaller temperature-dependence.

On the other hand, the flux-dependence $g(\varphi) = j(\varphi^{\frac{1}{3}})$ raises a serious objection to the concept of friction-hardening. The objection arises from the fact that plastic deformation is a slip process which occurs on a plane. If, then, the impedance to slip is purely a result of a random distribution of barriers on this plane, the dependence on the flux should be a $\varphi^{\frac{1}{2}}$ rather than $\varphi^{\frac{1}{3}}$ term. This objection is supported by the resistance data which show that for fluxes to $8 \cdot 10^{19}$ n/cm^2 the number of defects is proportional to the neutron flux. This result then indicates that the function $(\varphi^{\frac{1}{3}})$ is indeed a fundamental relationship. It would thus appear difficult to rationalize these results with the lattice friction scheme. It should be noted, however, that this evidence supports the source-hardening scheme only in a negative sense.

The very large slip steps observed in the electron microscope would also seem to offer support to the source-hardening scheme since an avalanche of dislocations would be expected once the stress had become large enough to overcome the obstacles to dislocation generation. While it may be possible to concoct a model on the friction-hardening scheme to account for the large slip steps, the model must, of necessity, be cumbersome and hence less satisfying than that required for source hardening.

It would seem that the experiment of measuring the yield stress following bombardment at 25 °K and after warm up to 80 °K would be a critical experiment to distinguish between these two models. If one assumes that some form of defect migration occurs at 30 °K to 50 °K then one should expect the yield stress to increase after the anneal if the source-hardening picture were utilized, since the mobility of the defect would enable more defects to reach the dislocation. On the other hand, the yield stress would be expected to decrease if the lattice friction picture were utilized, since the mobility of the defect would result in an annihilation of some of the barriers to the motion of the dislocation lines. The results as we have seen have shown that the large annealing peak has not appreciably affected the yield stress (*).

It is somewhat difficult to rationalize this experiment with either picture. The source-hardening picture requires that some of the defects (due to the formation of crowdions or to a focusing effect) travel large distances to the vicinity of the dislocation sources at the low bombardment temperatures. There is, indeed, good evidence that defects do interact with dislocation lines at bombardment temperatures of 20 °K from the fact that the logarithmic decrement and the elastic constants are changed by bombardment at 20 °K. There is also evidence that defects are formed near dislocations, probably the result of a focusing effect, from the fact that the radiation-induced resistivity is enhanced in a severely deformed crystal. On the other hand, it is also observed that the changes in decrement and elastic constants greatly increase during the 30 to 50 °K bombardment (**).

The results of this experiment also raise serious objections to the lattice friction scheme. It is difficult to conceive of barriers formed by bombardment which would not be changed by the migration of a radiation-induced defect The low-temperature shear-stress measurements while extremely important are very difficult to interpret in a positive sense.

In summary, then, although the evidence is by no means conclusive, radiation damage is most probably the result of an interaction of radiation defects with the dislocation sources. Perhaps the most satisfying conclusion to be derived from this work is the fact that radiation hardening appears to be completely analogous to solution-hardening. For example, one finds a one-to-one correspondence between the deformation characteristics of α-brass and samples which

(*) It is interesting to note that if the assumption is made that interstitials become mobile and are annihilated at vacant lattice sites, then the low-temperature yield stress experiment requires that defects other than single vacancies and single interstitials must be present on bombardment at 20 °K.

(**) A detailed discussion of the low-temperature experiments becomes considerably involved and will be postponed to a subsequent publication.

have been reactor-irradiated. The stress-strain curve with the Lüders band, the fact that the latent plane hardens faster than the active plane (overshoot), the temperature-dependence of the flow stress, the high step height of the slip bands, and the appearance of cross-slip are characteristic of deformed α-brass and of neutron-irradiated copper. It thus appears that if an understanding of the basic mechanisms of hardening is gained for either of these materials both will be understood.

It might be worth pointing out that radiation hardness is not analogous to work-hardening. This is immediately obvious when the stress-strain curve, the temperature-dependence of the flow stress, and the slip lines are considered. It is also significant that no recrystallization is observed on annealing the radiation hardness. It can be argued, however, that dislocation loops may form in neutron-irradiated copper from the condensation of vacancies. It is difficult to believe that these can play a significant role in radiation-hardening from the low temperature at which radiation hardness can be recovered. The fact that the radiation-hardening occurs at temperatures as low as 25 °K and that a much higher temperature would be required for vacancy migration and coagulation raises a serious objection to a theory attributing the major source of hardening to dislocation loops.

REFERENCES

[1] D. S. Billington: private communication.

[2] H. P. Yockey, M. R. Jeppson and C. D'A. Hunt: *Phys. Rev.*, **81**, 663 (1951); A. B. Martin, S. B. Austerman, R. R. Eggleston, J. F. McGee and M. Tarpinian: *Phys. Rev.*, **81**, 664 (1951).

[3] H. B. Huntington: *Phys. Rev.*, **94**, 1092 (1953).

[4] H. G. Cooper, J. S. Koehler and J. W. Marx: *Phys. Rev.*, **97**, 599 (1955).

[5] J. W. Corbett and R. M. Walker: *Phys. Rev.*, **110**, 767 (1958); J. W. Corbett, J. M. Denney, M. D. Fiske and R. M. Walker: *Phys. Rev.*, **108**, 954 (1959); J. W. Corbett, R. B. Smith and R. M. Walker: *Phys. Rev.*, **114**, 1452, 1460 (1959).

[6] T. H. Blewitt, R. R. Coltman, D. K. Holmes and T. S. Noggle: *Dislocations and Mechanical Properties of Crystals, Lake Placid 1956*, edited by J. C. Fisher, W. G. Johnston, R. Thomson and T. Vreeland jr. (New York, 1957).

[7] R. R. Coltman, Howe and Busby: *Solid State Division Progress Reports*, ORNL-2614, Physics and Mathematics, TID-4500, 14th ed. (1958).

[8] J. Doulat and Weill: *Cryogenics*, **4** (1960).

[9] D. O. Mapother and F. E. L. Witt: *Rev. Sci. Instr.*, **26**, 843 (1955).

[10] R. R. Coltman, T. H. Blewitt and T. S. Noggle: *Rev. Sci. Instr.*, **28**, 375 (1957); T. H. Blewitt and R. R. Coltman: *Experimental Cryophysics*, edited by F. E. Hoare, L. C. Jackson and N. Kurti (London, 1961), p. 274.

[11] T. H. Blewitt, R. R. Coltman and C. E. Klabunde: unpublished.

[12] T. H. Blewitt and R. R. Coltman: *Solid State Division Progress Report* (1952).
[13] G. D. Magnuson, W. Palmer and J. S. Koehler: *Phys. Rev.*, **109**, 1990 (1958).
[14] T. H. Blewitt, R. R. Coltman, C. E. Klabunde and J. K. Redman: Oak Ridge National Laboratory, unpublished.
[15] T. H. Blewitt, R. R. Coltman and C. E. Klabunde: *Solid State Annual Report*, ORNL-2614, (1959), p. 65.
[16] T. H. Blewitt, R. R. Coltman and T. S. Noggle: Oak Ridge National Laboratory (unpublished).
[17] T. H. Blewitt and R. R. Coltman: *Experimental Cryophysics*, edited by F. E. Hoare, L. C. Jackson and N. Kurti (London, 1961) p. 274.
[18] C. J. Meechan and A. Sosin: *Phys. Rev.*, **113**, 422 (1959).
[19] T. H. Blewitt, R. R. Coltman, C. E. Klabunde and J. K. Redman: *Solid State Division Annual Progress Report*, ORNL-3017, UC-34, Physics and Mathematics, TID-4500, 15th ed. (1960).
[20] T. H. Blewitt, R. R. Coltman, C. E. Klabunde and T. S. Noggle: *Journ. Appl. Phys.*, **28**, 639 (1957).
[21] W. M. Lomer and A. H. Cottrell: *Phil. Mag.*, **46**, 711 (1955).
[22] T. H. Blewitt, R. R. Coltman and C. E. Klabunde: *Austral. Journ. Phys.*, **13**, 24, 347 (1960).
[23] T. H. Blewitt, R. R. Coltman, C. E. Klabunde and J. K. Redman: *Solid State Division Annual Progress Report*, ORNL-3017, UC-34, Physics and Mathematics, TID-4500 (1960), p. 21.
[24] T. H. Blewitt, R. R. Coltman, T. S. Noggle and D. K. Holmes: *Bull. Am. Phys. Soc.*, **1**, 130 (1956).
[25] T. H. Blewitt, R. R. Coltman and C. E. Klabunde: *Phys. Rev. Lett.*, **3**, 132 (1959).
[26] W. F. Giauque and P. F. Meads: *Journ. Am. Chem. Soc.*, **63**, 1897 (1941).
[27] T. H. Blewitt, R. R. Coltman and C. E. Klabunde: to be published.
[28] T. E. Nilan and A. V. Granato: *Phys. Rev.*
[29] F. W. Jones and C. Sykes: *Proc. Roy. Soc.* (*London*), A **457**, 213 (1936).
[30] *Amer. Inst. of Phys. Handb.* (New York, 1957), p. 4-42.
[32] R. Vook and C. Wert: *Phys. Rev.*, **109**, 1529 (1957).
[33] T. H. Blewitt, R. R. Coltman and C. E. Klabunde: to be published.
[34] A. K. Seeger: *Second Intern. Conf. on Peaceful Uses of Atomic Energy*, **6**, 20 (1958).
[35] J. Silcox and P. Hirsch: *Phil. Mag.*, **4**, 1356 (1959).
[36] P. B. Hirsch: private communication.
[37] R. Barnes: This volume p. 860.
[38] L. Trewordt: *Phys. Rev.*, **109**, 61 (1958).
[39] J. B. Sampson and C. W. Tucker jr.: *Phys. Rev.*, **105**, 1117 (1957).
[40] R. W. Simmons: private communication.
[41] T. H. Blewitt: *Phys. Rev.*, **91**, 1115 (1953).
[42] T. H. Blewitt, R. R. Coltman and J. K. Redman: *Journ. Appl. Phys.*, **28**, 651 (1957).
[43] T. H. Blewitt and R. R. Coltman: *The effect of reactor irradiation on the stress-strain curves of copper*, AECD-3095; NSAS:3260 (1951).
[44] T. H. Blewitt and R. R. Coltman: *Phys. Rev.*, **82**, 769(A) (1951).
[45] T. H. Blewitt and R. R. Coltman (reported by G. Kinchin and R. Pease): *Progress in Physics*, **18**, 1 (1955).
[46] R. E. Jamison and T. H. Blewitt: *Phys. Rev.*, **91**, 237(A) (1953).
[47] D. K. Holmes, J. K. Redman, T. H. Blewitt and R. R. Coltman: *Bull. Am. Phys. Soc.*, **4**, 130 (LA9) (1956).

[48] E. SCHMID and W. BOAS: *Plasticity of Crystals* (London, 1950).
[49] R. E. JAMISON and T. H. BLEWITT: *Phys. Rev.*, **86**, 651(A) (1952).
[50] V. GOLER and G. SACHS: *Zeits. Phys.*, **55**, 581 (1929).
[51] R. R. COLTMAN, T. H. BLEWITT and T. S. NOGGLE: *Rev. Sci. Instr.*, **28**, 375 (1957).
[52] J. K. REDMAN, R. R. COLTMAN and T. H. BLEWITT: *Phys. Rev.*, **91**, 448(A) (1953).
[53] P. COULOMB and J. FRIEDEL: *On the formation of cavities along dislocations*, in *Dislocations and Mechanical Properties of Crystals*, edited by J. C. FISHER, W. G. JOHNSTON, R. THOMSON and T. VREELAND jr. (New York, 1957), Sect. **8**, p. 555.

The Mechanism of Radiation-Hardening of F.C.C. Metals by Fast Neutrons.

A. SEEGER and U. ESSMANN

Max Planck-Institut für Metallforschung - Stuttgart
Institut für theoretische und angewandte Physik der Technischen Hochschule - Stuttgart

1. – Introduction and basic facts on radiation-hardening.

Radiation-hardening is the effect of irradiation on the plastic properties of solids. In order to avoid the complications due to ionization effects, we shall confine ourselves to metals, with our main emphasis on f.c.c. metals, which are the only ones that have been studied in detail.

Sometimes radiation-hardening is understood in a restricted sense as the increase of the critical shear stress τ_0 for plastic deformation caused by irradiation. At least for copper, this aspect seems to be fairly well understood now. As we shall see, the increase in critical shear stress induced by fast neutron bombardment is very closely related to the mechanism and the nature of radiation damage in metals, and we shall therefore discuss it in some detail. Particularly informative in this connection is recent electron microscopy work done at Harwell. The experimental part of the present paper will be mainly concerned with the more general aspect of the effect of previous irradiation (by fast neutrons) on the stress-strain curve, *i.e.* with the mechanism of plastic deformation of radiation-hardened crystals. We shall see that here the interpretation of the experimental facts is less clear at present, and that a number of questions are still open.

Our experimental knowledge on radiation-hardening of f.c.c. metals owes a great deal to the work of the Oak Ridge group (whose main findings have recently been made available in a comprehensive form [1]), with important contributions from Brookhaven [2], from the Harwell group [3, 4], and others. The evidence on the increase in critical shear stress of copper due to irradiation has been discussed elsewhere together with the conclusions that can be drawn from it [5]. Three experimental facts seem to be particularly important: *a*) Radiation-hardening is almost independent of the temperature of irradiation, provided this is not too high. This demonstrates that the defects responsible for the hardening are formed practically independent of the irradiation temperature. *b*) Most of the radiation-hardening does not yet anneal out at a temperature where practically all the point defects are known to have annealed out (this statement is not true for aluminum). This indicates that more complicated defects than point defects must be responsible for the hardening. *c*) The critical shear stress of neutron irradiated f.c.c. metals is strongly temperature-dependent. This enables us to derive some characteristic properties of the defects responsible for the hardening, as will be discussed in more detail in the later sections.

One of the present authors has given a detailed theory of the nature of radiation damage by fast neutrons with particular emphasis on radiation-hardening in heavy f.c.c. metals such as copper [5-7]. In the next two sections we shall briefly outline this theory and discuss it in the light of recent experimental work.

2. – The model of neutron irradiation damage of f.c.c. metals.

Fig. 1 gives schematically a picture of the radiation damage of a f.c.c. metal. A *primary knock-on atom P* coming from the left collides with the atoms on lattice sites with a mean free path decreasing with decreasing kinetic energy. If in such a collision enough energy is transferred, the stationary atom may be displaced from its lattice site, leaving behind a vacant lattice site (*vacancy*). It may come to rest as an interstitial (*) close to this vacant site, forming together with it a so-called close Frenkel pair (for short: *close pair*). Another possibility is that enough kinetic energy has been transferred to the *secondary knock-on* for this to displace further atoms from their lattice sites, thus giving rise to a

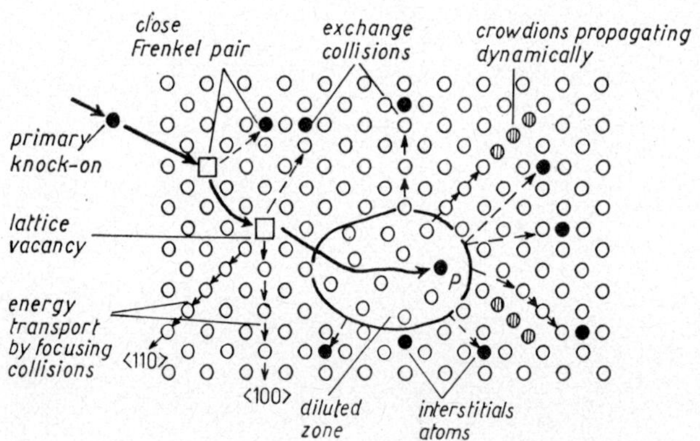

Fig. 1. – Radiation damage model. *P* denotes the position in which the primary knock-on comes to rest.

(*) For simplicity, in Fig. 1 all interstitials have been drawn as if in an otherwise perfect crystal they would possess cubic symmetry, although it is now known that they are in the so-called dumb-bell configuration with tetragonal symmetry.

cascade of displacements [8]. The secondary knock-on may displace another atom into an interstitial site, replacing it on its original lattice site (*replacement collisions*) [9]. Recent computer work on the dynamics of radiation damage [10] has shown that chains of replacement collisions along cube directions as shown in Fig. 1 may be quite frequent. Such *replacement chains* constitute one of the mechanisms by which an interstitial can be created at a site away from the corresponding vacant site (*). Another mechanism for the transport of matter over rather large distances is the mechanism of *dynamic crowdion propagation*, also shown in Fig. 1. By SILSBEE [11] and later on by other workers [9, 12, 13] it was shown theoretically that there is a focusing tendency for collisions in a closely spaced row of atoms. As was pointed out earlier [5], this focusing tendency may enable interstitial atoms in the crowdion configuration to propagate along a close-packed direction dynamically (*i.e.*, overcoming the energy barriers by kinetic energy and not by thermal fluctuations). The work on the computer [10] has shown that this process indeed can occur, and has also given some information on the threshold for displacement of atoms from their lattice sites and the energy loss during propagation. At present, theory has not yet clearly established whether a static crowdion (say in copper) is a stable configuration or not. There is, however, indirect evidence [14, 7] that it is metastable with respect to the dumb-bell configuration of the interstitial. A dynamic crowdion may therefore come to rest in a perfect crystal environment as a crowdion, or, if its propagation is suddenly stopped by an unpenetrable obstacle like a dislocation, a stacking fault, or an impurity atom—with kinetic energy to help the transformation—as an ordinary (dumb-bell) interstitial. Evidence for the latter possibility has recently been found by MEECHAN, SOSIN and BRINKMAN [14] from the effect of previous cold-work on radiation damage and annealing of electron-bombarded copper.

Replacement chains and dynamic crowdions provide a mechanism for transfer of both matter and energy. Silsbee's [11] original idea of *focusing collisions* involves only transfer of energy. VINEYARD *et al.* [10] have shown that in their computer model of a f.c.c. crystal two kinds of such « *focusons* » are possible: one propagating along the close-packed rows ⟨110⟩, focusing in the way envisaged by SILSBEE [11], and another one propagating along the less densely packed ⟨100⟩-directions in which the focusing is mainly due to the confining action of neighboring atomic rows. The focusons are essentially confined to the energy range below threshold; above the threshold energy one observes dynamic crowdions or replacement chains, depending on the crystallo-

(*) Replacement chains in ⟨100⟩-directions may be looked upon as strongly correlated successive jumps by the intersticialcy mechanism, using kinetic energy rather than thermal fluctuations to overcome the migration barrier.

graphic direction of the collision chain. Focusing collisions will only lead to formation of lattice defects if they are suddenly defocused by an obstacle, with enough kinetic energy available to create a Frenkel pair. LEIBFRIED [13] has discussed this process in some detail and attributed to it the enhancement of the low-temperature radiation damage rate by previous cold-work.

The work of THOMPSON [15, 16] on ejection of atoms in crystallographic directions from bombarded foils demonstrates experimentally the importance of focusing effects in the noble metals. At the present time we have no detailed experimental information on the relative importance in radiation damage experiments on bulk material of the three types of collision chains: crowdion propagation, replacement chains, and focusing collisions. On theoretical grounds it appears, however, that the first one should dominate, since the crowdions have a much larger range than the replacement chains, and since the energy of a focuson is always less than the threshold energy for displacements [10]. This should make defect production by focusons a rare event.

For our radiation damage model the transport of matter by crowdions is particularly important. BRINKMAN pointed out some time ago [17] that in a metal like copper a fast-moving atom should collide towards the end of its path with almost any atom it passes, thereby creating a large number of displacements. Crowdions and replacement chains will carry away a substantial fraction of the displaced atoms from their vacant sites. The interstitials leave behind a *diluted zone* of reduced density [5, 6]. The essential feature of this configuration is that the zones will not completely recover at the temperature where all point defects are mobile, as any configuration of individual point defects would do. In fact, once the interstitial atoms have annealed out, self-diffusion is required to remove these diluted zones. This agrees very well with the experimental facts on radiation-hardening, which, in our model, is due to the obstacles provided by these zones to dislocation movement. The name « zones » has been chosen in analogy to the hardening action of Guinier-Preston zones in precipitation-hardened alloys. As will be discussed in the next section, the same laws hold indeed for the increase of the critical shear stress of Guinier-Preston zones and for neutron radiation-hardening.

Our picture is a modification of Brinkman's [17] original *displacement spike*, whose essential feature was that the atoms ejected from the region at the end of the path of a fast particle formed a belt of interstitials surrounding a central hole (multiple vacancy). This configuration would be unstable and collapse. In an ordered alloy, of course, the order would be destroyed in the region of the hole and the belt. In a pure metal, the region would be perfect again save for close Frenkel pairs, which in turn would anneal out at rather low temperatures. The Brinkman mechanism alone is therefore unable to account for the facts on radiation-hardening. As an additional feature, however, it should also be present in our model, since not all of the displacements will be carried away by crowdions or replacement chains. Some of them will rather lead to interstitials close to the diluted zone. If such a situation is mechanically unstable, it will immediately rearrange itself with the same effects on order in alloys as in the displacement spike.

It is obvious that the rather ill-defined atomic arrangement inside a diluted zone will at higher temperatures follow the tendency to take up a more regular arrangement. It is not known at present what the configuration of lowest free energy of such a region under the restraint of a fixed number of missing atoms is. Possibilities are a hole in the material, dislocation rings, stacking-fault arrangements similar to those found in quenched gold [18], or quasi-crystalline structures of lower density such as a body-centered region in a face-centered cubic environment. The transition between two such structures would again involve dislocation lines.

It has been proposed [5, 7] that the « energy paradox » [19, 20] observed in the low-temperature annealing of neutron-bombarded copper has to do with the rearrangement in the zones. If this is true, the final configuration of the zones would have to give a rather small contribution to the electrical resistivity. This would exclude any sizeable participation of stacking faults in the final arrangement in the case of copper, since the reflexion coefficient of stacking faults for conduction electrons in noble metals is known to be rather large [21]. In gold, however, where no large drop of the electrical resistivity in the low-temperature annealing of neutron radiation damage is observed, stacking faults could play an important role [7, 22]. The concept that a large fraction of the stage I annealing of neutron-irradiated copper is due to the arrangement of the zones rather than the recombination of close Frenkel pairs explains very easily the differences in the low-temperature annealing kinetics after neutron bombardment [23, 24] and after electron bombardment [25-27]. It should be stressed, however, that this concept is not an essential part of our radiation-hardening model.

Since most of the preceding discussion refers to copper, let us finally discuss the question as to what extent the model is applicable to other metals. The essential factors are the mean free path of a fast atom towards the end of its path (determining the extension of the diluted zone and the number of atoms displaced from it) and the frequency of dynamic crowdions and replacement chains (determining what fraction of the displacements are actually carried away and what fraction get stuck in the unstable interstitial belt). The first factor was discussed in some detail by BRINKMAN [17], who showed that large atomic weight and close-packing of the atoms are favorable for the formation of displacement spikes. The initiation of dynamic crowdions is favorable if the conditions for focusing are favorable, *i.e.* if the atoms have large and hard ion cores. It is obvious that these conditions are not well fulfilled in aluminum. We expect, therefore, no zones or only very small zones for this metal. It is indeed observed that the radiation-hardening in this metal anneals out with an activation energy of 0.55 eV [2], approximately the energy of migration of single vacancies, suggesting very strongly that in this metal neutron radiation damage is largely due to point defects and not to zones. Our model should be applicable, however, to silver and gold, with the above-mentioned additional detail of a possible importance of stacking faults.

3. – Experimental tests of the radiation-hardening model.

The main experimental evidence for the existence of the « zones » comes at present from the nature of the increase of the critical shear stress τ_0 due to neutron irradiation. In Section 2 we have already discussed how the model accounts for the effect of the temperature of irradiation and the annealing behavior. Fig. 2 illustrates schematically that the hardening effect is due to the cutting of the zones by moving dislocations. Irrespective of what the detailed configuration of the obstacle is, the cutting process can be characterized by two parameters, the cutting energy U_0 and the cutting distance x_0. U_0 can be considered as the energy required to cut the obstacle into two halves, or as the energy necessary to increase the interface to the perfect surroundings. x_0 is the distance over which the applied stress has to supply the required energy. Its geometrical meaning depends on the nature of the obstacle. For certain kinds of obstacles x_0 will be smaller than the diameter of the obstacles. An example for this is a ring of an unextended dislocation, in which case x_0 would be approximately equal to the diameter of the dislocation core. In terms of these two parameters U_0 and x_0, the number N_z of obstacles per unit area of the glide plane, and the number N of dislocation lengths per unit volume that are held up by these obstacles, the increase in critical shear stress τ_0 at low temperatures is given as a function of absolute temperature T and strain rate $\dot{\varepsilon}$ by [5, 6] (*)

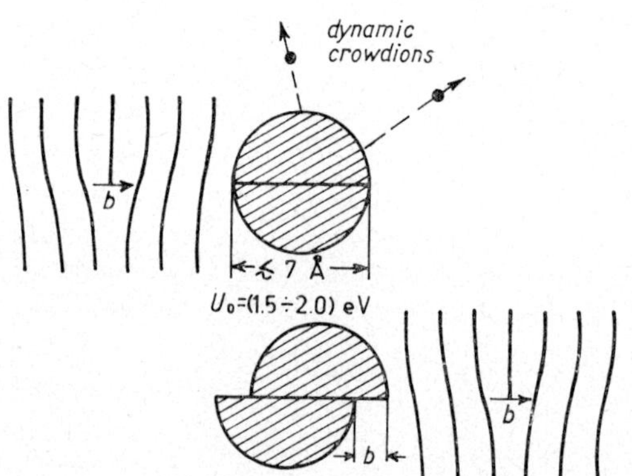

Fig. 2. – Dislocation cutting through a depleted zone (schematic).

$$(\tau_0)^{\frac{2}{3}} = A - BT^{\frac{2}{3}}, \tag{3.1}$$

(*) We are grateful to Dr. CH. SCHWINK for pointing out that the factor $\frac{3}{2}$ had to be included in eq. (3.3).

$$A = (N_z/Gb)^{\frac{1}{3}} \cdot (U_0/4x_0 b)\,, \tag{3.2}$$

$$B = A \cdot \left(\frac{3k}{2U_0} \log \frac{Nbv_0}{N_z\dot{\varepsilon}}\right)^{\frac{2}{3}}, \tag{3.3}$$

where G is the shear modulus, b the modulus of the Burgers vector, and k Boltzmann's constant.

In Fig. 3 we have plotted the data of BLEWITT *et al.* [1] on the critical shear stress of neutron-irradiated copper single crystals in such a way that eq. (3.1) gives a straight line. The relation eq. (3.1) is indeed obeyed. Very good agreement with this equation was found by MAKIN, WHAPHAM, and MINTER [4] for the so-called lattice hardening component of the yield stress of polycrystalline copper. An example of their results is shown in Fig. 3 after reducing the tensile stresses to shear stresses by dividing by 2.3. If we assume a reasonable value for the logarithm occuring in eq. (3.3) (~ 20), we find an experimental value for U_0 between 1.5 and 2.0 eV. An experimental value for x_0 is more difficult to obtain, since the number of zones created per fast neutron hit must be known. No detailed calculations with the neutron spectrum used in these experiments have been done. It appears that the experiments are compatible with experimental values for x_0 between 1.5 Å and 7 Å.

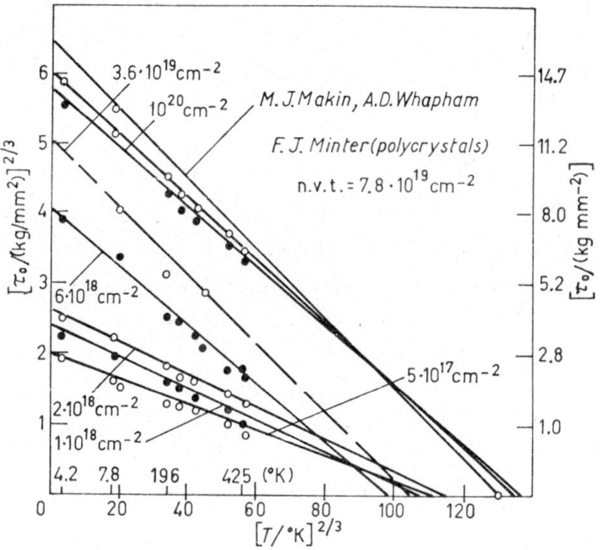

Fig. 3. – Dependence of the critical shear stress τ_0 of neutron-irradiated copper single crystals on temperature and integrated neutron flux. (Measurements of BLEWITT *et al.* [1]).

KELLY [28] has recently shown that eq. (3.1) is obeyed for the temperature-dependent part of the critical shear stress of Al-Cu single crystals containing G.P.I zones. Transmission electron micrographs show that during plastic deformation the G.P.I zones are indeed intersected by the dislocations. We can take these observations as an experimental proof that the dislocation theory of the intersection process is correct.

BLEWITT *et al.* [1] report that the critical shear stress of copper single crystals (as measured at room temperature) depends on the integrated flux density φ as $\varphi^{\frac{1}{3}}$ over a rather wide range of φ. The one-third power law is very hard to understand theoretically, and no convincing derivation has yet been given. Our model predicts a $\varphi^{\frac{1}{2}}$-dependence of the critical shear stress at $T=0$ with saturation effects at higher integrated flux densities. The critical shear stresses extrapolated to $T=0$ in Fig. 3 can indeed be fitted to a ($\varphi^{\frac{1}{2}}+$ saturation)-law. MAKIN and MINTER [3] have studied the φ-dependence of the « lattice hardening component » σ_i of the yield stress of irradiated polycrystals, which may be compared with the critical shear stress τ_0 of single crystals. For copper and nickel they find that σ_i can be about equally well represented by a linear function of $\varphi^{\frac{1}{3}}$ or as being proportional to the quantity $(1-\exp[-\varphi/\varphi_s])^{\frac{1}{2}}$. The latter relation is a possible form of the ($\varphi^{\frac{1}{2}}+$saturation)-law. φ_s denotes the flux at which the saturation effects become significant. The representation of σ_i as a linear function of $\varphi^{\frac{1}{3}}$ involves an incubation period, *i.e.* the extrapolation of the measured yield stresses to $\varphi=0$ gives a stress lower than the yield stress of the unirradiated crystals. Both relations involve two adjustable parameters. From the theoretical point of view, however, the ($\varphi^{\frac{1}{2}}+$saturation)-law is much more attractive than the ($\varphi^{\frac{1}{3}}+$incubation period)-law, which presents the additional difficulty of a physical explanation for the incubation flux. The saturation effect in the critical shear stress should begin long before appreciable overlap of the diluted zones starts, due to the fact that crowdions may be captured by the zones. This should lead to a dispersion in the sizes of the zones at large φ. In this context, reference might be made to the radiation-annealing effect and the low-temperature internal friction data as additional evidence for the importance of dynamic crowdions. A more detailed discussion can be found elsewhere [5].

According to our analysis, the defects responsible for the radiation-hardening in the as-irradiated state are too small to be seen by transmission electron microscopy. MAKIN *et al.* [4, 29] have found that mild annealing of irradiated copper at 306 °C reduces the yield stress at low temperatures much more than at high temperatures. As these authors point out, this means that the distribution of the sizes of the zones changes in such a way that large zones become relatively more frequent than small zones. In a suitable temperature range, according to our model large vacancy clusters should even *grow* at the expense of small clusters. In a transmission electron microscopy study MAKIN, WHAPMAN and MINTER [4, 29] were indeed able to show that during annealing at 306 °C an increasing number of defects with diameters of the order of 25 Å become visible. It seems very likely that these have grown from the small defects that were responsible for the radiation-hardening in the as-irradiated condition. Additional evidence for this view will be discussed below.

In strongly irradiated copper SILCOX and HIRSCH [30] observed dislocation loops which were rather larger than the defects discussed in the preceding paragraph. They attribute the radiation-hardening to these loops and propose a model very similar to that of SEEGER [5, 6] for the formation of loops, *e.g.*, also involving the emission of dynamic crowdions from spikes. Although they ascribe the radiation-hardening to the forest action of these defects, they do not give a quantitative treatment. An attempt to give a quantitative basis to their considerations appears us to be beset by a number of serious difficulties. Clusters of the order of 10^3 to 10^4 vacancies per spike are required, which seems to be incompatible with our present knowledge of neutron damage. Any substantial growth of the loops by diffusion processes seems to be incompatible with the virtual independence of the radiation-hardening of the radiation temperature. The total number of loops is too small by at least one order of magnitude to account for the observed hardening. The dependence of the density and size of the loops observed by SILCOX and HIRSCH on the integrated flux density seems to be uncorrelated with the variation of the hardening.

The large loops observed and discussed by SILCOX and HIRSCH have also been observed by MAKIN *et al.* [4] (Fig. 4 shows some examples). The quantitative studies of these authors on the numbers and sizes of these loops as a function of neutron irradiation and flow stress substantiate the conclusions that have been drawn from the observation of SILCOX and HIRSCH.

MAKIN *et al.* [4, 29] were able to show that the density of small defects in copper that had been mildly annealed after irradiation shows a good correlation with the flow stress, whereas for the large loops this is not the case. Furthermore, they found that near a grain boundary there is a denuded zone of the large defects but not of the small defects. This is what would be expected if the large defects form by a migration process whereas the small defects are formed by localized events and grow by migration over short distances.

We may summarize the preceding discussion as follows. The loops of the type observed by SILCOX and HIRSCH are so infrequent (at least at medium integrated fluxes) that they can at best play a secondary rôle in radiation-hardening. On the other hand, the small defects discovered by MAKIN *et al.* [4, 29] behave in all respects as if they had grown from the invisibly small zones of our model. We may therefore take these observations as an indirect proof for the existence of these small hardening zones.

A more direct proof for their existence might be furnished by X-ray small angle scattering experiments. As estimated elsewhere [7] with a simple model of small dislocation loops for the hardening defects, at sufficiently high integrated flux densities the small angle X-ray scattering from these should be large enough to be measurable on single crystals. Such experiments are under way at Stuttgart. It is hoped that they will give information on both the size and the number of the defects, and that they will thus provide a critical test of our model.

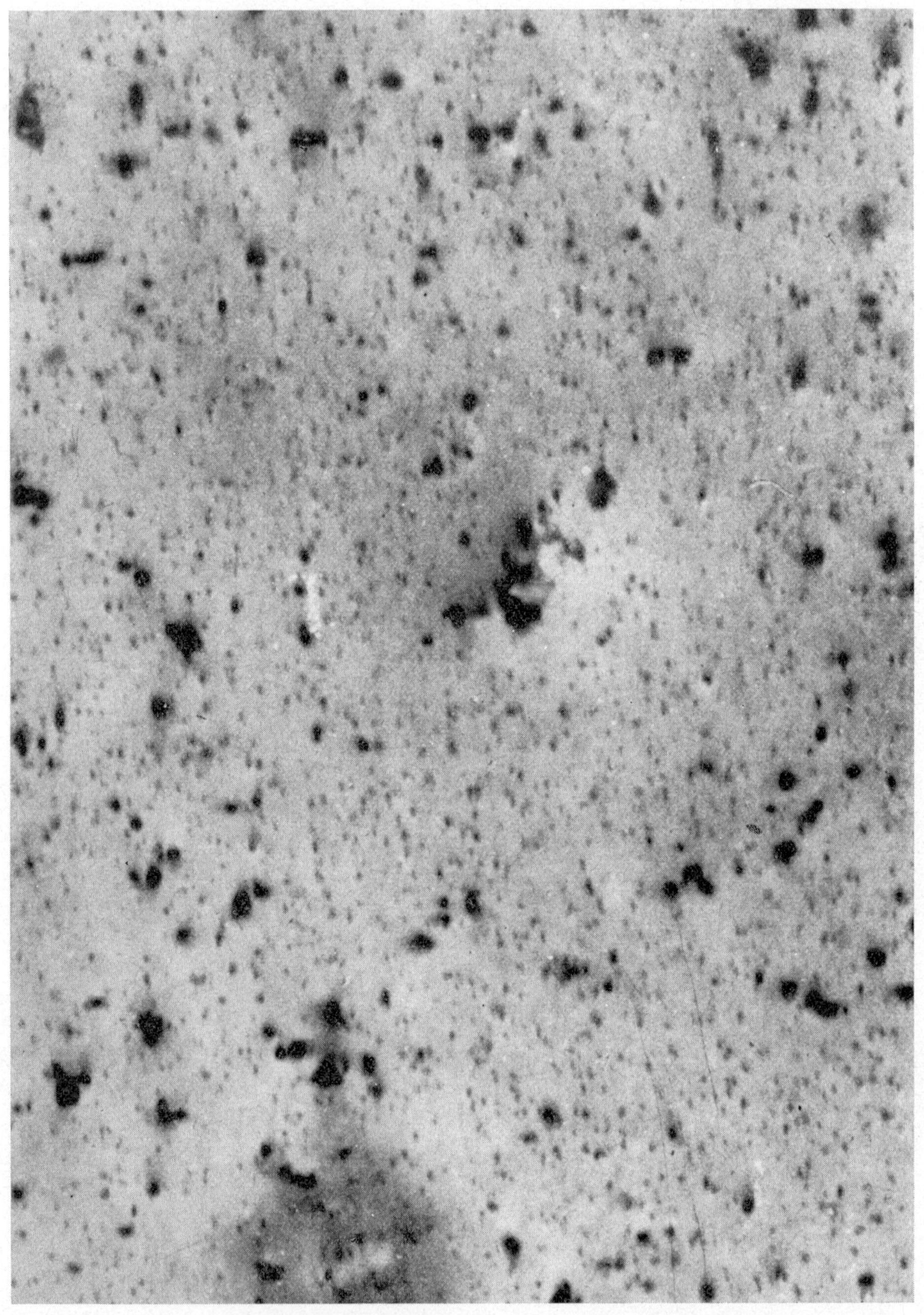

Fig. 4. – Radiation damage in copper as revealed by transmission electron microscopy. Magnification 200 000× (after M. J. MAKIN).

4. – Experimental methods for the study of the work-hardening of irradiated copper single crystals [31].

We investigated in some detail by replica electron microscopy the slip line pattern of three deformed copper single crystals that had been irradiated in the pile. All the crystals had the same crystallographic orientation in the middle of the crystallographic triangle. They were irradiated in the graphite reactor in Mol (Belgium) with an integrated thermal flux density $nvt = 6.7\cdot10^{17}$ neutrons/cm². Judging from the comparison of the critical shear stresses, this corresponds to an integrated flux density $nvt = 2\cdot10^{17}\ \text{cm}^{-2}$ in the scale used by the Oak Ridge group [1].

The crystals were deformed in tension with an average strain rate of $1.5\cdot10^{-4}\ \text{s}^{-1}$ either in a liquid oxygen bath ($T = 90\ ^\circ\text{K}$), at room temperature ($T = 293\ ^\circ\text{K}$), or at $T = 513\ ^\circ\text{K}$ in a furnace under an inert atmosphere of N_2 and H_2.

The shear-stress–shear-strain curves of these crystals are shown in Fig 5. At the points marked on the stress-strain curves the tensile tests were

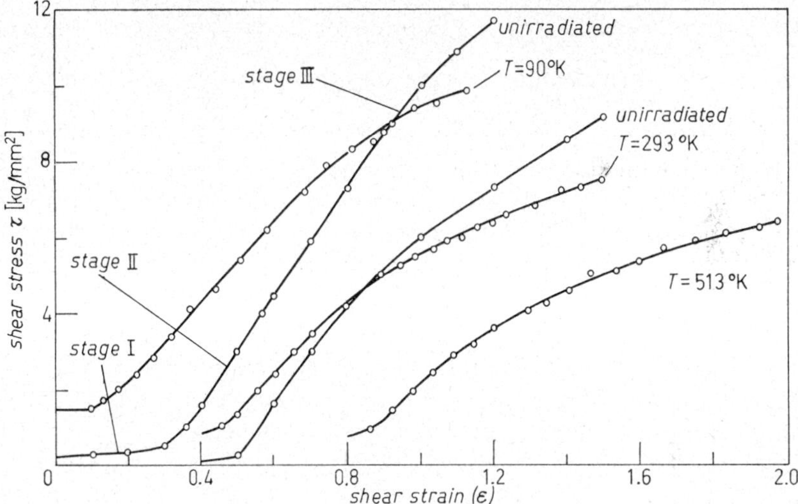

Fig. 5. – Stress-strain curves of neutron irradiated copper single crystals at three different temperatures, compared with the curves of unirradiated crystals deformed at 90 °K and 293 °K.

interrupted in order to study the surface by optical microscopy or to prepare carbon replicas for examination in the electron microscope. The electron microscopy techniques and the evaluation of the slip line data were essentially those described by MADER [32].

Before the plastic deformation and at points indicated in the stress-strain curve the crystals were polished electrolytically. By this procedure it was possible to attribute the observed slip line pattern to a certain strain interval, thus giving us information on the slip processes in this interval. Fig. 6 (taken

Fig. 6. – The « wooden disks » model of a single crystal with close-packed glide planes. *a*) The undeformed crystal. *b*) Plastic deformation by simultaneous slip on one glide plane along a close packed direction. *c*) Plastic deformation by local slip in various slipped zones in the glide plane. A short slip line appears where a slipped zone meets the surface.

from [33]) shows in a schematic way how this behavior is related to dislocation theory. Fig. 6*a* gives a model of a crystal with close-packed slip planes. Fig. 6*b* shows how translation on one of the glide planes in the slip direction indicated by the arrow (one of the close-packed directions and also the direction of the Burgers vector of the dislocations in Fig. 6*c*) created a slip step on the surface. It is these steps that are studied in the electron micrographs. In reality, however, the translation does not occur simultaneously over the whole glide plane. Rather, the slip spreads gradually over the glide plane by the movement of dislocations, dislocation lines forming the boundaries between the slipped and the unslipped parts of the plane or between regions of different amount of slip. Fig. 6*c* shows three systems of dislocation rings that have spread over part of the glide plane. Where such a system of rings is intersected by the surface, a slip step is created. The height of the slip step is proportional to the number n of dislocations in the ring and depends furthermore in a known way on the orientation of the crystal and of the surface. The length of the slip step is directly related to the slip distance of the dislocations (*), whereas the number of slip lines gives information on the number of dislocations per unit area, *i.e.* the dislocation density. At each end of a slip line a group of dislocation lines runs into the interior of the crystal. We can therefore also obtain information on the geometrical arrangement of these groups.

The information obtainable from slip line observations is most useful for building up a dislocation theory of work-hardening, provided the surface markings are typical and representative for the dislocation processes in the bulk material. That this is so has been shown in some detail for the plastic deformation of *unirradiated* f.c.c. single crystals [32-35]. Since at present nothing is known to the contrary we shall assume that the equivalence of surface pattern and bulk properties also holds for *irradiated* f.c.c. single crystals.

5. – Experimental results (**).

Fig. 5 shows the stress-strain curves and their temperature-dependence. Superficially the stress-strain curves might appear similar to those of the unirradiated crystals. There is a stage I of little or no work-hardening, followed by a stage II of rapid work-hardening. In the final stage III of the stress-strain curve the rate of work-hardening decreases again. However, the initial stage of the work-hardening curve of the irradiated crystals is entirely different from the so-called easy glide region of the unirradiated crystals and more related to the yield phenomenon and the elongation zone observed in alloys, as already stressed by BLEWITT *et al.* [1].

The initial part of the stress-strain curve of the irradiated crystals is serrated. The crystal deforms under an average load which remains constant. The observation of slip lines shows that the glide is not uniform. It starts at one or both of the grips and spreads gradually through the crystal. The region covered with slip lines is called a Lüders band. Fig. 7 shows the appearance of the Lüders band in the optical microscope. The sharpness of the Lüders band (characterized by the width of the region in which slip has begun but has not yet obtained the final value corresponding to the end of the elongation zone) varies considerably with the temperature of deformation. At 90 °K the front of the Lüders band extends over the whole length of the crystal, whereas at 513 °K the transition region between the slipped and the unslipped crystal has a width of the order 1 mm to 1 cm only.

The strong slip lines visible in the optical microscope (comp. Fig. 7) may

(*) For an exception to this see Sect. **6**·4.

(**) Part of these results have been published elsewhere [5, 31, 36].

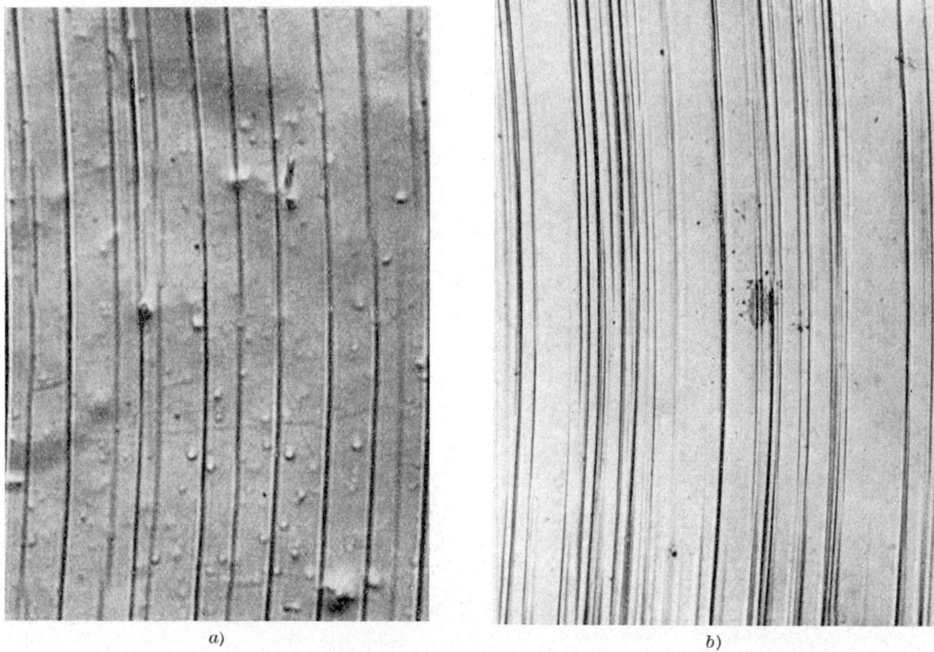

a) *b)*

Fig. 7. – Optical micrographs 250×. *a*) Temperature of deformation 513 °K, end of the elongation zone. The crystal surface is uniformly filled up with slip bands. *b*) Temperature of deformation 90 °K. The elongation zone is much longer and at the end of the elongation zone the slip bands are more densely packed.

Fig. 8. – Electron micrograph 7 500×, temperature of deformation 513 °K, fine structure of a slip line cluster generated in the elongation zone.

be further resolved in the electron microscope. Fig. 8 and 9 show two examples from crystals deformed at 90 °K and 513 °K. It is seen that a line visible in the optical microscope is in reality a cluster of very fine individual slip lines grouped together. At low temperatures the slip lines appear to be

Fig. 9. – Electron micrograph 7 500×, temperature of deformation 90 °K, fine structure of a slip line cluster generated in the elongation zone at low temperature.

more closely spaced and somewhat longer than at high temperatures. The amount of slip per individual line, however, is larger at higher temperatures. Tables I and II summarize some of the results on slip line observations at the end of the elongation zones.

TABLE I. – *Temperature-dependence of the arrangement of slip line clusters (slip bands) at the end of the elongation zone.*

T (°K)	τ_0 (kg/mm²)	Number of clusters per cm on the crystal surface (measured where the slip lines are normal to the crystal axis)	Amount of slip per cluster (Å)	Extension of elongation zone (shear strain) ε	Width of the regions between clusters free of slip lines, measured normal to the glide plane (μm)
90	1.50	$25 \cdot 10^2$	2 600	0.09	3
293	0.90	—	—	0.03	—
513	0.69	$6 \cdot 10^2$	2 000	0.017	13

TABLE II. – *Structure of the slip line clusters in the elongation zone.*

T (°K)	Number of slip lines per cluster	Slip per individual slip line	Approximate slip line length (μm)
90	50	50 Å only a small fraction of lines have a thickness between 100 to 200 Å	100
513	less than 50	more than at 90 °K	60

During the propagation of the Lüders band of the primary glide system, slip lines of other slip systems appear. These secondary slip traces belong frequently to the cross slip plane and sometimes to the so-called unpredicted glide plane. Pronounced slip on secondary systems stops when the primary slip has completely covered the crystal. Slip on both secondary glide planes is much more frequent at higher temperatures than at lower ones, and has been very rarely observed on the crystal deformed at 90 °K. Fig. 10 shows

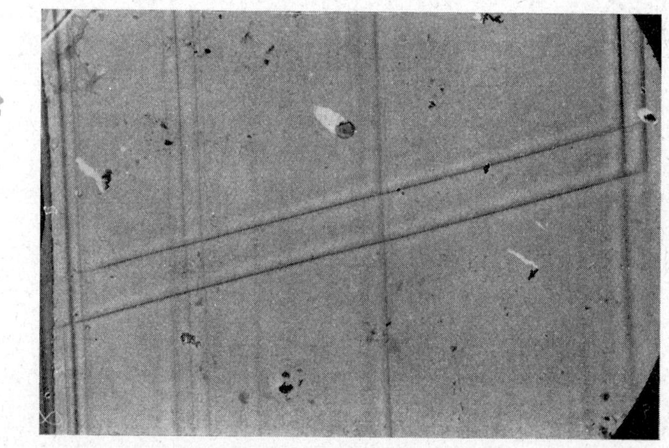

Fig. 10. – Electron micrograph 5000×, temperature of deformation 513 °K, pronounced cross slip traces in the elongation zone. The heights of the cross slip lines correspond to about 150 dislocation on the cross slip plane.

an example of cross slip intersecting or connecting the slip lines of the primary system. From the displacements of the primary lines at the intersections it is estimated that the number of dislocations leaving the crystal through the cross slip line was $n = 160$.

At the end of the elongation zone the whole surface of the crystals is covered uniformly with the slip clusters discussed above. Further glide proceeds by slip in the regions between the clusters. Occasionally cross slip traces are observed, the length of which, however, decreases with increasing strain. After a short transition stage of increasing curvature (which is more extended

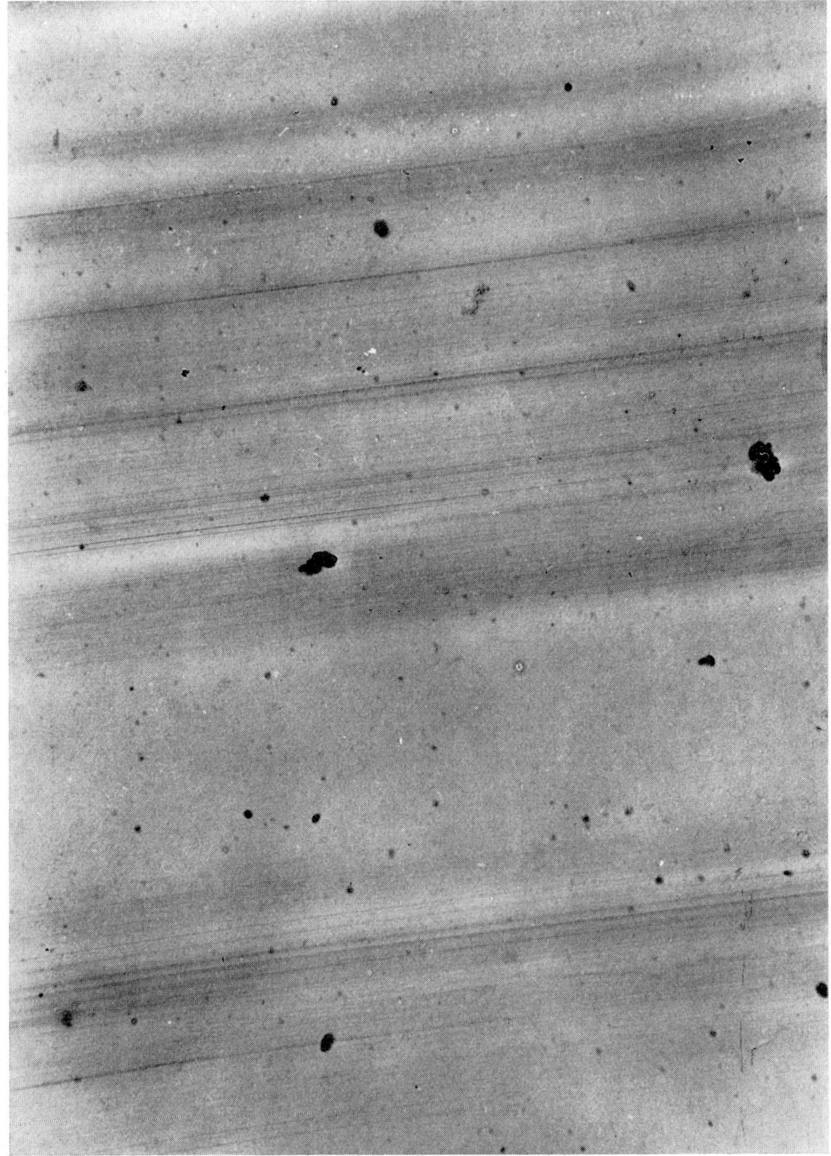

Fig. 11. – Electron micrograph 12 000 ×, temperature of deformation 90 °K, slip lines at the beginning of stage II. The slip lines are more clustered than those in stage II of unirradiated crystals.

at lower temperatures than at higher ones) the slope of the stress-strain curve assumes a constant value ϑ_{II}, which in our experiments was 10.5 kg/mm², practically independent of the temperature of deformation. If anything, the

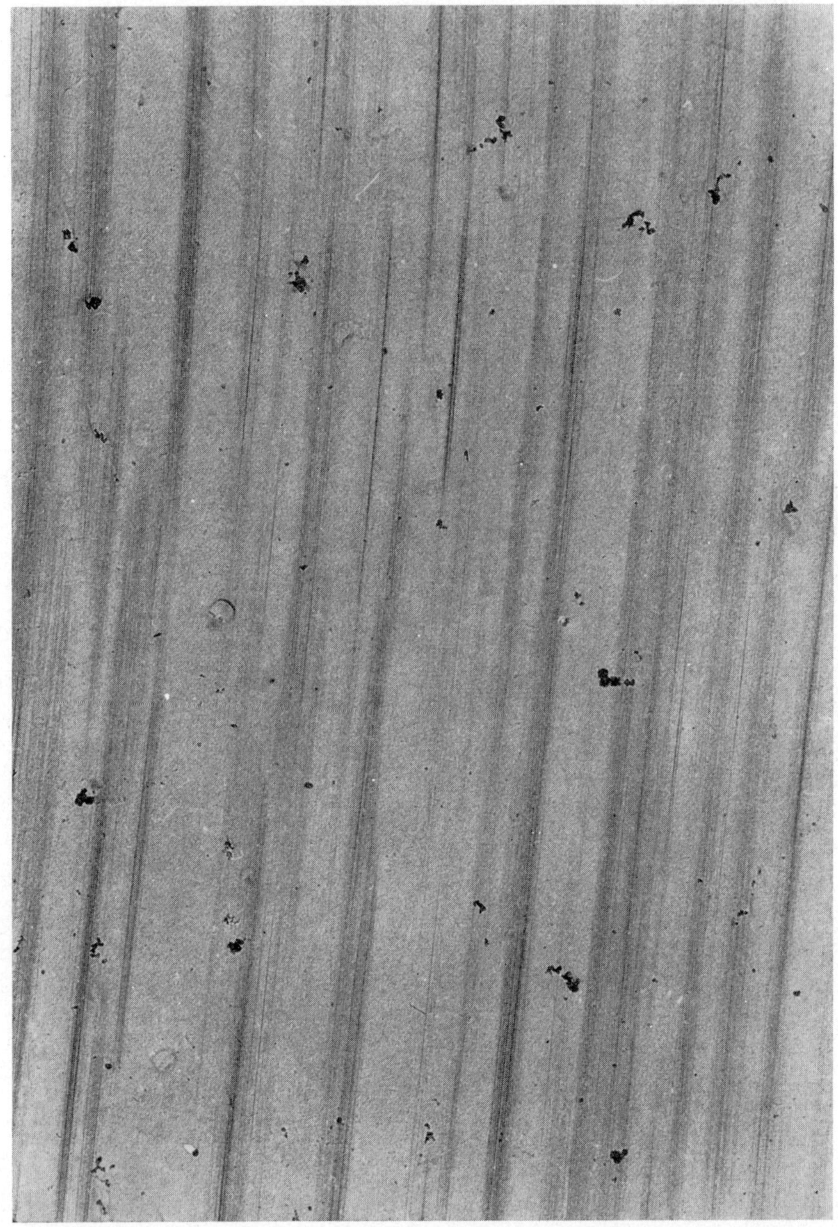

Fig. 12. – Electron micrograph 12 000×, temperature of deformation 90 °K, end of stage II. The length of the active slip lines has decreased during stage II.

ratio ϑ_{II}/G (G = shear modulus) increased slightly with increasing temperature, contrary to what is found for unirradiated crystals.

Fig. 11 and 12 show two typical electron micrographs of stage II. The individual slip lines are still clustered, although not as strongly as in the elongation zone or as later in stage III. The grouping of slip lines is similar to that found by MADER [32] on unirradiated copper single crystals in «structurized fine slip» of stage II, although more pronounced. The slip line pattern appears to be independent of the temperature of deformation. The same statement holds for the frequency of cross slip traces. The tendency for grouping diminished with increasing strain. Whereas at the beginning of stage II the clusters comprise 50 to 100 individual lines, they contain only 10 to 20 lines at the end of stage II.

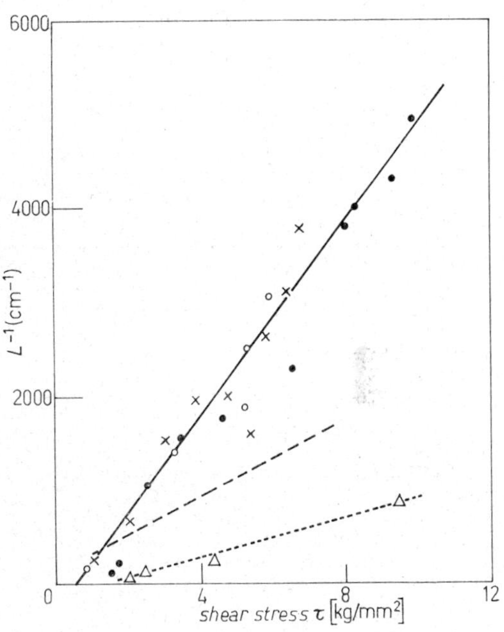

Fig. 13. – Variation with shear stress τ of the reciprocal of the average length L of active slip lines at different temperatures of deformation (● 90 °K, × 293 °K, ○ 513 °K) and of the clusters at 90 K (△). The dashed line gives the length of the active slip lines of unirradiated crystals according to MADER [32].

The length L of the individual slip lines (measured at the top surface) decreases with increasing stress and strain. Fig. 13 shows that L^{-1} is a linear function of stress (independent of the temperature of deformation), *i.e.*

$$L = \Lambda'/(\tau - \tau^*) . \tag{5.1}$$

In stage II, L^{-1} is a linear function of the strain, too:

$$L = \Lambda/(\varepsilon - \varepsilon^*) . \tag{5.2}$$

The parameters in the eqs. (5.1) and (5.2) are

$$\Lambda' = 2.1 \cdot 10^{-3} \frac{\text{kg}}{\text{mm}^2} \cdot \text{cm} , \qquad \tau^* = 0.6 \frac{\text{kg}}{\text{mm}^2} .$$

$$\Lambda = 2 \cdot 10^{-4} \text{ cm} , \qquad \varepsilon^* = 0.02 .$$

For unirradiated copper single crystals of the same crystallographic orientation MADER [32] finds in stage II: $\Lambda = 4 \cdot 10^{-4}$ cm. Relation (5.1) also holds for the length of the clusters of the irradiated crystals with Λ' being about four times larger than for individual slip lines.

Per definitionem, stage III begins at the stress τ_{III} where the stress-strain curves depart measurably from linearity. As it does for unirradiated crystals, τ_{III} decreases markedly with increasing temperature (Fig. 14) (*). Once τ_{III} is

TABLE III. – *Experimental data on overshooting and fracture.*

T (°K)	First traces of conjugate slip seen in the optical microscope		Onset of conjugate slip		Fracture		$(\tau_{co}/\tau_{pr} - 1)$
	shear strain (ε)	τ (kg/mm²)	shear strain (ε)	τ (kg/mm²)	shear strain (ε)	τ (kg/mm²)	
90	1.04	9.57	1.1	9.86	1.12	9.86	0.16
293	0.83	6.57	1.1	7.46	1.10	7.46	0.16
513	0.48	4.11	1.1	6.25	1.18	6.36	0.16

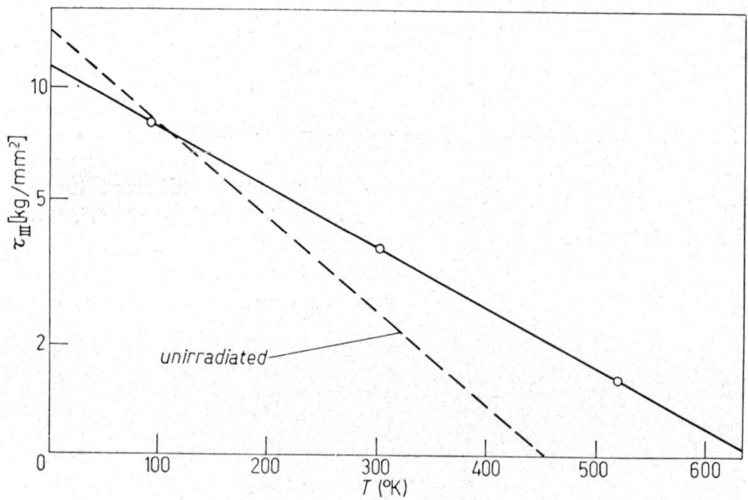

Fig. 14. – τ_{III} (the shear stress at which the stress-strain curve deviates from the linear stage II) as a function of the temperature of deformation. The dashed line corresponds to unirradiated crystals [22, 34].

(*) The accuracy of our τ_{III}-values is limited due to the repeated polishing of the crystals and subsequent variations in the crystal diameters.

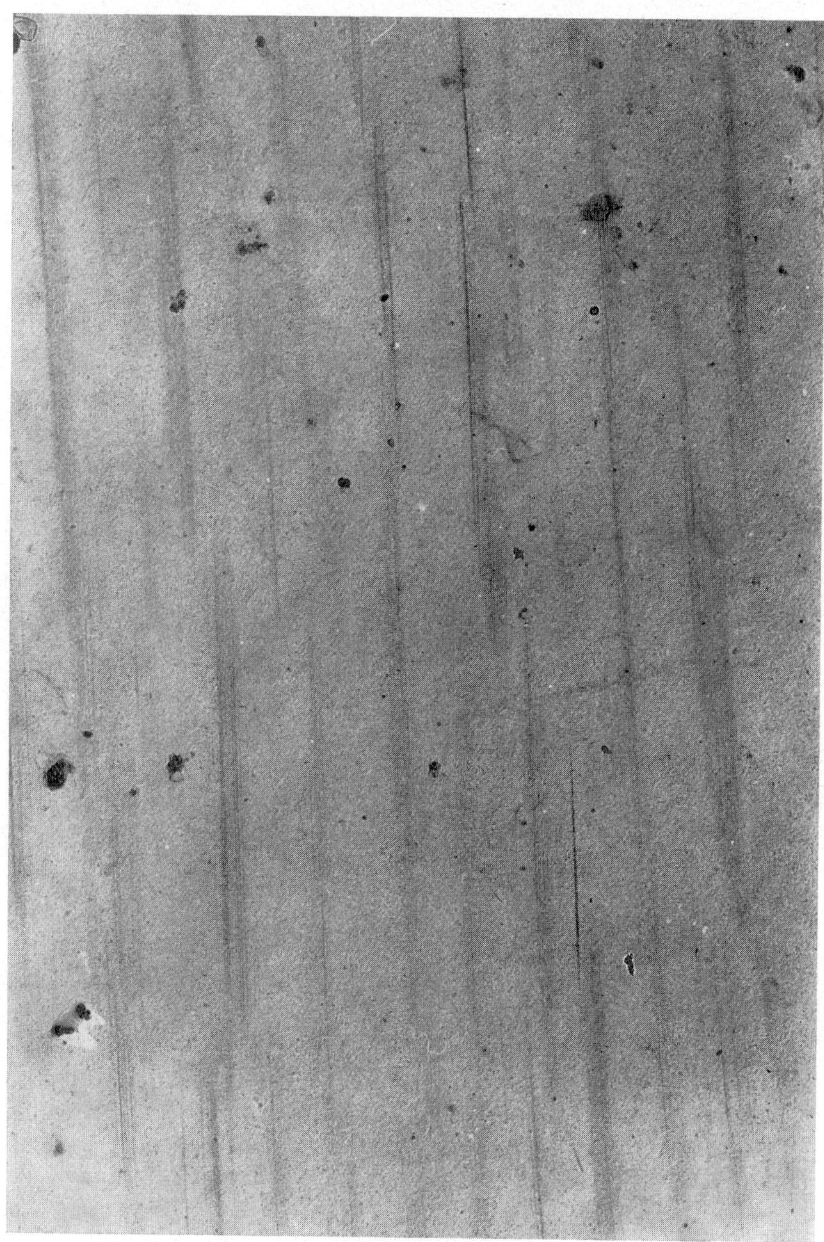

Fig. 15. – Electron micrograph 12 000×, temperature of deformation 90 °K, slip-line pattern in stage III, showing fragmented slip bands.

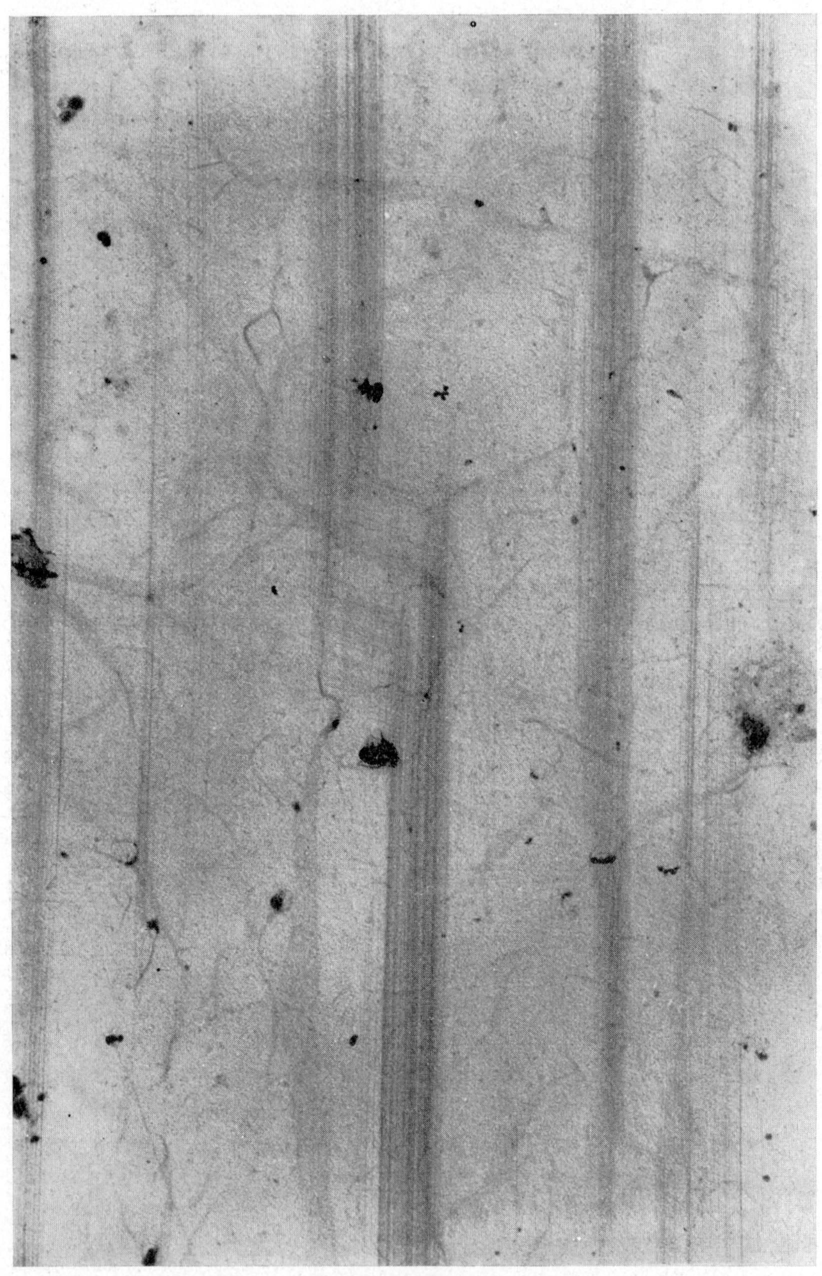

Fig. 16. – Electron micrograph 12 000 ×, temperature of deformation 513 °K, slip-line pattern in stage III, showing fragmented slip bands connected by thermally-activated cross slip.

Fig. 17. – Electron micrograph 7 500 ×, temperature of deformation 513 °K, fanning of slip lines on the side surface (Burgers vector nearly parallel to surface).

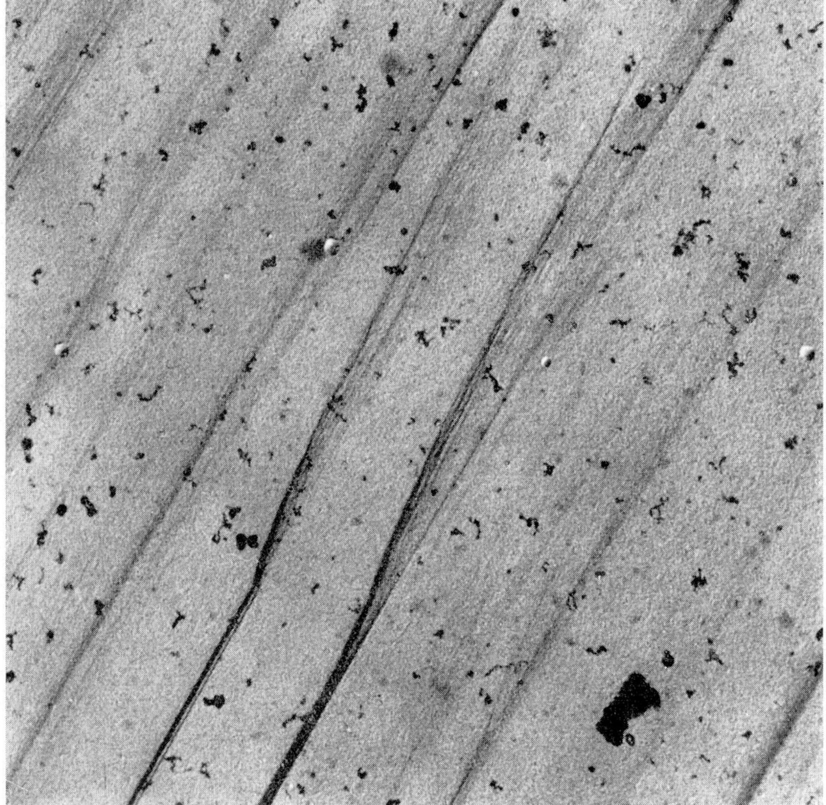

Fig. 18. – Electron micrograph 12 000 ×, temperature of deformation 773 °K, pronounced fanning of slip lines on the side surface of an unirradiated crystal.

TABLE IV. – *Comparison of the stress-strain curves and slip line characteristics between unirradiated copper crystals, irradiated copper crystals, and α-brass crystals, with special reference to the temperature-dependence.*

Property or stage	Unirradiated Cu single crystals	T-dep.	Irradiated Cu single crystals nvt$=2\cdot10^{+17}$ cm^{-2}	T-dep.	70/30 α-brass single crystals	T-dep.
critical shear stress (at 293 °K)	0.1 kg/mm²	weak	sharp yield point 0.9 kg/mm²	strong	sharp yield point 1.3 kg/mm²	strong
initial part of stress-strain curves (stage I)	easy glide, homogeneous fine-slip $n=10\ldots15$ [39]	intermediate (extension)	elongation zone, Lüders band, clustering, glide on cross-slip and unexpected plane $n\approx20$	strong (extension)	elongation zone, Lüders band [40] cross-slip [41] $n\approx100$	weak (extension)
stage II $\vartheta_{II}=$const	$L=\dfrac{\Lambda}{\varepsilon-\varepsilon^*}$; $\Lambda=4\cdot10^{-4}$ cm T (°K) | $\vartheta_{II}/G\cdot10^{-3}$ 90 | 3.15 293 | 3.08 structurized fine slip, traces of secondary slip, few kink bands $n=20\ldots25$	weak (ϑ_{II}/G)	$L=\dfrac{\Lambda}{\varepsilon-\varepsilon^*}$; $\Lambda=2\cdot10^{-4}$ cm T (°K) | $\vartheta_{II}/G\cdot10^{-3}$ 90 | 2.32 293 | 2.44 513 | 2.67 slip lines clustered, similar to structurized fine slip, no kink-bands, overshooting $(\tau_{co}/\tau_{pr})-1=0.16$ $n\approx25$	weak (ϑ_{II}/G)	T (°K) | $\vartheta_{II}/G\cdot10^{-3}$ 83 | 3.08 293 | 2.48 473 | 2.20 strong individual lines on cross-slip and conjugate plane, overshooting $(\tau_{co}/\tau_{pr})-1=0.25$ [40] $n\approx140$ [41]	stronger (ϑ_{II}/G)
stage III	fragmented slip bands, cross-slip, abundant kink-bands	strong (τ_{III})	fragmented slip bands, cross-slip, abundant kink-bands	strong (τ_{III})	Not observed, since onset of conjugate system occurred before τ_{III} was reached	weak according to theory (τ_{III})

reached, cross slip appears rather frequently. The slip proceeds mainly by glide on lines grouped into slip bands. Typical examples are shown in Fig. 15 and Fig. 16. These pictures are very similar to the corresponding ones obtained for unirradiated crystals. The relationship between the processes occurring in stage III in irradiated and in unirradiated crystals appears to be rather close.

Cross slip traces are only found on or near the top surface. On the side surface the crystal deformed at 513 °K showed the phenomenon of « fanning » of slip lines (Fig. 17), first observed on zinc single crystals deformed at (relatively) high temperatures [37]. The same phenomenon can also be observed on unirradiated copper single crystals, as the example (Fig. 18) of a crystal deformed at 773 °K shows.

With respect to kink-band formation the irradiated crystals seem to behave in essentially the same way as unirradiated crystals [38]. The density of kink-bands increased rapidly after the beginning of stage III.

The final experimental result which we wish to discuss is the overshooting of the crystal orientation over the symmetry plane between the primary and the conjugate slip system, reported already by Blewitt *et al.* [1]. For the crystal orientation chosen in our experiments the resolved shear stress τ_{co} in the conjugate glide system becomes equal to the resolved shear stress τ_{pr} in the primary system at the shear strain $\varepsilon = 0.71$. As Table III shows, however, slip continues on the primary system, until the ratio $\tau_{co}/\tau_{pr} = 1.16$ is reached. As can be seen from in Table III the crystal orientation employed is not very suitable for the study of conjugate slip, since the crystals broke very soon after the conjugate slip system had taken over.

6. – Discussion of the plastic deformation of irradiated single crystals.

6·1. *General discussion.* – The preceding experimental results can be characterized very briefly in the following way. At the beginning of the deformation both the stress-strain curve and the slip line pattern are very different from that of unirradiated crystals. The region of jerky flow following the yield stress τ_0 of the irradiated crystals bears practically no resemblance to the easy glide region of the unirradiated crystals. From the beginning of the linear part of the stress-strain curve (stage II) onwards, the work-hardening curves of the irradiated and of the unirradiated crystals have the same shape, although the quantitative details are somewhat different. The slip line patterns differ noticeably from each other at the beginning of stage II, but become increasingly similar, at least qualitatively, with increasing strain. However, with respect to the phenomenon of overshooting, irradiated crystals differ from unirradiated copper crystals, which show very little overshooting, rather drastically even at very high strains.

In terms of our radiation damage model the general characteristics of the plastic deformation of neutron-irradiated copper single crystals can be accounted for in a general way by supposing that during the deformation the « zones », which are responsible for the increase of flow stress due to irradiation, become gradually uneffective during deformation, and that the larger the deformation the more the dislocation processes resemble those occuring in the unirradiated crystals. This is rather gratifying, since the cutting of the dislocations through the zones will decrease them in size and effectiveness and eventually destroy them completely. The overshooting phenomenon might appear to present a serious difficulty to such a picture. It may be argued, however, that the work-hardened state built up during stage I and stage II is unlikely to be quite the same as in an unirradiated crystal. It could be different in such a way that the latent hardening in the conjugate slip system is larger. As a matter of fact, slip traces of the conjugate slip plane are never seen on irradiated crystals until τ_{co} is larger than τ_{pr}, in striking contrast to the behavior of unirradiated crystals. On the other hand, slip on the cross slip plane and on the unpredicted plane are not nearly as rare.

As stressed by BLEWITT *et al.* [1], neutron-irradiated copper crystals resemble the behavior of α-brass and some other alloys just in those respects in which they differ most from unirradiated crystals: elongation zone, Lüders-band propagation, and overshooting. In Table IV we have therefore carried out a comparison between the experimental results on unirradiated copper, neutron irradiated copper, and α-brass.

Our compilation shows that the analogy between α-brass and irradiated copper is far from being complete. In α-brass the Lüders strain (*i.e.*, the strain at the end of the elongation zone) is practically independent of temperature, whereas it is strongly temperature-dependent in neutron-irradiated copper. Whereas in α-brass the number n of dislocations per slip line is rather large (with a wide scatter between individual lines), it is small in neutron irradiated crystals. The similarity between optical micrographs of α-brass and irradiated crystals is not borne out by the more revealing electron microscope studies. These show that in the early stage of deformation the fine slip lines of irradiated copper are much more grouped together than the stronger lines of α-brass. The temperature-dependence of ϑ_{II}/G has opposite sign in the two cases. On the other hand, the appearance of cross slip before stage III is reached is very similar indeed to that on α-brass single crystals. (This type of cross slip should be clearly distinguished from the thermally activated cross slip prevailing in stage III, desirably by a different name.)

6'2. *The evidence for the destruction of the zones during deformation.* – After the general discussion let us now consider the interpretation of the experimental results in greater detail. We shall first take up the evidence for the gradual destruction of the hardening zones during plastic deformation. As has been shown in Section **3**, the zones give rise to a rather strong temperature-dependence of the critical shear stress of *irradiated crystals*. The temperature-dependence of the critical shear stress or of the flow stress after plastic deformation of *unirradiated* crystals (which is due to dislocation interactions) is much smaller. Plastic deformation should therefore reduce the temperature-dependence of the flow stress of irradiated crystals in such a way that forl arge strains it will approach that of deformed unirradiated crystals (*). The following experimental procedure allows us to test his prediction. Interrupt the deformation of an unirradiated crystal, change the testing temperature at each interruption between two temperatures T_1 and T_2, and study the flow-stress ratio τ_2/τ_1, where $\tau_2 =$ flow stress at the higher temperature T_2 and $\tau_1 =$ flow stress at the lower temperature T_1. MAKIN [43] has carried out a large number of such change-in-temperature tests on irradiated polycrystalline copper. He showed, furthermore, that corresponding tests on single crystals gave qualitatively, although not quantitatively, similar results. We feel therefore justified in discussing Makin's findings [43] in connection with our single crystal experiments.

MAKIN finds that τ_2/τ_1 decreases with increasing deformation, starting from the value corresponding to the yield stress of an irradiated crystal. After a tensile deformation of slightly more than 20% extension the flow stress ratio reaches that of unirradiated copper which had undergone the same amount of deformation. Applied to single crystals this means that after a shear strain ε of about 0.6 the contribution of the zones to the flow stress should be negligibly small. The gradual reduction of this contribution (which has the « normal » temperature-dependence) gives rise to an apparent contribution to the work-hardening rate ϑ_{II} of irradiated crystals that increases with increasing temperature. Let us compare deformations at 90 °K and 293 °K. Table IV shows that the difference in the reduced work-hardening rates at these two temper-

---

(*) It has proven fruitful to consider the flow-stress τ at any given strain ε as the sum of a contribution τ_s which decreases with increasing temperature on account of thermal activation and a contribution τ_G which is temperature-independent except for the temperature variation of the elastic constants. From the equation

$$\tau = \tau_s + \tau_G$$

follows for the work-hardening rates

$$\frac{d\tau}{d\varepsilon} \equiv \vartheta = \vartheta_s + \vartheta_G \,.$$

In the following discussions we shall make use of this scheme; for more details see *e.g.* [42].

atures is

$$(6.1a)\qquad \left.\frac{\vartheta_{II}}{G_t}\right|_{90°K} - \left.\frac{\vartheta_{II}}{G}\right|_{293°K} = 7\cdot 10^{-5}\,,$$

for unirradiated crystals, and

$$(6.1b)\qquad \left.\frac{\vartheta_{II}}{G}\right|_{90°K} - \left.\frac{\vartheta_{II}}{G}\right|_{293°K} = -\,12\cdot 10^{-5}\,,$$

for irradiated crystals.

The difference in the temperature-dependent part (*) of the work-hardening rate ϑ_s between irradiated and unirradiated crystals amounts therefore to

$$(6.2)\qquad \vartheta_s = -\,19\cdot 10^{-5} G\,.$$

For irradiated crystals the difference between the critical shear stress at 90 °K and that at 293 °K is (Fig. 5)

$$\tau_0\,(90\,°\mathrm{K}) - \tau_0\,(293\,°\mathrm{K}) = 0.60\ \mathrm{kg/mm^2}\,.$$

A small part of this (about 0.05 kg/mm²) comes from the original dislocation network of the crystal and is not reduced by the subsequent deformation. We may therefore expect that the destruction of the zones gives us a negative contribution to the temperature-dependent part of the work-hardening rate

$$(6.4)\qquad \vartheta_s = -\,\frac{0.55}{0.6}\ \mathrm{kg/mm^2} = -\,0.92\ \mathrm{kg/mm^2} = -\,20\cdot 10^{-5}\, G\,.$$

($G = 4\,560$ kg/mm²). The agreement between the calculated value, eq. (6.4), and the experimental value, eq. (6.2), is good.

According to the preceding picture the negative ϑ_s-contribution must disappear at strains large enough for the majority of the zones to be destroyed. We expect therefore an increase in the work-hardening rate at $\varepsilon = 0.6$ This effect should be most pronounced at very low temperatures, since at these

(*) In order to simplify the wording we take as « the temperature dependent part » simply the difference between ϑ/G at 90 °K and 293 °K.

temperatures $-\vartheta_s$ is largest, and stage II is most extended. The stress-strain curve of a copper single crystal deformed at 4.2 °K after irradiation by an integrated neutron flux of $nvt = 2 \cdot 10^{18}$ cm^{-2} shows indeed at $\varepsilon = 0.63$ an increase in ϑ_{II} of the order of 75 %, which is the right order of magnitude for the irradiation and temperature involved (Fig. 12, ref. [1]).

The preceding evidence lends considerable support to the destruction hypothesis. A further piece of evidence corroborating the view that the majority of the zones become ineffective after shear strains of about 0.6 is the fact that the slip line pattern in stage III (*i.e.*, at large strains) appears to be almost the same in irradiated crystals and in unirradiated crystals. The shear stress at the beginning of stage τ_{III} of irradiated crystals shows a qualitatively similar temperature-dependence as in unirradiated crystals (Fig. 14). In the latter case it was possible [22, 34] to relate the variation of τ_{III} with temperature and strain-rate quantitatively to the stacking-fault energy and the dislocation arrangement of the metal. In view of the very limited data available it is too early to say whether a similar analysis seems to be possible or not for irradiated f.c.c. metals. It should be kept in mind, however, that at higher temperatures stage III begins at strains where a large fraction of the zones have not yet been eliminated. This is bound to give rise to complications in the analysis of τ_{III}.

6·3. *Yield phenomenon and work-softening effect.* – As mentioned earlier, the beginning of the plastic deformation of irradiated crystals differs in a characteristic way from that of unirradiated crystals, particularly by the existence of a yield phenomenon (accompanied by Lüders-band propagation) and by the rather pronounced clustering of slip lines into bands. We should like to suggest that both of these phenomena have their origin in the destruction of the zones by gliding dislocations. Generally speaking, yield phenomena, elongation zones, and Lüders-band propagation occur whenever slip proceeds more easily in regions which have slipped before than in undeformed regions, *i.e.* if the local coefficient of work-hardening is negative. In our case such a negative coefficient of work-hardening is provided by the destruction mechanism discussed in Section **6·2**. The elongation zone terminates at a strain where the negative work-hardening rate due to the zone destruction is balanced by an opposite and equal « normal » work-hardening rate due to dislocation interactions. The latter is in general not very temperature-dependent. From what we have said in Section **6·2** it is clear that the amount of this negative contribution to the work-hardening rate is larger the lower the temperature. The proposed mechanism explains therefore, at least qualitatively, the temperature-dependence of the stage I of irradiated crystals. It should be noted that this explanation differs from that of the qualitatively similar temperature-dependence of the extension of stage I of the unirradiated crystals [42].

As discussed in Section **2**, the « zones » may be looked upon as a special arrangement of vacant lattice sites. It appears likely, therefore, that during the intersection of the zones some of these vacancies attach themselves to the intersecting dislocations, and, by disappearing at dislocation jogs, cause the dislocations to climb. By such a climbing process slip can be transferred to a neighboring parallel slip plane. As has been demonstrated in zinc single crystals deformed at intermediate and high temperatures [37, 42], such a process can give rise to a clustering of slip lines similar in appearance to the slip bands in stage III of f.c.c. metal crystals. The slip bands in zinc differ, however, from the stage III slip bands by the phenomenon of fanning, which is the surface marking left behind by climbing dislocations. On our irradiated crystals we have observed this fanning process only rarely. This is not surprising, since the climbing process gives rise to surface steps large enough to be visible in surface replicas only if a substantial number of dislocations climb along approximately the same path. This is unlikely to be the case in irradiated crystals, where the vacancy sources, *i.e.* the zones, are dispersed. Although we do not have direct evidence for this view, we are of the opinion that the pronounced clustering of the slip lines on little or moderately deformed irradiated crystals occurs by a climbing process similar to that operating in zinc.

KUHLMANN-WILSDORF, MADDIN and WILSDORF [44] have discussed at some length the various ways in which point defects, which may be either dispersed or condensed in dislocation rings, may interact with moving dislocations. These authors consider in particular the plastic deformation of quenched metal crystals. Some of their discussions (which include the mechanism of slip-band formation) may be relevant for our present discussion, since in addition to the zones in the irradiated crystals a small concentration of dislocation loops and point defects should be present. (The majority of the point defects have annealed out during the irradiation.) GREENFIELD and WILSDORF [45] have indeed observed that the density of dislocation loops visible in irradiated copper foils is reduced after the passing of dislocations.

Another group of phenomena likely to be related to the destruction of the zones are those connected with the *work-softening* effect of irradiated polycrystalline copper, discovered by MAKIN [43]. MAKIN observed that at small strains (below 12%, which for single crystals may correspond to $\varepsilon = 0.3$) a change-in-temperature test of the type described in Section **6**·2 is accompanied by a yield drop and the propagation of a Lüders band at the temperature T_2, if the temperature of deformation is changed from the temperature $T_1 = -195\,°C$ to a temperature T_2 above about $-100\,°C$. The drop in flow stress occuring during the testing at the higher temperature is irreversible and appears to occur mainly at the expense of the temperature-dependent part of the flow stress. No similar phenomenon appears if the temperature of deformation is changed from the higher temperature T_2 to the lower temperature T_1. Such change-in-temperature tests may therefore safely be employed to study the reversible temperature variation of the flow stress.

A possible explanation (similar to one of those discussed by MAKIN [43]) is as follows. The work-softening phenomenon is related to the existence of small zones, comprising only very few vacant sites. If such small zones are bisected by dislocations, vacancy clusters such as divacancies, trivacancies, etc., are generated. Some of these clusters are mobile at temperatures above $-100\,^{\circ}$C. When the temperature of deformation changes from liquid-nitrogen temperature to $T_2 = -100\,^{\circ}$C, some of these clusters may migrate to dislocation lines held up by large zones, and help them to climb over these obstacles. This means effectively that the flow stress is lowered due to the mobility of the small clusters. This gives rise to a negative coefficient of work-hardening with all the consequences indicated above. The strongly localized deformation following the yield drop will lead to a further elimination of zones and therefore reduce the temperature-dependent part of the flow stress further. An alternative explanation of the work-softening phenomenon may be based on the inhomogeneity of the deformed crystal. In the glide bands the ratio τ_s/τ_G is lower than in the regions between the glide bands, where the hardening zones have not yet been intersected by dislocations. As a consequence, after a change to a higher temperature the glide will tend to spread into the regions between the glide bands. Dislocation groups piled up at low temperature at the end of the slip lines may be dissolved by cross slip or by an annihilation with groups of opposite sign. The softening mechanism would in this case be similar to the classical work-softening mechanism of unirradiated f.c.c. crystals [42] (*).

The annealing characteristics observed by MAKIN [43] could be explained in both ways. The yield drop and the irradiation work-softening are eliminated by a 60 min anneal at 300 °C in copper. As discussed in Section 3 such a relatively light annealing treatment removes mainly the small clusters and changes the temperature-dependence of the flow stress accordingly.

A critical test of the preceding views would be provided by a deformation experiment in which the temperature is changed from, say, liquid-helium temperature to liquid-nitrogen temperature, since it is known that below liquid-nitrogen temperature none of the defects generated by plastic deformation (which include presumably all the smaller vacancy clusters) are mobile. We would therefore expect no work-softening effect in such an experiment if the first mechanism operates exclusively, and hope to carry out such tests in the near future.

(*) As a matter of course the « normal » work-softening phenomenon should also occur in irradiated crystals if the change-in-temperature test is performed in such a way that at the temperature T_2 the crystal is well within stage III.

6'4. *Work-hardening and slip line pattern in stage II.* – From a quantitative point of view the work-hardening of *unirradiated* f.c.c. single crystals is best understood in stage II [42, 46]. The main features in which stage II of neutron-*irradiated* crystals differ are as follows:

1) the magnitude of the reduced work-hardening rate ϑ_{II}/G is smaller;

2) the temperature-dependence of ϑ_{II}/G is reversed;

3) the slip lines are more clustered then in the structurized fine slip of unirradiated crystals;

4) the slip lines are shorter (see Section **5**), although their variation with stress and strain obeys the same law as in unirradiated crystals.

Item 2 has already been discussed in Section **6'2**. To summarize: the « normal » negative temperature coefficient of ϑ_{II}/G (caused by the « forest » contribution to the dislocation interaction) is overcompensated, at least for small or intermediate strains, by an apparent positive temperature-dependence due to the elimination of the zone hardening.

The explanation of item 3 is similar to that given in Section **6'3** for the banding of the slip lines in the Lüders-band region. Part of the vacancies contained in the intersected zones disappear in the moving dislocations and cause them to climb by a limited amount. This process transfers slip from one glide plane to a near parallel one and causes the slip lines to cluster, although to a lesser extent than in stage I. Such a mechanism needs little or no thermal activation and is therefore able to account for the weak temperature-dependence of the slip-line characteristics.

Let us now turn to the discussion of items 1 and 4, which are to some extent interrelated. Under the *assumption* that work-hardening is mainly due to long range stress the following can be shown by quite general arguments [42, 46]. The ratio ϑ_G/G is independent of the temperature of deformation, the metal, the impurity content, and to some extent also of the dislocation arrangement. The numerical value is approximately

$$\vartheta_G = \frac{1}{2}\cdot\frac{1}{6\pi^3}\cdot G = 2.7\cdot 10^{-3} G\,. \tag{6.5}$$

For both irradiated and unirradiated crystals it is impossible to measure ϑ_G directly, since in order to eliminate ϑ_s completely one would have to go to rather high temperatures, at which stage II has become too short for accurate evaluation of ϑ_{II}. For irradiated crystals, however, an estimate can be made by using the theory of Section **6'2**. For the crystals employed in our experiments this gives

(6.6) $$\vartheta_G = 2.5\cdot 10^{-3} G\,.$$

A similar estimate based on Table IV and other data [47] on ϑ_{II} suggests that for unirradiated crystals

(6.7) $$\vartheta_G = 2.9\cdot 10^{-3} G\,.$$

Although it appears that the experimental value of ϑ_G is by 5% to 8% larger for unirradiated crystals than for irradiated crystals (*), both values seem to be of the right magnitude in order to be explained by the long-range stress field of dislocations.

The length of the slip lines (item 4) is related to the work-hardening rate according to the formula [42, 46]

(6.8) $$\vartheta_G = \alpha \sqrt{\frac{nb}{\Lambda}}\cdot G\,,$$

where n and Λ have the meaning explained in Section **4** and Section **5**, b is the modulus of the Burgers vector, and α is a geometrical factor that depends somewhat on the character of the dislocations involved. We shall consider the slip-line length due to screw dislocations, in which case $\alpha \approx 1/2\pi$. As was mentioned at the end of Section **4**, eq. (6.8) has been well confirmed by the data on unirradiated f.c.c. single crystals. Since n is about the same for irradiated and unirradiated copper crystals and since the corresponding Λ-values differ by about a factor of 2 (Table IV), eq. (6.8) gives for irradiated crystals a value which is too large by about a factor of 1.5. How can we understand this discrepancy? Since eq. (6.5) is based on the same picture and on the same theoretical ideas as eq. (6.8), it is unlikely that the theoretical basis of eq. (6.8) is at fault. A possible explanation of the discrepancy would be that the surface markings are not representative for the bulk material, *i.e.* that neither n nor L (or Λ) can be obtained from surface observations. This appears to us as rather unlikely in view of our general experience with slip-line data. Furthermore, the question why in this respect irradiated and unirradiated crystals differ from each other would still be unsolved.

(*) This difference indicates a difference in the dislocation pattern (possibly related to the presence of the zones) which may also be responsible for the different overshooting behavior.

We think that the discrepancy connected with eq. (6.8) is to be resolved in the same way as in stage III of unirradiated crystals. If eq. (6.8) is applied to stage III, it gives too small a work-hardening rate, since ϑ_G is smaller and n is larger than in stage II, whereas Λ is about the same. However, the quantity L (or Λ) that enters into the theory is not necessarily the slip-line length but the slip distance of the dislocations. In stage III the slip distance is larger than the length of a slip line, since the dislocations may leave their original glide planes and continue their glide motion on parallel glide planes. We have already given arguments to explain why in stage II the dislocations undergo a limited amount of (not thermally activated) climb that transfers them from one glide plane to a neighboring one. This would also result in an effective slip distance larger than the slip-line length. In order to reach agreement with the observations the effective slip distance has to be about twice the slip-line length. The slip distance would then be about half the length of the clusters, which does not seems to be unreasonable.

7. – Concluding remarks.

In the present paper we have pointed out how the question of the mechanism of radiation-hardening of pile-irradiated crystals is related to the more general question of the nature of the radiation damage by fast neutrons. Much of our more detailed discussion referred to copper. The majority of the general ideas and techniques should apply to the other heavier f.c.c. metals as well. Unfortunately, experimental results on these metals are lacking.

We have shown that a picture of the damaged state of a metal can be built up which explains very well the facts on radiation-hardening in the narrower sense, that is the increase in critical shear stress caused by the neutron bombardment. The situation is more involved with respect to the plastic deformation of irradiation-hardened crystals. We have applied to this problem the experimental techniques and theoretical approaches that had proven successful for the study of the plastic deformation of unirradiated crystals. We were able to account for some of the observations quantitatively. With respect to other observations we had to be content with a qualitative explanation. Nowhere did we come across facts which would clearly fall outside our picture of radiation-hardening. We may therefore be confident that further studies along these lines will help us to arrive at a final picture of the processes in irradiation-hardened metals.

* * *

The authors would like to thank Professor DEHLINGER and Drs. DIEHL, KRONMÜLLER, and MADER for their interest and discussions, and Drs. MAKIN and WHAPHAM for making available their results before publication and for supplying Fig. 4. The authors' thanks are also due to the Deutsche Forschungsgemeinschaft for the support of the experimental work reported in this paper and to their colleagues in Mol, in particular Dr. J. SPAEPEN, for the irradiation of the crystals.

REFERENCES

[1] T. H. BLEWITT, R. R. COLTMAN, R. E. JAMISON, and J. K. REDMAN: *Journ. Nucl. Materials,* **2**, 277 (1960).
[2] A. W. MCREYNOLDS, W. AUGUSTYNIAK, M. MCKEOWN, and D. B. ROSENBLATT: *Phys. Rev.*, **98**, 418 (1955).
[3] M. J. MAKIN and A. J. MINTER: *Acta Met.*, **8**, 691 (1960).
[4] M. J. MAKIN, A. D. WHAPHAM, and F. J. MINTER: *Symposium on Lattice Defects and Mechanical Properties of Solids* (Cambridge, 1960).
[5] A. SEEGER: *Proc. Second Intern. Conf. Peaceful Uses Atomic Energy* (Geneva, 1958), vol. **6**, p. 250; (New York, 1958).
[6] A. SEEGER: *Zeits. Naturforschg.*, **13***a*, 54 (1958).
[7] A. SEEGER: *Progress in Nuclear Energy. Metallurgy and Fuels* (in press).
[8] G. H. KINCHIN and R. S. PEASE: *Rep. Progr. Phys.*, **18**, 1 (1955).
[9] G. H. KINCHIN and R. S. PEASE: *Journ. Nucl. Energy*, **1**, 200 (1955).
[10] J. B. GIBSON, A. N. GOLAND, M. MILGRAM, and G. H. VINEYARD: *Phys. Rev.*, **120**, 1229 (1960).
[11] R. H. SILSBEE: *Journ. Appl. Phys.*, **28**, 1246 (1957).
[12] G. LEIBFRIED: *Journ. Appl. Phys.*, **30**, 1388 (1959).
[13] G. LEIBFRIED: *Journ. Appl. Phys.*, **31**, 117 (1960).
[14] C. J. MEECHAN, A. SOSIN and J. A. BRINKMAN: *Phys. Rev.*, **120**, 411 (1960).
[15] M. THOMPSON: *Phil. Mag.*, **4**, 139 (1959).
[16] R. S. NELSON and M. THOMPSON: *Proc. Roy. Soc.*, (London) A **259**, 458 (1961).
[17] J. A. BRINKMAN: *Journ. Appl. Phys.*, **25**, 961 (1954).
[18] J. SILCOX and P. B. HIRSCH: *Phil. Mag.*, **4**, 72 (1958).
[19] T. H. BLEWITT: *Vacancies and Other Point Defects* (Institute of Metals Monograph and Report Series no. 23) (London, 1958), p. 213.
[20] T. H. BLEWITT, R. R. COLTMAN, and C. E. KLABUNDE: *Phys. Rev. Lett.*, **3**, 132 (1959).
[21] A. SEEGER: *Can. Journ. Phys.*, **34**, 1219 (1956).
[22] A. SEEGER, R. BERNER and H. WOLF: *Zeits. Phys.*, **155**, 247 (1959).
[23] T. H. BLEWITT, R. R. COLTMAN, D. K. HOLMES and T. S. NOGGLE: *Journ. Appl. Phys.*, **28**, 639 (1957).
[24] T. H. BLEWITT, R. R. COLTMAN, C. E. KLABUNDE and J. DIEHL: *Bull. Am. Phys. Soc.*, **4**, 135 (1959).
[25] J. W. CORBETT and R. M. WALKER: *Phys. Rev.*, **110**, 767 (1958).
[26] C. J. MEECHAN and A. SOSIN: *Phys. Rev.*, **113**, 422 (1959).
[27] J. W. CORBETT, R. B. SMITH and R. M. WALKER: *Phys. Rev.*, **114**, 1452 (1959).
[28] A. KELLY: *Symposium on Lattice Defects and Mechanical Properties of Solids* (Cambridge, 1960).

[29] M. J. MAKIN, A. D. WHAPHAM and F. J. MINTER: *Phil. Mag.*, **6**, 465 (1961).
[30] J. SILCOX and P. B. HIRSCH: *Phil. Mag.*, **4**, 1356 (1959).
[31] U. ESSMANN, S. MADER and A. SEEGER: *Zeits. Metallkde.*, **52**, 443 (1961).
[32] S. MADER: *Zeits. Phys.*, **149**, 73 (1957).
[33] A. SEEGER and S. MADER: *Trans. Ind. Inst. Met.*, **13**, 249 (1960).
[34] R. BERNER: *Zeits. Naturforschg.*, **15a**, 689 (1960).
[35] CH. LEITZ: *Diplomarbeit* (Stuttgart, 1960).
[36] A. SEEGER, S. MADER and U. ESSMANN: *Symposium on Lattice Defects and Mechanical Properties of Solids* (Cambridge, 1960).
[37] A. SEEGER and H. TRÄUBLE: *Zeits. Metallkde.*, **51**, 435 (1960).
[38] S. MADER and A. SEEGER: *Acta Met.*, **8**, 513 (1960).
[39] A. SEEGER, H. KRONMÜLLER, S. MADER and H. TRÄUBLE: *Phil. Mag.*, **6**, 639 (1961).
[40] G. R. PIERCY, R. W. CAHN and A. H. COTTRELL: *Acta Met.*, **3**, 331 (1955).
[41] J. T. FOURIE and H. G. WILSDORF: *Acta Met.*, **7**, 339 (1959).
[42] A. SEEGER: *Kristallplastizität, Encyclopedia of Physics*, vol. VII/**2** (Berlin, Göttingen, Heidelberg, 1958).
[43] M. J. MAKIN: *Acta Met.*, **7**, 233 (1959).
[44] D. KUHLMANN-WILSDORF, R. MADDIN and H. G. F. WILSDORF: *ASM Seminar on « Strengthening Mechanisms in Solids »* (Philadelphia, 1960).
[45] L. G. GREENFIELD and H. G. F. WILSDORF: *Naturwiss.*, **47**, 395 (1960).
[46] H. KRONMÜLLER and A. SEEGER: *Journ. Phys. Chem. Sol.*, **18**, 93 (1961).
[47] J. DIEHL and R. BERNER: *Zeits. Metallkunde.*, **51**, 522 (1960).

Radiation Damage in Body-Centred Metals.

M. W. Thompson

Atomic Energy Research Establishment - Harwell

1. - Introduction.

The study of body-centred metals has been stimulated by two considerations. The first of these was the obvious necessity of making a comparison between these metals and the face-centered metals, which have been more extensively studied. The second was the practical advantage which many b.c.c. metals have by virtue of their relatively high melting points. These have been found to lead to correspondingly higher, and experimentally more convenient, temperatures of damage recovery.

2. - General experimental observations.

In Fig. 1 the fractional increase in electrical resistivity of molybdenum and tungsten [1] is plotted *vs.* fast neutron dose. Irradiations were carried out at 30 °C, measurements of resistance at 0 °C. In each case there is as an initial

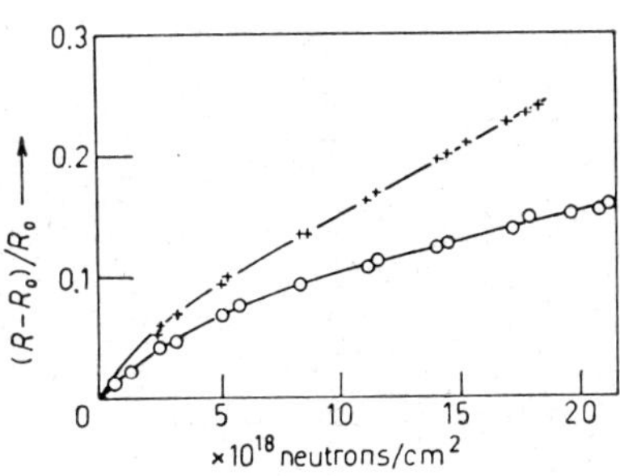

Fig. 1. – The fractional increase in resistance with fast neutron dose for molybdenum (lower curve) and tungsten (upper curve). Irradiations were carried out at 30 °C; measurements at 0 °C [1].

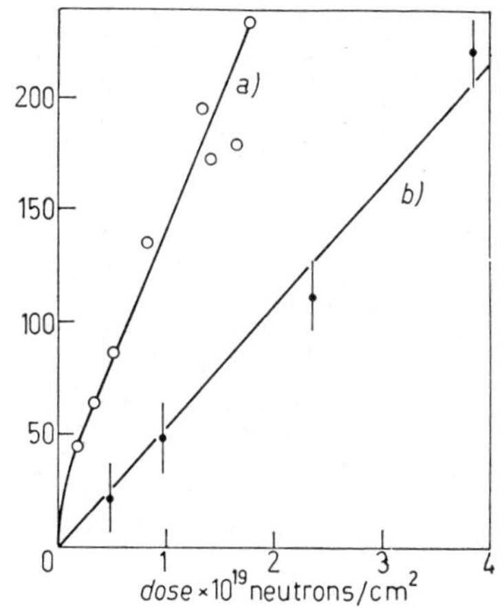

Fig 2. – Fractional change in parts per million of length (upper curve) and lattice parameter of molybdenum. Irradiations with fast neutrons at 30 °C [2].

tendency to saturate followed by a steadier increase. The corresponding changes in lattice parameter and linear dimensions of molybdenum [2] are shown in Fig. 2. The fact that the fractional length change is greater than the fractional lattice change suggests that there is a preponderance of vacancy damage after bombardment at 30 °C. (See lecture by Prof. FRIEDEL.)

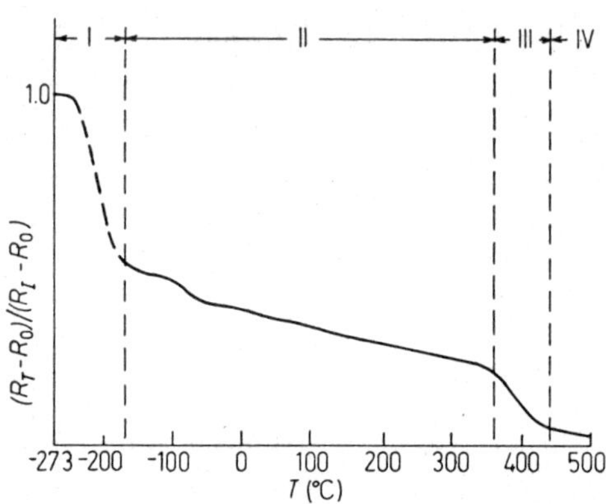

Fig. 3. – A schematic recovery curve for the electrical resistance of tungsten after a 140 h irradiation at 4 °K in a flux of 10^{12} n cm^{-2} s^{-1}. Showing the recovery stages I, II, III and IV [3].

The result of annealing a tungsten sample irradiated at 4 °K is shown in Fig. 3 where the ratio of excess resistance after annealing to temperature T for 30 min to the excess resistance immediately following irradiation, is plotted against T [3]. Recovery occurs in four main stages; the first below — 170 °C, the second between —170 and 350 °C, the third between 350 and 450 °C and the fourth above 450°C. In stage II the first derivative of the recovery curve, $\mathrm{d}R/\mathrm{d}T$, shows a series of small peaks. Measurements of the activation energy of the recovery rate process show that the energy rises from 0.25 to 1.7 eV in stage II and is 1.7 eV in stage III.

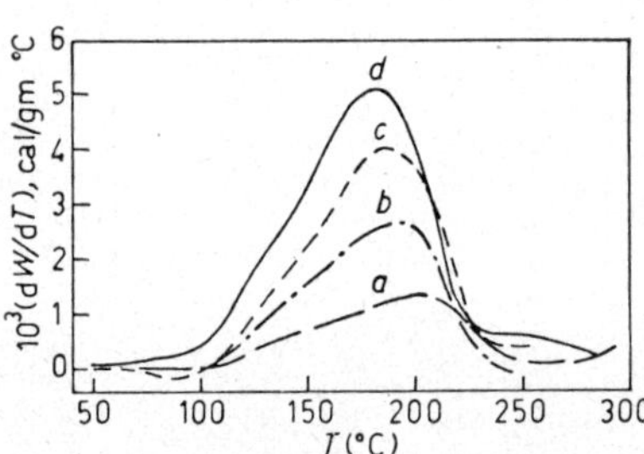

Fig. 4. – The stored energy release $\mathrm{d}S/\mathrm{d}T$ from molybdenum versus temperature: rate of rise 1.2° min^{-1} [1]. (*a*) dose, $1.7\cdot10^{18}$ n cm^{-2} at 30 °C; (*b*) dose, $4.5\cdot10^{18}$ n cm^{-2} at 30 °C; (*c*) dose, $8{,}2\cdot10^{18}$ n cm^{-2} at 30 °C; (*d*) dose, $13.3\cdot10^{18}$ n cm^{-2} at 30 °C.

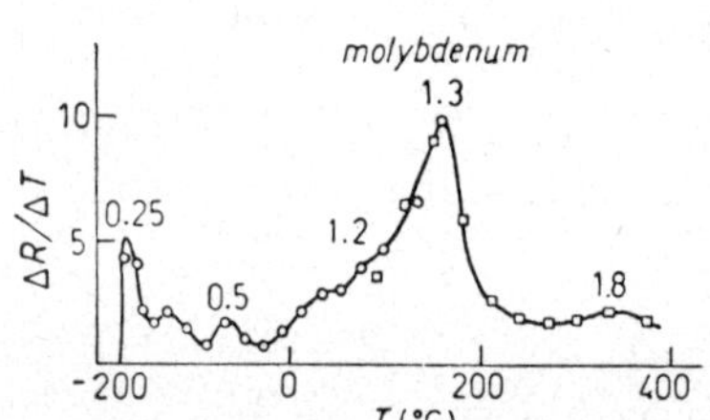

Fig. 5. – Differential recovery curve for electrical resistance of molybdenum irradiated with $2\cdot10^{18}$ n cm^{-2} at — 196 °C; figures above the curve show activation energies in eV [1].

In neutron-irradiated molybdenum the recovery curve is similar to tungsten but with an overall shift to lower temperatures. In Fig. 4 and 5 the stored energy release is compared with $\mathrm{d}R/\mathrm{d}T$ over stages II and III ([1]). The ratio of stored energy released to resistivity recovered over stage III is constant as a function of dose which suggests that the same process is responsible for both phenomena. The assumption that interstitial-vacancy annihilation is responsible with an energy release of 10 eV per pair leads to a concentration of the order 10^{-5} pairs annihilated in stage III per 10^{18} n cm^{-2} and a resistivity of 20 μΩ cm per 1 % concentration of pairs. This latter figure shows the resistivity of molybdenum to be considerably more sensitive to damage thane for instance, copper.

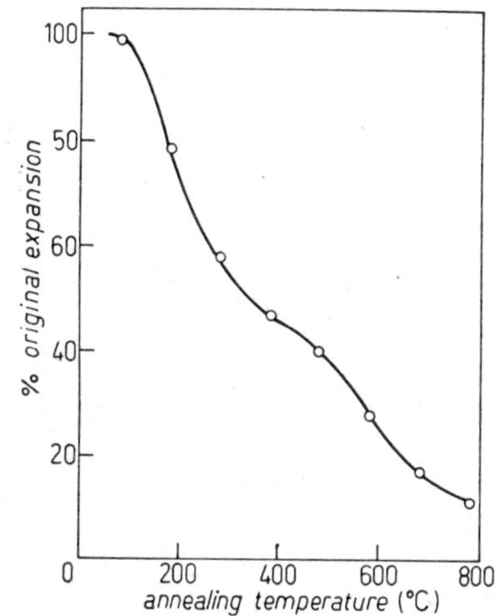

Fig. 6. – Recovery curve of length change for molybdenum irradiated with 10^{18} n cm^{-2} at 30 °C [2].

The recovery of length changes in molybdenum [2] (Fig. 6) shows the same features as resistivity and stored energy and over stage III also follows the changes in lattice parameter [4]. If we again assume that stage III is due to i-v annihilation and that a 1 % concentration of pairs produces roughly a 1 % lattice expansion, then for 10^{18} n·cm^{-2} the order of 10^{-5} pairs per atom are annihilated in stage III.

3. – The comparison of various metals.

In making a comparison between the general features of damage and recovery in b.c.c. and f.c.c. metals one is struck by the similar behaviour in later stages of annealing. In the great majority of recovery studies after irradiation, cold-work and quenching a pronounced stage III occurs at a temperature given very approximately by $T_m/5$, where T_m is the absolute melting point. In Table I activation energies E and recovery temperatures T for this stage have been collected for a variety of metals. A remarkable correlation exists between the ratios E/T_m which have a value close to $5 \cdot 10^{-4}$ eV deg^{-1} in all cases. This may be taken as an indication that the same recovery mechanism occurs in all metals in stage III. Furthermore, as this stage has been associated with vacancy migration in quenching experiments [5] it seems likely that this is the common stage III mechanism.

The comparison of recovery in stage I is less revealing as even metals of the same system show differing behavior [6].

The electron microscope observations on f.c.c. metals (see lectures by

TABLE I.

Metal	T_m (°K)	Damage	E (eV)	T (°K)	$\frac{E \cdot 10^4}{T_m}$	T/T_m	Reference
Ag f.c.c.	1 234	C. W.	0.65	230	5.3	0.17	MAINTVELD, 1952
Al f.c.c.	933	irrad.	0.55	190	5.9	0.20	MC REYNOLDS *et al.*, 1955
		quench	0.44	300	4.7	0.32	BRADSHAW and PEARSON, 1957*b*
		quench	0.52	270	5.6	0.3	DE SORBO and TURNBULL, 1959
Au f.c.c.	1 936	C. W.	0.6	290	5.2	0.22	MAINTVELD, 1957
		quench	0.82	310	6.1	0.23	BAURLE and KOEHLER, 1957
		quench					BRADSHAW and PEARSON, 1957*a*
Cu f.c.c.	1 356	irrad.	0.68	250	5.0	0.19	OVERHAUSER, 1955
		C. W.	0.67	230	5.0	0.17	EGGLESTON, 1952
Mo b.c.c.	2 893	irrad.	1.3	420	4.5	0.15	KINCHIN and THOMPSON, 1957
		C. W.	1.26	430	4.4	0.15	MARTIN, 1957
Nb b.c.c.	2 220	irrad.	1.3	420	5.9	0.19	MAKIN, 1959
Ni f.c.c.	1 728	C. W.	1.0	500	5.8	0.28	NICHOLAS, 1955
Pt f.c.c.	2 047	irrad.	1.2	420	5.9	0.21	DUGDALE, 1952
		quench	1.1	570	5.4	0.2	BRADSHAW and PEARSON, 1956
W b.c.c.	3 643	irrad.	1.7	670	4.7	0.18	KINCHIN and THOMPSON, 1957
		C. W.	1.7	620	4.7	0.17	SCHULTZ, 1959

Prof. HIRSCH) suggest that the final stage IV recovery is associated with aggregates. Information about the state of aggregation of point defects in b.c.c. metals is unfortunately scarce and few, if any, electron microscope observations have been made. However, some measurements of the low-temperature thermal conductivity of the superconductor niobium [7] are of considerable interest. In the superconducting state thermal conduction is due only to phonons and consequently is affected only by defects comparable in size with the phonon wavelength. At the temperatures concerned this is of the order 100 Å. In the presence of a magnetic field however, the superconductor reverts to the normal state where heat is carried by electrons whose short wavelength allows them to interact only with small ($\sim$ 1 Å) defects. After 10^{18} n·cm^{-2} at 30 °C it was found that both in the normal and superconducting state niobium had suffered a loss of conduction in the normal state corresponding to a point defect concentration of the order 10^{-4}. There was also a loss of conduction in the superconducting state (Fig. 7), and if this is attributed to small dislocation loops, then an increase of $3\cdot10^{9}$ cm^{-2} in dislocation density is deduced. Assuming these to be due to point defect condensation, a concentration of 10^{-5} aggregated into 100 Å loops will explain the observed effect, which seems in reasonable agreement with the directly observed effects in f.c.c. metals.

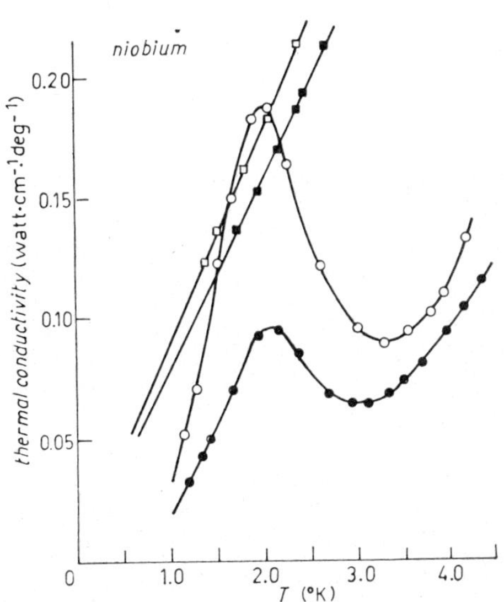

Fig. 7. – Low-temperature thermal conductivity of niobium in normal and superconducting states before and after irradiation with 10^{18} n cm^{-2} at 30 °C [7] □ normal state; ■ normal state irradiated; ○ superconducting state; ● superconducting state irradiated.

4. – Detailed considerations and the mechanisms of stages I and II.

A clue to the mechanism of stage II is provided by the recovery of cold-worked tungsten samples which, according to the ideas presented above, should

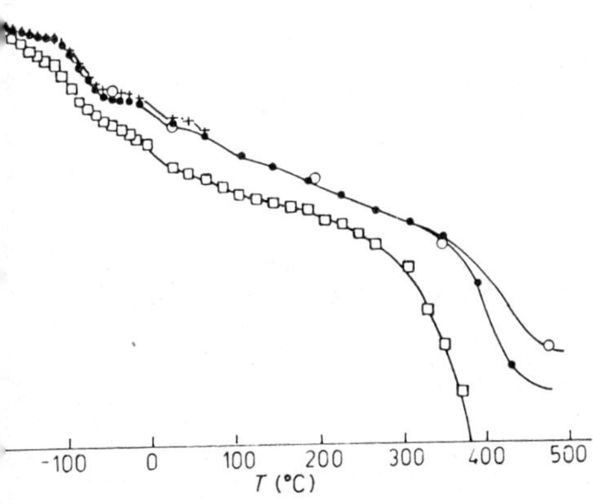

[Fig.] 8. – Recovery of electrical resistance in [tungst]en irradiated for 140 h in a flux of [10^{12} n] cm^{-2} s^{-1} at -196 °C [3]. (A) 100 μm grains; [(B) 1]0 μm grains; (C) 1 μm grains; (D) 1 μm[, ...], initial concentration of vacancies present [due t]o cold-work. + type A; ● type B; ○ type C; □ type D.

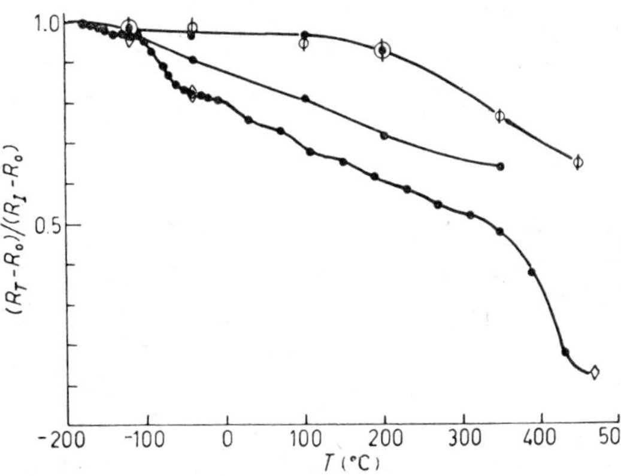

Fig. 9. – The effect of dose on recovery curves for the electrical resistance of tungsten [3]. Upper curve: 1 h exposure in 10^{12} n cm^{-2} s^{-1}. Middle curve: 12 h exposure in 10^{12} n cm^{-2} s^{-1}. Lower curve: 140 h exposure in 10^{12} n cm^{-2} s^{-1}. ● Type B, specimen 1. ◊ Type B, specimen 2. ⌽ Type B, specimen 3.

have had an excess of vacancies before irradiation. It appears from Fig. 8 that their presence enhances recovery in stage II and it therefore seems reasonable to associate this stage with interstitials. That it cannot be simply due to such defects first becoming mobile is shown by the dependence of stage II on dose; this is demonstrated in Fig. 9. A dual association is suggested however, by Fig. 10 in which the recovery of two samples having differing impurities is compared. This observation may be compared with the results of BLEWITT, COLTMAN and KLABUNDE [8] and MARTIN [9] on doped copper which have shown the marked influence of impurities on stage II.

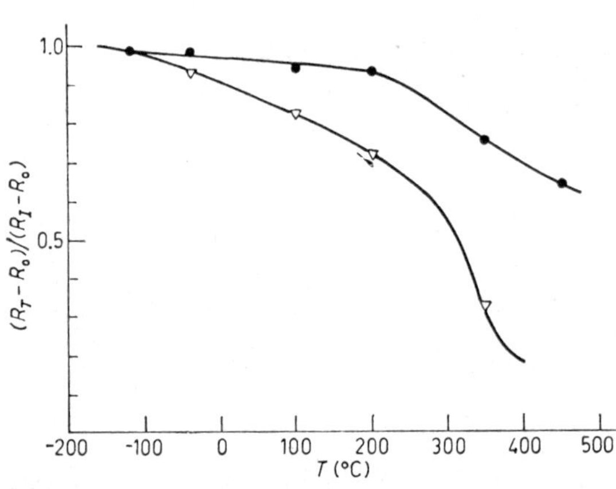

Fig. 10. – The effect of purity on recovery curves of electrical resistance of tungsten irradiated for 1 h in 10^{12} n cm^{-2} s^{-1} [3]. ● Type B; ▽ type E.

The dose-dependence of this stage may be explained by attributing it to the release of interstitials trapped on impurities, and also possibly dislocation lines and other centres of strain. At low doses (1 hour at 10^{12} n·cm^{-2}·s^{-1}) the concentration of damage is of the order 10^{-7} which is much lower than the concentration of impurities which might be of the order 10^{-4}. As annealing proceeds under such conditions the interstitials released from shallow traps should become attached to deeper ones rather than annihilate vacancies which are present at a much lower concentration. Such a process of changing traps could occur with little net change in resistivity.

There is an unfortunate lack of detailed information on recovery below liquid-nitrogen temperature in b.c.c. metals although Blewitt's results [6] show that recovery of niobium starts below 10 °K after a neutron irradiation at 4 °K. By a process of elimination it seems reasonable to assign stage I to interstitial migration in some form.

5. – Theoretical treatment of damage and recovery.

A simple theoretical treatment of damage accumulation and recovery will now be derived from the above model. Let C be the concentration of interstitials or vacancies produced, C_t the concentration of interstitials present on traps, C_b the concentration of interstitials which have escaped to boundary sinks, V the concentration of free vacancies, T the total concentration of traps and B the effective concentration of boundary sinks. Two cases will be considered: irradiation temperature below stage I and in stage II.

Below stage I the concentration of interstitials and vacancies will, as a first approximation, be equal to C as neither defect is mobile. If a and b are respectively the resistivity due to unit concentration of interstitials and vacancies then the resistivity increase will be

(1) $$\Delta\varrho = (a+b)C\,.$$

However as damage accumulates the increased probability of cascade regions overlapping and hence of new interstitials being produced at old vacant sites (and vice versa), will cause a tendency to saturate. Thus if C increase to $C+\mathrm{d}C$ a fraction mC of the extra $\mathrm{d}C$ will annihilate pre-existing defects, where m is the number of sites around a defect at which instant annihilation will occur.

Thus

$$\mathrm{d}V = \mathrm{d}C - mC\,\mathrm{d}C\,,$$

whence

$$V = C - \tfrac{1}{2}mC^2$$

and

(2) $$\Delta\varrho = (a+b)(C - \tfrac{1}{2}mC^2) \qquad \text{for } C \ll 1.$$

Assuming $m \simeq 8$ for b.c.c. metals the correction will only amount to 1% when C reaches $0.25\cdot10^{-2}$.

We shall next consider the case when irradiation occurs in the temperature range of stage II. This is the condition frequently encountered in practice when metals of moderate or high melting point are irradiated near room temperature. When C increases by $\mathrm{d}C$ the extra interstitials have the choice of annihilating vacancies already present at concentration V, of attaching themselves to unfilled traps present at a concentration of $(T-C_t)$ or of migrating to sinks of which there is an effective concentration B. Since vacancies can only be lost through annihilation by interstitials, their concentration must equal the concentration of interstitials lost to either sinks or traps, *i.e.*,

(3) $$V = C_t + C_b\,.$$

By simple proportion the increase in C_t is

$$\mathrm{d}C_t = T\,\mathrm{d}C/\{C_t + B + (T - C_t)\}\,,$$

i.e.,

$$\mathrm{d}C_t = T\,\mathrm{d}C/\{C_b + B + T\};$$

similarly

$$\mathrm{d}C_b = E\,\mathrm{d}C/\{C_b + B + T\}\,,$$

hence

(4) $$C_b = (B+T)\{[1 + 2BC/(B+T)^2]^{\frac{1}{2}} - 1\}$$

and

(5) $$C_t = T\{1 - \exp[-C_b/B]\}\,.$$

The resistivity increase is given by

(6) $$\Delta\varrho = (a_t + b)C_t + bC_b\,,$$

where a_t is the mean resistivity coefficient for trapped interstitials.

The variable C must next be related to the irradiation dose. Suppose that we are dealing with neutron irradiation and that the cross-section for a neutron hit is δ and the number of displaced atoms is n. Then in a flux φ for a time t:

(7) $$C = n\,\delta\varphi t\,.$$

The value of T will depend on the impurity concentration, which might typically be 10^{-4}, and also the dislocation density. If 10 sites exist on each atom plane intersected by a dislocation line then for a density of 10^{10} lines cm^{-2} a trap concentration of 10^{-4} might again be expected. The effective concentration of boundary sinks will be given in order of magnitude by the ratio of lattice sites at the grain boundary to the total sites in the grain, *i.e.*,

$$B \sim 6/dA^{\frac{1}{3}}\,,$$

where A is the atomic density and d the linear grain dimension. For 10 μm grains $B \sim 10^{-4}$.

Evaluation of expression (6) has been made using the data of Table II in which A, B and C refer to 100, 10 and $1\times1\times25$ μm grains and assuming

TABLE II. – *Estimated sink concentrations* $(\cdot 10^4)$ *for four types specimen.*

Type	B	$\sum T_r$	T_1	V_0'	Temp. of annealing (°C)
A	0.05	0.20	0.05	0	2 000
B	0.50	0.30	0.15	0	1 500
C	5.00	1.00	—	0	500
D	5.00	1.00	—	2.00	none

$a_t \simeq b \simeq 10^3\ \mu\Omega$ cm per unit concentration. The results are plotted as a function of C in Fig. 11.

From the analytical form of (6) it will be seen that the term due to trapping saturates whereas that due to vacancies left by interstitials lost to boundaries increases steadily with slight negative curvature. Large grain size therefore initially favours trapping and a large initial slope is associated with greater initial curvature as traps fill up. In small grains the loss to boundaries is more important and a steady, but initially less rapid, increase results. Comparing these predictions with the experimental curves in Fig. 12 and 13 shows them to be in accord with observation.

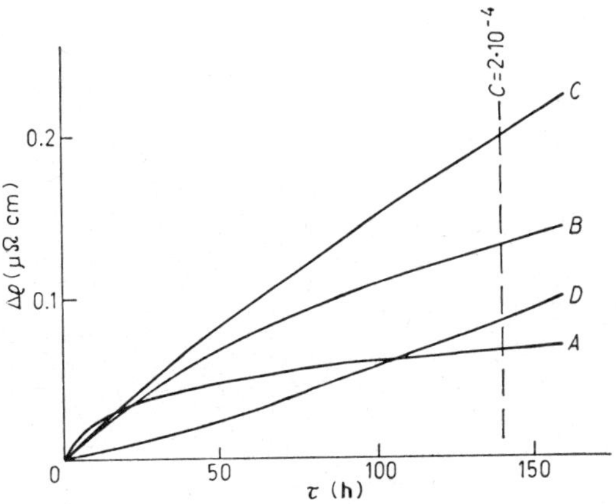

Fig. 11. – The resistivity increase as a function of irradiation time in a neutron flux of 10^{12} n cm^{-2} s^{-1}; calculated from theory for tungsten. [3]. (A) 100 μm grains; (B) 10 μm grains; (C) 1 μm grains; (D) 1 μm grains, with initial concentration of vacancies $2\cdot10^{-4}$, showing the annealing action of spikes assumed to affect 10^5 atoms each.

The above consideration may be extended to a system with many traps, T_r with interstitial resistivity coefficients a_r. The expression for $\Delta\varrho$ is then formally similar but with a group of terms representing accumulation on traps, all of which however, saturate with the same time constant thus leading to identical net results.

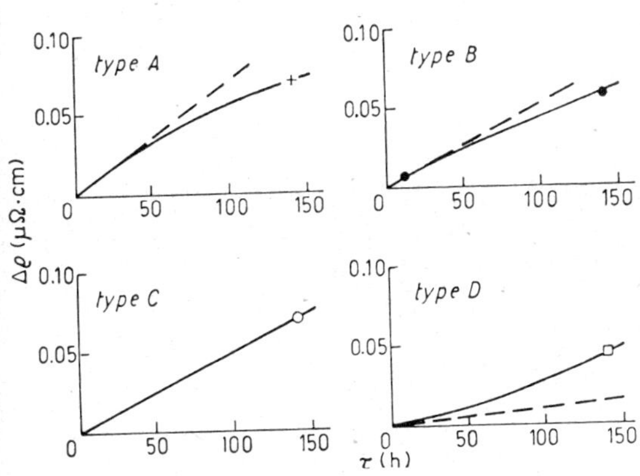

Fig. 12. – Experimental curves showing resistivity increase of tungsten specimens as in Fig. 11, slope at the origin is obtained from increment after 1 h irradiation. Neutron flux 10^{12} n cm^{-2} s^{-1} [3].

This detailed form has been extended [3] to the recovery process in stage II. The principles of the calculation are as follows: the temperature is supposed to be raised just enough to release interstitials from the first trap (T_1, a_1) and these are then distributed amongst the $(T_r - C_r)$ unfilled traps of type r $(\neq 1)$, the B boundary sinks and the $(C_b + C_t)$ vacancies, by simple proportion as above. The resistivity change due to unit concentration changing from trap 1 to trap r is $(a_1 - a_r)$ that due to unit concentration going to sinks is a_1 and that due to annihilating vacancies $(a_1 + b)$. The complete expression for $\Delta\varrho_1$ the resistivity recovery due to annealing from trap 1, is then constructed and the ratio $\Delta\varrho_1/\Delta\varrho$ obtained. This represents the height of the step on the recovery curve due to trap 1.

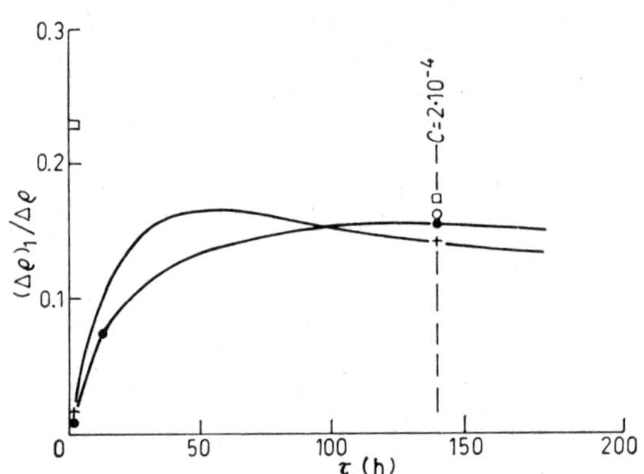

Fig. 13. – Recovery in stage II of tungsten between -120 and -40 °C as a function of irradiation time in 10^{12} n cm^{-2} s^{-1}. The solid lines represent theoretical curves which have been fitted to observations at $t = 140$ h using the data in Table II [3]. + Type A; ● type B; ○ type C; □ type D.

Since this expression contains the coefficients a, which are unknown, the assumption is made that all a_r are equal so that the term involving $(a_1 - a_r)$ cancels out and then for $B \sim 10^{-4}$.

Approximately

$$\Delta\varrho_1/\Delta\varrho \simeq 0 \qquad \text{as} \qquad C \to 0\,,$$

which is the observed phenomenon that stage II is small for low doses.

In Fig. 13 theoretical curves of $\Delta\varrho_1/\Delta\varrho$ are plotted *vs.* C for specimens of different grain size, the curves having been fitted to one experimental point. It will be seen that the remaining points lie on the curve showing the theoretical expression to have the correct dependence on C.

REFERENCES

[1] G. H. Kinchin and M. W. Thompson: *Journ. Nucl. Energy*, **6**, 4, 275 (1958).
[2] J. Adam and D. G. Martin: *Phil. Mag.*, **3**, 132*a* (1958).
[3] M. W. Thompson: *Phil. Mag.*, **5**, 51, 278 (1960).
[4] D. L. Gray: U.S.A.E.C.-H.W.-57903, unclassified report (1958).
[5] J. E. Baurle and J. S. Koehler: *Phys. Rev.*, **107**, 1493 (1957).
[6] T. H. Blewitt: private communication (1960).
[7] K. Chandhuri, K. Mendlessohn and M. W. Thompson: *Cryogenics*, **1**, 1, 47 (1960).
[8] T. H. Blewitt, R. R. Coltman and C. E. Klabunde: *Journ. Appl. Phys.*, **28**, 630 (1957).
[9] D. G. Martin: private communication (1958).

Radiation-Enhanced Diffusion in Metals (*).

A. C. DAMASK (**).

Pitmann-Dunn Laboratories, Frankford Arsenal - Philadelphia, Penn.

1. – Introduction.

Diffusion takes place in a large class of solids by means of a vacancy mechanism. One of the reasons for increased diffusion rates at high temperature is that the equilibrium number of vacancies increases with increasing temperature. Irradiation of a solid by high-energy electrons, γ-rays, or heavy particles displaces atoms and creates vacancies as one of the defects. The presence of these vacancies in excess of the thermal equilibrium number leads to an acceleration of the diffusion rate, a process termed radiation-enhanced diffusion. This account will be confined to substitutional alloys in which diffusion takes place by the vacancy mechanism, since there is no evidence that irradiation can assist interstitial diffusion.

2. – Radiation effects [1].

2·1. *Electrons.* – When a metal is bombarded with electrons of sufficient energy, atoms are displaced from their original positions and leave behind vacant lattice sites. An electron from an average laboratory accelerator has about 1 to 2 MeV energy, and imparts only about 50 eV to a copper atom. Experiments with variable electron energy have shown the displacement energy of a copper atom to be about 25 eV (for most atoms in solids it is between 10 and 30 eV). Since electrons also lose energy by interaction with the electrons in the metal, it is highly improbable that an electron will produce more than one displacement collision; in fact the probability is high that it will produce

(*) Supported in part by the U. S. Atomic Energy Commission.

(**) Guest Scientist at Brookhaven National Laboratory, Upton, N. Y.

none. If the struck atom does not have enough additional kinetic energy to move more than a few atomic distances, it will probably return and recombine with the vacancy it has left, so that some of the vacancies useful to diffusion are lost before they can contribute many jumps. The major limitation of electron irradiation is its low penetration into solids, and the effects are confined to small specimens.

2·2. *γ-rays.* – Irradiation by γ-rays is simply a less efficient case of electron irradiation. First the γ-ray must create a Compton or photoelectron, which then provides internal bombardment. Since it is a two-step process, the photons are less efficient than direct electron bombardment. A change caused by one hour of electron irradiation would take about three months of γ-irradiation, with average available sources.

2·3. *Neutrons.* – The most important damage effects in a reactor arise from the fast neutrons which have an energy distribution up to 10 MeV with the largest intensity around 1 MeV. The atoms in a metallic crystal present such a small cross section to the fast neutrons that the mean free path between collisions is of the order of 1 to 10 cm. Although the struck atoms are uniformly distributed, the resulting damage is quite severe in local regions. The maximum energy that can be imparted to the struck atoms is of the order of 100 000 eV. The atoms present a relatively large cross-section to this energetic knock-on, which increases with decreasing energy. Since the knock-on strikes other atoms with more than enough energy for displacement, cascades of displacementsc an result, and the defects created are no longer simple vacancies or interstitials. Clusters of defects are formed, and recent machine calculations at Brookhaven [2] show that many interstitials are formed at larged istances from the collision because of the dynamic crowdion effect. More violent spike events may also occur, which can result in highly strained regions or even regions of altered crystal orientation [3].

Because of these displaced and replaced atoms, one of the additional effects of heavy-particle bombarment of alloys is the destruction of ordered arrangement and the breaking apart of precipitates [4]. Another effects would be the enhancement of nucleation of new phases [5], since nucleation in a lattice occurs preferentially at points where it can relieve internal strains. Thus, neutron or other heavy-particle bombarment can 1) enhance diffusion, 2) enhance nucleation, and 3) break up precipitated or ordered regions. However, because of the different mechanisms of damage by different types of irradiation described above, destruction of order or re-solution of precipitates is not expected with electron or γ-irradiation, nor has it been observed [6]. With these latter types of irradiation only one atom is displaced to create the vacancy, but the vacancy can interchange many atoms to more preferable sites during its migration.

Therefore with electron or γ-irradiation only enhanced diffusion should be observed.

3. – Radiation-enhanced diffusion.

Since high-energy irradiation produces vacancies as one of the defects, an excess steady-state vacancy concentration can be maintained in a crystal in a radiation field. Therefore diffusion rates can be increased at temperatures at which thermal diffusion is very low. The concentration of excess vacancies is usually too small to cause observable bulk diffusion effects, but microdiffusion effects such as ordering or precipitation can be observed indirectly.

Neutron-enhanced diffusion can be used as a guide to the *minimum* overall change in an alloy at the temperature of irradiation; with electron or γ-radiation the total effect will be at least as large. Four examples of diffusion-enhancement by neutron-irradiation will be examined briefly: long-range order, changes in precipitation, clustering, and short-range order.

3·1. Cu_3Au. – Below ≈ 400 °C, long-range order develops in Cu_3Au, and the equilibrium order at 250 °C is 0.85. Above 400 °C long-range order is absent. Neutron-irradiation is expected to induce two competing processes: the diffusion-enhancement of the vacancies tending to order the material and the displacement effects of the knock-ons tending to disorder it. Fig. 1 shows that the experimental result is as expected [7]. The initially disordered specimen decrease in resistivity, which indicates ordering, and the ordered specimen increases in resistivity, which indicates disordering. The final result is some intermediate equilibrium value of order. Also, as expected from the previous arguments, when both « ordered » and disordered Cu_3Au are irradiated with electrons or γ-rays, the only effect is to increase order [6]. The minimum temperature at which the motion of the vacancies becomes observable can be measured. With irradiation at low temperatures, no effect other the slight resistivity-increase due to the defects themselves is observed. Upon warming the sample, when the vacancies begin to move, measurable decreases in

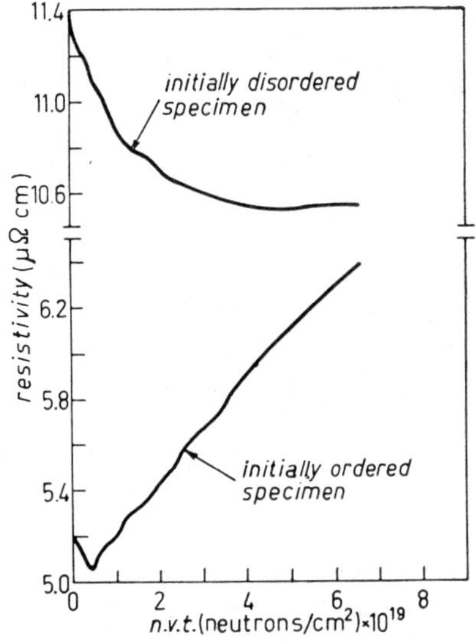

Fig. 1. – Resistivity of initially ordered and disordered Cu_3Au during neutron irradiation at 80 °C (ref. [7]).

resistivity are noted. This occurs at about 80 °C for Cu_3Au [8]. However, in unirradiated samples virtually no observable change in resistivity is noted below 100 °C. Thus, the irradiation-produced vacancies render the range of free-energy decrease between 80° and 200 °C observable in this alloy.

3·2. *Nickel-Beryllium* [9]. – This alloy is an example of a precipitating system. The solid solution of beryllium in nickel is ferromagnetic and the amount of beryllium in solution can be determined from the Curie temperature. The temperature at which the vacancies moved was not determined, but a comparison was made between the change with time in Curie temperature of a sample in a reactor and that of one outside, both at 300 °C. Fig. 2 shows a definite increase in precipitation rate under irradiation, even though the number of thermal vacancies present is rather large at this temperature.

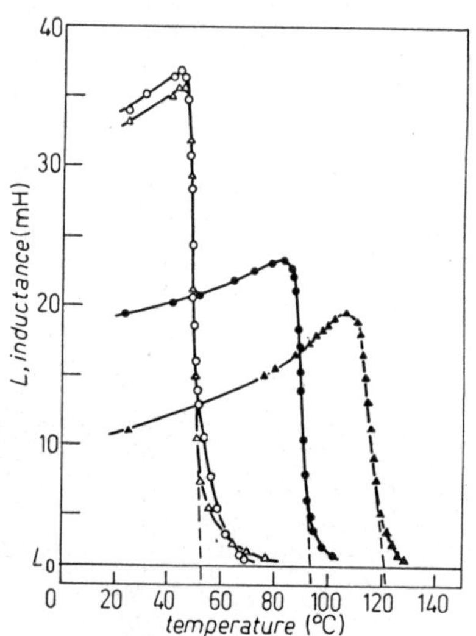

Fig. 2. – Inductance *vs.* temperature curves for nickel-beryllium (ref. [9]); ○ initial values; △ initial values; ● specimen heated at 300 °C for 1 month; ▲ specimen irradiated at 300 °C for 1 month.

3·3. Cu-Ni [10]. – The copper and nickel in this alloy tend to cluster. Ryan, Pugh and Smoluchowski observed an increase in the magnetic susceptibility of these alloys after neutron-irradiation which, without clustering, would require the assumption of an unreasonably large magnetic moment per nickel atom.

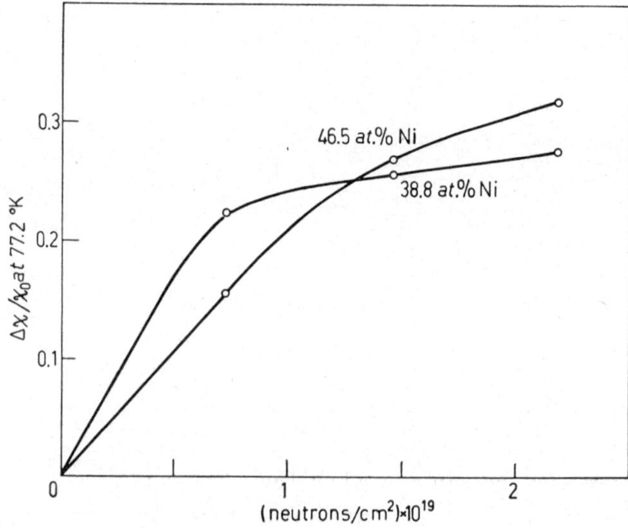

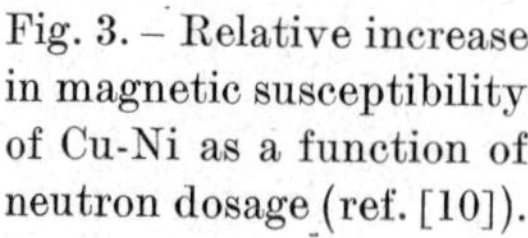
Fig. 3. – Relative increase in magnetic susceptibility of Cu-Ni as a function of neutron dosage (ref. [10]).

They showed that the susceptibility increases with irradiation time (Fig. 3), and that the increase could be removed by subsequent annealing in the temperature range where self-diffusion becomes important. They concluded that Cu-Ni is a clustering alloy and that the radiation produced vacancies which enhanced diffusion at low temperatures.

3·4. *α-Brass.* – This alloy is useful because the phenomenon of enhanced diffusion can be isolated. In α-brass decrease in electrical resistivity is associated with an increase in short-range order. Neutron-irradiation does not

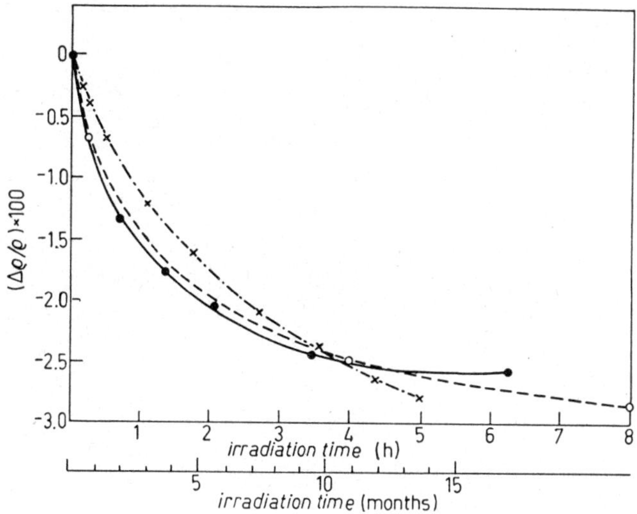

Fig. 4. – Change in electrical resistivity of α-brass with neutron, electron, and γ-irradiation (ref. [12]). Fluxes: neutron $= 10^{12}$ nv (fast), electron $= 2.6 \cdot 10^{14}$ electrons/cm² s, ^{60}Co γ = 850 000 *R*; I) 50 °C: – – – neutrons, —— electrons (time scale in hours); II) 20 °C: –·–·– γ-rays (time scale on months).

seem to destroy short-range order, and no long-range order is present. Also, for small deviations from equilibrium, the rate of ordering obeys simple exponential kinetics [11]. Fig. 4 shows a comparison of the effects of neutron, electron, and γ-irradiation of α-brass [12]. At these temperatures there is no thermal change in the material, because, although it is not in its lowest free-energy state, the rate of atomic motion is zero in terms of human lifetime. The observed decrease in electrical resistivity indicates increasing short-range order. At higher temperatures this change in resistivity can be quenched in, as shown by the solid points of Fig. 5. The sample is held at each temperature for the proper length of time (obtained from the Arrhenius equation for diffusion) to achieve equilibrium and then quenched, and the resistivity is measured at liquid-nitrogen temperature. Some typical times are indicated by the arrows. The open circle in Fig. 5 indicates the result of a few hours of electron-irradiation (Fig. 4). The time required to achieve this state by thermal means alone would be 30 000 years. A resistivity decrease has since been found in the reactor at 0 °C which would require millions of years to attain thermally:

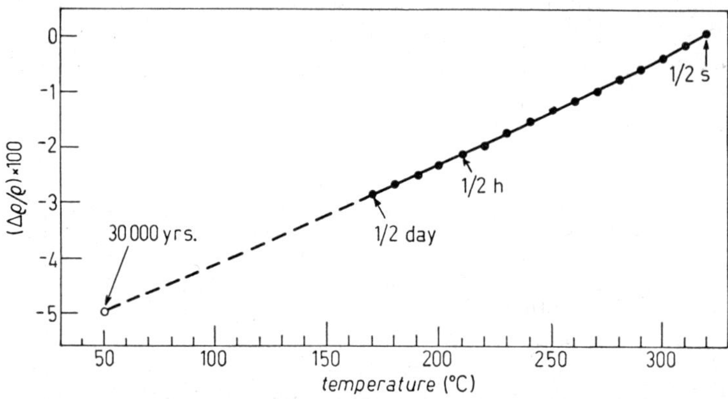

Fig. 5. – Equilibrium resistivities of α-brass measured at liquid-nitrogen temperature. Arrows are example times to achieve equilibrium. Open circle at 50 °C is the value obtained by electron-irradiation (ref. [11]).

the lower the temperature the more striking the effect. Somewhat similar behavior has been reported for the short-range [13] ordering alloy Al-Cu [14] which the writer believes can be interpreted in essentially the same way as that of α-brass [15].

3'5. *Quantitative description.* – The diffusion rate in a radiation field will now be developed on more fundamental grounds. The variation of diffusion-enhancement with temperature is found to depend on the manner in which the defects are removed from the crystal [16]. If recombination is negligible and the defects migrate either to the surface or to dislocations in the crystal at a rate proportional to their concentration (linear case), the rate of change of the number of excess (irradiation) vacancies may be expressed as $\mathrm{d}V/\mathrm{d}t = K - K_v V$. K is the rate of production of excess vacancies, which is a function of the flux, and K_v is a proportionality constant for the rate of removal of the vacancies. Under steady state conditions $\mathrm{d}V/\mathrm{d}t = 0$ and, therefore, $V = K/K_v$. Further, $K_v = \alpha_v \nu_v \lambda^2$, where α_v is the number of vacancy traps in the crystal, ν_v is the jump frequency, and λ is the jump distance. The thermal diffusion coefficient D is given by $D = V_0 \nu_v \lambda^2$, where V_0 is the number of thermal vacancies. The diffusion coefficient under radiation, D', is proportional to the sum of the thermal and radiation-induced vacancies, *i.e.*, $D' = (V + V_0)\lambda^2 \nu_v =$

$= (K/\alpha_v \nu_v \lambda^2)\, \lambda^2 \nu_v + V_0 \lambda^2 \nu_v$, or $D' - D = K/\alpha_v$. Thus the enhancement of diffusion $D' - D$, is equal to a constant and independent of temperature. This is shown in Fig. 6, where the solid line is a plot of thermal D *vs.* $1/T$. (Since $D \propto 1/\tau$ and τ, the mean atomic jump time, is the measured quantity in these experiments, the abscissa is given as $1/\tau$.) The dashed line is the theoretical plot of the above equation for D'. When the thermal concentration of vacancies is small, $D' = K/\alpha$ and there is no temperature-dependence. At high temperatures, where D is very large, only the thermal process is observable. Data similar to those shown in Fig. 4 were taken in the reactor and plotted as open circles in Fig. 6. The simple theory is seen to compare quite favorably with experiment. The diffusion coefficient may be estimated from $D = (a^2/12)(1/\tau) = 10^{-16}\,(1/\tau)$ where a is the lattice parameter, which yields $D' - D \simeq D' = K/\alpha \simeq 10^{-20}$ cm/s. This is an extremely small diffusion coefficient for bulk diffusion, but the preceding experiments show that the microdiffusion effects are readily observable.

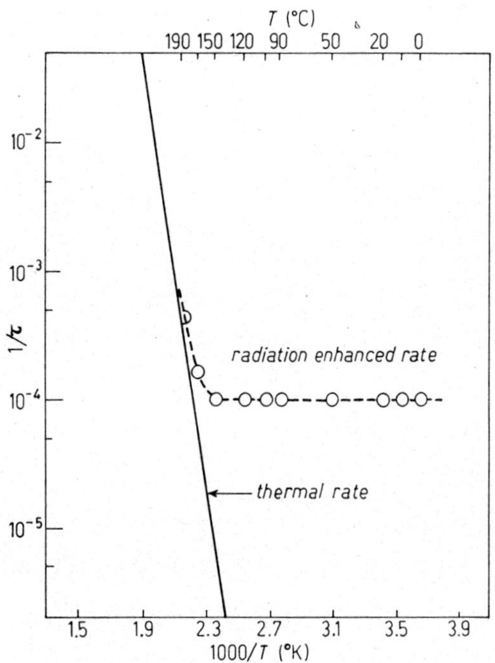

Fig. 6. – Rate of ordering $(1/\tau)$ *vs.* $1/T$ for α-brass. Solid line: thermal rate. Dashed line: theoretical radiation-enhanced rate for linear annealing of defects. Circles: experimental points (ref. [16]).

Although these data were taken with neutron irradiation, Fig. 4 shows the amount of electron irradiation which would produce equivalent results.

This simple theory has been extended to the cases in which the defects are removed by recombination and by both recombination and linear anneal [17]. The case of recombination is characterized by only the direct recombination of vacancies and interstitials which are generated in equal numbers by irradiation. Assume first that V_0 is small compared to V. It is also assumed that interstitials migrate much faster than the vacancies (the opposite case is easily treated by symmetry). Thus, if V and i are the number of vacancies and interstitials respectively, and ν_i is the jump frequency of the interstitials, the simplest direct recombination is described, in steady state, by the relation

$$\mathrm{d}V/\mathrm{d}t = K - \nu_i V i = 0\,,$$

and $V=i$. Thus in steady state,

$$V=i=(K/\nu_i)^{\frac{1}{2}},$$

and

$$D_v' = (K^{\frac{1}{2}}/(A^i)^{\frac{1}{2}})\,\lambda^2 A^v \exp\left[-(E_m^v - \tfrac{1}{2}E_m^i)/kT\right] + D_v\,,$$

where E_m^v and E_m^i are the migration energies of the vacancies and interstitials respectively and A^v and A^i are their respective entropy terms. In this case $(D'-D)$ depends exponentially on $1/T$ with the characteristic activation energy given by the esponential part of the above equation. Also note that D' depends on the square root of the flux in contrast to the linear flux-dependence in the case of the linear annealing of defects. The influence of V_0 on annealing in this case can be taken into account. If

$$\mathrm{d}V/\mathrm{d}t = K - \nu_i(V+V_0)i = 0\,,$$

then

$$V=i=-\frac{V_0}{2}+\frac{1}{2}\sqrt{V_0^2+\frac{4k}{\nu_i}}\,,$$

which can be compared numerically to the simpler cases. It is found that this correction is important in the temperature region where enhanced diffusion just becomes significant.

If both annealing to surfaces and recombination are important, then one has to solve the equation involving both effects simultaneously:

$$\mathrm{d}V/\mathrm{d}t = K - K_v V - \nu_i(V+V_0)i = 0\,.$$

After considerable reduction one finds

$$V=-\tfrac{1}{2}(\alpha\lambda^2+V_0)+\tfrac{1}{2}\sqrt{(\alpha\lambda^2+V_0)^2+\frac{4K}{\nu_v}}\,.$$

This must be solved numerically and at low temperatures where the enhancement is large one finds a square root of flux-dependence and an effective activation energy of $\frac{1}{2}E_m^v$.

These results are summarized in Table I.

The conditions under which the experiments were performed agree well with the case of linear annealing and thus tend to confirm this simple theory. The results were somewhat dissapointing, however, in that the case which was observed is the only one which does not yield information on the migration energy of the defects. Experiments are in progress with γ-radiation [18]

TABLE I. – *Characteristics of enhanced diffusion for various annealing mechanisms.*

Annealing mechanism	Activation energy for enhanced diffusion	Dependence of enhanced diffusion on rate of defect generation (flux)
Linear (direct to surfaces)	0	Linear
Bimolecular recombination of interstitials and vacancies	— $E^{\text{v}}_{\text{m}} - \frac{1}{2}E^{\text{i}}_{\text{m}}$	Square root
Bimolecular recombination plus linear anneal	$\frac{1}{2}E^{\text{v}}_{\text{m}}$	Square root

and, although not complete, they show a temperature-dependence of enhanced diffusion. This indicates a different mechanism of vacancy removal, probably because a great deal of vacancy-interstitial recombination can take place. This difference in mechanism as well as the lower irradiation temperature are possibly the reasons for the deviation of the γ curve from the others in Fig. 4.

The above equations for the linear case show that for neutron irradiation of α-brass the flux-dependence should be linear. A ground test of a nuclear rocket engine in America afforded a convenient means for an experimental determination of the flux-dependence, because the flux could be varied simply by placing samples at different distances from the source (*). This effectively gave only air as the absorbing medium with essentially no change in the energy spectrum, but some difficulties were encountered due to the reflection of neutrons from the ground and other objects in the vicinity of the engine. However, the diffusion coefficient *vs.* flux was essentially linear, in confirmation of the simple theory [19].

3·6. *Visual observation of enhanced diffusion.* – Because of the extremely small contribution to the diffusion coefficient from neutron-irradiation, all the above examples involved indirect measurements of microdiffusion. Recent work at Brookhaven has provided the first direct observation of enhanced diffusion [20]. Barnes *et al.* have bombarded copper with α-particles from a cyclotron [21]. Subsequent heating produced void formation in the copper within the band of the deposited heliun atoms. Their explanation is that the helium precipitates out as small gas bubbles in those parts of the metal where the helium atoms receive vacancies from nearby sources. An identical experi-

(*) This experiment was performed with the assistance of the Los Alamos Scientific Laboratory.

ment was performed at Brookhaven in which two samples received α-bombardment and then one was heated in the reactor for 10 days at 425 °C and the other kept at the same temperature outside. The reactor specimen (Fig. 7) clearly shows a greater void density which, we conclude, arises from the radiation excess vacancies.

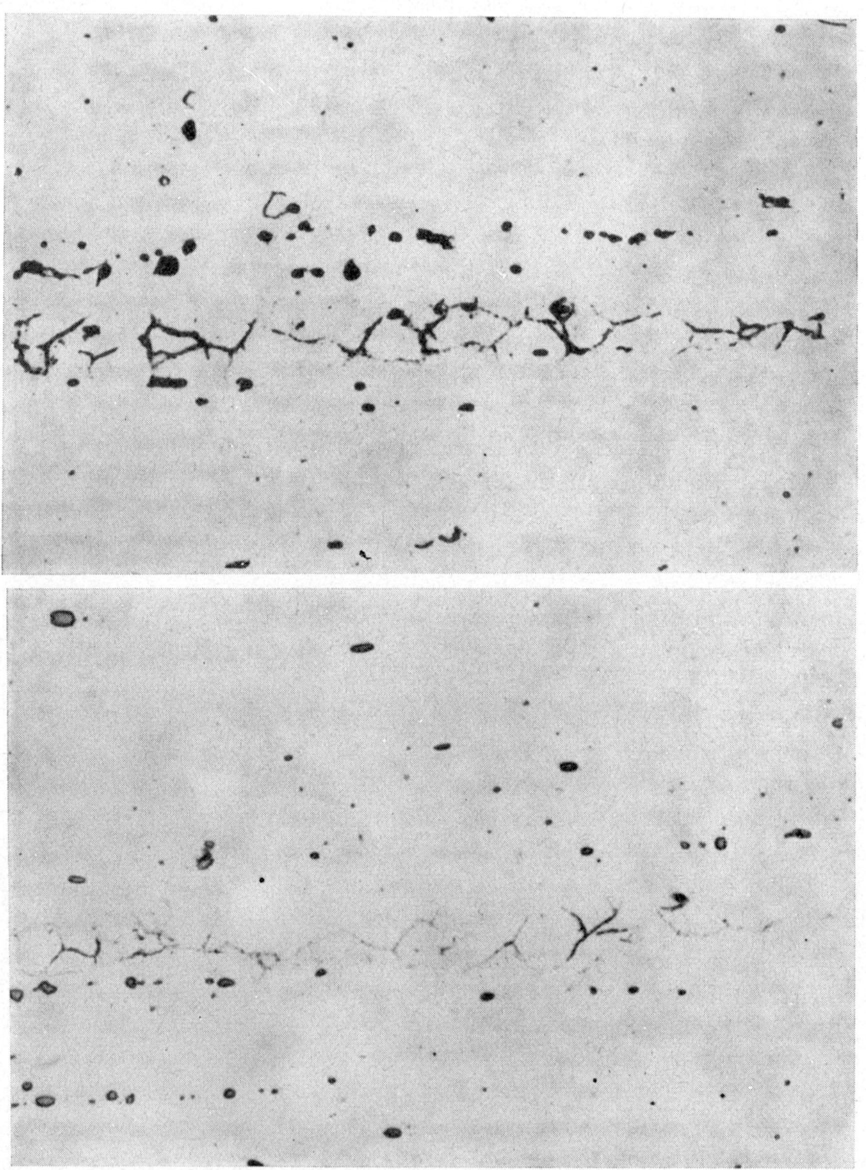

Fig. 7. – Copper bombarded by α-particles and heated 10 days at 425 °C. Upper picture: heating in reactor. Lower picture: heating outside reactor. Center horizontal band in pictures is position of imbedded helium (ref. [20]).

4. – Application.

Most atomic rearrangements in alloys do not obey the simple exponential kinetics of α-brass. Any rate more complex than exponential would progress more slowly towards equilibrium. One type of experiment which could be performed without achieving equilibrium is the determination of phase boundaries at low temperatures. When excess vacancies are introduced and some sensitive property of the atomic arrangement such as electrical resistivity is measured, only the alloy concentrations which are not in their lowest free energy states would exhibit a change upon irradiation. Thus very short irradiation of a series of concentrations should delineate the phase boundary. For these purposes only electron or γ (or other electromagnetic) irradiation should be used, so that any observed changes can be assigned to diffusion alone.

These « cold diffusion » methods have many other applications [22] in the study of solids. One of these is controlled diffusion of junctions into transistors by electron irradiation. This type of experiment has been performed on the diffusion of arsenic into germanium using the X-rays from an electron VAN DE GRAAFF beam [23]. At 700 °C the ratio of diffusion coefficient with irradiation to that without was 3.8. According to the theory presented here, this ratio would be much higher at lower temperatures.

4'1. *Excess vacancy generation by cold work.* – In the equations discussed previously the constant K is proportional to the number of excess vacancies in steady state in the solid, and although it was related to radiation-produced

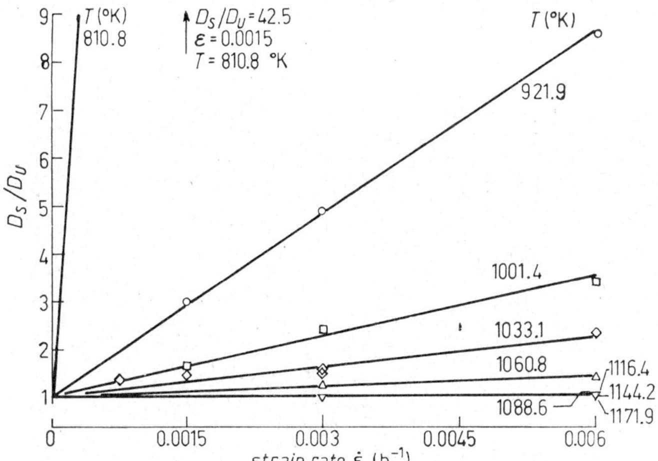

Fig. 8. – The ratio of the diffussion coefficient in strained silver to the diffusion coefficient in unstrained silver *vs.* the strain rate at various temperatures (ref. [24]).

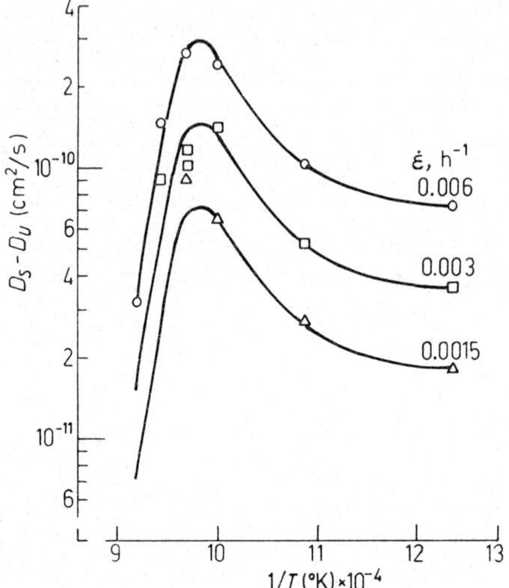

Fig. 9. – The logarithm of the difference in diffusion coefficients in strained and unstrained silver *vs.* the reciprocal absolute temperature for various strain rates (ref. [24]).

vacancies, the equations are not limited to solids in a radiation field. Moving dislocations also generate vacancies and experiments have been performed by FORESTIERI and GIRIFALCO [24] on the self-diffusion of silver under a constant strain rate. Fig. 8 shows the initial data plotted as the ratio of D_s, the diffusion coefficient at a constant strain rate, over D_u, the unstrained diffusion coefficient, *vs.* the strain rate. It is seen that at low temperatures, where the excess vacancies are expected to play an important role, this ratio increases very rapidly with increasing strain rate. At high temperatures, where the strain-generated vacancies are dominated in number by the thermal vacancies, there is no observable effect. If vertical cuts are made on this figure and the data plotted as $D_s - D_u$ *vs.* $1/T$, the points of Fig. 9 are given. The curves of Fig. 9, however, were derived in the following manner. The equation of the most general case developed here

$$\mathrm{d}V/\mathrm{d}t = K - K_v V - \nu_i(V + V_0)i = 0 \,,$$

was modified by the following assumptions. The generation rate of vacancies, K, was set equal to a constant plus a temperature-dependent term, $K = C_1 + C_2 \exp[E^*/kT]$. From the calculation of DAMASK *et al.* [25] it was assumed that divacancies are more mobile than single vacancies and that trivacancies are not mobile at all. Thus, if two vacancies collide they form a divacancy

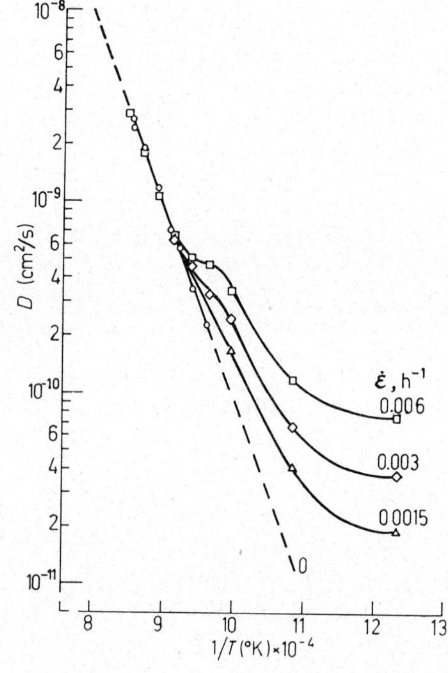

Fig. 10. – The logarithm of the diffusion coefficient of silver *vs.* the reciprocal absolute temperature for various strain rates (ref. [24]).

which continues to contribute to diffusion unless it meets another vacancy in which case all three become fixed and can no longer contribute. Since the divacancy is the faster moving defect, its jump frequency is the rate-controlling term. Although reference [24] develops the case more rigorously, in its simplest concept the above equation is modified by changing the jump frequency and the concentration of the interstitials to those of the divacancy. There are admittedly many adjustable parameters, but reasonable choices can be made to give the curves of Fig. 9 which are seen to fit the data very well. It may well be that intestitials are produced in large numbers and they become the dominating term, but the same equation, with suitable modifications, would apply. From a plot of simply D *vs.* $1/T$, the curves of Fig. 10 result. When low strain rates are used, there is a low probability of interaction between vacancies before they anneal to the surface, and the general case would be expected to reduce to the simple linear annealing case. The curve of lowest strain rate in Fig. 10 is seen to be quite similar to the irradiation curve of Fig. 6.

It, therefore, seems that the equations presented here are most general and that future considerations such as relative number of defects present, collision probabilities, etc. will be introduced as modifications to these basic forms.

REFERENCES

[1] G. J. Dienes and G. H. Vineyard: *Radiation Effects in Solids* (New York, 1957).

[2] G. H. Vineyard J. B. Gibson, A. N. Goland and M. Milgram: *Bull. Am. Phys. Soc.*, **5**, 26 (1960).

[3] J. A. Brinkman: *Journ. Appl. Phys.*, **25**, 961 (1954).

[4] A. Boltax in *Symposium on Radiation Effects on Materials* vol. **1** (1956), pp. 183-190; ASTM Spec. Tech. Pub. no. 208 (Philadelphia, Pa., 1957).

[5] J. Fleeman and G. J. Dienes: *Journ. Appl. Phys.*, **26**, 652 (1955).

[6] D. E. Thomas in *Nuclear Metallurgy,* vol. **3**, Table I, p. 24, Inst. of Met. Div. Spec. Rep. no. 3, AIME (New York, 1956).

[7] H. L. Glick, F. C. Brooks, W. F. Witzig and W. E. Johnson: *Phys. Rev.*, **87**, 1074 (1952).

[8] R. A. Dugdale: *Phil. Mag.*, **1**, 537 (1957).

[9] R. H. Kernohan, D. S. Billington and A. B. Lewis: *Journ. Appl. Phys.*, **27**, 40 (1956).

[10] F. M. Ryan, E. W. Pugh and R. Smoluchowski: *Phys. Rev.*, **116**, 1106 (1959).

[11] A. C. Damask: *Journ. Appl. Phys.*, **27**, 610 (1956).

[12] A. C. Damask: *Journ. Phys. Chem. Solids*, **4**, 177 (1958).

[13] C. R. Houska and B. L. Averbach: *Journ. Appl. Phys.*, **30**, 1525 (1959).

[14] M. S. Wechsler and R. H. Kernohan: *Journ. Phys. Chem. Solids*, **7**, 307 (1958).

[15] A. C. Damask and G. J. Dienes: *Journ. Phys. Chem. Solids*, **12**, 105 (1959).

[16] G. J. Dienes and A. C. Damask: *Journ. Appl. Phys.*, **29**, 1713 (1958).
[17] W. M. Lomer: AERE (Harwell), Report 1540 (1954), unpublished.
[18] A. C. Damask and R. E. Larsen: unpublished.
[19] R. E. Larsen, A. C. Damask and G. J. Dienes: *Bull. Am. Phys. Soc.*, **5**, 182 (1960).
[20] A. N. Goland: *Phil. Mag.* (in press).
[21] R. S. Barnes, G. B. Redding and A. H. Cottrell: *Phil. Mag.*, **3**, 97 (1958).
[22] A. C. Damask: U. S. Patent 2, 911, 533.
[23] N. L. Peterson and R. E. Olgilvie: *Trans. Met. Soc. AIME*, **215**, 873 (1959).
[24] A. F. Forestieri and L. A. Girifalco: *Journ. Phys. Chem. Solids*, **10**, 99 (1959).
[25] A. C. Damask, G. J. Dienes and V. G. Weizer: *Phys. Rev.*, **113**, 781 (1959).

Radiation-Damage Studies Using Dislocation Properties.

D. K. Holmes

Oak Ridge National Laboratory (*), *Solid State Division - Oak Ridge, Tenn.*

1. – The contribution of dislocations to the elastic constants.

T. A. Read [1] in 1940 suggested that the presence of dislocations would lower the modulus of a crystal (as compared with the « perfect » crystal) and introduce anelastic damping centers. The work of J. S. Koehler [2], especially in the late 1940's and early 1950's, established this effect very precisely; and observations of changes in elastic moduli and internal friction due to irradiation soon became a matter of interest both to radiation-damage theory and to dislocation theory.

Basically, the physical situation is, at present, thought to be as shown in the accompanying Fig. 1. If a crystal is under applied stresses, the dislocations inside feel a local force per unit length which is directly proportional to the local shear stress, acting across their glide planes. Suppose the force couple, F_a, shown, corresponds to a shear stress on the crystal, σ_s. Then, taking this stress to be uniform through the crystal, the force per unit length of dislocation line, F, is given by

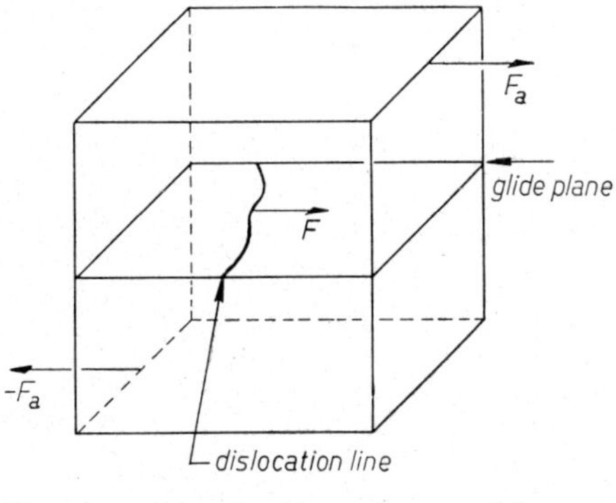

$$F = \sigma_s b \, , \tag{1}$$

Fig. 1. – The shearing of a crystal containing dislocations.

(*) Oak Ridge National Laboratory is operated by Union Carbide Corporation for the U.S. Atomic Energy Commission.

where b is the magnitude of the Burgers vector of the dislocation. There is an elastic strain of the crystal from the applied stress, given by

$$\varepsilon_e = \frac{\sigma_s}{\mu}, \tag{2}$$

where μ is the shear modulus of the crystal. If the dislocation can move some distance in its glide plane before becoming « stuck » so that the force, F, cannot move it further, then there will occur an additional strain of the crystal resulting from the slip of the top half of the crystal over the bottom half as the dislocation moves. This extra strain, ε_D, is directly proportional to the area A swept out by the dislocation (see Fig. 2) as it moves under the applied stress.

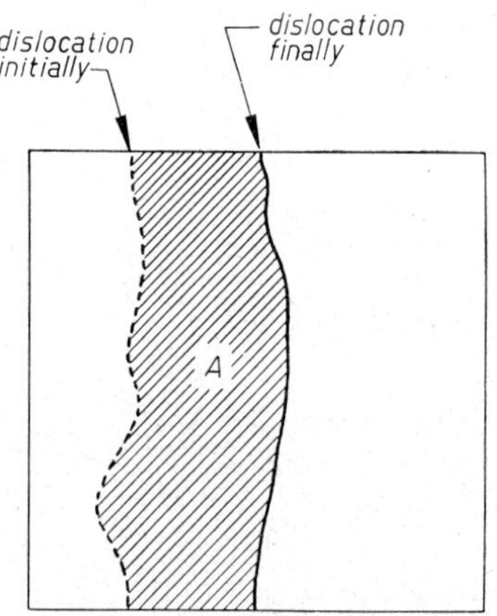

Fig. 2. – The glide plane.

For one dislocation line in a unit volume of the crystal

$$\varepsilon_D = bA \quad \text{(unitless)}. \tag{3}$$

For an array of many dislocations, eq. (3) still holds with A interpreted as the total area swept out by *all* the dislocations in a unit volume. Thus, the effect of the presence of dislocations, which are able to move some, is to « weaken » the crystal, *i.e.*, to lower its effective modulus; thus

$$\varepsilon_T = \varepsilon_e + \varepsilon_D = \frac{\sigma_s}{\mu_{\text{eff}}}, \tag{4}$$

and from eq. (2)

$$\mu_{\text{eff}} = \frac{\mu}{1 + \mu\varepsilon_D/\sigma_s}. \tag{5}$$

Further, if the stress is oscillatory, the dislocations may be able to move back and forth between the extreme positions; but there will, in general, be a frictional loss as they do so. So, under oscillatory stress there will be centers of energy dissipation in the crystal at each mobile dislocation line. Thus, there will be a measurable internal friction or logarithmic decrement of the crystal associated with the presence of dislocations; we will denote this by Δ_D and note that the decrement of the crystal may be written as

$$\Delta = \Delta_D + \Delta_B, \tag{6}$$

where Δ_B is the «background loss», *i.e.*, all losses other than to dislocations. The contribution of dislocations to the internal friction is somewhat more difficult to calculate than the contribution to the modulus for two reasons:

a) Most basically, the fundamental coupling by which moving dislocations lose energy to the lattice has not as yet been clearly established.

b) But even if a simple model is taken such as the usual one, that the frictional force on a dislocation is proportional to its velocity, the result for the decrement must be obtained by solving completely the equation of motion, which in turn depends on another unknown quantity, the exact nature of the dislocation network in the crystal, and of the physical barriers to their motion.

2. – The resonant bar experiment and experimental parameters.

In practical experiments the shear stress is not simple and uniform as pictured here; in fact, the shear modulus itself is seldom measured. As an example of a typical experimental setup, consider the resonant bar of Fig. 3. The bar is mounted in the center and driven from one end in a longitudinal model. The amplitude of motion is measured at the other end. The frequency of the applied stress is varied through the lowest resonant mode and the required mechanical properties measured. The modulus, in this case Young's modulus, E, is proportional to the square of the resonant frequency and the decrement is proportional to the half-width of the resonant peak. In such an experiment the dislocation motion is quite complicated. For example, if the bar is a single crystal of copper, there are four sets of [111] planes which act as glide planes; the compression and extension of the longitudinal waves will, in general, exert shear stresses across these planes which will be different for the four different sets. Further, the dislocations may be edge, screw, or mixed, and their possibilities for motion correspondingly variant. As a final point, the dislocation density may very well not be uniform over the length of the bar; and it must be noted that the highest strains are always at the center. Most of these parameters are at present unknown, so progress is always made by assuming simplifying models of the nature of the dislocation network of the crystal.

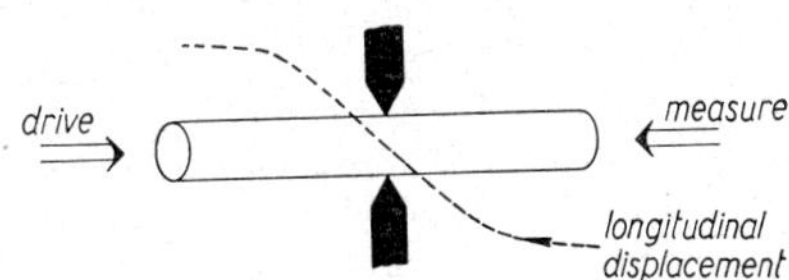

Fig. 3. – Resonant bar.

There are many other experimental arrangements, but we only need concern ourselves with two important parameters which may vary from experiment to experiment.

a) *The strain amplitude* ε_0. This may vary from 10^{-8} to 10^{-4} (rarely greater) and is, of course, of the greatest importance since it determines the maximum force on the dislocation lines, essentially through a relationship of the type

$$F_{\max} = \alpha\mu\varepsilon_0 b\,, \tag{7}$$

where α is an orientation factor which takes the component of the applied forces along the direction of the Burgers vector. In general, the dislocation contribution to the physical properties increases with increasing strain amplitude since the greater force usually causes greater motion of the lines, since certain barriers to motion in the crystal are overcome. Thus, Fig. 4 is typical of such results. Very often the low-strain-amplitude region shows the behavior schematized by the curve of Fig. 4, and this «strain-amplitude-independent» range can be very useful.

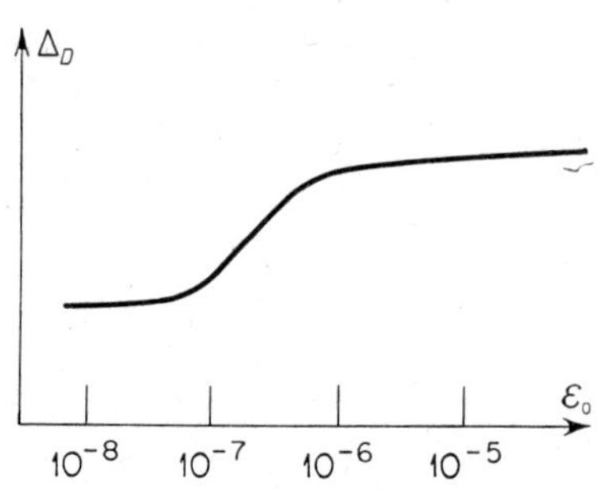

Fig. 4. – Decrement *vs.* strain amplitude (schematic).

b) *The applied frequency.* This also is very effective in determining dislocation motion and may vary over even greater ranges than the strain amplitude. The significant point is that, in this field, a given experimental arrangement is generally useful only over about an order of magnitude in the frequency. For example, the resonant bar may typically resonate at 10 000 Hz; by using higher harmonics (30 000, 50 000, etc.), the response to higher frequencies may be tested; but experimental difficulties with the higher modes limit this technique severely. Some of the important methods are:

1) Torsion-pendulum studies on wires are used in the few Hz range.

2) Flexural modes of thin bars are used in the range of a few hundred to a few thousand Hz.

3) Resonant bars are used in the 10 000 to 20 000 Hz range.

4) Pulsed sound waves are used in the MHz and higher range.

3. – Irradiation and the « pinning » of dislocations.

If in any way the dislocation motion can be completely quenched [3], the modulus of the « perfect » crystal will be observed; and the background decrement only will appear. The two important means by which this has been accomplished to date are:

a) by introducing impurity atoms, substitutionally or interstitially, which tend to cluster around dislocations and impede their motion. For example, KOEHLER annealed copper crystals in hydrogen and successfully quenched dislocation motion;

b) by irradiation. As an example, some results from resonant-bar experiments on copper single crystals are given in Table I [4]. Here the decrement and Young's modulus of the original (well-annealed) crystal, Δ_0 and E_0, respectively, are given with the corresponding quantities Δ_f and E_f after various irradiations (somewhat above room temperature) with fast neutrons in the Oak Ridge National Laboratory Graphite Reactor. As can be seen from eq. (5), the quantity in the sixth column is directly proportional to the dislocation strain; thus

TABLE I.

Crystal	E_0 (dyn/cm²)	Δ_0	E_f (dyn/cm²)	Δ_f	$(E_f-E_0)/E_0$ (%)	Integrated flux (nvt)
1*A*	$1.227\cdot10^{12}$	$24.8\cdot10^{-3}$	$1.34\cdot10^{12}$	$0.7\cdot10^{-3}$	+9.55	$15\cdot10^{17}$
2*A*	1.008	2.2	1.023	0.4_5	1.49	$10\cdot10^{17}$
2*B*	1.013	5.5	1.028	1.0	1.48	$3.1\cdot10^{15}$
2*C*	1.021	2.5	1.032_5	1.2	1.13	$10\cdot10^{17}$
3*A*	1.460	5.7	1.472	0.3_5	0.82	$10\cdot10^{17}$
3*B*	1.474	1.0	1.477	0.3_5	0.22	$8.5\cdot10^{15}$
4*A*	1.107	5.4	1.149	0.8	3.80	$2.4\cdot10^{14}$
83*A*	1.142	3.6	1.196	1.0	4.72	$4.8\cdot10^{18}$

$$\frac{E_f - E_0}{E_0} = \left(\frac{\mu}{\sigma_s}\right)\varepsilon_D\,. \tag{8}$$

It may be seen that in all these crystals the decrement falls and the modulus rises, which is consistent with the idea that some products of the fast-neutron bombardment are pinning down the dislocations. This is, of course, not conclusive from this simple before-and-after type of experiment, although there is a pertinent side point, that the irradiation of some of these crystals was continued to a factor of three greater dose than that at which the change was first observed without any further changes greater than one part in 10^4. It might be expected that, if the observed changes were due to a « bulk » effect rather than to a dislocation-pinning effect, the range of 10^{17} to 10^{19} nvt would be a range of monotonically changing properties. We are thinking, for example, of vacancies and interstitials as produced by fast-neutron bombardment and their effects on the modulus and decrements. But, again, this is not conclusive, though it is difficult to imagine how these defects could decrease the decrement so dramactically. Now look at a more detailed presentation of the changes in these two properties (Fig. 5). As a function of increasing fast-neutron irradiation, the modulus rises and the decrement falls somewhat more

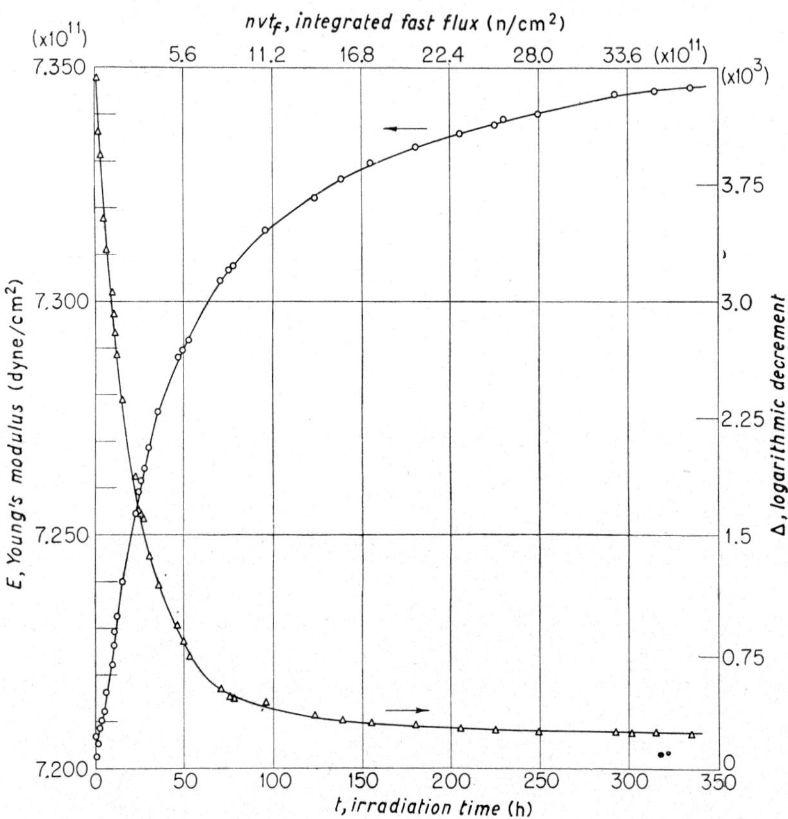

Fig. 5. – Young's modulus (○) and logarithmic decrement (△) *vs.* irradiation time, crystal 5*A*. The flux is $3.1 \cdot 10^6$ neutrons/cm²·s, and the maximum strain amplitude is $5 \cdot 10^{-8}$.

rapidly. Of interest here is the final total irradiation at which these properties seem to have saturated,

$$(\text{nvt})_{\text{final}} \sim 3 \cdot 10^{12} \text{ neutrons/cm}^2 .$$

It seems difficult to imagine that the atomic fraction of vacancy-interstitial pairs is greater than 10^{-9} after this dosage, and it is further difficult to imagine that this small fraction could produce these effects. The theory of the quenching of dislocation motion, which we shall present later, shows conclusively that the observed changes are directly connected with the dislocation structure of the crystal. (In fact, the solid lines in Fig. 5 are just the theoretical curves.)

It is concluded, then, that in room-temperature irradiations the direct effects on the elastic constants of the presence of vacancies and interstitials is not seen up to quite high total bombardments with fast neutrons. On the

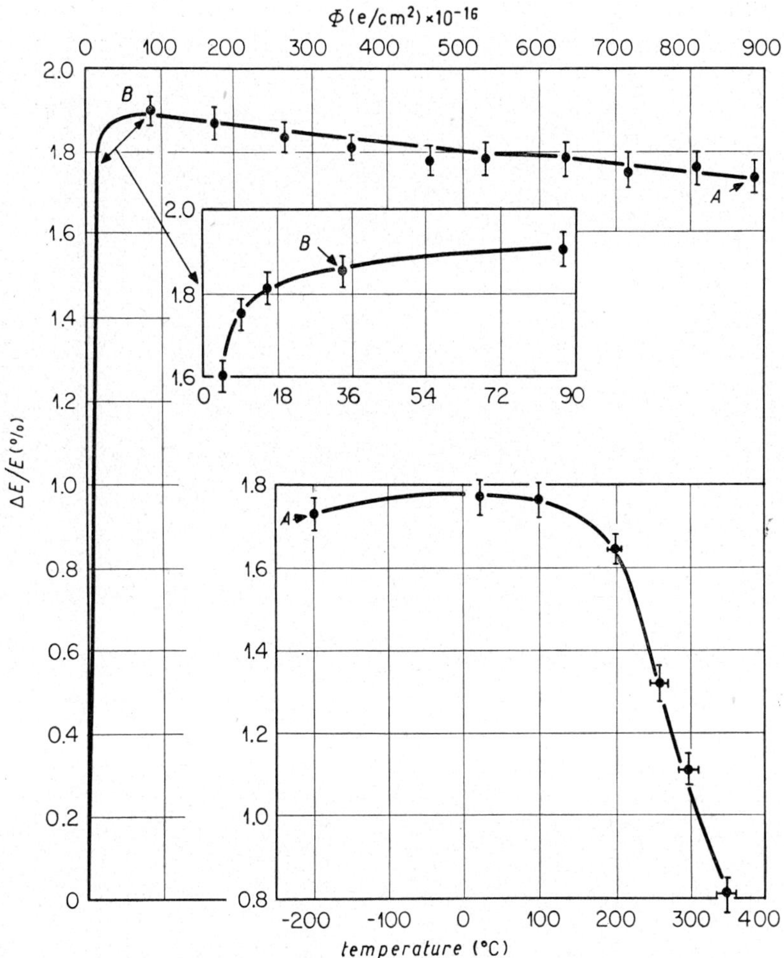

Fig. 6. – The variation of the modulus with electron irradiation. [H. DIECKAMP and A. SOSIN: *Journ. Appl. Phys.*, **27**, 1417 (1956)].

other hand, DIECKAMP and SOSIN [5], in using electron irradiation at liquid-nitrogen temperature (Fig. 6), found that the initial rapid rise (dislocation-associated) in the modulus was followed by a slow decrease, which they attribute to the creation of point defects in the lattice.

4. – The bowing-string model.

The « bowing string » model, which has been quite successfully applied toward predicting the dislocation behavior, was first discussed in detail by J. S. KOEHLER. The principal idea is that the dislocations in the well-annealed crystal are not free to move but are pinned down at somewhat widely spaced points either by impurity atoms or crossing points with other dislocations. Thus, when they feel the force resulting from the local shear stress, they can only « bow out » between these points. This type of behavior is illustrated in Fig. 7. This bowing out is limited by the line tension of the dislocation, much as in the case of a bowing string. This line tension is just the energy

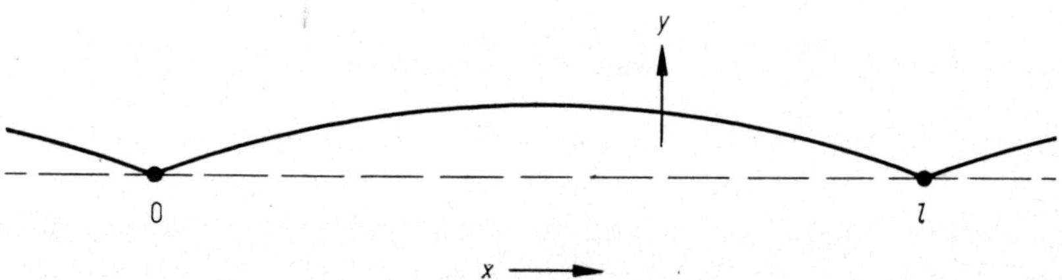

Fig. 7. – The « bowing string » model of dislocation motion. Approximate form for displacement: $y(x, t) = (\sigma_s(t)b/2T)\ x(l - x)$.

per unit length of a dislocation, which we will denote by T, and is given very closely by

$$T = \tfrac{1}{2}\mu b^2 . \tag{9}$$

Statically, the balance can be written (in the notation of Fig. 7)

$$T\,\frac{\mathrm{d}^2 y}{\mathrm{d}x^2} = \sigma_s b . \tag{10}$$

The form of the loop is

$$y(x) = \frac{\sigma_s b}{2T}\, x(l - x) , \tag{11}$$

fixing the end points at $x = 0$ we and 1. On the basis of this simple model, we may calculate the contribution to the strain of one dislocation as (see eq. (3))

$$\varepsilon_D = \frac{\sigma_s}{6\mu}\, l^3 . \tag{12}$$

If there are $N(l)$ dislocation loops per unit volume having lengths between l and $l+\mathrm{d}l$, the total contribution of all dislocations is

(13) $$\varepsilon_D = \frac{\sigma_s}{6\mu}\int_0^\infty l^3 N(l)\,\mathrm{d}l\,,$$

neglecting the difference between dislocations on different glide planes and their different orientations factors.

The decrement is more difficult to calculate since we must use the dynamic equations. This is usually written as

(14) $$\varrho\,\frac{\partial^2 y}{\partial t^2} + B\,\frac{\partial y}{\partial t} + T\,\frac{\partial^2 y}{\partial x^2} = \sigma_s^{(0)} b\cos\omega t\,.$$

In eq. (14), ϱ is the effective mass per unit length of the dislocation. The frictional force on the dislocation has been taken as proportional to the velocity of the dislocation line through a constant of proportionality, B, the « damping constant »; and a simple harmonic force has been assumed. In the general case this equation has a somewhat cumbersome solution, but there is a very useful solution in the low-frequency, low-damping range obtained by neglecting the first two terms. The inertia term can be seen to be negligible for low enough frequencies (for long enough free lengths) when it is realized that a typical resonant frequency (undamped) for dislocation loops is $\sim$1 000 MHz. The solution is then

(15) $$y(x, t) = \frac{\sigma_s b}{2T}\,x(l-x)\cos\omega t\,,$$

and the energy loss per cycle may be calculated as

(16) $$\Delta\varepsilon = \int_0^l \mathrm{d}x \oint B\left(\frac{\partial y}{\partial t}\right)^2 \mathrm{d}t\,.$$

Then the contribution to the decrement of one dislocation loop of length l per unit volume may be calculated as

(17) $$\Delta_l = \frac{\Delta\varepsilon}{2W}\,,$$

where W is the maximum energy stored (elastically) during a cycle (per unit volume),

$$W = \frac{\sigma_s^2}{2\mu}, \tag{18}$$

in the simple case. Finally

$$\Delta_l = B\omega \frac{\pi}{60T} l^5 . \tag{19}$$

Note that, while the contribution to strain varies as the cube of the loop length, the contribution to the decrement varies as the fifth power.

5. – The loop-length distribution.

Two forms have been widely used for the loop-length distribution, $N(l)$ (which must be assumed since little is known of its true nature). These are the exponential and the δ-function. The latter is analytically simple and corresponds to the case of all lengths being the same. The former may also have some physical reality since it corresponds to randomly arranged pinning points along the line. The analytic forms are:

a) δ-function:

$$N_\Delta = \frac{L_0}{l_0} \delta(l - l_0) , \tag{20}$$

b) exponential:

$$N_e(l) = \frac{L_0}{l_0^2} \exp\left[-\frac{l}{l_0}\right]. \tag{21}$$

Here L_0 = the total length of dislocation line per unit volume =

= the number of dislocation lines threading one cm²;

l_0 = the average loop length.

The final expressions for the dislocation effect are [6], then, using the equations above [7]

$$\left(\frac{\Delta\mu}{\mu}\right)_D = \left[\frac{1}{6} L_0 l_0^2\right] [3\,!]_e , \tag{22}$$

$$\Delta_D = \left[B\omega \frac{\pi}{60T} L_0 l_0^4\right] [5\,!]_e . \tag{23}$$

The forms for the two distributions are the same but the results differ by numerical factors. The first bracket alone in each case gives the δ-function result, while the exponential result is to be obtained by including (as a multiplier) the factor in the second bracket. Note that we can already use the results of Table I [4] in this model; using the exponential result, eq. (22), we find that $L_0 l_0^2 \sim 0.01$. If we believe that $L_0 \sim 10^7$ in a well-annealed crystal, then $l_0 \simeq 3 \cdot 10^{-5}$ cm.

6. – The time-dependence of the irradiation changes.

There is another important way of looking at these results if we recognize that the average loop length, l_0, is just the reciprocal of the average number of pinning points per unit length of dislocation line, n_0,

$$l_0 = \frac{1}{n_0}\,. \tag{24}$$

For the moment, let us use the exponential distribution. Now the assumption is that products of irradiation migrate over to the dislocation line (at room temperature) and, in some way, act as, supposedly, random pinning points. Thus, the calculation on the basis of the exponential distribution applies throughout the irradiation if we interpret the number of pinning point, n_t, as the *total* number, original plus radiation-produced,

$$n_t = n_0 + n_r\,. \tag{25}$$

In the small-irradiation range we may take the number of pinning points produced by irradiation as simply linear in time (for a constant flux)

$$n_r = n_0 \gamma t\,, \tag{26}$$

where γ is a (presently unknown) constant involving neutron flux, cross-section, defect mobilities, etc. Now we are ready to predict the time-dependence of the dislocation properties in the reactor (using eq. (22) and (23)) by

$$\frac{\Delta\mu}{\mu}(t) = \frac{L_0 l_0^2}{(1+\gamma t)^2}\,, \tag{27}$$

$$\Delta_D(t) = \left(\frac{2B\omega\pi}{T}\right)\frac{L_0 l_0^2}{(1+\gamma t)^4}\,. \tag{28}$$

For convenience we define new quantities which will be simple functions of time:

(29) $$y^{-\frac{1}{2}} = \sqrt{\frac{\Delta\mu/\mu(t)}{\Delta\mu/\mu(0)}} = 1 + \gamma t\,.$$

(30) $$z^{-\frac{1}{4}} = \sqrt[4]{\frac{\Delta_D(t)}{\Delta(0)}} = 1 + \gamma t\,.$$

The data of Fig. 5 are replotted in Fig. 8 to show this linear behavior [8]. The agreement is quite startling [9]. Indeed, results such as these may be regarded as the principal reason why the bowing-string model, with the simple frictional law, is so highly regarded in spite of the fact that it has numerous drawbacks, as will be discussed.

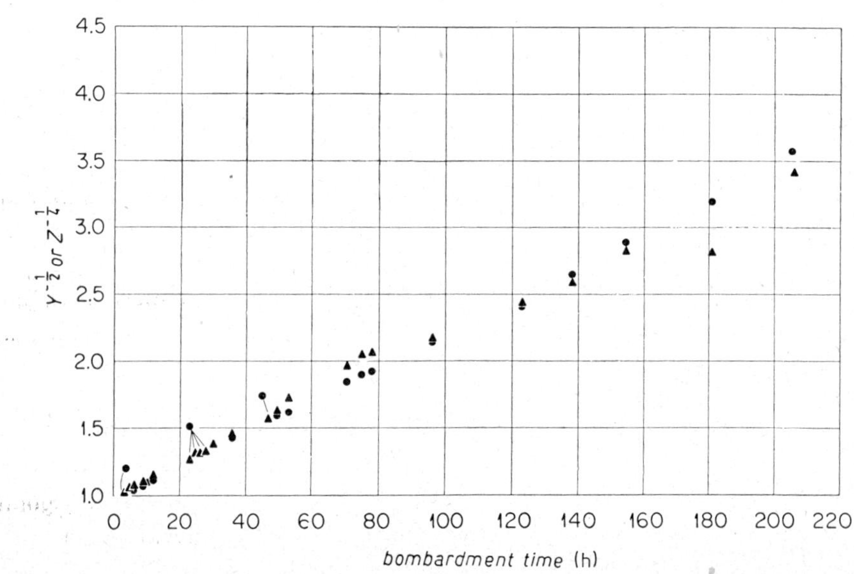

Fig. 8. – The change in modulus and decrement with fast-neutron irradiation (room temperature). [D. O. THOMPSON and V. K. PARE: *Journ. Appl. Phys.*, **31**, 528 (1960).]

From this kind of data we can get essentially three experimental results: $L_0 l_0^2$; $BL_0 l_0^4$; γ. But they include *four* unknowns. To utilize the data as well as we can, we relate γ to the neutron flux by

(31) $$\gamma = \frac{n \sum_s \varphi}{L_0}\,.$$

Equation (31) essentially says that the number of pinning points produced per unit length of dislocation line per second in a flux, φ, is the total number of neutron-nucleus scattering collisions multiplied by the number of effective pinning points, n, produced per collision, distributed over the total length of dislocation line, L_0. Here we regard « n » as the unknown. In Table II [4] we summarize the values for L_0 and l_0 which may be obtained from the experimental data (on copper) by assuming various values for n.

TABLE II.

Crystal	$n=1$	$n=10$	$n=100$
5A l_0	$6.9_5 \cdot 10^{-5}$ cm	$3.2 \cdot 10^{-5}$ cm	$1.5 \cdot 10^{-5}$ cm
L_0	$1.8_5 \cdot 10^{7}$ cm^{-2}	$8.6 \cdot 10^{7}$ cm^{-2}	$40 \cdot 10^{7}$ cm^{-2}
5B l_0	$6.4 \cdot 10^{-5}$ cm	$2.9^5 \cdot 10^{-5}$ cm	$1.4 \cdot 10^{-5}$ cm
L_0	$1.5 \cdot 10^{7}$ cm^{-2}	$7.0 \cdot 10^{7}$ cm^{-2}	$32 \cdot 10^{7}$ cm^{-2}

7. – The general use of dislocation pinning to study irradiation-produced defects.

With considerable confidence in the bowing-string model, we may now use changes in dislocation properties to study irradiation-produced defects. As a simple example, we may test our understanding of the production of defects by various types of incident radiation. We have already seen examples of the use of two bombarding particles, fast neutrons and energetic electrons (Fig. 6), though at different temperatures. More directly, we compare irradiation by γ-rays and fast neutrons [10] (Fig. 9) (γ-rays of $E_\gamma \sim 1.25$ MeV

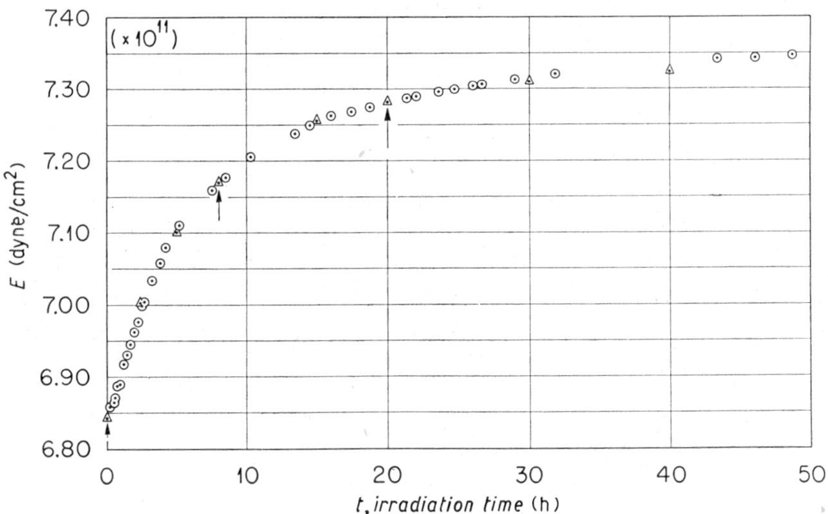

Fig. 9. – The variation of the Young's modulus of a copper single crystal with time of exposure to γ-rays. Circled dots are data points; triangles enclose points calculated from eq. (1) of the text. The arrows indicate fitting points used to obtain eq. (1).

from ^{60}Co). The data of Fig. 9, showing modulus changes with irradiation, were taken on one of the same crystals which was used for fast-neutron irradiation (subsequently annealed to remove all damage effects), and the results fit well with the $1/(1+\gamma t)^2$ form of eq. (27). However, the rate constant, γ, is such that on the basis of eq. (31) (using the appropriate γ-ray flux and γ-ray displacement cross-section) it may be shown that the effective number of pinning points per γ-ray « hit » is about a factor of 80 lower than that for fast neutrons. This is very much in line with what would, in general, be expected since a γ-ray of this energy produces hardly more than one displaced atom, while a fast-neutron hit will produce (theoretically) something like 100 displaced atoms.

Even more interesting are the experiments using one type of radiation at several different sample temperatures since this can indicate something about defect mobilities at various temperatures. Presumably, point defects must get to the dislocation line in order to act as effective pinning points. Fig. 10

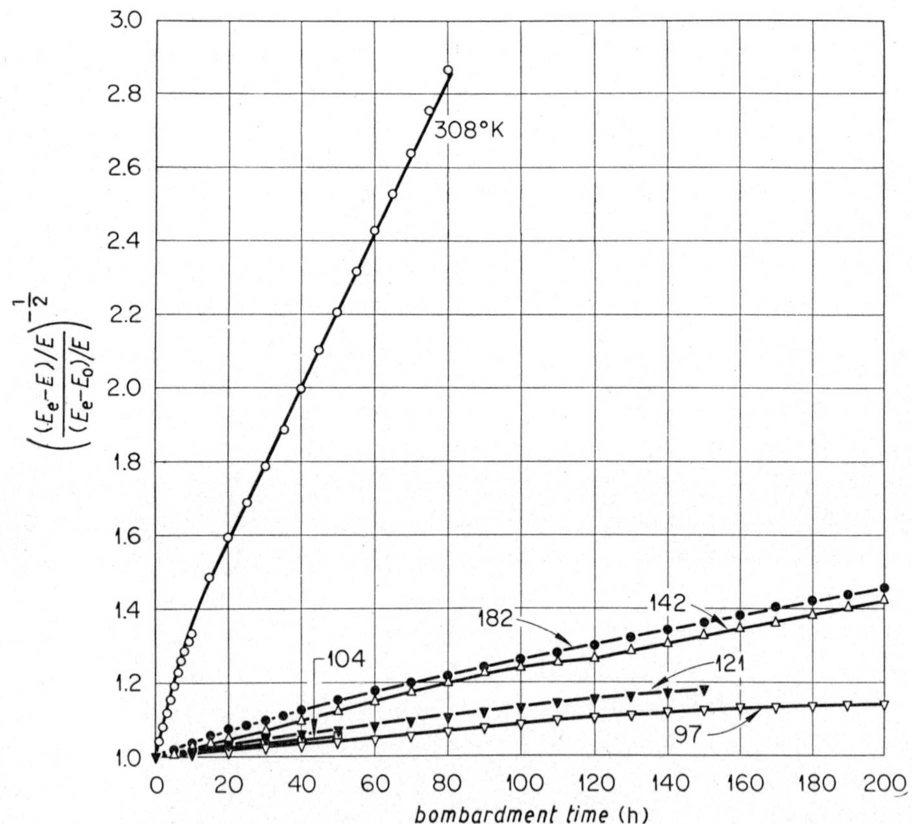

Fig. 10. – The change in modulus with fast-neutron irradiation at various temperatures [D. O. Thompson and V. K. Pare: *Journ. Appl. Phys.*, **31**, 528 (1960)].

shows some modulus curves [8] plotted *vs.* $y^{-\frac{1}{2}}$ (as in Fig. 8). Here the room-temperature (308 °K) curve is compared with curves for several other temperatures (all at the same fast-neutron-flux level). An interesting point is that the curve are not quite straight lines for this particular sample. THOMPSON and PARE [8] have shown that this is most likely due to the presence of two different populations of dislocations which pin at different rates, for some reason. But the outstanding feature of this data is the vastly different pinning

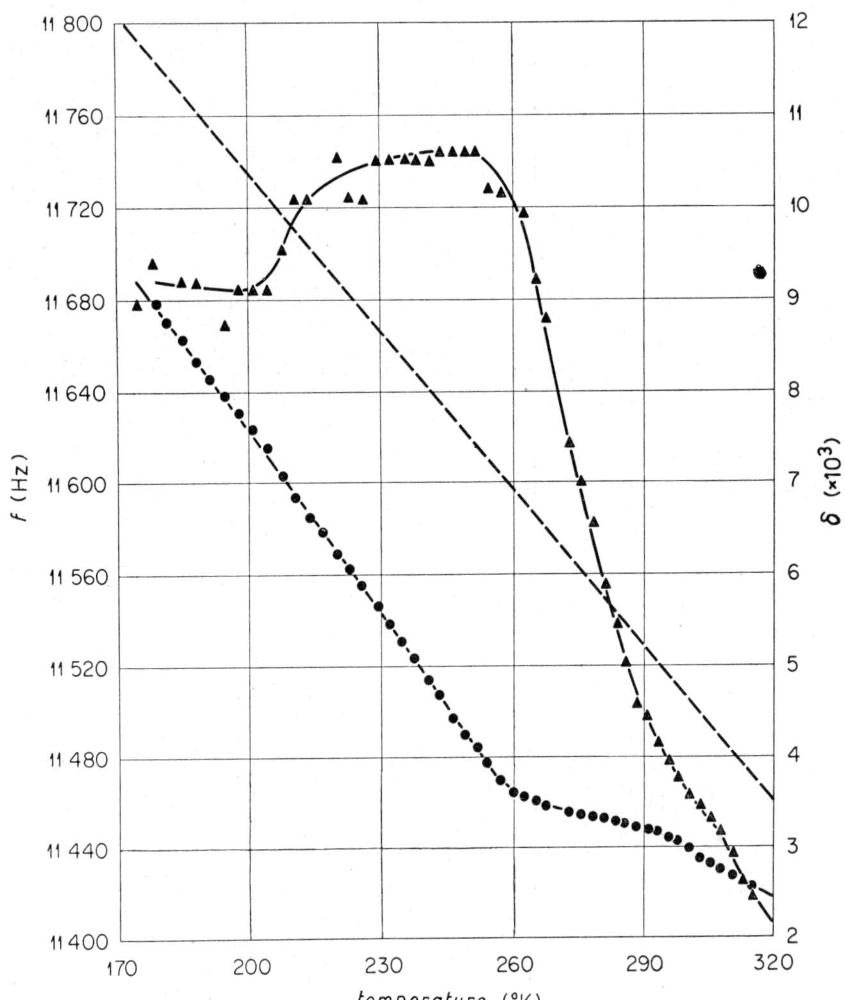

Fig. 11. – The change in resonant frequency and decrement with temperature upon warming-up from fast neutron irradiation at 168 °K. [D. O. THOMPSON and V. K. PARE: *Journ. Appl. Phys.*, **31**, 528 (1960)]. ● resonant frequency; ▲ logarithmic decrement; – – – « saturated » resonant frequency.

rates for the dominant group of dislocations at the various temperatures. It is, in fact, tempting to conclude that some irradiation-produced defect which is mobile at 308 °K is immobile at 182 °K. This effect is also seen visibly in Fig. 11, which shows the decrement and modulus changes with increasing temperature after fast-neutron irradiation at about 170 °K. Note that the modulus (as measured here by the resonant frequency) is expected to fall with rising temperature in the crystal (note the dashed curve). The significant feature of these curves is the abrupt fall in the decrement as the temperature of the sample rises above 250 °K. These are just the effects expected if de-

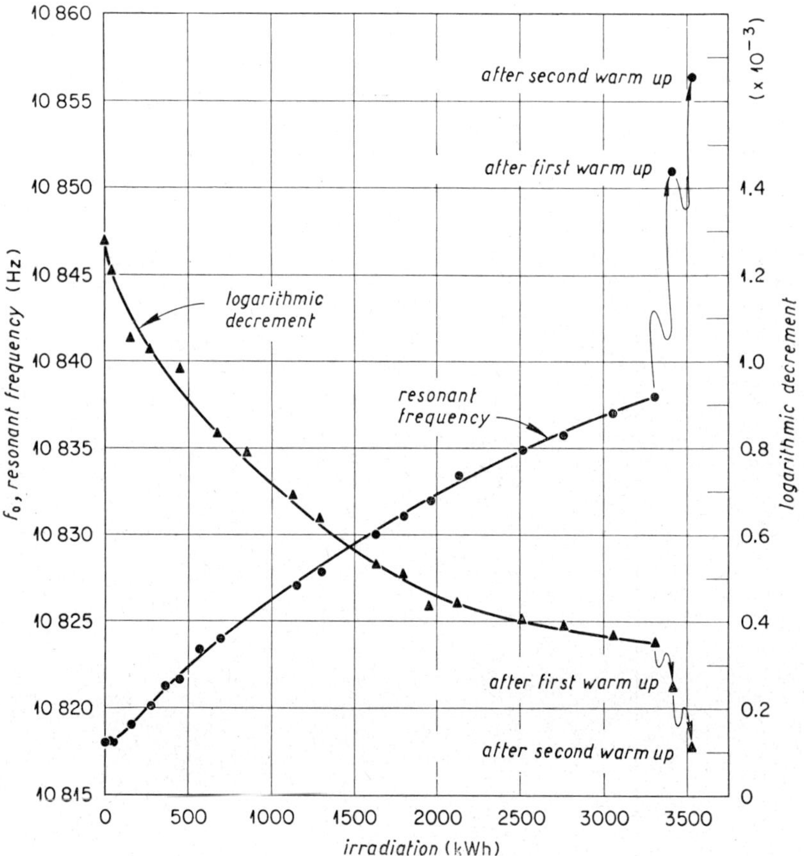

Fig. 12. – The change in resonant frequency and logarithmic decrement with fast neutron irradiation (20 °K). [D. O. THOMPSON, T. H. BLEWITT and D. K. HOLMES: *Journ. Appl. Phys.*, **28**, 742 (1957)].

fects suddenly started moving over to the dislocation lines, acting as pinning points; the dislocation motion is reduced, the decrement falls, and the modulus rises toward its values in the dislocation-free crystal. It seems unavoidable to associate this effect with the stage III annealing observed in this temperature range of the irradiation-produced resistivity in copper.

Going to still lower temperatures of irradiation, we show in Fig. 12 the decrement and modulus changes with fast-neutron irradiation at about 20 °K [11]. Analysis shows that these curves cannot be explained on the basis of neutron hits near the dislocation lines unless very large ranges are

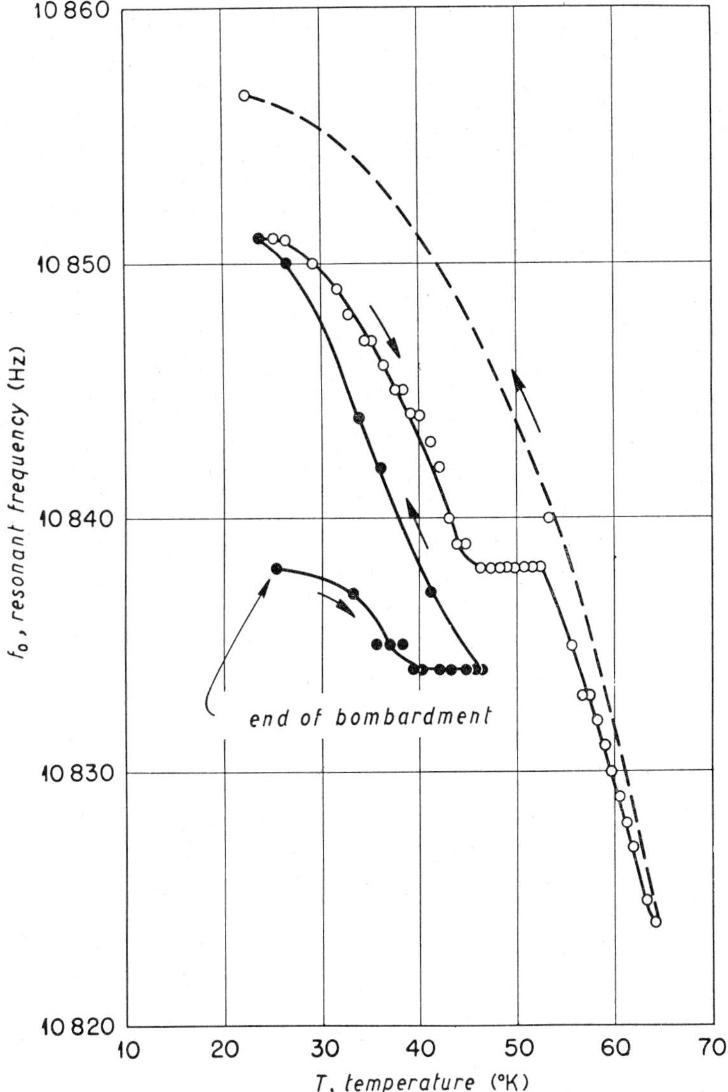

Fig. 13. – The change in resonant frequency with temperature upon warming-up from fast-neutron irradiation at 20 °K. [D. O. Thompson, T. H. Blewitt and D. K. Holmes: *Journ. Appl. Phys.*, **28**, 742 (1957)].

allowed for the primary knock-on. On the other hand, evidence seems to indicate that in copper at 20 °K there are not any radiation-produced defects with any mobility in the bulk material. It has recently been suggested that the explanation of these curves may lie in the various lattice focusing effects.

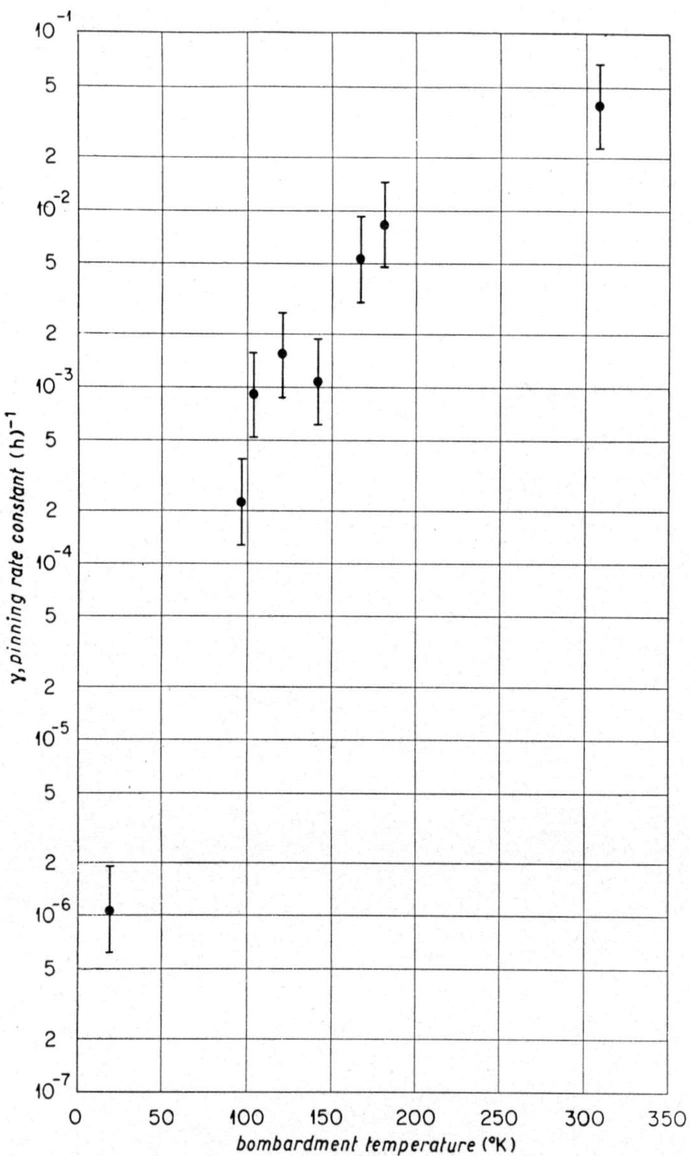

Fig. 14. – Pinning rate constant γ as a function of temperature. [D. O. THOMPSON and V. K. PARE: *Journ. Appl. Phys.*, **31**, 528 (1960)].

Fig. 13 shows the very interesting pinning action that occurred when this crystal was warmed up [11]. Some defect becomes mobile at around 35° K and migrates to the dislocation lines. Again, it seems unavoidable to associate this effect with stage I of the annealing of resistivity in copper.

The overall picture of the rate constant as a function of temperature is given in Fig. 14 [8]. This work (on copper) is as yet incomplete; but even the relatively meager coverage of the entire temperature range, as shown in Fig. 14, indicates the presence of two major regions of large changes which, as suggested above, may be associated with stages I and III of the annealing of damage-induced electrical resistivity. The association of annealing stages with basic defect mobilities is not as yet established in metals such as copper; but it *is* tempting to associate the two largest jumps in rate constant, *i.e.*, *a*) 20 to 100 °K and *b*) 180 to 320 °K, with the two simplest defects, interstitials and vacancies, respectively. It is to be noted that these experimental results most probably indicate mobility in the bulk lattice. The principle possibility for explaining the results otherwise lies in the fact that actually very few defects are needed (less than 10^{13} per cm^3) to pin completely all the dislocation lines present.

8. – The use of radiation-quenching of dislocation motion to study dislocation properties.

To the extent that radiation completely quenches all dislocation motion, a comparison of the properties before and after irradiation reflect the dislocation properties in the well-annealed, unirradiated crystal. For example, Fig. 15 shows the decrement and modulus (resonant frequency) as functions of temperature before and after irradiation [12]. In Fig. 16 [13] the differences are taken, and Δ_D and $(\Delta\mu/\mu)^2$ are plotted against temperature [12]. The subtraction process is such that these are the properties in the crystal before irradiation. The first point is that the dislocation properties show a strong temperature-dependence in this range. The second point is that plots of Δ_D and $(\Delta\mu/\mu)^2$ coincide quite well. This indicates, from eq. (22) and eq. (23), since

$$\Delta\mu/\mu \sim l_0^2 \qquad \text{and} \qquad \Delta_D \sim l_0^4\,, \tag{32}$$

that l_0 must be varying with temperature, while all other parameters must be relatively independent of temperature. THOMPSON and HOLMES [12] have suggested that this is a thermal unpinning process and have found theoretical reasons to expect the T^2 law, which seems to be a good fit to the data of Fig. 16.

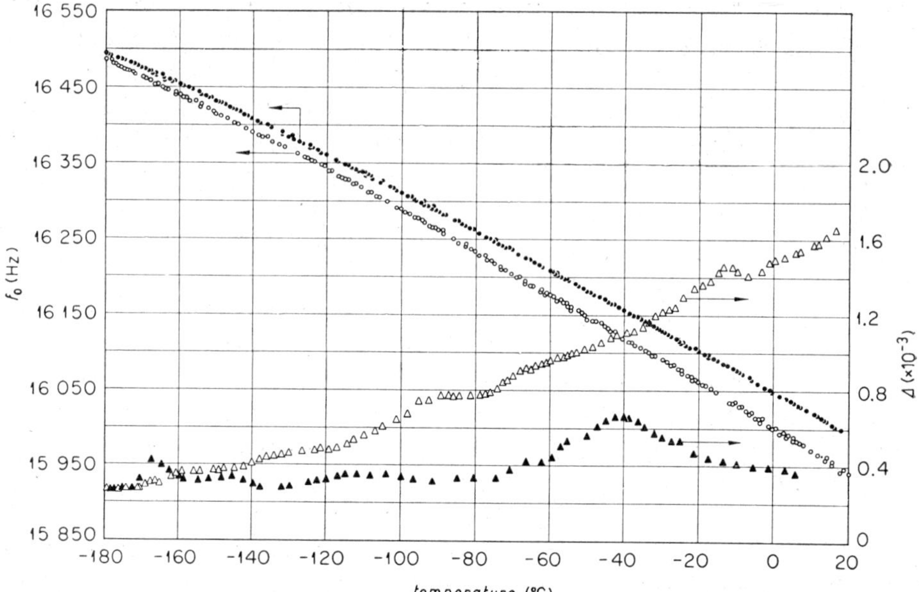

Fig. 15. – Resonant frequency and internal friction of crystal $3I_{16}$ before and after room-temperature irradiation. [D. O. Thompson and D. K. Holmes: *Journ. Appl. Phys.*, **30**, 528 (1959)]. △, ○ before irradiation; ▲, ● ofter irradiation.

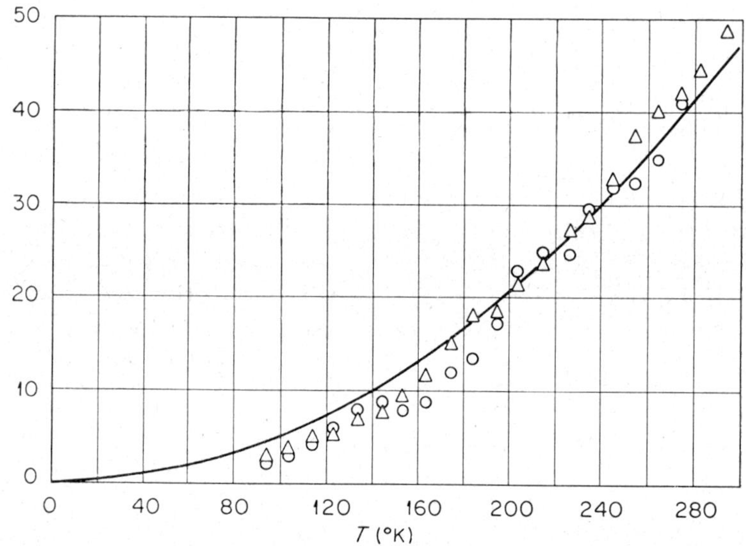

Fig. 16. – The temperature dependence of the dislocation contributions to the Young's modulus and decrement of copper. △ Δ_D, ⊙ $(\Delta\mu/\mu)^2$ (arbitrary scales); —— T^2 curve. $3I_{16}$ (annealed) [D. O. Thompson and D. K. Holmes: *Journ. Appl. Phys.*, **30**, 534 (1959)].

9. – The high-frequency range.

Recently, interest in high-frequency experiments (in metals) has increased. Some of these indicated that the damping constant, B, may be rather large, of the order of 10^{-4} to 10^{-3} (cgs). The present high-frequency machines, say, for copper, operate in the range of 5 to 100 MHz. This is still well below the resonance range of 1000 MHz so that it is thought to be worth-while to examine the fundamental equation for dislocation motion, eq. (14), in the approximation in which the inertia term only is dropped. The properties are then found to be given (for the δ-distribution) by

$$\left(\frac{\Delta\mu}{\mu}\right)_D \frac{1}{L_0 l_0^2} = \frac{1}{(kl_0)^3}\,\frac{\sinh kl_0 - \sin kl_0}{\cosh kl_0 - \cos kl_0}\,, \tag{33}$$

$$\frac{\Delta_D}{\pi L_0 l_0^2} = \frac{1}{(kl_0)^3}\left[kl_0 - \frac{\sinh kl_0 + \sin kl_0}{\cosh kl_0 + \cos kl_0}\right], \tag{34}$$

where

$$k^2 = \frac{\omega B}{2T}\,. \tag{35}$$

The asymptotic forms of these expressions are given in Table III. Since the decrement has been given the greatest attention, let us concentrate on it.

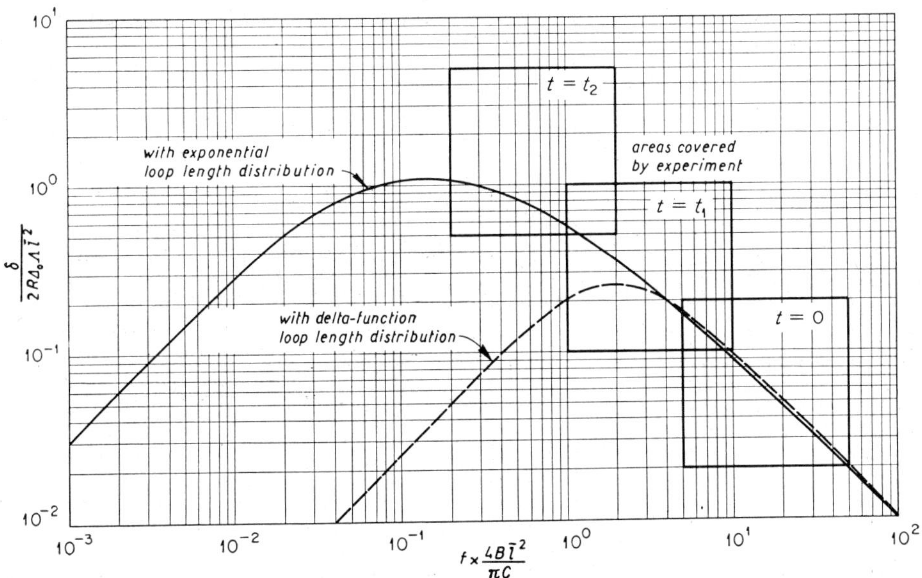

Fig. 17. – The theoretical variation of the decrement (attenuation) with frequency for two different loop-length distributions.

TABLE III.

	Low frequency	High frequency
$(\Delta\mu/\mu)_D$	$\frac{1}{6}L_0 l_0^2$	$\frac{L_0}{l_0}\left(\frac{2T}{\omega B}\right)^{\frac{1}{2}}$
Δ_D	$\frac{\pi\omega B}{60T}L_0 l_0^4$	$\frac{2\pi L_0 T}{\omega B}$

Fig. 17 shows the form of eq. (24) [14], along with the corresponding result for the exponential distribution.

It may at first seem surprising that a peak should be found in the decrement (in the absence of resonance effects); this is physically explained by the fact that, as the frequency is raised, the velocities of motion of the dislocation loops tend to become high; and the frictional force is very effective in limiting the amplitude of motion. If the lines are pinned and the loop lengths shortened, the asymptotic forms of Table III indicate that the left-hand side of the decrement curve will lower rapidly (Nl_0^4), while the right-hand side will be unchanged. Fig. 18 [15] shows some successive stages expected theoretically. One result has come out of this work. ALERS and THOMPSON [16] have found that the damping constant, B, in the high-frequency range seems to vary linearly with temperature in the range from liquid-nitrogen to room temperature. This clashes badly with the low-frequency results as given in Fig. 16 since B enters only into the decrement; and the results of Fig. 16 are neatly explainable on the thermal unpinning model.

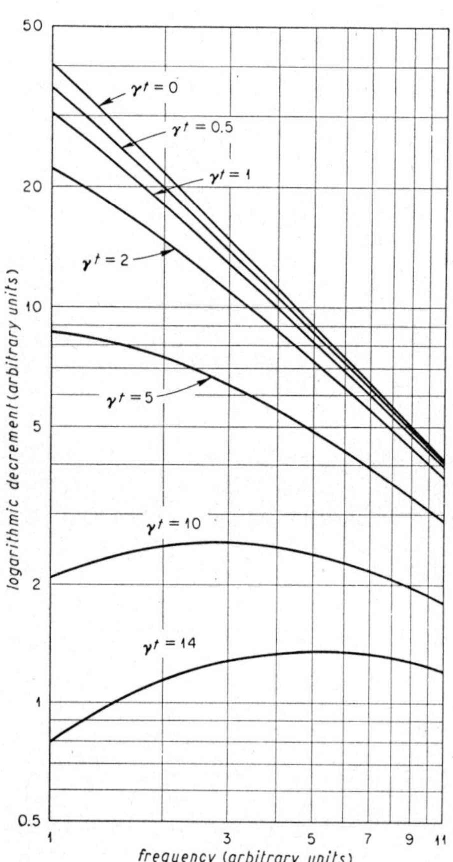

Fig. 18. – The theoretical change in the decrement-frequency-dependence with irradiation (t is the irradiation time).

10. – Objections and conclusions.

Looking at Table III, we may summarize the observations (on copper) to date. The l_0^2 and l_0^4 dependence of $(\Delta\mu/\mu)_D$ and Δ_D, respectively, in the low-frequency range seems well confirmed. The $1/\omega$ dependence of Δ_D in the high-frequency range is confirmed. But the linear dependence of Δ_D on ω in the low-frequency range has *not* been observed; and, indeed, it seems that there is experimental evidence contrary to this dependence. An interesting prediction of Table III is that the modulus effect should actually rise with irradiation. (Note the dependence on $1/l_0$!.)

One objection to the entire bowing-string model which has never been met is seen when we calculate the amplitude of motion of a dislocation loop ($l=3\cdot10^{-5}$ cm) when the total elastic strain is 10^{-7}. From eq. (11) this is

$$y\left(\frac{l}{2}\right)=\frac{\mu\varepsilon b}{2T}\frac{l^2}{4}\sim10^{-9}\text{ cm}\,.$$

Thus, the displacement of the center of the loop, at 10^{-7} (much lower strain amplitudes are used) is less than one atomic distance.

These are considerable theoretical weaknesses in our present position on dislocation pinning. The worst is that we do not know the exact nature of the pinning process. It cannot even be said to be certain at present that a single vacancy or a single interstitial can act as an effective pinning defect. If either or both do, it is not certain whether they join with the (edge) dislocation to form a jog or simply sit in the strain field of the dislocation and impede its motion.

Another problem is the nature of the loss of energy as the dislocation moves. The hope is that work of the kind discussed here can help toward establishing these quantities. For example, it may be possible to establish the velocity-dependence of the frictional force and, perhaps, to establish the binding energy between the defects and the dislocation lines by using larger strain amplitudes at which the dislocations tear away from the defects.

In conclusion, it seems certain that further work in this field can aid greatly in the acquisition of more knowledge of radiation-produced defects and of dislocations.

REFERENCES

[1] T. A. Read: *Phys. Rev.*, **58**, 371 (1940).

[2] J. S. Koehler: *Imperfections in Nearly Perfect Crystals* (edited by W. Shockley) (New York, 1952), p. 197.

[3] It should be mentioned that only a specially prepared, very pure crystal will have dislocations sufficiently mobile to give significant effects.

[4] D. O. THOMPSON and D. K. HOLMES: *Journ. Appl. Phys.*, **27**, 713 (1956).
[5] H. DIECKAMP and A. SOSIN: *Journ Appl. Phys.*, **27**, 1416 (1956).
[6] Still neglecting all different classes of dislocations and orientation factors.
[7] From eq. (5), we use as a measure of the modulus change

$$\frac{\mu - \mu_{\text{eff}}}{\mu} \equiv \frac{\Delta\mu}{\mu} \simeq \frac{\mu\varepsilon_D}{\sigma_s}.$$

[8] D. O. THOMPSON and V. K. PARE: *Journ. Appl. Phys.*, **31**, 529 (1960).
[9] The scatter at high doses is not important because the properties are too nearly saturated there for accuracy in taking differences.
[10] D. O. THOMPSON and D. K. HOLMES: *Journ. Phys. Chem. Solids*, **1**, 275 (1957).
[11] D. O. THOMPSON, T. H. BLEWITT and D. K. HOLMES: *Journ. Appl. Phys.*, **28**, 275 (1957).
[12] D. O. THOMPSON and D. K. HOLMES: *Journ. Appl. Phys.*, **30**, 525 (1959).
[13] Note that E_e/E_D is essentially $(\Delta\mu/\mu)_D$.
[14] The author is indebted to V. K. PARE for the privilege of using the drawings on which Fig. 17 and 18 are based.
[15] In Fig. 18 γ is the rate constant of eq. (26) and t is the bombardment time.
[16] G. A. ALERS and D. O. THOMPSON: *Journ. Appl. Phys.*, to be published.

Quenched-in Vacancies and Low-Temperature Diffusion in Al-Rich Alloys.

T. FEDERIGHI

Istituto Sperimentale Metalli Leggeri - Novara

1. – Introduction.

The electrical resistivity, hardness and other properties of many Al-rich alloys, quenched from a convient high temperature, change appreciably during the aging at about room temperature. Al-Cu, Al-Zn and Al-Ag are examples of Al-rich alloys which show the phenomenon.

Nowadays it is well known that these property changes are due to the segregation of a large fraction of the solute atoms into small clusters [1]; when these clusters have grown enough they can be identified with the solute rich and matrix-coherent zones which produce certain X-ray effects, and now usually called Guinier-Preston zones (extending this name, initially introduced for Al-Cu alloys, to the general case).

Following GUINIER [1, 2], the process of clustering or of zone formation can be called pre-precipitation to distinguish it from the true precipitation process which occurs usually at higher temperatures in Al-rich alloys.

An interesting characteristic of the phenomenon is that it takes place with a relatively high rate of diffusion. For example, it has been shown [3, 4] that the formation of zones at 20 °C occurs ad a rate 10^7 higher than the extrapolated one based on high-temperature meausurements; in the Al-Ag alloys the increase in the rate diffusion at -45 °C is esteemed about 10^{15} times [5]. In any case it is very easy to see that the equilibrium diffusion cannot account for the clustering process by considering that the mean time τ of jumping for an atom in f.c.c. metals [6] is $\tau = a^2/12D$ where « a » is the lattice parameter and D is the diffusion coefficient. By assuming $D_0 = 0.084$ cm²/s and $Q = 1.42$ eV for the diffusion of Cu in Al [7] in the expression $D = D_0 \cdot \exp[-Q/kT]$ one gets easily at 20 °C $\tau \sim 10^6$ s, which is too large to account for any clustering process.

Another interesting characteristic of pre-precipitation is that it is controlled by an activation energy of the order of 0.5 eV [5, 8-10] and this is too much lower than the usual activation energy values for solute diffusion in Al ($\sim$ 1.3 eV) [7].

The obvious meaning of these facts is that the diffusion in the quenched alloys differs in some way from that usually observed in the high-temperature range.

Several explanations to interpret these properties of the pre-precipitation have been advanced. Among these, the hypothesis originally advanced by SEITZ [11] and subsequently discussed by the A. [12] that this very high rate of diffusion might be due to an excess of thermal vacancies, frozen-in by quenching, appears very reasonable. The same hypotehsis can account easily, « a priori », for the low-activation energy of the phenomenon, since the contribution due to the formation of vacancies is no longer present in the activation energy for diffusion (which for equilibrium diffusion is the sum of the motion and formation energies of vacancies).

In the last few years the pre-precipitation phenomenon has been investigated extensively, expecially by resistivity measurements [5, 8-10, 13] since resistivity is very sensitive to the early stages of the process. The result is that nowadays there is plenty of experimental evidence about the role of quenched-in point defects in controlling the rate of clustering.

However, a comparison of the results obtained for several kinds of alloys shows clearly that the details of the kinetics, of the phenomenon can be quite different for the different kinds of alloys. The need arises, therefore, to investigate in a systematic way the several kinds of alloys and to interpret the different behavior in aging in terms of point defects.

The purpose or this lecture is to review briefly some experimental evidence about point defects in Al, to report a general model recently advanced for the kinetics of pre-precipitation [14] which should allow to easily interpretate the differences between the various alloys, and finally, to review shortly some experimental evidence obtained at Novara about the Al-Zn and Al-Mg_2Si alloys.

2. – Thermal vacancies in Al.

A lot of information about thermal vacancies in Al has been obtained in the last few years by means of resistivity measurements and electron microscopy on quenched specimens, and by means of lattice parameter, dilatation and resistivity measurements as a function of temperature.

The experimental evidence which has a bearing on the actual question can be syntesized as follows:

1) the recent experiments of SIMMONS and BALLUFFI [15] leave very little doubt that thermal point defects are vacancies in Al.

2) The formation energy of vacancies in Al is about 0.76 eV [15-18]; the ratio of the equilibrium concentration of vacancies at 550 °C and 20 °C

is about 10^8, which is just of the order of magnitude of the increase in the rate of diffusion.

3) After quenching, vacancies move at about room temperature [17-19]. Probably during the quenching or during the annealing out, vacancies couple together in dependence on initial concentration so that a definite activation energy cannot be observed; however values in the range 0.3 to 0.6 eV have been reported [18-20], and these are of the order of magnitude observed for the pre-precipitation phenomenon.

4) During the annealing the quenched-in vacancies tend to condense and to form dislocation loops [20]. The number of loops increases with quenching temperature. The consequence is that the mean number of jumps for the elimination of a vacancy decreases with quenching temperature, in agreement with results of resistivity measurements [18].

5) Loops are observed also in alloys, but upon increasing the content of solute or decreasing the quenching temperature, helical dislocations become predominant [21].

3. – General model for pre-precipitation.

Keeping in mind the previous results it is possible to give a picture of what one should expect about the kinetics of the pre-precipitation phenomenon [14].

At the quenching temperature solute atoms are pratically homogeneously dispersed in the matrix and a concentration C_v of vacancies will also be present. If we now quench to a sufficiently low temperature so that vacancies are not moving (liquid-nitrogen temperature), we should then observe:

1) some small solute clusters, whose number and size will depend on quenching rate and temperature;

2) some small dislocation loops originated by the condensation of vacancies;

3) dispersed solute atoms and point defects.

During the aging at about room temperature vacancies can move and one should then observe two separate processes:

I) the progressive annihilation of the excess of point defects which can be eliminated in several ways;

II) the diffusion of solute atoms, which, via the movement of defects, can move and gather into zones; this is the pre-precipitation process.

The two processes are independent, but, as said before, the kinetics of process II will be controlled by processes I. Therefore, to discuss the details of the kinetics of process II one has to establish in which way point defects are being eliminated when different kinds of solute atoms are present.

Recently G. THOMAS and the A. have advanced the hypothesis [14] that the principal factor controlling the details of the kinetics is the presence of the zones themselves; namely, they have supposed that the zones themselves are able to act as sinks for vacancies, and therefore most vacancies can be trapped inside or around zones, leading to an extinction of process I. In other words, process II can be dependent on process I, and vice versa: process II can control process I by a sort of feedback.

This « feedback » is dependent on the binding energy between vacancies and zones. If there is no interaction between them, vacancies can cross zones as if they were of pure solvent; therefore they will not be trapped by zones but will be eliminated as in pure Al, *e.g.*, at loops, etc. This seems to be just what was observed for the Al-Zn 10% [10].

If the interaction between vacancies and zones is strong, then when a vacancy reaches a zone it is trapped and it cannot go back into the matrix; in other words, it is virtually eliminated and the reaction will stop or slow down when zones are still small. This seems to be just what was observed for the Al-Mg_2Si 1.4% alloys.

Some results obtained for the Al-Zn 10% and Al-Mg_2Si alloys will now be synthesized.

4. – The Al-Zn alloys.

The Al-Zn 10% has been investigated extensively by resistivity measurements at liquid-nitrogen themperature, and many results have been published recently [18].

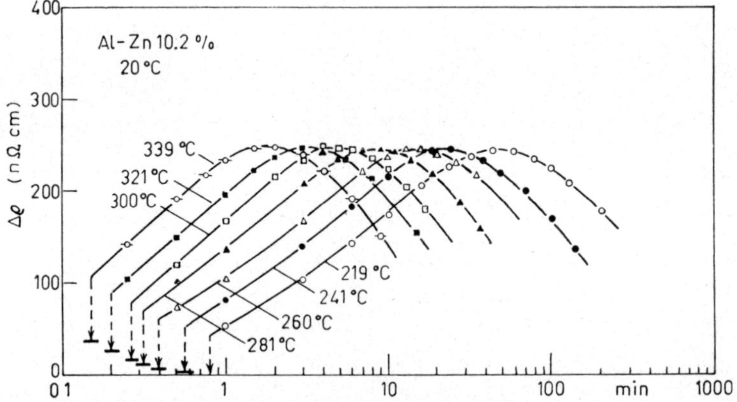

Fig. 1. – Effect of quenching temperature on the rate of variation in resistivity at 20 °C for the Al-Zn 10% alloy.

The experimental evidence about the kinetics of pre-precipitation in this alloy can be synthesized as follows (for more details see the original paper);

1) the rate of reaction increases with quenching temperature (Fig. 1), and the formation energy of vacancies is determined in (0.70 ± 0.02) eV (Fig. 2), in good agreement with the formation energy of vacancies in Al;

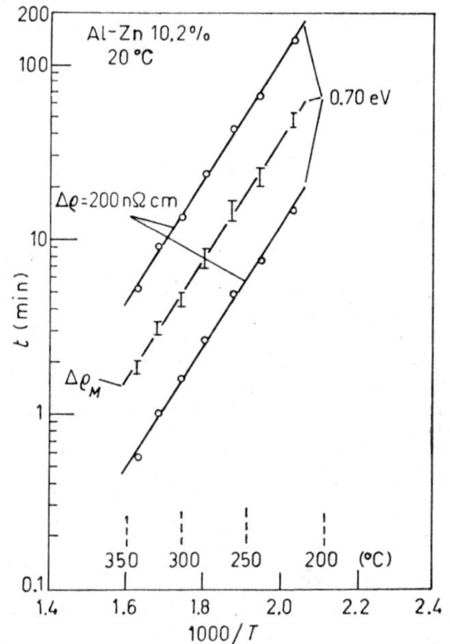

Fig. 2. – Plotting of the time to reach the maximum in resistivity ($\Delta\varrho_M$) and other values in resistivity, from the data in Fig. 1, to deduce the formation energy of vacancies in the alloy.

2) the time for complete reaction is just off the order of magnitude of the time for elimination of point defects in pure Al (Fig. 3);

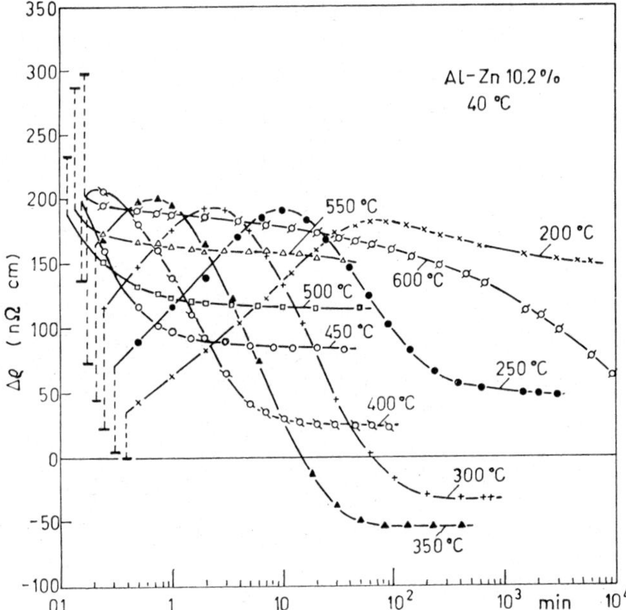

Fig. 3. – Isothermal aging curves at 40 °C after quenching from several temperatures. Note that the lower value in resistivity (*i.e.*, the higher size of zones) is reached after quenching from 350 °C. Note, also, that the time to complete the reaction is a few hours (*e.g.*, after quenching from 3(0 °C).

3) the final size of zones, as judged by the final value in resistivity, is dependent on the quenching temperature (Fig. 3): it is largest by quenching from a mean temperature as 350 °C, and it is lower for higher and lower quenching temperatures. This is just what one should expect if point defects were eliminated as in pure Al; the amount of diffusion is controlled by the product $C_v \cdot n$ where C_v is the concentration of quenched-in defects and n is the mean number of jumps for annihilation; the first factor is small at low quenching temperatures and the other at high quenching temperatures due to the formation of loops; therefore it is to be expected that the maximum value $C_v \cdot n$ is obtained for mean quenching temperatures.

In conclusion all the experimental evidence supports the view that in the Al-Zn 10% alloy vacancies are eliminated just as in pure Al, namely, there is no interaction between zones and vacancies. In very good agreement with this conclusion is the fact that THOMAS [21] has observed dislocation loops in the Al-Zn 10% alloy just in the same way as in pure Al.

5. – The Al-Mg_2Si alloy.

The kinetics of pre-precipitation in the Al-Mg_2Si 1.4% is quite different from that observed in the Al-Zn 10% alloy and it is just what one would expect when a strong interaction exists between vacancies and zones.

The results will appear in a separate paper [13], but it is possible to anticipate that the principal feature is that during the isothermal aging at about room temperature there is a relatively large variation in resistivity followed, after a sharp transition, by a very slow variation in resistivity. In other words, it is possible to distinguish two stages

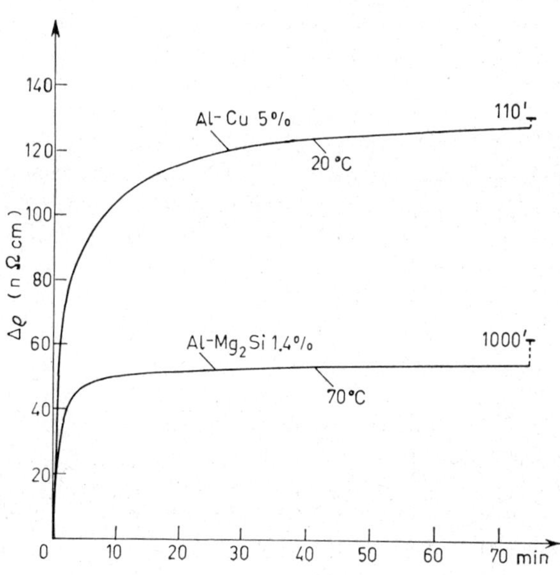

Fig. 4. – Isothermal aging curves for Al-rich alloys quenched from high temperature. The segment shows the variation observed after the given time. Note the sharp change after a few minutes in the variation in resistivity, expecially for the Al-Mg_2Si alloy.

in the phenomenon, called the fast and the slow reaction; the first occurs in a few minutes, whereas the second goes on for a very long time.

Now it is very easy to interpret the presence of the transition by assuming a strong interaction between vacancies and zones. During the fast reaction zones are forming but, as they are growing, the excess of vacancies is virtually eliminated from the matrix, since, as vacancies arrive at zones accompanying solute atoms, they are trapped near zones themselves. At the end of the fast reaction most vacancies are therefore trapped by the zones themselves, which should become very rich in vacancies; then a sort of equilibrium between vacancies inside (or around zones) and vacancies in the matrix will be established and the reaction will go on slowly, for a very long time, controlled by the concentration of vacancies in the matrix.

Another example of alloy which is thought to have the same behaviour as the Al-Mg_2Si, is given by the Al-Cu alloys; in these alloys the interaction between vacancies and zones seems to have an intermediate value between the Al-Zn and Al-Mg_2Si alloys.

Examples of isothermal aging curves for the Al-Mg_2Si and for the Al-Cu 5% are shown in Fig. 4; it is possible to see, expecially for the Al-Mg_2Si alloy, a sharp transition between the fast and the slow reaction.

6. – Conclusions.

Some experimental evidence supporting the role of quenched-in thermal vacancies in controlling the kinetics of the clustering process has been reviewed. Nowadays the aim is to study the details of the various kinds of alloys and to try to interpret them in terms of the interaction between vacancies and zones.

REFERENCES

[1] A. Guinier: *Adv. in Solid State Phys.*, **9**, 239 (1959).
[2] A. Guinier: *Trans. AIME*, **206**, 673 (1956).
[3] H. Jagodzinski and F. Laves: *Zeits. Metallk.*, **40**, 296 (1949).
[4] H. K. Hardy: *Journ. Inst. Met.*, **18**, 321 (1951).
[5] D. Turnbull and H. N. Treaftis: *Acta Met.*, **5**, 534 (1957).
[6] A. D. Le Claire: *Progress in Metal Phys.*, **4**, 265 (1953).
[7] J. W. H. Clare: *Metallurgia*, **57**, 273 (1958).
[8] W. De Sorbo, H. N. Treaftis and D. Turnbull: *Acta Met.*, **6**, 401 (1958).
[9] D. Turnbull, H. S. Rosembaum and H. N. Treaftis: *Acta Met.*, **8**, 160 (1960).
[10] C. Panseri and T. Federighi: *Acta Met.*, **8**, 217 (1960).

[11] F. Seitz: *L'Etat Solide* (Bruxelles, 1952), p. 377.
[12] T. Federighi: *Acta Met.*, **6**, 379 (1958).
[13] T. Federighi: *Resistometric Studies on* Al *Alloys*, to be published.
[14] T. Federighi and G. Thomas: *Phyl. Mag.*, **7**,127 (1962).
[15] R. O. Simmons and R. W. Balluffi: *Phys. Rev.*, **117**, 52 (1960).
[16] F. J. Bradshaw and S. Pearson: *Phil. Mag.*, **2**, 570 (1957).
[17] W. De Sorbo and D. Turnbull: *Acta Met.*, **7**, 83 (1959).
[18] C. Panseri and T. Federighi: *Phil. Mag.*, **3**, 1223 (1958).
[19] M. Wintenberger: *Compt. Rend. Acad. Sci.*, **242**, 128 (1956).
[20] P. B. Hirsch, J. Silcox, R. E. Smallman and K. H. Westmacott: *Phil. Mag.*, **4**, 897 (1959).
[21] G. Thomas: *Phil. Mag.*, **4**, 1231 (1959).

The Ferromagnetic After-Effect in Irradiated Nickel, and Its Application to the Study of Point Defects in F.C.C. Metals.

A. SEEGER, H. KRONMÜLLER, P. SCHILLER and H. JÄGER
Max-Planck-Institut für Metallforschung - Stuttgart

The usual and most convenient way to study the generation and the annealing of point defects in irradiated metals is by measuring the electrical resistivity. However, since all point defects increase the electrical resistivity of metals by comparable amounts, resistivity studies do not in general allow us to separate from each other the contributions due to different types of point defects, *e.g.* single vacancies, divacancies, and interstitials. We shall discuss here an experimental method which enables us to study separately those point defects in cubic metals which have a symmetry lower than cubic, *e.g.* tetragonal or trigonal symmetry.

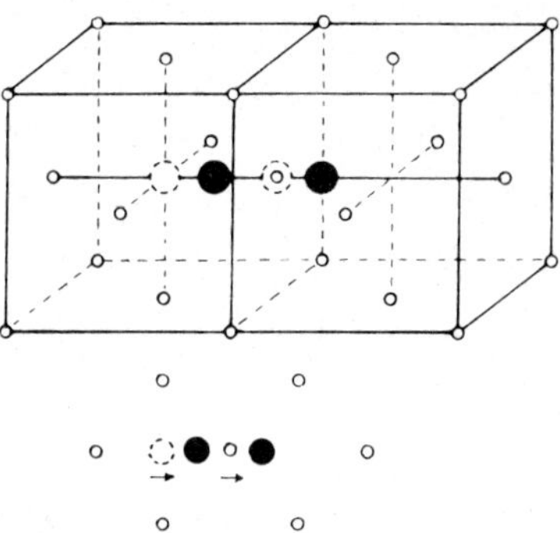

Fig. 1. – F.c.c. crystal containing an interstitial atom. Dashed circle represents an interstitial atom in the octahedral interstice with cubic symmetry of the environment. Full circles represent an interstitial in the interstitialcy (dumb-bell) configuration with tetragonal symmetry of the environment. Lower part: configuration of the atoms in a {100}-plane. The arrows indicate the movements leading from an octahedral interstitial to a dumb-bell.

Let us fix our attention on a specific example. GIBSON, GOLAND, MILGRAM and VINEYARD [1] and SEEGER, MANN and v. JAN [2] have found from calculations that the configuration of lowest energy of a copper interstitial atom in an f.c.c. copper crystal has tetragonal symmetry. Fig. 1 shows this so-called *dumb-bell configuration of an interstitial atom in an f.c.c. crystal.* Since a cubic crystal has three distinct ⟨100⟩-directions, there are three different kinds of sites for such a dumb-bell. Under conditions of statistical equilibrium, in an unstressed crystal, these three types of sites will be equally populated. If, however, a tensile stress, say, along the [100]-drection is applied, the dumb-bells with their tetragonal axes parallel to [100] will have a lower energy than those with their axes parallel to [010] or [001]. The equilibrium distribution under the applied stress will then have a larger population in the [100]-sites than in the [010]- and [001]-sites. In addition to the « elastic » strain caused directly by the applied stress, there will be an « anelastic » strain due to the excess of [100]-dumb-bells. If the external stress is suddenly applied at a time $t = 0$, the distribution of dumb-bells in the unstressed crystal « relaxes » with a certain relaxation time τ towards the new equilibrium distribution, the anelastic strain being proportional to $(1 - \exp[-t/\tau])$. The elementary step of this « relaxation » process is the jump of atoms over potential barriers. By well-known arguments the relaxation time τ of such a process depends on temperature according to

$$\tau = \tau_0 \exp[Q/kT], \tag{1}$$

where Q is the height of the potential barrier, and τ_0 is temperature-independent (in general of the order of magnitude of the reciprocal of an attempt frequency ν_0). k and T denote as usual Boltzmann's constant and the absolute temperature.

Let us now consider the application of an *alternating stress* of circular frequency ω to a crystal containing dumb-bells. If $\omega\tau \gg 1$, the distribution of the dumb-bells over the three kinds of sites is unable to follow the applied stress, and the anelastic strain is zero. If $\omega\tau \ll 1$, the anelastic strain follows the applied stress instantaneously and has always the magnitude it would have under static conditions. In both limiting cases there is no energy dissipation due to the redistribution of the dumb-bells. If, however, $\omega\tau = 1$ the anelastic strain is out of phase with respect to the stress by 45°, and the energy dissipation averaged over a vibrational cycle is a maximum. This maximum of the energy dissipation or « internal friction » can be studied either by varying the measuring frequency or by varying the relaxation time through a variation in the temperature according to eq. (1). Internal friction measurements, usually carried out at a fixed angular frequency ω, enable us, therefore, to study anisotropic defects, and to observe in particular their generation and annealing in radiation-damage experiments.

The applicability of these techniques, useful as they have proved, *e.g.*, for the study of carbon impurities in α-iron [3], to the study of point imperfections created by *radiation damage* is limited. The main limitation stems from the fact that the radiation damage is not in thermal equilibrium, and that the point defects tend to anneal out. Consider the specific example of a divacancy in an f.c.c. crystal. The elementary process by which the divacancy changes its orientation in the crystal is the same as that by which it migrates when annealing out, namely the jumping of an atom adjacent to both of the vacant sites into one of these empty sites. Suppose that on the average 1000 jumps are necessary for a divacancy to anneal out, and suppose further that we wish to observe these divancancies with an internal friction equipment working at $\omega = 1000$ Hz (corresponding to a measuring frequency $f = 1000/2\pi$ Hz $= 160$ Hz). The maximum in the internal friction will occur at a temperature T at which $\tau(T) = 10^{-3}$ s. At such a temperature, however, each divacancy undergoes 10^3 jumps per second, which means that at that temperature we have only a measuring time of one second available before the majority of the defects we want to study have annealed out. The conclusion to be drawn from this is that unless we are studying very large effects and use extremely sensitive equipment, we are limited in such studies to the frequency range around or below 1 Hz. This means that in general we are confined in these internal friction studies to the use of the torsion pendulum, and that we cannot use the more sensitive equipment developed for higher frequencies.

There is also a problem of signal-to-noise ratio. The height of the maximum in the internal friction is of the order of magnitude of the ratio of anelastic strain to elastic strain. Since on account of the tendency to thermal disorder only a fraction of the defects can be oriented under the applied stress the internal friction effects are small unless we work either with extremely large defect concentrations or with defects exhibiting a very pronounced deviation of their surrouding strain fields from cubic symmetry. Calculations [2] show that for an atomic concentration c of dumb-bell interstitials in copper the ratio of anelastic strain to elastic strain is of the order $20\,c$. This means that a concentration of $c = 10^{-4}$ should be easily detectable by internal friction measurements. On the other hand, the strain around divacancies appears to be so small that it would seem very difficult to observe internal friction due to divacancy reorientation.

The first mentioned difficulty can be overcome by taking resort to *after-effect measurements* rather than internal friction experiments. The simplest experiments of this kind would be to apply a static stress at a temperature T at which the relaxation time τ is of the order of minutes to hours, and to observe the gradual increase of strain with time. This is the typical procedure of creep experiments, and any creep mechanism operating at this temperature (*e.g.*, dislocation movement) will interfere with the observation of the point defects. The mechanical after-effect is therefore not at all a sensitive tool for our purpose, although it has been successfully used in similar studies of atom movements in alloys [4].

In ferromagnetic metals, these difficulties can be overcome by the use of the *ferromagnetic after-effect*, in particular the disaccommodation of the initial susceptibility. This experiment consists in demagnetizing the material and measuring the initial susceptibility as a function of time. Let us describe the mechanism of the time variation of the initial susceptibility for the example of dumb-bell interstitials in nickel. If the demagnetizing process is carried out carefully, ferromagnetic domain-walls will be formed in regions of the crystal in which the three types of sites of the dumb-bells are equally populated. In a ferromagnetic crystal there are two kinds of interactions between the direction of magnetization and the dumb-bell orientation, namely on one hand an indirect one through the magnetostrictive stresses [5], and on the other hand a direct interaction depending on the angle between the direction of magnetization and the direction of the dumb-bell axis [6]. The latter one has not yet been calculated from first principles. Symmetry arguments tell us that it has the same general form as the magnetostrictive interaction, so that we do not have to consider it separately.

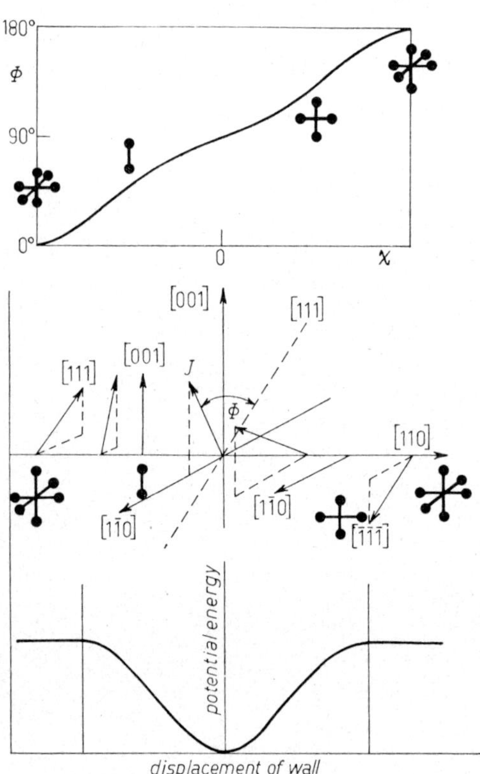

Fig. 2. – Rotation of the direction J of the magnetization in an [110] — 180° — domain wall, and preferred orientation of dumb-bell interstitials in the wall. Φ is the angle between the direction of magnetization and [111]. The lower part of the figure gives the potential well in which the domain wall moves under the influence of a small applied field.

The direction of easy magnetization of nickel and, therefore, the direction of magnetization within the domains is ⟨111⟩. Since all ⟨100⟩-directions form the same angle with each ⟨111⟩-direction, there is no tendency for a redistribution of the dumb-bell orientations within the domains after the demagnetization. In the domain-walls, however, the magnetization rotates gradually from the ⟨111⟩-direction of one domain to that of the adjacent one. Therefore, the potential energy of the three types of sites will in general be different inside the domain walls, and the dumb-bells tend to redistribute themselves accord ing to the new equilibrium (Fig. 2). While they do so, they lower the free energy of the system and deepen the potential well in which the domain wall is located. The average curvature of these potential wells is measured by applying an a.c. magnetic field of, say 1 000 Hz, of relatively small amplitude, and observing the initial susceptibility in an a.c. bridge. As the new equilibrium of the dumb-bell orientations is approached with the relaxation time τ, the mobility of the domain walls and therefore the initial susceptibility decreases with the same relaxation time. The use of a mutual inductance bridge [7, 8] enabled us to measure relative changes in the susceptibility of the order 10^{-5}. Among the methods discussed in this paper the susceptibility measurements are certainly the most sensitive ones.

The measurement of the ferromagnetic disaccommodation has been used successfully by various schools in the study of interstitial carbon atoms in α-iron, *e.g.* by the Grenoble school [9] and the Amsterdam school [10]. MOSER, DAUTREPPE and BRISSONNEAU [11] have used this technique in studying the radiation damage of pile-irradiated α-iron. They found that after room-temperature irradiation a defect with an activation energy of relaxation of about 1.2 eV gave rise to a relaxation phenomenon between 25 °C and 100 °C. After irradiation at liquid-nitrogen temperature they found a relaxation phenomenon between 80 °K and 100 °K with an activation energy of 0.3 eV, and a weaker one at higher temperatures with an activation energy of about 0.6 eV. The relaxation effect associated with the activation energy of about 1.2 eV does not appear after the low-temperature irradiation. The authors make no definitive proposals for the assignment of certain defects to these observations. Such an assignment will have to await further experiments on radiation-damaged iron.

We have carried out *radiation-damage experiments* on carbonyl *nickel* that was irradiated in a swimming pool reactor (München) with an integrated flux density $\varphi = nvt = 4 \cdot 10^{17}$ fast neutrons/cm² (energies above 0.1 eV) [12]. Fig. 3 shows a logarithmic plot of the time variation of the initial permeability $\mu(t)$, which apart from very short times, is to a good approximation exponential:

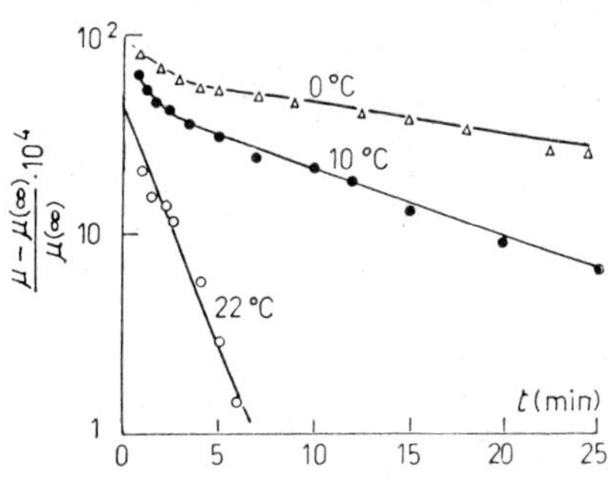

Fig. 3. – Time variation of the initial permeability of pile-irradiated Ni at different temperatures.

$$\mu(t) = \mu(\infty) + [\mu(0) - \mu(\infty)] \exp[-t/\tau] . \tag{2}$$

The relaxation times are plotted in an Arrhenius plot in Fig. 4 (open squares). It is seen that they follow well the law eq. (1).

The defect responsible for the relaxation phenomenon is also generated by *plastic deformation of nickel*, as shown in Fig. 4. The black squares are the relaxation times observed after cold-working of nickel wires [13]. The disaccommodation phenomenon found by MORKOWSKI [14] in stressed nickel wires between 10.3 °C and 59.6 °C appears to have the same origin, although the author does not explicitly give relaxation times.

In order to extend the range of relaxation times for an accurate determination of the activation energy, we carried out experiments with the *torsion pendulum*. Fig. 5 shows the internal friction δ of a nickel wire stretched by $\varepsilon = 160\%$ as a function of temperature during the warming-up and the subsequent cooling. In Fig. 6 we have plotted the difference between the heating and the cooling curve, showing that for the frequency $f = 0.16$ Hz (corresponding to $\tau = 1$ s) there is an internal friction maximum at $T = 351$ °K. The maximum anneals out at and above 100 °C. A second maximum, annealing at a lower temperature, was found at about 40 °C. In Fig. 4 we have inserted the relaxation times obtained for the higher maximum. It is seen that they fall on a straight line together with those from the susceptibility measurements. The measured relaxation times cover four powers of ten and enable us to deduce accurate values for the parameters in eq. (1):

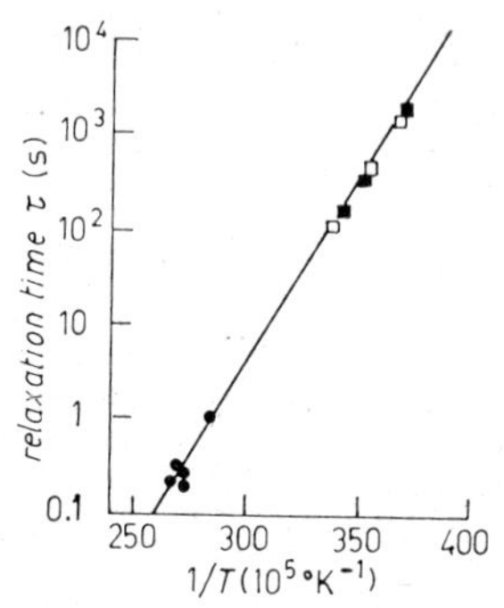

Fig. 4. – Relaxation times τ in a logarithmic plot as a function of the reciprocal absolute temperature T. □: magnetic disaccommodation after neutron-irradiation; ■: magnetic disaccommodation after cold-work; ●: obtained from internal friction measurements after cold-work.

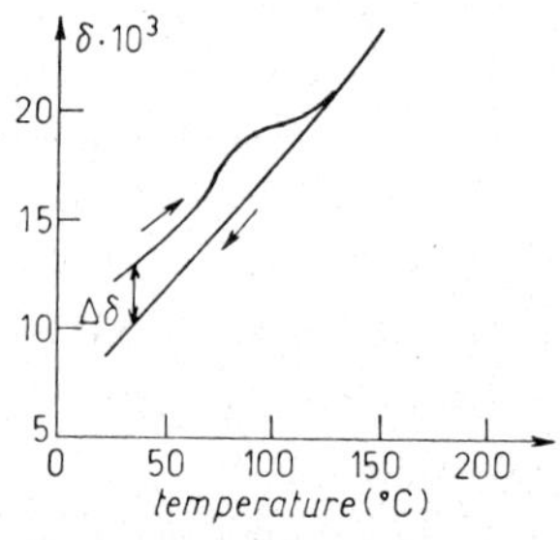

Fig. 5. – Internal friction as a function of temperature of a cold-worked nickel wire stretched 160%. Vibrational frequency $f = 0.16$ Hz (δ = logarithmic decrement).

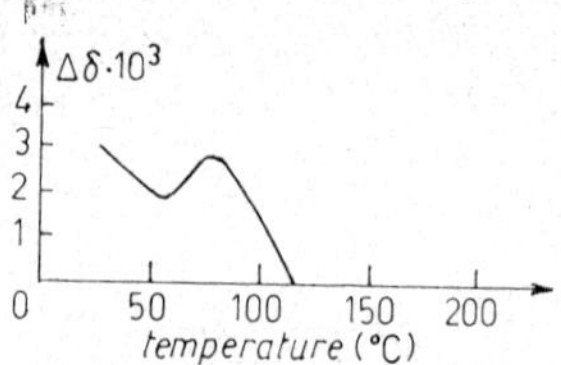

Fig. 6. – Difference of internal friction between the warming-up and the cooling-down curves in Fig. 5.

$$\begin{cases} Q = (0.81 \pm 0.01)\ \text{eV} \\ \tau_0 = 2.6 \cdot 10^{-12}\ \text{s}\,. \end{cases} \tag{3}$$

Internal friction experiments on *pile-irradiated nickel* wires showed an increase in the internal friction in the temperature range between 50 °C and 100 °C, which annealed out in the same temperature range as the effects shown in Fig. 4 and Fig. 5. On account of the residual reactivity of the irradiated nickel, we had to use rather small integrated fluxes, which did not enable us to obtain reliable values for the temperature T_{max}. With higher doses, the maximum should also be clearly observable.

Disaccommodation measurements were also performed on *quenched nickel* wires. Although the quenched wires showed an after-effect of the susceptibility (in all probability related to the initial (curved) parts in Fig. 3), we did not observe relaxation times fitting into the plot Fig. 4.

Preliminary observations indicated that the defect causing the relaxation effect of Fig. 4 annealed out with an activation energy W higher than Q as given in eq. (3). Since the knowledge of the energy of migration W would help to identify the defect, we tried to obtain an accurate value of W by the method of MEECHAN and BRINKMAN [15]. In this method isothermal and isochronal annealing curves on identical specimens are compared with each other as indicated in Fig. 7. The logarithm of the time interval $\Delta\tau_i$ corresponding to the same annealing effect as that of an isochronal anneal at the temperature T_i is plotted against $(kT_i)^{-1}$. If and only if the process is governed by a single activation energy W, a straight line is obtained, and the (negative) slope of this line is equal to the energy of migration W. Fig. 8 (open circles)

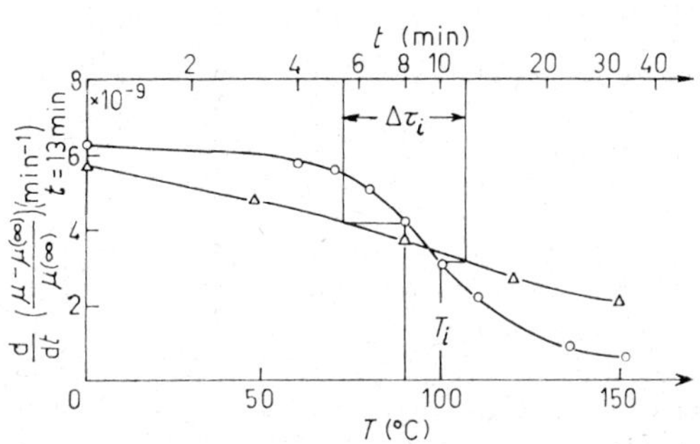

Fig. 7. – Recovery of disaccommodation in Ni after neutron irradiation. The ordinate represents the rate of the change of relative permeability $p=(d/dt)([\mu(t)-\mu(\infty)]/\mu(\infty))$ after 13 min at 10 °C. △: isothermal recovery at $T_a = 100$ °C; ○: isochronal recovery for annealing intervals $\Delta t = 10$ min. The analysis of Brinkman and Meechan is indicated for the temperature $T_i = 100$ °C.

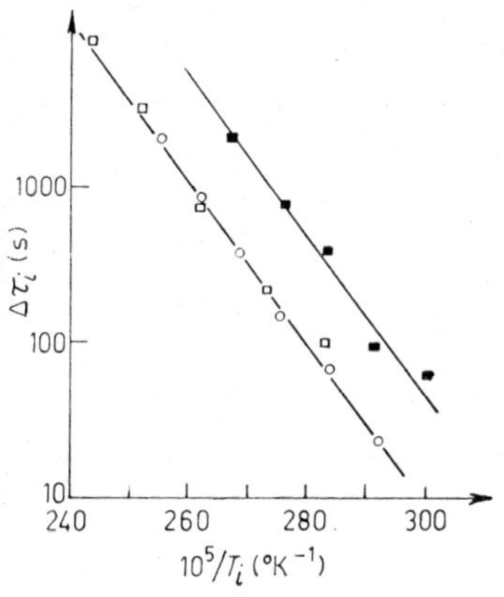

Fig. 8. – Determination of the activation energy of recovery by the method of Brinkman and Meechan. ○: recovery of magnetic disaccommodation after pile-irradiation. ■: recovery of electrical resistivity after cold-work (SOSIN and BRINKMAN [16]). □: recovery of electrical resistivity after electron bombardment (SOSIN and BRINKMAN [16]).

shows that the single activation criterion is well fulfilled, and that the activation energy of migration is

$$W = 1.02 \pm 0.03 \text{ eV}. \tag{4}$$

Figure 9 gives the isothermal recovery curve of Fig. 7 in a p^{-1} *vs.* time plot. A straight line is obtained, showing that the defect responsible for the relaxation phenomenon anneals out by second-order kinetics. Using the same analysis [15], SOSIN and BRINKMAN [16] have studied the annealing of the electrical resistivity of cold-worked and of electron-irradiated nickel. Their results are also plotted in Fig. 8, showing that within experimental accuracy they obtain the same activation energy of migration as we. There seems to be little doubt that they have been studying the same defect as we have.

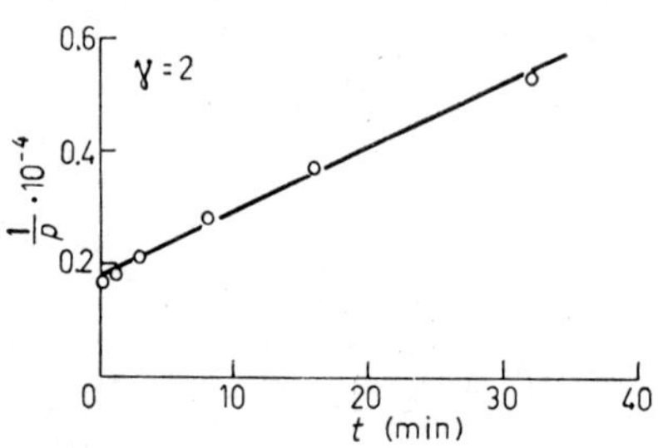

Fig. 9. – Isothermal annealing of the relaxation effect after neutron irradiation (annealing temperature $T = 100\,^{\circ}\text{C}$). A chemical rate equation $\mathrm{d}p/\mathrm{d}t = -\alpha p^{\gamma}$ wit $\gamma = 2$ (second-order kinetics) is obeyed.

This brings us to the identification of the defect. By detailed arguments, SOSIN and BRINKMAN [16] assign their recovery process to the migration of interstitial atoms. We have every reason to attribute our relaxation phenomenon to interstitial atoms in the dumb-bell configuration. As we have seen, the energy of relaxation Q is lower by about 20 % than the energy of migration. This is possible for dumb-bells but not for divacancies. The dumb-bells can « rotate » from one $\langle 100 \rangle$-orientation to another without shifting their center of gravity and, therefore, without involving a migration process (Fig. 10). If the energy of activation for the rotation is lower than that for the migration, the former will be observed as the activation energy of the relaxation process. Due to mathematical difficulties the calculations on interstitials in copper [2] have not yet given a clear answer whether for a dumb-bell the energy of migration or the energy of rotation should be lower. At the moment we have to accept the experimental result. Further evidence for our assignment is that the defect is generated by both cold-work and plastic deformation, but not by quenching. This is

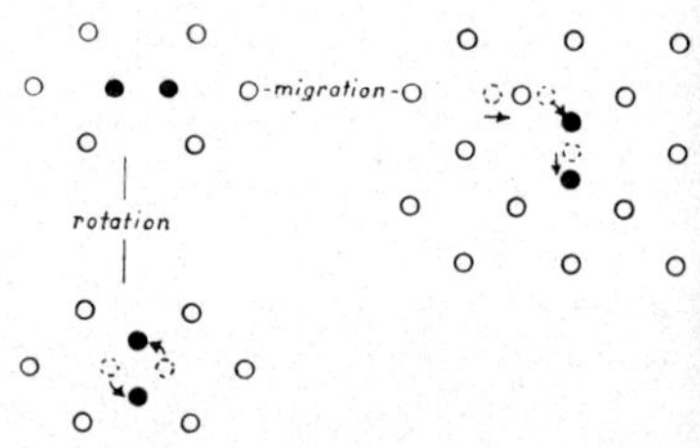

Fig. 10. – « Rotation » *vs.* « migration » of dumb-bells. The arrows indicate the projection on the $\{100\}$-plane of the atom movements in the two modes of elementary motions of the dumb-bells.

what we would expect for interstitial atoms. The relaxation strength in the internal friction experiments appears right for interstitial atoms, but not for vacancy groups. Experiments that would check whether the ⟨100⟩-direction is indeed the preferred direction of the defect have not yet been carried out. They could be done either by observing the dependence of the internal friction on the orientation of a single crystal (the effect should be zero for crystals with axes parallel to ⟨111⟩) or by measuring the dependence of the disaccommodation on the amplitude of the a.c. magnetic field for larger fields (measuring the so-called stabilization field [6]).

The preceding discussion shows how useful the susceptibility measurements are for the study of particular point defects. Historically, the relaxation effect due to interstitials in f.c.c. crystals had been predicted by the theory [13], and only later was it shown that the energy of migration of these defects agreed with that observed by SOSIN and BRINKMAN [12]. The implication is that annealing stage III in the f.c.c. metals [17] has to be ascribed to interstitial migration.

The second order of the annealing kinetics agrees with that observed in stage III after electron bombardment by SOSIN and BRINKMAN [12]. The interpretation of the annealing kinetics is that the interstitials anneal out by migration to an annihilation with vacancies that are present in approximately the same concentration as the dumb-bell interstitials. It appears difficult to account for the annealing kinetics by any other model for the relaxation process. In particular, second-order kinetics would *not* be expected if the relaxation effect were due to the re-orientation of impurity-vacancy or impurity-interstitial pairs, and if the rate-determining step for the recovery were the decomposition of these pairs.

We shall conclude with a few remarks on related phenomena. We have measured the *elastic modulus of plastically deformed nickel* bars in the frequency range at about 1 000 Hz, and we have found that the modulus defect recovers strongly in the same temperature range in which the relaxation phenomenon anneals out. We attribute this to the migration of interstitial atoms to dislocations and their pinning action. The same explanation presumably holds for the annealing of the background of the internal friction in Fig. 5.

Divacancies should in principle give rise to a similar relaxation phenomenon with the requirement $Q = W$ as discussed above. For intensity reasons we cannot expect to observe this in internal friction experiments, unless dislocation lines act to « amplify » the effect. This may be the case in the 40 °C-maximum of the internal friction of cold-worked nickel. We suspect further that below room temperature the movement of divacancies contributes to the disaccommodation effect in both quenched and irradiated wires. We have, however, not yet carried out a complete analysis of these observations, since under these conditions another mechanism — presumably associated with more extended defects — interferes. This mechanism seems to be responsible also for the deviations at short times of the plots in Fig. 3 from straight lines. The investigations on these questions are pursued actively, and we hope to have soon more definitive results.

* * *

The authors would like to thank the reactor personnel in München and the Deutsche Forschungsgemeinschaft for their support.

REFERENCES

[1] J. B. Gibson, A. N. Goland, M. Milgram and G. H. Vineyard: *Phys. Rev.*, **120**, 1229 (1960).

[2] A. Seeger, E. Mann and R. Van Jan: *Journ Phys Chem. Sol.*, **23**, 639 (1962).

[3] C. Zener: *Elasticity and Anelasticity of Metals* (Chicago, 1948).

[4] A. S. Nowick: *Progress in Metal Physics*, **4**, 1 (1953).

[5] J. L. Snoek: *Physica*, **6**, 161, 591 (1939); **8**, 711 (1941).

[6] L. Néel: *Journ. Phys. Rad.*, **12**, 339 (1951); **13**, 249 (1952).

[7] H. Wilde: *Arch. elektr. Übertr.*, **6**, 354 (1952).

[8] D. Gerstner: *Dissertation* (Stuttgart, 1960).

[9] P. Brissonneau: *Journ. Phys. Chem. Sol.*, **7**, 22 (1958).

[10] G. W. Rathenau: *Magnetic Properties of Metals and Alloys*, American Society for Metals (1958), p. 168.

[11] P. Moser, D. Dautreppe and P. Brissonneau: *Compt. Rend.*, **250**, 3963 (1960).

[12] H. Kronmüller, A. Seeger and P. Schiller: *Zeits. Naturfor.*, **15***a*, 740 (1960).

[13] A. Seeger, P. Schiller and H. Kronmüller: *Phil. Mag.*, **5**, 853 (1960).

[14] J. Morkowski: *Acta Phys. Polon.*, **18**, 75 (1959).

[15] J. C. Meechan and J. A. Brinkman: *Phys. Rev.*, **103**, 1193 (1956).

[16] A. Sosin and J. A. Brinkman: *Acta Met.*, **7**, 478 (1959).

[17] H. G. Van Büren: *Imperfections in Crystals* (Amsterdam, 1960).

Effets du rayonnement neutronique sur les matériaux magnétiques.

G. Montalenti

Istituto Elettrotecnico Nazionale « G. Ferraris » - Torino

Pour mieux comprendre l'effet d'une irradiation aux neutrons rapides sur les matériaux magnétiques il est utile de classer ces derniers en quatre catégories: aimants permanents; alliages à haute perméabilité; métaux ferromagnétiques très purs (Fe, Ni); ferrites.

1. – Aimants permanents.

Des expériences sur les aimants permanents ont été exécutées, en 1958 et 1959, par Sery, Gordon, Lundesten [1-2] et par Fennel et coll. [3]. Les doses de neutrons rapides employées étaient de l'ordre de $(10^{17} \div 10^{18})$ n/cm^2. Les matériaux examinés étaient du type: Al/Ni/Co, ferrites de Ba ainsi que des aciers de différentes compositions. On n'a pas rencontré des variations signifiantes dans les propriétés magnétiques. Compte tenu des théories de Kersten [4] et Néel [5] on peut en déduire que des tensions internes n'ont pas été produites en mesure sensible et, en plus, qu'il n'y a pas eu des variations sensibles ni dans le nombre ni dans les dimensions des précipités. En effet, il est déjà bien connu, depuis les travaux de Néel [5] que le champ coercitif est fortement dépendant des dimensions des précipités.

2. – Alliages ferromagnétiques à haute perméabilité.

Les premières expériences sur ces matériaux ont été conduites en 1956, par Sery, Fischell et Gordon [6]. D'autres résultats ont été obtenus par les mêmes Auteurs en 1958 [7]. Aucune variation n'a été observée sur les propriétés qui ne sont pas dépendantes de la structure, comme l'intensité d'aimantation à saturation. On a observé de considérables diminutions sur la valeur de la perméabilité initiale et maximum, ainsi que de considérables augmentations de la valeur du champ coercitif. Dans les Figs. 1, 2, 3, sont représentés les résultats les plus significatifs obtenus sur de différents alliages en fonction

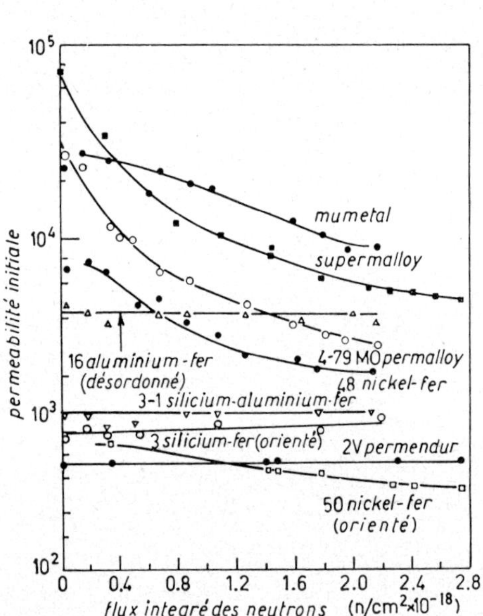

Fig. 1. – Perméabilité initiale en fonction de l'intensité du flux de neutrons incidents. (D'après GORDON [7], 1958).

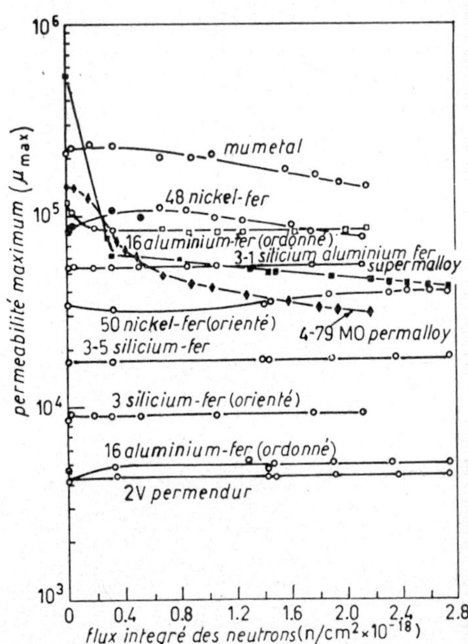

Fig. 2. – Perméabilité maximum en fonction de l'intensité du flux de neutrons incidents. (D'après GORDON [7], 1958).

de la dose des neutrons incidents. Comme on voit, sur les alliages du type « Permalloy », on observe une forte diminution (parfois de 90 %) de la perméabilité maximum et de la perméabilité initiale, ainsi qu'une forte augmentation du champ coercitif. Dans la Fig. 4 (d'après GORDON [7]) est représenté un cycle d'hystérésis avant et après l'irradiation d'un Supermalloy (alliage de Fe-Ni de propriétés magnétiques exceptionnelles). On remarque une très forte augmentation du champ coercitif et une diminution très marquée de la rectangularité du cycle d'hystérésis.

D'autres expériences, d'un remarquable intérêt, ont été faites par SCHINDLER et SALKOWITZ [8] sur des alliages Fe-Ni. Ces Auteurs ont démontré que le recuit d'un alliage désordonné sous champ magnétique équivaut à une irradiation de neutrons sous champ magnétique. Le cycle d'hystérésis devient plus rectangulaire: il y a une création d'énergie d'anisotropie induite.

En résumant on peut conclure ainsi: par irradiation aux neutrons d'un alliage de propriétés magnétiques élevées on produit une diminution marquée de la perméabilité initiale et de la perméabilité maximum, ainsi qu'une très nette augmentation du champ coercitif. En plus, par irradiation aux neutrons sous champ magnétique d'un alliage qui n'a pas de superstructure d'orientation, on peut créer de l'energie d'anisotropie induite, c'est à dire, on peut obtenir des cycles d'hystérésis rectangulaires. Quelles sont les causes de ces faits?

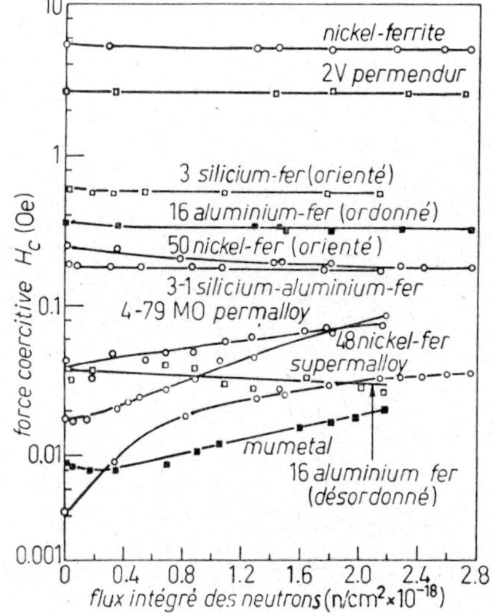

Fig. 3. – Champ coercitif en fonction de l'intensité du flux de neutrons incidents. (D'après GORDON [7], 1958).

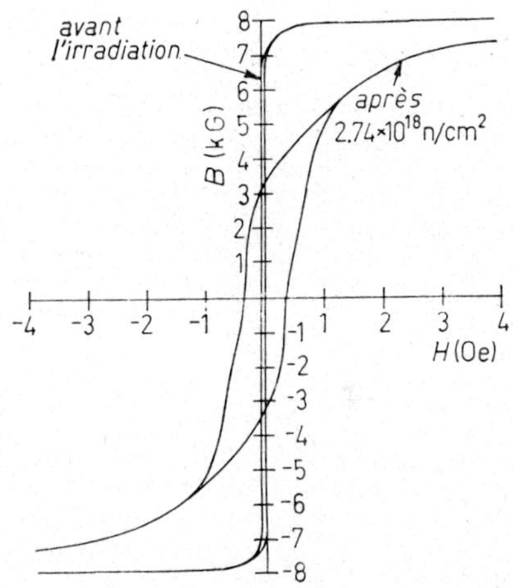

Fig. 4. – Cycle d'hystérésis du Supermalloy après et avant l'irradiation. (D'après GORDON [7], 1958).

A priori différentes causes sont possibles. L'irradiation peut produire des anneaux de dislocations, (des tensions internes); ou bien des lacunes, ou bien de petites quantités d'atomes interstitiels qui subsistent encore à température ambiante; ou bien des « clusters » de défauts; ou bien des variations de l'état d'ordre de l'alliage. Pour décider quelle est la cause responsable parmi celles envisagées, il est utile de résumer la théorie de NÉEL [9] sur les superstructures d'orientation.

Considérons, pour simplicité, un réseau cubique; si l'on dissout une petite quantité d'atomes B de substitution il y aura un certain nombre de couples d'atomes BB (Fig. 5). On admet, avec NÉEL [9], qu'il existe entre le vecteur d'intensité d'aimantation $\boldsymbol{J}_s$ et le couple d'atomes BB une énergie

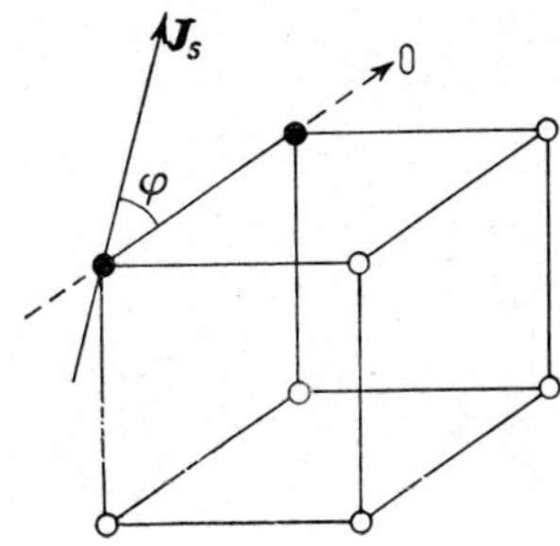

Fig. 5. – Interaction entre le couple d'atomes BB de substitution dissous dans le réseau et le vecteur intensité d'aimantation.

d'intéraction du type

$$w = w_1 \cos^2 \varphi \tag{1}$$

où φ est l'angle entre $\boldsymbol{J}_s$ et la direction du couple BB.

Si l'on recuit à matériel saturé, c'est à dire sous champ magnétique, les couples BB auront tendence à s'orienter dans la direction du champ magnétique. Après la suppression du champ magnétique le vecteur $\boldsymbol{J}_s$ va conserver la même orientation. On aura créé ainsi une énergie induite d'anisotropie. Dans le cas le plus simple, l'expression de l'energie induite d'anisotropie est donnée par

$$E_d = - W_0(\alpha^2\alpha'^2 + \beta^2\beta'^2 + \gamma^2\gamma'^2)$$

où $\alpha, \beta, \gamma;\ \alpha', \beta', \gamma'$ sont respectivement les cosinus directeurs de $\boldsymbol{J}_s$ pendant le recuit sous champ magnétique et pendant la mesure. La quantité W_0 est exprimé par

$$W_0 = \frac{n_{\mathrm{BB}} w_1(T_2)}{3kT_1}\, w_1(T_1)\,, \tag{2}$$

où n_{BB} est le nombre des couples des atomes BB dissous dans le réseau; w_1 est l'énergie d'interaction de chaque couple BB avec le vecteur $\boldsymbol{J}_s$; T_1 et T_2 sont, respectivement, la température à laquelle se passe la diffusion et la température de mesure de la E_d. Pour ce qui suit, il est utile d'observer que, comme a démontré FERGUSSON [10], la w_1 est une fonction fortement décroissante de la température.

Il a été démontré par l'auteur et ses collègues [12] que l'on peut avoir énergie d'anisotropie induite par un recuit sous champ magnétique aussi même lorsque l'on a diffusion des atomes interstitiels ou bien des dislocations [12].

Pour résoudre le problème au sujet des causes des phénomènes observés sur les matériaux magnétiques irradiés, il est nécessaire de faire une analyse quantitative. Suivant [11] les méthodes de calcul de Seitz et Köhler la concentration d'atomes interstitiels produite dans un métal par irradiation de neutrons rapides est de l'ordre de 10^{-3} avec un flux incident de l'ordre de 10^{18} n/cm^2, si l'on admet que le spectre d'énergie des neutrons soit celui du réacteur de Oak Ridge. D'après les mesures de résistance spécifique, en tenant compte de la petite énergie de diffusion des atomes interstitiels, on peut déduire que, à température ordinaire, il y aura une fraction très modeste des interstitiels produits (entre 1% et 0.1%). Dans notre cas, on aurait une concentration de l'ordre de $(10^{-5} \div 10^{-6})$ atomes interstitiels. Nous avons montré [12] que du Fe, contenant du C à l'état interstitiel, peut donner, par recuit sous champ magnétique, de l'énergie d'anisotropie induite. Mais, avec des concentrations atomiques de l'ordre de 10^{-4} atomes de C, on obtient une énergie d'anisotropie très limitée: moins que 100 erg/cm³. On pourrait aisément démontrer que des bilacunes ou des dislocations, à des concentrations raisonnables, donneraient des énergies d'anisotropie induites encore plus petites.

Des mesures quantitatives d'énergie d'anisotropie induite ont été faites pour la première fois par J. PAULEVE et D. DAUTREPPE de l'école de Grenoble.

Un alliage Fe-Ni (50%-50%) a été bombardé aux neutrons rapides sous un champ magnétique. Les résultats obtenus sont indiqués en Fig. 6. Comme l'on voit, les valeurs de l'énergie d'anisotropie induite sont assez fortes. On peut arriver jusqu'à 10^4 erg/cm³ avec 10^{18} n/cm² de neutrons incidents. Des valeurs si élevées ne pourraient certainement pas être obtenues avec des atomes interstitiels ou avec d'autres types de défauts. Par recuit d'alliage non bombardé à 500 °C approximativement (comme il est nécessaire pour la diffusion des couples d'atomes) sous champ magnétique on obtient des valeurs à peu près de 1 000 erg/cm³ pour l'énergie induite d'anisotropie. Cela s'explique aisément en rappelant la [2]. L'énergie de couplage: intensité d'aimantation-couple d'atomes, dépend fortement de la température. Un recuit à température ordinaire, comme il est possible par bombardement à cause de l'augmentation de la mobilité des atomes, équivaut à une forte augmentation du facteur $w_1(T_1)$ de la (2).

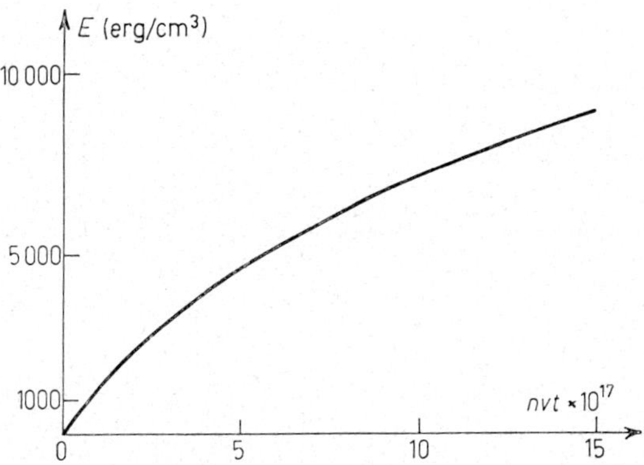

Fig. 6. – Energie d'anisotropie en fonction de la dose de neutrons rapides pour un alliage Fe-Ni (Fe 50%; Ni 50%). Irradiation exécutée sous champ magnétique. (D'après J. PAULEVE [12-*bis*], 1960).

Pour confirmer que, pendant le bombardement avec neutrons rapides sur des alliages ferromagnétiques, les phénomènes plus marqués sont dus à des circonstances d'ordre-désordre il est utile de rappeler les expériences de ARONIN [16]. Cet auteur a irradié avec 10^{20} n/cm² un alliage ordonné de Ni-Mn; il a observé, pour le composé Ni_3Mn, une diminution de l'ordre de 80%, sur l'induction de saturation. Comme on sait, dans cet alliage la valeur de $\boldsymbol{J}_s$ dépend de l'état d'ordre. Mais dans ce cas le phénomène fondamental est dû à une autre cause: un ordre-désordre qui n'est pas changé par le champ magnétique extérieur. Tandis que l'ordre-désordre des superstructures est dû au couplage du vecteur $\boldsymbol{J}$ aux couples d'atomes de substitution dissous dans le réseau ou à d'autres défauts anisotropes.

En conclusion: dans les alliages ferromagnétiques à haute perméabilité, du type Fe-Ni on observe:

1) une création d'énergie d'anisotropie induite qui croît au fur et à mesure que la dose des neutrons croît;

2) une nette diminution de la perméabilité initiale et maximum;

3) augmentation du champ coercitif.

Le phénomène 1) peut être interprété seulement en supposant que l'irradiation crée, même à température ordinaire, un ordre dans les couples d'atomes de substitution dissous.

La clef de l'interprétation est donnée par la théorie de NÉEL [9] et TANIGUCHI [13] sur les superstructures d'orientation. Les phénomènes 2), 3) peuvent aussi être interprétés comme conséquences du phénomène d'ordre de superstructure. Par contre, on ne peut pas exclure que des anneaux de dislocations ou d'autres défauts peuvent contribuer d'une façon sensible à empirer les propriétés magnétiques. Ces questions deviendront plus claires après les expériences sur le fer très pur.

3. – Métaux très purs.

Les expériences sur des métaux ferromagnétiques très purs (Fe et Ni) connues jusqu'ici sont deux. L'une a été faite par l'auteur et ses collègues [14]. L'autre a été faite par MOSER, DAUTREPPE et BRISSONNEAU [15], de l'école de Grenoble. Dans notre expérience on a irradié des échantillons toriques de fer très pur obtenu dans notre Laboratoire, doués de propriétés magnétiques exceptionnelles. (Maximum de perméabilité: 180 000; champ coercitif: 2 A/m.) Les résultats sont donnés dans le Tableau I et la Fig. 7. On voit que la diminution de la perméabilité maximum est très nette, ainsi que l'augmentation du champ coercitif. Sur le Ni (perméabilité maximum 5 000) on n'a observé aucune variation. Il est utile de rappeler que le Ni est particulièrement instable; même la courbe de première aimantation du matériel non bombardé peut être obtenue avec une précision assez modeste.

Pour expliquer les résultats obtenus sur le Fe très pur on peut faire des hypothèses. On peut admettre, par exemple, que des anneaux de dislocations restent à la température ambiante. Sur cuivre irradié des dislocations ont été observées au microscope électronique par HIRSCH et coll. [20]. En tenant compte de la théorie de VICENA [21] qui donne l'interaction entre les dislocations et les parois de Bloch, on peut estimer que, après irradiation avec à peu près 10^{18} n/cm^2, il reste à température ambiante 10^7 dislocations/cm^2 environ ce qui équivaut à des tensions internes de l'ordre de 10^6 à 10^7 dyn/cm^2.

TABLEAU I. – *Variations des proprietés magnétiques du fer très pur après et avant l'irradiation avec neutrons rapides.* (*D'après* MONTALENTI [14], 1960).

Echantillons		T 11 A	T 13 A	T 20 A
Champ coercitif H_c	avant irrad.	2.4 A/m	2.3 A/m	2.4 A/m
	après irrad.	2.9 A/m	3.1 A/m	3.2 A/m
Variation de H_c		0.5 A/m	0.8 A/m	0.8 A/m
Perméabilité maximum	avant irrad.	145 000	135 000	190 000
	après irrad.	120 000	96 000	152 000
$\int \Delta H \cdot dJ$		11 J/m³	9.8 J/m³	10.3 J/m³

Irradiation avec neutrons rapides (> 1 MeV)

Dose:

T 11 A: $1.2 \cdot 10^{18}$ neutrons rapides et $1.24 \cdot 10^{19}$ flux total de neutrons n/cm²
T 13 A: $1.3 \cdot 10^{18}$ neutrons rapides et $1.3 \cdot 10^{19}$ flux total de neutrons n/cm²
T 20 A: $1.3 \cdot 10^{18}$ neutrons rapides et $1.3 \cdot 10^{19}$ flux total de neutrons n/cm²

Cette valeur apparait raisonnable. Une autre hypothèse pour expliquer les faits observés est la suivante. Quand les atomes interstitiels diffusent dans un

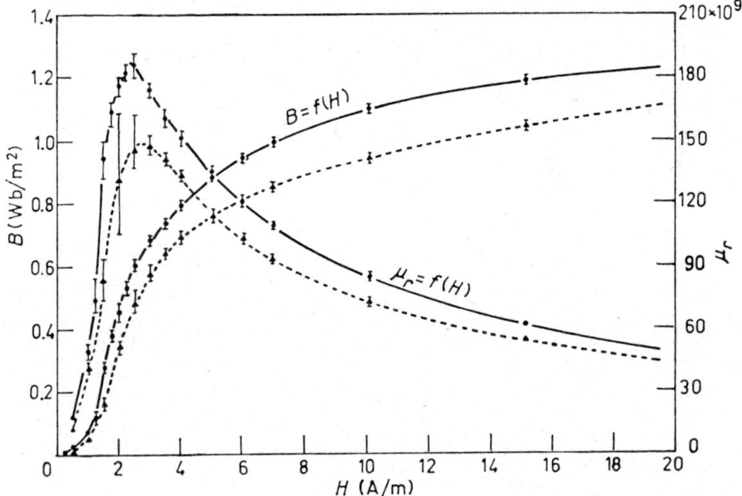

Fig. 7. – Fer très pur. Courbe de la perméabilité et de première aimantation avant et après l'irradiation. Dose: $1.3 \cdot 10^{18}$ neutrons rapides/cm² et $1.3 \cdot 10^{19}$ neutrons total/cm². (D'après MONTALENTI [14], 1960).

matériel magnétique qui n'est pas saturé, on crée dans chaque domaine de Weiss une énergie d'anisotropie K_u ayant la valeur minimum dans la direction du vecteur J_s relatif au domaine considéré. Si l'on considère le mouvement des parois de Bloch pour domaines à 90° on peut conclure que le mouvement de la paroi sera empêché par des fluctuations d'énergie d'anisotropie d'un domaine à l'autre. En généralisant l'expression de Kersten pour le calcul du champ coercitif dû aux fluctuations de tensions internes on a

$$H_c = \frac{1}{p} \frac{K_u}{J_s} \frac{d}{l}, \tag{3}$$

où p est le rapport entre les parois à 90° et celles à 180°; d est l'épaisseur de la paroi de Bloch; l la longueur du domaine; K_u l'énergie d'anisotropie induite en chaque domaine par les éléments (p. ex. interstitiels) qui sont mobiles à la température à laquelle on a irradié le matériel. Suivant des considérations dont il faut se passer ici pour brieveté, on peut appliquer la (3) au cas du Fe très pur. Si l'on admet que seulement 1% des atomes interstitiels soit le résidu à la température ambiante, on obtient des valeurs de H_c seulement 100 fois plus petites que celles observées. Il est évident que des considérations de ce type là auront un sens quantitatif seulement lorsque l'on aura des résultats expérimentaux bien plus nombreux et précis. Des expériences de recuit à des températures différentes pourront mieux expliquer le type de défaut responsable des phénomènes observés dans le Fe pur. Il est sage, pour le moment, de ne pas tirer des conclusions pressées. L'expérience de l'Ecole de Grenoble est d'un intérêt particulièrement vif. Il est utile, pour l'envisager, de faire quelques considérations élémentaires sur le traînage de diffusion. S'il y a dans un fer des interstitiels d'azote ou de carbone, la courbe de première aimantation tracée immédiatement après désaimantation et celle tracée après un temps très long ne coïncident pas (Fig. 8). NÉEL [22] a démontré que le maximum du segment intercepté par une droite parallèle à l'axe du champ magnétique (c'est-à-dire le champ de traînage) est une fonction linéaire de la concentration des interstitiels diffusant. Si l'on examine la perméabilité initiale en fonction de la température, on observe une chute caractéristique. Nous avons démontré [12] qu'un phénomène semblable se passe dans le cas de la diffusion des dislocations ou des couples d'atomes de substitution. En bref, le phénomène magnétique du traînage de diffusion peut être utilement étudié pour déterminer les constantes de diffusion des défauts anisotropes tels que

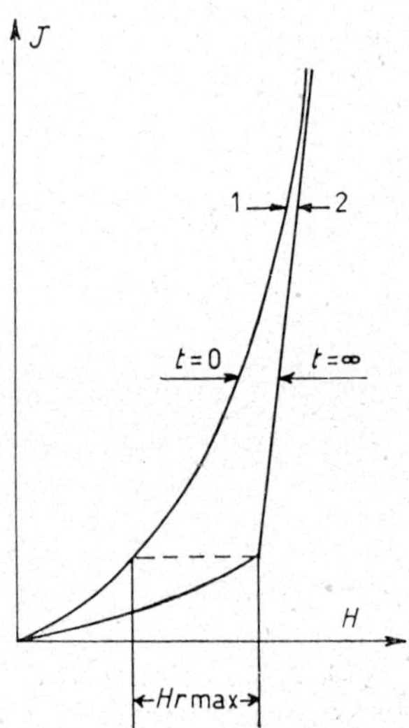

Fig. 8. – Courbe de première aimantation. (1) Immédiatement après désaimantation; (2) un temps très long après la désaimantiation.

les interstitiels dans un réseau *cc*, les bilacunes, les couples d'atomes, les dislocations, etc..

MOSER, DAUTREPPE et BRISSONNEAU [15] ont ainsi étudié ce qui se passe dans le Fe pur après irradiation aux neutrons rapides avec des doses de l'ordre de 10^{18} n/cm². Une partie de leurs résultats est indiquée dans la Fig. 9 et dans la Fig. 10. On a observé trois bandes de traînage: la troisième entre 25 °C et 100 °C ((300÷370) °K) est provoquée par des défauts qui ont une énergie d'activation de 1.2 eV. La première bande a été trouvée entre 80 et 100 °K, et les défauts ont une énergie d'activation de 0.3 eV, la deuxième bande, moins intense, est à la température de 200 °K environ, avec une énergie d'activation de 0.6 eV. La première bande, qui a une énergie d'activation très modeste, est certainement due à des atomes interstitiels du Fe dans la matrice du Fe. Pour les autres bandes, les types de défauts, peuvent être différents: « clusters », bilacunes, lacunes attrappées par des impuretés, etc. Seulement d'autres expériences pourront éclairer la question. Les mêmes A. n'ont

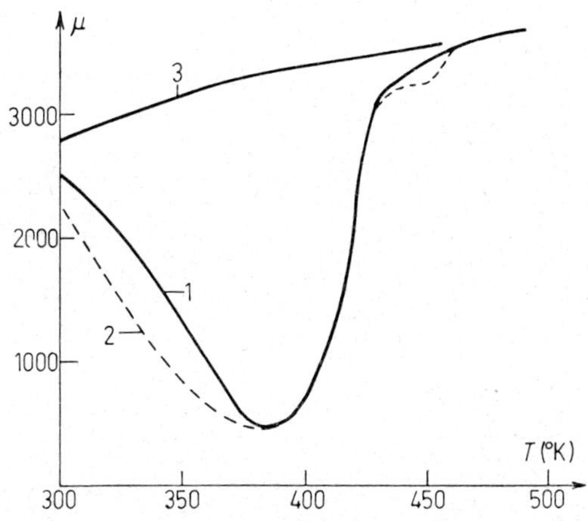

Fig. 9. – Fer pur. Bande de traînage pour un échantillon irradié avec $1.7 \cdot 10^{18}$ nvt à 25 °C. (D'après MOSER [15], 1960). 1) 60 s après désaimantation; 2) 270 s après désaimantation; 3) retour après montée en température.

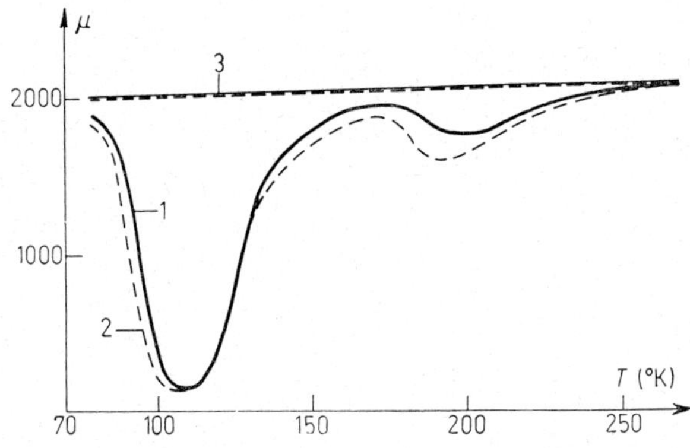

Fig. 10. – Fer pur. Bande de traînage pour un échantillon irradié avec $2.4 \cdot 10^{17}$ nvt à 78 °K. (D'après MOSER [15], 1960). 1) 70 s après désaimantation; 2) 160 s après désaimantation; 3) retour après montée en température.

trouvé aucune bande de traînage sur le Ni bombardé à la température ordinaire. En conclusion, les expériences de l'auteur et de l'école de Grenoble sur le Fe pur ont démontré clairement que, à la suite d'un bombardement aux neutrons rapides, des défauts d'autre nature qui persistent à la température ordinaire se forment à côtè des interstitiels. Sur la nature de ces défauts il est pour l'instant imprudent de faire des anticipations: de nombreuses autres expériences seront nécessaires.

4. – Ferrites.

SALKOVITZ et autres [17] ont examiné plusieures ferrites commerciales. Sur les mesures à très basse fréquence on a observé une bien nette augmentation du champ coercitif. Dans quelques cas on a observé des augmentations de 100 %. Sur les cycles d'hystérésis on a observé la même déformation caractéristique qu'on a observé sur les alliages: une diminution de rectangularité du cycle d'hystérésis. Les mêmes auteurs ont observé des variations signifiantes sur les propriétés à haute fréquence. HENRY et SALKOVITZ [18] ont aussi signalé des variations de la valeur de l'induction de saturation (entre 3 % et 15 %) pour des ferrites γ-Fe_2O_3 et Fe_3O_4 irradiées à la température de 4.2 °K. La dose des neutrons rapides était de 10^{17} n/cm^2.

SAKIOTIS et autres [19] ont observé des variations signifiantes aussi sur des propriétés en haute fréquence.

Il est imprudent de tirer des conclusions sur les causes des effets observés. Il faut expérimenter sur des échantillons bien connus et non pas commerciaux.

5. – Conclusions générales.

Les phénomènes observés sur les matériaux magnétiques après irradiation aux neutrons rapides ont la clef de leur interprétation dans la théorie de NÉEL [22] et TANIGUCHI [13] sur les superstructures d'orientation. Cette théorie, bien confirmée par l'« expérience », est basée sur l'hypotèse d'une énergie de couplage entre le vecteur intensité d'aimantation et les couples d'atomes de substitution dissous dans le réseau. Cette énergie donne origine à la superstructure d'orientation. Certainement d'autres défauts peuvent contribuer d'une façon sensible à empirer les propriétés magnétiques. Cette cause devient essentielle dans le cas de métaux très purs.

REFERENCES

[1] R. S. Sery, D. I. Gordon et R. H. Lundsten: *Bull. Am. Phys. Soc.*, **4**, 137 (1959).

[2] D. I. Gordon, R. S. Sery et R. H. Lundsten: Office of Naval Research, Washington (1959), pp. 253-292.

[3] C. B. Fennel, N. H. Hancock et R. S. Barnes: AEREM/TN-48 (Atomic Energy Research Establishment, Harwell, Berkshire, 1958).

[4] C. Kittel: *Rev. Mod. Phys.*, **24**, 541 (1949).

[5] L. Néel: *Cahiers de Phys.*, **25**, 1 (1944).

[6] R. S. Sery, R. E. Fischell et D. I. Gordon: *Trans. Amer. Inst. Elec. Engrs.*, **77**, 453 (1957).

[7] D. I. Gordon et R. S. Sery: *Intern. Conf. on Solid State Physics in Electronics, Brussels 1958* (London, 1960), p. 824.

[8] A. I. Schindler, E. I. Salkovitz et G. S. Ansell: *Journ. Appl. Phys.*, **30**, suppl. no. 4, 282-S (1959).

[9] L. Néel: *Journ. Phys. et Rad.*, **15**, 225 (1954).

[10] E. T. Fergusson: *Compt. Rend.*, **244**, 2363 (1957).

[11] G. Biorci, A. Ferro et G. Montalenti: *Effect of neutron bombardment on the magnetic properties of iron.* Technical note I *b* -A.R.D.C. Contract A.F. (514)-1331 (September 1958).

[12] G. Biorci, A. Ferro et G. Montalenti: *Magnetic viscosity and annealing in magnetic field. Theory of the magnetic viscosity due to solute atom pairs.* A.R.D.C Contract A.F. (514)-1331 Technical report 3*a* (November 1959).

[12-*bis*] J. Pauleve et D. Dautreppe: *Compt. Rend.* (en cours de publication).

[13] S. Taniguchi: *Sc. Ref. Res. Inst. Tohoku Univ.*, A **7**, 269 (1955).

[14] G. Biorci, A. Ferro et G. Montalenti: *Effect of neutron bombardment on the magnetic properties of iron and nickel of very high permeability.* A.R.D.C. Contract A.F. (514)-1331 Technical Report 3*b* (February 1960).

[15] P. Moser, D. Dautreppe et P. Brissonneau: *Compt. Rend.* (en cours de publication).

[16] L. R. Aronin: *Journ. Appl. Phys.*, **25**, 344 (1954).

[17] E. I. Salkovitz, A. I. Schindler, N. G. Sakiotis et G. S. Ansell: *Intern. Conf. on Solid State Physics in Electronics, Brussels 1958* (London, 1960), p. 808.

[18] W. E. Henry et E. I. Salkovitz: *Journ. Appl. Phys.*, **30**, 287-S (1959).

[19] E. I. Sakiotis, E. I. Salkovitz et A. I. Schindler: *Intern. Conf. on Solid State Physics in Electronics, Brussels 1958* (London, 1960), p. 817.

[20] J. Silcox et P. B. Hirsch: *Phil. Mag.*, **4**, 1359 (1959).

[21] F. Vicena: *Czechosl. Journ. Phys.*, **5**, 4 (1955).

[22] L. Néel: *Journ. Phys. et Rad.*, **13**, 249 (1952).

Radiation Damage in Uranium.

Fission Damage in Metals.

J. A. BRINKMAN

Atomics International, Research Division - Canoga Park, Cal.

1. – Introduction.

One of the more important practical problems resulting from neutron irradiation is fission damage in fuel materials. The program for these two lectures is to formulate a theoretical model for fission damage in uranium and to compare this theory with the available experimental evidence. Although the experimental work is not extensive at present, it is our belief that in the near future additional observations will be made which will make possible a more complete picture of fission damage.

The distribution of energy among the various particles produced by a typical fission event in uranium 235 is given in Table I [1].

TABLE I. – *Distribution of fission energy.*

Kinetic energy of fission fragments	162 MeV
β-decay energy	5
γ-decay energy	5
Neutrino energy	11
Energy of fission neutrons	6
Instantaneous γ-ray energy	6
	195 MeV

The great bulk of the energy is carried off by the two fission fragments, and it is the damage produced by these fragments with which we are primarily concerned. The other effects are not always negligible but can be treated by the theory which has been developed in the lectures by Drs. HOLMES and LEIBFRIED.

2. – Method of calculation.

In order to make our calculation, there are several approximations which will be made. The first is to substitute only two types of fragments, one heavy and one light, for the many chemical species which are present among fission fragments. This is a reasonable approximation, as may be seen from the mass spectrum in Fig. 1 [1]. The mass spectrum is fairly sharply peaked around two mass numbers, so that we can take $m_L = 96$ a.m.u., for the light fragment, and $m_H = 137$ a.m.u., for the heavy fragment. From the principle of energy and momentum conservation, we determine the distribution of energy between the two particles to be

$$E_L = 95 \text{ MeV};$$

$$E_H = 67 \text{ MeV}.$$

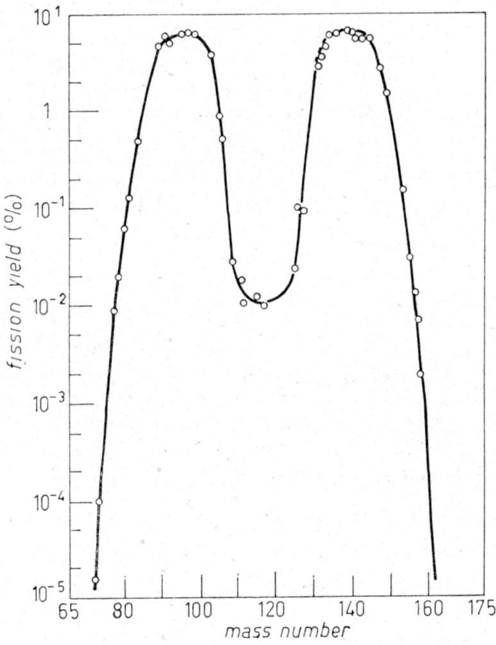

Fig. 1. – Fission yields of products with various mass numbers (after GLASSTONE and EDLUND).

For the nuclear charge the following figures may be taken:

$$Z_L = 39 ; \qquad Z_H = 55 .$$

These two figures do not add up to 92, the reason being that extremely rapid β-decay frequently changes the nuclear charge during the time of flight of the fragments. The total atomic charges are energy-dependent as may be seen in Fig. 2 [2].

Secondly, we shall make the approximation (which at first glance seems drastic) that the total atomic charge is zero. This is not such a bad approximation as it may seem, however, since we are concerned only with energy loss due to collisions with the atoms, and not with that due to electron excitation and ionization. Furthermore, the atomic collisions of primary importance are those in which the nuclei approach each other so closely that the shielding effect of the outer electrons, which are the missing ones, would not be important even if they were present.

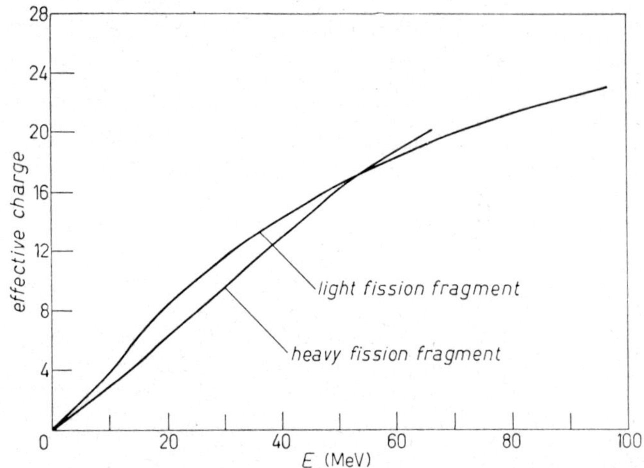

Fig. 2. – Dependence of effective charge of light and heavy fission fragments on energy.

The third approximation to be made is the use of classical mechanics in computing the energy spectrum of primary knock-ons. Although this is not completely justifiable, it is necessary, since the correct quantum-mechanical calculation is not available. In view of this limitation, we shall expect only a little better than order of magnitude agreement.

Fourthly, we use the momentum approximation. The justification for this is given later, but for the moment it is based on the fact that fission fragment tracks actually observed show rather infrequent large-angle scattering events, while the track segments between such events are extremely straight.

The cross-section for transferring an energy in excess of T to a lattice atom is given by

$$\sigma(E, T) = \pi p^2 , \tag{1}$$

where E is the kinetic energy of the fission fragment, and p is the impact parameter. This can be related to the quantities defined by Dr. Holmes [3] in his lectures as follows:

$$\sigma(E, T) = \int_T^{T_{\max}} \sigma_s(E) K(E, T') \, \mathrm{d}T' .$$

There is a mean free path associated with this cross-section, which is

$$l(E, T) = \frac{1}{N_0 \sigma(E, T)}, \tag{2}$$

where N_0 is the spatial density of lattice atoms.

In the momentum approximation, the energy transferred is

$$T = I^2/2M, \tag{3}$$

where M is the mass of the lattice atom, and I is the momentum transferred, given by

$$I = -\left(\frac{2m}{E}\right)^{\frac{1}{2}} \int_p^\infty \frac{p}{(r^2 - p^2)^{\frac{1}{2}}} \left(\frac{\partial V}{\partial r}\right) \mathrm{d}r, \tag{4}$$

where m is the mass of the fission fragment, and $V(r)$ is the potential energy of interaction of the fission fragment and a lattice atom when their nuclei are separated by a distance r. To evaluate T for a given collision characterized by an impact parameter p, we must determine $V(r)$, differentiate it and substitute into eq. (4) to obtain I, and substitute this result into eq. (3). The atomic interaction potential function which we will use is described in the next section.

3. – Atomic interaction potential.

A satisfactory potential-energy function has not yet been formulated which is satisfactory both for general use over sufficiently large ranges of interatomic separations and for use in determining interaction energies between atoms of arbitrary atomic numbers. Therefore, for the present calculations, we shall use a new empirical potential which will be demonstrated to be generally valid for radiation-damage calculations covering a wide class of interacting atoms. The empirical relation to be used is

$$V(r) = (AZ_1Z_2e^2) \frac{\exp[-Br]}{1 - \exp[-Ar]}. \tag{5}$$

It can be seen that the small-r approximation of this expression is simply the Coulomb repulsive interaction of two atoms,

$$\lim_{r \to 0} V(r) \to \frac{Z_1Z_2e^2}{r}. \tag{6}$$

In such an expression as eq. (5), when $B \gg A$, B can generally be assumed to be of the order of $Z_{\text{eff}}^{\frac{1}{3}}/a_0$, where Z_{eff} is an effective average atomic number for the two atoms. In order that Z_{eff} be equal to Z for like interacting atoms and that $Z_1 < Z_{\text{eff}} < Z_2$ for unlike interacting atoms, we choose Z_{eff} as the geometrical mean of Z_1 and Z_2. For our purposes, therefore, we shall define

$$B = Z_{\text{eff}}^{\frac{1}{3}}/Ca_0 \,, \tag{7}$$

where

$$Z_{\text{eff}} = \sqrt{Z_1 Z_2} \,, \tag{8}$$

and C is an adjustable constant of the order of unity.

At large separations, eq. (5) approximates an exponential repulsion of the Born-Mayer type, a form which is frequently used for calculations of the interaction energies between atoms separated by distances comparable with normal interatomic distances:

$$\lim_{r\to\infty} V(r) \to (AZ_1 Z_2 e^2) \exp[-Br] \,. \tag{9}$$

If eq. (9) is an adequate approximation to eq. (5) at a separation of one normal interatomic distance, then both A and B in eq. (9) can be evaluated for a particular metal ($Z_1 = Z_2$) from elastic constant data in the manner described by HUNTINGTON [4]. When this is done, the value for B for such a metal as copper is such as to require that the value of C in eq. (7) be chosen as approximately unity. The corresponding value of B for copper is such as to allow eq. (9) to be used as an adequate approximation of eq. (5) at the interatomic separation for copper, 2.55 Å. However, it is found that a value for C of unity allows eq. (9) to be used as a reasonably accurate approximation for eq. (5) at one interatomic distance only for $Z \leqslant 30$; it becomes quite unsatisfactory for $Z \geqslant 70$. For such a metal as uranium ($Z = 92$) a value of C equal to about 1.5 or greater is required in order that this approximation be reasonably valid. Since we wish this approximation to be valid for all metals, we shall choose $C = 1.5$ for general use in eq. (5). The greatest error introduced by this choice is expected when eq. (5) is applied to the lighter elements. However, if one compares the function $V(r)$ as a function of r for copper for values of C equal to both 1.0 and 1.5 in eq. (7), it is found that even in this case the discrepancy is not serious in the range of importance for radiation-damage calculations.

Having chosen a value for C, B is determined for any choice of Z_1 and Z_2. To determine the appropriate value for A, we shall make use of measured compressibility values. This procedure, of course, limits our determinations of A to those cases where $Z_1 = Z_2$. We further limit our determination to those metals having a face-centered-cubic structure. Then, since the Born-Mayer form, eq. (5), is intended to represent that portion of the interaction between two atoms which results from the overlap of closed shells of electrons, we can write the contribution to the bulk modulus which results from this portion of the interaction as

$$K' = \frac{2}{3} N_0 \left(r^2 \frac{\partial^2 V}{\partial r^2} \right)_{r=r_0}, \tag{10}$$

where V is given by eq. (9). Here, r_0 represents the normal interatomic separation in the metal. Making use of the relationship,

$$N_0 = \frac{\sqrt{2}}{r_0^3}, \tag{11}$$

and solving eq. (10) for A, the following expression is obtained:

$$A = \frac{3\, K' \exp\,[B r_0]}{2^{\frac{4}{3}} N_0^{\frac{1}{3}} B^2 Z_1 Z_2 e^2}. \tag{12}$$

In addition to K', there are other contributions to the bulk modulus such as those which arise from interactions involving electrons outside the closed shells. We shall express the experimentally measured bulk modulus for metals as the sum

$$K = K' + K'', \tag{13}$$

where K'' includes all contributions to K other than K'.

As HUNTINGTON has shown, for such monovalent metals as copper, silver, and gold, the dominant contribution to K is K', and K'' results primarily from the conduction electrons and takes on a particulary simple form:

$$K'' = \frac{2}{5} N_0 E_F \frac{m_0}{m_0^*}, \tag{14}$$

where N_0, the density of atoms, has been substituted for the density of conduction electrons, since these quantities are equal. Here, m_0 represents the electronic mass, m_0^* the effective mass of the conduction electrons, and E_F the Fermi energy for the metal. Table II gives the experimentally observed bulk moduli for these three metals, the calculated values of K'', the corresponding values of K' obtained by use of eq. (13), and the resulting values of A calculated from eq. (12) by choosing $C = 1.5$. An empirical correlation which accurately represents the Z-dependence of A for these three metals is

$$A = \frac{0.95\cdot 10^{-6} Z^{\frac{7}{2}}}{a_0}\,, \qquad \text{when} \qquad C = 1.5\,. \tag{15}$$

We have applied this empirical expression to uranium by taking the appropriate « average » interatomic distance for r_0, as defined by eq. (11). Even

TABLE II. – *Compressibilities and values of parameter A for copper, silver and gold.*

Metal	K (dyn/cm²)	K'' (dyn/cm²)	K' (dyn/cm²)	A (cm⁻¹)
Cu	$1.421\cdot 10^{12}$ (a)	$0.281\cdot 10^{12}$	$1.14\cdot 10^{12}$	$2.28\cdot 10^{7}$
Ag	$1.087\cdot 10^{12}$ (b)	$0.215\cdot 10^{12}$	$0.87\cdot 10^{12}$	$1.39\cdot 10^{8}$
Au	$1.803\cdot 10^{12}$ (b)	$0.179\cdot 10^{12}$	$1.62\cdot 10^{12}$	$7.45\cdot 10^{8}$

(a) See Ref. [5] (b) See Ref. [6]

though uranium does not have a face-centered-cubic structure, this procedure is reasonable since uranium does fairly closely approach a close-packed lattice structure. In this manner, a value of $0.644\cdot 10^{12}$ dyn/cm² for K'' is obtained for uranium. The observed value for K is $1.016\cdot 10^{12}$ dyn/cm², leaving a difference of $0.372\cdot 10^{12}$ dyn/cm² to be ascribed to K''. Certainly it is fair to conclude that we have constructed an empirical atomic interaction potential function from data obtained on copper, silver, and gold, which yields a value of K' which is not more than 50% in error for uranium. It is found that this error limit also holds for nickel, cadmium, zinc, platinum, and tungsten, in which cases K'' can be estimated with reasonable accuracy.

The foregoing treatment can only be applied with confidence to interactions between like atoms. To make eq. (15) applicable to the interactions between unlike atoms, we simply assume

$$A = \frac{0.95\cdot 10^{-6} Z_{\text{eff}}^{\frac{7}{2}}}{a_0}\,, \tag{16}$$

where Z_{eff} is defined as in eq. (8). Substituting eq. (16) and (8) into eq. (5) taking $C = 1.5$, we obtain

$$V(r) = 1.9\cdot 10^{-6} Z_{\text{eff}}^{11/2} E_{\mathrm{R}} \frac{\exp\left[-Z_{\text{eff}}^{\frac{1}{3}} r/1.5 a_0\right]}{1 - \exp\left[-0.95\cdot 10^{-6} Z_{\text{eff}}^{\frac{7}{2}} r/a_0\right]} \tag{17}$$

as the empirical potential which we shall use for the calculations to follow. Here, E_{R}, the Rydberg energy, has been substituted for $e^2/2a_0$. The error which arises when eq. (17) is used for calculating the interaction energies between unlike atoms is greater than the error for the calculation involving like atoms since the substitution of Z_{eff} for Z in eq. (12) is not rigorously correct. However, a reasonable estimate of the magnitude of this additional error can be obtained by comparing three interaction energies given by this potential: 1) the interaction between two atoms both having atomic number Z_1, 2) the interaction between two atoms both having atomic number Z_2, and 3) the interaction between two atoms having atomic numbers Z_1 and Z_2, respectively. For atomic separation distances of interest and importance in the calculations which are to follow, and when Z_1 represents the atomic number of a fission fragment and Z_2 that of a uranium atom, 1) and 3) generally differ by less than an order of magnitude, and 2) lies near the geometrical mean of 1) and 3). Certainly 2) must lie between 1) and 3), and this fact in itself implies that our potential in the case of unlike atoms has an error not more than a factor of two or three greater than that for like atoms. A more realistic estimate would probably be an additional 50% error over that for like atoms.

Fortunately, the fractional uncertainty in the cross-sections calculated by use of such a potential is generally appreciably less than that in the magnitude of the potential itself. An error of an order of magnitude in the value of the potential at a particular value of r, for example, will usually result in an error of not more than a factor of two in the cross-section for a particular energy transfer to a lattice atom. The calculations to be made of the numbers of defects produced by fission fragments are therefore believed to be somewhat better than order-of-magnitude calculations, the probable errors generally being less than a factor of two.

It should be mentioned at this point that a somewhat lower value of C for use in evaluating both A and B in eq. (5) would probably be desirable if one were interested in obtaining a potential for use only with elements having atomic numbers less than about 50. Nevertheless, for general use in radiation-damage calculations, we have confidence that eq. (17) is a reasonably reliable function for all metals whose atomic number exceeds 25. This contention is supported by the fact that both the large and small r behaviors can be shown to be reasonably accurate, and also by the fact that the function decreases monotonically with increasing r and changes smoothly from one asymptotic form to the other over the proper range of r.

We should also point out that the important range of r over which the atomic interaction potential must be known for radiation-damage calculations does not extend to r_0; a knowledge over the range $r < 0.7 r_0$ is quite adequate. We feel that eq. (17) is reliable over this range. It should not be used near $r = r_0$, however, since the implicit assumption has been made in deriving it that all interatomic distances (atomic radii) are close to those of copper, silver and gold. It is therefore not a satisfactory potential for use in calculating such quantities as the formation and migration energies of point defects in metals.

4. – Mean free path conclusions.

We are now prepared to use the potential energy expression, eq. (5), to evaluate the impulse, I, in eq. (4), which can then be put into eq. (3) to determine the energy transfer, T. Since in the momentum approximation, the energy transfer in a collision is always proportional to $1/E$, we can put these two quantities together and evaluate the product:

$$TE = \frac{m}{M} p^2 A^2 Z_1^2 Z_2^2 e^4 [B\,F(A, B, p) + (A - B) F(A, A + B, p)]^2 , \tag{18}$$

where $F(A, B, p)$ is defined by

$$F(A, B, p) = \int_p^\infty \frac{\exp[-Br]\,\mathrm{d}r}{(r^2 - p^2)^{\frac{1}{2}}(1 - \exp[-Ar])^2} = \sum_{\nu=0}^{\infty} (\nu + 1) K_0[(B + \nu A)p] , \tag{19}$$

where K_0 is the modified Bessel function of the second kind, also known as the Bessel function of the third kind.

Choosing particular values of p, the impact parameter, we can evaluate both the mean free path, l, and the product TE. Such calculations have been performed for both the heavy and light fission fragments in a uranium lattice. The results are plotted in Fig. 3.

As a specific example, let us calculate the mean free path between atomic

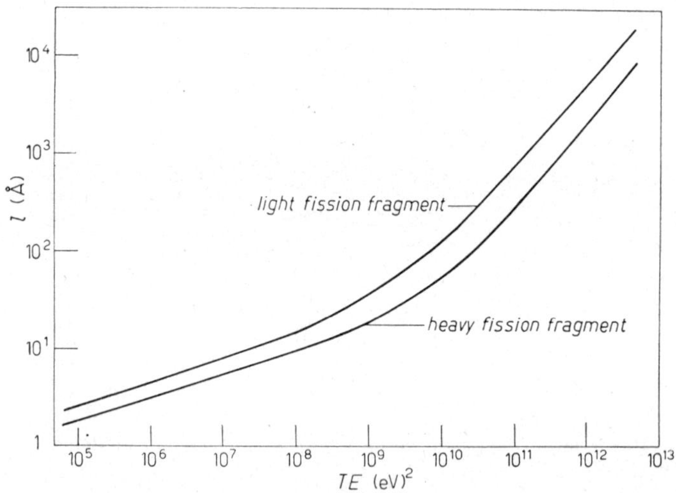

Fig. 3. – Energy-dependence of mean free path (l) of light and heavy fission fragments in uranium between production of successive knock-ons having energies in excess of T.

displacements for fission fragments in uranium taking the displacement energy $T_D = 50$ eV. Although displacements might be made with less energy, since the region where the displacement probability function varies from zero to unity is probably about 60 eV in copper, as shown by Dr. VINEYARD [7], and may be more in uranium, this seems to be a reasonable value for the effective displacement energy.

For the heavy fragment, we obtain the mean free path at an energy, $E = 30$ MeV, or about half of its original energy: l_H (30 MeV, 50 eV) = 25 Å. Similarly for the light fragment, taking an enegy of 45 MeV: l_L (45 MeV, 50 eV) = 40 Å. This gives us an idea of the mean distance between displaced atoms along the path of the fission fragment, all of which have energies of at least 50 eV, and many of which have considerably more energy.

The mean free path for large-angle scattering events can be calculated by use of the hard-sphere model in the manner described by Dr. LEIBFRIED [8]. For both the light and heavy fragments, the result is

$$l_{\text{H.S.}} \simeq 10^6 \text{ Å} .$$

This correctly predicts that fission fragment paths are mostly straight lines, along which atomic displacements are made, while large angle scattering events are rare. If we consider only the portions of the tracks produced by fission fragments during the time their energy is high ($E > 10$ MeV), we expect to find a large-angle scattering event in only about one fission fragment track in ten, since the average track length is of the order of 10^5 Å. In the final portions of the tracks, however, the large angle scattering events become more numerous.

The reason for the apparent discrepancy between the mean free paths calculated by 1) the momentum approximation and 2) the hard-sphere approximation lies in the fact that two distinctly different mean free paths can be determined. The first, $l_{\text{disp}}(E, T)$, is the mean free path between the production of successive knock-on atoms having energies in excess of T, and is correctly calculated by use of the momentum approximation when $E \gg T$. The second $l_{\text{col}}(E)$, is the mean free path between successive large-angle scattering events. It is calculated with good accuracy by use of the hard-sphere approximation, and is useful in determining ranges of moving atoms in solids, when their initial energy does not exceed about 1 MeV. Such atoms lose the greater fraction of their energy in hard-sphere collisions. Fission fragments, on the other hand, lose most of their energy in electronic energy losses and in low-angle displacement collisions. If one plots the differential scattering cross-section, $d\sigma/dT$, as a function of T (following Dr. LEIBFRIED) [8], the ranges of validity and the respective usefulness of each of these approximations can be more clearly understood (see Fig. 4). Note that when $T_D > T'_D$, where $T'_D \sim 0.1\, T_{\max}$, the hard-sphere approximation gives the better estimate of the total displacement cross-section (area under exact curve to the right of T_D), since the shaded areas cancel each other to a large extent. However, when $T_D \sim T''_D$, where $T''_D \ll 0.1\,T_{max}$, the shaded area on the left increases rapidly, and eventually (for very small T_D) the area to the right of T'_D becomes a negligible portion of the entire area. For fission fragments, this condition is fulfilled, and, as will be seen later, for treating the damage produced by high-energy knock-ons ($T \sim 5 \cdot 10^4$ eV), it is also a good approximation. When the hard-sphere approximation is used for treating collisions of such particles, it must be kept in mind that the mean free paths calculated only represent the straight-line distances travelled between large-angle scattering events; they are not at all representative of the average distance between successive displacements of atoms.

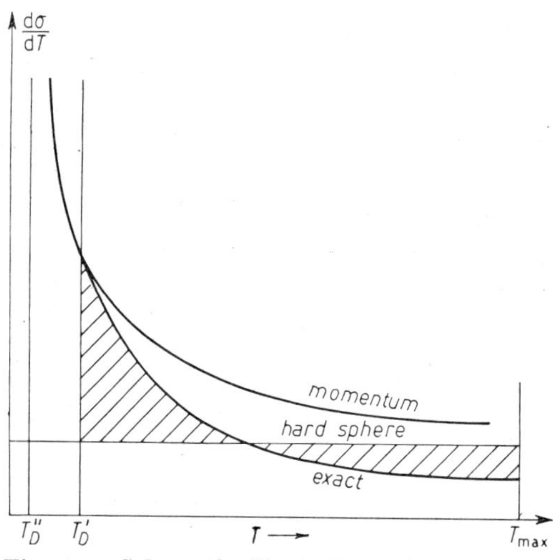

Fig. 4. – Schematic illustration of ranges of validity of momentum and hard-sphere approximations.

5. – Primary knock-on energy spectra.

We may define the quantity $N_{L,H}(T)$ as the total number of primary knock-ons produced by the light (subscript L) and heavy (subscript H) fission fragments, respectively, with energies in excess of T,

$$N_{L,H}(T) = \int\limits_{E_{L,H(min)}}^{E_{L,H(max)}} \left(\frac{\partial R}{\partial E}\right)_{L,H} \frac{dE_{L,H}}{l_{L,H}(E,\,T)}\,. \tag{20}$$

Here R is the residual range and $(\partial R/\partial E)$ is the slope of the range-energy curve, taken from empirical range-energy data, thus circumventing the problem of energy loss by electron excitation. The lower limit of the integral is the smallest energy that the fission fragment can possess and still be capable of making an atomic displacement with energy in excess of T:

$$E_{L,H}(\min) = \frac{(M + m_{L,H})^2}{4Mm_{L,H}}\,T\,.$$

The upper limit $E_{L,H}(\max)$ is the initial fission fragment energy.

The result of integration of eq. (20) is shown if Fig. 5. An approximate analytical expression fitting these curves over the range of 25 eV to 10^5 eV,

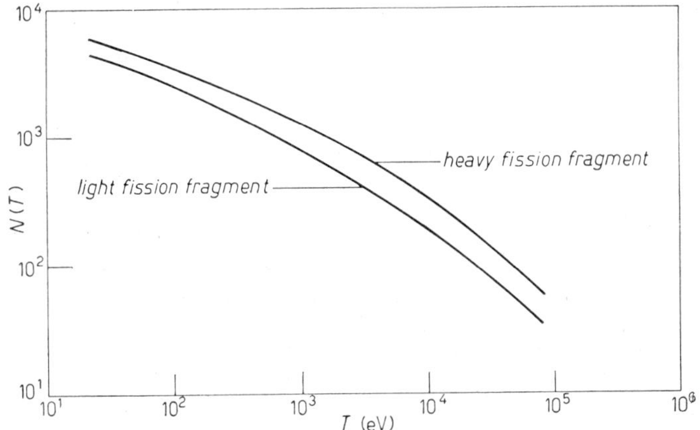

Fig. 5. – Number of primary knock-ons produced by light and heavy fission fragments in uranium, having energies in excess of T.

within $\sim 2\%$ (up to 10^6 eV $\sim 5\%$) has been formulated:

$$N_{\mathrm{L,H}}(T) = \exp\,[d_{\mathrm{L,H}}]\, T^{-(a_{\mathrm{L,H}}+b_{\mathrm{L,H}}\ln T)}\,,$$

where

$$\begin{aligned} a_{\mathrm{L}} &= 0.1006\\ a_{\mathrm{H}} &= 0.0488\\ b_{\mathrm{L}} &= 0.0342\\ b_{\mathrm{H}} &= 0.0354\\ d_{\mathrm{L}} &= 9.02\\ d_{\mathrm{H}} &= 9.16 \end{aligned}$$

and T is measured in eV.

6. – Lattice energy transfer calculations.

The total energy transferred to the lattice by a fission fragment is of interest since the total number of displaced atoms in the lattice is approximately proportional to this quantity. We define $\mathscr{E}_{\mathrm{L,H}}(T)$ as the total energy supplied to all struck atoms which receive energies less than T, by light and heavy fission fragments, respectively. This is given by

$$\mathscr{E}_{\mathrm{L,H}}(T) = \int_0^T T' \left(-\frac{\partial N_{\mathrm{L,H}}(T')}{\partial T'}\right) \mathrm{d}T'\,. \tag{22}$$

$N_{L,H}(T)$ is the function shown in Fig. 5, and the negative derivative is taken since we are interested in the numbers of displacements with energies *less* than T. This derivative is shown in Fig. 6.

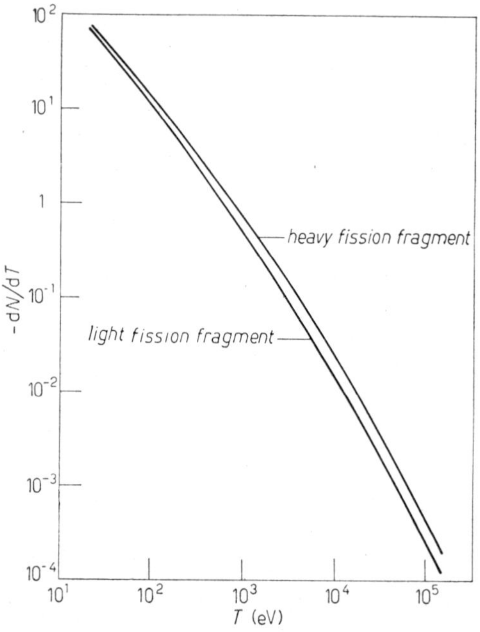

It may be seen that the heavy fragment produces considerably more damage than the light one, though this fact is somewhat obscured by the logarithmic plot. The energy transferred to primary knock-ons having initial energies lying within any specific energy range, *e.g.* between T_1 and T_2, is then given by: $\mathscr{E}_{L,H}(T_2) - \mathscr{E}_{L,H}(T_1)$.

The validity of this expression is still limited to the region where T is small with respect to T_{max}. T_{max} for the heavy fragment is 62 MeV, and for the light fragment 78 MeV. Thus, at this time we are not justified in using such an expression above 1 MeV, but we shall see later that we can use it over the entire energy range.

Fig. 6. – Energy spectra of primary knock-ons produced by light and heavy fission fragments in uranium.

Integration of eq. (22) gives the following result:

$$\mathscr{E}_{L,H} = \frac{1}{b^{\frac{1}{2}}_{L,H}} \exp\left[d_{L,H} + \frac{(1-a_{L,H})^2}{4b_{L,H}}\right] \cdot \left\{\frac{\sqrt{\pi}}{2}[1 \pm \mathrm{Erf}\,(\pm\, t_{L,H})] - b^{\frac{1}{2}}_{L,H} \exp\left[-t^2_{L,H}\right]\right\}. \tag{23}$$

Here

$$\mathrm{Erf}(t) \equiv \frac{2}{\sqrt{\pi}} \int_0^t \exp\left[-t'^2\right] \mathrm{d}t' , \tag{24}$$

is the error function, which is tabulated, and

$$t_{L,H} \equiv b^{\frac{1}{2}}_{L,H} \ln T - \frac{1-a_{L,H}}{2b^{\frac{1}{2}}_{L,H}} . \tag{25}$$

The positive signs in the square brackets of eq. (23) are used when $t > 0$, the negative signs when $t < 0$.

Some values of $\mathscr{E}_L$ and $\mathscr{E}_H$ for various values of T are given in Table III.

TABLE III.

T (eV)	$\mathscr{E}_L$ (MeV)	$\mathscr{E}_H$ (MeV)
$T_D =$ 50	0.06	0.07
400	0.37	0.47
40 000	4.95	7.82
10^6	24	42
$T_{L(max)} = 77.8 \cdot 10^6$	25.5	—
$T_{H(max)} = 62.1 \cdot 10^6$	—	44.6

The upper limit of validity of the expression for $\mathscr{E}_{L,H}$ would be expected to be about $T = 10^6$ eV, but the table has been extended to include the maximum energies which can be transferred to primary knock-ons by the light and heavy fission fragments, respectively. Since the additional energy transferred to the lattice in both cases is less than ten percent in going from 10^6 eV to the maximum energy, and taking account of the fact that the momentum approximation always overestimates the energy transfer, we may conclude that the extension of the calculation to the entire energy range is justified.

In point of fact, the « true » value of $\mathscr{E}_L$ for $T = T_L$ (max) should lie somewhere between 24 and 25.5 MeV, and the « true » value of $\mathscr{E}_H$ for $T = T_H$(max) between 42 and 44.6 MeV.

The greatest amount of energy transfer to the lattice occurs via those primary knock-ons having initial energies lying in the range between 40 000 and 10^6 eV. These are all high-energy knock-ons capable of producing a high concentration of localized damage. The mean free path between such collisions is some thousands of ångströms in general.

Adding up the energies, $\mathscr{E}_L(T_{L(max)})$ and $\mathscr{E}_H(T_{H(max)})$, we find that 70 MeV, or about 45% of the total kinetic energy (162 MeV) of the fission fragments is transferred directly to lattice atoms, the remainder being given to the electrons. There is a notable difference in the behavior of the two fragments: the heavy fragment transfers about $\frac{2}{3}$ of its total energy to the lattice, while the light fragment transfers about $\frac{1}{4}$ of its energy to the lattice. It is also significant to note that the concept of an ionization threshold, as discussed by Dr. HOLMES [3], cannot even be considered in the case of fission fragments. This can be seen by considering the dependence of a quantity, F, on E, where

$$F(E) = \frac{(\mathrm{d}E/\mathrm{d}X)_{at}}{(\mathrm{d}E/\mathrm{d}X)_{at} + (\mathrm{d}E/\mathrm{d}X)_{el}},$$

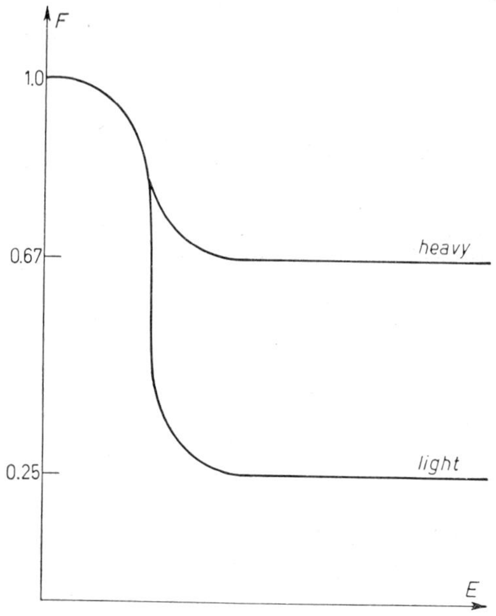

is the fraction of the energy being lost by the fragment along its path, which is being transferred to the lattice. Curves similar in form to those illustrated idealistically in Fig. 7 are obtained.

If the sharp ionization threshold assumption were realistic, these curves would both drop to zero, instead of to a more or less constant value given approximately by $\mathscr{E}(T_{max})/E_{max}$.

Fig. 7. – Dependence of fraction of energy loss by light and heavy fission fragments which is transmitted to lattice atoms on energy.

7. – Fission damage model.

We can now begin to formulate a general picture of the kind of damage produced in the lattice. We draw a straight line to represent the path of the fission fragment in the high-energy range ($E > 0.1\,E_{max}$). Every 25 Å on the average, for the heavy fragment and 40 Å for the light fragment, a displaced atom will be produced. Many of these will have enough energy to produce additional displacements. Every few thousand ångstroms a high-energy event occurs resulting in a cascade of displacements and a region of highly concentrated damage. There will be a fairly large number (of the order of 100) of these « spikes » produced along the total length of the fragment's path, which is of the order of 10^5 Å.

These spikes, in many cases, will be much more important in the case of fission fragment damage than in the case of fast-neutron experiments, and there are certain physical property changes which must be ascribed to these regions of high local damage.

Fission fragment tracks have been observed in electron-microscopy studies on platinum and UO_2 by BIERLEIN and MASTEL [9] at Hanford; and by NOGGLE and STIEGLER [10] at Oak Ridge. A structure indicating localized regions of high damage was observed although their spacing along the tracks seems to be somewhat too small. Workers at other laboratories (Harwell and Brookhaven) have observed similar effects in other materials.

7·1. *Displacement spikes.* – Many of the primary knock-ons having energies in excess of 40 000 eV may be able to produce considerable numbers of displacements along the straight segments of their paths, which may be of the order of 100 Å or more in length. In order to calculate the two mean free paths involved, namely that for large angle collisions and that for production of lattice displacements, we again use the same equations and potential function, with the momentum approximation, but now for uranium in uranium. Since we are primarily interested in primary knock-ons having initial energies of the order of 10^5 eV, we must keep in mind the limitation of the momentum approximation, namely that the transferred energy must be small compared with the energy of the incident particle. Before performing these calculations for uranium, however, let us, as an example, first do the same in copper, a material with which we have considerably more familiarity from both theory and experiment.

Calculations can be made for copper in copper using the Huntington potential [4],

$$V(r) = (0.053\ \text{eV}) \exp[13.9\,(r_0 - r)/r_0]\,. \tag{26}$$

In this case we take the threshold displacement energy to be 25 eV and calculate the mean free path for displacements, l_{disp}, by the momentum approximation, and the mean free path for large-angle collisions, l_{col}, by the hard-sphere approximation. Results are given in Table IV.

TABLE IV.

E (eV)	$T_D E$ (eV)^2 ($T_D = 25$ eV)	l_{col} (Å)	l_{disp} (Å)
55	$1.35 \cdot 10^3$	1.98	1.67
1 100	$2.8 \cdot 10^4$	5.4	2.62
8 400	$2.1 \cdot 10^5$	16.4	3.8
58 000	$1.45 \cdot 10^6$	223	5.9

It may be seen that atomic displacements are made not only at the junctions of the tracks, but also along the straight line portions, particularly at high energy. In the case of uranium, which has a higher mass, the difference between the two mean free paths is even greater.

The calculations for copper show that even at 58 000 eV a primary knock-on produces secondaries about once every two atomic distances without experiencing noticeable angular deflection. A nonuniform damage is produced along the tracks, since secondaries of all energies become more closely spaced as the primary slows down.

It is also seen that the mean free path for displacement becomes equal to one interatomic distance at about $E = 1000$ eV. In this region it is no longer possible to think of individual displacements, since all the vacancies are connected and the displaced atoms move outward in a coherent manner. The details of what happens to the lattice at this point and beyond are not at all well understood, and are difficult to calculate. The lattice change produced by the dynamic action of this primary and all the secondaries before this energy is transformed to heat, is referred to as a *displacement spike* (Fig. 8).

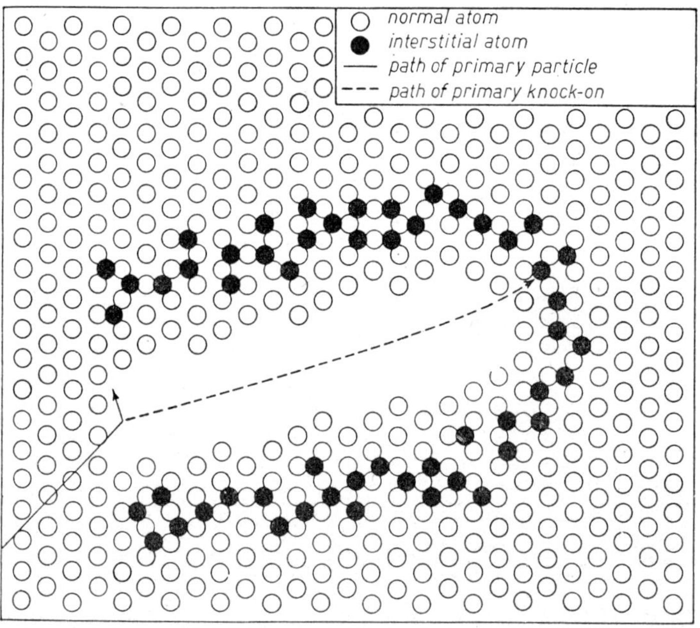

Fig. 8. – Schematic representation of interstitial atoms around a multiple vacancy during production of a displacement spike.

We may emphasize that the coherent motion outward of the displaced atoms is not equivalent to heat, since heat consists of randomized motion. The displacement spike, which is due to the dynamic action, should then be clearly distinguished from the thermal spike. The secondary knock-ons travel outward a few atom distances from the path of the primary, a shell of interstitials is formed, and a large elongated vacant region is left in the center. Due to the pressure exerted by the shell of interstitials, collapse may follow, giving rise to a disordering effect. Focussing has been neglected here, but it may be present and lead to some long-range transport of matter and energy.

To estimate the energy expended in a displacement spike, we may calculate the energy of the primary knock-on at which the mean free path becomes equal to one interatomic distance. The values of such energies, T_2, for several metals have been calculated and are presented in Table V, using eq. (17) as the atomic interaction potential. T_2 is calculated from the defining equation:

$$l_{\text{disp}}(T_2, T_D) = r_0 ,$$

where r_0 represents one interatomic distance. In face centered cubic metals:

$$r_0 = \left(\frac{\sqrt{2}}{N_0}\right)^{\frac{1}{3}},$$

and we shall take this as the definition of r_0 in uranium also.

TABLE V.

Metals	T_2 (eV)
Cu	4 000 (1000 for Huntington potential)
Ag	4 500
Au	80 000
U	79 000

These results have been obtained, using the potential in eq. (17), on the assumption that $T_D = 25$ eV for all of these materials. In U and Au, as already pointed out, it is probably better to assume that $T_D = 50$ eV, in which case the values for T_2 are 40 000 eV for these metals. If focussing is not important, the numbers of atoms involved in such a spike can be approximately calculated by dividing the energy among the atoms, with an energy density of the order of 1 eV per atom, as pointed out by Dr. THOMPSON [11].

On the basis of this picture, some displacement spike effects may be predicted which will cause property changes subject to experimental observation: 1) disordering of superlattice alloys; 2) long-range mixing of the atoms of the material (the material originally in the center of the spike is redistributed into a larger region leading to radiation-induced diffusion); 3) radiation annealing (after the spike has taken place, the final structure will not be influenced by the original state of the material, *e.g.*, the presence of Frenkel defects in the material).

We are now in a position to calculate the total energy spent in the production of displacement spikes in uranium. We shall assume the threshold displacement energy for uranium to be $T_D = 50$ eV, giving the corresponding value, $T_2 = 40\,000$ eV. A lower threshold for the production of displacement spikes, T_1, is assumed to be 400 eV [12], without further discussion except to say that it is not a very sensitive parameter. We also need the maximum transferable energies for the light and heavy fission fragments. These are $T_{L(max)} = 77.8$ MeV, and $T_{H(max)} = 62.1$ MeV.

Another quantity, $\mathscr{E}^*_{L,H}(T)$, is defined as the total energy expended in the production of displacement spikes by those primary knock-ons having initial energies less than T. It is

$$(27)\quad \begin{cases} \mathscr{E}^*_{L,H}(T) = \displaystyle\int_{T_1}^{T} T' \left(-\frac{\partial N_{L,H}}{\partial T'}\right) dT' = \mathscr{E}_{L,H}(T) - \mathscr{E}_{L,H}(T_1) & \text{for } T_1 < T < T_2 \\ \text{and} & \\ \mathscr{E}^*_{L,H}(T) = \mathscr{E}_{L,H}(T_2) - \mathscr{E}_{L,H}(T_1) + \displaystyle\int_{T_2}^{T} T_2 \left(-\frac{\partial N_{L,H}}{\partial T'}\right) dT' & \text{for } T_2 < T < T_{L,H(max)} . \end{cases}$$

This energy can be calculated from expressions already given; the total amounts of energy expended by the light and heavy fragments in the production of displacement spikes are

$$\mathscr{E}^*_L(T_{L(max)}) = 7.0 \cdot 10^6 \text{ eV} ,$$

$$\mathscr{E}^*_H(T_{H(max)}) = 11.7 \cdot 10^6 \text{ eV} .$$

Adding these energies, we find that about 19 MeV is expended in the production of the spikes per fission event. Assuming the distribution of this energy to be about 1 eV per atom, we obtain the total volume of the spikes produced by one fission event as $1.9 \cdot 10^7$ atoms.

7·2. *Frenkel defects.* – The numbers of Frenkel pairs produced can be calculated using the basic equation $\nu(T) = T/2T_D$ developed by Dr. HOLMES. The initial primary knock-on energies can be divided into three ranges, for each of which we calculate the number of Frenkel defects as follows:

$$(1)\quad T_D < T < T_1: \quad \nu(T) = T/2T_D ,$$

$$(2)\quad T_1 < T < T_2: \quad \nu(T) = 0$$

$$(3)\quad T_2 < T: \quad \nu(T) = \frac{T - T_2}{2T_D} .$$

In the first range, spike production is not possible, so all the energy transferred to the lattice is expended in the production of Frenkel defects. In the second range, only displacement spikes are produced. In the third range, Frenkel defects are produced until the energy is degraded to T_2, after which all the energy goes into spike production.

Let $n_{L,H}$ be the total number of Frenkel pairs produced by a fission fragment,

$$n_{L,H} = \int_{T_D}^{T_{max}} \nu(T') \left(-\frac{dN_{L,H}}{dT'} \right) dT' . \tag{28}$$

Integration of eq. (28), making use of relationships previously given, gives

$$n_L = 2.1 \cdot 10^5 ,$$

$$n_H = 3.7 \cdot 10^5 .$$

The total number of Frenkel pairs produced per fission event in uranium is thus $n = 5.8 \cdot 10^5$. Therefore, even though in the present model we have expended a substantial amount of the energy of the fission fragments in the production of displacement spikes, we still predict that more Frenkel defects will be produced than previous models have estimated. The reason for this is that the atomic interaction potential is considerably stronger; as a consequence more energy is transferred to the lattice.

8. – Experimental evidence.

8·1. *Electron-microscope observations.* – Fission tracks in thin films of various materials have been observed by several workers by electron microscopy. Both NOGGLE and STIEGLER [10], and BIERLEIN and MASTEL [9] have studied them in thin films of UO_2, and BIERLEIN and MASTEL have studied them in nonfissionable thin films as well.

Fig. 9 shows fission tracks in UO_2 films photographed by NOGGLE and STIEGLER. Fig. 9*a* shows a typical transmission photograph of a 100 Å thick film after an irradiation of $5 \cdot 10^{15}$ thermal neutrons per cm^2. It is significant to note that: 1) the tracks consist primarily of straight lines, in agreement with the fact that the calculated mean free path between large-angle scattering events is larger than the average track length; 2) the tracks are of the order of 100 Å in diameter; and 3) the tracks are all lighter than the background, indicating a net loss of material from such films whose thickness is comparable with the track diameter.

Fig. 9*b* shows a preshadowed carbon replica of the free surface of a UO_2 film which had been irradiated in place on its substrate and shows the surface disturbances which occur as a result of the passage of fission fragments through the film. These surface disturbances associated with the tracks are somewhat variable in nature; in some cases they appear as distinct furrows or grooves, with or without displaced material immediately adjacent to the tracks; in other cases the tracks appear as linear arrays of particles or bulges at the

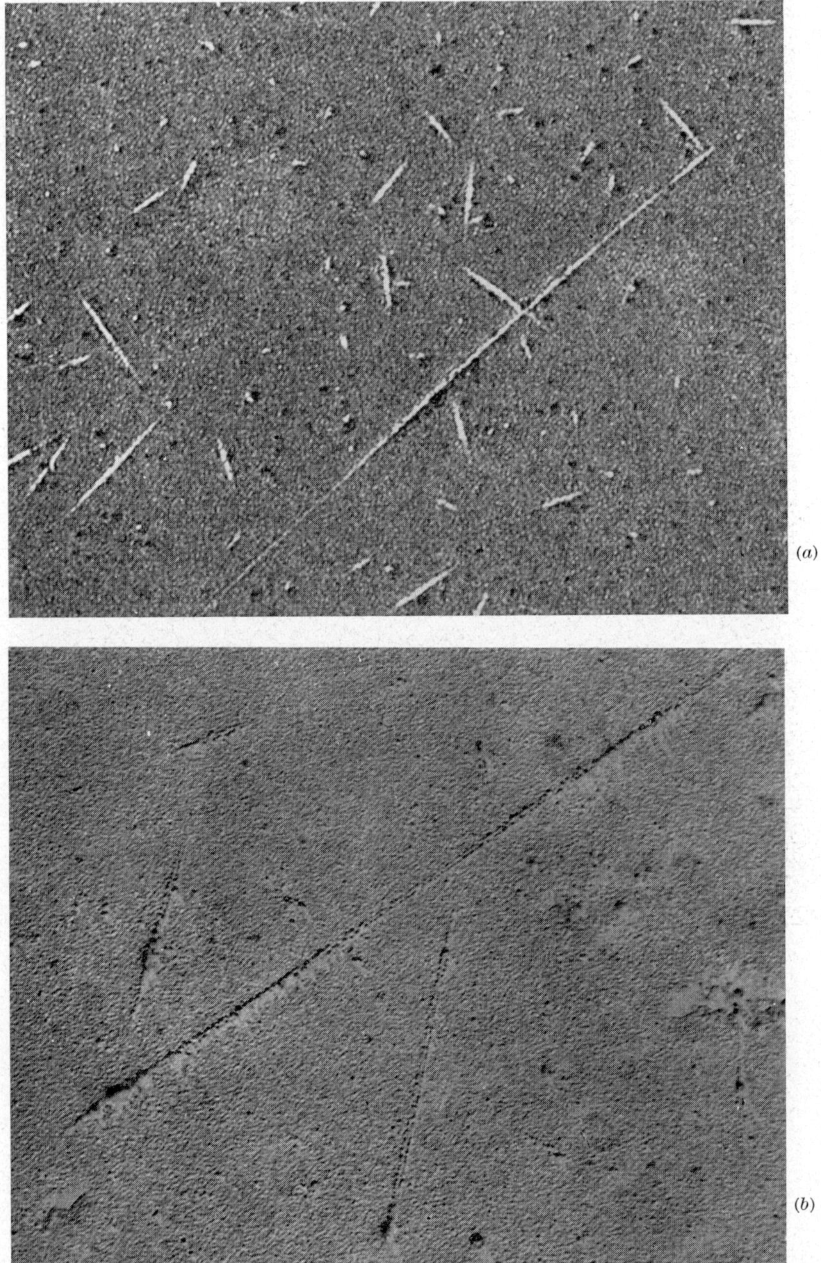

Fig. 9. – Electron micrographs of fission fragment tracks in UO_2, by T. S. NOGGLE and J. O. STIEGLER. *a*) 100 Å thick OU_2 after dose of approximately $5\cdot10^{15}$ nvt thermal; 50000×. *b*) Carbon replica of the free surface of a UO_2 film. Note the variation in the surface topography between different tracks, along the track, and at their ends. Several types of tracks are seen in the replicas—furrows, linear arrays of clumped particles, and bulging of the surface; 25000×.

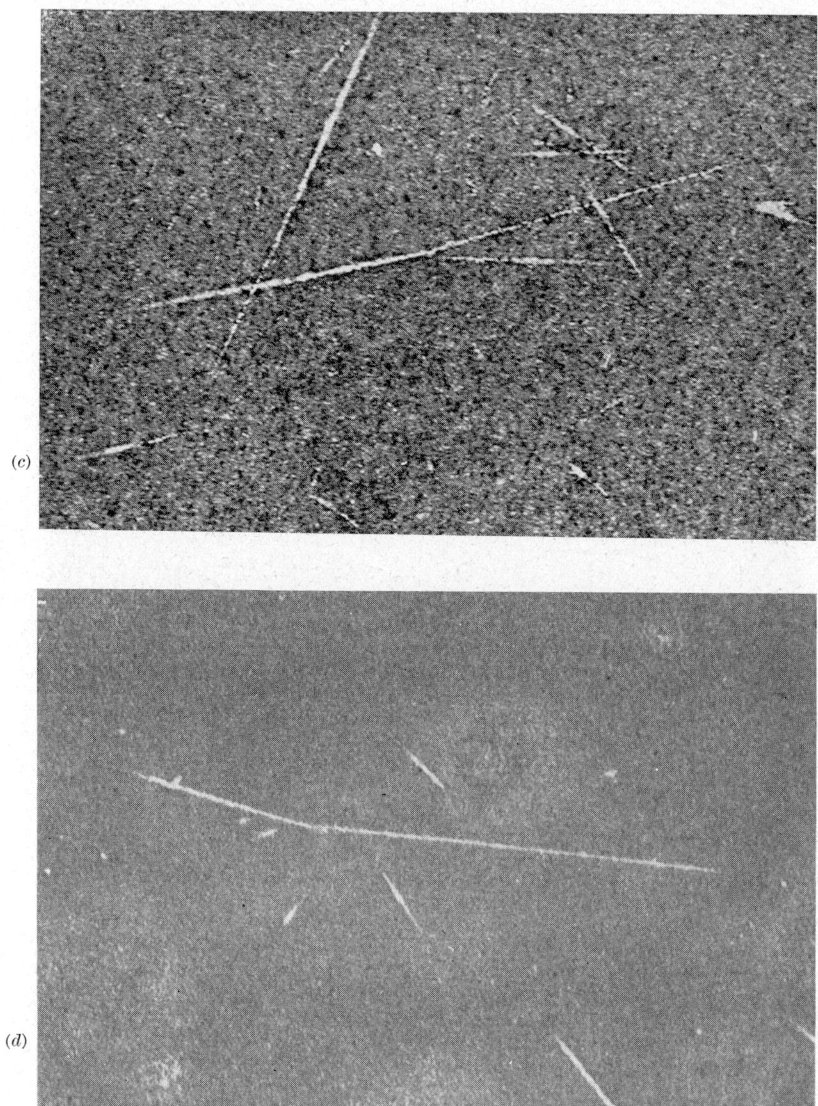

(c)

(d)

Fig. 9 – Electron micrographs of fission fragment tracks in UO_2, by T. S. NOGGLE and J. O. STIEGLER. c) Rutherford scattering of a fission fragment. Fission fragment of mass 85 has struck an oxygen atom in the lattice. The energy of the incident particle is shared approximately equally between the two atoms after the event, and each must have in excess of (35÷40) MeV of energy—sufficient for both to dissipate at a rate in excess of 1000 eV/Å; 25000×. d) Bent track probably represents an encounter with an uranium atom since only mass 80 or less fission fragments could be deviated through thus large an angle by an oxygen atom. If the struck atom is uranium, the energy imparted to it is on the order of 1.5 MeV. It would dissipate energy at a rate of about 400 eV/Å, which is too low for registration to occur; 25000×.

surface. This variable appearance is interpreted as reflecting the depth from the free surface at which the fission fragments traveled and also upon the specific rate of energy input to the film. The tracks or portions thereof which show particle build-up or bulging appear to give random spacings between these regions of displaced material with an average spacing of the order of a few hundred ångströms. These fluctuations in the distribution of the displaced material may represent the contribution of displacement spikes to the track registration, although their observed spacing is an order of magnitude smaller than the calculated value.

Fig. 9*c* and 9*d* show examples of large angle scattering events, the first with an oxygen atom, and the second presumably with an uranium atom. The

Fig. 10. – Electron micrographs of fission fragment tracks in platinum by T. K. Bierlein and B. Mastel.

frequency of occurrence of such events has not yet been determined for a comparison with that predicted from the calculated mean free paths between such events, but it seems to be of the proper order of magnitude. For a more complete description of the nature of these tracks, as well as of the required energy-dissipation rate of 1000 eV/Å for registration of the tracks to occur, the reader is referred to the work of NOGGLE and STIEGLER.

Fig. 10 shows fission fragment tracks in platinum, photographed by BIERLEIN and MASTEL [9]. A thin film (less than 100 Å) of platinum was evaporated onto a carbon substrate, polystyrene latex spheres were deposited on it, and the film was then shadow-coated with UO_2 at an angle of 15°. The spheres measure $1.1 \cdot 10^4$ Å in diameter. Fission fragments originate in the UO_2; however, when they are observed in the shadow they produce tracks in uncoated platinum. Fig. 10 is a transmission photograph of a track in such a film. It is significant to note that a series of holes is produced in the platinum film along the track. These holes average some 150 Å in diameter, and the mean free path of the fission fragment between events responsible for their production is about 200 Å. The observed sizes of these holes seem quite compatible with our theoretical model for displacement spikes and the manner in which they are produced by fission fragments. Their spacing, however, is apparently an order of magnitude less than that to be expected on the basis of our calculations. Whether or not each is the direct result of the production by the fission fragment of a primary knock-on platinum atom having an initial energy of the order of 10000 eV or more cannot be stated at present. Further experiments of this type are urgently needed. It is possible, for example, but seems quite unlikely that this represents the region very near the end of the track of a fission fragment where the spacing of spikes is much smaller than in the early portion. For a more detailed discussion of these and similar tracks, the reader is referred to the work of BIERLEIN and MASTEL.

8·2. *Radiation-annealing.* – Evidence for radiation-annealing due to displacement spikes is obtained from an experiment in which thorium was first irradiated with 9 MeV protons until the change in electrical resistivity with exposure saturated, and was subsequently irradiated with 18 MeV deuterons. The temperature of irradiation was 133 °K and the resistivity measurements were made at 83 °K. At the onset of the second irradiation a decrease in resistivity was observed, and a lower saturation value of resistivity was reached. This effect may be attributed to radiation-annealing due to displacement spikes [12]. Deuterons of this energy have a finite cross-section for the production of fission in thorium, so that fission fragments are produced giving rise to displacement spikes. The measurements are shown in Fig. 11. This effect provides evidence of a qualitative nature for radiation-annealing produced by displacement spikes.

More quantitative evidence is obtained from the measurements by QUERE and NAKACHE [13] of the curvature of the resistivity change *vs.* burn-up curve in uranium. The analysis of this curve, presented by Dr. BLIN [14] in a subsequent lecture, leds to a figure for the size of the « fission spike » which is $1.0 \cdot 10^7$ atoms. On the basis of our model, this should represent the total volume of displacement spikes produced by a fission event. This result compares reasonably well with our figure of $1.9 \cdot 10^7$ atoms. It should be pointed out that the occurrence of radiation-annealing implies that the spike collapses, since this is the only proposed displacement-spike mechanism by which radiation-annealing can be accomplished.

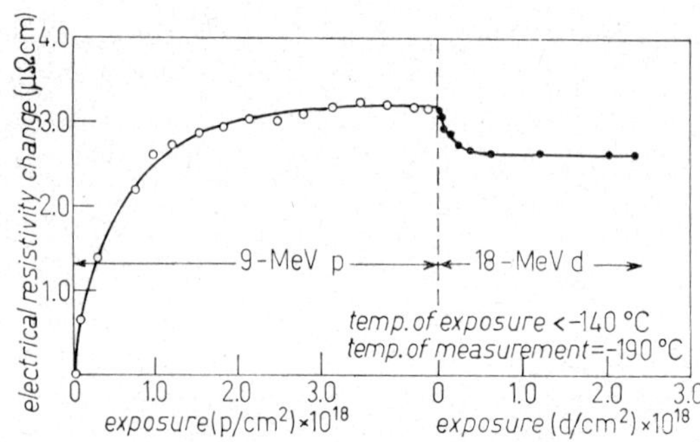

Fig. 11. – Electrical resistivity change produced by proton and deuteron irradiation of thorium.

8·3. *Frenkel defect resistivity.* – The figure obtained for the number of Frenkel pairs produced per fission event can be used to estimate the initial slope of the incremental resistivity *vs.* burn-up curve. If one assumes that the resistivity increase due to Frenkel pairs in uranium is $3\ \mu\Omega\cdot\text{cm}$ per atomic per cent of persisting defects, then the number of defects that one calculates from the initial slope of the curve of Quere and Nakache, taken at liquid-nitrogen temperature [14], is a factor of five to ten lower than our calculated result. The fact that the calculated value is too high is consistent with the fact that three assumptions have been made in this calculation, all of which tend to overestimate the persisting Frenkel defect concentration. These assumptions are: 1) the displacement probability of an atom is unity whenever the energy imparted to it exceeds T_D, 2) thermal recovery of Frenkel pairs is negligible at liquid-nitrogen temperature, and 3) no radiation-annealing results from the interaction of the thermal and displacement spikes produced by a given fission fragment with the Frenkel pairs produced by the same fragment.

8·4. *Radiation-induced diffusion.* – BLEIBERG [15] has studied phase changes in the alloy U+9 wt% Mo, produced as a consequence of fission of the uranium. The same phenomenon has also been studied by KONOBEEVSKY [16]. This particular alloy can exist in either the γ phase or the $\alpha+\varepsilon$ structure. The γ phase is a metastable solid solution, but can be quenched in at room temperature or below. The microstructure of the $\alpha+\varepsilon$ material consists of lamellae which are alternately rich and poor in molybdenum. The ε phase has the composition U+15% Mo, and the α phase is U+0.5% Mo. The spacing of the lamellae is normally about one micron, but depends to some extent on the temperature at which the transformation has occurred in the alloy. When the $\alpha+\varepsilon$ material is irradiated by internal fission, it transforms spontaneously to the γ phase. The net effect of the radiation is to diffuse the Mo from the ε phase lamellae into those of the α phase, and so distribute the molybdenum uniformly throughout the solid. This, then, is radiation-induced diffusion. The transformation to the γ phase occurs because this is the stable phase at all temperatures for the alloy when the Mo is uniformly distributed.

To explain the effect, we consider an idealized model of the displacement spike. The large multiple vacancy comprising the transient central hole is considered spherical, as in the spike itself, the two spheres being concentric. The radius of the central hole will be denoted by R_1 and the radius of the entire spike, by R_2. The volume of the spike is

$$V_2 = KT = (4/3)\pi R_2^3 , \tag{29}$$

where T is either the initial energy of the primary knock-on producing the spike or the maximum displacement-spike energy, which ever is least, and $K=(N_0 \times 1\ \text{eV/atom})^{-1}$. The volume of the central hole is just the volume occupied by the number of atoms displaced directly in producing the multiple vacancy, $\nu(T)$,

$$V_1 = \frac{\nu(T)}{N_0} = \frac{4}{3}\pi R_1^3 . \tag{30}$$

The material originally contained within the central hole will, after the occurrence of the spike, be distributed throughout the entire spike, since these atoms are driven outward with varying initial energies. The actual final distribution of this material is difficult to calculate with any degree of accuracy, since one must know the spectrum of the initial energies of all of these atoms, which consist chiefly of secondary and tertiary knock-ons, and also the range-energy curve for them in the energy range below 1000 eV. We will assume that their final distribution throughout the volume of the sphere of radius R_2 is uniform. Our model, for calculation purposes then, is one in which all of the material originally within V_1 is finally distributed uniformly throughout V_2, and all of the material originally within V_2 but outside of V_1 is displaced radially inward during collapse of the central hole in such a manner that the net flow of matter out of any volume element within the spike is zero.

We now consider the consequences of the occurrence of a displacement spike in an alloy in a region in which there exists a concentration gradient of one of the constituents, A. We denote the concentration of A by C_A and choose a co-ordinate system such that the concentration gradient at the origin is in the x-direction. We consider the concentration gradient to be constant over the dimensions of the spike. We shall let x denote the distance from the $x=0$ plane to the center of the spike, and locate the spike such that $R_1 < x < R_2$, as shown in Fig. 12. From geometrical considerations, the fraction of the volume of the spike located to the left of the $x=0$ plane is

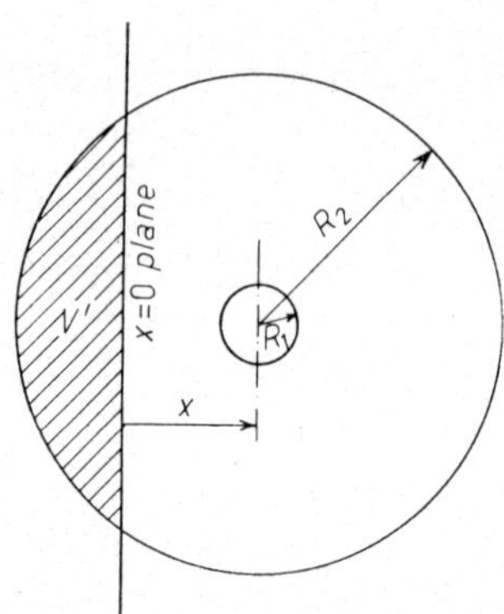

Fig. 12. – Model for calculating mass trasport within a displacement spike.

$$\frac{V'}{V_2} = \frac{1}{2} - \frac{x}{R_2}\left(\frac{3}{4} - \frac{x^2}{4R_2^2}\right). \tag{31}$$

This fraction also represents the fraction of the material originally contained in the central hole which is moved from right to left across the $x=0$ plane by the action of the spike. The total amount of A moving right to left across the $x=0$ plane is therefore $(V_1V'/V_2)\,C_A(x)$, to the approximation that R_1 is sufficiently small relative to R_2 that the C_A may be considered constant within V_1. The same total volume of material, (V_1V'/V_2), must move from left to right across the $x=0$ plane during collapse. The concentration of A in this material, however, is $C_A(0)$. Therefore, the amount of A moving across $x=0$ to the right is $(V_1V'/V_2)\,C_A(0)$. The difference,

$$(V_1V'/V_2)[C_A(0) - C_A(x)] = \frac{V_1V'x}{V_2}\frac{\partial C_A}{\partial x}, \tag{32}$$

is the net amount of A which has moved to the right across $x=0$.

We next calculate the total current density, J_A, of A across the $x=0$ plane from left to right, per unit area, due to all spikes which interest this plane. The fission rate per unit volume is

$$R_f = N_f \varphi_{th} \sigma_f, \tag{33}$$

in a thermal reactor. Here N_f is the spatial density of fissionable atoms, φ_{th} is the thermal neutron flux, and σ_f is the fission cross-section per fissionable atom. The number of spikes produced per unit time per unit volume by knock-ons with initial energies between T and $T+\mathrm{d}T$ is $R_f(-\mathrm{d}N/\mathrm{d}T)\,\mathrm{d}T$. The number produced per unit time per unit volume having radii between R_2 and $R_2+\mathrm{d}R_2$ is then $R_f(-\mathrm{d}N/\mathrm{d}T)(\mathrm{d}T/\mathrm{d}R_2)\,\mathrm{d}R_2$. The total contribution to the current density across the $x=0$ plane by all spikes having radii between R_2 and $R_2+\mathrm{d}R_2$, and whose centers lie between x and $x+\mathrm{d}x$, is then

$$R_f(\mathrm{d}N/\mathrm{d}T)(\mathrm{d}T/\mathrm{d}R_2)(\partial C_A/\partial x)(V_1V'/V_2)x\,\mathrm{d}x\,\mathrm{d}R_2\,.$$

From symmetry considerations, an equal contribution will result from those spikes produced between $-x$ and $-(x+\mathrm{d}x)$. To obtain the total current density of A across $x=0$, we must integrate over both x and R_2, maintaining $x<R_2$:

$$J_A = 2\int_{R_2(\min)}^{R_2(\max)} \mathrm{d}R_2 \int_0^{R_2} \mathrm{d}x R_f \left(\frac{\mathrm{d}N}{\mathrm{d}T}\right)\left(\frac{\mathrm{d}T}{\mathrm{d}R_2}\right)\left(\frac{\partial C_A}{\partial x}\right)\frac{V_1 V' x}{V_2}\,. \tag{34}$$

Since $\partial C_A/\partial x$ is assumed constant over the range of integration, this equation can be written in the form of Fick's law governing diffusion in a system having a concentration gradient in the x-direction:

$$J_A = -D_1 \frac{\partial C_A}{\partial x}\,, \tag{35}$$

where

$$D_1 = -2R_f \int_{R_2(\min)}^{R_2(\max)} \mathrm{d}R_2 \int_0^{R_2} \mathrm{d}x \left(\frac{\mathrm{d}N}{\mathrm{d}T}\right)\left(\frac{\mathrm{d}T}{\mathrm{d}R_2}\right)\frac{V_1 V' x}{V_2}\,. \tag{36}$$

The limits, $R_2(\min)$ and $R_2(\max)$, are the values of R_2, as given by eq. (29), which correspond to T_1 and T_2, respectively; V'/V_2 is given by eq. (31); $\mathrm{d}T/\mathrm{d}R_2$ is obtained by differentiating eq. (13); V_1 is given in terms of R_2 by substituting eq. (29) into the first half of eq. (30); and

$$\frac{\mathrm{d}N}{\mathrm{d}T} = \frac{\mathrm{d}N_L}{\mathrm{d}T} + \frac{\mathrm{d}N_H}{\mathrm{d}T}\,, \tag{37}$$

the latter two quantities being obtained in the case of uranium from Fig. 5.

Eq. (36) gives only that contribution to the radiation-induced « diffusion coefficient » resulting from the action of displacement spikes produced by primary knock-ons with initial energies in the range T_1 to T_2. In addition, a number $N(T_2)$, of displacement spikes of maximum size, $V_2(T_2)$, are produced by each fission event. The contribution to the diffusion coefficient resulting from their action is

$$D_2 = 2R_f N(T_2) \int_0^{R_2(\max)} \mathrm{d}x\, V_{1(\max)} \left(\frac{V'}{V_{2(\max)}}\right) x\,, \tag{38}$$

where the subscript (max) denotes the values of the appropriate quantities when $T=T_2$. The total radiation-induced diffusion coefficient is

$$D = D_1 + D_2\,. \tag{39}$$

BLEIBERG [15] found the diffusion coefficient to be proportional to the fission rate, as predicted by eq. (36), (38), and (39). For a fission rate

$$R_f = 5.25\cdot 10^{12}\ \text{cm}^{-3}\,\text{s}^{-1}\,, \tag{40}$$

he found the diffusion coefficient to be

$$D = (1.4 \pm 0.6)\cdot 10^{-18}\ \text{cm}^2/\text{s}\,. \tag{41}$$

When eq. (36) and (38) are evaluated for Bleiberg's experimental conditions, using the present model, and substituted into eq. (39), a calculated value is obtained for the radiation-induced diffusion coefficient which lies within the experimental error limits of the measured value.

9. – Conclusions.

We can conclude from all the above considerations that the model considered gives not only the correct number of atoms in an average spike but also the correct distribution of displacement spike sizes. Since the radiation-annealing effect is proportional to the third power of the average spike radius, and the radiation-induced diffusion coefficient is proportional to the fifth power of the same quantity, we have an indication that the calculation of the average radius is substantially correct. Thus, it is seen that the present model gives reasonably accurate predictions of 1) the number of Frenkel defects produced per fission event, 2) the total volume of displacement spikes produced per fission event, and 3) the average size of the individual displacement spikes produced by fission in uranium.

Although the model is at present very crude, and further experimental evidence is desirable, we feel that at least some indication of its validity has been obtained and that its preliminary success warrants further experimental testing.

* * *

The author is grateful to C. J. MEECHAN for considerable help in carrying out the detailed calculations. Gratitude is also expressed to T. S. NOGGLE and J. O. STIEGLER and to T. K. BIERLEIN and B. MASTEL for providing electron photomicrographs of fission tracks and advance copies of their manuscripts.

BIBLIOGRAFIA

[1] From S. Glasstone and M. C. Edlund: *The Elements of Nuclear Reactor Theory* (New York, 1952).
[2] J. Knipp and E. Teller: *Phys. Rev.*, **59**, 659 (1941).
[3] D. K. Holmes: This volume p. 182.
[4] H. B. Huntington: *Phys. Rev.*, **91**, 1092 (1953).
[5] W. C. Overton and J. Gaffney: *Phys. Rev.*, **98**, 969 (1955).
[6] J. R. Neighbors and G. A. Alers: *Phys. Rev.*, **111**, 707 (1958).
[7] G. H. Vineyard: This volume p, 291.
[8] G. Leibfried: This volume p. 227.
[9] T. K. Bierlein and B. Mastel: to be published in *Journ. Appl. Phys.*
[10] T. S. Noggle and J. O. Stiegler: to be published in *Journ. Appl. Phys.*
[11] M. W. Thompsom: This volume p. 753.
[12] J. A. Brinkman: *Am. Journ. Phys.*, **24**, 246 (1956).
[13] Y. Quere and F. Nakache: *Journ. Nucl. Materials*, **1**, 203 (1959).
[14] J. J. Blin: This volume p. 888.
[15] M. L. Bleiberg: *Journ. Nucl. Materials*, **1**, 182 (1959).
[16] S. T. Konobeevsky: *Journ. Nucl. Energy*, II **3**, 356 (1956).

Atomic Displacement and Impurity Effects in Fissile Metals.

R. S. Barnes

Atomic Energy Research Establishment - Harwell

1. – Introduction.

In addition to the normal effects occuring in any irradiated metal, those which suffer a nuclear transmutation are severely damaged by the transmutation products which usually have high kinetic energy. Also as the transmutation products come to rest within the metal they add to the impurities already there and permanently change its properties. Many metals of importance in the applications of atomic energy come into this category. They include the fuel materials, uranium, plutonium and thorium, materials containing boron which are used for control, beryllium, which is a moderator and canning material, lithium, etc. Table I [1] lists some of the isotopes which transmute to give inert gas atoms as products, the last column giving an estimate of the amount of the inert gas which is produced by a dose of $10^{24}\ n\cdot cm^{-2}$.

Table I. – *Some isotopes which transmute into inert gas atoms.*

Target isotope	Reaction	Reaction energy (MeV)	Threshold energy (MeV)	Cross-section in barns	Gases produced	Vol./unit vol. of target for dose of $10^{24}\ n\cdot cm^{-2}$
^{6}Li	(n, α)	4.70	slow	950	$2\,^{4}He$, ^{3}He	$2.8\cdot10^{6}$
^{9}Be	(n, α)	−0.64	0.71	0.050	$2\,^{4}He$, ^{3}H	$5.7\cdot10^{2}$
^{9}Be	(n, 2n)	−1.66	1.84	0.20	$2\,^{4}He$	$2.0\cdot10^{3}$
^{10}B	(n, α)	2.26	slow	3990	^{4}He	$3.1\cdot10^{7}$
U nat.	fission	180	slow	4.2	Xe, Kr	$3\ \cdot10^{3}$

These inert gases are in general the most important product and some of their effects will be dealt with later. The amount of energy involved in the reactions varies (see column 3, Table I). For instance, those in beryllium are endothermic and will only proceed with fast neutrons. The reactions in uranium and boron are both exothermic and occur with thermal neutrons with considerable release of energy. The greater the energy liberated in the reaction the greater is the damage to the metal. There will be little or no extra damage to beryllium, for instance, and the main effects will be due to the impurities which result from the transmutation.

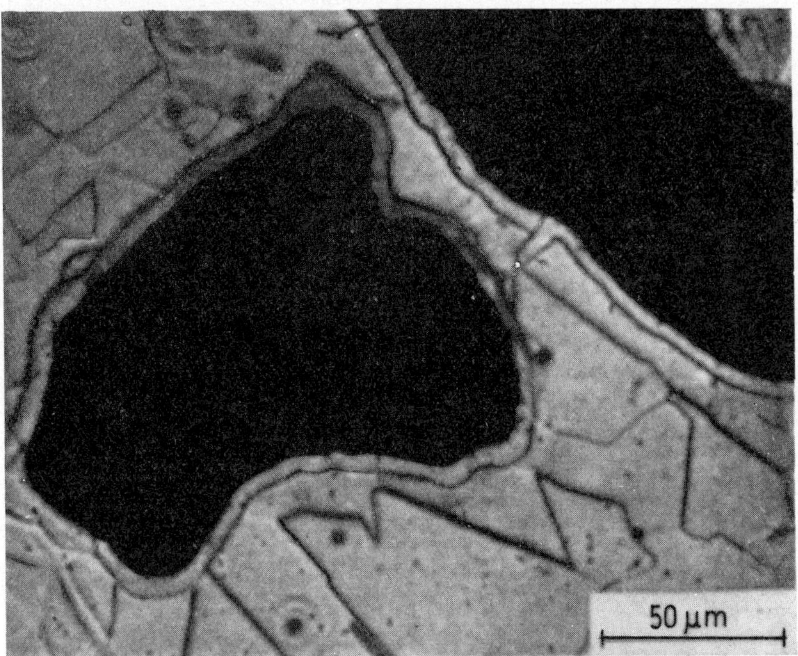

Fig. 1. – Particles of uranium dioxide embedded in a stainless steel matrix showing fission fragment damage around the particles [2]. ×300.

The effect of these transmutations is not confined to the materials in which the transmutations occur. Depending upon their kinetic energy, the products travel some distance through the solid, and those produced near the surface escape and affect nearby materials during irradiation. Fig. 1 [2] shows some uranium dioxide particles embedded in a stainless steel matrix and then irradiated; the fission products from the particles have penetrated approximately 10 μm into the stainless steel and locally altered its etching behaviour. Up to one half the maximum concentration of the fission products can occur in the surrounding medium. This damage occurs in any material in contact with a transmuting material and will be most general when the two are intimately mixed together.

2. – Displacement effects.

As a measure of the extra number of displaced atoms produced in a fissile material about three orders of magnitude more point defects are produced in natural uranium than in uranium depleted of the fissile isotope ^{235}U. Thus

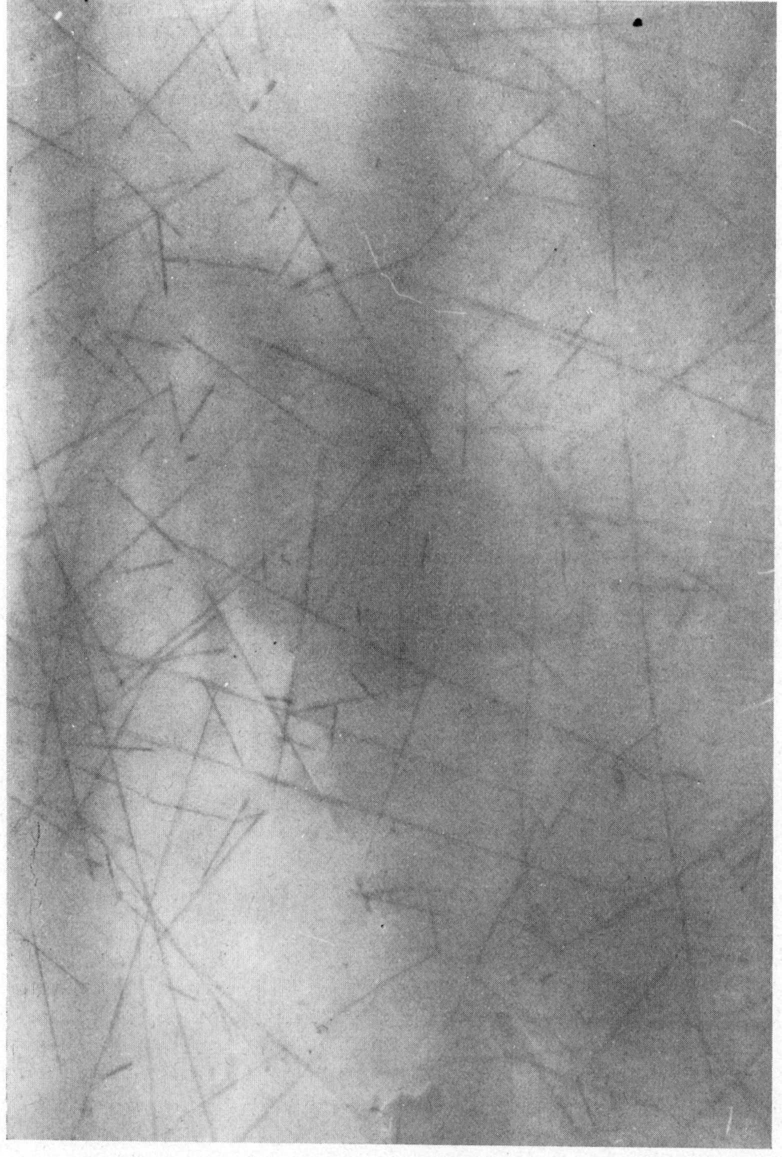

Fig. 2. – Fission fragment tracks in thin-cleaved sheets of mica. ×40 000.

this type of metal shows significant irradiation effects at much lower doses than do normal metals.

The distribution of the damage in fissile metals is very different from that in nonfissile metals where the occasional « primary knock-ons » are of relatively low energy. Fig. 2 reveals the distributions of damage caused by these

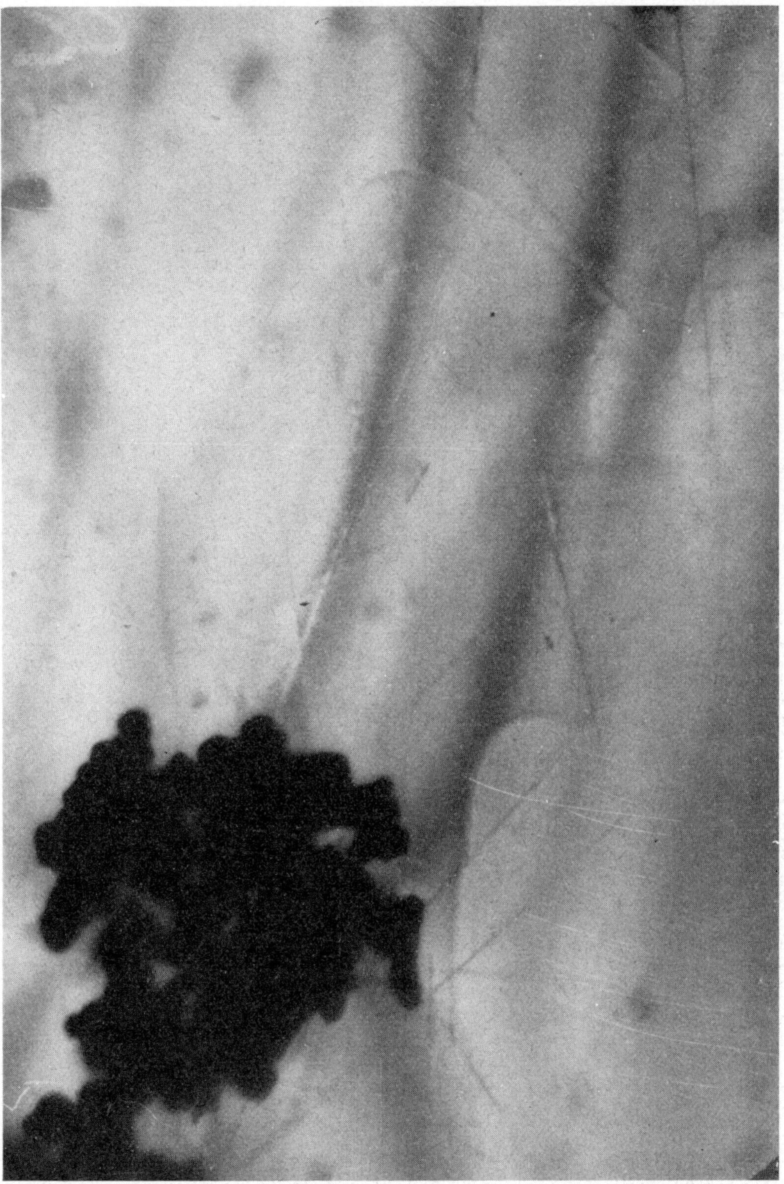

Fig. 3. – Motion of dislocations impeded by fission tracks in mica. $\times 40\,000$.

highly charged fission products. To obtain electron micrographs such as this, a sheet of mica was placed in contact with a layer of uranium and irradiated in BEPO for five minutes [3]. Some of the fission fragments which left the surface of the uranium entered the surface of mica and produced the long tracks which can be clearly seen as black lines in the transmission electron micrographs. The sheet of mica was repeatedly cleaved until the surface layer was thin enough ($\sim$1 000 Å) to transmit electrons in the electron microscope. The length of tracks varies greatly, but tracks up to 7 μm long have been seen. This variation results from the random direction of entry of the fragments into the mica surface; only those entering the mica at a glancing angle to the surface produce as long tracks. The number of tracks observed corresponds to the number of fission fragments entering the mica, so that the tracks must be visible along most of their length. The width of the tracks is about 100 Å and they are very uniform along their whole length. Secondary tracks frequently originate along the main track which deviates a degree or so at this point. Fig. 3 (*) demonstrates that the fission track obstructs the motion of dislocation lines in the mica, cusps occurring in the dislocation line where it intersects the fission track.

The interpretation of these observations is not clear but the contrast effects in the microscope are consistent with there being a strain field around the tracks. Electron microscope observations of very thin evaporated films ($\sim$100 Å thick) of uranium dioxide [4-5] and metals [6] reveal similar tracks, but here the tracks are white as more electrons are transmitted at the tracks (whereas in mica electrons are scattered from the tracks). It appears that atoms are ejected from these very thin films, leaving a depleted surface furrow. In the much thicker mica it seems possible that the atoms ejected from the immediate vicinity of the particle come to rest within the film some distance away from the track, generating a local strain field, which produces the contrast. The tracks can be annealed in mica, the material returning to its original transparency due to the disappearance of the strain field. These photographs illustrate the very localized and yet intense damage which is produced by these very heavily ionized fission fragments which travel with great momentum through the crystal.

Electron microscopy is also helping our understanding of the eventual behaviour of the point defects produced by irradiation. The first information on the detailed high-temperature behaviour of point defects came from quenching experiments which have already been discussed [7]. The electron micrographs shown in Fig. 4 show hexagonal dislocation loops in a quenched aluminium-magnesium alloy [8]. The dislocation loops, which are produced

(*) In this case uranium dioxide particles where deposited upon the surface of the mica and a collection of them can be seen in the bottom left-hand corner.

by the aggregation of vacancies on $\{111\}$ planes, initially (a) contain a stacking fault (hence the dark centres) but after a short time (b) this is eliminated by the dislocation reaction:

$$\frac{a}{3}[111] + \frac{a}{6}[11\bar{2}] \rightarrow \frac{a}{2}[110] .$$

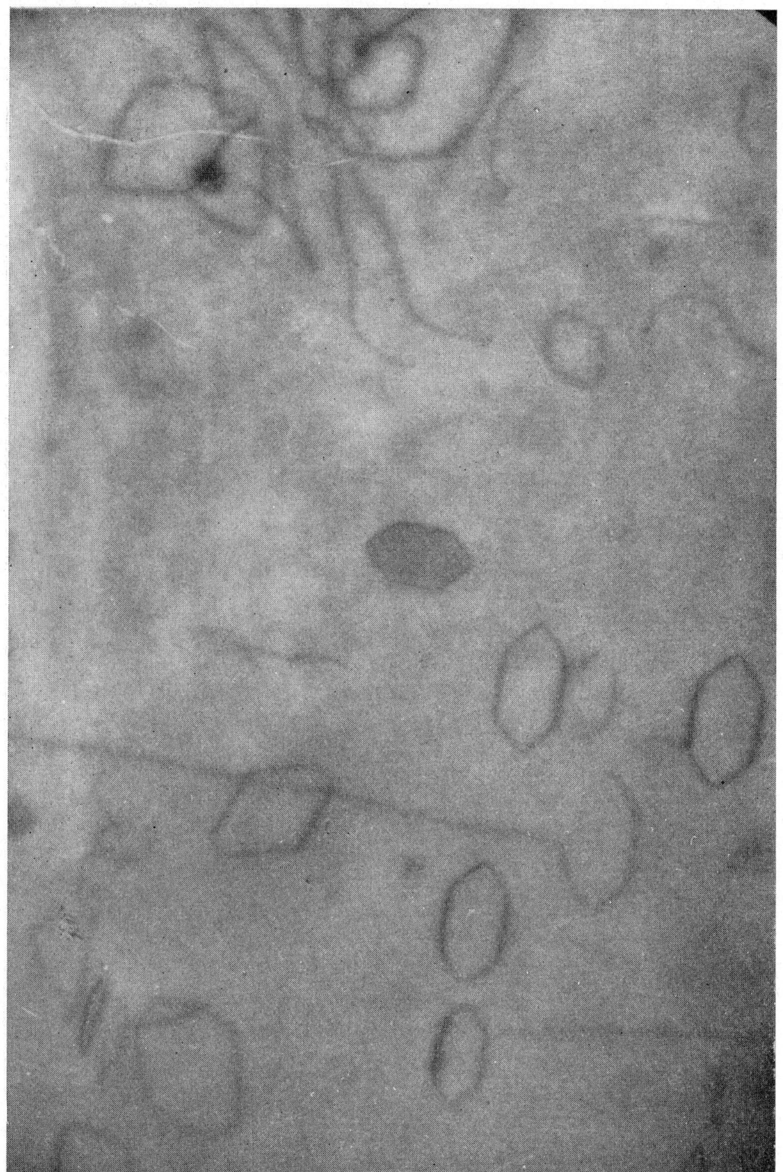

Fig. 4a. – Prismatic dislocation loops in an Al 3% Mg alloy quenched from 550 °C into 20 °C oil showing loops containing stacking faults.

Irradiated metals have a somewhat similar appearance but the scale of the clusters is smaller and they are less regular. Fig. 5 shows a thin film of copper which had been bombarded with $1.4 \cdot 10^{17}$ α-particles cm^{-2} and contains many irregular defects. These can be separated into two kinds; the large

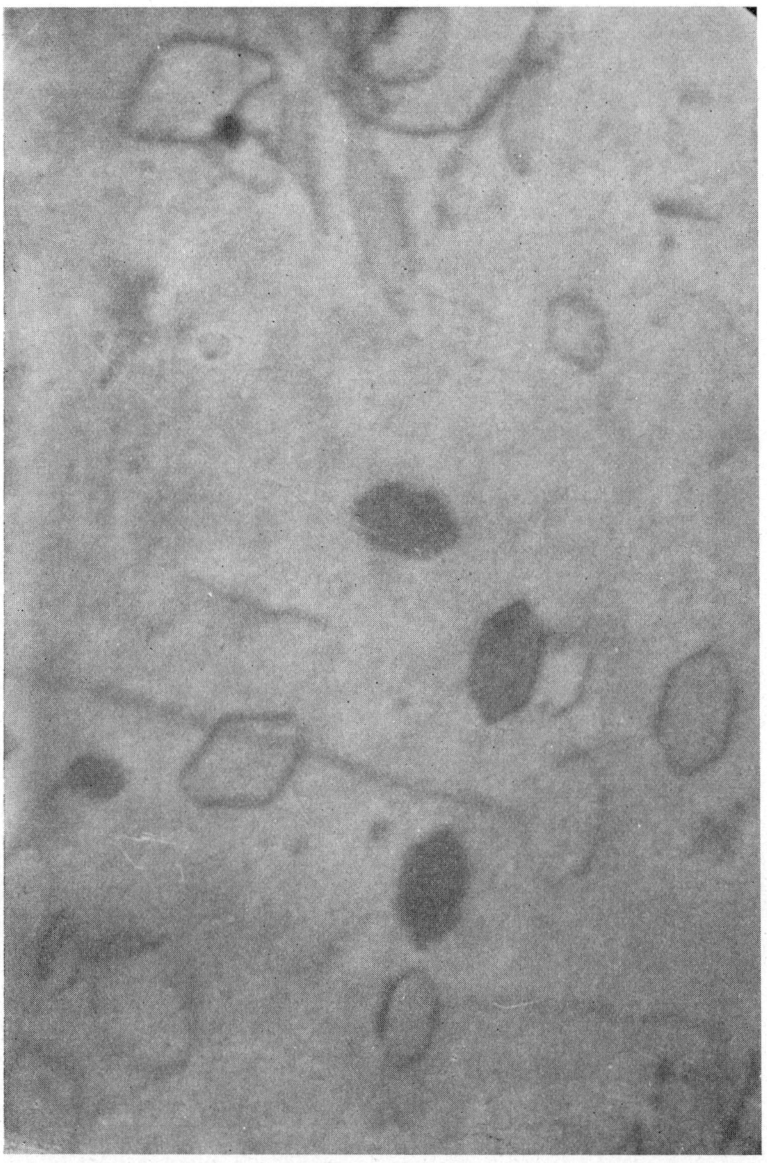

Fig. 4*b*. – Prismatic dislocation loops in an Al 3% Mg alloy quenched from 550 °C into 20 °C oil: a later photograph showing the same loops which have lost their stacking faults [8]. ×40 000.

clusters, which are about 200 Å in radius and look very much like irregular dislocation loops, and the more numerous small black dots, which are about 20 Å in radius. It is believed that the large loops are clusters of interstitial atoms and the small dots clusters of vacancies [9]. Near a grain boundary

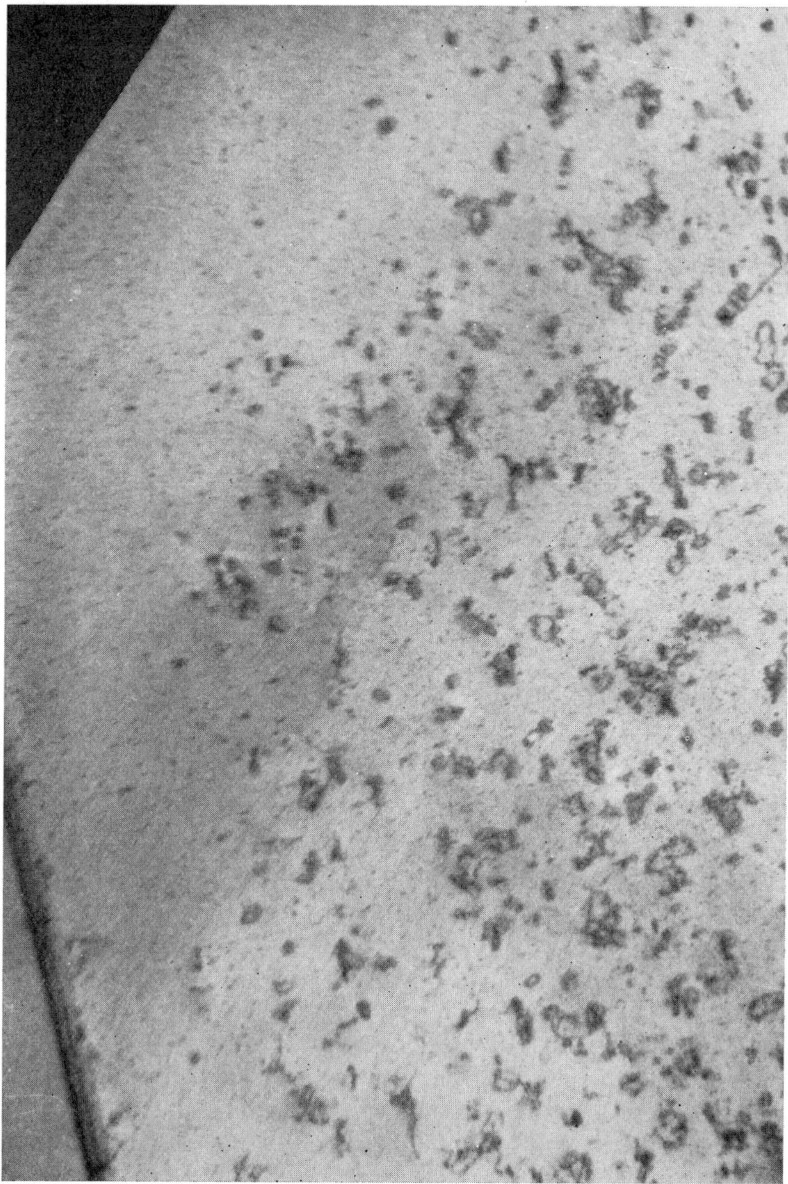

'ig. 5. – Thin film of copper taken from a foil which had been bombarded with $1.4 \cdot 10^{17}$ α-particles cm^{-2} [9]. $\times 40\,000$.

there is a region which is denuded of the larger clusters; however, the small defects continue right up to the grain boundary, suggesting that the defects are formed from different point defects. If foils containing these defects are annealed at 350 °C for four hours the loops disappear, and Fig. 6 shows a sequence of photographs taken during the anneal of a film in the « hot stage »

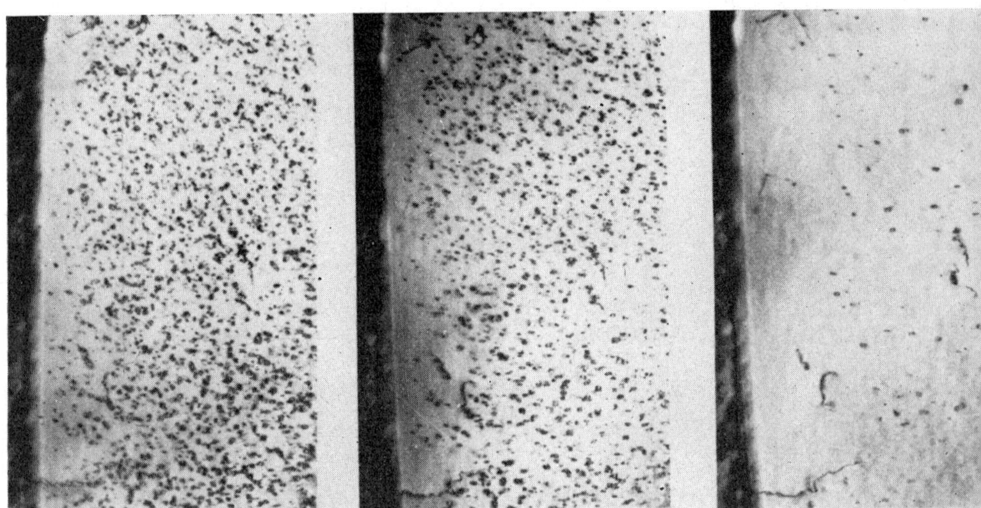

Fig. 6. – Three successive photographs taken at about 350 °C on the « hot stage » showing annealing of the clusters in copper [9]. ×20 000.

of the elctron microscope, where these clusters have practically disappeared in the last photograph. At a temperature of 350 °C vacancies can be generated and diffuse and one would expect vacancies to diffuse from the vacancy clusters to the interstitial clusters, eventually annihilating them both.

These foils where bombarded by placing them in a cyclotron beam. If a stack of foils is used, then the α-particles come to rest in one of the foils and this foil, in addition to containing the interstitial atoms and vacancies contains also many helium atoms. Fig. 7 shows such a film. However, when this foil is heated to 350 °C the large loops do not disappear but become more regular and *grow* as is shown in Fig. 8. The helium atoms form gas bubbles and obtain the necessary space by acquiring vacancies from the dislocation loops, which become so large that eventually they meet one another and form a three-dimensional dislocation network (Fig. 9*a*, which has a magnification only $\frac{1}{8}$ that of Figs. 7 and 8). The growth of these loops while producing vacancies shows them to consist of clusters of interstitial atoms and not of vacancies. Close examination of these films reveals small helium bubbles lying upon the dislocation lines, and Fig. 9*b* shows these, the film having been tilted to reduce the contrast from the dislocation lines. The small white dots ($r \sim 40$ Å) are due to the helium bubbles which give a locally enhanced electron transmission. The total volume of these helium bubbles in a unit volume of

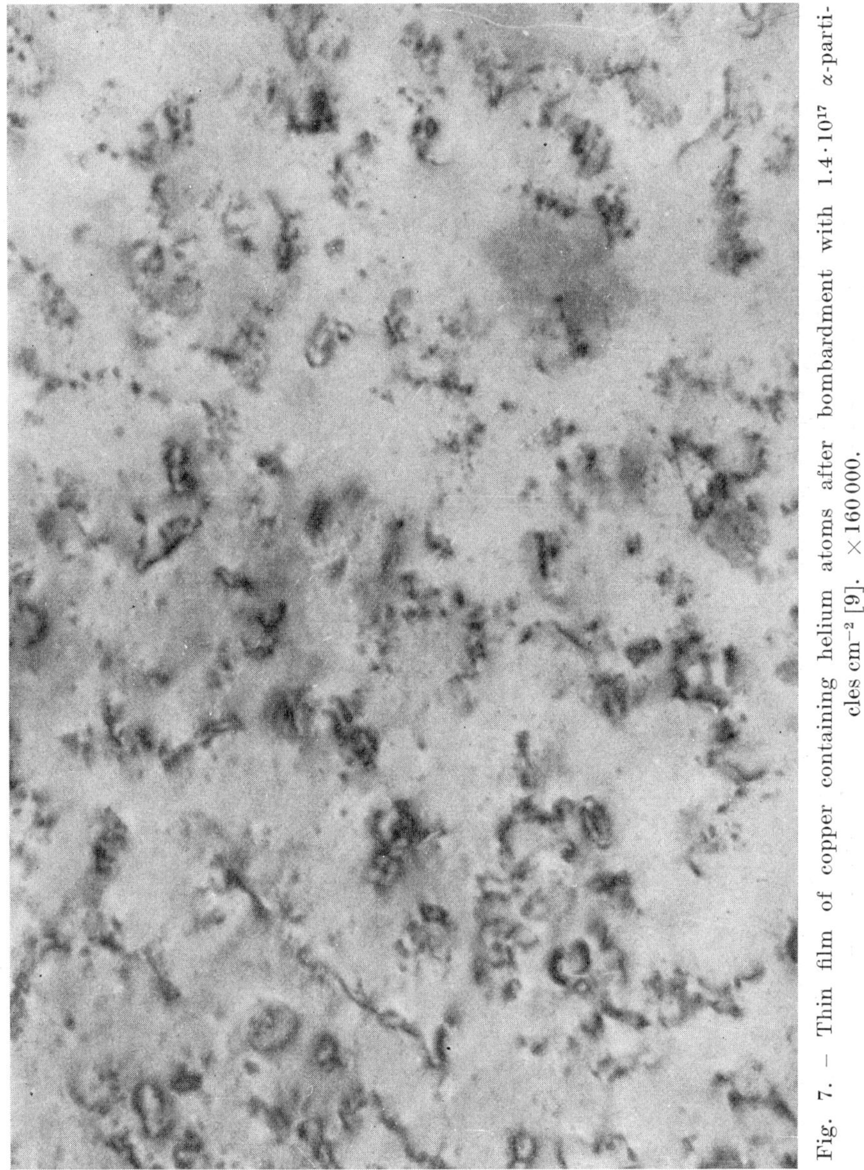

Fig. 7. – Thin film of copper containing helium atoms after bombardment with $1.4 \cdot 10^{17}$ α-particles cm^{-2} [9]. $\times 160\,000$.

metal, divided by the atomic volume of a copper atom, gives the number of vacancies that these bubbles contain. The number of vacancies given off by the interstitial loops can also be estimated from their increase in area. There is rough agreement between these values as there should be if the model is correct.

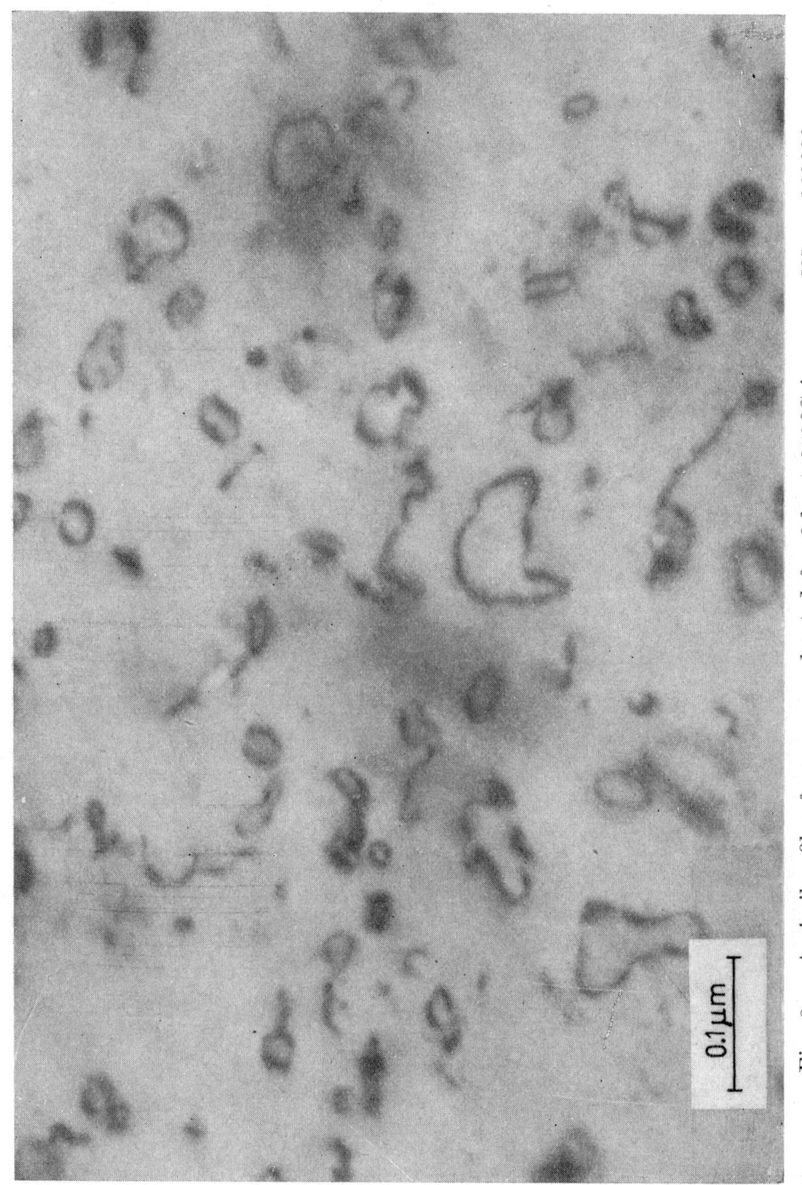

Fig. 8. – A similar film from copper heated for 2 h at 350 °C in vacuo [9]. × 160000.

If the background dots are clusters of the vacancies the number of vacancies they contain should, in regions away from sinks, equal the number of interstitial atoms. Table II shows some of the values, admittedly rough, of the radius and number of the loops and the dots taken from various photographs. There is little difference between the values for films containing helium

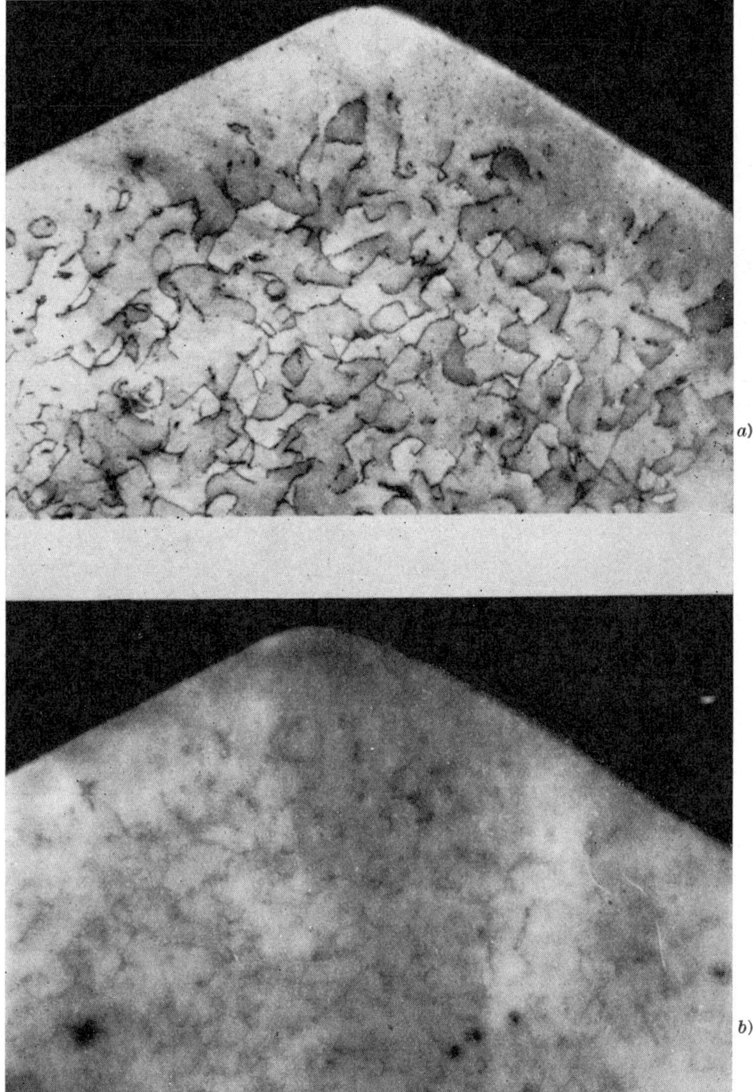

Fig. 9. – The same copper film showing: *a*) the dislocation network, and I) the small bubbles lying upon the network. ×20 000.

and those which do not. There are $1.6 \cdot 10^{14}$ interstitial atoms cm^{-2} of the film and as the films are about 1 000 Å thick this means that the number of interstitials is $\sim 2 \cdot 10^{19}$ cm^{-3} and their atomic concentration $\sim 10^{-4}$. The number of vacancies the dots represent can be estimated similarly. Once again there is not a very marked difference in the values. If these dots represent

TABLE II.

	Radius (cm)	No. cm^{-2} (n)	No. of atom spaces in	
			loops $(4\pi/\sqrt{3})(r/a)^2$ n	spheres $(16\pi/3)(r/a)^3$ n
Displacements	$2.2 \cdot 10^{-6}$	$4.2 \cdot 10^{9}$	$1.2 \cdot 10^{14}$	—
Displacements	$2.2 \cdot 10^{-6}$	$6.4 \cdot 10^{9}$	$1.8 \cdot 10^{14}$	—
He+displacements	$1.6 \cdot 10^{-6}$	$1.4 \cdot 10^{10}$	$2.0 \cdot 10^{14}$	—
Displacements	$2.5 \cdot 10^{-7}$	$9.0 \cdot 10^{10}$	$3.6 \cdot 10^{13}$	$5.0 \cdot 10^{14}$
He+displacements	$1.9 \cdot 10^{-7}$	$1.2 \cdot 10^{11}$	$2.4 \cdot 10^{13}$	$3.0 \cdot 10^{14}$
He bubbles	$4.0 \cdot 10^{-7}$	$1.4 \cdot 10^{11}$	—	$3.2 \cdot 10^{15}$

small dislocation loops the number of vacancies they contain is less by about a factor of 5 than the number of interstitial atoms previously estimated. If the dots represent spherical voids, then there are about 3 times as many vacancies as interstitial atoms. There is some evidence (see below) that the dots are tetrahedra of vacancies. It appears, therefore, that the vacancies and interstitials produce separate clusters, those of interstitials being platelike and best described as dislocation loops (although these loops are rather irregular) and those of vacancies being smaller three-dimensional clusters.

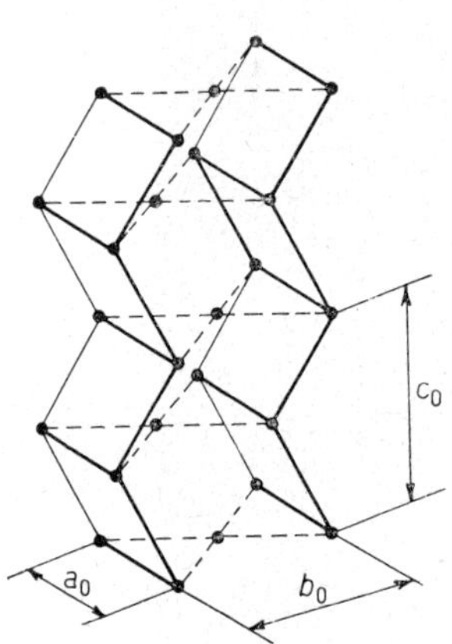

Fig. 10. – Crystal structure of α-uranium.

In uranium many of these vacancy and interstitial clusters will form, and their nature will be influenced by the anisotropic crystal structure. The widest spacing in the uranium crystal is between the b planes (see Fig. 10), and the bonds across this plane are weak. Thus interstitial plates would form on the b planes during irradiation and produce an expansion in the b direction. Uranium does change its shape during irradiation, growing in the b direction by about 10% per year in a moderate flux of 10^{12} thermal neutrons cm^{-2} s^{-1} at room temperature. It has now been established that the rate is an order of magnitude greater at liquid-nitrogen temperature than at room temperature [10]. If sufficient damage can be induced in other anisotropic crystals, *e.g.* by bombarding them with energetic fission fragments, they also grow [10]. However, during this growth the volume of the crystal does not increase; there is an equal contraction in the a direction, and no change in the c direction. The contraction in the a direction could result from vacancies condensed in plates on the a planes. It is unlikely that vacancies could diffuse to form such a configuration at liquid-nitrogen temperatures. However, if the vacancies are formed as three-dimensional clusters, as is suggested by the previous electron micrographs of fission fragment tracks, then these could collapse by the slip process described by JONES and MITCHELL [11]. (Very high pressures to cause such collapse would arise around these clusters by virtue of the locally high temperatures and resulting thermal expansion.) This would cause dislocation spirals to form and these would have as their Burgers vector the slip vector which in uranium lies in the a direction [12]. Each turn of the spiral is equivalent to a dislocation loop formed from vacancies and with its Burgers vector in the a direction. Thus there would be a contraction in the a direction equal to the expansion in the b direction caused by the equivalent number of interstitial atoms. This model of growth would be consistent with a greater growth at low temperatures when there would be less annihilation of the vacancies by the interstitial atoms. This annihilation would be complete at the temperature of self-diffusion ($\sim$ 500 °C) where the growth rate is zero. The growth rate would show little dependence upon the number of dislocations already in the material before irradiation, and BUCKLEY [10] has shown that slight extension of crystals does not alter their growth rate.

There are several consequences of the growth of anisotropic materials during irradiation. One is that if one takes a polycrystalline material its surface becomes very roughened during irradiation due to the differential growth in neighbouring surface grains. Another conseguence is that this differential growth in neighbouring grains raises a stress at the grain boundaries until the metal eventually yields. The metal is thus weakened and has a much lower creep strength, as was demonstrated by ROBERTS and COTTRELL [13].

3. – Impurity effects.

The impurity atoms introduced into a fissile metal range over the whole of the centre of the periodic table, from ^{72}Zn to ^{161}Tb, and as one would imagine their effects are difficult to enumerate and understand. In other metals the transmutation products are well defined. Because the number of atoms is increased by transmutation the volume of the material will increase. However, the inert gases xenon, krypton and helium, are frequent products of these nuclear reactions, *e.g.* in fissile metals xenon and krypton account for about 10 atomic percent of the fission products. Because these elements are normally gaseous (by lowering their pressure they reduce their free energy), they can occupy a very large volume and so play a dominant role in the behaviour of these metals. Natural uranium which has been bombarded with 10^{21} thermal neutrons cm^{-2} will contain about 3 cm^3 (at N.T.P.) of xenon and krypton in each cm^3 of uranium, and if the gas could attain atmospheric pressure without escaping, the uranium would froth up to four times its original volume.

Already, it has been shown that the interaction between the impurity atoms and the vacancies and interstitial atoms, caused by atomic displacement, is important and that these two types of irradiation damage cannot entirely be treated separately. In the case of the inert gas atoms the interaction is very striking because of the great capacity for clusters of these atoms to absorb vacancies [14]; this is the way they increase the volume they occupy. The inert gas atoms which are produced interstitially in the crystal form gas bubbles by nucleation upon lattice imperfections. The small dots seen in the electron micrographs, and which we believe to be clusters of vacant lattice sites, could provide such nuclei. Some of these defects in copper which has been heated to 400 °C for 1 hour after bombardment with α-particles are shown at high magnification in Fig. 11. After this heat treatment the large loops formed from clusters of interstitial atoms have disappeared and the remaining small clusters (between 25 and 70 Å in radius) can be seen to have crystallographic shapes. In this instance they appear to be triangular, some with their apexes pointed upwards, others downwards. This and their apparent stability at such high temperatures suggest that if the dots represent vacancy clusters their best description is tetrahedra of the stacking fault such as was seen in quenched gold [15]. Gas atoms might be expected to stabilize such three-dimensional clusters which would act as bubble nuclei. The number of helium bubbles which appear is roughly equal to the number of these small defects (Table II). It is possible that these and the dislocations themselves are the nuclei for these bubbles; the majority of the bubbles are seen to lie upon the dislocation network which forms by the growth of the dislocation loops.

The pressure of the gas in these bubbles (radius $<$ 40 Å) is about 5 000 atmospheres and is balanced almost exactly by the pressure (p) exerted by the surface energy (γ) of the metal ($p = 2\gamma/r$). The size and number of the bubbles changes little until temperatures of about 700 °C are reached in copper, and then they rapidly coarsen in the neighbourhood of vacancy sources, *e.g.* grain boundaries. This coarsening can be seen clearly in Fig. 12 where bubbles of about 1 000 Å appear near to the grain boundary after heating to 750 °C for two hours. Beyond a certain distance from the grain

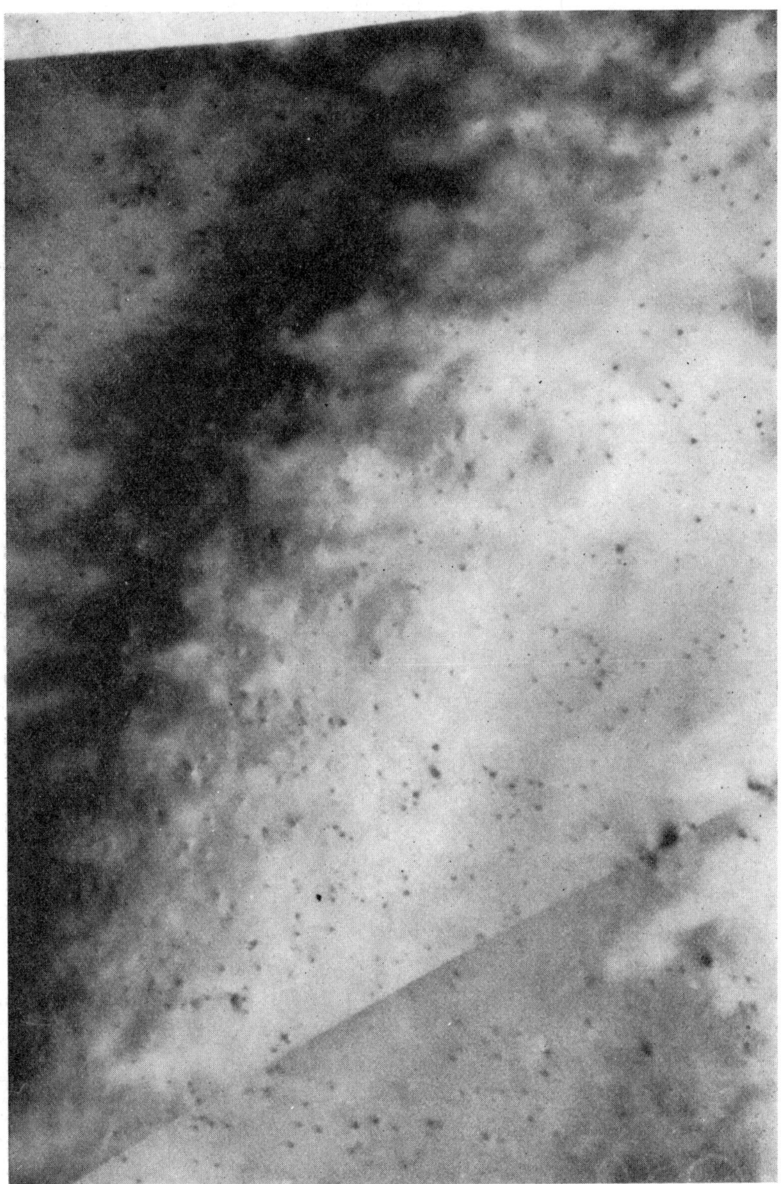

Fig. 11. – Triangular black dots in a copper film bombarded with α-particles and then annealed for 1 h at 400 °C. ×160 000.

boundary (1.7 μm) the original dislocation network is still preserved and the small bubbles lying upon it have been little changed. The amount of gas contained in the smaller number of large bubbles is the same as was previously contained in the small bubbles, but the pressure (which is still balanced by

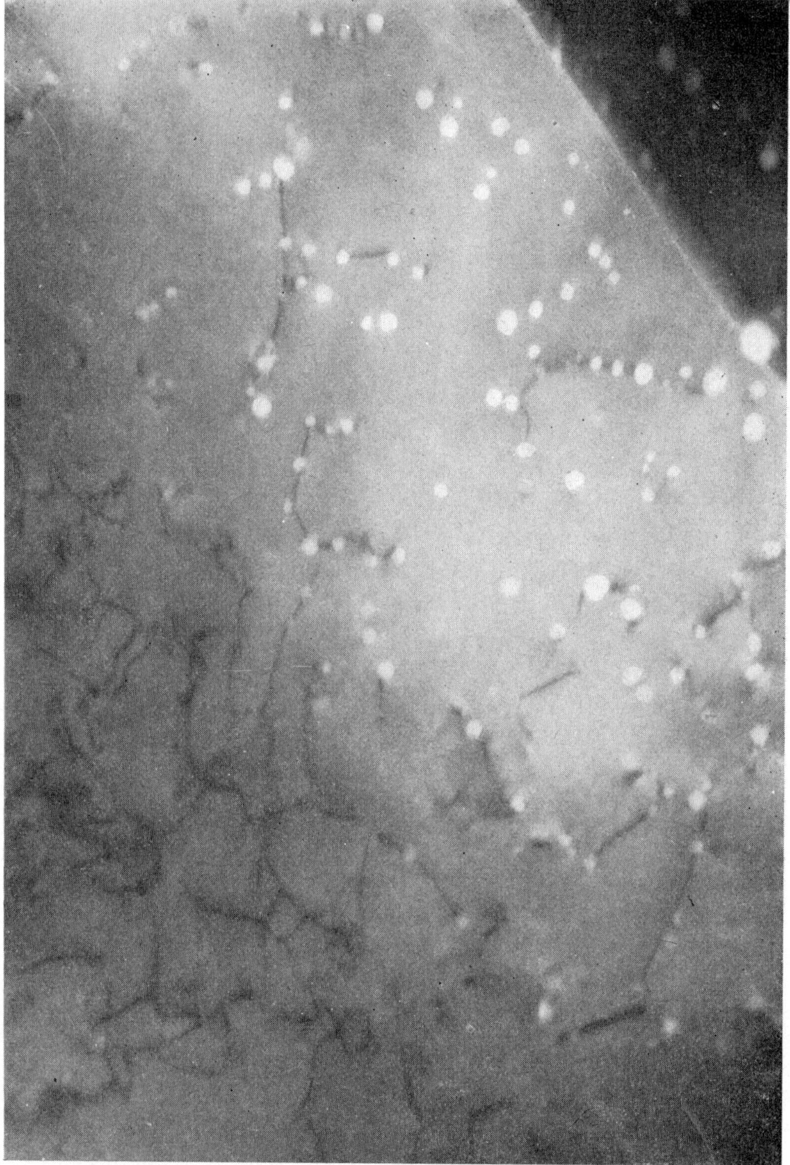

Fig. 12. – Copper film containing large helium bubbles near a grain boundary after heating for 2 h at 750 °C [9]. ×40 000.

the surface energy) is considerably lower and thus the volume of the region has increased. The extra space has been obtained by the bubbles acquiring vacancies from the grain boundary.

Replicas taken from grain boundary regions show a similar situation, although here the very small bubbles and dislocation lines cannot be seen. Fig. 13 shows a replica taken from the electro-polished surface of a copper sample which had been heated to 800 °C for 2 hours. The grain boundary runs diagonally across the photograph from the top right to the bottom left corner, but only the central section of this boundary is able to provide vacancies and permit the local growth of the helium bubbles. Examination shows that where either of the two grains is twinned, the nature of the boundary is so altered that it is unable to provide vacancies. The nature of the boundary is so radically altered that it is only able to conduct vacancies to a very small extent, as can be seen by the slight cusp at each extremity. Ordinary optical micrographs, although unable to resolve individual bubbles, show clearly the importance the nature of the boundary has in determining its ability to provide vacancies [16]. The boundary between two twins of common parent grain is a good source of vacancies, as illustrated in Fig. 14, whereas the coherent twin boundaries and noncoherent twin boundaries are unable to generate vacancies. However, noncoherent twin boundaries which connect with a good vacancy source are able to conduct vacancies along their length and thence to gas bubbles lying away from the true vacancy source. A free surface is perhaps the most obvious source of vacancies. Fig. 15 illustrates the generation of vacancies at the surface of a void which existed in the copper before the helium was injected; many bubbles can be seen around the void, in striking contrast with the very small number around a nearby inclusion.

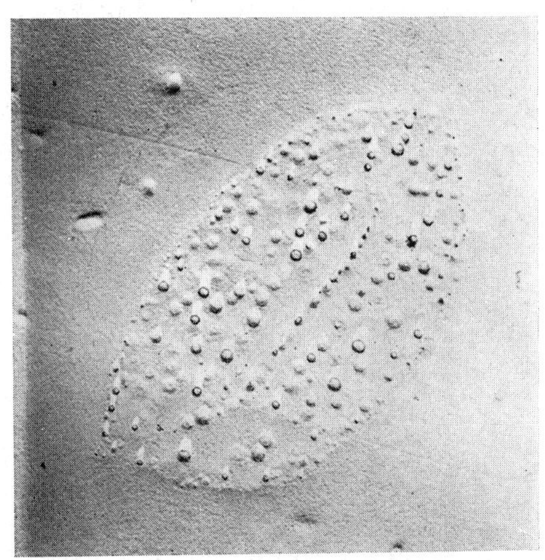

Fig. 13. – A grain boundary which is only a vacancy source between the two twin boundaries (one in each grain) [16]. ×1 800.

Thus, it appears that the growth of the bubbles is in the early stages controlled by the supply of vacancies and that the volume the gas occupies is a measure of the number of vacancies supplied. The large number of vacancies involved is demonstrated by the fact that volume increases of greater than 10% have been observed.

These effects, which have been illustrated in copper which has been injected with helium by a cyclotron, also occur in metals which transmute upon irradiation with neutrons. Fig. 16 shows a replica taken from a section of α-uranium which has been irradiated to 0.09% burn-up, by fission, of its atoms at 500 °C, and which has increased in volume by 1.3 % [14]. The small bubbles of xenon and krypton (~ 500 Å in radius) with larger bubbles lying

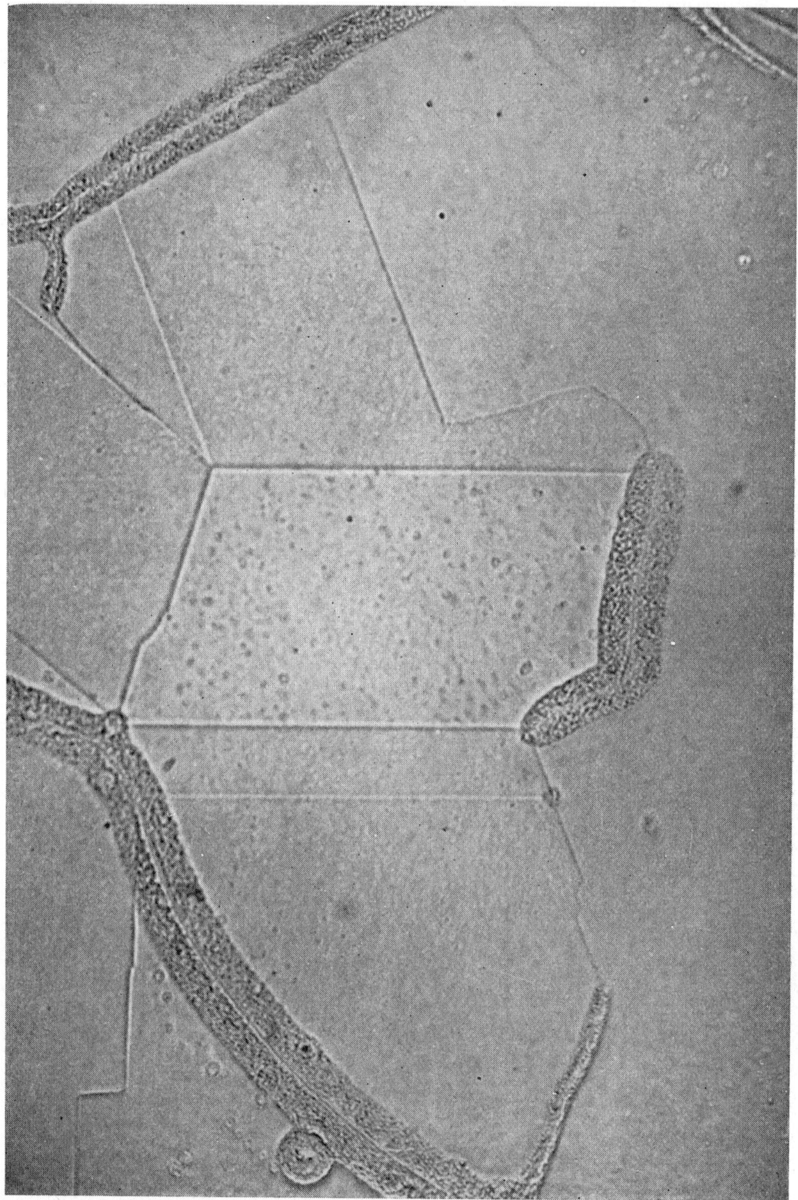

Fig. 14. – Bubble formation at twin boundaries [16]. ×750.

along the grain boundary, can be seen largely by virtue of their shadows. Small carbide inclusions in the bottom left corner have had little influence upon the behaviour of the gas. About 3 cm^3 of helium are produced in each cm^3 of beryllium during irradiation by $1.5 \cdot 10^{21}$ fast neutrons cm^{-2}, and Fig. 17

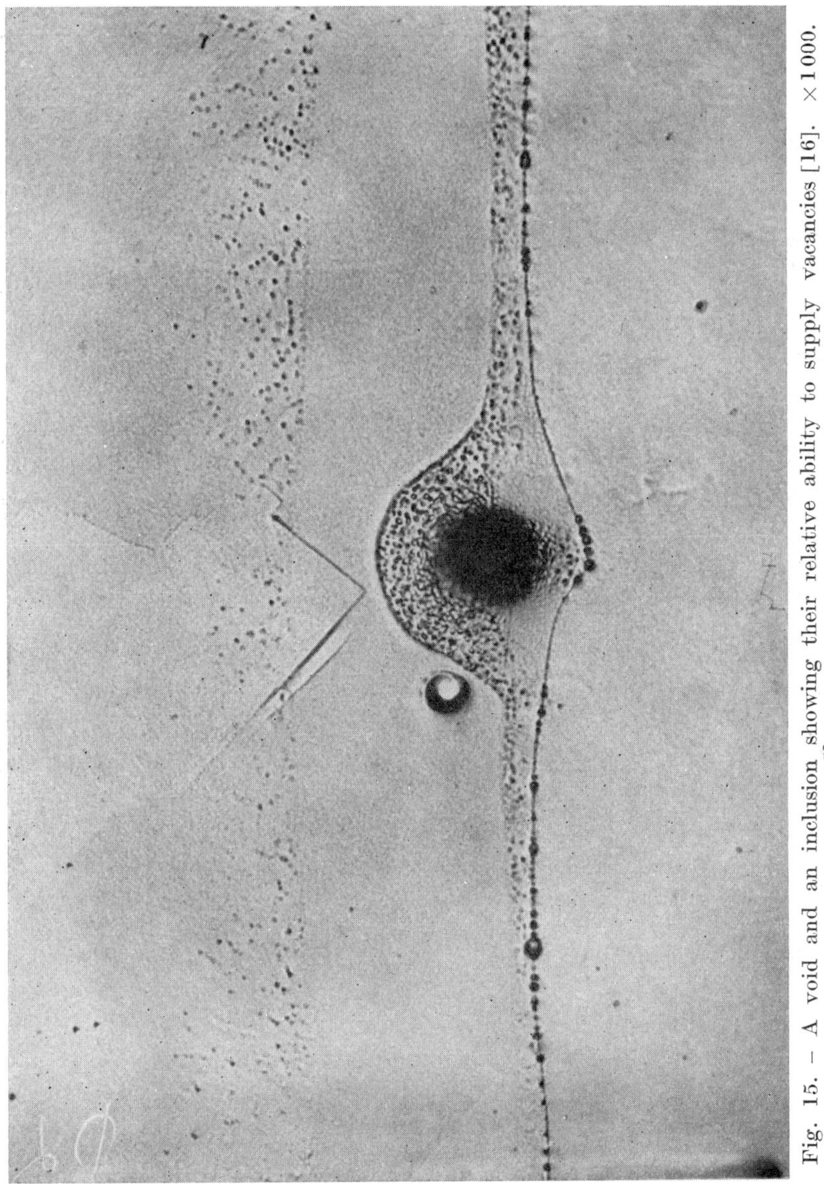

Fig. 15. – A void and an inclusion showing their relative ability to supply vacancies [16]. $\times 1000$.

shows a thin film of such a piece of beryllium which had been, subsequently heated for 1 hour at 900 °C [18]. There are a few bubbles lying on the horizontal grain boundary, and there is a striking difference in the number and size of the bubbles lying in the two neighbouring grains. This difference would result in a differential volume increase in the two grains and induce considerable

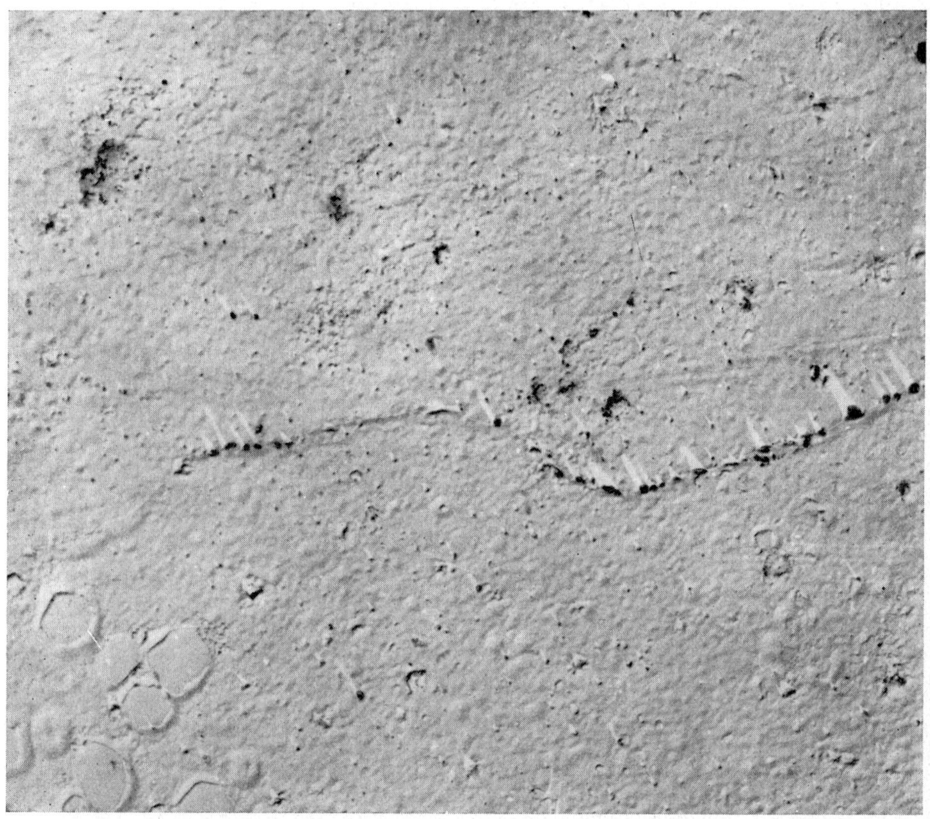

Fig. 16. – Shadowed replica of α-uranium after 0.09% burn-up at 500 °C [17]. ×40 000.

stress upon the grain boundaries. On heating the bubbles coarsen further, and eventually large tears occur at the grain boundaries, possibly because of the unequal volume increase in the individual grains. The overall volume increase can be measured and compared with the size and number of bubbles the material contains. While the metal contains bubbles of only 100 Å the change in volume cannot easily be measured. It is only when the bubbles attain the size of about 1 000 Å that the material shows a measurable volume increase, and a further increase occurs at higher temperatures as the bubbles become larger. Once the bubbles radius (r) or the number per unit volume (n) is known, the volume occupied by the gas (δV) can be calculated from the following relation [19], which merely assumes that the gas obeys the perfect gas laws and that the pressure is determined solely by the surface energy:

$$\frac{\delta V}{V} = \frac{4}{3}\pi r^3 n = \frac{mkTr}{2\gamma}\,,$$

where m is the amount of gas per unit volume, k is Boltzmann's constant and T the absolute temperature.

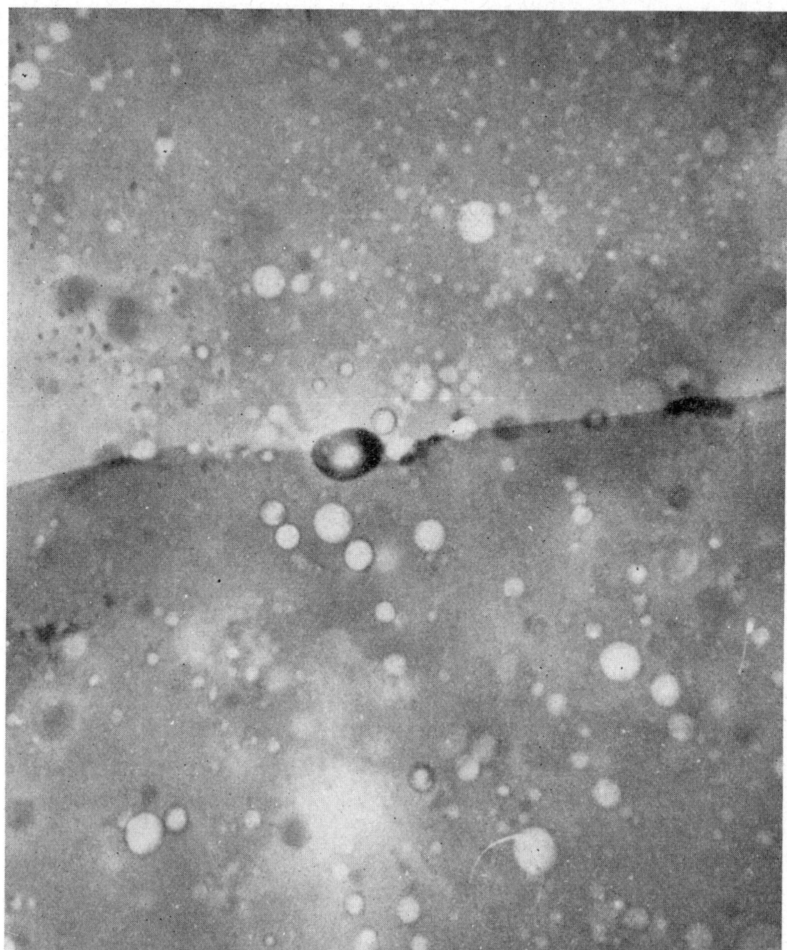

Fig. 17. – Thin film of beryllium after bombardment with $1.5\cdot10^{21}$ fast neutrons cm^{-2} and subsequent heating at 900 °C for 1 h [18]. ×10 000.

The bubbles impede the motion of grain boundaries. For instance, the recrystallized grain size can be retained almost up to the melting point of a metal if it contains many gas atoms. However, if the metal is severely worked, the grain boundaries will move upon subsequent heating, and in such circumstances very large bubbles appear upon the grain boundary and in positions

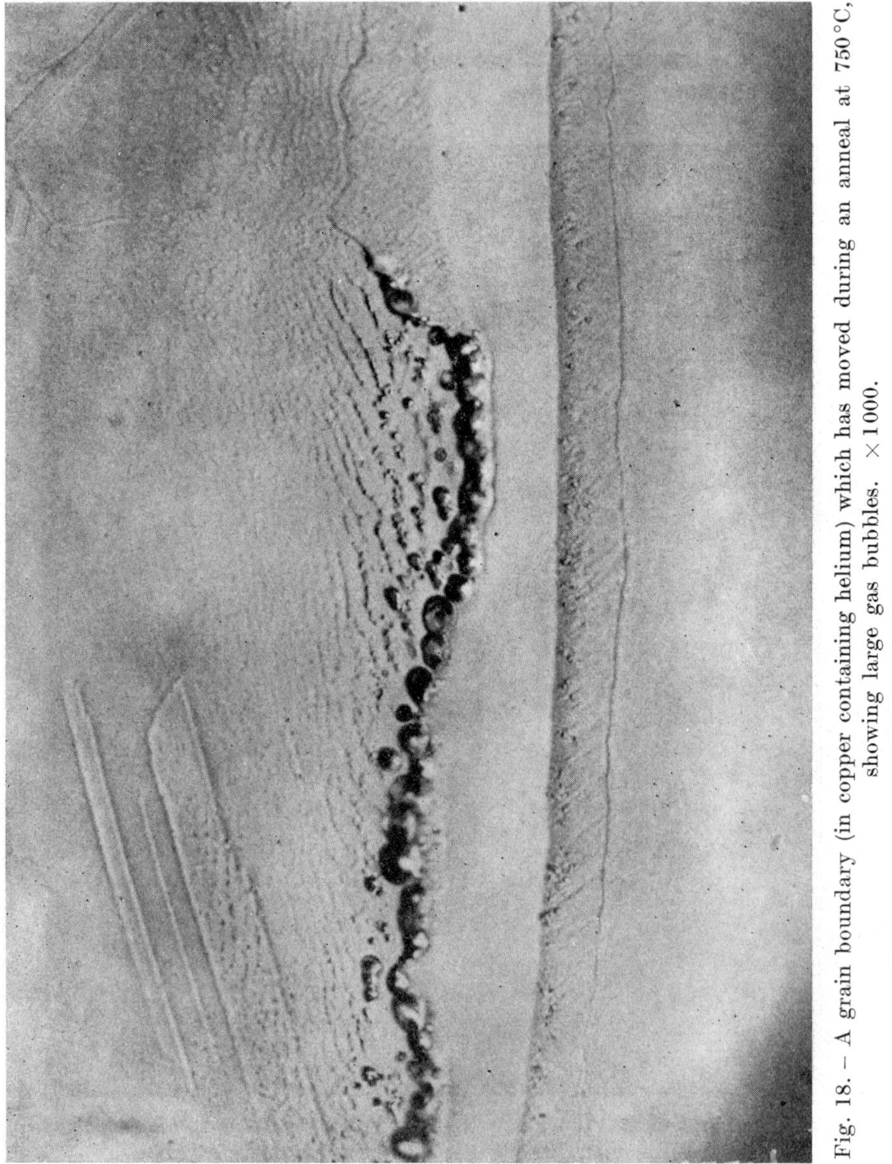

Fig. 18. – A grain boundary (in copper containing helium) which has moved during an anneal at 750 °C, showing large gas bubbles. × 1000.

previously occupied by it (Fig. 18). It is as though the grain boundary had repeatedly swept the gas lying in its path and bubbles formed on the boundary which had then broken away leaving a trail of bubbles. Whatever the mechanism, it appears that moving grain boundaries are able to induce very large gas bubbles in the metal at temperatures far below those necessary for their normal growth to this size. In anisotropic metals, such as uranium and beryllium, thermal cycling can generate internal stresses and these may be sufficient to cause grain boundaries to move with resultant large swelling. It is known that if uranium is thermally cycled larger swellings do occur, and movement of the grain boundaries may be the cause.

4. – Mechanical properties.

The point defects and impurities produced during the irradiation both tend to harden the metal. However, at high temperatures the impurities alone will be effective.

The bubbles, from their first appearance when they are only 100 Å in size, lie along dislocations lines. Several rows of bubbles can be seen in aluminium in Fig. 19. The bubbles are closely spaced and occasionally one can see a small bubble next to one several times larger; this suggests that the escape of helium atoms from the small bubble to the large is slow if it occurs at all, even though there is a dislocation line joining the two to assist such migration. Bubbles lying on the dislocation with this frequency will obviously very much affect the behaviour of the dislocation line. The application of stress will merely bow the individual segments of the dislocation line between the neighbouring bubbles, the image force on the dislocation line ensuring that the dislocation leaves the surface of the bubble normally. It is only when the stress (σ) is sufficiently great so that the segment is a complete semicircle that it is possible for the dislocation line to break away from the bubbles. That this is true is illustrated in the sequence of photographs shown in Fig. 20. Here a thin film has been stressed nonuniformly in the electron beam of the microscope such that it bows between two neighbouring bubbles, the sequence showing that the bow increases even beyond the situation where the two dislocations meet. (Such an array of bubbles, if their centres do not lie on the slip plane, makes a very simple series of Frank-Read sources.) The stress needed to free the dislocation lines is given by the expression $\sigma = Gb/L$, where G is the shear modulus, and L the spacing between neighbouring bubble centres. Thus, when L is small the bubbles lying on the dislocation lines harden the metal.

Microhardness indentations on a piece of copper which had been injected with helium atoms showed that the region containing the helium atoms was much harder than the metal through which the α-particles had passed and which contained only displaced atoms [20]. In addition to this initial diffe-

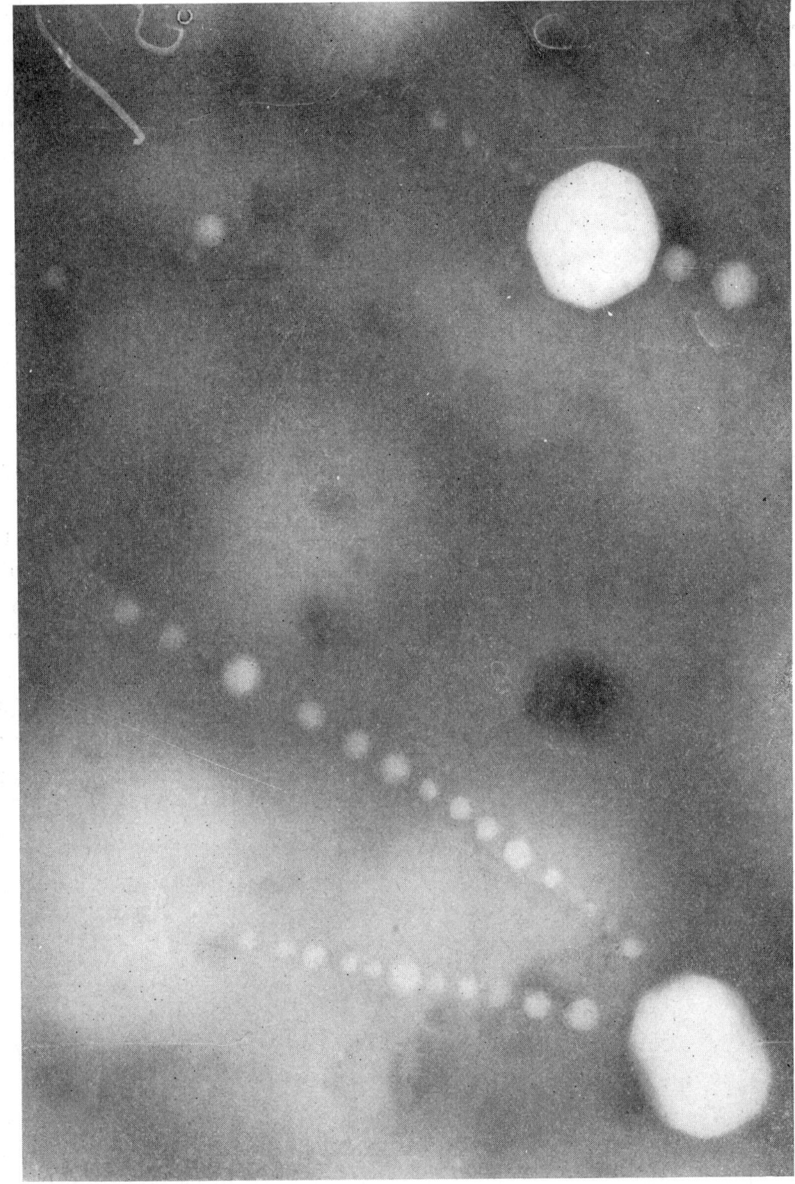

Fig. 19. – Helium bubbles in a thin film of aluminium after heating for 1 h at 600 °C. ×40 000.

rence in hardness there was a marked difference in the annealing behaviour of the two regions, as might be expected from the difference in annealing behaviour of the thin film shown in Figs. 6 and 8. The region containing only displaced atoms recovered its original hardness after heating for one hour

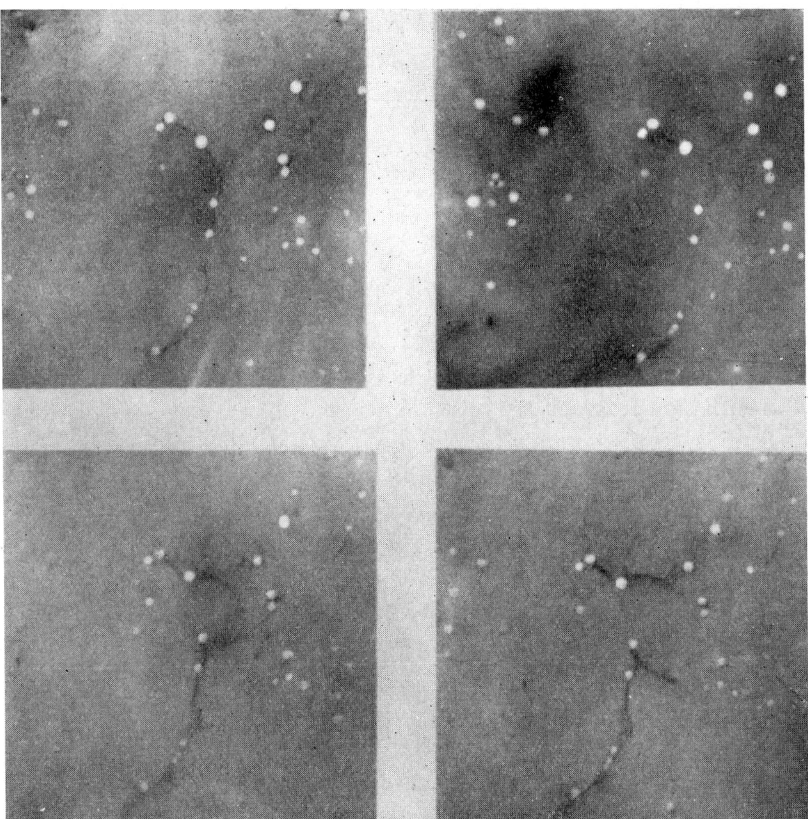

Fig. 20. – Sequence showing the movement of a dislocation line impeded by bubbles lying upon it. ×23 000.

at 300 °C, but the region containing helium atoms in addition did not recover even after heating to temperatures as high as 850 °C (see Fig. 21). Eventually this latter region, lying about 0.2 mm from the bombarded surface, recovered and was then softer than was the original material. This happened

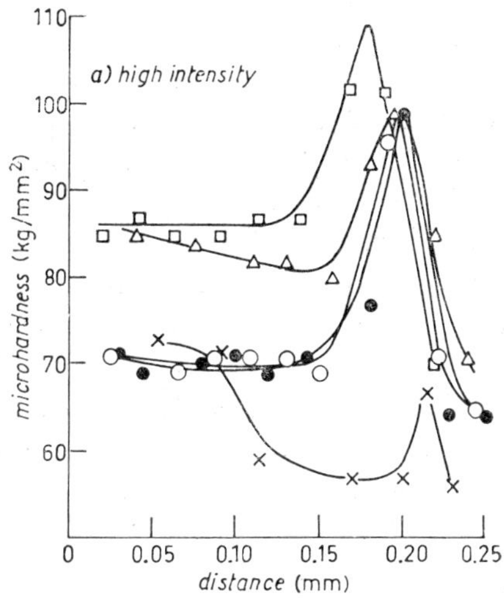

Fig. 21. – Microhardness of a copper block which has been bombarded with α-particles which have penetrated 0.2 mm where helium atoms deposit [20]. □ as irradiated; △ 200 °C; ● 300 °C; ○ 700 °C; × 850 °C.

when the bubbles became so large that their spacing was greater than 10^{-4} cm. Highly irradiated beryllium behaves similarly, becoming much harder after a high irradiation dose, and this hardening can only be removed by heating at high temperature.

5. – Summary.

More displaced atoms are produced in metals which transmute if there is a release of energy during the transmutation, and the distribution of the displaced atoms is very different from that in metals which do not transmute; for instance, fission fragments produce damage very local to their long straight tracks. In anisotropic crystals this large number of displaced atoms combined with their localized distribution results in growth of the crystal which can manifest itself in many ways, such as surface wrinkling and low creep strength. However, these displacement defects are only important below the self-diffusion temperature.

The impurities, which result in all transmutations, produce changes at all temperatures of irradiation providing that the number of impurities introduced is comparable to or greater than the number already present. In some important metals the impurity levels far exceed the original ones. The inert atoms helium, xenon and krypton are all frequent products of these transmutations and have a marked effect upon the properties of the material because of their gaseous character. It appears that the point-defect clusters produced by the irradiation are able to act as nuclei for the formation of gas bubbles and also as sources for the vacancies necessary for the growth of these bubbles. There appears, however, to be a limit to the number of vacancies available from this source and consequently the growth of bubbles is limited; large bubbles of helium only occur when copious supplies of vacancies become available to them from the permanent vacancy sources such as the grain boundaries and free surfaces. This large scale trapping of vacancies in the material produces the volume increase observed in these metals.

The bubbles which generally lie upon the dislocation lines within the material impede their motion and harden the material, the hardening being inversely proportional to the spacing between adjacent bubbles. As the helium bubbles coarsen, this hardening effect diminishes. Thus, both the volume increase and hardening are determined by the number of bubbles per unit volume. This vital parameter depends upon the scale of the nuclei or their ability to coarsen. Thus, in metals containing a large amount of gas either the bubbles are small and closely spaced when there is little volume increase but the metal is hardened, or the bubbles are large and widely spaced when there is a considerable increase in volume but little hardening.

* * *

I am grateful to Dr. G. W. GREENWOOD and Mr. K. H. WESTMACOTT for allowing me to use their previously unpublished photographs.

REFERENCES

[1] R. S. BARNES and G. B. REDDING: *Atomics*, 166 (1958).
[2] D. W. WHITE, A. P. BEARD and A. H. WILLIS: *Paris Conf. Fuel Element Technology* (1957).
[3] E. C. H. SILK and R. S. BARNES: *Phil. Mag.*, **4**, 970 (1959).
[4] T. S. NOGGLE: to be published.
[5] T. K. BIERLEIN: to be published.
[6] J. KELSCH: to be published.
[7] P. B. HIRSCH: This volume p. 39.
[8] K. WESTMACOTT: to be published.
[9] R. S. BARNES and D. J. MAZEY: *Phil. Mag.*, **5**, 1247 (1960).
[10] S. N. BUCKLEY: to be published.
[11] D. A. JONES and J. W. MITCHELL: *Phil. Mag.*, **3**, 1 (1958).
[12] R. W. CAHN: *Acta Met.*, **1**, 49 (1953).
[13] A. C. ROBERTS and A. H. COTTRELL: *Phil. Mag.*, **1**, 711 (1956).
[14] R. S. BARNES, G. B. REDDING and A. H. COTTRELL: *Phil. Mag.*, **3**, 97 (1958).
[15] J. SILCOX and P. B. HIRSCH: *Phil. Mag.*, **4**, 72 (1959).
[16] R. BARNES: *Phil. Mag.*, **5**, 635 (1960).
[17] G. W. GREENWOOD: to be published.
[18] J. RICH, P. WALTERS and R. S. BARNES: A.E.R.E. R. 3449 (1960).
[19] R. S. BARNES: *Nuclear Metallurgy*, **6**, 21 (1959).
[20] T. K. GHOSH, C. J. BEAVERS and R. S. BARNES: *Journ. Inst. Metals*, to be published.

Effets des radiations dans l'uranium.

J. BLIN

Centre d'Etudes Nucléaires de Fontenay-aux-Roses,
Department du Plutonium - Fontenay-aux-Roses (Seine)

Introduction.

Les effets de l'irradiation de l'uranium en pile sont complexes du fait que les dégats créés par le passage d'une particule de fission sont importants et de natures variées et qu'en plus il s'agit d'un matéraiu anisotrope. Ces effets sont sans doute nettement plus complexes que ceux du bombardment du cuivre par des électrons, qui commencent seulement à être débrouillés.

Le nombre atomique élevé de cet élément et sa grande réactivité vis-à-vis de l'oxygène ont de plus empêché de faire jusqu'à présent des études au microscope électronique par transmission qui eussent permis d'analyser directement les degâts dûs à la fission. Ainsi actuellement se trouve-t-on en présence d'un grand nombre d'études de changements de propriétés physiques par irradiation, études faites d'ailleurs sur des matériaux polycristallins assez peu isotropes. Dans une première partie nous ferons le point de ces études sans chercher aucunement à les grouper autour d'une interprétation de l'effet d'une pointe de fission et cela simplement pour délimiter nos connaissances expérimentales.

Dans une seconde partie nous décrirons un certain nombre d'expériences qui visent au contraire à préciser un modèle de la pointe de fission et nous indiquerons comment se pose actuellement le problème de la « croissance ».

I. – L'uranium irradié.

Ce matériau a été très étudié en raison de son intérêt pratique et l'on se trouve en présence d'un grand nombre de données expérimentales, quelquefois contradictoires, tout au moins en apparence. De la masse importante de documents nous dégageons ceux qui sont les plus significatifs.

Les effets les plus apparents dans l'uranium sont la « croissance », c'est-à-dire le changement de forme sans changement de volume notable et le « gonflement », c'est-à-dire un changement de volume important et presque isotrope. Le Dr. BARNES a exposé dans sa conférence tout ce qui a trait au gonflement. Si l'on voit maintenant assez clair dans le problème du gonflement, en grande partie à cause des travaux de BARNES et de ses collaborateurs, il n'en est pas du tout de même pour la croissance où la situation est assez mauvaise.

1. – La croissance.

Le phénomène a été clairement montré et defini dans le rapport de S. H. PAINE et J. H. KITTEL [1]. La Fig. 1 représente le motif élémentaire de l'uranium et les coefficients de croissance (G) dans chaque direction cristallographique. G est défini par

$$G = \frac{1}{\tau} \log \frac{l_1}{l_0},$$

où l_1 et l_0 sont les dimensions initiales et finales dans une direction et τ le taux de combustion.

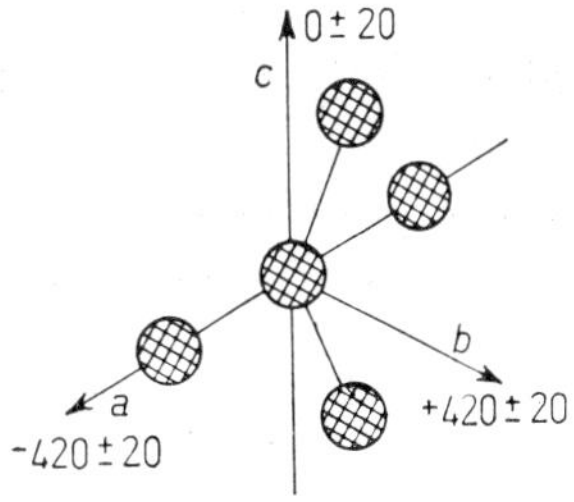

0 ± 20
c
b
a
+420 ± 20
-420 ± 20

Fig. 1. – Coefficient de croissance (G) de l'uranium α dans les différentes directions cristallographiques.

1·1. *Rôle de la température.* – Peu d'expériences on été faites à basse température (azote liquide). Aucune ne prouvait l'existence d'une croissance importante (voir par exemple HOLDEN [2]). Des résultats récents semblent indiquer le contraire. On manque là d'une donnée expérimentale fort importante.

C'est pour des températures voisines de 100°C que l'on trouve le plus de résultats publiés. Dans le domaine de 75° à 150°C KITTEL et PAINE [3] indiquent, dans un travail portant sur un grand nombre d'échantillons, une légère décroissance de G (Fig. 2). Ces résultats sont à comparer avec des mesures de rides à la surface des éléments combustibles. Ces rides sont dues à ce que ces éléments sont constitués d'uranium en gros cristaux et que chaque cristal développe une bosse à la surface du barreau. ELDRED *et al.* [4] donnent une série de courbes indiquant les hauteurs moyennes des rides pour une irradiation donnée et une température donnée. Ces renseignements sont statistiques mais vont également dans le même sens que ceux de KITTEL et PAINE comme le montre très clairement la Fig. 3. Nous avons porté sur cette figure le quotient du coefficient de ride par le taux de combustion en fonction de la température. Ce coefficient est en quelque sorte une mesure de G.

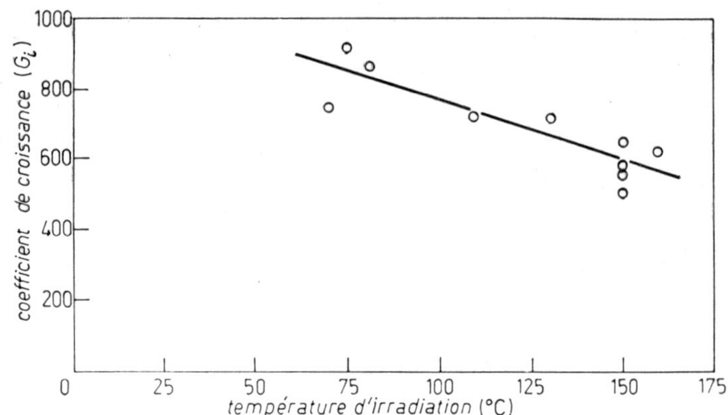

Fig. 2. – Effect de la température d'irradiation sur le coefficient de croissance de l'uranium laminé à 300 °C.

Les résultats relatifs aux températures supérieures à 350°C sont très rares. PUGH mentionne [5] une expérience faite sur un pseudo-cristal obtenu par changement de phase. Les dimensions du cristal en inch étaient $1.5 \times \times 0.08 \times 0.01$ et la désorientation des domaines de 5°. Un tel cristal ne croit pas à 500°C alors qu'à 200° un cristal analogue donne $G = 500$.

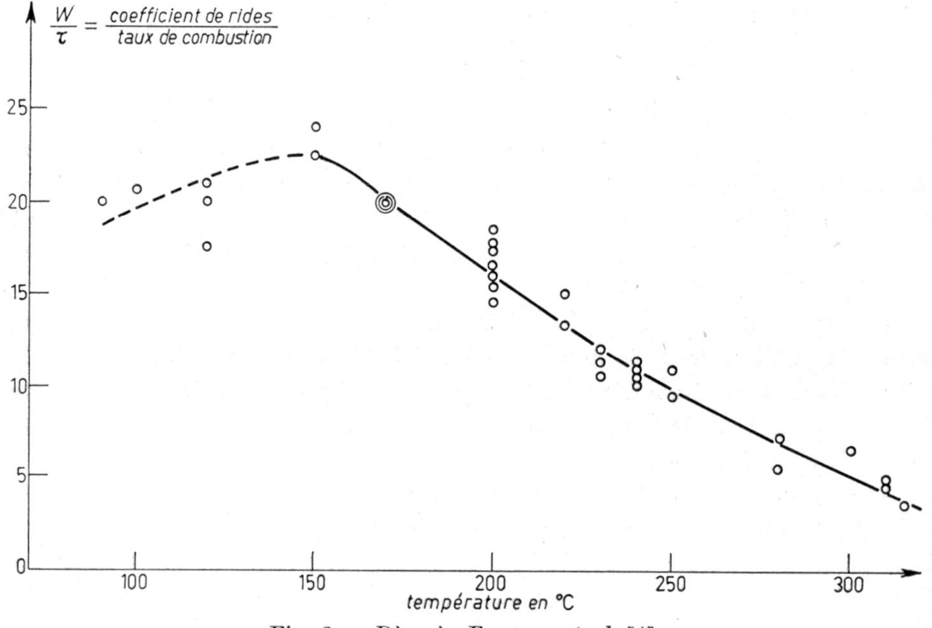

Fig. 3. – D'après ELDRED *et al.* [4].

On peut être tenté de tracer une « courbe » décrivant l'allure de la variation de la croissance en fonctoin de la température. Cela n'est pas justifié du fait que les mesures faites à la température de l'azote liquide sont trop rares et trop peu comparables aux autres.

1·2. *Rôle de la perfection des cristaux.* – Une des raisons qui ont empeché le progrès des expériences sur la croissance est la difficulté de préparer de bons cristaux ou tout au moins de contrôler la déorientation dans les pseudo-cristaux. Paine et Kittel [6] ont irradié dans les mêmes conditions des cristaux de changement de phases et des bons cristaux obtenus par croissance de grains. La croissance des seconds est plus faible que celle des premiers sans que l'on puisse avancer de valeurs précises.

Les joints de grains ne jouent qu'un rôle mineur dans la croissance. Sur ce point important on se reportera aux expériences décrites dans la référence [7] qui sont les plus claires à ce sujet.

1·3. *Aspect micrographique de l'uranium irradié.* – Il est impossible de ne pas faire état, en parlant de la croissance, de l'aspect micrographique de l'uranium irradié.

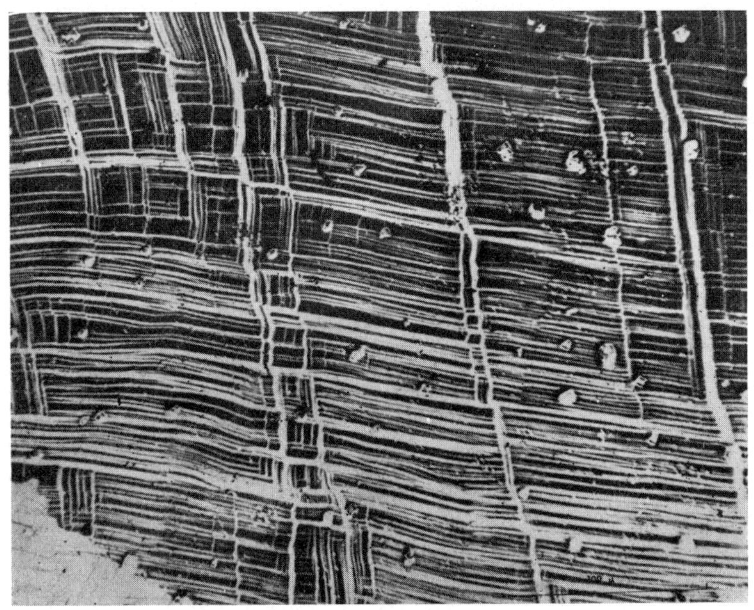

Fig. 4.

La Fig. 4 est relative à un barreau ayant un taux de combustion de $2.2 \cdot 10^{-4}$. On y remarque des macles très abondantes. Ces macles sont généralement assez droites et bien que l'on observe des régions de macles courbes telles que

Fig. 5.

celles de la Fig. 5, on peut dire que le principal processus de déformation est le maclage.

Fig. 6.

Une étude de détail des cisaillements dans ces cristaux révèle des déformations locales importantes de l'ordre de 25 % pour 0.02 % de taux de combustion, ce qui amène à des coefficients de croissance de l'ordre de 1000 et cela pour des barres d'uranium irradiées à moins de 300°C. Jusqu'à ce taux de combustion et pour ces températures on peut donc admettre que les cristaux se déforment *presque comme s'ils étaient seuls* et d'une façon sensiblement proportionnelle au taux de combustion. Ce résultat révèle également le rôle très faible du nombre des grains.

Une étude de matériaux plus irradiés montre qu'il n'y a pas proportionnalité du nombre des macles visibles au microscope optique et du taux de combustion lorsque celui-ci devient dix fois plus grand ($2 \cdot 10^{-3}$). On peut se demander s'il y a saturation de la déformation ou si une étude au microscope électronique révèlerait des macles plus nombreuses et plus fines.

Ces macles sont très stables et ne disparaissent que très lentement même par des recuits à 600°C, sans doute à cause des produits de fission qui bloquent la migration des joints (Fig. 6).

2. – Structure cristallographique.

On peut schématiser rapidement les résultats en disant qu'il n'y a que peu de changement dans la structure de l'uranium irradié. Si on fait le diagramme d'un échantillon très irradié on trouve un certain élargissement des raies qui n'a rien de surprenant si on le rapproche de sa micrographie et un très léger changement de paramètre.

Si par contre on désire entrer dans le détail on peut dire qu'il n'y a presque aucune expérience satisfaisante. Tout d'abord parce que la *température* d'irradiation joue un rôle particulièrement important. On a pu mettre en évidence [8] un changement de largeur de raie par un recuit de 94 h à 100 °C dans un morceau d'uranium laminé à 40 % de réduction de section. D'autre part jusqu'à maintenant presque personne n'avait d'appareil permettant d'éliminer le rayonnement $K\alpha_2$ ce qui fait que les mesures de paramètres de haute précision sur des raies un peu larges n'ont guère de sens.

On peut donc affirmer simplement que, malgré l'importance de la perturbation que crée une particule de fission, la structure est très peu perturbée.

Remarquons qu'il n'en est pas toujours ainsi et que si dans certains cristaux contenant de l'uranium (UO_2 par exemple) on peut atteindre des taux de combustion supérieurs à 1 % sans altérer la structure, dans d'autres elle est totalement détruite. Cest le cas par exemple de U_3O_8, U_3Si, U_6Fe, etc.

La Fig. 7 montre par exemple le diagramme du composé U_3Si avant et après irradiation. On constate une transformation complète de la structure qui devient pratiquement amorphe.

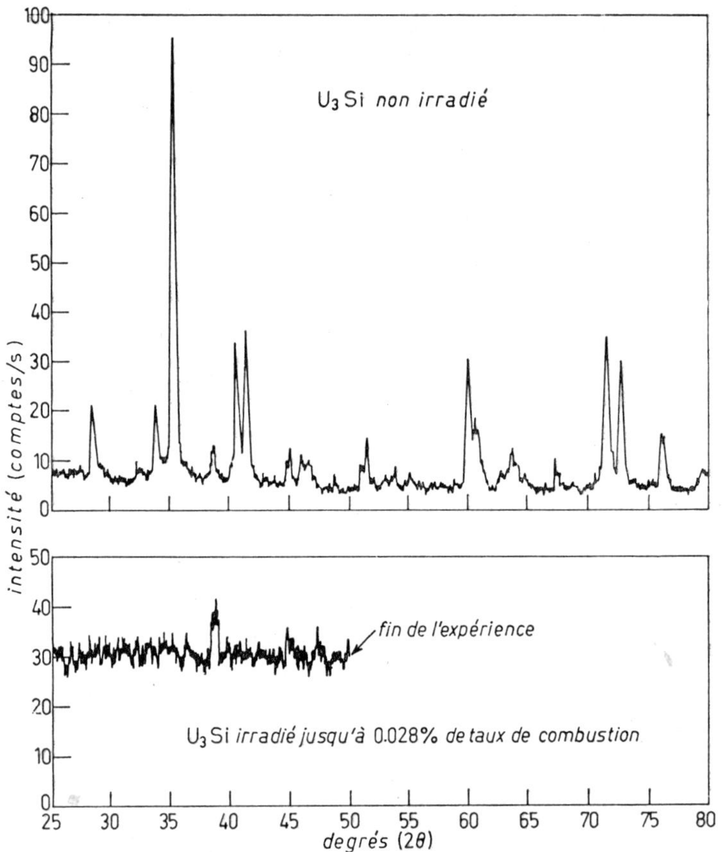

Fig. 7. – Diagramme de diffraction de la phase U_3Si avant et après irradiation.

3. – Propriétés mécaniques.

3·1. *Tractions sur un matériau recuit puis irradé.* – Pour bien voir l'ensemble des changements apportés aux propriétés mécaniques par l'irradiation il faut commencer par étudier l'effet de doses très faibles de neutrons.

Une étude de la dureté [9] faite sur un uranium polycristallin, soigneusement recuit puis refroidi lentement, montre une discontinuité dans les mesures pour un flux intégré de 10^{15} neutrons/cm² (Fig. 8). Ce flux intégré correspond à $0.4 \cdot 10^{15}$ atomes de fission par cm³ et en admettant un nombre de dislocations à l'état recuit de 10^7/cm² on voit que ce flux correspond à la saturation des dislocations par les produits de fission. Une telle situation devrait se traduire sur de bons monocristaux par l'apparition d'un « yield point ».

Si on accroît le flux intégré le métal durcit ensuite lentement. Comme pour les autres matériaux irradiés la limite élastique est beaucoup plus affectée par l'irradiation que la limite à rupture. L'élongation à rupture est par contre radicalement diminuée. Pour caractériser l'effet de l'irradiation le mieux

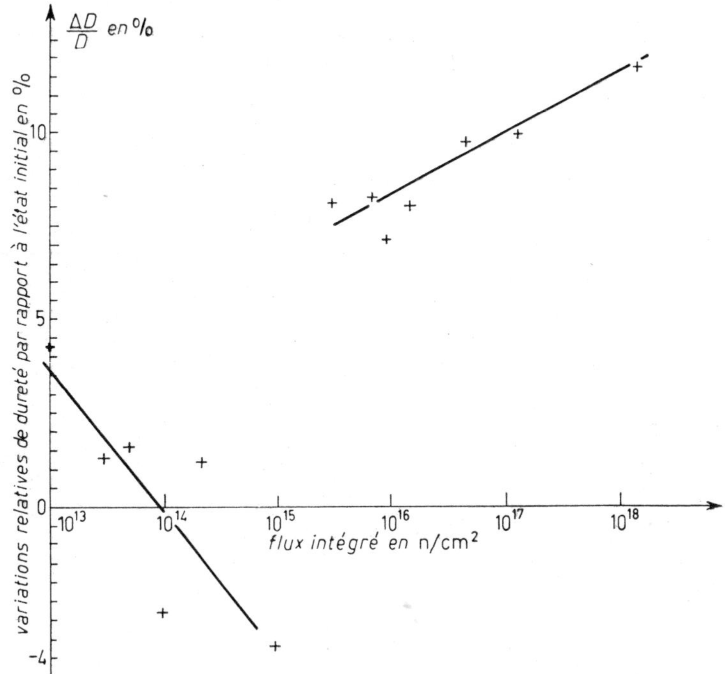

Fig. 8. – Variation de la dureté d'un uranium irradié progressivement.

semble de choisir la limite à 0.2 % d'allongement et cela d'autant plus que, comme on le sait, il n'y a pas à proprement parler de limite élastique dans l'uranium polycristallin avant irradiation.

Il est difficile de trouver des résultats couvrant un très large intervalle de flux. Les mesures faites par BUSH [10] partent de 10^{16} neutrons/cm² pour aller jusqu'à 10^{20} avec toutefois un hiatus au voisinage de 10^{18}. Ces mesures faites sur un uranium polycristallin irradié à la température ordinaire indiquent un accroissement *lent* de la limite élastique qui est deux fois plus grande pour les taux d'irradiation élevés qu'à l'état initial (Tableau I et Fig. 9).

Toutes ces mesures tendent à prouver que les propriétés mécaniques du

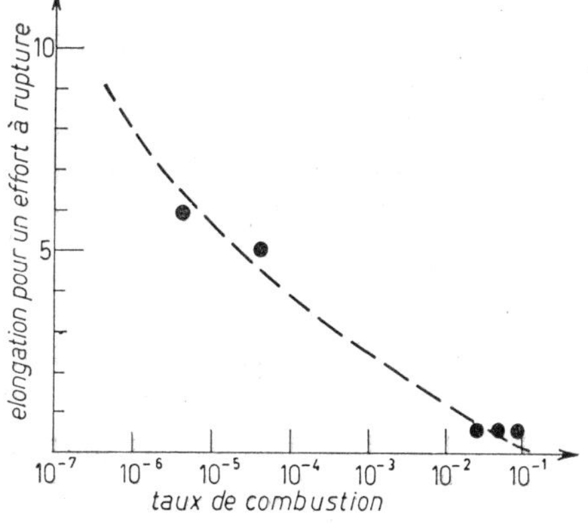

Fig. 9. – Elongation pour un effort à rupture. D'après S. H. BUSH [10].

matériau irradié dépendent beaucoup *plus des produits de fission que des défauts du réseau au dessus d'un taux d'irradiation très faible.* Si en effet la perturbation

TABLEAU I. – *Effet de l'exposition à température ordinaire sur les propriétés mécaniques de l'uranium.*

Echatillon moyen de six contrôles	Exposition totale taux de combustion %	Tension d'allongement à 0.2% en 1000 psi.	Elongation % dans 1 in.
O	0	37.5	19.0
A	$4\cdot10^{-6}$	35.4	6.0
B	$4\cdot10^{-5}$	41.2	5.2
C	0.018	57	0.6
D	0.031	72	0.6
E	0.075	79	0.6
F	0.100	73	0.6

que l'on observe par micrographie était responsable de cet accroissement de dureté, on observerait une discontinuité dans les propriétés mécaniques dans un domaine de flux voisin de 10^{19}, ce qui n'est pas.

3·2. *Mesures de dureté et de largeur de raies de diffraction sur de l'uranium écroui avant irradiation.* – Toutes ces mesures ne nous éclairent pas sur les propriétés mécaniques de l'uranium pendant l'irradiation. Avant d'aborder cette question nous parlerons de deux séries de mesures relatives à un uranium écroui puis irradié.

MADSEN [11] a étudié la dureté Brinell d'un uranium écroui par laminage. La Fig. 10 indique l'évolution de la dureté en fonction du flux intégré. Le point principal est qu'aprés une irradiation de $5\cdot10^{15}$ neutrons par cm^2 on observe une chute sensible de la dureté qui par ailleurs ne varie guère quand on augmente le flux intégré.

Cette expérience est à rapprocher de celles faites par KONOBEEVSKI [12] d'une part et TARDIVON d'autre part [8] sur les largeurs de raies d'un uranium laminé puis irradié. Le travail de TARDIVON indique nettement que c'est entre 10^{17} et 10^{18} que se produit un changement net de la largeur de raies (Fig. 11). Dans cette expérience la température de l'échantillon était maintenue au dessous de 60 °C et l'on s'était assuré qu'aucun recuit ne se produisait à cette température. En poursuivant l'irradiation le diagramme de diffraction se stabilise et reste toujours très différent de celui du métal recuit.

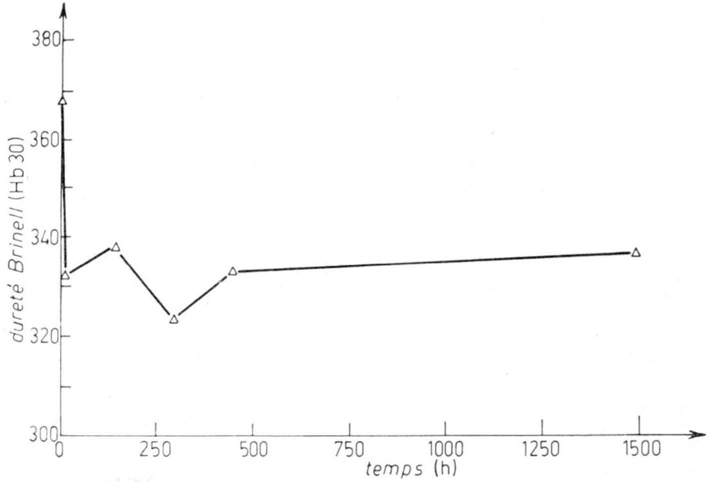

Fig. 10. – Changement de dureté d'un uranium écroui en fonction de la durée d'irradiation irradié en fluxe de 10^{11} neutrons/cm$^2\cdot$s.

De ces deux expériences on peut conclure que les particules de fission créent une perturbation suffisante pour faire disparaître un grand nombre de dislocations. On notera d'ailleurs que la dureté est nettement plus sensible à ce revenu par irradiation que la largeur des raies de diffraction, le changement se produisant pour au plus $5\cdot10^{15}$ dans un cas et pour environ 10^{17} dans l'autre.

Il s'agit là d'un effet de revenu contraire à l'effet de durcissement dont on parle dans le paragraphe précédent ce qui renforce l'idée qu'il est dû aux défauts créés par la particule de fission ou à l'échauffement qu'elle produit. On peut donner à ce phénomène le nom de *revenu par irradiation*.

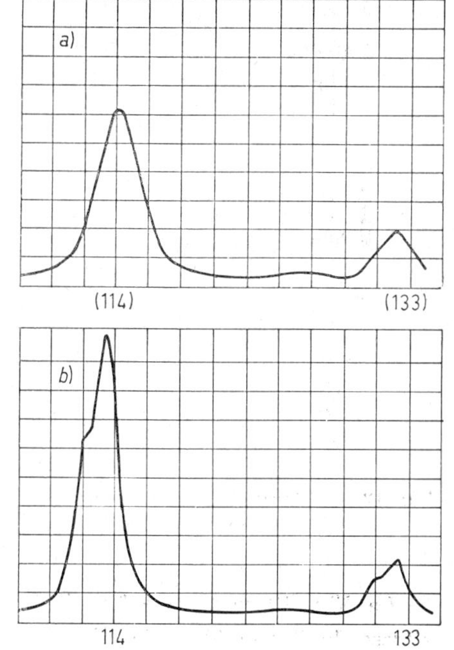

Fig. 11. – Changement de la largeur des raies (114) et (133) d'un uranium écroui au cours d'une irradiation: *a*) echantillon no. 9 avant irradiation; *b*) echantillon no. 9 après irradiation $1\cdot10^{18}$ n/cm^2.

3·3. *Fluage sous irradiation.* – Le fluage sous irradiation de l'uranium a été étudié avec quelques détails per ZAIMOVSKY *et al.* [14] d'une part ainsi que par ROBERTS et COTTRELL [13]. Les résultats russes sont relatifs à une température de 220°C, ceux des Anglais à une température d'une centaine de degrés. A ces températures le fluage de l'uranium est tout à fait négligeable. La vitesse de fluage est accrue par plusieurs ordres de grandeurs dès que l'on fait l'essai sous irradiation.

Il semble qu'une certaine confusion se soit établie à ce propos du fait que l'on n'ait pas distingué entre le fluage sous faible et sous forte charge. Les expériences qui ont été faites prouvent deux choses:

1) l'irradiation peut faire apparaître un fluage là où de toutes façons il n'y en aurait pas eu, la contrainte exercée étant inférieure à la limite élastique du matériau irradié.

2) l'irradiation peut accélérer le fluage par plusieurs ordres de grandeur sous forte charge.

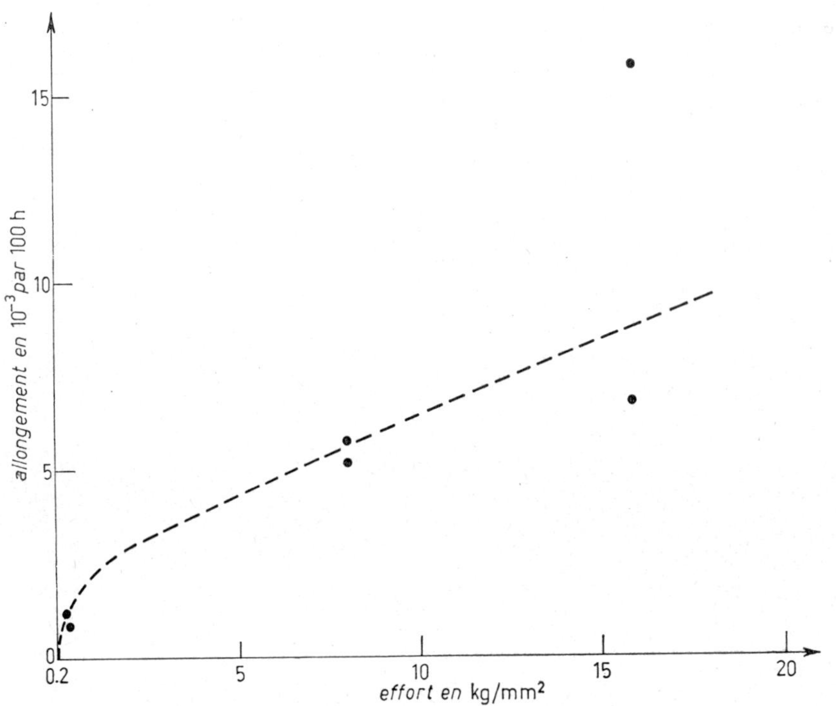

Fig. 12. – Vitesse de fluage en fonction de la contrainte pour l'uranium en cours d'irradiation. Résultats de ZAIMOVSKY *et al.* [14].

La Fig. 12 rassemble les résultats russes qui montrent comment varie la vitesse de fluage (dans la période linéaire) en fonction de la charge pour un flux de $6 \cdot 10^{12}$ neutrons/cm² et une température de 220°C. Les données expérimentales sont dispersées mais il est clair qu'il n'y a pas proportionnalité entre la vitesse de fluage (v) et la contrainte (σ) dans le domaine de contraintes consideré ($(0 \div 15)$ kg/mm²). Par contre ZAIMOVSKY a clairement montré (Fig. 13) que le fluage était proportionnel au flux instantané de neutrons sur l'échantillon.

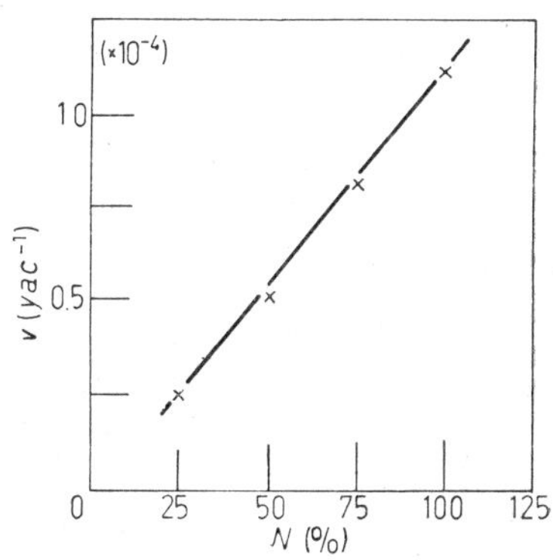

Fig. 13. – Fluage sous irradiation. Vitesse de fluage en fonction de flux.

La Fig. 14 permet de comparer les résultats anglais et russes dans le domaine des contraintes très faibles: inférieures à 1.5 kg/mm². Les Anglais ont montré qu'il y avait alors très sensiblement proportionnalité entre v et σ (courbe 1).

Si on essaie alors à partir des indications de flux de comparer les valeurs de v/σ obtenues par les Russes et les Anglais on trouve un écart égal à un facteur de 10. Sans être contradictoires on voit cependant que les expériences ont besoin d'être améliorées. Une analyse plus détaillée des résultats expérimentaux montre d'ailleurs qu'on ne peut les rapprocher davantage.

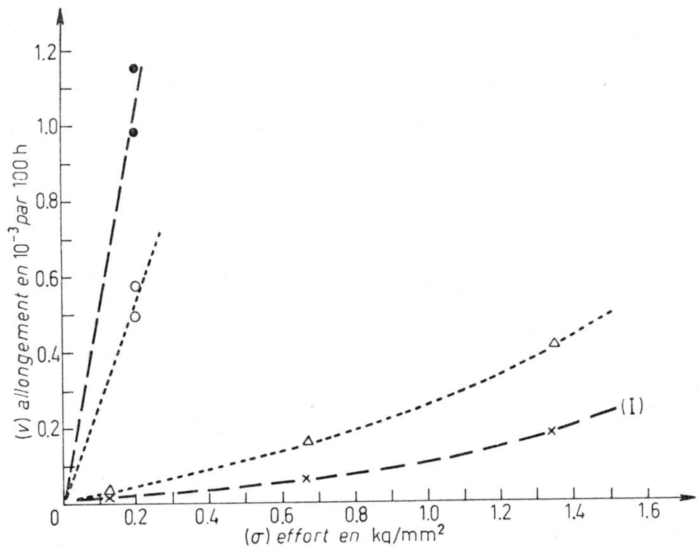

ig. 14. – Comparaison des résultats russes et anglais relatifs au fluage de l'uranium ›us irradiation. ● Russes $\varphi = 6 \cdot 10^{12}$; × Anglais $\varphi = 1.3 \cdot 10^{12}$; ○ Russes ramenés à $\varphi = 3 \cdot 10^{12}$; △ Anglais ramenés à $\varphi = 3 \cdot 10^{12}$.

4. – Liaisons entre les différentes propriétés de l'uranium irradié.

Les observations faites sur l'uranium irradié s'expliquent presque toutes par la « croissance » sans éclairer toutefois son mécanisme. A cela près, elles s'articulent assez bien les unes aux autres comme nous allons le montrer.

Le point essentiel est que la forme des cristaux change sans que la structure cristallographique soit altérée, chaque particule de fission amenant le changement de place d'environ 200 atomes ($G/2$) à la température ordinaire. Par conséquent seule l'accumulation très lente des produits de fission modifie le crista d'uranium. D'après ce que l'on sait de la solubilité des autres atomes dans l'uranium il n'y a rien d'étonnant à ce que le durcissement soit notable même pour des concentrations en produit de fission de 10^{-3}. La structure de l'uranium α vient de l'existence de liaisons à caractère covalent qui rendent difficile la mise en solution d'un grand nombre d'atomes.

4·1. *Faibles irradiations.* – Les cristaux se déforment donc par croissance augmentant autour d'eux les tensions. Quand celles-ci dépassent en moyenn une certaine valeur σ_y il y a relâchement d'une grande partie des tensions soi par maclage soit par glissement. Cette valeur σ_y n'est pas nulle comme dan le cas de l'uranium recuit non irradié d'après ce qu'indiquent les mesures de dureté mentionnées au paragraphe I-3·1. Elle croît lentement avec le tau d'irradiation à cause des produits de fission. Le nombre des macles est don au début proportionnel au taux d'irradiation. Le métal ne durcit cependan pas malgré l'accumultation de ces macles et de ces glissements. Le bombardement assure en effet un recuit continuel comme le montrent les expérience décrites dans le paragraphe I-3·2. En s'appuyant en particulier sur la diminution de la largeur des raies de diffraction on constate qu'il suffit de 10^{17} fissions/cm³ pour accomplir cette décroissance, ce qui représente un taux de combustion très faible: $0.4 \cdot 10^{-6}$.

Il est maintenant facile de montrer que si pendant cette période de faible irradiation on exerce une contrainte σ sur un materiau polycristallin on obse vera un fluage si petite que soit σ. Nous venons de dire que la croissance amène une déformation plastique quand les contraintes qu'elle crée dépasser une valeur σ_y. Quand on exerce une contrainte supplémentaire σ on peu distinguer deux sortes de régions dans le métal. Les régions A où les effor sont accrus et les régions B où il sont diminués. Si le *matériau est isotrope* nombre de ces régions est égal. Dans les régions A on atteindra la contrain σ_y au bout d'un temps

$$t_A = \frac{\sigma_y - \sigma}{E \cdot G'} \, .$$

E désignant le module d'Young du métal et G' la vitesse de croissance du cristal. Dans les régions B le temps nécessaire pour dépasser σ_y sera un peu plus long et égal à

$$t_B = \frac{\sigma_y + \sigma}{E \cdot G'} \,.$$

En supposant que les efforts moyens s'annulent quand on dépasse σ_y et que l'amplitude moyenne des déformations (ε_m) est constante on trouve une vitesse de fluage:

$$v = \left(\frac{1}{\sigma_y - \sigma} - \frac{1}{\sigma_y + \sigma}\right) E\varepsilon_m \cdot G' \,,$$

qui lorsque σ est petit devant σ_y s'écrit

$$v = \frac{\sigma}{\sigma_y} \cdot G' \cdot \frac{E\varepsilon_m}{\sigma_y} \,,$$

$E\varepsilon_m/\sigma_y$ est évidemment un coefficient de l'ordre de l'unité. On retrouve donc la formule indiquée par COTTRELL.

Les valeurs introduites dans ce calcul sont des valeurs moyennes. Les principales hypothèses sont que:

1) Les contraintes moyennes s'annulent après la déformation. Tenir compte d'une valeur résiduelle des contraintes moyennes (σ_m) revient à changer σ_y en $\sigma_y - \sigma_m$ ce qui ne change pas grand chose à notre raisonnement.

2) La déformation ε_m est constante. Cette hypothèse est justifiée car les barrières qui limitent le glissement dépendent de la structure des cristaux qui n'est que peu affectée par l'irradiation tout au moins au début.

3) Le métal considéré *n'a pas de texture*. C'est là une hypothèse importante et qui peut expliquer les désaccords entre les résultats russes et anglais. Les expériences russes étaient faites en effet sur un matérieu à forte texture.

Il faut remarquer qu'une oscillation de température, même faible peut provoquer le fluage de l'uranium par le même processus. La dilatation de l'uranium étant anisotrope la dilatation thermique crèe des tensions de même que la croissance.

L'explication de l'accélération du fluage que l'on observe sous de *fortes charges* est à notre avis assez différente. Elle est donnée simplement par les expériences de revenu par irradiation (I-3·2). On sait en effet que le fluage est le résultat de la compétition de deux phénomènes: l'écrouissage et le revenu. Le revenu est alors simplement créé par l'irradiation.

4·2. *Fortes irradiations* (taux de combustion supérieur à 0.05 %). – Peu d'études ont été faites dans ce domaine. Il est cependant évident que la situation est beaucoup plus compliquée. Les cristaux sont plus durs à cause des produits de fission. D'autre part la structure micrographique est totalement modifiée du fait du brassage intense créé par l'irradiation; tout ce qui vient d'être dit serait donc à reprendre dans ce domaine.

II. – Expériences sur les pointes de fission.

1. – Modèle de pointe de fission.

Ce modèle est développé en détail dans la conférence du Dr. BRINKMAN. Nous nous contenterons ici d'un modèle beaucoup plus simple, les expériences dont il est question dans ce chapitre étant encore très rudimentaires.

Une particule de fission perd une partie de son énergie sous forme d'ionisation et une partie en collision. La proportion de ces deux phénomènes n'est pas déterminée expérimentalement dans le cas de l'uranium.

L'énergie perdue en ionisation se retrouve finalement sous la forme d'agitation thermique. Il n'est cependant pas correct de parler de température — cette notion étant liée à un équilibre thermodynamique — et encore moins d'appliquer à la propagation de cette énergie des coefficients ordinaires de conductibilité thermique. On peut simplement dire que cette énergie est répartie de façon *continue*, avec une répartition que nous ne connaissons pas.

Au contraire, comme l'indique le Dr. BRINKMAN dans sa conférence, les dégats créés par les collisions apparaissent comme des nuages d'imperfections, chaque nuage correspondant à un atome éjecté par un choc coulombien avec la particule de fission. Aussi peut-on schématiser la situation en disant que les imperfections sont réparties un peu comme les feuilles d'une branche d'arbre (qui elle serait droite). Il se peut d'ailleurs que dans bien des cas les feuilles se recouvrent. Nous considérerons donc un modèle de pointe de fission constitué d'un tube cylindrique de longueur égale à la trajectoire d'une pointe de fission.

Le premier problème expérimental dont nous parlerons est de mesurer le volume v de ce tube qui correspond au *volume d'action d'une particule de fission.*

Le second problème est de déterminer *l'importance comparée* des effets dûs aux *oscillations* du réseau et des effets dûs aux *collisions.*

2. – Saturation de la résistance électrique de l'uranium irradié.

L'étude de la saturation de la résistance électrique de l'uranium irradié est un moyen de mesurer le volume v.

2·1. *Saturation a température ordinaire.* – A cette température on sait que le nombre des défauts qui subsistent sur la trace d'une particule de fission est faible. C'est ce qu'indiquent les résultat de cristallographie.

Si l'on admet qu'une particule de fission efface dans le cylindre considéré les défauts qui subsistent après le passage des particules précedentes on peut mesurer le volume v de ce cylindre.

Soit en effet K le nombre de défauts par unité de volume qui sont créés par unité de temps et qui subsistent après le passage des particules de fission. Soit V le nombre de fissions par unité de temps et de volume et $N(t)$ le nombre de défauts existant au temps t par unité de volume dans l'uranium. On a la relation d'équilibre

$$\mathrm{d}N(t) = K\,\mathrm{d}t - Vv\,N(t)\,\mathrm{d}t\,,$$

d'où

$$N(t) = N(W)\big(1-\exp[Vvt]\big)$$

$$N(\infty) = K/Vv\,.$$

Ceci suppose:

$$N(0) = 0\,.$$

On se reportera au papier de Y. QUÉRÉ et F. NAKACHE pour une description plus détaillée de cette expérience dans laquelle il faut en fait considérer le revenu d'origine thermique — revenu dont on peut finalement tenir compte de façon exacte.

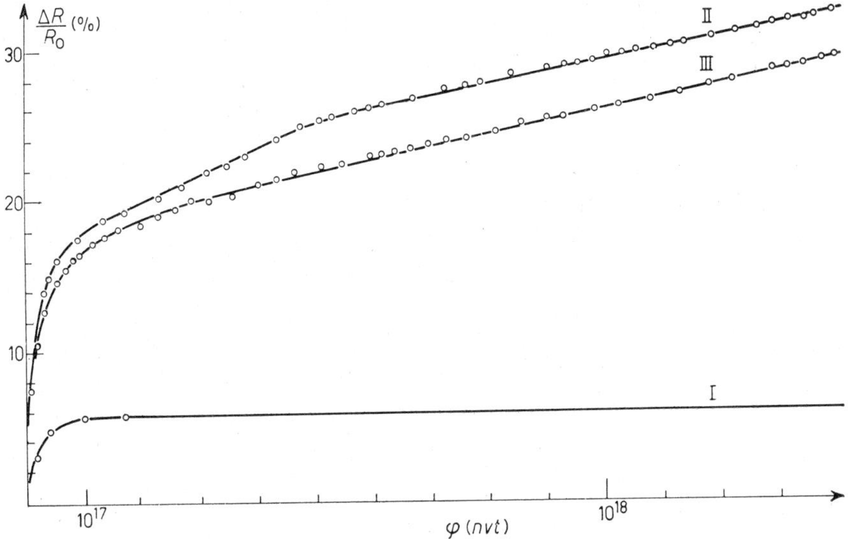

Fig. 15. – Changement de résistance électrique d'un uranium irradié en cours d'irradiation. I) U recuit (irrad. temp. ambiante); II) U recuit (irrad. 77 °K); III) U écroui irrad. 77 °K.

Les expériences faites par Y. QUÉRÉ et F. NAKACHE à la température ordinaire confirment ce modèle et donnent pour v la valeur de $2 \cdot 10^{-16}$ cm³. En admettant un parcours moyen de $5 \cdot 10^{-4}$ cm pour les particules de fission on trouve un diamètre de 80 Å pour le cylindre où se fait sentir leur effet (courbe I, Fig. 15).

La croissance ne gène en rien les observations car en supposant que l'on ait un allongement de fil égal au coefficient de croissance on obtient une augmentation de résistance de l'ordre de $1.6 \cdot 10^{-3}$ pour un flux de 10^{18} négligeable devant l'accroissement obtenu.

2'2. *Saturation a la température de l'azote liquide.* – Nous avons alors fait la même expérience à basse température (80 °K) (résultats non publiés). Les courbes II et III correspondent respectivement à un métal recuit puis soigneusement refroidi et à un métal écroui. Les points essentiels mis en évidence par cette expérience sont qu'à *basse température* il n'y a *pas de saturation rapide de la résistance électrique* et que la *notion de volume de fission est bien valable.*

A partir d'un certain flux intégré la résistance de l'uranium recuit ou celle du métal écroui croissent linéairement et de la même façon. Les produits de fission ne rendent pas compte de cet accroissement linéaire. Pour un flux intégré de 10^{18} neutrons/cm² la concentration des produits de fission est d'environ $8 \cdot 10^{-6}$ et l'accroissement de résistivité de 8% soit de 1 μΩ cm (à 80 °K). Cela amènerait à des changements de résistance électrique de 1000 μΩ cm pour 1% de produit de fission ce qui est invraisemblable.

Une explication est que la croissance à basse température est importante. Si tel était le cas le coefficient de croissance à basse température devrait être 50 fois plus élevé que le coefficient trouvé à 100°C. On ne peut rien dire contre cette explication, certaines mesures préliminaires venant au contraire la renforcer.

En fait la croissance n'est peut être pas seule à être responsable de cet accroissement linéaire, il se peut que certains défauts comme par exemple des boucles de dislocations subsistent en nombre proportionnel à celui des fissions. Une point de fission ne fait en effet pas disparaître une boucle de dislocations assez grande pour n'être affectée que sur une partie de son contour.

Notons que si l'explication due à la croissance est exacte, les dislocations ne jouent qu'un rôle mineur. La courbe III est en effet située en dessous de la première ce qui indique que les dislocations ne font que manger un certain nombre de défauts.

Si l'on soustrait de la courbe de résistance électrique l'accroissement linéaire en question on obtient (Fig. 16) des courbes qui dans le cas du métal recuit ou écroui sont très sensiblement affines de la courbe obtenue par irradiation à la température ordinaire. La courbe correspondant au métal recuit possède un petit méplat qu'il ne nous est pas possible d'interpréter actuellement. Par contre le début des courbes a été soigneusement tracé. Cette affinité des courbes autorise à parler du volume perturbé par la fission, cette notion ne devant en principe *pas dépendre de la température* du milieu, tout au moins tant que celle-ci est inférieure à la température moyenne atteinte dans la pointe de fission.

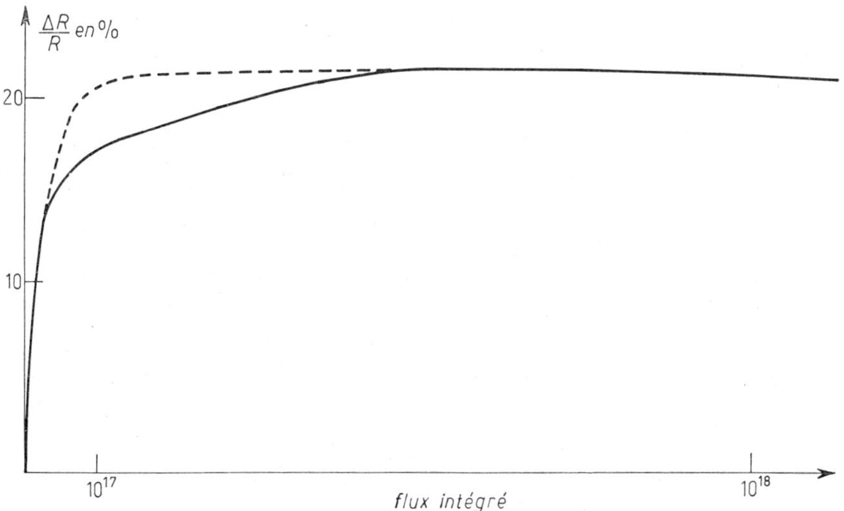

Fig. 16. – —— Courbe déduite de la courbe de changement de résistivité (80 °K) en soustrayant la partie linéaire. – – – Courbe affine de la courbe de changement de résistivité (0 °C).

On remarque que le métal contenant des dislocations possède un nombre de défauts à l'équilibre plus petit que celui du métal recuit. Les dislocations étant des puits pour les défauts cette différence est très normale. Il faut cependant remarquer que de ce fait les dislocations devraient se saturer ou disparaître, cela semble ne se faire que pour des irradiations beaucoup plus longues.

3. – Mise en désordre des alliages U_2Mo.

Cette expérience est destinée à évaluer l'importance relative des effets des oscillations du réseau et des collisions.

Nous avons ainsi été amenés à étudier la mise en désordre des alliages U_2Mo. Le diagramme d'équilibre uranium-molybdène est représenté sur la Fig. 17. La phase U_2Mo a une structure quadratique et on peut dire qu'elle est formée de trois cubes centrés (structure de la phase γ) superposés et légèrement aplatis. L'aplatissement est de l'ordre de quelques pour cent. Le volume total de la maille est par contre égal à celui de trois mailles γ à mieux que 10^{-3} près. On voit qu'un échauffement au dessus de 600°C de ces alliages les transforme en uranium γ de structure cubique centrée.

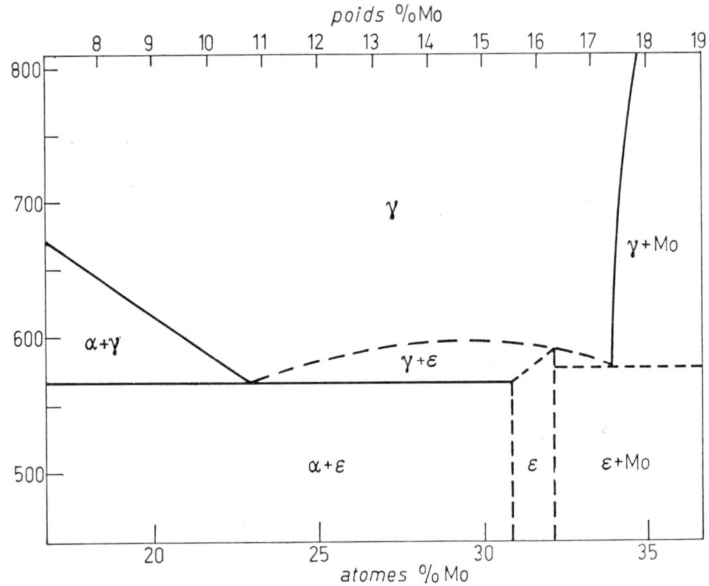

Fig. 17. – Diagramme d'équilibre du système U_2Mo d'après DWIGHT.

On peut se demander si les oscillations du réseau sont assez importantes pour que la phase U_2Mo soit fondue et que par refroidissement on obtienne la structure γ (on sait en effet que la transformation de la phase γ en U_2Mo est lente comme toutes les transformations de mise en désordre). La fusion étant

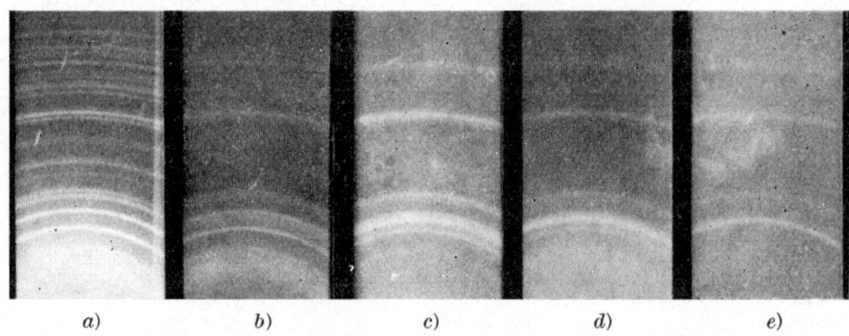

Fig. 18. – D'après WITTELS et SHERILL: ORNL. ZrO_2: diagrammes Debye-Scherrer d'échantillons irradiés par les fragments de fission. *a*) non irradié; *b*) après irradiation avec $7.66 \cdot 10^{14}$ paires de fragments de fission/cm^3; *c*) après irradiation avec $6.67 \cdot 10^{15}$ paires de fragments de fission/cm^3; *d*) après irradiation avec $1.07 \cdot 10^{16}$ paires de fragments de fission/cm^3 transformés 80%; *e*) après irradiation avec $3.39 \cdot 10^{16}$ paires de fragments de fission/cm^3 complètement transformés.

un phénomène qui ne dure que pendant un petit nombre de périodes d'oscillations du réseau elle peut se produire dans la pointe de fission.

Dans une telle hypothèse on aurait par irradiation un certain nombre de tubes transformés en phase γ. Si le volume total de ces tubes devient notable on peut s'attendre à voir apparaître des raies de la structure γ. Ces raies devraient se superposer à celles de la structure quadratique.

Cette façon de voir peut encore se renforcer si l'on considère les expériences de M. C. WITTELS et F. A. SHERILL [16] dans lesquelles des raies de la phase cubique de la zircone stable à haute température apparaissent en même temps que disparaissent celles de la phase monoclinique (Fig. 18).

L'expérience montre que la situation est tout à fait différente dans le cas de la phase U_2Mo. J. BLOCH [17] a observé que les raies de cette phase qui est quadratique se rapprochent au cours de l'irradiation pour aboutir finalement au diagramme de la structure cubique γ. A aucun moment on a une coexistence des raies des deux phases. Cette variation continue de paramètre est d'ailleurs associée à la disparition des raies d'ordre (Fig. 19).

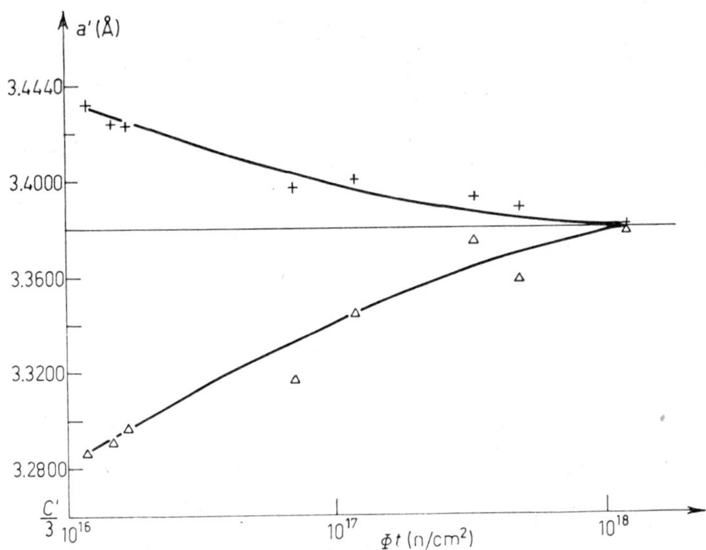

Fig. 19. – Changement de paramètre de la phase quadratique U_2Mo par irradiation.

Cette expérience montre que les oscillations du réseau ne constituent pas le phénomène essentiel et que ce sont les collisions qui assurent la mise en désordre. Cette conclusion est confirmée du fait que le paramètre varie de façon continue. Le désordre s'établit ainsi à l'aide de défauts ponctuels ou linéaires. Le volume de la phase γ (3 mailles) est en effet très sensiblement égal (à 10^{-3} près) à celui de la maille de la phase U_2Mo. Si par conséquent un volume notable passait en bloc de la structure U_2Mo à la structure γ aucun effet à longue distance ne se ferait sentir donc aucun changement de paramètre. L'effet des pointes de fission est donc de créer le désordre point par point ou le long de certaines lignes.

Cette expérience est également intéressante parce que la mise en désordre peut se faire par des *permutations de positions entre atomes*; on peut donc se demander si le nombre de ces permutations n'est pas très supérieur à celui des défauts créés et si de ce fait la vitesse de mise en désordre n'est pas très supérieure dans cette expérience à celle qui est obtenue dans l'expérience précédente. C'est le contraire qui est exact. *La mise en désordre demande un flux environ dix fois plus élevé pour être achevée* (à la température ordinaire) que la saturation de la résistance électrique. Cela signifie en gros qu'il faut que 10 pointes de fission recouvrent un certain volume avant qu'il ne change de phase. Cette valeur est cohérente avec ce que l'on sait par ailleurs comme le montre le calcul développé ci-dessous (Section II-4).

Pour aller plus avant dans l'interprétation de cette mise en désordre nous avons refait la même expérience à la température de l'azote liquide [18] tout en effectuant les mesures de diffraction à la température ordinaire. Cela suppose donc que les défauts gelés à la température de l'azote liquide ne modifient pas trop le désordre obtenu à cette température en reprenant leur état d'équilibre à la température ambiante. Cela étant admis, on observe (Fig. 20) que la mise en désordre est seulement un peu plus lente à la température de l'azote liquide. Le rapport des vitesses de mise en désordre n'autorise à mettre en jeu aucun phénomène activé thermiquement car il est bien trop petit.

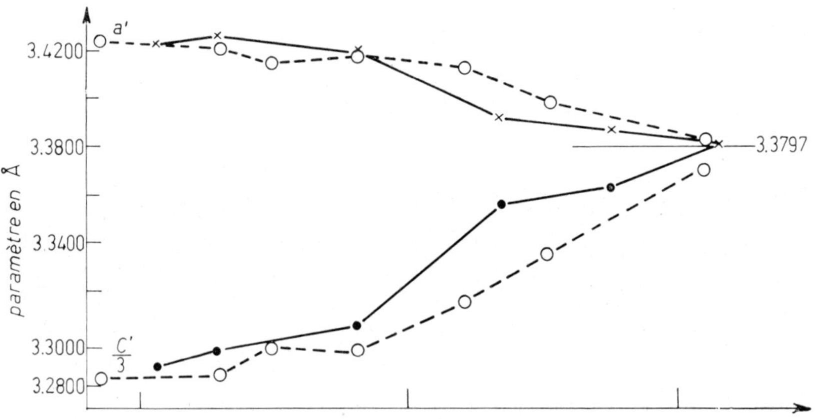

Fig. 20. – Changement de structure de la phase U_2Mo. —— Irradiation à la température ambiante. - - - Irradiation à 78 °K.

En résumé le désordre s'établit donc point par point et d'une façon qui dépend assez peu de la température du milieu. Cette dernière expérience établit donc *l'influence prépondérante des collisions pour créer des défauts sur les effets d'échauffement* et infirme donc le modèle de thermal spike.

Il faut souligner que ces résultats ne sont sûrement valables que dans le cas d'un métal.

4. – Le problème de la croissance.

Si les défauts qui subsistent après le passage d'une particule de fission sont peu nombreux — Section II-2 — il en est de même de ceux qui produisent la croissance. En admettant un nombre de 300 000 atomes déplacés par fission on voit d'après ce qui a été dit au début du paragraphe I-4 qu'environ 1/1000 des défauts créés sert à la croissance. Il est donc clair que la plupart d'entre eux se recombinent après quelques sauts. La densité des défauts est de 10 % dans la pointe de fission d'après ce que nous savons de son volume ($2\cdot10^{-16}$ cm^3 soit $8\cdot10^6$ atomes) et du nombre (300 000) d'atomes déplacés. Il est par conséquent bien normal qu'une recombinaison intense se produise dès que la particule de fission est passée.

Le problème central est donc de savoir quand et comment disparaissent les défauts qui produisent la croissance.

Il peut tout d'abord s'agir de collisions provoquant des « crowdions dynamiques » comme le suggère GONSER [19]. Cette explication nous semble faible car l'effet d'anisotropie de la structure α devrait porter sur tous les défauts créés. Cet effet serait donc très faible. D'autres arguments concourent à écarter cette explication. On comprend mal dans ce modèle comment la croissance peut disparaître avec la température (décroissance certaine de 100 à 350°C). Le changement d'anisotropie dans ce domaine est très petit. D'autre part les joints de grains devraient jouer un rôle fondamental d'après cette théorie, ce qui n'est pas.

On est donc amené à penser que parmi les défauts qui viennent d'être créés après la fission un certain nombre diffusent et disparaissent en provoquant la croissance. Une simple diffusion anisotrope des défauts jusqu'à leur disparition ne peut d'ailleurs suffire à expliquer ce phénomène. On serait en effet amené à des formules pour le coefficient F de la forme:

$$G \simeq A \exp\left[-\frac{E_1}{kT}\right] - B \exp\left[-\frac{E_2}{T}\right].$$

Un examen de la dépendance de ces courbes en fonction de la température T montre que pour les valeurs usuelles de E_1 ou E_2 (au moins 0.5 eV) cette fonction croît toujours avec T.

Il faut donc analyser le comportement des lacunes et des interstitiels. Des recherches sont actuellement entreprises pour savoir si la diffusion des lacunes est anisotrope dans l'uranium [20]. Le comportement des interstitiels peut être très différent. Ceux-ci auront tendance à écarter les « tôles ondulées » de la structure de l'uranium. Ils auront ainsi une forte tendance à diffuser dans la direction [100]. En se condensant ils peuvent donner naissance à de petites boucles de dislocation de vecteur de Burgers [100] qui peuvent ensuite se déplacer vers la surface du cristal sous l'effet de contraintes thermiques.

Avec ces hypothèses qui ont d'ailleurs été déjà plusieurs fois avancées, le schéma de la croissance serait le suivant:

1) Presque tous les défauts se recombinent.

2) Les interstitiels diffusent suivant la direction [100] et se rassemblent dans des plans [100] pour donner de petite boucles de vecteur de Burgers [010]. Un certain nombre sont mangés par les dislocations mais ce phénomène n'est sans doute pas essentiel.

3) Les lacunes diffusent d'une façon sensiblement isotrope ce qui est le cas de l'étain par exemple (ref. [21]) et se condensent sur les plans de moindre énergie superficielle; on ne connaît rien sur l'orientation de ces plans actuellement. Pour expliquer la croissance il faudrait que ces plans soient des plans (100).

La décroissance de G avec la température s'expliquerait alors par une recombinaison plus intense des défauts quand la température augmente. Il suffit d'ailleurs pour cela qu'un seul type de défaut se déplace.

5. – Conclusion.

En fait le substratum expérimental nécessaire à une explication de la croissance n'est pas encore acquis. Deux données importantes sont nécessaires:

1) Une courbe de G en fonction de T, notamment aux basses températures.

2) Des examens par microscopie électronique par transmission montrant les déchets qui subsistent après la fission.

REFERENCES

[1] Rapport de la Conférence de Genève (1955), no. P/745.
[2] A. N. Holden: KAPL 1149.
[3] J. H. Kittel et S. H. Paine: *Nucl. Sci. Eng.*, **3**, 258 (1958).
[4] V. W. Eldred, G. B. Greenough et P. Leech: Rapport de la Conférence de Genève (1958), no. P/50.

[5] S. F. Pugh: Rapport de la Conférence de Genève (1955), no. P/443.
[6] S. H. Paine et J. H. Kittel: A.N.L. 5676 (1958).
[7] R. Resnick et L. Seigle: *Second Nucl. Eng. and Sci. Conference*, paper no. 63.
[8] D. Tardivon: *Nuclear Metallurgy*, **6**, 39 (1959).
[9] J. Bloch, J. P. Mustelier, P. Bussy et J. Blin: *Etude sur l'uranium irradié*, Rapport de la Conférence de Genève (1958), no. P/1158.
[10] S. H. Bush: *Irradiation effects in uranium*, Rapport H. 51444.
[11] P. E. Madsen: *Effect of irradiation on the hardness of* αU, Rapport A.E.R.E. M/R 741.
[12] S. T. Konobeevski, K. P. Dubrovin, B. M. Levitsky, L. D. Panteleev et N. F. Pravdyuk: *Quelques phénomènes physico-chimiques provoqués par irradiation dans les matériaux fissiles*, Rapport de la Conférence de Genève (1958), no. P/2192.
[13] A. C. Roberts et A. H. Cottrell: *Creep of* α *uranium during irradiation with neutrons*, Rapport A.E.R.E. M/R 1969.
[14] A. S. Zaimovsky, G. Y. Sergeev, V. V. Titova, B. M. Levitsky et Y. N. Sokursky: *Influence des propriétés et de la structure de l'uranium sur son comportement sous irradiation*, Rapport de la Conférence de Genève (1958), no. P/2191.
[15] *Journal des Matériaux Nucléaires*, **1**, 203 (1959).
[16] J. Block: *Phys. Rev. Lett.*, **3**, 176 (1959).
[17] M. C. Wittels et F. A. Sherill: *Journ. des Matériaux Nucléaires*, **1**, 90 (1960).
[18] Résultats non publiés de J. Bloch et J. Doulat.
[19] U. Gonser: *Journ. of Nuclear Materials*, **2**, 43 (1960).
[20] Au Laboratoire « Argonne National Laboratory » en particulier: voir par exemple A.N.L. 6099 S. J. Rothman, p. 102.
[21] J. D. Meakin et E. Klokholm: *Trans. of AIME*, **218**, 463 (1960).

Special Seminars.

Thermoelectricity and Direct Conversion Systems.

J. A. KRUMHANSL

Cornell University, Department of Physics - Ithaca, N. Y.

1. – Introduction.

Radiation damage in solids originally arose as a technological problem in the operation of reactors. The desire to understand radiation effects has given incentive to substantial progress in basic science, which in its turn has stimulated further advances in technology. Currently, we hear of various devices for direct conversion of heat into electrical energy. It is the author's feeling that within the next decade or so study and design of these devices will become an integral part of the technology associated with reactors.

In these lectures an attempt will be made to present, first, the general principles that are common to all forms of energy converters, and then applications of these principles in some particular energy converting systems.

Since the audience constitutes a « school », this approach is adopted in preference to review of constructional and technological details of practical or existing direct energy conversion devices.

2. – Review of thermostatics and irreversible thermodynamics.

Thermodynamics as a subject has had two principal eras in its development. The accomplishments of the first era, dealing with systems in equilibrium or processes accomplished by a sequence of steps each essentially of an equilibrium nature, have by now encompassed virtually all of the theoretical and experimental content necessary to make equilibrium thermodynamics (better called « thermostatics ») quite complete as a fundamental subject in physics.

The second era, which is still evolving, comprises the formulation and application of principles suitable to describe interacting systems which are not in thermostatic equilibrium. In many ways such problems are far more important and challenging to the imagination. The understanding of transport processes in solids, liquids, and gases, the systemization of description in chemical kinetics, the relation of fluctuation theory to transport phenomena all have the common feature of variety and, therefore, usefulness that dynamic systems hold to advantage over static systems. Many have contributed to this evolution [1]—ONSAGER, DE GROOT, PRIGOGINE, CALLEN, LAX, to mention a few. The primary purpose of basing a discussion of energy conversion on this formalism of irreversible thermodynamics (or, simply « thermodynamics ») is that modern energy conversion concepts depend in an *essential* way on phenomena occurring primarily in nonequilibrium systems.

It is the task of this section of the discussion to review very briefly the structure of irreversible thermodynamics in such a form as to be particularly directed to application in the energy conversion problem; also, since application is our motivation, it is not the intent to be comprehensive in the development of the basic principles of this subject.

The principal features of « thermodynamics » which we wish to note, and which extend beyond the postulates of thermostatics, are:

1) the extension and use of static concepts to some properties of systems which are not in equilibrium;

2) the extension from discrete to continuous systems;

3) the concept of entropy production in nonequilibrium systems and the Onsager relations.

These ideas are completely extra-thermostatic, but are essential in specifying heat and energy balance in nonequilibrium systems. Moreover, it is in this part of the structure of the formalism that the relation between flows and driving forces is systemized.

Consider the first of these—the use of thermostatic concepts in nonequilibrium problems. It is clear that the first law, being simply a statement of energy conservation, will apply without conceptual modification to heat and energy transfer between components of or regions in a nonequilibrium assembly.

To discuss the domain of applicability of the second law, it is necessary to recognize the need to re-examine definitions of entropy. What is done is to postulate the concept that « local » rather than « global » (PRIGOGINE, CALLEN, Ref. [1]) calculation of the entropy (or for that matter, other thermostatic extensive quantities) can be made in terms of « local » intensive parameters. The justification of this view can be regarded simply as a postulate (CALLEN [1], Chapter 15) or as plausible on mechanistic (statistical) grounds in systems described by distribution functions differing not too drastically from the equilibrium distribution function (DE GROOT [1] p. 221).

Proceeding from this postulate the second law is exhibited in terms of:

first, specification of the change in entropy in familiar form but with « local » meaning,

$$T\,\mathrm{d}S = \mathrm{d}U + p\,\mathrm{d}V - \sum_{\gamma} \mu_{\gamma}\,\mathrm{d}n_{\gamma} \tag{2.1}$$

(where the symbols have the standard meaning temperature, entropy, internal energy, pressure, volume, chemical potential, concentration), and second, in the statement that for purely internal changes in the system (or each defined subsystem) $\mathrm{d}S_i \geqslant 0$, where $\mathrm{d}S_i$ is the entropy change due to transfer within the system (usually irreversible).

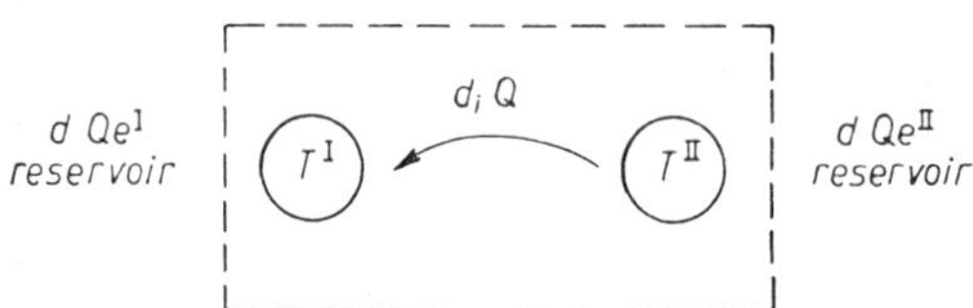

Fig. 1. – A system consisting of two subsystems having different « local » temperatures, T^{I} and T^{II}.

Perhaps the simplest example which can be used to illustrate the application of these quasi-static postulates is the transfer of heat between two closed but interacting phases, as illustrated in Fig. 1.

The total entropy change is

$$\mathrm{d}s = d_e S + d_i S = \frac{d_e Q^{\mathrm{I}}}{T^{\mathrm{I}}} + \frac{d_e Q^{\mathrm{II}}}{T^{\mathrm{II}}} + d_i I_Q \left(\frac{1}{T^{\mathrm{I}}} - \frac{1}{T^{\mathrm{II}}}\right). \tag{2.2}$$

The application of the postulates above then yields (by the first law $\mathrm{d}U = \mathrm{d}Q$ in this example, since $\mathrm{d}V$ and $\mathrm{d}n_{\gamma}$ are zero)

$$\frac{d_i S}{\mathrm{d}t} = \frac{d_i Q^{\mathrm{I}}}{\mathrm{d}T}\left(\frac{1}{T^{\mathrm{I}}} - \frac{1}{T^{\mathrm{II}}}\right) > 0 \,. \tag{2.3}$$

From (2.3) one concludes that Q^{I} will be positive if $T^{\mathrm{I}} > T^{\mathrm{II}}$ and vice versa, in accord with experience. In this example the « local » parameter concept is particularly plausible, and the use of the postulate of positive internal entropy production is quite obvious. Similar examples including volume changes, particle transfer (chemical reactions) and combinations thereof can easily be developed for interacting discrete subsystems.

In the development of this example, with generalization of thermostatic concepts, we have introduced the irreversible entropy production rate (2.3). Consequences of this will be examined in connection with the third of the points previously itemized—entropy and energy balance in energy conversion devices.

Before proceeding to the next item in this outline (the extension to continuous systems), it is perhaps worth noting that the extension of thermostatic concepts so far has not included any explicit restriction to situations where the flows are linear functions of the driving forces (temperature differences in the above example) which produce them. Thus, at least this much of the formalism of irreversible thermodynamics can be and has been applied with care to nonlinear problems, such as chemical reactions; the point is emphasized since subsequent application to the thermionic energy converter might prompt this question.

The extension to continuous systems is now presented on the basis of reasonableness; more extensive discussion can be found in the standard references. We can use eq. (2.1) and the above example as a guide to what is required. Equation (2.1) is a relation involving *changes* in the extensive variables with parametric dependence on the values of the local intensive parameters. In reactions involving discrete systems, as in conventional thermostatics, changes can be labeled by an index, *i.e.*, n_γ the number of particles in the γ-th phase. In continuous systems the *changes* in question are flows or currents. Thus, we make the replacements

$$\left\{\begin{array}{lll} \mathrm{d}U & \to J^0 & \text{energy current,} \\ \mathrm{d}n_\gamma & \to J^\gamma & \text{particle current of } \gamma\text{-th species,} \\ \mathrm{d}s & \to J^s & \text{entropy current.} \end{array}\right. \tag{2.4}$$

Terms in (2.1) related to $\mathrm{d}V$ can be related [7] to the tensor gradient of velocity of the center of mass $\boldsymbol{v}$; in solid state and thermionic applications these need not be considered, but must be included in discussing more general systems such as magnetohydrodynamic devices. In systems with no net mass flow ($\boldsymbol{v}=0$), eq. (2.1) then assumes the form

$$T\boldsymbol{J}^s = \boldsymbol{J}^0 - \sum \mu_\gamma \boldsymbol{J}^\gamma \,. \tag{2.5}$$

The usual differential manipulations applied to flow fields apply. For example, the entropy production per unit volume would be given by

$$\dot{S} = \frac{\partial s}{\partial t} + \boldsymbol{\nabla}\cdot\boldsymbol{J}^s \,, \tag{2.6}$$

where $\dot{S}$ is the net entropy source strength due to external heat reservoirs and internal irreversible terms such as (2.3) (see (2.8)). Of course, any of these « extensive » flow parameters can be expected to depend on local values of the intensive parameters, *i.e.*, temperature, composition, local electrical potential.

To summarize, the extension of thermostatic to continuous systems consists primarily of the replacement of extensive parameter changes by currents which are defined as a continuum field, and secondarily in the extension of pseudothermostatic relations such as (2.1) to the currents, *i.e.*, (2.5) and (2.6).

This brings us to the third item in this survey—entropy production and the related transport equations. We are led more or less directly to the very important and quite extra-« thermostatic » role of entropy production by noting that starting from (2.1) we calculated a rate of production of entropy in an internal irreversible process, *i.e.*, heat transfer between two subsystems. Entropy production rates are of the form

$$\dot{S}_i = \dot{U}_i\left(\frac{1}{T^{\text{I}}} - \frac{1}{T^{\text{II}}}\right). \tag{2.7}$$

If we denote by X_i the *extensive* parameters, then (2.7) is a special case of a general form [1]

$$\dot{S}_i = \sum_i F_i \dot{X}_i\,. \tag{2.8}$$

From (2.1), X_i may be U, V, or n_γ, for example. This equation is then interpreted by denoting the $\dot{X}$ as « fluxes » or « currents », and the F_i as « affinities » or « forces ». Note that (2.8) results simply from the extension of thermostatics and « linearity » between F_i and X_i has not been invoked.

The terminology of « fluxes » and « forces » is obviously appropriate, since it is just the fact that $F_i \neq 0$ that produces the flux X_i. In the previous example, $F_U = \left((1/T^{\text{I}}) - (1/T^{\text{II}})\right)$ and it is just the temperature difference that produces the heat flow. Specifically, in the case of discrete interacting systems, the forces which produce currents are simply the differences in the differential entropy representation intensive parameter coefficients of the extensive parameter changes. Thus

$$\left\{\begin{array}{lcc} & \dot{X}_i & F_i \\[1ex] \text{Heat flow} & \dot{U} & \Delta\left(\dfrac{1}{T}\right), \\[2ex] \text{Expansion changes} & V & \Delta\left(\dfrac{P}{T}\right). \\[2ex] \text{Particle transfer} & n_\gamma & \Delta\left(\dfrac{\mu_\gamma}{T}\right), \end{array}\right. \tag{2.9}$$

where the symbol $\Delta(\;)$ means the difference between its argument for the two discrete interacting phases.

The extension of the relations (2.9) to continuous systems follows in a plausible way. As (2.1) relates differential entropy change to differential extensive parameter changes, and the transition to the continuum is accomplished by replacing extensive parameter differentials by current flow fields, we can write

$$\boldsymbol{J}^s = \sum F_i \boldsymbol{J}^i \,, \tag{2.10}$$

where $\boldsymbol{J}^s$ is the entropy current density, $\boldsymbol{J}^i$ is the current density for the extensive parameter X_i, and F_i is the intensive parametric coefficient in (2.1) or (2.6).

For applications to energy conversion in continuous systems the most important point concerned with entropy production is: in a continuous system, simply as a consequence of the existence of flows, there must be a production of entropy at every point in the flow field. There may in addition be other external sources or sinks of heat, particles, etc., which contribute to the total entropy balance, but the flow-produced entropy is an intrinsic property of the nonequilibrium state of the system.

We can use a special flow (Callen) as a computational device to compute the entropy production at a point due to the existence of currents; again reference is made to systems with vanishing net matter flow, *i.e.*, $\boldsymbol{v}=0$. Consider uniform flow in a steady state. Using (2.6) and (2.10) we can write

$$\left\{\begin{aligned} \dot{S}_i &= \frac{\partial S}{\partial t} + \boldsymbol{\nabla}\cdot\boldsymbol{J}^s, \\ \dot{S}_i &= \frac{\partial S}{\partial t} + (F_i \boldsymbol{\nabla}\cdot J^i + J^i\cdot\boldsymbol{\nabla} F_i)\,. \end{aligned}\right. \tag{2.11}$$

Under the particular assumptions made $\partial S/\partial t = 0$ (steady state) and $\boldsymbol{\nabla}_i J^i = 0$ (uniform flow) whence

$$\dot{S}_i = \sum_i \boldsymbol{J}^i\cdot\boldsymbol{\nabla}_i\,. \tag{2.12}$$

Though this has been calculated for a special case, the intrinsic flow induced entropy production has this form in general. Following Callen we rewrite (2.12) as

$$\dot{S}_i = \sum \boldsymbol{J}^i\cdot\mathscr{F}_i\,, \tag{21.3}$$

where now $\mathscr{F}_i = \boldsymbol{\nabla} F_i$ is the «force» associated with the extensive parameter current $\boldsymbol{J}^i$. $\mathscr{F}_i$ depends parametrically only on the local values of the intensive parameters and their gradients. This entropy production (2.13) is the continuum equivalent of (2.8); in analogy with eq. (2.9) the currents and related driving forces can be tabulated as follows:

energy current density	$\mathscr{F}_0 = \nabla\left(\dfrac{1}{T}\right)$,
particle current density	$\mathscr{F}_\gamma = -\nabla\left(\dfrac{\mu_\gamma}{T}\right)$,
total matter flow	$\mathscr{F} = \nabla\left(\dfrac{p}{T}\right)$.

Thus, in continuous systems there is an entropy production proportional to the product of currents and forces.

While we have identified these forces as cause of the currents, we have not discussed the explicit form of the relation between these two quantities. Obviously, the most general equation relating currents and forces will have the form

$$J^i = \sum_j L_{ij}\mathscr{F}_j + \sum_{jk} L_{ijk}\mathscr{F}_j \cdot \mathscr{F}_k + \dots . \tag{2.14}$$

The L_{ij}, L_{ijk}, etc., are the « kinetic coefficients » and are functions of the local intensive parameters.

In general, the properties of the kinetic coefficients L_{ij} ... are not determined beyond the linear approximation. We now quote the fundamental Onsager theorem regarding the kinetic coefficients L_{ij}. For situations where the *first term* on the right-hand side of (2.14) suffices, microscopic reversibility is sufficient to establish that

$$L_{ij}(\boldsymbol{H}) = L_{ji}(-\boldsymbol{H}) , \tag{2.15}$$

where $\boldsymbol{H}$ is the applied magnetic field if there is such. The importance of this symmetry relation is that it reduces the number of independent kinetic coefficients and also makes possible the justifications of pseudothermostatic treatments (KELVIN) of phenomena such as thermoelectricity.

This completes the brief review of those ingredients of the formalism of irreversible thermodynamics of primary interest in application to energy conversion. Many topics in this subject of both past and current interest (particularly fluctuations and nonlinearity) have been completely omitted in this introduction. The reader is referred to LAX [2] and BERNARD and CALLEN [3] for recent reviews.

3. – General considerations for energy converters.

Ordinarily, the next step in the application of the « thermodynamics » we have developed so far consists in application to the specific local transport equations of diffusion, thermoelectricity, chemical reactions, and so forth. This approach is a natural one if it is the local behavior which is of primary interest.

On the other hand, our primary interest is in systems rather than local phenomena. Ultimately, an understanding of the local phenomena in a particular system will be necessary; on the other hand, if it is possible to develop an overall framework against which all energy-conversion systems might be compared, it would simplify the comparative evaluation of the many and varied systems being proposed.

This objective can be accomplished to quite a surprising degree, without detailed discussion of specific phenomena, following the extremely interesting ideas presented by TOLMAN and FINE [4]. While fully cognizant of unresolved fundamental physical questions of validity in the extension of thermostatics to « pseudothermostatics », their work was addressed to an application of basic principles to practical systems. The present approach will not be identical, since it profits by the extensive developments in « thermodynamics » since their paper was written, but the writer wishes to direct attention to their work as a fruitful conceptual statement of the « system » approach.

Most of the present interest in energy-conversion systems is directed toward continuous flow systems rather than cyclic systems of the more conventional type; moreover, the « direct » conversion systems use charged particles as the working fluid. Therefore, we now proceed to a description of systems in which heat (and perhaps fuel) is supplied and removed to establish currents in a continuous working fluid, which currents then can be made to do work by their flow through some load. Moreover, we will restrict ourselves to steady-state situations.

The kind of system one might have in general is shown suggestively in Fig. 2. Of course, this schematic system is general enough to include a tremendous variety of systems—turbines, magnetohydrodynamic generators, thermoelectric, thermionic systems and so forth. There is a basis for subdividing these according to whether the system is primarily convective or diffusive in regard to energy transfer. Further details of this differentiation will be discussed in Section **4**, but they are not of primary concern in the following deductions of general systems limitations.

The discussion of Section **2** postulated that it was possible to extend thermostatics to nonequilibrium situations by the use of the concepts of « local » extensive and intensive parameters. Furthermore, the externally induced changes of the extensive parameters were added to internal changes to obtain *total* changes in such quantities as entropy, internal energy, etc. Finally, specific attention was given to the internal *irreversible* entropy production due to fluxes set up by the nonequilibrium conditions.

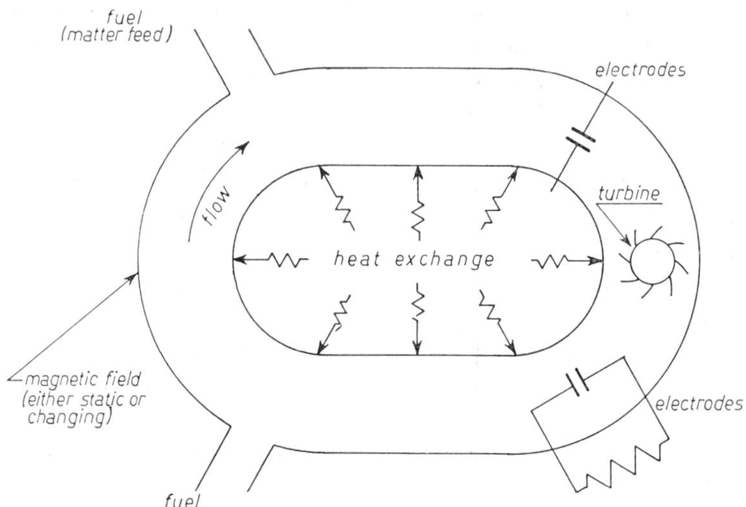

Fig. 2. – A general energy-conversion system.

We now apply these ideas, following TOLMAN and FINE. Consider the first law; suppose that at each point in the fluid we can place particle sources or sinks and that at each point we may make contact with a heat reservoir supplying heat at the local temperature. Let ΔU be the total change in internal energy of the system, ΔW the work done by the system, ΔU_γ^n the energy supplied by the injected γ-th species of injected fuel and ΔQ the external heat supplied to the n-th element of volume. These Δ « changes » may be referred to a cycle for cyclic systems, or may be « per unit time » in a continuous system. The specific form applicable in continuous systems is given by eq. (4.2). We thus have

$$\Delta U = \sum_n \sum_\gamma \Delta U_\gamma^n + \sum_n \Delta Q_M - \Delta W \,. \tag{3.1}$$

In continuous systems, the sums are really integrals over the volume of the system.

In similar fashion, and using the generalization of (2.2), plus the assumption of steady state,

$$\Delta S = \Delta S_e + \Delta S_i = 0 = \sum_\gamma S_\gamma + \sum \frac{Q_M}{T_M} + \Delta S_i \,. \tag{3.2}$$

In this expression ΔS_i is the irreversible entropy production which we have previously discussed in (2.3) and (2.13). Its important role with respect to the efficiency of the overall energy conversion system can now be examined.

In many applications, the system gives off heat either by design or accident to some surrounding environment at temperature T_0. Multiplying (3.2) by T_0 and subtracting from (3.1) gives

$$\Delta W = \sum_{\gamma} (\Delta U_{\gamma} - T_0 \Delta s_{\gamma}) + \sum \frac{T_M - T_0}{T_M} \Delta Q_M - T_0 \Delta S_i \,. \tag{3.3}$$

The role of the irreversible entropy production in the overall system performance is now manifestly clear. Since ΔS_i is *necessarily* positive, it subtracts from the work done by the fuel supplied (the first term) and the heat supplied (the second term).

The power and generality of the arguments leading to (3.3) can be recognized by illustrating the use of this limiting principle for the two most prominent « termoelectric » systems—the solid state thermoelectric system and the thermionic system.

Consider first a simple thermoelectric system to which heat Q_H is supplied at the hot junction only, and removed at the cold junction; no carriers are supplied or removed. Then (3.3) becomes

$$\Delta W = \frac{T_H - T_0}{T_H} \Delta Q_H - T_0 \Delta S_i \,. \tag{3.3a}$$

The exact calculation of the internal (irreversible) entropy generation for this case will be discussed later. We can make a simple approximation as follows. In the steady state, we must have $\Delta S_{\text{total}} = 0$; therefore $\Delta S_U = -\Delta S_e \cdot$ Since ΔS_e is produced only by heat put in at T_H and (negative heat) at T_0, we simply need to know these. The one assumption which we make on plausibility arguments concerns distribution of the internal $I^2 r$ heat; half goes to each junction. It is usual to assume as a first approximation that the termoelectric power α is independent of temperature. Defining Q_f as the thermal heat flow,

$$(3.4)\quad \left\{ \begin{aligned} \Delta S_i &= -\frac{Q_H}{T_H} - \frac{Q_0}{T_0}\,, \\ \Delta S_i &= -\frac{1}{T_H}\left(I\alpha T_H + Q_f - \tfrac{1}{2} I^2 r\right) - \frac{1}{T_0}\left(- I\alpha T_0 - Q_f - \tfrac{1}{2} I^2 r\right), \\ \Delta S_i &= Q_f \left(\frac{1}{T_0} - \frac{1}{T_H}\right) + \frac{I^2 r}{2}\left(\frac{1}{T_0} + \frac{1}{T_H}\right). \end{aligned} \right.$$

Note the heat flow and ohmic loss terms.

From (3.3-a) the efficiency $\eta = W/Q_H$ becomes (η_c = Carnot efficiency)

$$\eta = \eta_c - \frac{Q_f \eta_c + I^2 r(T/T_H)}{I\alpha T_H + Q_f - \frac{1}{2} I^2 r}, \tag{3.5}$$

where

$$T = \frac{T_H + T_0}{2}.$$

This expression has the form derived in a different way by IOFFE. It is physically sensible: when $I \to 0$, $\eta \to 0$. There is an upper limit to I such that $\alpha(T_H - T_0) = Ir$ where again the efficiency is zero, *i.e.*, all thermoelectric « power » goes into internal heating. There is an optimum value at I_M found by differentiating (3.5) with respect to I which to the approximations made here agrees with Ioffe's expression

$$\eta = \eta_c \frac{M - 1}{M + (T_0/T_H)}, \tag{3.6}$$

with $M = \sqrt{1 + Z\bar{T}}$ and $Z = \alpha^2 \sigma / \varkappa$, where σ is the conductivity. Thus, without detailed examination of local phenomena we have deduced the principal features of the conventional thermoelectric converter.

Let us pause to summarize the content so far of this section, and of the above example, in terms of the elements of irreversible thermodynamics reviewed in Section **2**. First, in (3.1) and (3.2) we have made use of the postulate extending thermostatics to nonequilibrium systems, implicitly using the concept of « local » meaning of the thermostatic parameters. Second, we have utilized the concept of entropy production in a steady-state nonequilibrium process; moreover, we have made use of the fact that this must be a positive quantity. Third, we have in (3.3) a rearrangement of the equations resulting from these postulates, along lines suggested by TOLMAN and FINE, which is fruitful.

In the example chosen, we have not made explicit use of one of the items discussed in Section **2**—the formulation for continuous systems . Actually, it is only through an application of this part of the theory that the precise current and temperature distribution in a thermocouple can be determined in terms of the applied heats and electrical loads; this will be the subject of Section **4**.

Another example which is particularly suited to applications of the methodology so far developed is the thermionic diode. The following assumptions can reasonably be met in practice:

a) by introduction of a small amount of an easily ionizable gas, space charge effects can virtually be suppressed;

b) at the same time, the number of gas atoms and ions necessary for space charge suppression is not so great as to limit the electron mean free path essentially, so that electrons emitted from one electrode are free to travel without scattering to the other electrode;

c) we assume plane parallel geometry;

d) we neglect thermoelectric effects in the metal leads.

Under these circumstances, the system is essentially identical to one in which heat and particles are transferred between two discrete subsystems—the cathode and the anode. The situation is shown schematically in Fig. 3.

Rewriting (3.3-*a*),

$$W = \frac{T_H - T_0}{T_H} Q_H - T_0 \Delta S_i \,. \tag{3.3a}$$

Again, the central problem in calculating the practical efficiency is that of calculating the irreversible entropy production ΔS_i.

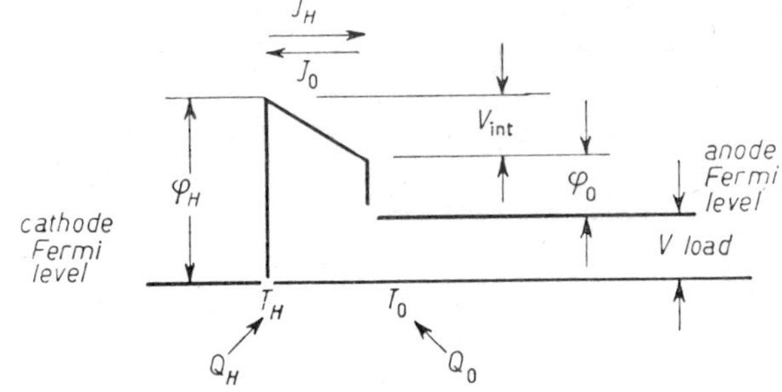

Fig. 3. – Schematic of potential distribution in a thermionic diode.

Assuming saturation conditions the various contributions per unit area are as follows (*):

a) Heat transfer between the electrodes in the electron gas, and the resulting entropy production. This is [5, 6]

$$\Delta S_{ie} = (J_H 2kT_H - J_0 2kT_0)\left(\frac{1}{T_0} - \frac{1}{T_H}\right). \tag{3.7}$$

b) The entropy production due to transfer of particles between phases. This is

$$\Delta S_{i\Phi} = (J_H - J_0)\left(\frac{\varphi_H}{T_H} - \frac{\varphi_0 + V_{int}}{T_0}\right). \tag{3.8}$$

where the φ_H and $\varphi_0 + V_{int}$ are electrochemical potentials, *i.e.*, $\varphi = eW_H$ where W_H is the work function.

(*) The J_H and J_0 here are particle (electron) currents; the electrical currents are $I = eJ$, where e is the electron charge.

c) The entropy production due to heat radiation from the hot to cold electrodes. This is

$$\Delta S_{i\,\mathrm{RAD}} = S_B(T_H^4 - T_0^4)\left(\frac{1}{T_0} - \frac{1}{T_H}\right), \tag{3.9}$$

where S_B is the Stefan-Boltzmann radiation constant.

d) Any entropy production due to cathode or anode resistance,

$$\Delta S_{iR} = \frac{e^2(J_H - J_0)R_H}{T_H} + \frac{e^2(J_H - J_0)^2 R_0}{T_0}. \tag{3.10}$$

e) Any entropy production due to heat flow through leads and other parasitic heat paths,

$$\Delta S_{iK} = \eta_{\mathrm{eff}}(T_H - T_0)\left(\frac{1}{T_0} - \frac{1}{T_H}\right). \tag{3.11}$$

A discussion of all possible cases would involve us in a morass of algebra. In any practical case $2kT_H$ or $2kT_0$ are much less than φ_H or $\varphi_0 + V_{\mathrm{int}}$; we will therefore neglect ΔS_{ie}. The internal electrode and lead resistance terms ΔS_{iR} will also be neglected. The heat input of the hot electrode is also approximately ($J = S_H - J_0$) given by

$$Q_H = J\varphi_H + S_B(T_H^4 - T_0^4) + \eta_{\mathrm{eff}}(T_H - T_0)$$

or, letting the sum of the last two terms be denoted simply by Q_F, the efficiency expression becomes

$$\eta = \frac{T_H - T_0}{T_H} - T_0\,\frac{\left[J\left(\dfrac{\varphi_H}{T_H} - \dfrac{\varphi_0 + V_{\mathrm{int}}}{T_0}\right) + Q_F\left(\dfrac{1}{T_0} - \dfrac{1}{T_H}\right)\right]}{J\varphi_H + Q_F}. \tag{3.12}$$

In optimizing the efficiency, we must specify what parameters can be adjusted. For example, we can assume that the source temperature T_H and sink temperature T_0 are specified, then we can adjust φ_H and $\varphi_0 + V_{\mathrm{int}}$ by choice of electrode materials and load resistance. The actual conditions for maximizing are again algebraically tedious, but HOUSTON has shown by direct numerical calculation that one condition is essentially that $\varphi_H/T_H = (\varphi_0 + V_{\mathrm{int}})/T_0$, which makes the particle transfer entropy production zero. Inserting this condition, (3.12) takes the simple form

$$\eta = \eta_c\left[1 - \frac{1}{1 + J\varphi_H/Q_F}\right]. \tag{3.13}$$

It can easily be seen that for small $\bar{Z}$, $\eta \to 0$; that is, all the input heat simply supplies the heat current. Maximum efficiency is obtained for $J\varphi_H/Q_F$ maximum. With the relation between φ_H and $\varphi_0 + V_{\text{int}}$ which minimizes the particle transfer entropy production,

$$\frac{J\varphi_H}{Q_F} = \frac{\varphi_H a T_H^2 \exp[-\varphi_H/kT_H](1 - T_0^2/T_H^2)}{S_B(T_H^4 - T_0^4) + \eta_{\text{eff}}(T_H - T_0)} . \tag{3.14}$$

Given the environmental (sink) temperature T_0, one can study (3.14) as a function of T_H. The general behavior is shown in Fig. 4.

For reasonably sensible values of the electrode material parameters, it should be possible to obtain a maximum value of $J\varphi_H/Q_F = 1$ and obtain half the thermodynamic efficiency. Practical systems have not achieved this as yet, because of material problems.

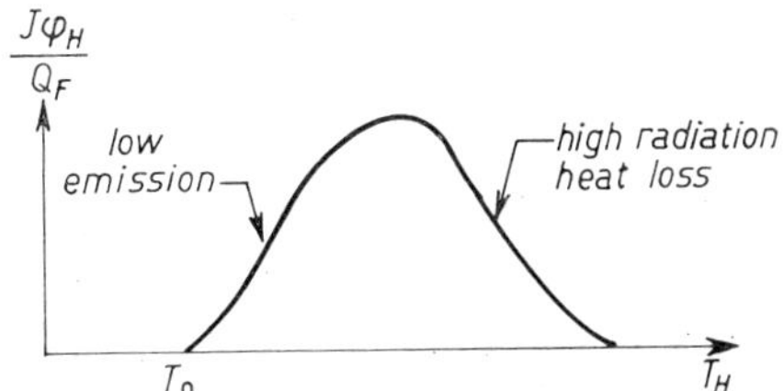

Fig. 4. – The efficiency of a thermionic diode converter depends on the ratio of the heat supplied for electron emission $J\varphi_H$ to the heat Q_F flowing through leads or by radiation.

In this section we have shown how it is possible to apply the postulates of irreversible thermodynamics to two important forms of thermoelectric energy conversion systems. Using this approach, it is possible to avoid the necessity of coping in detail with local transport phenomena in each system as a new problem; this unification has considerable merit.

4. – Defining equations for energy converters.

The previous sections have illustrated the particular role which irreversible entropy production plays in limiting the efficiency of energy converters in general. However, the examples chosen were simple enough so that it was straightforward to write down the entropy production terms.

In the case of the general heat engine, we supply fuel, heat, and do external work on the circulating fluid. To prescribe the system in detail we need some orderly procedure for determining the dependent variables such as the fluid flow, the electrical current, the heat current, etc., in terms of these prescribed heat, particle, and force distributions acting on the system.

To achieve a definition of the problem in a sufficiently general way is not trivial, since a wide variety of physical phenomena can be involved. Presuming that we wish to cover continuous flow systems with working fluid comprising mixtures of charged particles, the following ingredients must be present in a complete description of the behavior of a system:

1) Kinematic descriptive equations for fluid flow fields—including the concept of motional derivatives $D/Dt = \partial/\partial t + \boldsymbol{v}\cdot\nabla$, and including equations of continuity.

2) Mechanics – the macroscopic mechanical motion of the fluid is prescribed according to Newton's laws, *i.e.*, the domain of fluid mechanics. Energy and momentum transfer take place via the net or « convective » fluid motion.

3) Electrodynamics – if the particles in the working fluid are charged, then the electromagnetic fields defined by Maxwell's equations couple to the mechanical motion through the Lorentz force. Two limiting cases are of interest: first, when the motion of the fluid is entirely responsible for the fields, which is the magnetohydrodynamic regime; second, if the fields are « impressed » upon the system and maintained by external means—this is the usual regime of transport phenomena in solids.

4) Thermostatics – in the course of the fluid motion it is compressed and accelerated. Assuming that the molecular distribution can follow this motion in a « local » sense, the behavior of the system thus must also be governed by the first and second laws of thermostatics, and by a « local » equation of state. In « convective » fluid motion, this is the extent of the intentional need for thermal concepts.

5) Thermodynamics – when there is negligible macroscopic mechanical motion of the system, there can still be « diffusive » transfer of energy, such as heat flow and electrical currents, which arise from temperature and electric potential gradients. In fact, we can now recognize that the development of the « transport » equations in Section **2** implicitly referred to « diffusive » transport. In the general case this diffusive transport will be superimposed on the convective motion; as such it may be undesirable, *e.g.*, heat loss by « conduction » through the working fluid in a turbine.

At the present time, it appears that either of the limiting cases of « convective » or « diffusive » conversion systems has merit. The various forms of magnetohydrodynamic generators [9] now being developed to extract energy from an ionized gas driven between electrodes and in a static magnetic field are examples of the former. Solid state and thermionic systems are examples of the latter, *i.e.*, the physical behavior is essentially unchanged by idealizing the ions in the system as having infinite mass.

In the context of this conference, the principal interest is in solid-state systems, so the remainder of the discussion will be directed toward establishing the defining equations for such systems. Actually, the framework for the general case has been established by FIESCHI, DE GROOT, MAZUR and VLIEGER [7] wherein they consider: continuity and conservation of particles; fluid mechanics of momentum, stress and kinetic energy of the macroscopic motions; internal thermostatics, and « diffusive » thermodynamics—all for mixtures of charged particles in electromagnetic fields. Their interest was in applications to galvanomagnetic and thermogalvanomagnetic effects. We can pass to the present thermoelectric problem by letting $\boldsymbol{v}$ (the center-of-mass velocity) $\to 0$, and by restricting consideration to systems in which we do not inject particles or do mechanical work. The coupling to the system is then made solely by thermal or electrical means—heat reservoir contact the system at various positions and temperature and electrical currents are taken out of (and returned to) the system to do work in external loads.

In this limiting case, the defining equation which « couples » the heat sources and electrical loads to the system using the entropy and balance equations of continuity is

$$\frac{\partial s}{\partial t} + \nabla \cdot \boldsymbol{J}^s = \dot{s}_i + \frac{\dot{q}}{T}, \tag{4.1}$$

where s, $\boldsymbol{J}^s$, $\dot{s}_i$ have been previously defined as the entropy density per unit volume, entropy current (2.6) and flow entropy production (2.13); $\dot{q}$ is the externally supplied heat transfer rate to the system—in general, a function of position and local temperature. Similarly for energy balance

$$\frac{\partial u}{\partial t} + \nabla \cdot \boldsymbol{J}^0 = \dot{u}_i + \dot{q} + \dot{u}_e, \tag{4.2}$$

where u is the energy density per unit volume, $\boldsymbol{J}^0$ the energy current, $\dot{u}_i$ the internal energy generation due to flows (we have not defined this, but it can be shown to be related to Joule heating and thermoelectric effects by the approach used to develop (2.11), (2.12), (2.13) and using the relation (2.6)), $\dot{q}$ is again the rate of local supply of external heat, and finally the important term $\dot{u}_e$ represents the rate at which (negative) energy is transferred from the load to the system. For a load resistance R_L assumed to be inserted at a point, x_0 in a circuit carrying electrical current I, the term $\dot{u}_e \simeq - I^2 R_L \delta(x - x_0)$ where $\delta(x - x_0)$ is the conventional « δ » function centered at x_0.

For steady state systems, $s/t = 0$, $\partial u/\partial t = 0$. There are also a number of particle conservation conditions $\nabla \cdot \boldsymbol{J}^\gamma = 0$.

Having identified the coupling relations between the system and its heat and electrical environment, we now must say precisely what the structure of the problem of a « thermoelectric » conversion system is: given a system with prescribed configuration and composition, the temperature distribution and electric fields determine the currents $\boldsymbol{J}^i$ and the forces $\mathscr{F}_i$ in the system (through the transport coefficients L_{ij}, L_{ijk}, etc., (2.5)). The electrical fields and temperature gradients are then « coupled » to the heats and loads by substituting for the $\boldsymbol{J}^i$ and $\mathscr{F}^i$ that appear in (4.1) and (4.2). In general, for three components each of electric field $\mathscr{E}$ and temperature gradient ΔT the problem is only completely determined when the conservation conditions $\nabla\cdot\boldsymbol{J}_\gamma$ plus boundary conditions on the flows are satisfied.

All of this now can be best illustrated by specific example. Consider the idealized « one-dimensional flow » standard thermocouple circuit. Assume steady state $\partial S/\partial t=0$, and consider one carrier species (electrons) only. It is instructive to identify the usual thermoelectric effects from the entropy balance eq. (4.1) plus three other considerations:

1) The heat current $\boldsymbol{J}^Q=T\boldsymbol{J}^s$—a « local » relation.

2) The heat current arises from two causes—particle current and temperature gradient. Define Ts^* as the mean heat carried per unit particle current and $\boldsymbol{J}^{Q*}$ as the heat current which would be produced by the temperature gradient with no particle current (the usual zero electrical current heat conduction). Then

$$\boldsymbol{J}^Q=Ts^*\boldsymbol{J}^1+\boldsymbol{J}^{Q*}\,, \tag{4.3}$$

where $\boldsymbol{J}^1$ is the electron particle current.

3) As shown in any of the basic references, in an electric field, the μ_γ defined in (2.1) and appearing throughout the subsequent discussion should really be generalized to « electrochemical » potential $\bar{\mu}_\gamma=\mu_\gamma+e\varphi$ where φ is the electric potential, *i.e.*, $-\nabla\varphi=\mathscr{E}$ the electric field.

With these assumptions, one can substitute in (4.2) to obtain two instructive alternate forms of the « coupling » equations,

$$\nabla\cdot\boldsymbol{J}_Q=T\boldsymbol{J}^1\cdot\mathscr{F}_1+\dot{q}\,, \tag{4.4}$$

where $T\mathscr{F}_1=-\nabla\bar{\mu}_1$. Or alternatively, using $\nabla\cdot\boldsymbol{J}^1=0$ for divergenceless flow

$$\nabla\cdot\boldsymbol{J}^{Q*}=\boldsymbol{I}\,\mathscr{E}-\boldsymbol{I}\cdot\frac{1}{e}[\nabla(\mu_1+Ts^*)]_{x\dot{q}}\,, \tag{4.5}$$

where $\boldsymbol{I}=eJ^1$.

The physical interpretation of (4.5) is quite straightforward:

1) $\boldsymbol{J}^{Q*}$ is the conventional (nonthermoelectric) heat current given by $-\varkappa\nabla T$, where $\varkappa$ is the thermal conductivity.

2) $\boldsymbol{I}\cdot\mathscr{E}$ = rate at which current does electrical work.

3) The second term on the right-hand side of (4.5) is linear in the current I and proportional to the gradient of a quantity which depends on composition and temperature. Symbolically, we can write

$$\nabla = \nabla T \frac{\partial}{\partial T} + \nabla c \frac{\partial}{\partial c}, \tag{4.6}$$

where T and c are temperature and composition, respectively. Two familiar limiting forms of this term occur. To a very good approximation (see Appendix A) this $s^* \simeq s$, the local equilibrium entropy of the carrier, so $\mu_1 + Ts^* = u_1 - Ts + Ts^* \simeq u_1$, where u_1 is the mean (local) energy of the carriers.

For uniform composition (along the thermocouple legs) $\nabla c = 0$ and

$$\boldsymbol{I}\cdot\frac{1}{e}\nabla(\mu_1 + Ts^*) = \boldsymbol{I}\cdot\nabla T\left(\frac{1}{e}\frac{\partial u_1}{\partial T}\right), \tag{4.7}$$

but $\partial u_1/\partial T$ is simply the « specific heat » of the electrons and $(1/e)(\partial u_1/\partial T) = \tau$ is the familiar Thomson coefficient.

On the other hand, across a sharp junction $\nabla T = 0$, but there is a change in the mean energy per carrier and this discontinuity ∂u_1 will be equivalent to a heat of $(\partial u_1/e)$ per unit current, which is simply the well-known Peltier heat π_{AB}.

In the first approximation for semiconductor thermoelements, the Thomson heat is small compared with Joule heat. If heat is supplied only at the junctions, $\dot{q} = 0$ along the arm of thermocouple and (4.5) becomes

$$\frac{\mathrm{d}^2 T}{\mathrm{d}x^2} = \frac{\sigma\mathscr{E}^2}{\eta} = \frac{I^2}{\sigma\varkappa}, \qquad T = T_0 + \left[(T_H - T_0) - \frac{I^2}{\sigma\varkappa}\frac{L^2}{2}\right]\frac{x}{L} + \frac{I^2}{\sigma\varkappa}\frac{x^2}{2}. \tag{4.8}$$

Where: $x = 0$; $T = T_0$ when $x = L$; $T = T_H$ and the heat flow $-\varkappa(\mathrm{d}T/\mathrm{d}x)$ at hot junction becomes (unit cross-section),

$$Q = -\varkappa\left(\frac{\mathrm{d}T}{\mathrm{d}x}\right) = -\frac{\varkappa(T_H - T_0)}{L} + \frac{I^2 L}{2\sigma}. \tag{4.9}$$

The sense of the co-ordinate x is positive from T_0 to T_H; thus this is an external heat flow into the hot junction, consisting of the normal heat flow minus half the internal heat generated. This derivation is the basis for division of the internal Joule heat assumed in Section **3**. It can be seen that this neglects the Thomson heating effects. In semiconductor thermoelements this is ordinarily well justified; actually, as IOFFE and GOLDSMID [8] have shown, this neglect can to good approximation be included in figure-of-merit calculations by using the mean thermoelectric power in the expressions derived neglecting the Thomson effect.

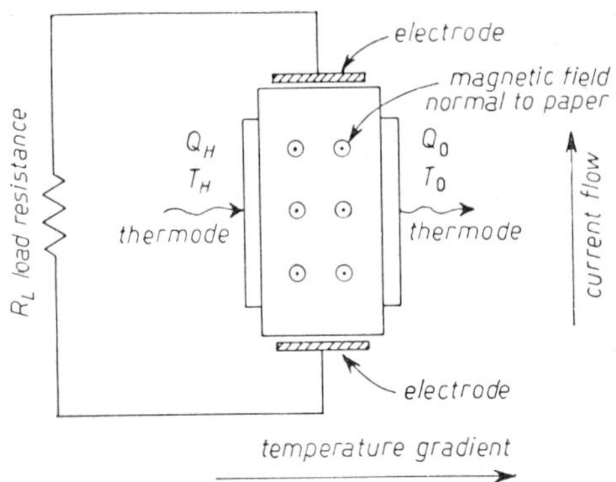

Fig. 5. – A Nernst-Ettingshausen generator utilizing transverse thermomagnetic effects.

The simple thermocouple has been straightforward because it is one-dimensional, in addition to being quite familiar. As a somewhat more interesting example of the application of the general methods, consider next a Nernst-Ettingshausen converter.

This generator, illustrated schematically in Fig. 5, is based on the principle that when a heat current flows through a conductor in the presence of a magnetic field normal to the direction of heat flow, an electric voltage is induced in a direction normal to both the heat flow and magnetic field vectors (see Chapter 17 of Callen's book).

Again (4.1) and (4.2) apply. In the steady state $\partial s/\partial t = 0$; also it is assumed that there are no internal heat sinks, *i.e.*, all heat. The generalized currents and forces are, respectively,

$$J^i \equiv J^0_x,\ J^0_y;\ J^1_x,\ J^1_y\,,$$

$$\mathscr{F}^i \equiv \frac{\partial}{\partial x}\left(\frac{1}{T}\right), \quad \frac{\partial}{\partial y}\left(\frac{1}{T}\right); \quad \frac{\partial}{\partial x}\left(\frac{\bar{\mu}_1}{T}\right), \quad \frac{\partial}{\partial y}\left(\frac{\bar{\mu}_1}{T}\right).$$

Apparently there are eight dependent variables J^i and $\mathscr{F}^i$ to be determined. Four of these are related by the equations

$$\boldsymbol{J}^i = \underline{\boldsymbol{L}}\mathscr{F}^i$$

as discussed in Section **2**. The elements of the 4×4 matrix $\underline{\mathbf{L}}$ satisfy the Onsager relations

$$L_{ij}(\boldsymbol{H}) = \tilde{L}_{ij} - (\boldsymbol{H})$$

where H is the magnetic field. These equations together with (4.1) comprise five equations; three more equations can be found by specifying boundary conditions (*):

(*) It is quite possible to have more defining equations than necessary; the additional equations then are of the nature of « compatibility » relations which might exclude certain types of boundary condition assumptions.

a) If the thermodes are insulators, electrical current in the direction of heat flow is zero:

$$J_x = 0 . \tag{4.10}$$

b) Similarly, if the electrodes are taken as perfect thermal insulators,

$$J_y^Q = J_y^0 - \bar{\mu}_1 J_y = 0 . \tag{4.11}$$

c) The voltage developed between A and B equals the difference in electrochemical potential $\bar{\mu}_1$, between the electrodes, which also equals the voltage across the load:

$$\mu_{1B} - \mu_{1A} = IR_L . \tag{4.12}$$

Thus we have an orderly procedure for specifying the determining equations for heat and particle flows. To emphasize again, the combination of the equations (4.1), (4.2) and (2.14) suffice to determine completely the coupling between heat and work sources and sinks. The transport relations and boundary conditions complete the specification of the problem.

The solution of these equations for the Nernst-Ettingshausen generator has not been completed at this writing.

5. – Brief considerations of practical systems and concluding remarks.

The intent of this discussion has been to concentrate on the basic principles relating to thermoelectric systems. However, we might note some of the material aspects of current systems in this concluding section.

For semiconductor systems $\bar{Z} = \alpha^2 \sigma \varkappa^{-1}$. Using a standard formula (see also Appendix A), this can be written as

$$\bar{Z} = \frac{\left(\dfrac{k}{e}\right)^2 \left(\gamma + \dfrac{\zeta}{kT}\right)^2 e^2 \mu_m N_e(T) \exp\left[-\zeta/kT\right]}{\varkappa_e + \varkappa_1} , \tag{5.1}$$

where: k = Boltzmann's constant,

$\varkappa_e$ = electronic thermal conductivity,

$\varkappa_1$ = lattice thermal conductivity,

μ_m = electron mobility,

γ depends on scattering mechanism,

ζ = Fermi level measured with respect to band edge.

When $\varkappa_e \ll \varkappa_1$, (5.1) is optimized by maximizing $x^2 e^{-x}$, where $x = (\gamma + (\zeta/kT))$. The following considerations then are desired:

1) ionic scattering with $\gamma = 4$;

2) small $\varkappa_1$;

3) large mobility and large effective mass m^* (though these requirements are somewhat mutually exclusive);

4) thermoelectric power $\simeq 200\ \mu\text{V}\cdot\text{deg}$.

The problem has been discussed by GOLDSMID [8]. Fig. 6 gives a graph for the maximum efficiency of a thermoelectric generator with $\bar{Z}T$ temperature independent and the cold junction at 300 °K. Some results from radiation-damage studies are as follows:

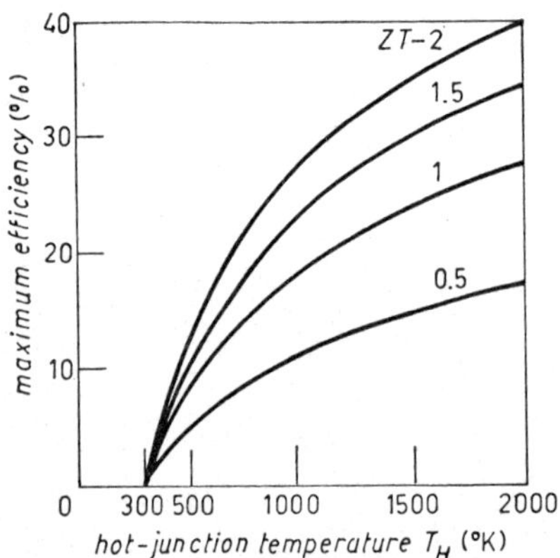

Fig. 6. – Maximum efficiency of a thermoelectric converter for various values of the parameter ZT and T_0 at 300 °K.

1) $\varkappa_1$ is decreased by radiation, which is desirable; but at high temperatures $\varkappa_1$ is limited mostly by anharmonicity, so that the differential gain is not great.

2) Successful materials, such as Bi_2Te_3, depend on high mobility and slight degeneracy. Radiation effects are expected to be extremely detrimental to high-mobility semiconductors.

3) The high-temperature thermal conductivity of solids varies almost universally according to the law (KEYES [10])

$$\varkappa \sim T_m^{\frac{3}{2}},$$

(T_m = melting temperature). Though irradiation may decrease $\varkappa$, the amount by which the high-temperature thermal conductivity can be changed is not enough to be of significance in increasing $\bar{Z}$. One may say that at the present time semiconductor thermoelements of the conventional doped semiconductor type do not look too promising for direct conversion use in reactors.

We turn briefly to thermionic converters. The present-day limitation on the efficiency of these systems is the radiation heat loss from the hot electrode:

$$Q_{\text{Rad}} \sim S_B T_H^4 .$$

One wants to keep the average temperature low, but this requires a very efficient emitter, and therefore low work-function cathode materials. Neutralization of space charge can be brought about by surface ionization at the hot electrode ($\varphi_H > V_I$, where V_I is ionization potential of gas atoms); by non-equilibrium injection methods; and by radiation ionization.

We also need φ_0 to be small for $T_0/T_H \ll 1$; presently available electrode materials of low work-function are not very stable. Assuming $T_0 = 500°$, $\varphi_0 = 1.2$ eV (which is possible for special photosurfaces), we find that to get appreciable emission current we must have T_H at least 1500°. It has been possible to attain overall efficiencies of 20 per cent in laboratory devices using special materials (Cs condensed on W or Mo for which $\varphi_0 = 1.4$ eV, at $T_H = 2000°$).

Radiation effects on thermionic systems might be as follows:

1) Since the electrodes are metallic, direct radiation-damage effect on electrical properties is much less serious than in semiconductor elements.

2) Radiation-induced corrosion with Cs present will be a problem. Low work-function collector electrodes are not very stable.

In principle, overall efficiencies of 40 per cent or more can be attained by thermionic devices. The first large-scale engine of the direct conversion type to compete against conventional equipment might well use a combination of all the above principles.

* * *

The author wishes to acknowledge support from the John Simon Guggenheim Foundation for a fellowship of study in this general area during 1959. He also wishes to acknowledge subsequent support from the United States Atomic Energy Commission and from the Office of Naval Research for this research. Finally, he wishes to acknowledge the hospitality and assistance in preparation of the manuscript at the Oak Ridge National Laboratory.

APPENDIX A

Some conventional thermoelectric considerations.

In the usual form, the transport equations (CALLEN) for thermoelastic systems are (no magnetic field):

$$-J^1 = \bar{L}_{11}\frac{1}{T}\nabla\bar{\mu} + \bar{L}_{12}\nabla\left(\frac{1}{T}\right), \tag{A.1}$$

$$J^Q = \bar{L}_{12}\frac{1}{T}\nabla\bar{\mu} + L_{22}\nabla\left(\frac{1}{T}\right). \tag{A.3}$$

(A.2) can be related to (4.2) by rewriting

$$\text{(A.3)}\qquad \dot{T}\boldsymbol{J}^s = \boldsymbol{J}^Q = \frac{-\bar{L}_{12}}{T\bar{L}_{11}} J^1 + \frac{\bar{L}_{11}\bar{L}_{22}-\bar{L}_{12}^{-2}}{\bar{L}_{11}} \nabla\left(\frac{1}{T}\right),$$

$$\text{(A.4)}\qquad = Ts^*J^1 + J^{Q*}\,.$$

The isothermal electrical conductivity is $e^2\bar{L}_{11}/T$, the zero current thermal conductivity from (A.3) is $(\bar{L}_{11}\bar{L}_{22}-\bar{L}_{12}^2)/\bar{L}_{11}T^2$. The thermoelectric power α which experimentally is found as the rate change of open circuit thermocouple voltage with temperature is found to be simply $\alpha = s^*/e$. In all of these, e is the charge of the carrier.

Physical considerations for various kinds of semiconductors can be conveniently discussed in terms of the plausible (and locally rigorous) relations:

$$\text{(A.4)}\qquad T\boldsymbol{J}^s = J_0 - \mu J^1\,,$$

$$\text{(A.5)}\qquad Ts^* = \lim_{J^1\to 0}\frac{J_0-\mu J^1}{J'} = \text{mean energy per unit particle current as measured with respect to the Fermi level}\,.$$

Using the conventional band picture of conduction, it is clear that there are two contributions to Ts^* in (A.5)—first, the mean energy of the carriers measured with respect to the band edge and second, the energy separation of the Fermi level from the band edge. The former will have the form λkT and the latter can be denoted by ζ. Then we arrive at the usual expression for the thermoelectric power α:

$$\text{(A.6)}\qquad \alpha = \frac{s^*}{e} = \frac{k}{e}\left(\gamma + \frac{\zeta}{kT}\right).$$

This physical viewpoint can also be applied to mixed valency semiconductors, such as $Li_xNi_{(1-x)}O$. In these the conduction process arises by electrons hopping over randomly distributed potential barriers. Using rate theory, the mean current across a barrier of length « a » along the electric field direction and of height « b », the conductivity, and current are related by

$$\text{(A.7)}\qquad J^1 = \mathscr{E}\frac{aJ^+}{kT}\exp\left[-\frac{b}{kT}\right] = \sigma\mathscr{E}\,,$$

where J^+ is the « saddle point » current along the reaction coordinate. The carriers transport an energy b with respect to the bottom of the potential well, and the Fermi level is near the bottom of the well; thus again

$$\text{(A.8)}\qquad \alpha = \frac{s^*}{e} = \frac{k}{e}\left(\gamma + \frac{b}{kT}\right).$$

In either case (band or jump conduction) the conductivity is exponentially related to the thermoelectric power so the optimization of the thermoelectric figure of merit $\alpha^2\sigma\varkappa^{-1}$ sets a rather well-defined value of α, as noted following (5.1).

REFERENCES

[1] S. R. DE GROOT: *Thermodynamics of Irreversible Processes* (Amsterdam, 1952); H. B. CALLEN: *Thermodynamics* (New York, 1960); I. PRIGOGINE: *Thermodynamics of Irreversible Processes* (1955).

[2] M. LAX: *Rev. Mod. Phys.*, **32**, 25 (1960).

[3] W. BERNARD and H. B. CALLEN: *Rev. Mod. Phys.*, **31**, 1017 (1959).

[4] R. C. TOLMAN and P. C. FINE: *Rev. Mod. Phys.*, **20**, 51 (1948).

[5] J. M. HOUSTON: *Journ. Appl. Phys.*, **30**, 481 (1959).

[6] C. HERRING: *Phys. Rev.*, **59**, 889 (1941).

[7] See De Groot's book; also the generalization to the case of magnetic fields, see R. FIESCHI, S. R. DE GROOT and P. MAZUR: *Physica*, **20**, 67 (1954); R. FIESCHI, S. R. DE GROOT, P. MAZUR and J. VLIEGER: *Physica*, **20**, 245 (1954).

[8] H. J. GOLDSMID: *Brit. Journ. Appl. Phys.*, **11**, 209 (1960).

[9] R. J. ROSA: *Phys. Fluids*, **4**, 182 (1961).

[10] R. J. KEYES: *Phys. Rev.*, **115**, 564 (1959).

Theory of Sequential Processes and the Crystallization of High Polymers.

F. C. Frank and M. P. Tosi (*)

H. H. Wills Physics Laboratory, University of Bristol - Bristol

The paper reports on the results of a recent investigation which was mainly concerned with the interpretation of the crystallization processes of high polymers in terms of the kinetics of crystal growth. A formal discussion of the basic problem of the theory of nucleation was developed, which illustrates the assumptions involved in the steady-state treatments of nucleation processes and leads to general formulas applicable whenever the nucleation process can be schematized as a sequential process. The results hereby discussed have been published elsewhere [1].

1. – Theory of sequential processes.

The typical problem studied by the theory of nucleation is the transition of a physical system from one state of aggregation A to another state B, which is envisaged as involving the formation of nuclei of phase B inside phase A [2]. The transition occurs because phase A is thermodynamically unstable relative to *bulk* phase B: however, a free energy increase is associated with the formation of *small* nuclei of the new phase inside the original one, which effectively is in a metastable state. The initial increase of free energy implies that only nuclei of the new phase, formed as a result of fluctuations of energy or density or concentration, whatever the case may be, which have reached at least the critical stage in the transition process corresponding to the highest value of free energy, can grow at the expense of the original phase.

(*) Italian Research Council Fellow (1959-1960), on leave from the Istituto di Fisica Teorica, Università di Pavia. Now at the Solid State Science Division, Argonne National Laboratory, Argonne, Illinois.

The transition process is often schematized as a *sequential process*, *i.e.*, a process which proceeds through a denumerable sequence of stages 0, 1, 2, ..., ν, ..., with definite forward and backward transition probabilities α_ν and β_ν from each stage to the adjacent stages in the sequence, and zero transition probability between nonadjacent stages [3]. If $\eta_\nu(t)$ is the number of systems in the ν-th stage at time t, the net transition rate between the ν-th and the $(\nu+1)$-th stages is

$$(1) \qquad j_\nu(t) = \alpha_\nu \eta_\nu(t) - \beta_{\nu+1}\eta_{\nu+1}(t)$$

which, together with the continuity equations,

$$(2) \qquad \frac{\partial \eta_\nu(t)}{\partial t} = j_{\nu-1}(t) - j_\nu(t) = \alpha_{\nu-1}\eta_{\nu-1}(t) - (\alpha_\nu + \beta_\nu)\eta_\nu(t) + \beta_{\nu+1}\eta_{\nu+1}(t) \, ,$$

and appropriate initial or boundary conditions, is the basic equation of a time-dependent nucleation problem. Equation (2) is a second-order difference differential equation, and we accordingly expect its solution to be a linear combination of two independent solutions.

In the particular case of steady-state conditions, where the transition rate is a constant (j, say), the solution of eq. (2) can be written as the sum of a distribution proportional to a Boltzmann factor and of the purely flux-determined distribution:

$$(3) \qquad \eta_\nu = \Delta\eta_0 \exp\left[-\varphi_\nu/kT\right] + j \exp\left[-\varphi_\nu/kT\right] \sum_{n=\nu}^{\infty} \frac{1}{\alpha_n} \exp\left[\varphi_n/kT\right] ,$$

where

$$(4) \qquad \Delta\eta_0 = \eta_0 - j \sum_{n=0}^{\infty} \frac{1}{\alpha_n} \exp\left[\varphi_n/kT\right] ,$$

and φ_ν is the free energy of the ν-th stage relative to that of the zeroth stage. In deriving eq. (3), use has been made of the relation

$$(5) \qquad \alpha_\nu/\beta_{\nu+1} = \exp\left[-(\varphi_{\nu+1} - \varphi_\nu)/kT\right] ,$$

which follows at once from eq. (1), if one considers that the distribution is the equilibrium distribution when the transition rate is zero. The second term in the right-hand side of eq. (3) is identified as the purely flux-determined distribution: *its convergence at large* ν *is assured, provided the* α_ν *are not expotially diminishing.*

Volmer's method of idealizing the nucleation problem [4], so as to justify treatment of it by steady state methods, is to consider that systems reaching a specified large value μ of ν are removed from the ensemble and restored to the initial stage. The ensuing boundary conditions ($\eta_0 = \text{constant}$, $\eta_\mu = 0$) have the effect that in the distribution (3), $\Delta\eta_0$ has a very small negative value, and for all values of ν for which the free energy φ_ν exceeds φ_μ by more than a moderate multiple of kT the distribution differs negligibly from the purely flux-determined distribution. Hence the steady-state treatment of a nucleation problem consists essentially in isolating the flux-determined distribution. It is then possible to express the nucleation rate j in terms of the occupation number of any stage, η_ν:

$$j = \eta_\nu \exp[\varphi_\nu/kT] \Big/ \left(\sum_{n=\nu}^{\infty} \frac{1}{\alpha_n} \exp[\varphi_n/kT] \right), \tag{6}$$

or, in terms of the transition probabilities,

$$j = \eta_\nu \beta_\nu \Big/ \left(\sum_{n=\nu}^{\infty} \prod_{i=\nu}^{n} \frac{\beta_i}{\alpha_i} \right). \tag{7}$$

The nucleation rate can also be written in terms of the activation free-energy levels φ_ν^*, which are formally defined through the rate constants by the rate equations

$$\alpha_\nu = \frac{kT}{h} \exp[-(\varphi_\nu^* - \varphi_\nu)/kT], \tag{8}$$

$$\beta_{\nu+1} = \frac{kT}{h} \exp[-(\varphi_\nu^* - \varphi_{\nu+1})/kT]. \tag{9}$$

Eq. (6) can then be rewritten as follows:

$$j = \frac{kT}{h} \eta_\nu \exp[\varphi_\nu/kT] \Big/ \left(\sum_{n=\nu}^{\infty} \exp[\varphi_n^*/kT] \right).$$

In some problems, it is actually more convenient to relate the transition rate to the occupation number at the critical stage, where the free energy is highest.

2. – Nucleation theory of the crystallization of high polymers.

The salient fact characteristic of and peculiar to the crystallization of substances with very long chain molecules is the pleating of the molecules into segments, of a length of the order of magnitude of one hundred chain atoms, which is not, however, a marked length in the molecule. This fact is well established for crystallization from solution [5]. The leading problem in connection with polymer crystallization is to discover the factors which determine the segment length. Since equilibrium theories are bound to give a very shallow, broad minimum in the free energy with respect to segment length (if they lead to a minimum at all), as indeed was recently found in an equilibrium theory proposed by PETERLIN and FISCHER [6], one expects that, if it can be shown that the theory of crystal growth kinetics accounts for a uniform layer thickness, this will be the dominant determining factor in the practical case.

A kinetic theory of intramolecular crystallization in polymer molecules in solution has been given by LAURITZEN and HOFFMAN [7], on the assumption that there is no change in segment length after the first two pleats have been made. Their theory shows that the rate of primary nucleation has a maximum for a tabular nucleus having height $2l_0$, l_0 being the minimum height compatible with a net growth rate and depending on temperature, latent heat of crystallization and surface energy of the end faces of the crystal. Once the primary nucleus has been formed, the growth of the tabular crystal proceeds by secondary nucleation on its side surfaces. This process has also been considered by LAURITZEN and HOFFMAN [7], on the assumption that the first segment in each newly commencing strip on the edge of the (infinitely thick) crystal plate has a choice of length, but all subsequent segments have the same length.

It is difficult to eliminate the postulate of persistence of segment length, since otherwise the infinite summations entering the theory become intractable. However, if the probability of large fluctuations in segment length is small, it should be possible to take approximately into account the fluctuations in segment length by permitting just one more fluctuation to occur in the growth of the strip, but ignoring any fluctuation in segment length thereafter. An examination of the growth process in this schematization on a microscopic scale shows that, if the attachment of a chain segment is counted as one stage in the nucleation process, one has to deal with only three rate constants. These are α_0, the forward transition probability into the stage at which the fluctuation in segment length occurs, α, the subsequent forward transition probabilities which are all equal, and β, the backward transition probabilities which are all equal. Eq. (7) then reads

$$j = \eta_0 \alpha_0 (1 - \beta/\alpha) . \tag{11}$$

The rate constants can easily be expressed, through eqs. (8) and (9), in terms of a mean activation free energy for transition between stages, the supercooling, the latent heat of crystallization, the surface energies for the side and the end surfaces, and the segment lengths.

The theory confirms that there is a tendency to persistence in segment length, but nevertheless shows that the probability of a change is high. Its calculated magnitude is thus inaccurate. Nevertheless it seems likely that a more accurate treatment would retain qualitative features of the result obtained to this approximation. The most important such feature, when we allow a growing strip of width l_1 a single chance to fluctuate to a new width l_2, which it is obliged to retain thereafter, is that for a small value of l_1 the mean value of (l_2-l_1) (a mean weighted according to the distribution function in l_2 appropriate to that value of l_1, and hereafter denoted by $\langle l_2-l_1\rangle$) is positive; while, for a large value of l_1, $\langle l_2-l_1\rangle$ is negative. There is an intermediate value, l^*, of l_1 for which $\langle l_2-l_1\rangle$ is zero. l^*, defined by this condition, is identified as the stable width of the growing strip, in the sense that though fluctuations to greater and lesser widths occur, the subsequent fluctuations are biased towards a correction of the discrepancy; and likewise, whether at the first step in the commencement of the strip the width was large or small compared with l^*, the width in subsequent growth tends towards a condition of fluctuating about l^* as a mean value.

This value l^* is not taken to represent the resulting final layer thickness. For this we must consider the further problem of the deposition of successive strips. Subject to a certain limit on the supercoolings, l^* is finite when the width of the crystal surface on which the strip is being deposited is infinite. If this width is reduced, it begins to restrict l^* when it becomes of comparable magnitude. If we may suppose this restriction negligible for the « first » strip, we assuredly cannot for the « second » strip, which is deposited on the first: it will grow with a smaller stable width, and so in turn will the third strip deposited on the second. Our calculation shows that this sequence converges to a limiting width l^{**}, which we do identify (apart from the quantitative errors of the approximation) as the layer thickness which finally results. It is less than l^*, and indeed rather similar in magnitude to the Lauritzen and Hoffman result: but its meaning is significantly different.

The theory indicates that strips deposited on an initial strip narrower than l^{**} successively widen, to the same stable width l^{**} as for too broad an initial strip. Thus the theory agrees with the experimental observation that raising or lowering temperature during the growth of a crystal produces corresponding changes of thickness, to zones of greater or smaller thickness.

The theory in this form indicates different behaviour in three distinct ranges of supercooling (with reference to the ideal equilibrium temperature between the solution and crystals of very large layer thickness). In the first range, of small supercooling, whatever the thickness l may be in the nuclei provided (and it must be greater than l_0 if there is to be growth at all), it converges in the deposition of successive strips to l_0, and growth then ceases. Hence in this range no crystallization is to be observed (unless molecular rearrangement within the crystal allows its thickness gradually to increase, when there would be growth at a rate controlled by the rearrangement rate). In the next range of supercooling, l^{**} has a finite value greater than l_0, and the result should be crystallization at a finite rate to produce crystals with a layer thickness l^{**}. It is the behaviour in this range that we identify with the experimentally observed crystallization. The extent of each of these two ranges is of the order of about 10 or 20 degrees. At the bottom of the second range l^{**}, having been falling with falling temperature, rapidly rises to very large values. However, before this happens we think that another process sets in, intramolecular crystallization at many places within the same molecule, which should totally change the behaviour. The consequence of this process is likely to be the production of dendritic crystals instead of tablets, as is indeed observed at low temperatures.

There is an important difference in the nature of the crystals produced according to the above ideas compared with those of LAURITZEN and HOFFMAN. In the latter, the segment length is uniform within each crystal, but there is a variation among crystals, all grown at the same temperature. In our picture, all crystals grown at the same temperature have the same mean segment length, but there is variation of segment lengths in one crystal. This implies, further, that the crystal is likely to change after growth, by creeping displacements of the molecular chains tending to even out the segment lengths.

The results of the theory have been used to interpret the experimental temperature-dependence of the layer thickness for polyethylene [1], for which information is mot complete. There is good quantitative agreement between theory and observation for acceptable values of the relevant parameters, the only assumption in the fitting of the experimental data being that the highest temperature at which tabular crystals are formed (90 °C) corresponds to the boundary between the first two ranges of supercooling indicated by the theory. The value of the equilibrium temperature seems to lie between 110 and 115 °C, while the value of the surface energy of the side surfaces lies between 5 and 10 erg cm^{-2} and that of the surface energy of the end surfaces (containing the energy of the folds) is of the order of 100 erg cm^{-2}. For the latter energy a value of about 70 erg cm^{-2} can be estimated from spectroscopic data on smaller molecules. With the above values of the parameters, the theory predicts formation of dendritic crystals at temperatures of about 70 °C, in agreement with observation.

REFERENCES

[1] F. C. FRANK and M. P. TOSI: *Proc. Roy. Soc.* A **263**, 323 (1961).

[2] The application of nucleation theory to several types of phase transition has been described by J. FRENKEL: *Kinetic Theory of Liquids* (Oxford, 1946), ch. 7, and, for transitions in the solid state, by R. SMOLUCHOWSKI, in *Phase Transformations in Solids* (New York, 1951), p. 149.

[3] The implications of these assumptions have been discussed in ref. [1], Appendix. Here, the approximations involved in the lumping of a number of microstates of the system into one stage are discussed, with particular reference to the crystallization of high polymers.

[4] O. VOLMER: *Zeits. Phys. Chem.*, **119**, 277 (1926).

[5] A. KELLER: *Phil. Mag.*, **2**, 1171 (1957); A. KELLER and A. O'CONNOR: *Disc. Far. Soc.*, **25**, 114 (1958).

[6] A. PETERLIN and E. W. FISCHER: *Zeits. Phys.*, **159**, 272 (1960).

[7] J. I. LAURITZEN and J. D. HOFFMAN: *Journ. Res. NBS*, **64** A, 73 (1960).

Tipografia Compositori - Bologna - Italy